D1649268

FUNDAMENTAL PRINCIPLES OF MATHEMATICS

JOHN T. MOORE

Associate Professor of Mathematics
The University of Florida

Fundamental Principles of MATHEMATICS

HOLT, RINEHART AND WINSTON • NEW YORK

October, 1966

25804-0110

Printed in the United States of America

Library of Congress Catalog Card Number: 60-5113

To my Parkhill teachers

A. B. C.	A. L. H.
I. C. M.	J. H. Y.

PREFACE

The present book has been written to provide a basis for a two-semester program in freshman mathematics, either as a terminal course or as a preparation for further work in the calculus. There are many texts which survey the same general area as this one, and so it is perhaps of importance to mention some of the features of this book. For, while a glance at the chapter headings will show that most of the material that is usually covered in a freshman course is included, it is nonetheless true that there is scarcely a chapter which contains the usual presentation. An attempt has been made to bridge a small portion of the immense gap which exists between the traditional freshman course and what might be considered as modern mathematics. However, while new methods have been given, old techniques have not been discarded simply because they are old. For example, some of the techniques discussed in Chapter 6 for the graphing of functions are essentially the "Theorems on Loci" of *Elementary Analysis* by C. S. Slichter, to which reference is given in that chapter.

Perhaps the most important general feature of the book is the development of the material. I have tried to make the development orderly, by introducing and exploiting one basic concept at a time. The pace, particularly of the early chapters, is slow, so that a good foundation may be established; for without such a foundation, a study of mathematics is sure to crumble. I have tried to avoid making this a "cook" book, which attempts to show the student how to get answers to certain types of problems, regardless of whether he comprehends what he is doing. At the same time, I believe that it is almost as bad for a student to have only a nodding acquaintance with the theory of mathematics, so that even the simplest "practical" problems cannot be worked. Accordingly, keeping in mind both the budding mathematician and the future engineer and scientist, I have emphasized both basic ideas and their applications. I have tried to be realistic in my evaluation of the high-school training of the average college freshman, who is admittedly poorly prepared in elementary mathematics. A review of high-school algebra might appear to be a reasonable topic for the beginning of the book, but I am not sure that it is good from a psychological point of view to confront a new college student with material that he has seen before, however much he may be in need of it. The book then begins with ideas and concepts that are not usually covered even in a freshman college course, but which are basic for an understanding of modern mathematics. In order to help overcome any deficiencies which the student may have in elementary algebra, however, a review of high-school algebra has been included in the Appendix, to which he may refer either with or without the direction of an instructor. And at certain places in the main body of the text where a particular kind of algebraic manipulation is required, a few problems of that type have been inserted at the beginning of the Problem Sets, with appropriate references to the Appendix. The more difficult sections and problems have been starred and may be omitted, if desired, with no loss of continuity.

Beyond general comments, mention should also be made of a few specific points. The book opens with a discussion of sets, and, what is more important, the basic notion of a set plays a significant role in practically every chapter. Throughout the book, the concept of a function, along with its graphic representation, has been considered of prime importance; in fact, a large portion of the book has been built around the elementary functions, with special emphasis on their graphs. Relations and functions have been introduced as sets of ordered pairs, with particular attention being paid to their domains. In my own calculus classes, I have often found it difficult to test the students on the subject matter of calculus, in view of their general inability to sketch the graphs of even the most elementary functions. This may be considered a prime motivation for my emphasis in this direction. In an attempt to put some order into the generally confused situation with regard to the trigonometric functions, I have introduced both circular and degree-circular functions; the former are adapted to the radian measure of angles, while the latter are to be used with degree measure. This avoids any necessity for the directions, which are usually given almost apologetically to students, designating when to use radian measure in a formula.

The conic sections have been de-emphasized, though many of the usual results may be found in the Problem Sets. The parabola and hyperbola occur simply as special cases of power functions, while an ellipse is considered a uniformly distorted circle. It may be thought that too much has been attempted in differential calculus in Chapter 8, but I have felt that the derivatives of most of the elementary functions should be derived, in view of the central role of these functions in the text. If attention is paid to starred sections and problems, however, it would be possible to confine one's attention to power functions. It is not to be expected that the concepts of limit and continuity, which are introduced here, will be fully understood by any but the most superior students. In spite of this, I feel that a careful treatment of these topics is of sufficient importance to be included, with the hope that if the student comes in contact with them again, he will have a much better chance of mastering them at that time.

Whenever possible, the student is introduced to the proper mathematical language, and a few definitions are given which usually are not found in a freshman book. I have tried to make the definitions accurate; and if a proof cannot be made rigorous at this level, reference is made to this fact, and frequently only a statement of the result is given. It may be that I will be considered "fussy" for my frequent reference to the "measure" of a quantity, rather than to the quantity itself, as is customarily done. However, I feel that it should be emphasized that mathematics, in its usual algebraic setting, deals with *numbers*; and, for example, in a formula such as $A = \pi r^2$ for the area of a circle, A is a *number* and not an area, but rather a *measure* of area. Two review tests have been included at the end of each chapter, for a check of the students' mastery of the basic notions introduced therein. The tests are of equal difficulty, and should be considered as alternates rather than as graded tests.

The book was conceived prior to the organization of most of the presently numerous committees that are studying the undergraduate mathematics curriculum, particularly at the freshman level. But while I have not been influenced by any of these groups or their recommendations, it has been gratifying to know that in many instances we appear to hold a somewhat similar viewpoint. There is one noteworthy omission in this text—the topic of logic. For my own part, I have never felt that logic per se was a suitable diet for freshmen, excellent as it is as a mathematical discipline. Rather, I have felt that at this level it is more effective to instill mathematical rigor in the thinking of a student by using a more familiar mathematical environment, and one which is a little less abstract.

Finally, I believe that while mathematics is the "handmaiden" of the sciences, she is also the "queen" thereof. It is to be hoped that a student who reads this book will develop some appreciation for mathematics in its own right; for there is beauty in the theorems and propositions of mathematics, which makes its study worth while, in spite of as well as because of its many applications to science.

I have tried to keep in mind the varied needs and interests of people throughout the country, and so have made the book quite comprehensive in nature. Accordingly, it may be necessary to omit certain sections in the planning of a two-semester course, but this can be accomplished easily without serious loss of continuity. For example, if one wishes to assume familiarity with the real number system, Chapter 2 may be omitted; parts of Chapter 7 may be omitted, if there is no special interest in the applications of circular functions to wave motion; there are a number of sections in Chapter 14 which may be omitted, if the propositions of plane geometry are not of great interest; and Chapter 17 on probability and statistics may be omitted, if not considered important for the course at hand. There are many other possibilities, and only Chapters 1, 4, and 5 need be considered essential.

For any merits which this book may have, it would be difficult to give proper credit to all the institutions and persons concerned, though a few should be mentioned. There are many points of view which date back to valuable experience gained while at the University of Wisconsin; and, especially for the discussion on relations and functions, I owe much to the College of the University of Chicago, where I had the privilege of teaching for a short time. For my early interest in mathematics, I am indebted to the staff of the University of Western Ontario. In particular, I wish to thank Professor E. M. Beesley, of the University of Nevada, and Professors W. P. Morse, P. B. Patterson, and C. G. Phipps of the University of Florida, who read portions or all of the manuscript at various stages, and from whom I received valuable comments. To my many other colleagues at the University of Florida, with whom I have had many consultations, and especially to Professor F. W. Kokomoor for his continued encouragement, I also wish to tender my warmest thanks. Finally, I am greatly indebted to Dr. C. V. Newsom and the staff of the publisher for their assistance during the writing of this book.

JOHN T. MOORE

Gainesville, Florida
October, 1959

CONTENTS

Appendix [illegible]

FUNDAMENTAL PRINCIPLES OF MATHEMATICS

1

THE BASIC THEORY OF SETS

"Contrariwise," continued Tweedledee, "if it was so, it might be; and if it was, it would be; but as it isn't, it ain't. That's logic."

LEWIS CARROLL

1.1 The Nature of Sets

One of the most basic concepts in mathematics is that of a *set* or *class* of objects, though the student may be surprised to find that such a notion is even of a mathematical nature. The concept is, in fact, so basic that no completely satisfactory definition for it has been found. Under these circumstances we then accept it as undefined—but familiar—and proceed to build on it. We shall always think of a set as an unambiguous collection of objects, where by the word *unambiguous* we mean that it will always be possible to decide whether an arbitrary object is a member of the set. Sets which are not so restricted are sometimes useful in mathematics, but we shall have no use for them here. A set will usually be described with reference to some property which is possessed by each of its members, though this property may be merely that of membership in the set! Thus, we may speak of the set of fur-bearing animals in the United States, the set of Signs of the Zodiac, the set of people now living in Florida who were not born there, and the set which has for its members the city of Jacksonville, the star Aldebaran, and the President of the United States. The members of the first three of these sets have in common a physical property which is responsible for their inclusion in their respective sets; the only property that characterizes the members of the last set is that of fortuitous membership therein. The members of a set may be tangible objects like apples, people, and cities, or they may be intangible objects like colors, senses, and virtues. The members of a set may even be sets themselves. For example, the set known as the Chicago Cubs, itself a set of ball players, is a member of a set known as the National League—as any baseball fan knows. If the members of a set A are specified as $a, b, c, \cdots$, we shall describe the set by writing $A = \{a, b, c, \cdots\}$, the three dots indicating that all the members are not listed.

Whenever symbols are used to designate or "name" objects, there is an ever-present danger that the symbols will be confused with the objects, though in most instances it should be clear from the context which interpretation is desired. For example, the statements "James is a clever student" and "James is a 5-letter word" are both clear, though the first "James" refers to a definite person with the name "James," while the second "James" is merely a word or name, and without reference to any person. If a set is described by listing certain names or symbols, it is possible to interpret these as the elements of the set, or to regard the set as consisting of the *objects identified* by the names or symbols. The set {John, James, Henry} could be a set of people, or it could be a set of three proper names. There will be occasions when we shall use each interpretation, but to avoid ambiguity or repeated explanations, let us come to the following general agreement: *The elements of a set* {a, b, c, ···} *are the objects, of which* a, b, c, ··· *are names, except when designated otherwise, or when it is clear that the symbols are to be regarded as the objects, themselves.* Thus, in general, the set {John, James, Henry} will be a set of people, and the set {1, 2, 3} will be a set of numbers, but the set {?, #, *} will be a set of symbols. The only important instance when we shall consider symbols to be the objects in their own right occurs in Chapter 16, in connection with permutations and combinations. In that chapter we shall speak, for example, of the letters of the word BASSOON as comprising a set of 7 distinct, though not entirely distinguishable, letters.

The only important relation between a set and an object is that of membership: the object either *is* or *is not* a member of the set. For this reason a set may be a meaningful concept, even though it may be impossible or impracticable to list all of its members. It is clear that your pet poodle Fifi is a member of the set of all fur-bearing animals, even though no complete tabulation of the latter set is possible. On the other hand, the set of Signs of the Zodiac may be actually tabulated: Aries, Taurus, Gemini, Cancer, Leo, Virgo, Libra, Scorpio, Sagittarius, Capricornus, Aquarius, Pisces; and membership in this set can be checked by inspection. In general, if s is a member of a set S, we shall indicate this fact by writing $s \in S$; the denial of this—meaning that s is not a member of S—will be indicated by $s \notin S$.

The individual members of a set should be carefully distinguished from the set itself. For example, a bushel of apples and the apples in the bushel are not the same concept; to illustrate, the bushel can be split into half-bushels, while the individual apples remain unchanged. Even the physical properties of a set may be different from those of its members: the bushel of apples may be heavy, while the individual apples are light; one or two of the apples may be over-ripe or wormy, while the bushel as a whole is in good condition. Even a class of only one student in a college should not be identified with the student, for the class may be abolished by the Registrar, while the student will probably survive to register in another class! H. M. Tomlinson† writes in "Old Junk": "His shop has its native smell. It was of coffee, spices, rock-wool, cheese, bundles of wood, biscuits, and jute bags, and yet was none of these things, for their separate essences were so blended by old association that they made one indivisible smell, peculiar but not unpleasing when you were used to it."

Sometimes we wish to make a general statement about each and every member of a set without specifying any particular member. In this case a symbol like x may be used to stand for a representative member of the set. Thus, if $x \in A$, where A is a set of triangles, we know that x has three sides. It is of course essential, in any discussion involving x, that we know the set of which x is the representative member. Thus, the statement "Metal x is soft" is not significant, unless we know the set of which x is a member. Furthermore, while x may be an arbitrary member of the set, it should always be the *same* member throughout any discussion or nonsense may result. For example, if x is a member of the set of Governors of the 50 states, even such a trivial statement as "x is the Chief Executive of the state in which x lives" becomes ridiculous if x is not assumed to be the *same* Governor for both occurrences. This notation is often useful in the definition of a set. For example, if N is the set of natural numbers, the set of odd natural numbers can be denoted by $\{x \mid x \in N \text{ and } x \text{ is odd}\}$. In this notation, the statement after the vertical bar gives the requirement, that x must satisfy, in order to be a member of the set. Of course any other symbol, as well as x, may be used to designate the representative member.

PROBLEM SET 1.1

1. If A is the set of Boy Scout virtues, decide which of the following are true statements: (*a*) Loyalty $\in A$; (*b*) Cheerfulness $\notin A$; (*c*) Unkindness $\in A$; (*d*) Bravery $\in A$; (*e*) Cleanliness $\in A$; (*f*) Rudeness $\notin A$.
2. Give an example of a set having only (*a*) one member; (*b*) two members.
3. List the members of each of the following sets: (*a*) $\{x \mid x$ is a city in your state with population over 100,000$\}$; (*b*) $\{y \mid y$ is a capital city in New England$\}$; (*c*) $\{x \mid x$ is a course which you are now taking$\}$; (*d*) $\{z \mid z$ is a planet of our solar system$\}$.
4. Decide which of the following statements are true: (*a*) Mathematics $\in \{x \mid x$ is a biological science$\}$; (*b*) A right triangle $\notin \{y \mid y$ is a regular polygon$\}$;

† H. M. Tomlinson, *Old Junk* (New York: Knopf, 1920). For the discovery of this quotation, the author is indebted to the writers of *Fundamental Mathematics,* Vol. 1, The University of Chicago Press, 1948.

(c) A trapezoid $\notin \{x \mid x$ is a quadrilateral$\}$; (d) A U.S. Navy veteran $\in \{t \mid t$ is a U.S. veteran$\}$; (e) A pentagon $\in \{x \mid x$ is a quadrilateral$\}$.

5. Decide whether the members of the following sets are individual elements, or are themselves sets having more than one member: (a) The American League; (b) The Chapter of ΦBK at your college; (c) The national ΦBK organization; (d) The Ivy League football conference; (e) Your college basketball team.
6. Express each of the following in words: (a) $A \in \{x \mid x$ is a former President of the U.S.$\}$. (b) John $\notin \{z \mid z$ is the name of a girl$\}$; (c) $C \notin \{u \mid u$ is a right triangle$\}$; (d) $D \notin \{x \mid x$ is a capital city$\}$; (e) $E \in \{y \mid y$ is a river in South America$\}$.
7. Let A be the set of colleges in the Big Ten football conference. Which of the following are members of A? (a) The University of Wisconsin; (b) The University of Arizona; (c) The football team of the University of Ohio; (d) The football Head Coach of the University of Michigan; (e) Purdue University.
8. If A is the set of former Presidents of the United States, indicate the truth or falsity of each of the following: (a) John Hancock $\in A$; (b) Franklin Roosevelt $\in A$; (c) Oliver Wendell Holmes $\in A$; (d) Woodrow Wilson $\in A$; (e) Washington Irving $\in A$.
9. Name three members of the set of present Governors of the 50 States.
10. Let $A = \{x \mid x$ is an equilateral triangle$\}$, and $B = \{y \mid y$ is a triangle having all of its interior angles equal$\}$. State a theorem from plane geometry which asserts that the sets A and B are the same.
11. Decide whether or not the following sets can be conveniently tabulated: (a) $\{x \mid x$ is an animal$\}$; (b) $\{y \mid y$ is a man over 6 feet tall$\}$; (c) $\{t \mid t$ is a regular solid$\}$; (d) $\{x \mid x$ is a living human being$\}$; (e) $\{s \mid s$ is a New England state$\}$.
12. (a) If A is the set of fruit varieties grown in the U.S., name three members of the set $\{x \mid x \in A$ and x is sweet$\}$; (b) if A is the set of gases, name three members of the set $\{x \mid x \in A$ and x is combustible$\}$.
13. Which of the following are not to comprise the membership of a set, according to our policy in this book? (a) The five greatest living Americans; (b) The ten most brilliant students at your college; (c) The letters of the English alphabet; (d) The words spoken between 11 P.M. and 12 P.M. in your city on July 4, last year; (e) The months of the year.

1.2 Relations between Sets

One of the most familiar symbols in mathematics is that of *equality* (=), used to express the fact that two quantities are *equal.* The symbol occurs most frequently in statements that two numerical expressions are *equal in magnitude;* for example, $3 + 2 = 4 + 1$. But clearly, if the symbol is used in connection with elements which have no quality of magnitude, the meaning must be different from this. Thus, if we make the statement "The Empire State = New York State," we are stating that The Empire State and New York State are two *different names* for the same object—the State of New York. However, regardless of the special meaning of the symbol, the *Principle of Substitution of an Equal* will always be assumed to hold: if $a = b$, in any expression containing a we may replace a by b at some or all of its occurrences. We now apply this notion of equality to sets.

DEFINITION. Two sets A and B are equal and we write $A = B$, provided $a \in A$ if and only if $a \in B$.

Note. The phrase "if and only if" occurs frequently in mathematics, and is used to abbreviate a statement and its converse. Thus, the above condition is an abbreviation for the two statements:

1. If $x \in A$, then $x \in B$ (in symbols $x \in A \rightarrow x \in B$).
2. If $x \in B$, then $x \in A$ (in symbols $x \in B \rightarrow x \in A$).

These two statements may be abbreviated symbolically by $x \in A \leftrightarrow x \in B$, so that the preceding definition becomes: $A = B$ provided $x \in A \leftrightarrow x \in B$.

In other words, two sets are equal if and only if they contain the same elements. If A and B are not equal, we write $A \neq B$; this implies, of course, that one of the sets contains at least one element not a member of the other set.

DEFINITION. A set A is a *subset* of a set B if $x \in A \rightarrow x \in B$, and we indicate this by the notation $A \subseteq B$.

For example, if Y is the set of men in your county and X is the set of men in your county weighing over 150 lbs, then $X \subseteq Y$. The denial of the relation $A \subseteq B$ is $A \nsubseteq B$. It is clear that $A = B$ if and only if $A \subseteq B$ and $B \subseteq A$. If $A \subseteq B$ and $A \neq B$, we say that A is a *proper* subset of B and write $A \subset B$. Thus, in the symbolism of the above example, if there are men in your county weighing less than 150 lbs, we could write $X \subset Y$. For some purposes it is convenient to speak of the *empty* set as the set which has no elements. There is only one such set, and it is regarded as a subset of all sets: the set of persons named Phfph listed in your telephone directory, the set of seven-legged cows, and the set of four-sided triangles are illustrations of the empty set—and all the same set! We shall use the letter Z to indicate this set.

DEFINITION. Two sets are *disjoint* if they have no elements in common, i.e., the only common subset is the empty set.

It is possible to associate with any set a special set having members that are themselves sets.

DEFINITION. The set of subsets of a set A is called the *power set* of A. We shall frequently have occasion to refer to such a set of subsets.

If the members of two sets are paired off, one from each set, in such a way that no element in either set remains unpaired, we have obtained what we call a *one-to-one correspondence* between the elements of the sets. Whenever it is possible to do this, the two sets are said to be *cardinally equivalent* or to have the *same cardinal number*. For example, at a dance, the set of men has the same cardinal number as the set of women, provided everyone is dancing with someone of the opposite sex. Note that the concept of *same cardinal number* has been defined before that of *cardinal number*. However, we now come to this latter notion.

From the point of view of a mathematician, probably the most important set of elements, mentioned previously, is the set of natural numbers $\{1, 2, 3, \cdots\}$. This set will be mentioned frequently and will be denoted in the future by the letter N. While it is possible to define the natural numbers abstractly in terms of sets, we shall merely accept them as being completely familiar.

DEFINITION. A set has *cardinal number* n if its members can be put in a one-to-one correspondence with those of the subset $\{1, 2, 3, \cdots, n\}$ of N.

A set that has cardinal number n, where n is a natural number, is said to be *finite;* otherwise, a non-empty set is said to be *infinite.* The cardinal number of a finite set may be obtained, of course, by the process of *counting* the members, a process which actually sets up the one-to-one correspondence of the definition. If the members of an infinite set can be put in a one-to-one correspondence with the set N of natural numbers, the set is said to be *denumerable.* It should be realized that there may be, in general, many different ways of setting up such a correspondence; but any acceptable pairing of the elements must permit one to designate both the element of the set which is paired with an arbitrary natural number, and also the natural number which is paired with an arbitrary element of the set. A proper subset of an infinite set may have the same cardinal number as the whole set. For example, the set of even natural numbers has the same cardinal number as N and so is a denumerable set. To see this, we set up a correspondence in which each natural number of N is paired with the even natural number twice as large. Thus, we pair 1 with 2, 2 with 4, 3 with 6, etc., as indicated in the following array:

$$\begin{array}{cccccc} 1 & 2 & 3 & 4 & 5 & \cdots \\ 2 & 4 & 6 & 8 & 10 & \cdots \end{array}$$

It is evident that the correspondence is one-to-one, and so the sets have the same cardinal number, even though one is a proper subset of the other. The cardinal number of a denumerable set is usually labeled $\aleph_0$ (read "aleph zero"), $\aleph$ being the first Hebrew letter. We note in passing that we have not associated a cardinal number with the empty set.

PROBLEM SET 1.2

1. Use the definition of equality to show that the following relations hold for any sets A, B, and C: (*a*) $A = A$; (*b*) If $A = B$, then $B = A$; (*c*) If $A = B$ and $B = C$, then $A = C$.
2. Show that if $A = B$, $B = C$, and $C = D$ for any sets A, B, C, and D, then $A = D$.
3. If A, B, and C are triangles in a given plane, list some relations used in plane geometry which could replace equality (=), with the statements of Problem 1 still holding.
4. Examine each of the following sets, and list its subsets that have at least two members: (*a*) $\{1, 2, 5\}$; (*b*) $\{a, b, c, d\}$.
5. If B is the set $\{3, a, 5, *\}$ and $A \subset B$, list the possibilities for A.
6. Tabulate two other sets having the same cardinal number as the set $\{a, *, \&, 6, \#\}$.
7. Define two subsets, of the set of people in your state, which are (*a*) disjoint; (*b*) not disjoint.
8. Give two new illustrations of the empty set.
9. Let A, B, C, D, E, and F represent, respectively, the set of plane quadrilaterals, trapezoids, parallelograms, rectangles, rhombuses, and squares. Indicate the proper inclusion relation ($\subseteq$) between the following pairs of sets: (*a*) A, B; (*b*) B, E; (*c*) A, E; (*d*) E, F; (*e*) C, E; (*f*) D, F.
10. If $A = \{1, 2, 3, 4, 5\}$, and X is a set which simultaneously satisfies the conditions $\{1, 2\} \subseteq X$ and $X \subseteq A$, list the possibilities for X.
11. Let A, B, C, and D represent the sets of points within or on the indicated circles. Redraw the diagram for each part of the problem, and cross-hatch the region described by the sets:

(*a*) $\{x \mid x \in A \text{ and } x \in B\}$;
(*b*) $\{x \mid x \in A, x \in B, \text{and } x \notin C\}$;
(*c*) $\{x \mid x \in B, x \in C, \text{and } x \in D\}$;
(*d*) $\{x \mid x \in A \text{ and } x \notin B\}$.

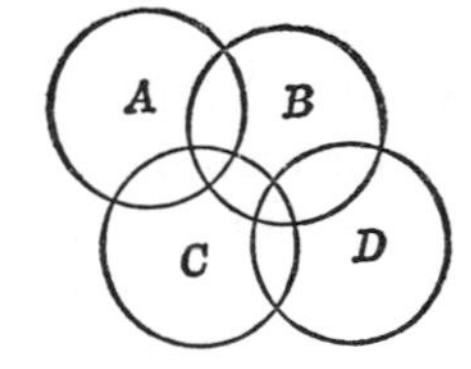

12. Classify the following sets as empty, finite, or infinite, the empty set being indicated by Z: (*a*) $\{x \mid x \in Z\}$; (*b*) $\{x \mid x \in N \text{ and } x + 1 = 2\}$; (*c*) $\{x \mid x \in N \text{ and } 2x = 1\}$; (*d*) $\{y \mid y \in N \text{ and } y \text{ is odd}\}$; (*e*) $\{t \mid t \in N \text{ and } t \text{ is prime}\}$; (*f*) The power set of N.
13. (*a*) Is the power set of the empty set the empty set?; (*b*) List the members of the power set of the set $\{1, 3\}$; (*c*) Is the set A a member of the power set of A?
14. Let $A = \{a, b, 5, 3\}$ and $B = \{b, c, 5, 3\}$. (*a*) List all the subsets of B. (*b*) Which subsets of B are proper subsets of A? (*c*) Which subsets of B are disjoint from A?
15. If $A = \{a\}$ and $B = \{b\}$, what can be said about a and b if (*a*) B is contained in A; (*b*) A and B are disjoint; (*c*) A and B are not disjoint?

16. Show that the set of odd natural numbers is a denumerable set.

17*. Refer to a more advanced book for a proof of the fact that the set of positive rational numbers is denumerable.

1.3 The Cartesian Set

We have mentioned that the only important relation existing between an element and a set is one of membership; from the point of view of the set itself, the order in which the elements may be listed is of no importance. Even subsets of the natural numbers, with their inherent property of order, could have been arranged in any order as far as our definition of the cardinal number of a set was concerned. However, there are many occasions when we must consider *ordered* sets, rather than the unordered type that we have been considering up to this time. It has been said that a recipe for success is (work, play), while (play, work) frequently leads to failure. The order does matter here! The position of a ship in the North Atlantic may be given by stating two numbers, the first being the number of degrees of north latitude and the second the number of degrees of west longitude. Thus, if a ship radios its position as (45, 60), its position is understood to be 45° north latitude and 60° west longitude, and not the reverse. Such a pair of numbers is called an *ordered pair*, with 45 the first and 60 the second *component* in this instance; it is distinguished in notation from an unordered set by the use of parentheses instead of braces.

It is not necessary that the two components of an ordered pair be members of the same set. If A and B are arbitrary sets, we can form ordered pairs of the form (a, b) with $a \in A$ and $b \in B$. For example, if $A = \{1, 2\}$ and $B = \{3, 4\}$ the following ordered pairs can be formed in this way: $(1, 3)$, $(1, 4)$, $(2, 3)$, $(2, 4)$. Two ordered pairs are said to be *equal* if their corresponding components are equal: $(a, b) = (c, d)$ if and only if $a = c$ and $b = d$.

DEFINITION. The set of all ordered pairs of the form (a, b), where $a \in A$ and $b \in B$, is known as the *Cartesian set* $A \times B$ *of* A *and* B.

The case of most frequent occurrence is where $A = B$, and in this case we obtain the *Cartesian set* $A \times A$ *of* A.

If A and B are finite sets, there is an excellent device for exhibiting all the elements of $A \times B$. A horizontal and an intersecting vertical line segment are drawn on a plane, and the elements of A are associated with distinct points of the horizontal line, while the elements of B are associated with distinct points of the vertical line. The points selected are arbitrary, but for the present we shall not select the point of intersection of the two lines. If horizontal and vertical lines are now drawn through all the points associated, respectively, with the elements of B and A, the result will be a network of lines intersecting in points which we may call "lattice" points. We shall associate the ordered pair (a, b) with the lattice point that is the point of intersection of the vertical line through a and the horizontal line through b. In Figure 1–1a we have shown a complete lattice diagram of $A \times B$, in which $A = \{a, b, c, d, e\}$ and $B = \{1, 2, 3, 4\}$.

If A or B is not finite, there are infinitely many ordered pairs in the set $A \times B$. However, if A and B are denumerable, the ordered pairs of $A \times B$ can still be indicated on an incomplete lattice diagram. For example, if $A = B = N$, we have shown in Figure 1–1b such an incomplete lattice diagram for $A \times B$, with only a scattering of ordered pairs indicated.

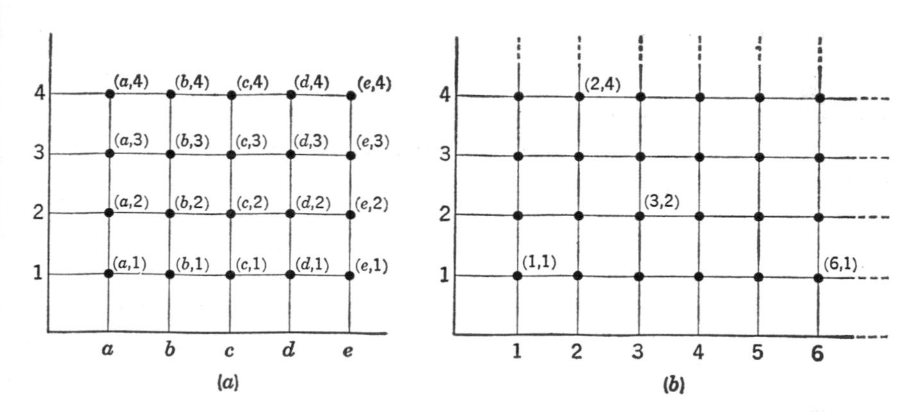

Figure 1–1

PROBLEM SET 1.3

1. List the elements of $A \times B$ for each of the following pairs of sets: (*a*) $A = \{2, 4, a\}$, $B = \{1, 2\}$; (*b*) $A = \{a, x, y\}$, $B = \{3, y, 1\}$; (*c*) $A = \{3, x, a\}$, $B = \{3, y, 1\}$.
2. List all the members of $A \times A$ where $A = \{1, 2, 3\}$.
3. On an appropriate lattice diagram, locate the elements of $A \times A$ if $A = \{1, 2, 3\}$.
4. If $A = \{x_1, x_2, x_3, x_4\}$, with all elements distinct, determine the cardinal numbers of the following sets: (*a*) $A \times A$; (*b*) The subset of $A \times A$ of those ordered pairs having identical first and second components; (*c*) The subset of $A \times A$ of those ordered pairs having distinct first and second components; (*d*) The subset of $A \times A$ of those ordered pairs having x_1 as their first component.
5. Make a lattice diagram of the Cartesian set $A \times A$ where $A = \{1, 2, 3, 4\}$, and answer the following questions relative to the diagram: (*a*) Where are all ordered pairs of the form (a, a) located?; (*b*) Where is an ordered pair of the form (b, a) located with respect to the location of (a, b)?; (*c*) Where are

all ordered pairs of the form $(a, 2)$ located?; (*d*) Where are all ordered pairs of the form $(3, b)$ located?

6. Draw a conclusion from each of the following statements: (*a*) $(x, 1) = (y, 1)$; (*b*) $(x, 2) \neq (y, 2)$; (*c*) $(x, 1) = (3, y)$; (*d*) $(x, y) = (y, x)$.

7. How many subsets are there of the set $\{a, b, c, d\}$? How many ordered pairs can be constructed, using the members of this set for components?

8. (*a*) What can be said about the number of elements of any Cartesian set $A \times A$?; (*b*) Describe the set $A \times A$ where $A = \{1\}$.

9. The idea of a Cartesian set can be extended to the set $A \times B \times C$ of all ordered triples (a, b, c), in which $a \in A$, $b \in B$, and $c \in C$. Write down all the elements of $A \times A \times A$ where $A = \{1, 2\}$.

10. If $A = \{2, a, *\}$, determine (*a*) all the subsets of A that have two members; (*b*) the power set of A; (*c*) the Cartesian set of A.

1.4 Operations on Sets

Let us suppose for the purpose of the present discussion, that all the basic elements to be considered are members of some given set or *universe* U. The various sets A, B, or C, which we shall introduce, will be subsets of U, i.e., members of the power set of U. We now propose to define operations on the subsets of U to obtain other subsets of U.

DEFINITION. The set $\{x \mid x \in A \text{ and } x \in B\}$ is called the *intersection* or *meet* of A and B and is indicated by $A \cap B$. The process, by means of which $A \cap B$ is obtained from A and B, is known as the *operation of intersection.*

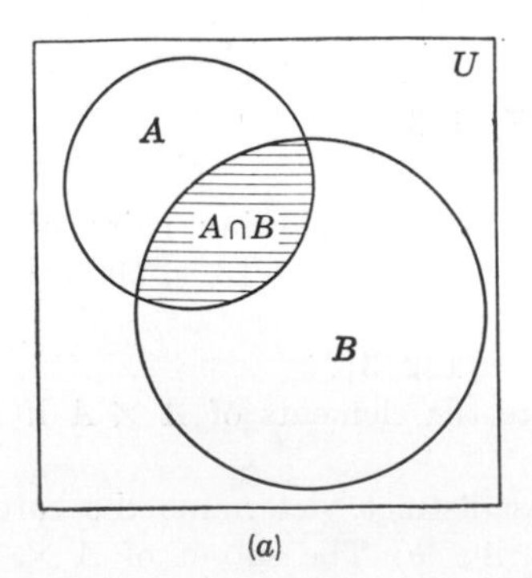

(a)

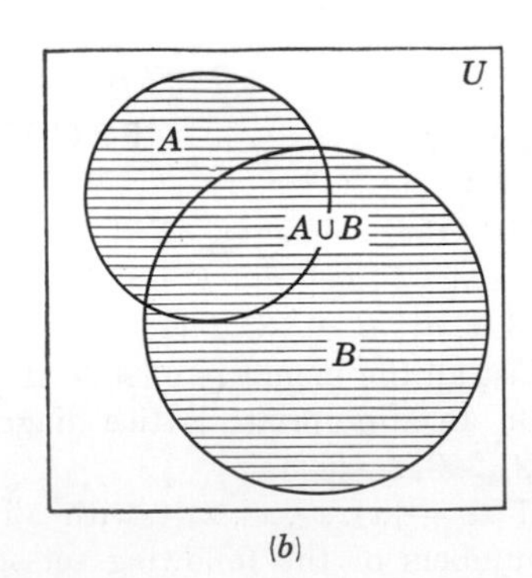

(b)

Figure 1–2

Clearly, $A \cap B$ is the set of elements common to A and B. For example, if $A = \{2, 3, 5, 8, 9\}$ and $B = \{2, 3, 4, 5, 6\}$, it is evident that $A \cap B = \{2, 3, 5\}$. A geometric illustration may be helpful. Thus, let U be the set of points in or on the square shown in Figure 1–2*a*, and let A and B be the sets of points in or on the indicated circles. The set $A \cap B$

is then the set of points common to both circles, and is shown cross-hatched in the figure; such a figure is known as a *Venn diagram.*

A process of combining *two* sets of a class of sets to form a third set of the class is called a *binary* operation on the class; the operation of intersection, denoted by $\cap$, is our first such example. It should be noted that the process of forming the Cartesian set from two sets is not this type of operation, because the resultant set is not a member of the original class. We now introduce another binary operation.

DEFINITION. The set $\{x \mid x \in A \text{ or } x \in B\}$ is called the *union* or *join* of A and B, and is denoted by $A \cup B$. The process, by means of which $A \cup B$ is obtained from A and B, is known as the *operation of union.*

In this definition, the word "or" is so interpreted that $A \cup B$ is the set of elements in A alone, in B alone, or in both A and B. For example, if $A = \{2, 4, 6\}$ and $B = \{1, 2, 3, 6\}$, the set $A \cup B$ is $\{1, 2, 3, 4, 6\}$. Again, if A and B are defined as in Figure 1–2*a*, the set $A \cup B$ is shown in the cross-hatched portion of Figure 1–2*b*.

The use of parentheses always indicates that the quantities inside them are to be treated as units. Thus, the expression $A \cap (B \cup C)$ would mean the intersection of A with the union of B and C. If we wished to indicate the union of $A \cap B$ with C, we would write $(A \cap B) \cup C$. An expression like $A \cap B \cup C$ would, of course, be ambiguous.

The two set operations of intersection and union are *binary* in the sense that *two* sets are combined to produce a third. The final set operation which we now describe, involves only *one* set—and the universe—and so may be called *unary.*

DEFINITION. The set $\{x \mid x \notin A\}$ is known as the *complement* of A, and is denoted by A'. The process, by means of which A' is obtained from A, is known as the *operation of complementation*, or the *"not" operation.*

It should be observed that the complement of a set depends on the universe, of which it is considered a subset; the elements of the complement are those elements of the universe that are not members of the set. The cross-hatched portion of the Venn diagram, Figure 1–3*a*, is the complement of the indicated point set A, in the universe U of points of the square.

The three operations that we have mentioned may be performed several times in succession, and the composite expression representing the resultant set may be somewhat complicated. In analyzing such a composite expression, extreme care must be taken in the treatment of quantities inside parentheses as units. Thus, in the Venn diagram, Figure 1–3*b*, the set $[A \cap (B' \cap C)]'$ is the indicated cross-hatched portion, with A, B, and C the sets of points inside the indicated circles. The convenience of using Venn diagrams in analyzing such an expression should be apparent.

If a set, described as a composite of other sets, turns out to be merely the universe U, the expression or representation of the set is called a *universal form.* On the other hand, if the composite set turns out to be the empty set—which we represent by Z—the expression of the set is called an *empty form.* For example, $(A \cap B) \cap (A' \cup B')$ is an empty form, while $(A \cap B) \cup (A \cap B') \cup (A' \cap B) \cup (A' \cap B')$ is a universal form.

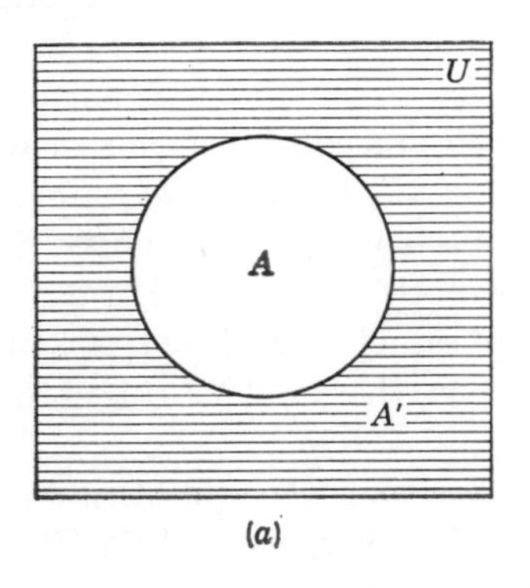

(a)

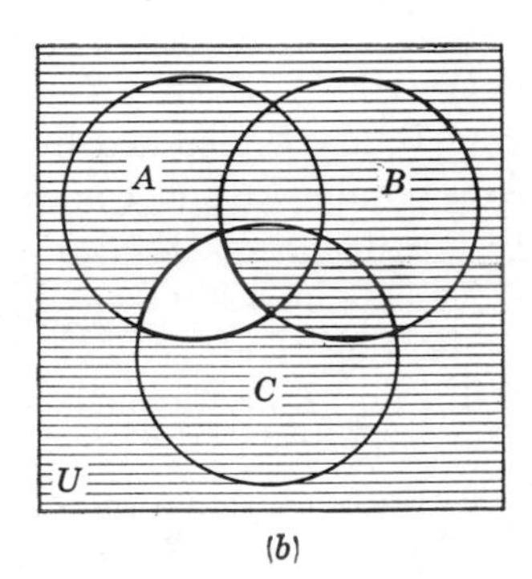

(b)

Figure 1-3

Frequently, it will be convenient to refer to a set $A \cap B'$ as the *difference* set $A - B$, containing those elements of A that are not elements of B. For example, if A is the set of prime natural numbers and B is the set of odd natural numbers, $A - B = \{2\}$. If $B \subset A$, then $A - B$ may be referred to as the *complement of B in A.*

PROBLEM SET 1.4

1. List the members of $A \cap B$ and of $A - B$ for each of the following pairs of sets: (*a*) $A = \{2, 3, 4\}$, $B = \{1, 4, 5\}$; (*b*) $A = \{a, b, c, 2, 3\}$, $B = \{2, c, d, 1, 3\}$; (*c*) A is the set of even natural numbers, B is the set of odd natural numbers.
2. Tabulate the members of $A \cup B$ and of $A - B$ for each of the following pairs of sets: (*a*) $A = \{2, 4, 6\}$, $B = \{1, 2\}$; (*b*) $A = \{a, x, y\}$, $B = \{2, 1, 6\}$; (*c*) $A = \{3, x, a\}$, $B = \{3, y, 1\}$.
3. If $A = \{2, 1, 5\}$, tabulate the members of $A \times A$, $A \cup A$, and $A \cap A$.
4. Describe $A \cap B$ if (*a*) A and B are disjoint; (*b*) $B \subset A$; (*c*) $A = B$; (*d*) $A \subseteq B$.
5. Prove the following: (*a*) If $D \subseteq A$, $D \subseteq B$, and $D \subseteq C$, then $D \subseteq A \cap (B \cap C)$; (*b*) $(A \cap B) \cap C \subseteq A \cap B$.
6. Show that $A \cap B \cap C$ has a definite meaning even without parentheses.
7. If $A = \{1, 2, 3\}$, $B = \{2, 3, 4\}$, $C = \{3, 4, 5\}$, and $D = \{4, 5, 6\}$, list the

members of each of the following sets: (*a*) $A \cap B$; (*b*) $A \cap B \cap C$; (*c*) $(A \cap B) \cup (C \cap D)$; (*d*) $(A \times A) \cap (C \times C)$; (*e*) $(C \times C) \cup (D \times D)$.

8. Let $C = \{1, 3\}$, A, and B be non-empty subsets of $U = \{1, 2, 3, 4, 5\}$. Determine the members of A in each of the following cases: (*a*) $A \cup B = \{4, 5\}$ and $B \subseteq A$; (*b*) $A \cap B = \{3\}$, $A \cup B = \{2, 3, 4\}$, and $B \cup C = \{1, 2, 3\}$; (*c*) $A \cup B = U$, $A \cap B = Z$, and $B = \{1\}$.

9. Illustrate each of the following sets with a Venn diagram, taking U to be the points inside a rectangle with A, B, and C the points in or on overlapping circles contained in U: (*a*) $A \cap B$; (*b*) $B \cap C$; (*c*) $A \cap B \cap C$; (*d*) $A \cap (B \cup C)$.

10. If $U = \{1, 2, 3, 4, 5\}$, list the members of the complement of each of the following sets: (*a*) $\{1\}$; (*b*) $\{2, 4\}$; (*c*) $\{1, 2, 4, 5\}$; (*d*) $\{5, 3, 2\}$; (*e*) $\{1, 3, 5\}$.

11. Let U be the set of natural numbers from 1 to 15 inclusive. Then if $A = \{2, 4, 6, 8, 10, 12, 14\}$, $B = \{1, 3, 5, 7, 9, 11, 13, 15\}$, and $C = \{3, 6, 9, 12, 15\}$, list the members of each of the following sets: (*a*) U'; (*b*) A'; (*c*) $B \cup C$; (*d*) $(B \cup C)'$; (*e*) $B' \cup A'$; (*f*) $(A \cup B) \cap C$; (*g*) $A - (B \cup C)$.

12. Using Venn diagrams or otherwise, establish the truth of: (*a*) $(A \cap B)' = A' \cup B'$; (*b*) $(A \cup B)' = A' \cap B'$.

Note. The above two results are known as "De Morgan's Laws," after the English mathematician De Morgan.

13. Use De Morgan's Laws (see Problem 12) to establish the following results: (*a*) $A' \subseteq (A \cap B)'$ and $B' \subseteq (A \cap B)'$; (*b*) $(A \cup B)' \subseteq A'$ and $(A \cup B)' \subseteq B'$; (*c*) $A \cap (A \cup B)' = Z$; (*d*) $A \cup (A \cap B)' = U$; (*e*) $[(A \cup B) \cap C]' = (A' \cap B') \cup C'$.

14. Classify each of the following as a universal form, an empty form, or neither: (*a*) $U \cap Z$; (*b*) $(A \cap U) \cup Z$; (*c*) $A \cup (A \cap B)'$; (*d*) $A \cap A'$; (*e*) $(A \cap B) \cup (A' \cap B')$; (*f*) $(A \cap C) \cap (C \cap A')$.

15. What relation, if any, holds between $A \times A$ and $A' \times A'$ for an arbitrary set $A \subset U$? Answer the same question for the power sets of A and A'.

16. Using Venn diagrams or otherwise, establish the truth of the following. (*a*) $A \cap (B \cup C) = (A \cap B) \cup (A \cap C)$; (*b*) $A \cup (B \cap C) = (A \cup B) \cap (A \cup C)$; (*c*) $A \cap (A \cup B) = A$ and $A \cup (A \cap B) = A$.

17. Let $N(A)$ be the cardinal number of the set A. Then, if A and B are finite sets, show that $N(A \cup B) = N(A) + N(B) - N(A \cap B)$.

18. If 60% of the employees of a certain firm are women and 70% are married, determine what percentage *at least* are married women. (Hint: Use the result of Problem 17.)

19. If 75% of the employees of the firm in Problem 18 have blonde hair, what percentage *at least* of the employees are blonde women? What percentage *at least* are married blonde women?

20. If $A = \{1, 2, 3\}$ and $B = \{\text{I, II, III}\}$, describe $A \cup B$ and $A \cap B$, if (*a*) the usual interpretation is given A and B; (*b*) the members of A and B are to be regarded as mere symbols.

21. If $A = \{2, 1, 3\}$ and $B = \{2, 1, 5\}$, describe $A \cup B$ and $A \cap B$, if (*a*) the usual interpretation is given A and B; (*b*) A is the set of digits of the numeral 213, and B is the set of digits of the numeral 215.

1.5* Mathematical Systems and Boolean Algebras

By this time, the student may be wondering what a discussion of sets and their operations has to do with mathematics; he always may have thought of mathematics as something quite different. So let us pause for a moment to consider what really constitutes mathematics.

High-school plane geometry—probably the only course of a really mathematical nature studied on that level—has introduced the student to the postulational method in mathematics. Certain concepts, e.g., point, line, and plane, were left undefined (though he had an intuitive notion of them) and the whole of geometry was built upon a system of initial propositions or axioms, involving these undefined concepts. New concepts were then defined in terms of the undefined ones, and theorems were proved on the basis of the axioms. In addition to the axioms, the student accepted, of course, certain rules of Aristotelian logic such as: (1) Either a statement is true or it is not true (Law of Excluded Middle); (2) Not both a statement and its denial can be simultaneously true (Law of Contradiction). But this was pretty much a matter of common sense!

On the other hand, a student who has had a course in high school algebra, where the procedure was probably quite different from that in geometry, may never have realized that it is also capable of a postulational treatment. In reality, the postulational method now is used in all of mathematics.

A mathematical system, from the modern point of view, is the resultant of the application of logic to a set of elements, relations, and operations, the characteristics of which are described by a consistent (i.e., noncontradictory) set of postulates. The nature of the system is completely determined by the choice of postulates. It has been said that all mathematics would be obvious to someone sufficiently clever to comprehend immediately all the logical consequences of a set of postulates. But actually, it is extremely difficult to discover all the consequences of even a very few simple axioms, and so mathematics is far from trivial. It is true, however, that mathematical discovery is different from that of other fields, in that any discovery which we make is in fact inherent in the postulates; our "discovery" means that we are only recognizing a consequence of what we have postulated.

If different sets of elements, relations, and operations are chosen, different mathematical systems arise, all of them equally valid. There is never a question of one being more nearly "right" than another; all must be consistent within themselves. Our choice of a system for investigation depends only on our personal interest in it or on its possible usefulness. The applied mathematician or scientist is most interested in "useful" systems, though it should be pointed out that the usefulness of a system is not always apparent at the outset. If a physical situation appears to satisfy the postulates of a mathematical system—with a suitable interpretation given to the elements, relations, and operations—the results of the mathematics can be tested experimentally in the physical system. If the physical results do not agree with the predictions of the mathematics, the wrong mathematical system has evidently been chosen—but the mathematics may still be correct. So mathematics works hand-in-hand with science. The planet Neptune was "discovered" by mathematics before it was observed in the sky; and the recent great advances in nuclear physics are due, in part, to the application of previously developed mathematical theories to problems on the structure of the atom.

The components of a mathematical system, as we have said, are elements, relations, and operations. The *algebra of sets* which we have introduced in this chapter, has for its elements a collection of sets including a universe U and the empty set Z, two relations designated by $=$ and $\subseteq$, two binary operations indicated by $\cap$ and $\cup$, and one unary operation indicated by $'$. We now generalize this notion.

DEFINITION. A mathematical system which has its relations, operations, and special elements *postulated* to satisfy the same laws as those of the algebra of sets, is called a *Boolean algebra.*

Any mathematical system has one relation, called an *equality* or *equivalence* relation, which allows us to designate when two members of the set are indistinguishable or the same element. We have already used the symbol $(=)$ to indicate such a relation, which must also obey the following laws:

1. $x = x$ for all x (reflexive).
2. If $x = y$, then $y = x$ (symmetric).
3. If $x = y$ and $y = z$, then $x = z$ (transitive).

Our definition of equality of sets obeys these laws, and so is a valid *equivalence relation.* (See Problem 1 of Problem Set 1.2.)

It is not necessary to postulate explicitly *all* the properties of the components of a Boolean algebra, because they can be derived from a relatively small list of axioms. With a small list of axioms, it is of course much easier to check the adaptability of a mathematical system to a given physical situation. As a matter of fact, it is possible to show that any non-empty set of objects Γ, having an equivalence relation and two operations $\cap$ and $'$ that satisfy the seven postulates given below, is a Boolean algebra.

1. A' and $A \cap B$ are uniquely defined members of Γ.
2. $A \cap B = B \cap A$.
3. $(A \cap B) \cap C = A \cap (B \cap C)$.
4. There exists an element Z in Γ, such that $A \cap A' = Z$ for all A in Γ.

5. If $A \cap B' = Z$, then $A \cap B = A$.
6. If $A \cap B = A$, then $A \cap B' = Z$.
7. If $A = B$, then $A' = B'$ and $A \cap C = B \cap C$.

If we wish to check the usual properties of a Boolean algebra, we must define the universe U, the operation $\cup$, and the relation $\subseteq$ as follows: (1) $U = Z'$; (2) $A \cup B = (A' \cap B')'$; (3) $A \subseteq B$ if $A \cap B = A$.

Since the above postulates are easily seen to be satisfied if Γ is the collection of all subsets of some set U, with $\cap$ and $'$ the usual operations for sets, it follows that the algebra so defined is a Boolean algebra. In the next section we give some other examples of Boolean algebras.

The results of the algebra of sets may sometimes be used to discover inconsistencies in sets of numerical data. We give an illustration of this in the setting of a fable.

ILLUSTRATION 1. The chieftain of a primitive tribe of Indians had a feeling that some of his men were cheating him of tax payments. According to the laws of the tribe, a tax had to be paid by any man owning three pieces of taxable property—teepees, horses, and squaws. The tribe practised monogamy and no man owned more than one horse or one teepee. The chieftain knew that none would admit guilt, and so decided on a trick scheme: he enquired of the 2000 men in his tribe how many owned a horse, a teepee, a squaw, a squaw and a horse, a squaw and a teepee, and a horse and a teepee. He knew that he might reasonably expect honest answers to these questions, the results of which are given in the table below. It was observed, moreover, that every man admitted ownership of at least one piece of property.

property	*number of men owning property*
horse	700
teepee	1300
squaw	1000
squaw and horse	400
squaw and teepee	500
horse and teepee	200

The chieftain knew a little about the algebra of sets—in particular the results of Problems 16a and 17 of Problem Set 1.4—and proceeded to analyze the information. He let H be the set of men owning a horse, T be the set of men owning a teepee, and S be the set of men owning a squaw, and reasoned as follows:

$$\begin{aligned} N(H \cup S \cup T) &= N[H \cup (S \cup T)] \\ &= N(H) + N(S \cup T) - N[H \cap (S \cup T)] \\ &= N(H) + N(S) + N(T) - N(S \cap T) \\ &\qquad - N[(H \cap S) \cup (H \cap T)] \end{aligned}$$

$$\begin{aligned} &= N(H) + N(S) + N(T) - N(S \cap T) \\ &\qquad - \{N(H \cap S) + N(H \cap T) \\ &\qquad - N[(H \cap S) \cap (H \cap T)]\} \\ &= N(H) + N(S) + N(T) - N(S \cap T) - N(H \cap S) \\ &\qquad - N(H \cap T) + N(H \cap S \cap T). \end{aligned}$$

On using the data of the table, this equation becomes

$$2000 = 700 + 1000 + 1300 - 500 - 400 - 200 + N(H \cap S \cap T),$$

which yields $N(H \cap S \cap T) = 100$. The chieftain then knew that exactly 100 men should be making tax payments to him.

Sometimes the methods of Boolean algebra can be used to untangle complicated verbal statements, as in the following illustration.

ILLUSTRATION 2. Let us try to draw an interesting conclusion from the following three statements: (1) All engineering students are ambitious; (2) No lazy student gets good grades; (3) Students, who do not get good grades, are not ambitious.

If we let A be the set of engineering students, B be the set of ambitious students, C be the set of lazy students, and D be the set of students who get good grades, the above three statements become in the notation of the algebra of sets: (1) $A \cap B = A$; (2) $C \cap D = Z$; (3) $D' \subseteq B'$.

From the corresponding Venn diagram, Figure 1–4, using the universe U of all students, we notice that $A \cap C = Z$, which means that *no engineering student is lazy*. There are, of course, other equally valid conclusions which could be drawn.

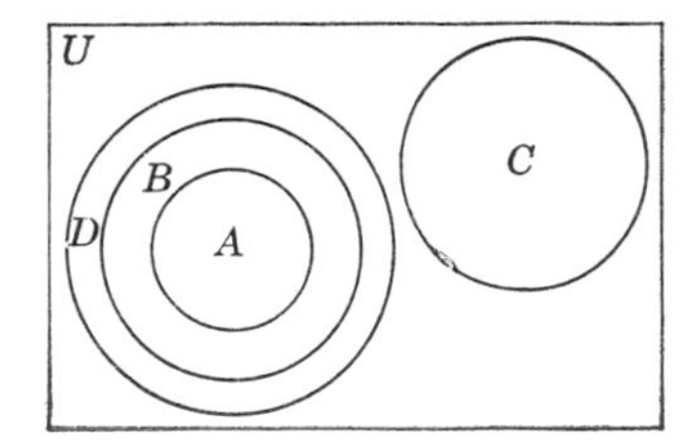

Figure 1–4

SUGGESTIONS FOR CLASS DISCUSSION

1. Think of a situation where the Law of Excluded Middle or the Law of Contradiction does not hold.
2. A set of postulates is said to be *independent* if no one of them can be derived from the others. Discuss possible advantages and disadvantages of an independent set of postulates.

3. Discuss the problem of the applied mathematician in trying to pick out a mathematical system to help in his study of some physical problem.
4. Discuss the famous remark of Bertrand Russell that "Pure mathematics is that subject in which we never know what we are talking about or whether what we are saying is true."†
5. What are some of the differences between mathematical research and research in physics and chemistry?
6. What do we mean by postulates being consistent? How can one test a set of postulates for consistency? (Hint: Suppose you can find an example or model satisfying the postulates?)

1.6* Illustrations and Applications of Boolean Algebra

ILLUSTRATION 1. Consider the set of integral divisors of 110, i.e., Γ is the set $\{1, 2, 5, 10, 11, 22, 55, 110\}$. If a and b are two members of Γ, let us interpret $a \cap b$ to mean the g.c.d. of a and b, and a' to mean the quotient if 110 is divided by a. The set Γ, with the usual definition of equality for its members and the interpretations just given for $\cap$ and $'$, then forms a Boolean algebra. A simple check of the seven postulates of the preceding section verifies this. For instance, the fourth postulate asserts the existence of an element Z such that for each integral divisor a of 110, the g.c.d. of a and the quotient of 110 divided by a is Z. Such an element for the above set Γ is the number 1. Similarly, postulate 5 asserts that if a and b' have no common factor except 1, then a divides b. A check reveals the truth of this for all possible a and b of Γ.

While a Boolean algebra may be considered a generalization of the algebra of sets, it is true that the elements of most Boolean algebras are not sets. For this reason it is customary to discard the "set" notation, except when the elements are actually sets or when there is apt to be confusion. In the new notation the elements Z and U are replaced by 0 and 1, respectively; and the operation symbols $\cup$ and $\cap$ are respectively replaced by $+$ and the juxtaposition of elements as in ordinary algebra multiplication. In general, we refer to these two operations as "addition" and "multiplication." Of course, the student must not associate with 0, 1, and the two operations, the meanings with which he is already familiar —although some similarity will be apparent in what follows.

It is a simple matter to check the validity of the following laws of operation, written in the new symbolism, by referring to the previously stated propositions of Boolean algebra. The first five are identical with rules of ordinary algebra:

$$a + b = b + a, \qquad a + (b + c) = (a + b) + c,$$
$$ab = ba, \qquad (a + b)(c + d) = ac + ad + bc + bd,$$
$$(ab)c = a(bc).$$

† Bertrand Russell, *Mysticism and Logic* (New York: Norton, 1929).

The next six laws are somewhat unusual, due to the special definitions of the operations:

$$a + a = a, \qquad a1 = a,$$

$$a + 1 = 1, \qquad a0 = 0,$$

$$aa = a, \qquad a + 0 = a.$$

The following three laws refer to the "not" operation:

$$a + a' = 1, \qquad aa' = 0, \qquad (a')' = a.$$

The last two that we list are De Morgan's Laws:

$$(ab)' = a' + b', \qquad (a + b)' = a'b'.$$

ILLUSTRATION 2. The simplest system that satisfies the postulates of a Boolean algebra contains only the two elements 0 and 1. We shall refer to this 2-element Boolean algebra as $B(0, 1)$. The operation table for this algebra is given below: the elements in the third and fourth columns are respectively the "sums" and "products" of the corresponding elements in the first two columns; the last column contains the complements of the elements in the first column.

a	b	$a + b$	ab	a'
1	1	1	1	0
1	0	1	0	0
0	1	1	0	1
0	0	0	0	1

ILLUSTRATION 3. A proposition is a declarative statement of some fact, such as "Some apples are red" or "A circle is round." While the truth or falsity of some propositions is in doubt or ambiguous, let us consider only those propositions that can be labeled definitely true or definitely false. Further, let us say that two propositions are "equal" (=) if they are both true or both false. Thus, if p is the proposition that "Some apples are red" and q is the proposition that "A circle is round," we say that $p = q$. Accordingly, if T is *any* true proposition and F is *any* false proposition, *every* proposition of the type we are considering is equal to either T or F.

Let us now define the symbol pq to mean the combined statement "p and q" and let p' be defined to mean "not p." Then using the above meanings of p and q, the symbol pq means "Some apples are red and a circle is round," while the symbol p' means "No apples are red." We now remark that the set of definitely true or definitely false propositions is a Boolean algebra with the operations of multiplication and complementation defined as above. To verify this we need merely check the seven postulates. For example, to verify postulate 2, we note that $pq = qp$ from the definition of multiplication; the element F plays the role of 0, and we note that $pp' = F$ for every p—verifying postulate 4. The other postulates may be checked in a similar manner. The meaning of the symbol $p + q$, in this setting, will be "either p or q or both." The operation table or "truth table" for this algebra of propositions is given below, its construction being similar to that of Illustration 2.

p	q	$p + q$	pq	p'
T	T	T	T	F
T	F	T	F	F
F	T	T	F	T
F	F	F	F	T

This Boolean algebra of propositions contains only two distinct elements T and F, and its resemblance to the 2-element Boolean algebra $B(0,1)$ of Illustration 1 should have been noticed. In fact, these two algebras are identical, except for notation: if we replace T and F in the above algebra by 1 and 0, respectively, and compare the operation tables, the two systems become indistinguishable. Thus, the algebra of propositions or the algebra of logic is a special Boolean algebra. Indeed, Boolean algebra was invented in this form, for it was introduced in 1854 by George Boole in a work entitled "An investigation of the Laws of Thought."

ILLUSTRATION 4. Recently there have been many applications of Boolean algebra to computing machinery and switching circuits. We shall give a few simple examples. A relay is a set of switches, controlled by an electromagnet which opens or closes certain contacts as it is energized. Thus, associated with each relay X of an electric circuit, there is the proposition "Relay X is energized," which may be indicated by x; and at any given instant this proposition is either true or false for each relay of the network. If we interpret x_1x_2 to mean that both relays X_1 and X_2 are energized, and x' to mean that relay X is not energized, the result of Illustration 3 shows that the set of x-propositions associated with a network of relays forms a 2-element Boolean algebra. In this case, the interpretation of $x_1 + x_2$ will be "Either relay X_1 or relay X_2 (or both) is energized."

First let us consider the simple series circuit of Figure 1–5a; the two switches, controlled by relays X_1 and X_2, are shown in their non-energized states, and for simplicity no relay coils have been included in the diagram. Along with the x-propositions of the relays, let us include the q-proposition of the lamp Q: "Lamp Q is lit." We are then to be concerned with the equation connecting the condition of lamp Q with the conditions of the relays. In this case, since *both* relays must be energized for the lamp to light, the desired equation is $q = x_1x_2$.

Similarly, the equation for the simple parallel circuit of Figure 1–5b

is seen to be $q = x_1 + x_2$. This equation results since the lamp will light provided *either* relay is energized.

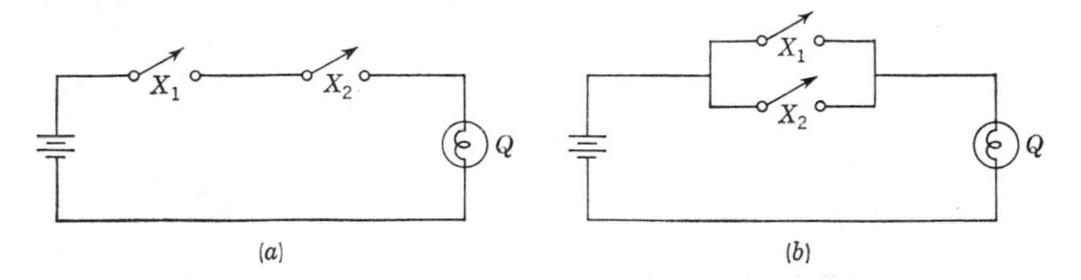

Figure 1–5

In Figure 1–6 we have shown a more complicated circuit. The relays X_1, X_2, and X_3 are of the multipole-double throw variety, with all switches shown as before in their unenergized states. Thus, if relay X_1 is energized,

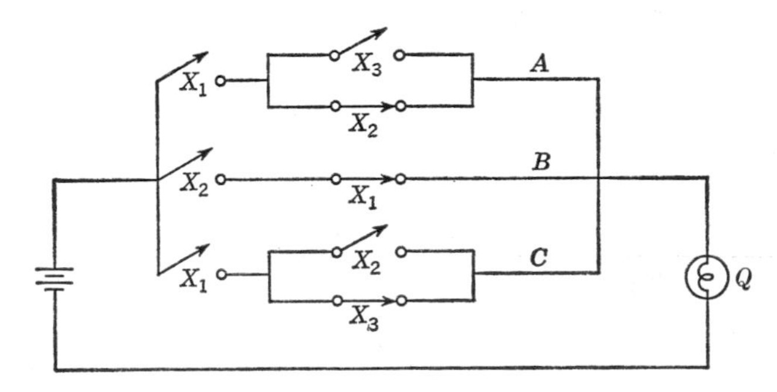

Figure 1–6

the arm of X_1 in branch A will close, its arm in branch B will open, and its arm in branch C will close. Since the lamp Q will light, provided current reaches it from any of the three arms, the equation of condition of Q at any time will be $q = x_1(x_3 + x_2') + x_2x_1' + x_1(x_3' + x_2)$.

If we apply the rules of operation for a Boolean algebra, however, this equation can be simplified. Thus

$$\begin{aligned} q &= x_1x_3 + x_1x_2' + x_2x_1' + x_1x_3' + x_1x_2 \\ &= x_1(x_3 + x_3') + x_1x_2' + x_2(x_1 + x_1') = x_1 + x_1x_2' + x_2 \\ &= x_1(1 + x_2') + x_2 = x_1 + x_2. \end{aligned}$$

It then appears that the complicated switching circuit of Figure 1–6 can be replaced by the simple equivalent circuit of Figure 1–7. We have simplified the original network by means of a Boolean algebra analysis.

ILLUSTRATION 5. Suppose we wish to control a hall light by both an upstairs and a downstairs switch; that is, with a single flip of either switch the light will go from on to off or from off to on. We can use Boolean algebra to help us design such a circuit.

Let D stand for the proposition "The downstairs switch is flipped," and U stand for the proposition "The upstairs switch is flipped." The

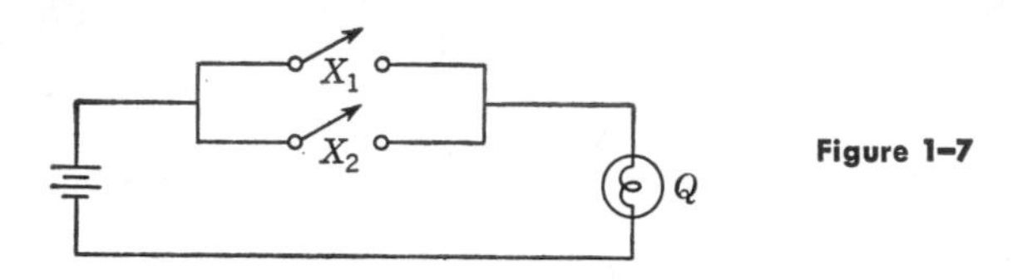

Figure 1–7

"addition," "multiplication," and "not" operations will be defined as in Illustration 3 for general propositions. Furthermore, let L stand for the proposition "The hall light is on." The Boolean algebra of these propositions is equivalent to the special Boolean algebra $B(0, 1)$, just as in the case of general propositions.

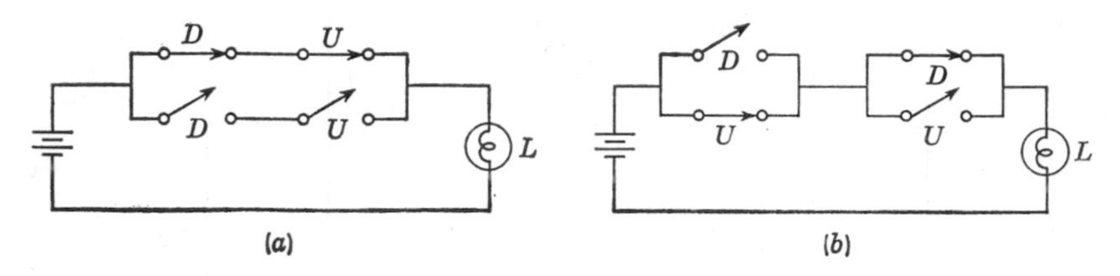

Figure 1–8

Let us design the circuit so that the light will be *initially on*—i.e., as soon as power is applied to the circuit. In this case we wish the light to be on if *neither* switch is flipped *or* if *both* switches are flipped. The equation of condition of the light may be then written $L = D'U' + DU$. The electrical circuit corresponding to this equation is shown in Figure 1–8*a*, all switches being shown in their "unflipped" state. Since $DD' = UU' = 0$, the above equation could also be written in the form $L = (D + U')(D' + U)$. The circuit diagram for this latter equation is shown in Figure 1–8*b*.

ILLUSTRATION 6. According to an old story, a traveler comes to a river bank with his possessions: a wolf, a goat, and a head of cabbage. The only boat available to ferry across is a small one and can carry only the traveler and one of his possessions. Unfortunately, if he leaves the goat and cabbage together the goat will eat the cabbage; and if he leaves the wolf and goat together the wolf will eat the goat. How does the traveler get all his possessions across the river safely? It is easy to find several solutions to the problem, but, to play this puzzle, let us construct a circuit diagram for a machine which will light a red light if part of the traveler's possessions are in danger, and which will light a green light if everything is secure.

Let T, G, W, and C represent, respectively, the propositions: "The traveler is on the initial side of the river"; "The goat is on the initial side of the river"; "The wolf is on the initial side of the river"; "The cabbage is on the initial side of the river." Furthermore, let D represent the proposi-

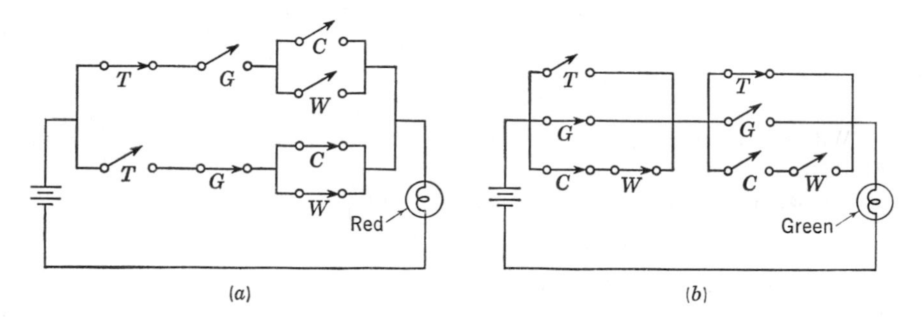

Figure 1–9

tion "There is danger." The following equation is then seen to be valid: $D = T'GCW + T'GCW' + TG'C'W' + TG'C'W + T'GWC + T'GWC' + TG'W'C + TG'W'C'$. On simplification, according to the rules of Boolean algebra, this equation reduces to $D = T'GC + TG'C' + T'GW + TG'W'$ or $D = T'G(C + W) + TG'(C' + W')$. The circuit for this equation is shown in Figure 1–9a; a red light comes on in the event of danger.

An application of De Morgan's Laws to the above equation yields $D' = (T + G' + C'W')(T' + G + CW)$, which is the equation representing the safe conditions. The corresponding "green light" circuit is shown in Figure 1–9b.

PROBLEM SET 1.6

1. Show that all seven postulates for a Boolean algebra are satisfied by the system discussed in Illustration 1.
2. Decide whether or not the following set Γ, with the indicated definitions for the operations $\cap$ and $'$, is a Boolean algebra. (a) Γ is the set of integral divisors of 15; a' is the quotient if 15 is divided by a and $a \cap b$ is the least common multiple of a and b; (b) Γ is the set of integral divisors of 24; a' is the quotient if 24 is divided by a and $a \cap b$ is the greatest common divisor of a and b; (c) Γ is the set of natural numbers; a' is the number 1 for any a and $a \cap b$ is the smaller of a and b.

3. What is the interpretation of $a \cup b$ in Illustration 1? Identify the element U in this illustration.
4. Use a Venn diagram to help you draw a conclusion from the following statements: Some laws are complicated; Every complicated law is confusing; No confusing law is satisfactory.
5. Let p and q be declaratory statements, as in Illustration 3, but let $p \cap q$ have the meaning of "p if and only if q" as defined in the table below.

p	T	T	F	F
q	T	F	T	F
$p \cap q$	T	F	F	T

With p' defined as usual, is this algebra of propositions a Boolean algebra?
6. Using Illustration 4 as a guide, explain the meaning of each of the following: (a) $x_1 \cap x_2 \cap x_3$; (b) $x_1 \cup x_2$; (c) $(x_1 \cap x_2')'$; (d) $(x_1' \cap x_2' \cap x_3')'$.
7. Draw an interesting conclusion from the following statements: No one reads the *Times* unless he is well educated; No polecat can read; Those who cannot read are not well educated.
8. If p and q are propositions, show that $p' \cup q$ means "p implies q" (in symbols $p \rightarrow q$) with the usual meaning for the symbol $\cup$. (Hint: $p \rightarrow q$ means that q must be true unless p is false.)
9. A *tautology* is a statement which is true regardless of the nature of the components of the statement, as for instance $(p \cap p')'$. Using Problem 8, which of the following are tautologies? (a) $p \rightarrow p'$; (b) $(p \rightarrow q') \rightarrow (q' \rightarrow p)$; (c) $(p \rightarrow q) \rightarrow (q' \rightarrow p')$.
10. Show that the usual definition of $p \cup q$ (Illustration 3) requires it to mean "p or q or both."
11. Before the date of a Sunday school picnic, a survey was made to determine the likes of the children. Of the 500 children in the Sunday school 400 liked candy, 350 liked ice cream, 200 liked chocolate cake, 150 liked ice cream and chocolate cake, 150 liked candy and chocolate cake, and 250 liked ice cream and candy. From the results of the survey, how many of the children liked all three items?
12. Use Boolean algebra to show that the following diagrams represent equivalent switching circuits.

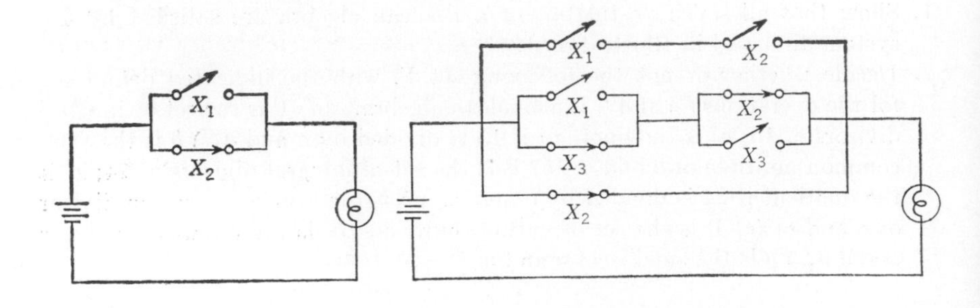

REVIEW TEST A

1. List the members of (*a*) the set A of natural numbers less than and prime to 20; (*b*) the set B of prime natural numbers between 10 and 25.
2. Referring to Problem 1, list the members of (*a*) $A \cap B$; (*b*) $A \cup B$.
3. If a is a member of the set $A = \{1, 2\}$ and b is a member of the set $B = \{1, 0\}$, list all the ordered pairs of the form (a, b). What is the name given to the set of all such ordered pairs?
4. If $A = \{\text{Lincoln, Washington, Jefferson}\}$ and $B = \{\text{Lincoln, Madison, Coolidge}\}$, list the members of the set $C = \{x \mid x \in (A \cap B)\}$.
5. If $A = \{1, 3, a, c\}$ and $B = \{1, 5, b, c\}$, find the largest subset $E \subset A$ and the largest subset $F \subset B$, such that $E \cap F$ is the empty set.
6. Let C be the set of mathematics sections, D be the set of freshman mathematics sections, and E be the set of graduate mathematics sections in your college. Use the symbols $\subset$ or $\supset$ to relate (*a*) C with D; (*b*) C with E. Describe $D \cap E$.
7. A certain Cartesian set has exactly 9 members, two of which are (a, b) and $(2, b)$, a, b, and 2 being distinct elements. Write down the remaining seven members of the set.
8. If $U = \{1, 2, 3, 4, 5, 6, 7, 8, 9, 10\}$, $A = \{2, 4, 6, 8\}$, and $B = \{1, 4, 6, 9\}$, and U is the universe of sets A and B, list the members of $(A' \cup B)'$.
9. If $A = \{1, 3\}$, tabulate the power set of the power set of A.
10. Is there any difference between a chocolate sundae without chocolate and a pineapple sundae without pineapple? Use this idea to illustrate the empty set.
11. Let the universe U be the set of points inside or on the square containing the following sets: A = the points inside or on a circle; B = the points inside or on a triangle; C = the points inside or on a rectangle. Suppose further that $A \subset B$ and $A \cap C$ is not empty. Use a Venn diagram to describe the set $(B \cap C) \cap A'$.
12. If A and B are sets, what is the meaning of the symbolic statement

$$A = B \leftrightarrow A \subseteq B \text{ and } B \subseteq A?$$

REVIEW TEST B

1. Tabulate the following sets: (*a*) the set A of states touched by the Mississippi river; (*b*) the set B of states, the names of which start with the letter M.
2. Referring to Problem 1, list the members of (*a*) $A \cap B$; (*b*) $A \cup B$.
3. If a is a member of the set $A = \{1, 3, 4\}$, and b is a member of the set $B = \{1, 5\}$, list all the ordered pairs of the form (a, b). What name is given to this set of ordered pairs?
4. If $A = \{1, 3, a, c\}$ and S is the power set of A, list all the members of S.
5. List the members of the Cartesian set $A \times A$, where $A = \{1, 3, 5\}$.

6. If $U = \{1, 2, 3, 4, 5, 6, 7, 8, 9, 10\}$ is the universe of the set $A = \{2, 4, 6, 8\}$, tabulate the set A'.
7. If $A = \{a, b, c, d\}$ and $B \subset A$, list the possibilities for B.
8. If $U = \{1, 2, 3, 4, 5, 6, 7, 8, 9, 10\}$ is the universe, $A = \{1, 3, 5\}$, and $B = \{3, 9, 10\}$, list the members of $(A \cap B')'$.
9. If $A = \{0, 1\}$, describe the power set of the power set of A.
10. Name two properties which are possessed by no object. Use these to illustrate the empty set.
11. Let the universe U be the set of points inside or on a plane equilateral triangle. Join the midpoints of the sides to form another triangle, the interior points of which comprise the set B. If C is the set of points inside or on the triangle formed by joining the midpoints of the second triangle, describe the set $C \cap B'$.
12. Give two methods for determining whether two finite sets have the same cardinal number.

REFERENCES

Books

ALLENDOERFER, C. B. AND C. O. OAKLEY, *Principles of Mathematics*, New York, McGraw-Hill, 1955. (Chaps. 1 and 5.)

ANDREE, RICHARD V., *Selections from Modern Abstract Algebra*, New York, Holt, 1957. (Chap. 3.)

COURANT, RICHARD AND HERBERT ROBBINS, *What is Mathematics?*, New York, Oxford, 1941. (Pp. 108–114.)

MAY, KENNETH O., *Elementary Analysis*, New York, Wiley, 1950. (Chap. 2.)

THE COLLEGE MATHEMATICS STAFF, *Fundamental Mathematics*, Chicago, The University of Chicago Press, 1948. (Vol. 1, Chaps. 2 and 3.)

American Mathematical Monthly

HOHN, FRANZ, "Some Mathematical Aspects of Switching," Vol. 62, p. 75 (1955).

LENNES, N. J., "The Foundations of Arithmetic," Vol. 45, p. 70 (1955).

MACLANE, SAUNDERS, "Symbolic Logic," Vol. 46, p. 289 (1939).

STABLER, E. R., "Boolean Algebra as an Introduction to Postulational Methods," Vol. 50, p. 106 (1943).

2

THE REAL NUMBER SYSTEM

God created the integers; all else is the work of man.

L. KRONECKER

2.1 Introduction

It may have appeared from our discussion of mathematical systems in the preceding chapter that these systems are quite independent of things physical and that it is a chance event if a scientist is able to make any use of them. While their use may be fortuitous, it nonetheless frequently happens that a system evolves along with and as an aid to the solution of a particular physical problem. Our system of real numbers today has a completely abstract description, independent of any physical interpretation, but it is still true that a historical development of the real number system is in large part the story of the evolution of the science of measurement. This science began with the measurement of the size of a *set* of objects, the natural numbers being used for this purpose; and as more comprehensive measurements were required, it became necessary to introduce new numbers, along with their "working" rules of operation, i.e., rules that made practical sense. When these numbers were seen later to be merely elements of a mathematical system satisfying certain postulates, all reference to the process of measurement was eliminated, and they were referred to as elements of an abstract mathematical system—with an application in the science of measurement! It would be beyond the purpose or scope of this book to give an abstract formal development of the real number system, which is possible today; we prefer rather to point out the different stages in its evolution, how the need for new numbers arose, and how the new numbers satisfied the need.

Before proceeding with this survey, however, it is perhaps appropriate to make a brief comment on the nature of the number concept. Our use of the natural number symbols in Chapter 1 has quite correctly implied that they are *names* of abstract entities known as *numbers*. But what is a number? This question has been asked often in the past, but not until modern times has a logically satisfactory answer been given.† The natural

† Bertrand Russell, *Introduction to Mathematical Philosophy* (London: George Allen and Unwin, Ltd., 1919).

numbers were created by the human mind to count the number of elements in a set and have no reference to the characteristics of these elements. Thus the cardinal number of a set is an abstraction of all sets having the same cardinal number as the given set. For example, the number 3 is an abstraction of all sets having three members, a statement which verbally appears to be circular, but which actually is not. Somewhat similar abstractions are possible for the rational, real, and complex numbers, but we shall not discuss this further. Fortunately, it is possible to work with numbers, regarded as measures of quantities, without knowing the philosophical relationship between their practical and abstract natures. For even a child knows the meaning of such a statement as "There are 3 apples in the bag," without any thought as to the meaning of the abstract concept of the number 3. We shall accept the notion of "number" then as being essentially intuitive. Since the symbols that we use for numbers are really names, as for instance the symbols $1, 2, 3, \cdots$, for the natural numbers, it would be proper to refer to these symbols as *numerals*. However, we shall follow the usual practice of designating a number by giving its customary symbolism, for example the "number 3," which is consistent with our agreement regarding the description of sets in Chapter 1.

2.2 The Natural Numbers

The natural numbers, usually designated by $1, 2, 3, \cdots$, are the familiar numbers of counting, and the relations and operations associated with these numbers may be considered to have arisen from problems connected with the process of counting.

Thus, the relations symbolized by $=$, $<$, and $>$ arise from an attempt to compare the sizes of different sets. Let A and B be sets having cardinal numbers m and n, respectively. If the elements of A and B can be put in a one-to-one correspondence, we say that $m = n$. If, on the other hand, A is exhausted before B in the process of establishing the correspondence, we say that $m < n$ or $n > m$, these two symbolisms meaning the same thing. Since any two natural numbers are the cardinal numbers of some two sets, it follows that for any two natural numbers m and n we are able to say: $m = n$ or $m \neq n$; $m < n$ or $m \nless n$; $m > n$ or $m \ngtr n$, where a relation symbol with a line drawn through it indicates the denial of the relation. Furthermore, for any two natural numbers m and n, either $m = n$, $m > n$, or $m < n$. It follows rather easily that the natural numbers can be *ordered* in a horizontal linear array, so that any number is *less than* ($<$) any number to the right of it, and *greater than* ($>$) any number to the left of it in the array. This is the "natural ordering" that is regularly followed when these numbers are indicated. The symbol $\leq$ is a combination of $=$ and $<$, so that $m \leq n$ means that m is *either* equal to or less than n, with a similar remark applying to the symbol $\geq$.

The *operations* of addition and multiplication arise from the desire to determine the cardinal number of the union of two or more sets, the cardinal numbers of which are known.

DEFINITION. If m and n are any two natural numbers, $m + n$ is the cardinal number of the union of two disjoint sets having cardinal numbers m and n respectively.

DEFINITION. If m and n are any two natural numbers, mn is the sum $n + n + \cdots + n$ (m summands).

The numbers $m + n$ and mn are said to be *unique* in the sense that each is one definite number. We have defined multiplication in terms of addition, and have in effect defined mn to be the cardinal number of the union of m disjoint sets, each having cardinal number n. The product mn is said to be a *multiple* of either m or n. For any two natural numbers m and n, the sum $m + n$ and the product mn are well-defined natural numbers, which is the meaning of the statement that the set of natural numbers is *closed* under the operations of addition and multiplication.

DEFINITION. If $m > n$, we define $m - n$ to be that natural number such that $(m - n) + n = m$; i.e., $m - n$ is the solution for x of the equation $x + n = m$.

DEFINITION. If m is a multiple of n, we define m/n to be that natural number such that $n(m/n) = m$; i.e., m/n is the solution for x of the equation $nx = m$.

The processes of determining the natural numbers $m - n$ and m/n from the numbers m and n are called *subtraction* and *division*, respectively. Unfortunately, the set of natural numbers is not closed under these two operations.

An attempt was made by G. Peano (1858–1932) to reduce the theory of natural numbers to the smallest possible set of postulates and undefined terms from which it could be derived Although his set has been shown to be not the smallest possible, nor does it uniquely define the natural numbers as we know them, the so-called *Peano postulates* have become standard characterizations of the natural numbers. The notion of "number" itself was left by Peano as one of the undefined terms.

PROBLEM SET 2.2

1. Indicate which of the following symbolic expressions represent natural numbers: $3 + 6$, $7 - 2$, $3/5$, $8 - 4$, $7/5$, $2 + 1$, $1 - 1$, $12/3$, $3 - 5$.
2. Define the following numbers and state which integers are equal to them: $5 - 2$, $6/2$, $7 - 3$, $20/5$.

3. Indicate the proper relation ($=$, $<$, or $>$) holding between 5 and each of the following natural numbers: 2, 7, 5, -3, $10 - 5$, 1, $10/5$, $20/4$, $12 - 2$.
4. Why is the set of natural numbers not closed under subtraction and division?

Note. Use the definitions of addition and multiplication as given, to verify each of the statements in Problems 5 through 9, for the natural numbers m, n, and r.

5. $m + n = n + m$ and $mn = nm$.
6. $(m + n) + r = m + (n + r)$ and $(mn)r = m(nr)$.
7. $m(n + r) = mn + mr$.
8. If $m + r = n + r$, then $m = n$; if $mr = nr$, then $m = n$.
9. If $m < n$, then $m + r < n + r$ and $mr < nr$.
10. Show that mn is the cardinal number of the set $A \times B$, if A and B are sets having respective cardinal numbers m and n.
11. If the two operations in the statement of Problem 7 are interchanged, is the equality sign still valid?
12. Assuming that $m - (n + r)$ and $(m - n) - r$ are natural numbers, use the definition of subtraction and any of the results in Problems 5 through 9 to prove that these numbers are equal.
13. Tabulate the set $\{x \mid x \in N \text{ and } 3 < x < 8\}$.
14. Tabulate the set $\{x \mid x \in N \text{ and } x^2 < 9\}$. ($x^2$ means xx.)
15. List the members of the following sets: (*a*) $\{x \mid x \in N \text{ and } 3 < x \leq 5\}$; (*b*) $\{y \mid y \in N \text{ and } 2 \leq y \leq 4\}$; (*c*) $\{t \mid t \in N \text{ and } 5 < t < 8\}$.

2.3 The Scalar Rational Numbers

The physical quantity that is measured by the natural numbers is the size of a set of objects, the cardinal number of a set being regarded as its size. In addition to counting, however, we may also wish to measure certain quantities such as length, time, and weight, and with only natural numbers at our disposal we must reduce this problem to one of counting. The procedure is familiar. Thus we select some unit of measurement—foot, minute, pound, etc.—to which we assign the measure 1, and then count the number of these units that are contained in the given quantity. The numerical answer to the problem depends, of course, on the unit adopted. When the natural numbers are so used to express the size of a physical quantity in terms of some arbitrary unit, they are usually referred to as *integers* or *whole numbers.* They are members of the general class of numbers used to measure *size* or *magnitude,* known as *scalar numbers* or simply as *scalars.* Thus, if we say that a mathematics class has 25 students, we are using 25 as a natural number, but if we say that the length of the classroom is 25 feet, we are using 25 as a scalar integer. The relations and operations on the scalar integers are, of course, the same as those on the natural numbers.

There is an additional number which is usually included in the set of scalar integers, but which is not a natural number. We are referring to the number 0, a number of which the characteristic defining properties are $m + 0 = m$ and $m0 = 0$, for any number m. This number 0, used in measurements for the size of a "sizeless" quantity, may not seem very important, for if we have any tangible quantity to measure, its measure will not be 0! However, the absence of a symbol for such a number was a principal reason for the slow advance in the art of calculation for a long period of time. To use the words of Dantzig†: "In the history of culture, the discovery of zero will always stand out as one of the greatest single achievements of the human race." Historically, it was introduced as a symbol for an empty column on a counting board, and only much more recently has it acquired the status of a number. Today, we regard 0 just as any other number. It may be used to measure a void quantity, but we shall refrain from calling it the cardinal number of the empty set, for there are difficulties†† with such a definition. Furthermore, we define $0 < m$ for any natural number m, so that 0 precedes 1 in the ordered array of natural numbers.

We are assuming complete familiarity with the rules associated with the relations and operations of the natural numbers or scalar integers including 0, but since the names of some of the rules may be unfamiliar, we list them below. In the sequel, these rules will be referred to as the Basic Laws of Arithmetic.

1. Commutative Laws: $m + n = n + m$; $mn = nm$.
2. Associative Laws: $(m + n) + r = m + (n + r)$; $(mn)r = m(nr)$.
3. Distributive Law: $m(n + r) = mn + mr$.
4. Identity Laws: The number 1 is the only number such that $m1 = m$, for any number m; the number 0 is the only number such that $m + 0 = m$, for any number m. These two numbers are known as the *identities* of multiplication and addition, respectively.
5. Cancellation Laws: $m + r = n + r$ if and only if $m = n$; $mr = nr$ if and only if $m = n$, provided $r \neq 0$.
6. Monotonic Laws: $m + r < n + r$ if and only if $m < n$; $mr < nr$ if and only if $m < n$, provided $r > 0$.

The above rules hold, of course, for arbitrary scalar integers m, n, and r, except as noted.

In making any sort of measurement of a physical quantity, except the cardinal number of a finite set, one of the first difficulties encountered is the fact that these measurements never "come out even." The measured

† Tobias Dantzig, *Number, The Language of Science* (New York: Macmillan, 1939), p. 35.

†† Garrett Birkhoff and Saunders MacLane: *A Survey of Modern Algebra*, rev. ed. (New York: Macmillan, 1953), p. 368.

length of a table is never exactly 5 feet, nor is the measured length of a time interval ever exactly 10 minutes. While it is impossible to eliminate this difficulty, we can reduce the size of the error by making our unit of measurement smaller, and this is usually done by subdividing the basic unit into "fractional" units. Our number system of scalar integers is not adequate for this type of measurement and so we need an extension. To be a satisfactory extension, the numbers of our new system must:

(1) satisfy the Basic Laws of Arithmetic, to justify their being considered "numbers";

(2) include the original numbers, so that nothing is lost in the extension;

(3) be suitable for the new measurement problem.

In case m is a multiple of n, we have already defined m/n to be a scalar integer. We now extend the meaning of this symbol, and define m/n to be a number for any scalar integers m and n ($\neq 0$), the operations and relations on these numbers being defined in terms of those on the scalar integers.

DEFINITION. If m and n ($\neq 0$) are scalar integers, m/n is known as a *scalar rational number*, the relations and operations on these numbers being defined as follows:

Addition. $m/n + r/s = (ms + nr)/ns.$

Multiplication. $(m/n)(r/s) = mr/ns.$

Equality. $m/n = r/s$ if $ms = nr.$

Less than. $m/n < r/s$ if $ms < nr.$

It is a simple but perhaps tedious application of the definitions to check the fact that the Basic Laws of Arithmetic are satisfied by these new numbers. For example, if m/n and r/s are any two scalar rational numbers, $m/n + r/s = (ms + nr)/ns = (nr + ms)/sn = (rn + sm)/sn = r/s + m/n$, so that the commutative law of addition is satisfied. Note that we are assuming the validity of the Basic Laws for scalar *integers.* It should be remarked in passing, that the definitions of the operations and relations, as given above, are really forced upon us by the requirement that the numbers *do* obey the Basic Laws, rather than by any practical use to which the numbers can be put. It can be shown, moreover, that the previous definition of m/n, in case m is a multiple of n, is consistent with the more general definition just given.

A scalar rational number of the form $r/1$ does not differ in any essential way from the scalar integer r. Thus, if we *identify* such numbers (i.e., we consider r and $r/1$ to be the same number), the set of scalar rational numbers will contain the set of scalar integers as a subset.

Since $(1/n)n = (1/n)(n/1) = 1/1 = 1$ (where we have just identified n with $n/1$ and $1/1$ with 1), it appears that we can interpret $1/n$ as the measure of a subunit of such a size, that the combined measure of n of them is equal to the basic unit. Since $1/n$ can be made arbitrarily small, it would appear that our measurement problem has been solved with the introduction of the scalar rational numbers. Thus, our extension is satisfactory, according to the criterion given above.

Any scalar rational number m/n may be regarded as the *quotient* of the scalar integer m by the scalar integer n, since $(m/n)n = (m/n)(n/1) = (mn)/n = m$. This property of being the quotient of two scalar integers is frequently used as the definition of a scalar rational number.

The definitions of subtraction and division, as given in Section 2.2, may be easily extended to apply to the scalar rational numbers. From a strictly arithmetic point of view, the principal advantage of the scalar rational numbers over the scalar integers is the fact that division is now always possible—except by 0. For if $(m/n)x = r/s$, we can solve for x and obtain the rational solution $x = (nr)/(ms)$. The system of scalar rational numbers is not closed under subtraction, however.

PROBLEM SET 2.3

1. Simplify the following: (*a*) $2 + 6(1 + 6) - 1$; (*b*) $36 - 5(4 + 2)$; (*c*) $(2 - 1) + (6 - 4)$; (*d*) $2 + 3(4 + 5) - 3$.
2. Simplify the following: (*a*) $2/3 + 1/4 + 1/2$; (*b*) $3/7 + 5/9 + 1/21$; (*c*) $5/6 + 1/3 + 1/2$; (*d*) $2/7 + 5/12 + 2/3 + 1/4 + 2/9$.
3. Simplify the following: (*a*) $(2/3)(1/6)(4/5)(3/1)$; (*b*) $(2/5)(1/4)/(4/5)$; (*c*) $[(1/2)(2/3)]/[(3/5)(2/7)]$; (*d*) $(1/2)(1/3 + 3/2)$.

Note. More problems like the above may be found in Section 1 of the Appendix.

4. Use two methods to simplify each of the following: (*a*) $5(4 + 6)$; (*b*) $3(2 + 4)$. What law did you use?
5. Simplify $2(7 - 2) + 5$. In how many ways can you do this, using only scalar integers?
6. Use the definition of equality to verify that a scalar rational number is unchanged, except in symbolism, if numerator and denominator are multiplied by the same scalar integer or scalar rational number.
7. Use the definition of equality of two scalar rational numbers to determine x from each of the following equations: (*a*) $2/3 = x/6$; (*b*) $7/5 = x/21$; (*c*) $1/x = 5/6$; (*d*) $3/7 = 9/x$.
8. If m, n, r, and s are scalar integers, use the Basic Laws to prove that
$$(m + n)(r + s) = mr + nr + ms + ns.$$
9. If m, n, r, and s are scalar integers such that $m/n = r/s$, show that (*a*) $n/m = s/r$; (*b*) $m/r = n/s$; (*c*) $(m + n)/n = (r + s)/s$.
10. Prove the commutative and associative laws for scalar rational numbers.
11. Prove the distributive and monotonic laws for scalar rational numbers.
12. Prove the cancellation law for scalar rational numbers.

13. If m, n, r, and s are scalar integers, use the Basic Laws to verify the following: (*a*) $(m + n) + (r + s) = (m + r) + (n + s)$; (*b*) $(m + n) + r = (m + r) + n$.
14. Indicate which Basic Laws are used to verify the following, for scalar integers m, n, r, and s: (*a*) $(mn)(rs) = [(mn)r]s$; (*b*) $[(mn)r]s = (mr)(ns)$.
15. To divide one scalar rational number by another, we invert the divisor and multiply. Verify the validity of this rule.
16. Prove that the distributive law and the uniqueness of the number 0 would require that $m0 = 0$ for any number m.
17*. A more formal definition of the scalar rational numbers can be given in terms of ordered pairs, as follows: The scalar rational numbers are ordered pairs (m, n) of scalar integers m and n ($\neq 0$), with addition and multiplication defined, respectively, by $(m, n) + (r, s) = (ms + nr, ns)$ and $(m, n)(r, s) = (mr, ns)$. Prove the first three of the Basic Laws using this notation.

2.4 The Rational Number System

The scalar rational numbers were devised, in part, to make more accurate the measurement of the size or magnitude of a physical object. And there is certainly no limit to the degree of accuracy of such a measurement that might be attributed to our extended number system. Thus, if we think of a number as a measure of the magnitude of an object or quantity, there might seem to be no practical reason for any further extension of the number system. As a matter of fact, the history of mathematics shows that it was a slow and halting process to introduce any new numbers. The fact that eventually negative numbers and complex numbers were accepted implies that either our concept of what constitutes a number has changed or else we have discarded certain notions of practicality!

It is common knowledge that many quantities require measurements involving more than mere magnitude. For example, it is generally accepted that $2 + 2 = 4$! But if one travels a distance of 2 yards from a fixed spot and then proceeds another 2 yards from the second spot, the final position is not necessarily 4 yards away from the original. It is clear that any measurement of distance that is to be unambiguous must involve a *direction* as well as a size. Quantities such as distance, velocity, and acceleration, measurements of which involve direction as well as size, are called *vector quantities;* they are measured by geometric elements called *vectors*, and the arithmetization of vectors calls for a new extension of our number system. In a later chapter we shall give a discussion of the arithmetic of these general vectors, with the introduction of complex numbers, but for the present we are concerned with a special class of vectors that involve only two mutually opposite directions. The numbers that we now introduce for this type of measurement are the familiar signed numbers, such as $-2/3$, $+1/4$, $-1/5$, etc.

For every scalar rational number r there are two *signed* numbers, a *positive* number $+r$ and a negative number $-r$. The scalar number r associated with a signed number is called its *absolute value* or *numerical value*, and is indicated by vertical bars around the symbol. Thus, $|+r| = |-r| = r$. These signed numbers are known as *rational* numbers, and if r is a scalar rational integer the corresponding rational numbers $+r$ and $-r$ are known as *rational integers* or simply *integers*. The number $+r$ is defined to operate exactly like the scalar number r, and for this reason the $+$ sign is usually omitted from the positive numbers, thus identifying $+r$ with r. The number $-r$ is defined to be the solution for x of the equation $x + r = 0$, i.e., $(-r) + r = 0$. The operations and relations on these signed numbers can now be defined according to the familiar rules of high-school algebra, though we omit a restatement of these rules. (See Section 2 of the Appendix.)

How does this latest extension of our number system "measure up," according to the criterion proposed in the preceding section? We have identified the positive rational numbers with the scalar rational numbers, so our requirement (2) is fulfilled. As for the measurement problem, we can regard the absolute value of a rational number as a measure of magnitude and use the sign to indicate the direction of the vector quantity. Thus, for example, $4/5$ and $-4/5$ would indicate two measurements of magnitude $4/5$, but the measurements indicate opposite directions for the measured quantity: the minus sign has taken care of the previous ambiguity of direction. Finally, if we check the Basic Laws of Arithmetic according to the rules of operation of these signed numbers, we find that most of them are satisfied by our new system. Just as with the scalar rationals, the definitions of the operations have been really forced upon us by the desire to have as many as possible of the Basic Laws remain valid, since we feel intuitively that a number should obey these laws. Thus, for example, our definition of multiplication makes $(-1)(-1) = 1$; but the distributive law would require this, for $(-1)[1 + (-1)] = 0 = (-1) + (-1)(-1)$. Since our new numbers involve a new concept—which we have identified with direction in their application—it would perhaps be too much to expect that *all* the Basic Laws would be satisfied. There is, however, only one exception, the *monotonic law*, which must now read: $MR < NR$ if and only if $M < N$, for any *positive* rational number R; $MR < NR$ if and only if $M > N$, for any *negative* rational number R. Thus, if a and b are positive rational numbers such that $a < b$, it follows that $-b < -a$.

If we define the result of the subtraction of S from R (i.e., $R - S$) in the usual way as the solution for x of the equation $S + x = R$, we now know that $x = R + (-S)$ is always a solution. Thus, the numbers $R - S$ and $R + (-S)$ are identified, and *the subtraction of any number is the same as the addition of its negative.* Also, if we represent the scalar numbers associated with R and S by r and s, respectively, the equation $Sx = R$ always has the rational number solution $x = R/S = \pm r/s$, provided $s \neq 0$; the minus sign is taken if R and S have opposite signs, while the plus sign is taken if these numbers have the same sign. This means that division (except by 0) is always possible. Thus, the system of rational numbers is closed, not only under addition and multiplication, but also under the inverse operations of subtraction and division (except by 0). In the sequel, we shall use the symbol $\bar{R}$ to designate the set of rational numbers, and I to designate the set of rational integers.

PROBLEM SET 2.4

1. Simplify the following: (*a*) $(2/3 - 1/2 + 4/5)(2/3 - 1/5)$; (*b*) $(2/3 - 4/5 + 1/9)(3/2 - 2/3 + 5/4)$; (*c*) $[(-3/4)(-2/3)(-1/8)]/(-6/5)$ (*d*) $(-2/3 - 4/5)/(2/5 - 1/9)$; (*e*) $[(-4/7)(-2/3)]/[(4/3)(-3/5)]$.
2. (*a*) Find the sum of the following: $2/3 - 1/4$, $3/5 + 1/3$, $-7/2 - 2/5$. (*b*) Subtract $1/4 - 2/3 + 1/2$ from $3/4 - 7/3$.
3. (*a*) Multiply $(1/5 - 2/7)$ by $(2/3 - 1/2 + 1/4)$. (*b*) Divide $(4/5 - 2/3 + 1/2)$ by $(2 - 7/4)$.

Note. More problems on the simplification of fractions may be found in Section 2 of the Appendix.

4. Give two reasons why the system of scalar rational numbers was not completely satisfactory.
5. Define the number -1.
6. What is the geometric effect of multiplying a rational number by -1?
7. Why do we say that the set of rational numbers is closed under the operations of subtraction and division (except by 0)?
8. What is the essential difference between a scalar number and a vector?
9. Under what conditions do we say that two signed numbers are equal?
10. Explain why the result of subtracting 3 from 5 is the same as that of adding -3 to 5.
11. Tabulate the set $\{x \mid x \in I, -1 \leq x \leq 3\}$.
12. List the members of the set $\{y \mid y \in I, |y| < 2\}$.
13. List the members of the set $\{t \mid t \in I, |t - 2| < 5\}$.
14. List two positive and two negative integers that are members of the set $\{x \mid x \in I, |x - 3| > 2\}$.
15. Tabulate the set $\{y \mid y \in I, |y - 3| < 1\}$.
16*. A more formal definition of rational numbers would define them as ordered pairs (m, n) of scalar rational numbers m and n, with addition and multiplication defined, respectively, as follows: $(m, n) + (r, s) = (m + r, n + s)$; $(m, n)(r, s) = (mr + ns, nr + ms)$. Use this symbolism and verify that the first three Basic Laws are satisfied.

2.5 The Real Number System

The system of rational numbers is quite adequate for all problems of practical measurement involving the size of a physical object, but there are still theoretical measurement-deficiencies in the system. For instance, there is no rational number which measures the theoretical length of a diagonal of a square having sides 1 unit in length. To show this, let us suppose that the diagonal is measured by a rational number p/q, where p and q are rational integers having no common factors. Then, by the Pythagorean Theorem, $p^2/q^2 = 1 + 1 = 2$, and so $p^2 = 2q^2$ (where $p^2 = pp$ and $q^2 = qq$). The square of any integer must contain any one of its factors an even number of times, and in particular both p^2 and q^2 must contain the factor 2 an even number of times, or not at all. But then the right side of the above equation must contain 2 an odd number of times, while the left side must contain 2 an even number of times, if at all. In view of the stated equality, this is a contradiction, and so the diagonal cannot be measured by a rational number. It is to resolve such theoretical difficulties that we must again extend our number system.

A *sequence* is a set, the elements of which are arranged in some definite order, the elements being then referred to as the *terms* of the sequence. The natural numbers 1, 2, 3, $\cdots$, arranged in their natural order, provide an example of a sequence of numbers. Other examples of number sequences are the finite sequence 2, 10, 4, 5 (with this or any other *definite* order), and the infinite sequence 1/2, 1/4, 1/8, $\cdots$, in which each successive term is obtained by multiplying the preceding term by 1/2. A symbol is said to be *indexed* if it is given a natural number subscript. For example, x_5 is indexed by the subscript 5. The index is frequently used as a device for ordering a set of symbols, and a general sequence of n terms may then be represented by: $a_1, a_2, a_3, \cdots, a_n$. When our interest is centered on the *whole* ordered array rather than on the particular terms of a sequence, the sequence is usually written as an ordered pair (a_1, a_2), an ordered triple (a_1, a_2, a_3), or more generally as an ordered n-tuple $(a_1, a_2, a_3, \cdots, a_n)$†; in this case however, the terms are usually referred to as *components*, as we have already seen. The use of parentheses rather than braces will always distinguish a sequence from an unordered set. A more detailed study of sequences will be made in Chapter 9, but for the present we need merely an understanding of the concept.

The procedure for converting a rational number into its "decimal" equivalent is familiar to the student. For example, the rational number 29/25 may be expressed as 1.16 by dividing 25 into 29. The symbol 1.16 is really just a short form for $1 + 1/10 + 6/100$, and the rule for the

† The notation (a_i), $i = 1, 2, 3, \cdots, n$ is also used for a sequence of n terms, the ith term of which is a_i.

addition of rational numbers may be used to check that this number is equal to 29/25. However, it is also well known that if the denominator of a fraction does not divide any power of 10, the division process does not terminate. For example, the number 1/3 becomes $0.\overline{3}$ and the number 107/495 becomes $2.\overline{16}$, a bar over certain digits indicating that those digits are repeated indefinitely. Since we cannot evaluate such a symbol as we did above, the question arises as to the meaning of such a "repeating decimal."

If we tentatively accept a repeating decimal as a designation for a number of some sort, we can use another method to show that this number must be a rational number. For example, consider the number $S = 6.\overline{2345}$. On multiplying by 10,000, this equation becomes $10{,}000\ S = 62{,}345.\overline{2345} = 62{,}339 + 6.\overline{2345} = 62{,}339 + S$, from which we obtain that $9{,}999 S = 62{,}339$. Thus, $S = 62{,}339/9{,}999$, a rational number. The method of this example, which can be completely justified in advanced analysis, is quite general, and so if a repeating decimal is to be accepted as a number, it must be identified with a rational number.

The "less than" relation permits us to think of the rational numbers in a linear array, ordered according to this relation. We can think of them as corresponding to points on a horizontal line, with a "rational point" r to the left of a "rational point" s if $r < s$. Let us designate a definite point on the line as corresponding to 0, and another definite point on the line as corresponding to 1, the distance between these two points being designated as the *unit distance.* We can now locate all positive rational numbers to the right of 0 and all negative rational numbers to the left of 0 so that the numerical distance from 0 to any number, in terms of the unit distance, is equal to its absolute value. We can always do this, since a scalar rational number is the measure of a definite distance on a line segment. In Figure 2–1, we have indicated a portion of such an arrangement of points, with only a scattering of numbers indicated on the *number scale.*

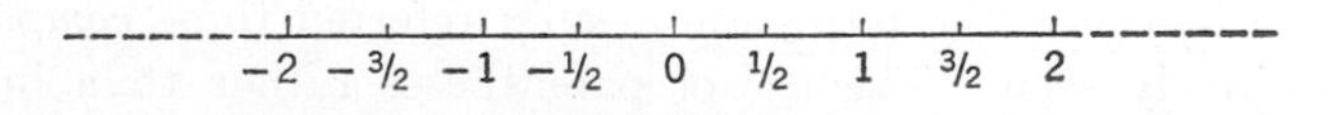

Figure 2–1

The rational numbers are located so densely upon the number scale that if r and s are any two rational numbers, there is another distinct rational number $(r + s)/2$ between them. In spite of this fact, however, the rational numbers can be shown to comprise a denumerable set.† On

† Richard Courant and Herbert Robbins, *What Is Mathematics?* (New York: Oxford, 1941), p. 79.

the other hand, it is easy to see that there are points on a number scale that do not correspond to any rational number. For example, if a circular arc is drawn as indicated in Figure 2–2, i.e., with center at the point O and the segment OT as a radius, the point P cannot be a rational point since we have already shown that the segment OP cannot be measured by a rational number. We are now about to introduce new numbers so that *every* point on the number scale will correspond to one of these numbers.

Figure 2–2

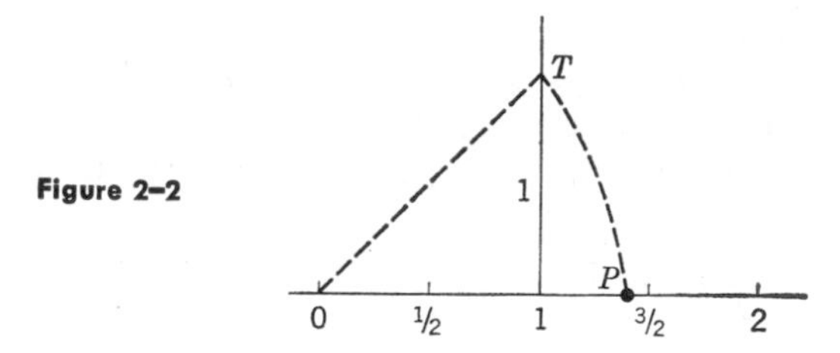

By an *interval* $[a, A]$ on a number scale, we shall mean the set of all points on the line segment between and including the points a and A; furthermore, the end points will be rational during the course of the present discussion. Thus, the integers separate the number scale into a set of intervals one unit long, the intervals overlapping at their end-points. Now let P be *any* point on the number scale, i.e., not necessarily corresponding to a rational number. If P lies on a boundary of one of the unit intervals, it will correspond to an integer; otherwise, it will lie inside one of the unit intervals and let us suppose for purposes of illustration that it lies inside the third positive interval, i.e., between 2 and 3. Let us designate this interval by I_1, and subdivide it into 10 equal parts. If P lies on one of the boundaries of these subintervals, it will correspond to a rational number and so a finite decimal, as we have already shown; otherwise, it will lie inside one of the subintervals, say the fourth, which we shall designate by I_2. Thus, P will lie between the points labeled 2.3 and 2.4. If the interval I_2 in turn is subdivided into 10 equal parts, the point P as before will either lie on one of the subinterval boundaries or inside a subinterval. In the former case, P will correspond to a finite decimal, while in the latter case let us suppose that the subinterval containing P is the eighth, designated by I_3; thus, P will lie between the points labeled 2.37 and 2.38 on the number scale. This procedure can be continued indefinitely, and either P will eventually lie on the boundary of some subinterval—and so correspond to a finite decimal—or P will always lie *inside* a subinterval. An infinite sequence of intervals $I_1, I_2, I_3, \cdots$, such that each is contained in the previous one $(\cdots I_3 \subset I_2 \subset I_1)$ and such that the length of I_n "tends to zero" as n increases, is known as a sequence of *nested intervals*. The expression "tends to zero" means that the lengths of the intervals eventually get arbitrarily close but never quite equal to zero. By our construction, the point P will either lie inside every interval of the sequence, or will correspond to a finite decimal. Let us suppose that the former situation holds. It is a *basic postulate of geometry* that every sequence of nested intervals with rational end-points contains—and so determines—one and only one point. (It is clear that such a sequence could not contain two distinct points, for the lengths of the subintervals will eventually be less than the distance between the points.) In our illustration, the point P, which is inside each subinterval, is determined by the sequence $I_1 = [2, 3]$, $I_2 = [2.3, 2.4]$, $I_3 = [2.37, 2.38]$, $\cdots$; moreover, we may consider the infinite decimal $2.37 \cdots$, thus determined, as a *new type of number* which corresponds to the point P, the three dots indicating that an indefinite number of digits may be obtained.

DEFINITION. A real number is an infinite decimal.

We may always regard a finite decimal as a repeating decimal with 0 the repeated digit, and so we have already seen that every rational number is equal to a repeating decimal and conversely. The non-repeating decimals are then new numbers, which we shall designate as *irrational* numbers. The rational and irrational numbers together comprise the *real number system.*

It is possible for more than one sequence of nested intervals to determine the same point, but this point will correspond to a unique infinite decimal except when such a number has a repeated digit 9. For example, the numbers $1.7\overline{9}$ and 1.8 must be regarded as equal, for the point determined by the nested intervals of $1.7\overline{9}$ is the point corresponding to 1.8. With this understanding, it can then be shown that there is a one-to-one correspondence between the set of points on a number scale and the set of real numbers. Such a scale is usually called an *algebraic scale*, and we may state the *Fundamental Postulate of Analytic Geometry* in the form: There is a one-to-one correspondence between the set of points of an algebraic scale and the set of real numbers. As a matter of fact—and this is an important item—our language will frequently imply that we are actually identifying the points of such a scale with the real numbers corresponding to them. Thus, we shall frequently speak of the "point" 2 or the "point" $\sqrt{3}$, etc., of an algebraic scale.

The development of the system of real numbers now makes it possible to assign a definite real number as the length of any line segment, and so the measurement of such segments is always possible.

Let a and b be two real numbers defined, respectively, by the sequences of nested intervals having ith terms $[a_i, A_i]$ and $[b_i, B_i]$. We define $a + b$ to be the number determined by the sequence, the ith term of which is $[a_i + b_i, A_i + B_i]$, and the product ab is defined to be the number determined by the sequence, the ith term of which is $[a_ib_i, A_iB_i]$. Furthermore, we define $a < b$ to mean that the number a is located left of the number b on an algebraic scale. It can be shown that all the rules of operation of the rational numbers remain valid for real numbers, though we shall not give a proof of this fact. (In practical computation, of course, any real number may be replaced by a rational number which approximates it to any desired degree of accuracy.) Hence, the real number system is a satisfactory extension of the rational number system. In the sequel, we shall use $R^{\#}$ to designate the set of real numbers, the sets previously labeled $\bar{R}$, I, and N being proper subsets of $R^{\#}$.

ILLUSTRATION 1. Find the positive real number, the square of which is 2.

Solution. We now know that such a number—corresponding to the point P of Figure 2–2—may be expressed as an infinite decimal. The procedure for finding the number is to determine a sequence of nested intervals that contain the corresponding point on an algebraic scale. Such a sequence would have for its ith term $[a_i, A_i]$, with $a_i^2 < 2$ and $A_i^2 > 2$. It is then easy to obtain, by actual computation, the following sequence: [1, 2], [1.4, 1.5], [1.41, 1.42], [1.414, 1.415], [1.4142, 1.4143], $\cdots$, and the real number thereby determined is the irrational number 1.4142 $\cdots$. We may designate this number by the symbol $\sqrt{2}$.

ILLUSTRATION 2. Construct a sequence of nested intervals that determines the number $\sqrt{2} + \sqrt{5}$.

Solution. The number $\sqrt{2}$ is determined by the sequence of Illustration 1. In a similar manner, the following sequence for $\sqrt{5}$ may be determined: [2, 3], [2.2, 2.3], [2.23, 2.24], [2.236, 2.237], [2.2360, 2.2361], $\cdots$. If the two sequences are now added by adding their respective terms, we obtain the following sequence: [3, 5], [3.6, 3.8], [3.64, 3.66], [3.650, 3.652], [3.6502, 3.6504], $\cdots$. This sequence then determines the number $\sqrt{2} + \sqrt{5}$, which we may write as 3.650 $\cdots$. It should be observed that the first interval of this latter sequence is 2 units long, and so each successive interval is twice as long as with the usual subdivision. This is, of course, illustrative of the fact that the same point and number may be determined by many sequences of nested intervals.

PROBLEM SET 2.5

1. Construct a sequence of nested intervals for $\sqrt{7}$, and determine to four decimal places the decimal representation of this number.
2. Express each of the following rational numbers as repeating decimals: (*a*) 2/3; (*b*) $-4/7$; (*c*) $-5/9$; (*d*) 4/5.

3. Express each of the following repeating decimals as a quotient of two integers: (*a*) $1.\overline{437}$; (*b*) $-2.\overline{0623}$; (*c*) $5.\overline{17457}$.
4. State whether the real number $0.2347\overline{9}$ is less than, equal to, or greater than each of the following: (*a*) $0.234\overline{623}$; (*b*) 0.23478; (*c*) $0.23457\overline{9}$.
5. Give an intuitive explanation of why we must have $0.\overline{9}$ equal to 1.
6. Construct a sequence of nested intervals for $\sqrt{3}$, and determine the decimal representation of this number to four decimal places.
7. Use the results of Problems 1 and 6 to construct a sequence of nested intervals for: (*a*) $\sqrt{3} + \sqrt{7}$; (*b*) $\sqrt{3}\,\sqrt{7}$. Represent each number as a four-place decimal.
8. Prove that $\sqrt{3}$ is not rational.
9. Classify each of the following numbers as a rational integer, a rational number, or an irrational number: -5, $\sqrt{9}$, $3\sqrt{3}$, 2, 1, $\sqrt{8}$, -5, $\sqrt{12}$.
10. Express the rational integer 3 as a quotient of two integers, and in two ways as an infinite decimal.
11. Show how to locate the square root of any integer on an algebraic scale, using ruler and compasses.
12. The difference between any two rational numbers is rational, but the difference between two irrational numbers is not necessarily irrational. Prove the first statement and give an example to illustrate the second.
13. If r is a rational and s an irrational number, show that $r + s$ is an irrational number. (Assume that $r + s$ is rational and get a contradiction.)
14. Indicate the following sets of points on an algebraic scale: (*a*) $\{x \mid x \in R^{\#}, x^2 < 4\}$; (*b*) $\{x \mid x \in R^{\#}, |x - 1| < 3\}$; (*c*) $\{y \mid y \in R^{\#}, -3 < y \leq 2\}$; (*d*) $\{y \mid y \in R^{\#}, |y - 1| > 3\}$.
15. Indicate the following sets of points on an algebraic scale: (*a*) $\{x \mid x \in R^{\#}, |x + 2| < 3\}$; (*b*) $\{x \mid x \in R^{\#}, |x - 2| > 2\}$; (*c*) $\{t \mid t \in R^{\#}, (t - 2)^2 \leq 1\}$; (*d*) $\{t \mid t \in R^{\#}, t^2 > 1\}$.

16*. Look up a proof, in a more advanced mathematics book, that the set of real numbers is not denumerable.

REVIEW TEST A

1. Use the inclusion relation $\subset$ to connect the four sets of numbers $R^{\#}$, $\bar{R}$, I, and N in a chain.
2. Let $A = \{\sqrt[3]{5}, 4, -3/2, \sqrt{25}, 4.\overline{216}, 1/3, \pi\}$. (*a*) List the rational numbers of A; (*b*) list the irrational numbers of A.
3. Use the symbol $>$ and arrange the numbers of set A in Problem 2 in descending order.
4. If $A = \{-3, -2, -1, 0, 1, 2, 3\}$, tabulate the set $\{x \mid x \in A, |x| < 2\}$.
5. Show, without counting, that the following sets have the same cardinal numbers: {3, *a*, *x*, #, \$, 1}; {4, 5, ?, =, 15, 0}. How would you show that the cardinal number of each of these sets is 6?

6. Which of the following are false? (*a*) $2 + 5 \neq 7$; (*b*) $-3 < 3$; (*c*) $2 \leq 2$; (*d*) $8 > -1$; (*e*) $4 > 4$; (*f*) $-|-2| < 2$; (*g*) $-|-4| = 4$; (*h*) $x^2 < 4 \leftrightarrow x < 2$.
7. Tabulate or describe the set $\{x \mid |x| < 2\}$, where (*a*) $x \in N$; (*b*) $x \in I$; (*c*) $x \in \bar{R}$; (*d*) $x \in R^{\#}$.
8. Use the Basic Laws of Arithmetic to prove each of the following, giving the justification at each step: (*a*) $(a + b)(c + d) = ac + bc + ad + bd$; (*b*) $(ab)(cd) = (cb)(ad)$.
9. Define $-(a + b)$, where a and b are scalar integers. Why is $-(a + b)$ equal to $-a - b$?
10. Solve each of the following equations for x: (*a*) $2/3 = x/9$; (*b*) $7/5 = x/10$: (*c*) $2/x = 8/7$.
11. State whether each of the following statements is true or false, giving a reason for your answer: (*a*) The number system consisting of the "square" numbers 1, 4, 9, $\cdots$ is closed under addition; (*b*) The number system of (*a*) is closed under multiplication; (*c*) The operation of division of two rational numbers is commutative; (*d*) The operation of addition of two rational numbers is commutative; (*e*) The number system consisting of the odd positive integers is closed under multiplication.
12. Find five terms of a sequence of nested intervals for $\sqrt{10}$, and write a four-decimal approximation to this number.

REVIEW TEST B

1. Let P and Q be operations, with PQ the operation consisting of P followed by Q. If we consider two operations to be equal (=) provided the results of the operations are the same, in which of the following is $PQ = QP$? (*a*) P = putting on socks, Q = putting on shoes; (*b*) P = putting on shirt, Q = putting on coat; (*c*) P = putting on hat, Q = putting on overshoes.
2. Let $A = \{2, -5, \sqrt{3}, 3/2, \sqrt{4}, \sqrt[3]{9}, 5/3, 0, -1/2, 1.\overline{234}, 1\}$. (*a*) List the rational numbers in A; (*b*) list the irrational numbers in A.
3. Use the symbol $<$ and arrange the numbers of set A in Problem 2 in ascending order.
4. Tabulate the set $\{x \mid x \in I, |x - 2| < 5\}$.
5. Prove that $\sqrt{5}$ is not a rational number.
6. Prove that $x + \sqrt{2}$ is irrational if x is rational.
7. Use definitions and the Basic Laws of Arithmetic to prove each of the following, giving the justification at each step: (*a*) $(a + b) - a = b$; (*b*) $x(y + 2t) = 2tx + xy$.
8. Draw a conclusion from each of the following statements: (*a*) $2x = 0$; (*b*) $xy = 0$; (*c*) $3xy \neq 0$.
9. Why is the number π not a rational number? Does $\pi = 22/7$? Discuss.
10. Express the repeating decimal $2.\overline{147}$ as a quotient of two integers.
11. Which of the following symbols are meaningless in the set of rational integers: $2 - 4$, $140 - 80$, $6 - 6$, $8/3$, $9/3$, $4/4$?

12. Is there any difference between the natural number 3, the positive integer +3, and the rational number 3/1? Discuss.

REFERENCES

Books

COURANT, RICHARD AND HERBERT ROBBINS, *What Is Mathematics?*, New York, Oxford, 1941. (Chaps. 1 and 2.)

DANTZIG, T., *Number, The Language of Science*, New York, Macmillan, 1941.

DUBISCH, R., *The Nature of Number*, New York, Ronald, 1952.

3

AN AID TO COMPUTATION

. . . nevertheless, there are certain branches of mathematics where calculation conserves its rights.

P. G. L. DIRICHLET

3.1 The Meaning of Exponents

If n real numbers, each equal to a, are multiplied together, an evident extension of the associative law of multiplication shows that the product is independent of the order in which the numbers are grouped. This common product for all such groupings, denoted by a^n, is called the nth power of the number a and n is known as an *exponent.* This natural number exponent then indicates how many times the number a, called the *base* number, is used as a factor. Thus, 5^4 is a short notation for the product $5 \cdot 5 \cdot 5 \cdot 5$, the number 4 being used here as an exponent. We now state the *Laws of Exponents,* which follow immediately from the definition of a natural number exponent and the Basic Laws of Arithmetic. The symbols a and b may be any real numbers but, for the present, the exponents m and n must be natural numbers.

Laws of Exponents

1. $a^m \cdot a^n = a^{m+n}$.
2. $(a^m)^n = a^{mn}$.
3. $(ab)^m = a^m b^m$.
4. $a^m/a^n = a^{m-n}$ if $m > n$;
   $= 1/a^{n-m}$ if $m < n$.

The operation that is the inverse of raising a number to the nth power for some positive integer n is that of finding an nth root. Thus, 3 and -3 are both 2th or "square" roots of 9 since $3^2 = (-3)^2 = 9$, and -3 is a 3th or "cube" root of -27 since $(-3)^3 = -27$. It is an important consequence of the Fundamental Theorem of Algebra, to be discussed in Chapter 10, that there are exactly n complex numbers that are nth roots of any real number a $(\neq 0)$. (The complex numbers comprise a further extension of our number system to be introduced later.) Exactly one of these nth roots is real and positive if a is positive, while if a is negative there is a real nth root only if n is odd, and in this case the real nth root is negative. In either of these two cases we refer to this unique real root as the *principal nth root* of a and indicate it by $\sqrt[n]{a}$, with n omitted from the symbol if $n = 2$. We emphasize that we have now given a meaning to this symbol, for any positive integer n if a is a positive real number, but only for a positive odd integer n if a is negative. Thus $\sqrt{4} = 2$ and $\sqrt[3]{-27} = -3$, but $\sqrt{-4}$ has not been defined. Later in the chapter we shall show how to compute rational number approximations to these nth roots, whenever they are defined, but for the present we are concerned only with the *meanings* of the symbols. We now extend the meaning of exponents, by defining them for *every rational* number power of a *positive real* number and *certain rational* number powers of a *negative real* number, our definitions being guided by the desire that the Laws of Exponents should remain valid. The situation is not unlike that which we encountered in extending the concept of a number, with the Basic Laws of Arithmetic leading the way.

Since a^n/a^n must equal 1 for any reasonable interpretation of a^n as a number, and since the fourth law of exponents would require that this quotient equal a^0, we make the

DEFINITION. $a^0 = 1$, for any real number $a \neq 0$.

If the "number" $a^{1/n}$ is to obey the second law of exponents, we must have $(a^{1/n})^n = a$ and so $a^{1/n}$ must be an nth root of a. In order to give the symbol an unambiguous meaning, we then make the

DEFINITION. $a^{1/n} = \sqrt[n]{a}$, for any real number a, and any positive integer n for which this principal nth root is defined.

Thus, for example, $4^{1/2} = 2$ and $(-8)^{1/3} = -2$; however, $(-4)^{1/2}$ is not defined, at present.

If the symbol $a^{m/n}$ has a meaning for positive integers m and n, the second law of exponents would require that it mean the same as $(a^m)^{1/n}$, and so we make the

DEFINITION. $a^{m/n} = (a^m)^{1/n} = \sqrt[n]{a^m}$, provided m/n is reduced to lowest terms and $\sqrt[n]{a^m}$ is defined. If $r/s = m/n$, $a^{r/s} = a^{m/n}$, whenever $a^{m/n}$ is defined.

The principal nth root of a^m is defined, except when a^m is negative and n is even; and in this latter case, since a is also negative, the principal nth root of a is also undefined. However, if $\sqrt[n]{a}$ is defined, we must have $(\sqrt[n]{a})^m = (a^{1/n})^m = a^{m/n}$, and so the symbols $(\sqrt[n]{a})^m$ and $\sqrt[n]{a^m}$ stand for the same number, when they are defined. Thus, for example, $\sqrt[3]{8^2} = (\sqrt[3]{8})^2 = 4$, the second form being the easier to simplify.

The first law of exponents, applied to a^{-r} for any positive rational r, would require that $(a^{-r})(a^r) = a^0 = 1$, and so the following definition is suggested.

DEFINITION. $a^{-r} = 1/a^r$ for any real number a, and any positive rational number r for which a^r is defined.

With the definitions just given, we have completed what might be called the second or "rational number" stage in the development of the exponent concept. If a is a positive real number, we have defined the number a^n, for any rational number n; however, if a is negative, the symbol a^n has meaning only for a rational number n, the reduced fractional form of which has an odd integer for its denominator.

If $[n_i, N_i]$ is the ith term of a sequence of nested intervals having rational end-points, $[a^{n_i}, a^{N_i}]$ is the ith term of an associated sequence of nested intervals, for any positive real number a. We can now make the following definition.

DEFINITION. Let a be an arbitrary non-negative real number. Then if n is the real number defined by the sequence of nested intervals, having $[n_i, N_i]$ for its ith term, a^n is the real number defined by the sequence of nested intervals, the ith term of which is $[a^{n_i}, a^{N_i}]$.

The definition of the number a^n, for a *negative* real number a and an arbitrary real number n, is somewhat complicated, and beyond the scope of this book. To illustrate the difficulty, however, suppose that we wish to define $(-3)^{\sqrt{2}}$ as a number, with $\sqrt{2}$ defined by a sequence of nested intervals, the lower boundaries of which are 1.4, 1.41, 1.414, $\cdots$. If we try to use the above definition to define $(-3)^{\sqrt{2}}$, the lower boundaries of the associated sequence of nested intervals will be $(-3)^{1.4}$, $(-3)^{1.41}$, $(-3)^{1.414}$, $\cdots$, i.e., $(-3)^{7/5}$, $(-3)^{141/100}$, $(-3)^{707/500}$, $\cdots$. However, while the first term of this sequence is a well defined number, the next two terms and many others are not defined, and so the indicated sequence of nested intervals is without meaning at this time. In Chapter 10, we shall make an extension of our number system, which will include a^n for every rational number n and every negative real number a, though even here the symbol a^n will not be given a universal meaning.

The definitions, that we have given for the numbers a^n, have been motivated by the Laws of Exponents, but this is not sufficient reason for assuming that these numbers then obey all these laws. This can be checked, however, and we are going to *assume without proof* that all the laws of exponents are satisfied by the numbers as we have defined them. Finally, we recall that any number $\sqrt[n]{a}$, that is defined, can be designated in exponential form by $a^{1/n}$. In view of the easy application of the Laws of Exponents, the student is urged to change any simplification problem involving radicals into an equivalent problem involving exponents, and afterwards revert to radical form if desired.

ILLUSTRATION 1. Simplify the following expressions, where x and y are real numbers:

$$(a)\quad \frac{\sqrt{x}\cdot\sqrt[4]{x^3}}{\sqrt[3]{x}};\qquad (b)\quad (3^{-2}+4^{-2})^{-1/2};\qquad (c)\quad \frac{x^{-1}+y^{-1}}{(x+y)^{-2}}.$$

Solutions.

$$(a)\quad \frac{\sqrt{x}\cdot\sqrt[4]{x^3}}{\sqrt[3]{x}} = \frac{x^{1/2}\cdot x^{3/4}}{x^{1/3}} = x^{(1/2+3/4-1/3)} = x^{11/12}$$
$$= \sqrt[12]{x^{11}}.$$

$$(b)\quad (3^{-2}+4^{-2})^{-1/2} = (1/3^2+1/4^2)^{-1/2} = (1/9+1/16)^{-1/2}$$
$$= (25/144)^{-1/2} = (144/25)^{1/2} = 12/5.$$

$$(c)\quad \frac{x^{-1}+y^{-1}}{(x+y)^{-2}} = \frac{1/x+1/y}{1/(x+y)^2} = \frac{(y+x)/xy}{1/(x+y)^2}$$
$$= \frac{(x+y)}{xy}\cdot\frac{(x+y)^2}{1} = \frac{(x+y)^3}{xy}.$$

ILLUSTRATION 2. If a and b are real numbers, express $\sqrt{6a^3b^2}/\sqrt[4]{2ab^5}$ in a form containing only one radical.

Solution.

$$\frac{\sqrt{6a^3b^2}}{\sqrt[4]{2ab^5}} = \frac{(6a^3b^2)^{1/2}}{(2ab^5)^{1/4}} = \left[\frac{(6a^3b^2)^2}{(2ab^5)}\right]^{1/4} = \left(\frac{36a^6b^4}{2ab^5}\right)^{1/4}$$
$$= \left(\frac{18a^5}{b}\right)^{1/4} = \left(\frac{18a\cdot a^4}{b}\right)^{1/4} = a\left(\frac{18a}{b}\right)^{1/4} = a\sqrt[4]{\frac{18a}{b}}.$$

PROBLEM SET 3.1

Note. Assume that the letters in the following problems represent arbitrary real numbers for which the associated symbols have been defined. More simple problems on exponents and radicals may be found in Section 8 of the Appendix.

1. For each of the following symbols that have been given a meaning, represent the number in simplest form: (*a*) $64^{2/3}$; (*b*) $(-64)^{2/3}$; (*c*) $(-4)^{3/2}$; (*d*) $4^{3/2}$; (*e*) 6^{-2}; (*f*) $1/4^{-2}$; (*g*) $(-2)^{\sqrt{2}}$; (*h*) $5/5^0$; (*i*) $-4^{3/2}$.
2. Express each of the following numbers as a radical: (*a*) $5^{2/3}$; (*b*) $6^{4/3}$; (*c*) $(-4)^{2/5}$; (*d*) $6^{-2/3}$; (*e*) $4^{-1/2}$; (*f*) $(-5)^{-3/5}$.

3. Express each of the following numbers in exponential form: (*a*) $\sqrt[4]{5x^3}$; (*b*) $\sqrt{5}$; (*c*) $\sqrt[3]{1/4}$; (*d*) $\sqrt[5]{3/2}$; (*e*) $\sqrt[5]{(5x)^2}$; (*f*) $\sqrt[5]{(-3/4)^2}$.
4. Indicate which of the following real numbers are negative: $5^{2/3}$; $(-2)^{5/3}$; $(-4)^{3/4}$; 3^{-2}; $4^{-1/2}$; $(-3)^{7/5}$; $(-4)^0$; $(-2)^{-2}$.
5. Simplify each of the following expressions: (*a*) a^2b^3/ab^2; (*b*) $a^2b^3a^3b$; (*c*) $(b^3)^4/b^5$; (*d*) $(2\cdot 3)^3\cdot 2^2\cdot 3^4$; (*e*) $(xy)^4/x^3y^2$.
6. Write each of the following as a fraction with denominator 1: (*a*) ab^2/c^3d^4; (*b*) $3x^3y^{-3}/4r^{-2}t^5$; (*c*) $a/x^3 + b/x^2 + c/x + d/x^{-1}$.
7. Write each of the following without negative exponents: (*a*) $3a^{-2}$; (*b*) $1/x^{-2}$; (*c*) $2a^3x^{-2}y^{-1/2}$; (*d*) x^4/y^{-5}; (*e*) $(3a^{2/3}b^{-1})/(5a^{-2/3}b)$; (*f*) $(-a^2)^{-3}$.
8. If $\sqrt{3} = 1.732\cdots$, explain why the concept of $(-2)^{\sqrt{3}}$, as the real number determined by a sequence of nested intervals having lower boundaries $(-2)^1$, $(-2)^{1.7}$, $(-2)^{1.73}$, $(-2)^{1.732}$, $\cdots$, would be meaningless with our present definitions.
9. Without attempting to evaluate, explain the meaning of the symbol 3^π, where $\pi = 3.14159\cdots$.
10. Simplify each of the following expressions: (*a*) $\dfrac{a^{-2}\cdot b^3}{x^{-1}\cdot y^{-4}}$; (*b*) $\dfrac{a^5\cdot b^{-3}}{3x^{-1}\cdot y^2}$; (*c*) $\left[\dfrac{a^6\cdot b^{-3}}{x^{-9}\cdot y^{-3/4}}\right]^{-1/3}$.
11. Reduce each of the following expressions to a single radical form: (*a*) $\dfrac{\sqrt[3]{x}\cdot\sqrt[4]{x^3}}{\sqrt{x^7}}$; (*b*) $\sqrt{a}\cdot\sqrt[3]{2b^2}\cdot\sqrt[4]{3a^2b}$; (*c*) $\sqrt{\dfrac{24x^5}{y}}\cdot\sqrt{\dfrac{y^2}{2x}}$; (*d*) $\sqrt{2\sqrt{2\sqrt{2}}}$.
12. Eliminate all negative exponents and simplify the result: (*a*) $\dfrac{x^{-2}+y^{-2}}{x^{-3}+y^{-3}}$; (*b*) $\dfrac{(x^2-y^2)^{-1}}{(x-y)^{-2}}$; (*c*) $\dfrac{x^{-3}\cdot y^{-3}}{x^{-3}+y^{-3}}$.

3.2 Scientific Notation and Approximate Computation

If a side of a square has been reported as 12 inches in length, it would be one's first impulse, in determining its area, to multiply 12 by 12 and obtain 144 square inches. However, a little reflection shows that this result may be misleading. The measurement, reported as 12, is apparently, in the absence of any information to the contrary, correct to the nearest unit only, and the "exact" length of a side is somewhere between 11.5 and 12.5 inches. The "exact" area then lies somewhere between $(11.5)^2$ or 132.25 and $(12.5)^2$ or 156.25 square inches; and it is clearly nonsense to report the area of the square as 144 square inches, with three non-zero digits, when even the second digit is in doubt. A more realistic approximation to the area would be 140 square inches, the final 0 merely locating the decimal point.

On the other hand, if the length of a side of the above square had been reported as 12.0 inches, one would understand that 12.0 is correct to the nearest tenth of a unit, with the "exact" length between 11.95 and 12.05 inches, and the "exact" area somewhere between the bounds of

142.8025 and 145.2025 square inches. A reasonable report of the area would then be 144 square inches, though even in this case there is some doubt about the correctness of the final 4. From the above discussion it appears that the numbers 12, 12.0, 12.00, etc., do not represent identical measurements, since a difference in accuracy is involved. Notice that we are distinguishing between the number 12 and a measurement of 12. The number 12 may, of course, be identified with the numbers 12.0, 12.00, etc.—and we have previously discussed such identifications—but the fact that a number 12 is a measurement implies that it is only an approximation to some unknown number, and further approximations such as 12.0 or 12.00 may not be valid. In answer to the whimsical query "When is 12 times 12 not equal to 144?" we may answer in all seriousness "When 12 is a measurement." In view of the fact that *all* measurements—apart from the cardinal number of a finite set—are inexact, the question of accuracy of a measurement and the reliability of a computation involving measured quantities is of great importance.

It is possible to indicate the accuracy of a measurement by actually giving the tolerance or possible error. For example, one could report a length as 124.58 ± 0.02 inches, indicating a possible error either way of 0.02 inches. Another method is to express all measurements in *scientific notation,* with the notation itself showing the tolerance. In this system, any measurement is written as a rational number between 1 and 10, multiplied by a power of 10, where the rational number expressed in decimal form contains *as many decimal places as the accuracy of the measurement warrants.* By this last remark we mean that all the digits in the rational number are actually measured digits. Thus, a measurement of 246.275, correct to the nearest thousandth unit, would be written as $2.46275(10)^2$; and a measurement of 40,000 would be written as $4(10)^4$, $4.0(10)^4$, $4.00(10)^4$, or $4.000(10)^4$, according as the measurement is correct to the nearest ten thousand, thousand, hundred, or ten units, respectively. The digits included in the decimal form of the rational number are called *significant digits,* and the number of these is the *number of significant digits* in the measurement.

In any computation involving *sums and differences,* the location of the decimal points in the various measurements is important in any consideration of the accuracy of the result, for the measurement with the least number of digits following the decimal point determines the number of decimal places in the answer. Thus, if two measurements have 3 and 5 decimal places, respectively, there should be only 3 decimal places in either their sum or difference. However, with products or quotients, the accuracy of the result is more dependent on the numbers of significant digits of the component measurements. A chain is as strong as its weakest link, and so we have selected the following rule for *products or quotients:*

> The number of significant digits to be retained in the final result is the *least* number of significant digits in any of the component measurements.

It is to be understood that in the use of a formula involving absolute constants, these constants may be assumed to have as many significant digits as desired; in other words, they may be ignored in any determination of the number of significant digits to be retained in the result of the computation.

The question of the accuracy of a computed result involving products and quotients is a difficult one. It might appear that the "best" result would be that which is midway between the two possible bounds. In the case of the square having sides 12 inches in length, this would give us a measure of area in square inches of 144.25, which is midway between the bounds of 132.25 and 156.25. But, as a matter of fact, a little reflection shows that the "exact" area is no more likely to be near 144.25 square inches, than any of the other possibilities within the bounds. The only true statement on accuracy, that we can possibly make, is that the area does lie between 132.25 and 156.25 square inches. The above rule then does not necessarily give us a "best" result, but merely gives us a definite procedure for selecting one of the infinitely many possible answers within the bounds, and one that does not imply more accuracy than is warranted. We shall follow this rule in the solutions of subsequent problems. In rounding off a digit, we shall add 1 if the succeeding digit is more than 5, and leave it unchanged if the succeeding digit is less than 5; if the succeeding digit is 5, followed by only zero digits, we shall round off the number so that the final digit is even. For example, if we round to three digits, 2.446 would be rounded to 2.45, 2.443 would be rounded to 2.44, while both 2.665 and 2.655 would be rounded to 2.66.

ILLUSTRATION 1. Determine the total weight of four objects, if their individual weights have been reported as 3147.2, 27.586, 146.287, and 5.12 grams.

Solution. If the measures of weight were to be added as abstract numbers, the total would be 3326.193. However, since the first mentioned object was weighed to only one tenth of a gram accuracy, the total weight should be reported as 3326.2 grams.

ILLUSTRATION 2. The altitude and a diameter of the base of a right circular cone have been measured as 12.156 and 5.42 inches, respectively. Determine the volume of the cone ($V = \pi d^2 h/12$).

Solution. If we replace d and h in the formula by the appropriate measurements and use $\pi = 3.14159$, the indicated computation would give $V = 93.4883 \cdots$. Since the diameter has been measured to only 3 significant digits, however, a more realistic approximation to the volume would be 93.5 cubic inches.

If measurements are written in scientific notation it is easy to *estimate* the result of a computation, and this is a good practice to follow even if one is going to make a more accurate computation later. The procedure is to express all the numbers involved, including the absolute constants, in scientific notation; then apply the laws of exponents to the powers of 10 and make a rough estimate of the answer, using one or two significant digits.

ILLUSTRATION 3. When an 80 h.p. engine rotates a drive shaft at 3600 r.p.m., the number T of pounds of torque developed is given by $T = \dfrac{44{,}000}{(3600)(2\pi/60)}$. Determine an approximation to T.

Solution.

$$T = \frac{[4.4(10)^4][6.0(10)^1]}{3.6(10)^3(2)(3.1)} = \frac{(4.4)(6)(10)^2}{(3.6)(6.2)} = 120,$$

approximately.

ILLUSTRATION 4. The measure F in foot-pounds of the centripetal force on a particle of weight W pounds, rotating at the rate of N r.p.m. on a circle having radii R feet in length, is given by the formula $F = 0.000341\ WRN^2$. Compute an approximation to F, using the measurements: $W = 20.12$, $R = 3.8$, $N = 268$.

Solution. An approximation to F is seen to be $(3.4)(10)^{-4}(2)(10)^1(3.8)(2.7)^2(10)^4$ or $(3.4)(7.6)(7.3)(10)^1$. If we replace the numbers 3.4, 7.6, and 7.3 by 3, 8, and 7, respectively, we see that 1700 is an approximation to F.

PROBLEM SET 3.2

1. Express each of the following numbers in scientific notation: 124.312, 0.00168, 0.000246, 364589, 1289.605, 0.00000067, 7854.358.
2. Express each of the following measurements in scientific notation, assuming that each is correct to the nearest thousandth of a unit: 24.0000, 248.2490, 0.00186, 2.38002, 12.6100.
3. A measurement has been recorded as 240,000. Express this in scientific notation in five different ways.
4. Explain the difference between measured lengths of 5 feet, 5.0 feet, and 5.00 feet.
5. Kasner and Newman† have defined a "googol" and a "googolplex" as the numbers symbolized, respectively, by 1 followed by one hundred zeros and 1 followed by a googol zeros. Express each number in scientific notation.

† Edward Kasner and James Newman, *Mathematics and the Imagination* (New York: Simon and Schuster, 1940).

6. If each of 9 roller bearings weighs 3.64 ounces, what is the combined weight of all 9? Obtain two different answers and discuss!

7. Determine (*a*) $a + b + c + d$ and (*b*) $(a - b) + (c - d)$ if a, b, c, and d are the following measurements: $a = 21.2867$, $b = 286.13$, $c = 5.08$, $d = 0.24186$.

8. If a, b, c, and d are the same as in Problem 7, determine a reasonable approximation to (*a*) a/b; (*b*) ac; (*c*) c/d.

9. One man measures the frontage of a rectangular lot as 50.12 feet, and another measures the depth as 186.25 feet. Determine the area of the lot.

10. If a person traveled 284.6 miles in 7.4 hours, both measurements having been read from instruments, what was his average velocity?

11. A rectangular box has a measured height of 12.6 feet, and a square base with sides that measure 4 feet in length. Compute the volume of the box.

12. If light travels at the rate of $186{,}000 \pm 500$ miles per second, find the distance in miles to a star 42 light years away (1 year = 365 days, 5 hours, 48 minutes, 46.0 seconds).

13. A right circular cylinder, having a height of h inches and base diameters d inches in length, has a volume of V cubic inches, where $V = \pi d^2 h/12$. Compute the volume if $h = 7.2$ and $d = 14.8$. How do you choose the number of digits for $\pi\,(\pi = 3.14159 \cdots)$?

14. The individual weights of three pieces of steel are given as 2880 ± 5 pounds, $13{,}400 \pm 50$ pounds, and 248 ± 0.5 pounds. What should be reported as the combined weight of the three pieces?

15. Find an approximation to the following: (*a*) $\dfrac{2x^2y}{4b}$ where $x = 124.8$, $y = 15$, and $b = 0.186$; (*b*) $\dfrac{256Rb^2x}{c}$ where $R = 12.56$, $x = 25{,}000$, $b = 18.28$, and $c = 180$.

16. Compute approximations to the following:

$$(a)\quad \frac{(284.5)(0.1840)}{(12000)(16.846)}; \qquad (b)\quad \frac{(0.0186)(0.24)}{(0.00256)(5.4)}.$$

3.3 The Meaning of Logarithms

Let us suppose that we wish to simplify the expression $\dfrac{8 \cdot 64^3 \cdot 32^2}{16^3 \cdot 128^2}$. If we write each base number occurring here as a power of 2 and use the laws of exponents, the computation is quite easy. Thus, the expression becomes

$$\frac{2^3(2^6)^3(2^5)^2}{(2^4)^3(2^7)^2} = \frac{2^3 \cdot 2^{18} \cdot 2^{10}}{2^{12} \cdot 2^{14}} = 2^{3+18+10-12-14} = 2^5 = 32.$$

It should be observed that the operations of multiplication and division for the given numbers were replaced by the simpler operations of addition and subtraction of the exponents, when the numbers were written as powers of 2. It is also apparent that this technique could be applied whenever the numbers involved are expressed as powers of *any one* number.

We are now going to show how *any* real number can be expressed approximately as a power of the number 10, so that we may always take advantage of the above simplified procedure.

When three real numbers b, x, and N are so related that $b^x = N$, we refer to the exponent x as the *logarithm* of N to the base b, and write $x = \log_b N$. In other words, the logarithm of a number to a given base is the exponent of the power to which the base must be raised to equal the number. The "exponential" equation $b^x = N$ and the "logarithmic" equation $x = \log_b N$ are equivalent; for example, $3^4 = 81$ is equivalent to $4 = \log_3 81$; and $6 = \log_{\sqrt{2}} 8$ is equivalent to $\sqrt{2}^6 = 8$. The identity $N = b^{\log_b N}$ is frequently useful.

While theoretically any positive number $b \neq 1$ could be used as a base, like 2 in the illustration above, the base 10 is generally used for a reason that will appear presently. Logarithms to the base 10 are called *common* logarithms, and in this book if no special base is indicated, the base 10 will be understood. Thus, if we write $\log 1000 = 3$, we shall mean $\log_{10} 1000 = 3$, a true statement since $10^3 = 1000$.

The common logarithm of any power of 10 is, of course, a whole number, and is the exponent that indicates the power. Thus, for example, $\log 10{,}000 = \log 10^4 = 4$, and $\log 0.001 = \log 10^{-3} = -3$; and since $10^0 = 1$, we have $\log 1 = 0$. The common logarithm of any "3-decimal" real number between 1 and 10 can be found expressed approximately as a 4-place decimal, with the help of Table 1 at the back of the book. At this time, we shall accept these logarithms as given without any discussion of how they may have been obtained. All decimal points have been omitted from this table, but we must assume that they are located immediately *after* the first digits of the numbers, of which the logarithms are listed, and immediately *before* the first digit of each logarithm. The logarithm of a number between 1 and 10 will then be some number between 0 and 1, as the definition of a common logarithm would require. For example, we find from the table that $\log 6.27 = 0.7973$, where we have inserted the decimal points as required, and have used the customary abbreviation "log" for logarithm. The next number, the logarithm of which can be read directly from the table, is 6.28, and the logarithm of this number can be observed to be 7 more in the fourth decimal place than the preceding logarithm. We now assume that the logarithms of two numbers, that are close together, differ by amounts proportional to their separation. Thus, if we wish to determine $\log 6.274$, for instance, we must add 4/10 of 7 to the fourth decimal digit of $\log 6.27$, and so $\log 6.274 = 0.7973 + 0.0003 = 0.7976$. By this method of "proportional parts," we can extend the table to include the logarithm of any rational number having 4 significant digits. In this example, the exponent of the power to which 10 must be raised to equal 6.274 is 0.7976, i.e., $10^{0.7976} = 6.274$, and the meaning of such a rational power of 10 has been discussed in Section 3.1.

In Section 3.2, we showed how any rational number can be expressed in scientific notation as a power of 10 multiplied by some number between 1 and 10. The discussion of the preceding paragraph, and the first law of exponents, then enable us to write down an approximation to the common logarithm of any rational number. Thus, suppose that we have symbolized the rational number N in scientific notation as $N = b(10)^x$, where x is an integer and b is a rational number such that $1 \leq b < 10$. The logarithm of b can be found approximately from Table 1, and so we may write $N = 10^{\log b}10^x = 10^{\log b + x}$, from which we obtain $\log N = \log b + x$. We reemphasize that x is an integer, and b is a rational number between 0 and 1.

ILLUSTRATION 1.

$$\begin{aligned}\log 287.6 &= \log 2.876(10)^2 = \log 2.876 + \log 10^2 \\ &= 0.4588 + 2 = 2.4588.\end{aligned}$$

ILLUSTRATION 2.

$$\begin{aligned}\log 0.002876 &= \log 2.876(10)^{-3} = \log 2.876 + \log 10^{-3} \\ &= 0.4588 - 3 = -2.5412.\end{aligned}$$

Two very important facts are illustrated in the above examples: the logarithm of any number less than 1 is negative; and the logarithms of any two numbers, having the same sequence of significant digits, differ at most by an integer, the contribution from the table to the logarithms being the same for both. It should be realized that this latter desirable condition would not exist if any base except 10 were chosen. This then explains the choice of base 10 for common logarithms.

The method of logarithms that we have discussed establishes a correspondence between the set of positive rational numbers with 4 significant digits and the set of rational numbers (positive, negative, and zero) with 4 digits following the decimal point. This correspondence could be extended if tables containing more significant digits were available, and the following important theoretical statement may be made: The correspondence between the set of all positive real numbers and the set of all real numbers, established by $x \leftrightarrow \log x$, is one-to-one. In other words, every positive real number has a *unique* real number as its logarithm, and every real number is the logarithm of some unique positive real number. We shall not attempt a formal proof of this general statement, however.

While the logarithm of a number that is less than 1 is negative, it will often be convenient—and sometimes necessary—to leave such a logarithm in a form exhibiting a positive decimal part. Thus, for some purposes, we shall wish to leave the logarithm of Illustration 2 in the form 0.4588 − 3. (Two alternate notations for this logarithm are $\bar{3}.4588$ and 7.4588 − 10, but we shall prefer not to use either of them.) It is always possible to put an arbitrary negative real number in this form, by the process of adding and subtracting 1. For example, $-2.3692 = -0.3692 - 2 = (1 - 0.3692) - 1 - 2 = 0.6308 - 3$. We must emphasize, however, that −2.3692 and 0.6308 − 3 are merely different symbolic forms of the *same* real number; sometimes we shall need one form, and sometimes the other.

It will often be necessary to find a number, the logarithm of which is known, and this process involves the use of a table of logarithms in reverse. Thus, for example, if $\log N = 3.8244 = 0.8244 + 3$, we know that $N = b(10)^3$, where $\log b = 0.8244$. The table of logarithms shows that the number 6.674 has 0.8244 for its logarithm, and so $N = 6.674(10)^3 = 6674$. Inasmuch as all the logarithms in the table are positive, it is clear that in this inverse process all negative logarithms must be written as the sum of a *positive* real number less than 1 and an integer. For example, if $\log y = -2.4639$, we must write this number in the form $0.5361 - 3$, as explained above; from the table, we see that $\log 3.436 = 0.5361$, and so $y = 3.436(10)^{-3} = 0.0003436$.

The definition of a common logarithm precludes the possibility of negative numbers having logarithms. However, this fact does not eliminate the use of logarithms in computations involving negative numbers; for the sign of the computed result can be obtained by inspection, and the negative signs otherwise ignored in the computation. Finally, we should always keep in mind that logarithms from a table are only rational number approximations to the real number logarithms, which exist from theoretical considerations.

PROBLEM SET 3.3

1. Find the common logarithm of each of the following numbers: (*a*) 126.5; (*b*) 346,000; (*c*) 1.867; (*d*) 24.84; (*e*) 857,600; (*f*) 12,000; (*g*) 986.0; (*h*) 3.343; (*i*) 12.00; (*j*) 56.57.
2. Find the common logarithm of each of the following numbers: (*a*) 0.2461; (*b*) 0.0014; (*c*) 0.2400; (*d*) 0.0000463; (*e*) 0.1469.
3. Write the common logarithm of each of the following numbers in two equivalent forms: (*a*) 0.1234; (*b*) 0.000186; (*c*) 0.02843; (*d*) 0.9431; (*e*) 0.00234.
4. Write each of the following equations in logarithmic form: (*a*) $5^x = 6$; (*b*) $2^3 = 8$; (*c*) $10^2 = 100$; (*d*) $\sqrt{2}^{\,a} = b$; (*e*) $5^{-2} = x$; (*f*) $10^{0.25} = 1.7783$; (*g*) $3^{-1/3} = a$; (*h*) $a^1 = a$.

5. Write each of the following equations in exponential form: (*a*) $\log_3 5 = x$; (*b*) $\log 1000 = 3$; (*c*) $\log_b 12 = 5$; (*d*) $\log_b \sqrt{2} = x$; (*e*) $\log_8 2 = 1/3$; (*f*) $\log 0.001 = -3$; (*g*) $\log 1 = 0$; (*h*) $\log \sqrt{1000} = 3/2$.
6. Determine each of the following by inspection: (*a*) $\log_3 81$; (*b*) $\log_5 25$; (*c*) $\log_2 16$; (*d*) $\log_6 36$; (*e*) $\log_2 1/8$; (*f*) $\log 0.001$.
7. Find x in each of the following equations: (*a*) $\log_{12} 1 = x$; (*b*) $\log x = -3$; (*c*) $\log_x 5 = -1$; (*d*) $\log_x 2 = 1/2$; (*e*) $\log_{16} x = -1/2$; (*f*) $\log_2 0.25 = x$.
8. Since $\log 3.3670 = 0.52724$, we must have $3.3670 = 10^{0.52724}$. What is the meaning of this last equality?

3.4 The Laws of Logarithms and Simple Calculations

Since logarithms are exponents, the laws of exponents may be written in an equivalent form known as the *Laws of Logarithms.* Let M and N be any two real numbers where $\log_b M = m$ and $\log_b N = n$. It follows that $M = b^m$ and $N = b^n$, and using the laws of exponents we then have $MN = b^m \cdot b^n = b^{m+n}$. Thus, $\log_b MN = m + n = \log_b M + \log_b N$. An easy generalization of this result gives us the

FIRST LAW OF LOGARITHMS. The logarithm of a product of numbers is equal to the sum of the logarithms of the numbers.

Using the same notation as above, we also have $M/N = b^m/b^n = b^{m-n}$, from which we obtain that $\log_b M/N = m - n = \log_b M - \log_b N$. We may state this result as the

SECOND LAW OF LOGARITHMS. The logarithm of the quotient of two numbers is the logarithm of the dividend minus the logarithm of the divisor.

Finally, consider the number M^N where $\log_b M = m$, as before. Then $M = b^m$ and $M^N = b^{mN}$, and so $\log_b M^N = mN = N \log_b M$. We then have the

THIRD LAW OF LOGARITHMS. The logarithm of a number expressed exponentially is the product of the exponent and the logarithm of the base.

We shall now illustrate the use of these Laws of Logarithms in the solutions of some simple problems.

ILLUSTRATION 1. Compute $N = (26.34)(0.0783)$.

Solution.

$$\begin{aligned} \log 26.34 &= \log 2.634(10)^1 = 0.4206 + 1 \\ \log 0.0783 &= \log 7.83(10)^{-2} = \underline{0.8938 - 2} \\ & \qquad\qquad\qquad\qquad 1.3144 - 1 = 0.3144 \end{aligned}$$

Thus, $\log N = \log 26.34 + \log 0.0783 = 0.3144$, and so $N = 2.062(10)^0 = 2.062$.

ILLUSTRATION 2. Compute $N = 0.4569/0.06528$.

Solution.

$$\begin{aligned} \log 0.4569 &= \log 4.569(10)^{-1} = 0.6598 - 1 = 1.6598 - 2 \\ \log 0.06528 &= \log 6.528(10)^{-2} = \underline{0.8148 - 2} \\ & \qquad\qquad\qquad\qquad 0.8450 \end{aligned}$$

Thus, $\log N = \log 0.4569 - \log 0.06528 = 0.8450$, and so $N = 6.999(10)^0 = 6.999$.

ILLUSTRATION 3. Compute $N = (0.0148)^{2/3}$.

Solution. $\log 0.0148 = \log 1.48(10)^{-2} = 0.1703 - 2$. Using the Third Law of Logarithms, $\log N = (2/3)\log 0.0148 = (2/3)(0.1703 - 2) = (2/3)(1.1703 - 3) = (1/3)(2.3406 - 6) = 0.7802 - 2$. Hence $N = 6.028(10)^{-2} = 0.006028$ or, rounding off to 3 significant digits, $N = 0.00603$.

The last illustration shows that great care must be taken in the manipulation of negative numbers, if written in the special form for negative logarithms. Of course, this form is merely a convenience and may be dispensed with if desired, for we again emphasize that a negative logarithm is merely a negative number. However, much time and effort will be saved if the student is able to make intelligent use of this special form. For this reason, we shall give a brief survey of the different arithmetic operations that may arise, with some brief comment on them, in the hope that the student will develop some facility for working with negative logarithms, as well as with positive ones.

ADDITION AND SUBTRACTION. If the operation is addition, we simply add the integral parts together, and the decimal parts together, and put our result in the standard form. If the operation is subtraction, it may be necessary, as in Illustration 2, to increase and decrease the minuend by 1, so that the decimal part of the result is positive.

ILLUSTRATIONS.

(*a*) *Addition:*

$$\begin{array}{ll} 0.5843 + 1 & \qquad 0.5843 - 1 \\ \underline{0.9421 - 3} & \qquad \underline{0.9421 - 3} \\ 1.5264 - 2 = 0.5264 - 1. & \qquad 1.5264 - 4 = 0.5264 - 3. \end{array}$$

(*b*) *Subtraction:*

$$\begin{array}{llll} 0.5843 + 1 = & 1.5843 + 0 & \qquad 0.5843 - 1 = & 1.5843 - 2 \\ \underline{0.9421 - 3} & \underline{0.9421 - 3} & \qquad \underline{0.9421 - 3} & \underline{0.9421 - 3} \\ & 0.6422 + 3. & & 0.6422 + 1. \end{array}$$

MULTIPLICATION AND DIVISION.

1. If a negative logarithm is to be multiplied by, divided by, or is the divisor of a number that is written as a decimal, the special form of the negative logarithm should not be used during the operation.

ILLUSTRATIONS.

(*a*) $(2.146)(0.486 - 2) = (2.146)(-1.514) = -(2.146)(1.514)$
$= -3.249.$

(*b*) $$\frac{0.146 - 2}{2.486} = \frac{-1.854}{2.486} = -\frac{1.854}{2.486} = -0.7458.$$

(*c*) $$\frac{2.146}{0.486 - 2} = \frac{2.146}{-1.514} = -\frac{2.146}{1.514} = -1.417.$$

2. If a negative logarithm, expressed as the sum of a positive decimal and a negative integer, is to be multiplied by a number in fractional form, it may be necessary to add and subtract some integer (like 1 in Illustration 3). This is necessary to insure that the product of the integer and the fraction is an integer.

ILLUSTRATION.

$$(1/3)(0.4855 - 1) = (1/3)(2.4855 - 3) = 0.8285 - 1.$$

In conclusion, we remark that the form in which a logarithm is left depends entirely on what arithmetic process is involved. If we wish to determine a number from its logarithm, however, the logarithm *must* be expressed as the sum of a *positive* decimal between 0 and 1, and an integer. Since problems in computation usually involve numbers that are measurements, we shall round off answers to such problems according to the rules given in Section 3.2. It is evident, however, that if the numbers are not measurements, it would not be necessary to so approximate our results.

PROBLEM SET 3.4

1. Determine the sum of the following numbers: (*a*) $0.4163 + 2$, $0.4861 - 2$; (*b*) $0.8154 - 2$, $0.9461 + 2$, $0.9462 + 3$; (*c*) $0.9162 - 4$, $0.3184 - 2$, $0.1516 - 1$; (*d*) $0.2674 + 3$, $0.9857 - 4$, $0.6765 + 2$.
2. Subtract the second number from the first in each of the following pairs: (*a*) $0.4165 + 2$, $0.8421 - 1$; (*b*) $0.5618 - 3$, $0.3284 - 5$; (*c*) $0.1643 + 4$, $0.4267 + 8$.
3. Multiply the numbers in each of the following pairs: (*a*) 1.86, $0.16 - 2$; (*b*) $0.48 - 1$, $0.16 - 2$; (*c*) $0.32 - 4$, $0.14 - 6$.
4. Divide the first number by the second in each of the following pairs: (*a*) $0.146 + 2$, $0.84 - 2$; (*b*) $0.843 - 1$, $0.321 - 4$; (*c*) $0.163 - 2$, 1.35.
5. Multiply the number $0.844 - 2$ by each of the following fractions: (*a*) 2/3; (*b*) 1/4; (*c*) 4/5.
6. Multiply the number $0.146 - 3$ by each of the following fractions: (*a*) 1/2; (*b*) 4/7; (*c*) 2/5.

7. Use the First Law of Logarithms to compute each of the following: (*a*) (14.38)(1.846); (*b*) (146.2)(0.0146); (*c*) (0.1284)(0.3654); (*d*) (0.2549)(21.84).
8. Use the Second Law of Logarithms to compute the quotient of the numbers in each pair listed in Problem 7, taking the second number as the divisor in each case.
9. Use the Third Law of Logarithms to compute each of the following: (*a*) $(21.56)^{1/3}$; (*b*) $(0.1847)^{2/3}$; (*c*) $(12.85)^{2.463}$; (*d*) $(0.1843)^{0.16}$.

3.5 Compound Calculations With Logarithms

Any computational problem involving products, quotients, powers, or root extractions, may be solved by successive applications of the Laws of Logarithms, with the use of Table 1. We shall now illustrate this, with the solution of several problems; the student is urged to pay particular attention to the arrangement of the work.

ILLUSTRATION 1. Compute $N = \dfrac{(7.186)(27.37)}{(0.04584)(6492)}$, by the approximation method of Section 3.2 with 1 significant digit, and also by logarithms.

Solution.

(*a*) An approximation to N is

$$\frac{(7)(3)(10)^1}{5(10)^{-2}(6)(10)^3} = \frac{(7)(3)(10)^0}{(5)(6)} = \frac{7}{10} = 0.7.$$

(*b*) $\log N = \log 7.186 + \log 27.37 - \log 0.04584 - \log 6492.$

$$\begin{aligned} \log 7.186 &= 0.8565 + 0 \\ \log 27.37 &= \underline{0.4373 + 1} \\ &\ 1.2938 + 1 = 0.2938 + 2 \end{aligned}$$

$$\begin{aligned} \log 0.04584 &= 0.6613 - 2 \\ \log 6492 &= \underline{0.8123 + 3} \\ &\ 1.4736 + 1 = 0.4736 + 2 \end{aligned}$$

$$\begin{array}{rcl} 0.2938 + 2 & = & 1.2938 + 1 \\ \underline{0.4736 + 2} & & \underline{0.4736 + 2} \\ & & 0.8202 - 1 \end{array}$$

Thus, $\log N = 0.8202 - 1$, and so $N = 6.610(10)^{-1} = 0.6610$.

ILLUSTRATION 2. If $0.0146^x = 1.36$, determine x.

Solution. If we take logarithms of both members of the equation, we obtain $x \log 0.0146 = \log 1.36$, and so $x = (\log 1.36)/(\log 0.0146) = (0.1335)/(0.1644 - 2) = (0.1335)/(-1.8356) = -(0.1335)/(1.8356) = -(0.1335)/(1.836)$, approximately.

$$\begin{aligned} \log 0.1335 &= 0.1255 - 1 = 1.1255 - 2 \\ \log 1.836 &= \underline{0.2639 + 0} = \underline{0.2639 + 0} \\ & \qquad\qquad\qquad\quad 0.8616 - 2 \end{aligned}$$

Hence, $\log |x| = 0.8616 - 2$, and so $|x| = 7.272(10)^{-2} = 0.07272$, and $x = -0.0727$, rounding off the result to 3 significant digits.

ILLUSTRATION 3. If $b^{0.12} = 0.307$, determine b.

Solution. If we take logarithms of both members of the equation, we obtain $0.12 \log b = \log 0.307$, and so $\log b = (\log 0.307)/0.12 = (0.4871 - 1)/0.12 = -0.5129/0.12 = -4.2742$ (by long division) $= (1 - 0.2742) - 5 = 0.7258 - 5$. Hence $b = 5.319(10)^{-5} = 0.00005319$, or 0.000053 on rounding off the result to 2 significant digits.

ILLUSTRATION 4. Compute $N = \sqrt[5]{\dfrac{(1.46)(0.0014)^2}{\sqrt{0.158}}}$.

Solution.

$$\begin{aligned} \log 1.46 &= &&= 0.1644 + 0 \\ 2 \log 0.0014 &= 2(0.1461 - 3) &&= \underline{0.2922 - 6} \\ & &&\quad 0.4566 - 6 \end{aligned}$$

$$\begin{aligned} 1/2 \log 0.158 &= 1/2(0.1987 - 1) \\ &= 1/2(1.1987 - 2) \\ &= 0.5994 - 1 \end{aligned}$$

Then $\log N = (1/5)$ (log numerator $-$ log denominator)

$$= (1/5)(0.8572 - 6) = (1/5)(4.8572 - 10) = 0.9714 - 2.$$

It follows that $N = 9.362(10)^{-2}$ or, rounding off to 2 significant digits, $N = 0.094$.

PROBLEM SET 3.5

1. Solve each of the following equations for N: (*a*) $N = (24.87)^{12.64}$; (*b*) $N = (0.0126)^{0.237}$; (*c*) $N = (0.02876)^{5.374}$.
2. Solve each of the following equations for b: (*a*) $12.01 = b^{251.4}$; (*b*) $0.01643 = b^{0.2345}$.
3. Solve each of the following equations for x: (*a*) $12.85 = (16.43)^x$; (*b*) $0.00187 = (21.5)^x$; (*c*) $0.08436 = (0.234)^x$.
4. Compute each of the following: (*a*) $\dfrac{(12.05)(0.1654)}{257.3}$; (*b*) $\dfrac{(137.5)(18.07)}{(0.0284)(1.573)}$; (*c*) $\dfrac{(186.3)(42.74)(0.0184)}{36000}$.

5. Compute each of the following: (a) $\frac{(26.43)^2\sqrt{14.3}}{(0.016)^3}$; (b) $\sqrt[3]{\frac{18.56(1.874)^2}{2.873}}$; (c) $\frac{\sqrt{(18.43)(164.3)}}{(0.014)^2}$.
6. Use logarithms to compute $\frac{\sqrt{386.4}\,(-2.834)^2}{(-68.31)(4.872)^2}$.
7. Compute (a) (log 284.3)(log 0.5135); (b) (log 186.2)/(12.59).
8. Use logarithms to compute (a) $\frac{\sqrt[3]{-284.2}\,\sqrt{36.43}}{(51.24)(-3.642)}$; (b) $2\pi\sqrt{\frac{I}{mgh}}$ (where $\pi = 3.142$; $I = 25{,}380$; $m = 431.2$; $h = 5.163$; $g = 980$).
9. Solve for x: (a) $(42.37)^{x-1} = 2436$; (b) $\frac{(1.03)^x - 1}{0.03} = 116.2$.
10. Solve for x: (a) $27(128.4)^{x+3} = 345.6$; (b) $12.43 \log (x - 4) = \log 28430$.

REVIEW TEST A

1. Give the definitions of the following numbers, where $x \in R^{\#}$: (a) x^3; (b) $x^{2/3}$; (c) x^{-2}; (d) x^0.
2. Simplify the expression $(a^{-1} + b^{-1})^{-1}$.
3. If $a^u = b$, determine x such that $b^x = a^2$.
4. Approximate each of the following numbers as powers of 10: 2, 1/2, 1/3, 5, 1.
5. Use scientific notation to find an approximation to $\frac{(128)(42)(10)^4(0.0123)}{(0.145)(84)(10)^{-3}}$.
6. If $\log \pi = 0.4972$, express $\sqrt{\pi}$ as a power of 10.
7. Use logarithms to compute $\frac{(21.07)(0.0284)}{1.78}$.
8. If $x = \frac{\log 100{,}000}{\log 100}$, find x.
9. If $(7.52)^{x-2} = 327$, determine x.
10. If $\log x + \log 10 = \log 5$, determine x.
11. Use logarithms to compute $\frac{(2.14)(58.4)^{3/2}}{\sqrt[3]{24.6}}$.
12. Use logarithms to compute $\sqrt[3]{\frac{(32.4)\sqrt{0.0286}}{\sqrt{0.123}}}$.

REVIEW TEST B

1. Give the definitions of the following numbers, where $y \in R^{\#}$: (a) y^4; (b) $y^{4/3}$; (c) $y^{-1/2}$; (d) y^1.
2. Simplify the expression $\frac{x^{1/3} \cdot x^{4/3}}{x^2 \cdot x^0}$.

3. Simplify the expression $\dfrac{x - y}{x^{-1} - y^{-1}}$.

4. At a point h miles above sea level, a measure p of atmospheric pressure is given by the formula $p = p_0e^{-0.193h}$. If this is expressed in the form $p = p_0(10)^{-mh}$, determine m ($e = 2.71828 \cdots$).

5. Use scientific notation to find an approximation to

$$\frac{(12000)(0.0124)(5)(10)^4}{(15.4)(72.5)(10)^{-5}}.$$

6. Find upper and lower bounds for $|x|$, if $2 \leq \log x^2 \leq 4$.

7. Use logarithms to compute $\dfrac{(0.00843)(228.4)}{0.1247}$.

8. If $\log(3x + 21) - \log(2x + 1) = \log 8$, find x.

9. Use logarithms to determine $435^{5/11}$.

10. Express each of the following in terms of logarithms of prime integers: (*a*) $\log \dfrac{\sqrt{6}}{\sqrt[3]{12}}$; (*b*) $\log \dfrac{\sqrt[3]{72}}{\sqrt[3]{15^2}}$; (*c*) $\log (4 \cdot 3 \cdot 2 \cdot 1)$.

11. Use logarithms to compute $\dfrac{\sqrt[3]{8.47}\,(0.129)}{\sqrt[3]{0.0084}}$.

12. Use logarithms to compute $\sqrt{\dfrac{128000(0.284)^3}{\sqrt{0.00240}}}$.

REFERENCES

Books

Dubisch, R., *Trigonometry,* New York, Ronald, 1955. (Chap. 12.)

Hall, Henry S. and Samuel R. Knight, *Higher Algebra,* London, Macmillan, 1950. (Chap. 16.)

Newsom, Carroll V. and Howard Eves, *Introduction to College Mathematics,* New York, Prentice Hall, 1954. (Chap. 4.)

4

RELATIONS AND FUNCTIONS

It is evident that the understanding of relations is a major concern of all men and women.

C. J. KEYSER

4.1 Introduction

In our development of the real number system in Chapter 2, we made numerous explicit references to the "equality" relation ($=$) and the "less than" relation ($<$); and in Chapter 1 much use was made of the relations of inclusion ($\subseteq$), complementation ($'$), and disjointness, though they were not referred to as "relations" at that time. It is the purpose of the present chapter to find a definition for this somewhat abstract idea of a *relation*, and to examine the concept a little more closely.

Whenever a physical object is described, we nearly always make use of the technique of "relating" it to other objects. Thus, we may say that object A "is heavier than" object B, orange P "is sweeter than" orange Q, or event p "occurred before" event q. These are illustrations of our intuitive notion of the relations "is heavier than," "is sweeter than," and "occurred before." When we say that Mary "is a sister of" John, Henry "is the father of" Joe, or Bernice "is the wife of" Bob, we are illustrating what might be described as "family" relations. In addition to the two *arithmetical* relations of "equality" and "less than" mentioned above, there are many others that are being used frequently, though we do not always refer to them as relations. For example, we may say that 2 "is a factor of" 8, 16 "is divisible by" 4, or 5 "is prime to" 12, all illustrating the use of arithmetical relations for which we have no common symbols. Let us now examine relations in general for properties that we may use eventually to characterize them.

A relation always involves elements of *two* sets, which may or may not be distinct. Thus, the relation "is less than" first appeared as a relation involving elements of the *single* set N of natural numbers. If we state that 2 "is less than" 5, the numbers 2 and 5 are both elements of the set N. On the other hand, if we remark that Joe "is the owner of" house

H, using the relation "is the owner of," two distinct sets are involved, one a set of houses and the other a set of people. Many of the relations with which we shall be most concerned will involve this double use of a single set.

Another point to notice is that a relation always associates elements of two sets in a *definite order*. Thus, the relation "is less than" may associate 1 with 4 *with the understanding* that "1 is less than 4" and not "4 is less than 1." Also, the relation "is the owner of" may associate Joe with house H, with the understanding that "Joe is the owner of house H" and not "house H is the owner of Joe."

Let us tentatively adopt the notation R for a relation of the type that has been under discussion, and let bRa be a short notation for the statement that b is in the relation R to a. For example, if R is the relation "is less than" ($<$), bRa means that b is less than a, i.e., $b < a$; and if R is the "equality" relation ($=$), bRa means that b equals a, i.e., $b = a$, etc. Inasmuch as a relation always connects two elements in a definite order, the notion of an ordered pair arises, and so let us make the following *agreement:* An ordered pair (a, b) will be said to *satisfy* the relation R, if bRa is a true statement. According to this agreement, the ordered pair (2, 1) satisfies the relation "is less than" because "1 is less than 2" is a true statement. Similarly, the ordered pair (4, 2) satisfies the relation "is a factor of," since 2 is a factor of 4; and (house H, Joe) satisfies the relation "is the owner of," because "Joe is the owner of house H" is alleged to be a statement of fact.

It might seem to be more natural to use (b, a) instead of (a, b) in the statement of the above agreement, so that (b, a) would satisfy the relation R if bRa is a true statement; however, the order that we have specified for the components of the ordered pair is the one preferred by mathematicians. Notice that if the parentheses around an ordered pair are omitted and the elements are preceded by the verbal description of the relation, the result reads like an index entry. For example, if we put the phrase "is less than" in front of the pair (5, 2) and remove the parentheses, we obtain "is less than 5, 2," which is a reasonable result. It is convenient to use this check if there is any doubt about the order of the components in an ordered pair satisfying a relation.

If the relation R involves elements of a single set U, we say that the relation is *in* U. On the other hand, if the first components of the ordered pairs that satisfy the relation are members of a set A, while the second components are members of a set B, we say that the relation is *from* A *to* B. Thus, the relation "is less than" may be defined *in* a set of real numbers, while the relation "is the owner of" may be defined *from* a set of houses *to* a set of people. If the sets involved in the relation are finite, there will be only a finite number of ordered pairs which satisfy the relation.

ILLUSTRATION 1. Let $U = \{1, 2, 3, 4\}$. If we examine the relation "is less than" in U, the following ordered pairs will be seen to satisfy the relation: (2, 1), (3, 1), (4, 1), (3, 2), (4, 2), (4, 3).

ILLUSTRATION 2. Consider the relation "is less than and is odd" in the set U, defined as in Illustration 1. In this case the following ordered pairs satisfy the relation: (2, 1), (3, 1), (4, 1), (4, 3). Notice that these elements comprise a *subset* of the set of elements in the preceding illustration.

ILLUSTRATION 3. Let $U = \{1, 2, 3, 4, 5, 6\}$. The following ordered pairs may be seen to satisfy the relation "is a multiple of" in U: (1, 1), (1, 2), (2, 2), (1, 3), (3, 3), (1, 4), (2, 4), (4, 4), (1, 5), (5, 5), (1, 6), (2, 6), (3, 6), (6, 6).

ILLUSTRATION 4. If A is the set of married women (living or dead) and B is the set of married men (living or dead), let us find some ordered pairs that satisfy the relation "is the husband of" from A to B. Two ordered pairs that satisfy this relation are (Josephine, Napoleon), and (Eleanor Roosevelt, Franklin D. Roosevelt), and one can think of many more!

PROBLEM SET 4.1

1. If $U = \{2, 3, 4, 8\}$, tabulate the set of ordered pairs that satisfy in U the relation (*a*) "is greater than"; (*b*) "is not less than"; (*c*) "is prime to"; (*d*) "is not equal to."
2. If $U = \{1, 3, 4, 8\}$, tabulate the set of ordered pairs that satisfy in U the relation (*a*) "is equal to"; (*b*) "is a factor of"; (*c*) "is a multiple of"; (*d*) "divides."
3. Let $U = \{1, 4, 7, 8\}$, and give a verbal description of a relation in U that is satisfied by all the ordered pairs of the set (*a*) $\{(7, 1), (8, 4), (8, 7), (7, 4), (4, 1), (8, 1)\}$; (*b*) $\{(1, 4), (1, 7), (1, 8), (4, 7), (7, 8)\}$; (*c*) $\{(4, 1), (7, 1), (8, 1), (8, 4)\}$.
4. Give a verbal description of a relation that is satisfied by the ordered pair (*a*) (the set of integers, the set of prime integers); (*b*) (your state, the Governor of your state); (*c*) (21, 7); (*d*) (7, 12); (*e*) (*Paradise Lost,* Milton); (*f*) (−5, 5).
5. Let U be the set of 50 states of the U.S.A. Find an ordered pair that satisfies in U the relation (*a*) "is west of"; (*b*) "has a larger population than"; (*c*) "is adjacent to"; (*d*) "is east of"; (*e*) "has a larger area than"; (*f*) "has more snowfall than."
6. If $U = \{R^{\#}, \bar{R}, I, N\}$, write down all the ordered pairs that satisfy in U the relation (*a*) "is included in"; (*b*) "is an extension of."
7. If $U = \{1, 2, 3, 4\}$, list all the ordered pairs that satisfy in U the relation (*a*) "is equal to"; (*b*) "is not equal to"; (*c*) "is different from 1 and divides"; (*d*) "is 2 larger than."
8. Write down the members of the set of first components, and the members

of the set of second components, of the ordered pairs that satisfy each of the relations in Problem 7.

9. Let A be the set of 50 states of the U.S.A., B be the set of State Capital cities, and R be the relation "is the State Capital of," from A to B. Write down the ordered pairs that satisfy the relation R, using the following first components: Florida, California, Michigan, Georgia, Ohio, West Virginia.

10. Using the notation of Problem 9, write down the ordered pairs that satisfy the relation R from A to B and that have the following second components: Springfield, Nashville, St. Paul, Albany, Baton Rouge, Jackson.

11. Let $U = \{1, 2, 3, 4, 5, 6\}$. If R is the relation "is divisible by and is even" in U, list the ordered pairs that satisfy R.

12. Let $U = \{2, 3, 4, 5, 6\}$. List the ordered pairs that satisfy the relation "is an integral multiple of" in U. If R is the relation "is the square of an odd integer and less than," are there any ordered pairs that satisfy R in U?

4.2 Relations and Their Graphs

We have seen that a relation always determines a set of ordered pairs, i.e., the set of pairs that satisfy the relation. For example, the relation "is less than" in U, where $U = \{1, 2, 3, 4\}$, determines the set of ordered pairs $\{(2, 1), (3, 1), (4, 1), (3, 2), (4, 2), (4, 3)\}$. For most purposes, this tabulated set of ordered pairs is just as good as any verbal description of this relation, and so it should not appear too far-fetched if we actually identify the set with the relation; i.e., we are proposing to identify the relation with the set of ordered pairs that satisfy it. Thus, if R is the above relation, we are now suggesting that $R = \{(2, 1), (3, 1), (4, 1), (3, 2), (4, 2), (4, 3)\}$. In Chapter 1 we defined the Cartesian set $A \times B$ of two sets A and B to be the set of all ordered pairs of the type (a, b) with a in A and b in B. It now appears that we are regarding a relation from a set A to a set B as a subset of $A \times B$, and a relation in U as a subset of $U \times U$. The following precise definition of the "relation" concept should now appear to be quite natural.

DEFINITION. A relation *from a set A to a set B* is a subset of $A \times B$; a relation *in* U is a subset of $U \times U$. The *domain* and the *range* of a relation are, respectively, the set of first and the set of second components of the ordered pairs of the relation. An ordered pair (a, b) may be said to *satisfy* a relation R if $(a, b) \in R$.

A relation from A to B will usually be described by giving some restrictive condition on its members, and the relation is to be identified with the set of *all* ordered pairs of $A \times B$ that satisfy the condition. For example, the relation from I to $R^{\#}$ defined by $y = \sqrt{x}$, is the set of *all* pairs (x, y) in $I \times R^{\#}$, such that $y = \sqrt{x}$. Similarly, if U is a set of real numbers, we shall identify the relation "is less than" in U with the set of *all* pairs (x, y) in $U \times U$, such that $y < x$, etc.

A method of graphing a Cartesian set $A \times B$ was discussed in Chapter 1, and in view of the above definition, it is only natural to consider a *graph of a relation from A to B* as the corresponding graph of the subset of $A \times B$ that constitutes the relation. A similar remark applies to a *graph of a relation in U*. In most instances, our relations will be subsets of $R^{\#} \times R^{\#}$, and it will be convenient to use, for the basic lines of our graphs, a pair of algebraic scales that intersect at their common 0 point, their positive directions being up and to the right; these scales are usually referred to as *axes*, if used in this way. A complete graph of $R^{\#} \times R^{\#}$ comprises all the points of the plane, where we are now associating each ordered pair $(a, 0)$ with the point a on the horizontal axis, and each ordered pair $(0, b)$ with the point b on the vertical axis. A graph of a relation may then consist of points in any or all four quadrants into which the axes separate the plane. It must be realized, of course, that if a relation from A to B (or in U) is being graphed, where A and B (or U) are subsets of $R^{\#}$, *only* points of $R^{\#} \times R^{\#}$ that are also in $A \times B$ (or $U \times U$) should be *even considered* for inclusion on the graph.

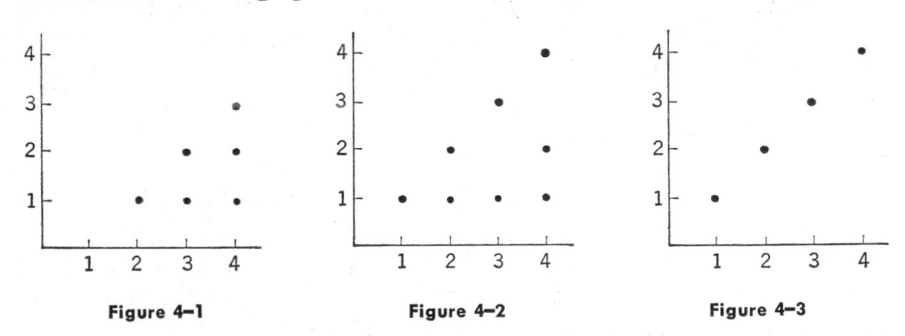

Figure 4–1 **Figure 4–2** **Figure 4–3**

ILLUSTRATION 1. If $U = \{1, 2, 3, 4\}$ and R is the relation "is less than" in U, then $R = \{(2, 1), (3, 1), (4, 1), (3, 2), (4, 2), (4, 3)\}$. The domain of R is the set $\{2, 3, 4\}$ while the range is $\{1, 2, 3\}$. A graph of this relation is shown in Figure 4–1.

ILLUSTRATION 2. If $U = \{1, 2, 3, 4\}$ and R is the relation "is a factor of" in U, then $R = \{(1, 1), (2, 1), (3, 1), (4, 1), (4, 2), (2, 2), (3, 3), (4, 4)\}$. The domain and the range of this relation both comprise the whole set U. A graph of R is shown in Figure 4–2.

ILLUSTRATION 3 Let $U = \{1, 2, 3, 4\}$. The relation "is equal to" in U is the set $\{(1, 1), (2, 2), (3, 3), (4, 4)\}$, a graph of which appears in Figure 4–3. Both the domain and the range are the whole set U.

In addition to the usual type of relation that we have been discussing, any number of new relations can be found by merely imposing some restriction on the components of the ordered pairs. We shall now illustrate this procedure.

ILLUSTRATION 4. Let $U = \{1, 2, 3, 4, 5, 6\}$ and define R to be a relation in U such that $(x, y) \in R$ if and only if $x - 2y = 0$, i.e., $R = \{(x, y) \mid (x, y) \in U \times U,\ x - 2y = 0\}$. The ordered pairs of R are $(2, 1)$, $(4, 2)$, and $(6, 3)$, a graph of this relation being shown in Figure 4–4*a*.

ILLUSTRATION 5. Let $A = \{-2, -1, 0, 1, 2, 3, 4\}$ and $B = \{-2, -1, 0, 1, 2\}$. Then if $R = \{(x, y) \mid (x, y) \in A \times B, x - 2y = 0\}$, we find that $R = \{(0, 0), (-2, -1), (4, 2)\}$. A graph of this relation is shown in Figure 4–4*b*, which should be compared with that of Figure 4–4*a*.

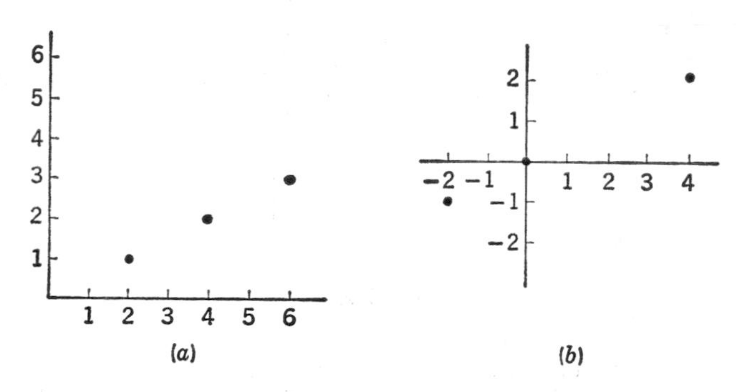

Figure 4–4

Illustrations 4 and 5 emphasize that two relations defined by the same equation are different if their domains are different. In Illustration 4, the domain is $\{2, 4, 6\}$ while in Illustration 5 it is $\{-2, 0, 4\}$.

ILLUSTRATION 6. Let $A = \{-3, -2, -1, 0, 1, 2, 3\}$ and $B = \{-5, -4, -3, -2, -1, 0, 1, 2, 3, 4, 5\}$, and let us define a relation R

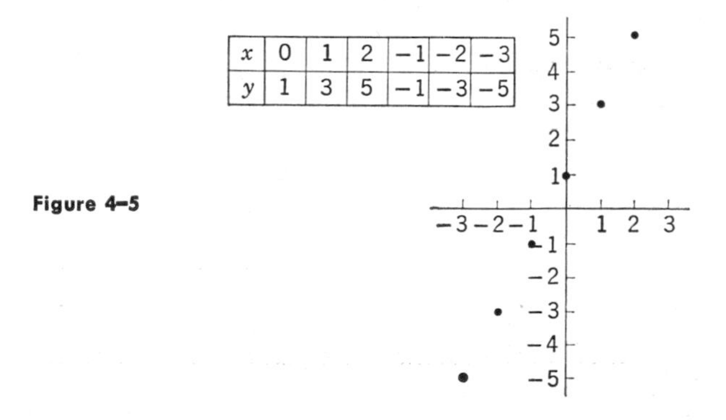

x	0	1	2	−1	−2	−3
y	1	3	5	−1	−3	−5

Figure 4–5

from A to B so that $R = \{(x, y) \mid (x, y) \in A \times B,\ 2x - y + 1 = 0\}$. It is convenient to construct a table of ordered pairs, the components of which satisfy the equation $2x - y + 1 = 0$, remembering that only numbers in A may be used for x and numbers in B for y. A graph of R, along with such a table, is shown in Figure 4–5.

ILLUSTRATION 7. Let $U = \{x \mid x \in I,\ -10 \leq x \leq 10\}$, and define the relation R in U by $R = \{(x, y) \mid (x, y) \in U \times U,\ x = y^2\}$. The table of ordered pairs in $U \times U$, having components which satisfy the equation $x = y^2$, is constructed as indicated and the graph of R is shown in Figure 4–6.

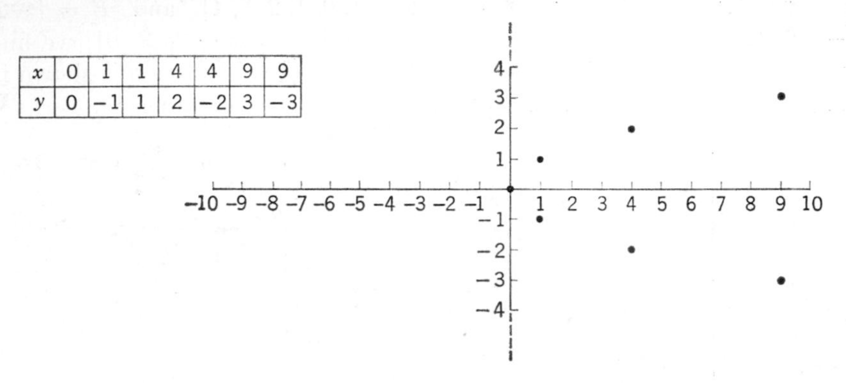

x	0	1	1	4	4	9	9
y	0	−1	1	2	−2	3	−3

Figure 4–6

Note. The following observations can be made about each of the above illustrations: the domain of the relation is the set of elements, associated with points on the horizontal scale that have at least one point graphed on the vertical line through each; the range has an analogous characterization, with respect to the points on the vertical scale.

PROBLEM SET 4.2

1. Solve each of the following equations for x: (*a*) $2x - 5 = 5x + 6$; (*b*) $(x + 5)(x - 2) = (x + 1)(x - 5)$; (*c*) $3x + 5 - x = 6x - 6$; (*d*) $2x^2 - (x + 1)(x + 5) = x^2 + 5x + 1$.
2. Solve each of the following equations for x in terms of y: (*a*) $xy + x - y^2 = 5$; (*b*) $y^3 + 2xy + y^2 - x - 4 = 0$; (*c*) $3y + xy^3 = 2xy^2 - 5$; (*d*) $2x - 3y + 5 = y^2$.
3. Solve each of the following equations for y in terms of x: (*a*) $2xy + 3x^2 - x = 2$; (*b*) $2x^2y - yx = 2x$; (*c*) $3 - y = 2xy + x^2$; (*d*) $x - 2y = 5 + 2x$.

Note. More problems on the solution of equations may be found in Section 6 of the Appendix.

4. A statement like "5 is a factor of 15" can be written in two abbreviated forms. Thus, if R is the relation "is a factor of" in I, we can write the above statement as either $5\,R\,15$ or $(15, 5) \in R$. Similarly, write each of the following statements in two ways: (*a*) 6 is divisible by 2; (*b*) 7 is prime to 12; (*c*) Joe is a brother of Mary; (*d*) -6 is less than -2; (*e*) A is disjoint from B; (*f*) Abraham is the father of Isaac.

5. Let $U = \{1, 2, 3, 4, 5, 6\}$, and consider the following elements of $U \times U$: $(1, 3)$, $(4, 1)$, $(6, 2)$, $(2, 6)$, $(5, 6)$, $(5, 2)$. (*a*) Which of the pairs belong to the relation "is less than" in U? (*b*) Which of the pairs belong to the relation "is a factor of" in U?
6. Let $U = \{1, 2, 3, 4, 5, 6\}$ and define $R = \{(2, 1), (5, 3), (1, 4), (1, 6)\}$. (*a*) What is the domain of R? (*b*) What is the range of R?
7. Let $R = \{(x, y) \mid (x, y) \in N \times N, y = x - 2\}$. (*a*) Which of the following pairs belong to R: $(0, 0)$, $(2, 1)$, $(3, 1)$, $(1, 3)$, $(4, 2)$, $(2, 5)$, $(-1, -3)$, $(-4, -6)$, $(3, -5)$? (*b*) Tabulate the range and the domain of R.
8. Let $A = \{0, 1, 2, 3\}$, $B = \{-3, -2, -1, 0, 1, 2, 3\}$, and define the relation R from A to B so that $R = \{(x, y) \mid (x, y) \in A \times B, x = y^2 + 1\}$. Graph the relation R.
9. Let $U = \{-5, -4, -3, -2, -1, 1, 2, 3, 4, 5\}$ and define the relation R in U by $R = \{(x, y) \mid (x, y) \in U \times U, x = y^2 + 1\}$. Graph R and compare with that of Problem 8.
10. Let $A = \{x \mid x \in I, -4 \leq x \leq 4\}$ and $B = \{y \mid y \in I, 0 \leq y \leq 4\}$. Graph the relation R from A to B, that is defined by $R = \{(x, y) \mid (x, y) \in A \times B, x^2 + y^2 = 16\}$.
11. Let $U = \{-3, -2, -1, 0, 1, 2, 3\}$. Graph the relation R in U where: (*a*) $R = \{(x, y) \mid (x, y) \in U \times U, x = 2\}$; (*b*) $R = \{(x, y) \mid (x, y) \in U \times U, y = -1\}$.

Note. Since a relation is a *set* of ordered pairs, the symbols $R_1 \cup R_2$, $R_1 \cap R_2$, and R' are defined for relations R_1, R_2, and R.

12. Let R_1 be the relation "is less than" and R_2 be the relation "is prime to" in U, where $U = \{-3, -2, -1, 0, 1, 2, 3\}$. Graph (*a*) $R_1 \cup R_2$; (*b*) $R_1 \cap R_2$; (*c*) R_1'.
13. Let the relations R_1 and R_2 be defined in N by: $R_1 = \{(2, 1), (1, 4), (2, 6), (-1, -5), (-2, -3), (1, 6)\}$; $R_2 = \{(1, 4), (-3, 4), (-2, -3), (1, 5), (-1, 6)\}$. (*a*) Graph $R_1 \cup R_2$. (*b*) Graph $R_1 \cap R_2$. (*c*) Tabulate the range and the domain of R_1; do the same for R_2.
14. If the domain of a relation R is a set U and the range is also U, can we conclude that $R = U \times U$?
15. Let $U = \{m, p, s, k, v\}$ and define R to be the relation "precedes in the alphabet" in U. (*a*) Graph R in U. (*b*) Tabulate the range and the domain of R.
16. If $U = \{x \mid x \in I, |x| \leq 5\}$, graph each of the following relations in U, giving the domain and the range in each case: (*a*) $R = \{(x, y) \mid (x, y) \in U \times U, xy \text{ is odd}\}$; (*b*) $R = \{(x, y) \mid (x, y) \in U \times U, x + y \text{ is even}\}$; (*c*) $R = \{(x, y) \mid (x, y) \in U \times U, x \text{ exceeds } y \text{ by } 1\}$; (*d*) $R = \{(x, y) \mid (x, y) \in U \times U, y = x^2 - 1\}$.

4.3 Functional Relations or Functions

Among the many possible relations from a set A to a set B are those having graphs intersected by each vertical line in at most one point.

These are called *functional relations* or simply *functions*. With the graphical picture in mind, we can now formulate the following definition.

DEFINITION. A *functional relation* (or *function*) f from a set A to a set B is a subset of $A \times B$ such that, if $(x, y) \in f$ and $(x, z) \in f$, then $y = z$; i.e., a relation is a function if no two distinct ordered pairs of the relation have the same first component.

Our definition of a function defines what was classically referred to as a *single-valued function*, but it has become customary in recent years to restrict the use of the word "function" to this case.

ILLUSTRATION 1. Let $U = \{x \mid x \in I,\ |x| \leq 10\}$. The relation R_1 in U defined by $R_1 = \{(x, y) \mid (x, y) \in U \times U,\ y = x^2\}$ contains the following ordered pairs: (0, 0), (1, 1), (2, 4), (3, 9), (−1, 1), (−2, 4), (−3, 9). Since no two ordered pairs of the relation have the same first

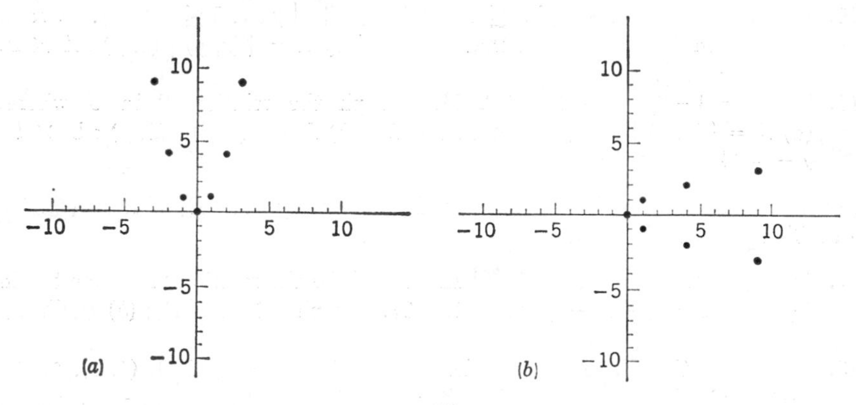

Figure 4–7

component, R_1 is a function. The graph, shown in Figure 4–7*a*, makes it clear that no vertical line could intersect it in more than one point. However, the relation R_2 in U defined by $R_2 = \{(x, y) \mid (x, y) \in U \times U, x = y^2\}$ contains the ordered pairs: (0, 0), (1, 1), (1, −1), (4, 2), (4, −2), (9, 3), (9, −3); and the pairs (1, 1) and (1, −1), for instance, have the same first component. Hence R_2 is not a function; this could also be observed from the graph of the relation shown in Figure 4–7*b*.

If a is an element of the domain of a function f, there exists one and only one element b in the range of f such that $(a, b) \in f$. The element b is uniquely determined by a and f, and so it is customary to represent b by $f(a)$, to be read "f of a." We caution at this point that $f(a)$ does not mean f multiplied by a, but is a symbol standing for the element in the range of f that is associated by f with the element a of its domain. We may then write $b = f(a)$ to indicate the *correspondence* between a and b induced by f, and refer to $f(a)$ or b as the *value of f at a*. Thus, a function f

from a set A to a set B always determines a correspondence that may be considered a *mapping* of some of the elements of A onto certain well-defined elements of B. If the domain of a function (or relation) is the set X, it frequently will be convenient to say that the function (or relation) is *on* X; the phrase "from A to B," that we have been using, has implied merely that the domain is a (possibly proper) subset of A.

In Problem 17 of Problem Set 1.4, we used the notation $N(A)$ to designate the cardinal number of the set A. While we were not thinking of N as a function at that time, the notation quite properly indicates that it is possible to do so. Thus, we may think of N as a function on the set of all finite sets, such that the value $N(A)$, for any finite set A, is its cardinal number. This notation will be used extensively in Chapter 17, and there should be no danger of confusing our use of N as a function with its use to indicate the set of all natural numbers.

We have just noted that a function always determines a mapping of the elements of one set onto those of another. The converse may also be true. Thus, given two sets A and B, if each element a of A is associated with some unique element b of B, and no two elements of B are associated with the same element of A, a function is defined on A to B; the function consists of all ordered pairs of the form (a, b) determined by the mapping. The rule of mapping, that defines a function, may be given by a verbal statement, a mathematical formula, or merely a table.

Through the years, the concept of a *function* has usually been identified with what we are calling the *functional value.* Thus, for example, if $y = f(x) = x^2$ is the rule that maps an element x of the domain of f onto the element y or $f(x)$ of its range, the quantity y was usually referred to as "the function $f(x)$." While this practice is established, we shall prefer to consider the *function* as a *set* of ordered pairs of the form (x, y), with y or $f(x)$ the *value of f at x.* Under these circumstances, however, we may sometimes wish to emphasize the *dependence* of the element y on the element x and refer to y as "a function of x"; this is in accord with common practice. We wish to emphasize a further point. In order to define a function properly, without listing all the ordered pairs in its membership, ordinarily three things must be given: the domain, the range, and the rule of mapping. For two functions may have the same domain and range but have different rules of mapping; or the rule of mapping may be the same for both functions, but their domains may be different. Thus, unless the domain and range of a function are clearly understood from the context, they should be specified along with the rule of mapping; this is ignored too frequently.

ILLUSTRATION 2. Let the membership of a set A consist of the states of California, Florida, Georgia, Michigan, New York, and Ohio; and let B be the set comprising the cities of Albany, Atlanta, Columbus, Lansing, Sacramento, and Tallahassee. Then a function f on A to B may be defined by the rule "$f(x)$ is the capital of x," and f consists of the following ordered pairs: (California, Sacramento), (Florida, Tallahassee), (Georgia, Atlanta), (Michigan, Lansing), (New York, Albany), (Ohio, Columbus).

ILLUSTRATION 3. Let $A = \{x \mid x \in I,\ 1 \leq x \leq 5\}$ and $B = \{x \mid x \in I,\ 1 \leq x \leq 100\}$. A function F on A to B may be defined by a mathematical formula, for instance, $F = \{(x, y) \mid (x, y) \in A \times B,\ y = 2x^2 + 3\}$. The domain of this function is the set A, while the range is $\{5, 11, 21, 35, 53\}$; the function F contains the pairs $(1, 5)$, $(2, 11)$, $(3, 21)$, $(4, 35)$, and $(5, 53)$.

ILLUSTRATION 4. An explicit table, such as the following, may be used to define a function.

x	-3	-2	-1	0	1	2	3
y	6	-3	5	2	6	5	-1

In this case the function consists of the following ordered pairs: $(-3, 6)$, $(-2, -3)$, $(-1, 5)$, $(0, 2)$, $(1, 6)$, $(2, 5)$, $(3, -1)$. The domain of the function is the set $\{-3, -2, -1, 0, 1, 2, 3\}$ and the range is $\{-3, -1, 2, 5, 6\}$. Note that the number of elements in the domain of a function can never be less than the number of elements in the range. Why?

ILLUSTRATION 5. Let $U = \{a, b, c\}$. Then, if f is the function on U that maps a onto b, b onto c, and c onto a, f consists of the pairs (a, b), (b, c), and (c, a). Such a function, defining a one-to-one mapping of the elements of a finite set onto itself, is also called a *permutation*. (See Chapter 16 for a more common use of this word.)

PROBLEM SET 4.3

1. If 1, -2, 0, and -3 are elements of the domain of a function f defined by $f(x) = 2x^3 - 3x + 1$, determine $f(1)$, $f(-2)$, $f(0)$, and $f(-3)$.

2. A function F is defined by $F(u) = u^2 + u + 1$. Assuming that -1, 1, 3, $1 + h$, and $1 - h$ are in the domain of F, determine: (*a*) $F(-1)$ and $F(1)$; (*b*) $F(1 + h)$ and $F(1 - h)$; (*c*) $\dfrac{2F(3) - F(-1)}{2F(1)}$.

3. The following table defines a function f:

x	2	4	6	8	10
$f(x)$	-3	-2	1	0	1

(*a*) Find $f(6)$ and $f(4)$. (*b*) What is the domain of f? (*c*) What is the range of f?

4. The function G, which has for its domain the set of positive integers from 1 to 100 inclusive, is defined by the equation $G(x) = x^3 + 1$. (*a*) Find $G(2)$, $G(5)$, and $G(10)$. (*b*) Is $G(-2)$ defined? (*c*) Determine $G(1) + 2G(2)$.
5. If $A = \{1, 3, 6\}$ and $B = \{0, 2, 4\}$, how many different functions from A to B are possible?
6. The following tables completely define certain relations:

(*a*)

x	1	2	3
y	-2	-5	-2

(*b*)

x	1	2	3
y	2	2	2

(*c*)

x	1	2	2
y	3	-1	-3

(*d*)

x	1	1	1
y	2	3	4

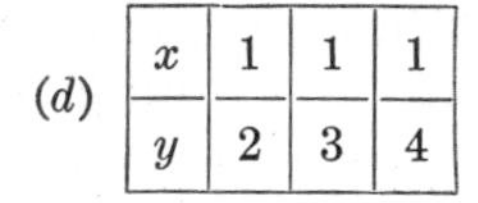

Which of these relations are functions, if x is regarded as an element of the domain and y the corresponding element of the range?
7. Let $A = \{1, 2, 3\}$ and $B = \{a, b, c\}$. If each of the following graphs is considered to define a relation from A to B (*a*) which of these relations are functions? (*b*) give the domain and range of each function defined. (*c*) give the domain and range of each relation that is not a function.

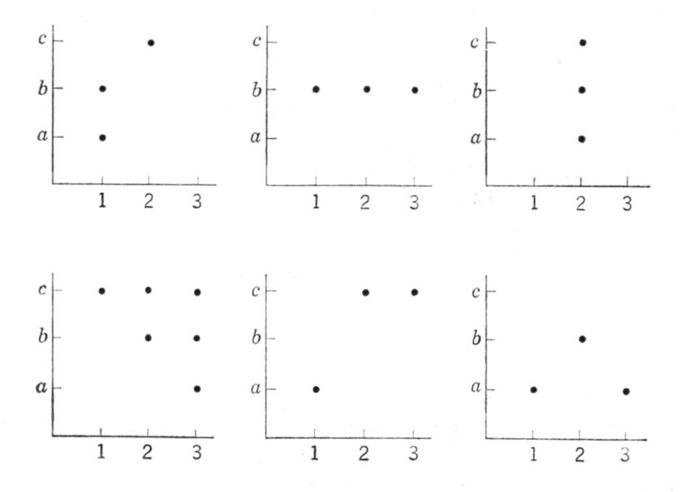

8. Let $A = \{-5, -3, 0, 1, 2\}$. If F is a function on A, with $F(x) = x^2 - 1$, write down the members of F.
9. Make up a table purporting to show the amount of rainfall in your city each week for the past six weeks. What are the domain and range of the function defined by the table?
10. With A and B subsets of I, a function f from A to B is defined by $f(x) = x^2 - 2$. (*a*) Graph f if its domain is $\{0, 1, 2, 3, 4, 5\}$. (*b*) Graph f if its domain is $\{-3, -1, 0, 3, 4, 5\}$.

11. The functions F_1 and F_2 are completely defined by the tables below. Graph each function.

x	1	3	2	4
$F_1(x)$	-3	0	1	2

x	1	4	6	8
$F_2(x)$	-2	5	1	6

12. Let A = set of books in your library and B = set of authors of books in your library. (*a*) Give a rule of mapping that would define a function on A to B. (*b*) Give a rule of mapping that would define a relation on B to A. (*c*) Why is the relation in (*b*) probably not a function?

13. A function G consists of the following ordered pairs: $(-2, 6)$, $(-1, 5)$, $(0, 7)$, $(3, 4)$, $(5, 10)$. (*a*) Find $G(3)$ and $G(-1)$. (*b*) Graph the function G. (*c*) Determine $[2G(5) - G(0)]/[G(-1)]$.

14. The following diagram illustrates a mapping of a set A into a set B, thereby defining a function F on A to B.

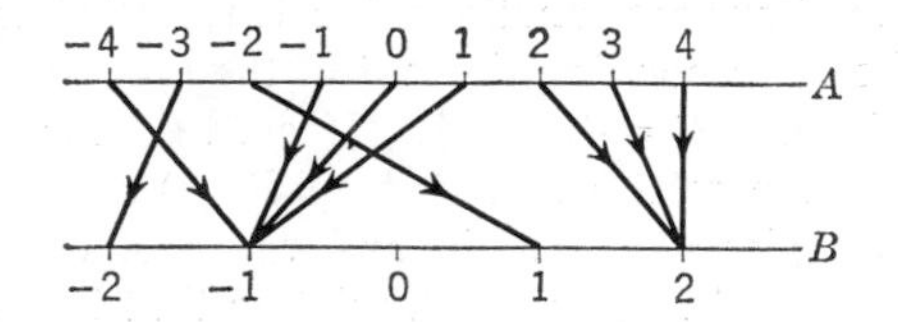

(*a*) What are the domain and range of F? (*b*) What are $F(-1)$ and $F(3)$? (*c*) Onto what element does the mapping take (i) -1; (ii) 3? (*d*) Does the inverse mapping of the elements from B to A define a function? Explain.

15. If $A = \{-4, -2, -1, 0, 1, 2, 4\}$ and $B = N$, graph the following functions:
(*a*) $f = \{(x, y) \mid (x, y) \in A \times B, y = 2x^2 + 1\}$;
(*b*) $F = \{(x, y) \mid (x, y) \in A \times B, y = 20/x \text{ if } x \neq 0, y = 0 \text{ if } x = 0\}$;
(*c*) $f = \{(x, y) \mid (x, y) \in A \times B, y = 20/x \text{ if } x \neq 0, y = 6 \text{ if } x = 0\}$.

16. If $A = \{-1, 0, 1\}$, the equation $x^2 + y^2 = 1$ defines a relation on A to A. Write down the elements of two subsets of this relation that are functions on A. Graph the relation and the two functions.

17. Which of the following relations in I are functions? Give the domain and range of each function. (*a*) $\{(x, y) \mid (x, y) \in I \times I,\ y = x^3\}$; (*b*) $\{(x, y) \mid (x, y) \in I \times I,\ y^4 = x\}$; (*c*) $\{(x, y) \mid (x, y) \in I \times I,\ x < y\}$; (*d*) $\{(x, y) \mid (x, y) \in I \times I, x^2 - y = 16\}$.

18. Let A be the set of all children and B be the set of all mothers. Show why the rule "is a child of" defines a function on A to B, and the rule "is the mother of" defines a relation on B to A.

19. If each natural number is mapped by the function F onto 0 or 1, according as the number is even or odd, what are $F(27)$, $F(22)$, and $F(2)$?

20. If f is the function that maps the last five years onto the respective championship school of the football conference to which your college belongs, list the members of this function. List the members of the domain and the range of f.

21. The counting process associates each element counted with a natural number. If f is the function defined by this correspondence in counting the elements of the set $\{a, *, \&, 6, \#\}$ in the written order, what are $f(\&)$ and $f(\#)$?

4.4. Extending The Domain

For any two sets A and B, the Cartesian set $A \times B$ is the set of all ordered pairs of the type (a, b) where $a \in A$ and $b \in B$, and we have represented $A \times B$ graphically by certain lattice points on a plane. As long as the sets A and B are finite, the order in which the elements of A and B are located on the horizontal and vertical line segments is unimportant. Thus, if $A = \{-1, 2, 3\}$ and $B = \{-5, -2, 5\}$, either of the two graphs in Figure 4–8 would represent $A \times B$ equally well; the elements of $A \times B$ would merely correspond to different points of the plane, in the two graphs.

The corresponding graphical representation of a relation or function on A to B could also be given equally well with either arrangement of the elements of A and B. For example, if a function f is defined by $f(-1) = 2$, $f(2) = 5$, and $f(3) = -5$, either graph of Figure 4–9 could represent the function; and it would be easy to produce other representations.

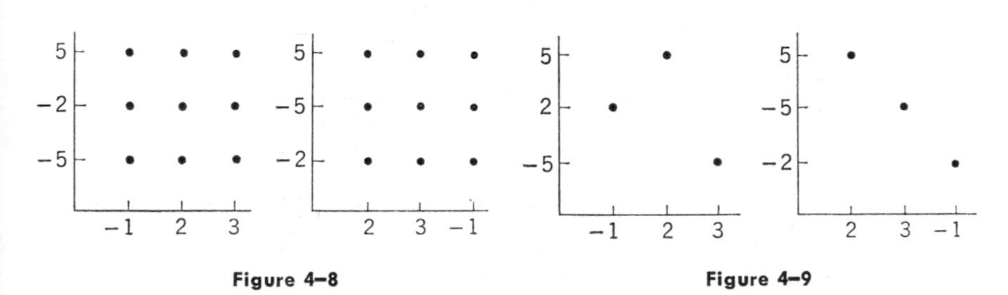

Figure 4–8 **Figure 4–9**

However, if the elements of the domain of a function are infinite in number, the actually "plotted" points are only a partial graph of the function, and it may be necessary to "interpolate" other points, i.e., to insert other points not accurately located. It would be impossible to do this if the elements of the domain and range were not arranged on the basic lines in an orderly fashion. It is for this reason that, if the domain and range of a relation are subsets of the set $R^{\#}$ of all real numbers, we have chosen a pair of *algebraic scales* as a basis for our graph; for it is the Fundamental Postulate of Analytic Geometry that each real number is associated with a *unique* point on such a scale. On each of the two scales we then have a complete representation of $R^{\#}$, and *every* point of the *plane* is a lattice point with respect to the real numbers represented on the scales. The Fundamental Postulate then implies that there is a one-to-one correspondence between the points of the plane and the set of ordered pairs of real numbers. In harmony with previous practice in connection with a single scale, we shall frequently identify the ordered pairs with the corresponding points of the plane. Thus, for example, we may speak of "the point (2, 3)" or "the point (−1, 1)."

If we use the method just described to graph a function or relation in $R^{\#}$, the resulting configuration of points assumes some geometrical significance. For if the point P is associated with the pair (a, b) on a graph, the component a is now the measure of distance of P from the vertical axis, in the units of the horizontal axis, while b is the measure of distance of P from the horizontal axis, in the units of the vertical axis. In this geometric setting, the numbers a and b are known, respectively, as the *abscissa* and *ordinate* of P, and together its *coordinates*; the pair (a, b) is then known as the *coordinate pair* of P. The point of intersection of the two axes, i.e., the point with coordinate pair $(0, 0)$, is the *origin* of this *Cartesian coordinate system*. If x is designated as a representative element of the domain of a relation, the horizontal axis is usually referred to as the *x-axis*; and if y is a corresponding element of the range, the vertical axis is known as the *y-axis*. In case symbols different from these are used, of course, the axes are named accordingly, but this is the customary symbolism. In this book, whenever we speak of a relation defined by an equation in x and y, we shall assume—unless otherwise directed—that x is an element of the domain and y is the corresponding element of the range. Under these circumstances, we shall refer to the plane of the graph as the *xy-plane*. In the case of a function f, however, we usually shall prefer the notation $f(x)$ to y.

There is one further item of terminology to which we wish to call attention. While one can conceive of an endless number of distinct Cartesian graphs of any given relation, if we consider distinct points as characterizing distinct graphs, inasmuch as they all convey the same information in essentially the same way, there is no good reason for distinguishing between them. Hence, we shall find it convenient to identify them all and refer to an arbitrary Cartesian graph of a relation R as *the* graph of R.

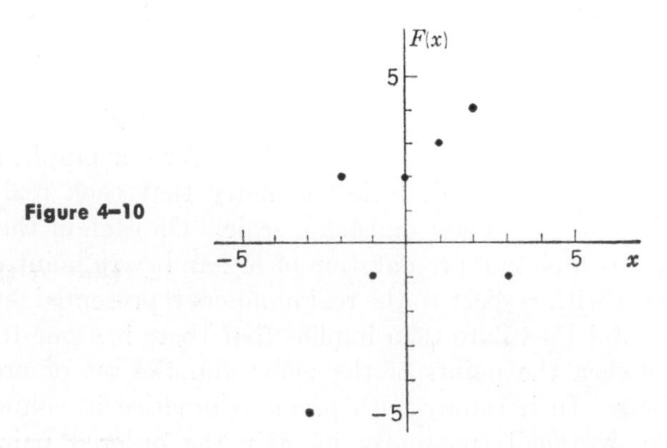

Figure 4–10

ILLUSTRATION 1. Graph the function f, completely defined by the following table.

x	-3	-2	-1	0	1	2	3
$F(x)$	-5	2	-1	2	3	4	-1

The result is shown in Figure 4–10.

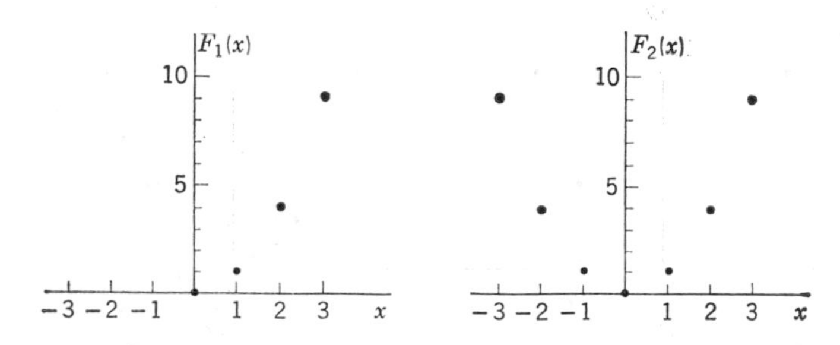

Figure 4–11

We have emphasized before that a function is not completely defined by a rule unless the domain is specified or assumed, because it is possible to define many different functions using the same rule. For example, consider the following two functions in I:

$$F_1 = \{(x, y) \mid (x, y) \in I \times I,\ y = x^2,\ 0 \leq x \leq 3\};$$

$$F_2 = \{(x, y) \mid (x, y) \in I \times I,\ y = x^2,\ -3 \leq x \leq 3\}.$$

The functions F_1 and F_2 are defined by the same rule, but since their domains are different they are distinct functions; their graphs are shown in Figure 4–11.

Consider now the functions defined on D by $y = x^2$, where D stands successively for the following subsets of $R^\#$: (*a*) $\{x \mid x \in I,\ |x| \leq 3\}$; (*b*) $\{x \mid x$ is an integral multiple of $1/2,\ |x| \leq 3\}$; (*c*) $\{x \mid x$ is an integral multiple of $1/4,\ |x| \leq 3\}$; (*d*) $\{x \mid x \in \bar{R},\ |x| \leq 3\}$; (*e*) $\{x \mid x \in R^\#,\ |x| \leq 3\}$. Each of these functions may be considered an extension of the function which precedes it, as is indicated by the graphs of Figure 4–12. Although the points on the graph of (*d*) do not form a smooth curve as in the case of (*e*), these two graphs will appear to be the same, since the rational numbers are so dense on the x-axis. If we should let D be enlarged still further to be the set $R^\#$ of all real numbers, the graph is a smooth curve that is infinite in extent, a portion of which is identical to that of (*e*). In the language of geometry, we may refer to $y = x^2$ as *an equation of the curve*, and to the curve as *the locus of the equation* $y = x^2$. It should be observed that there are many distinct equations having identical loci, for example $y = x^2$ and $2y - 2x^2 = 0$, and so it would not be proper to speak of *the* equation of a curve, without further specifications.

Whatever we have said about extending the domain of a function applies equally well to relations in general. If the domain of a function or relation is not finite, it is impossible to tabulate the function or relation or to graph it completely. However, it is possible in such cases to find as

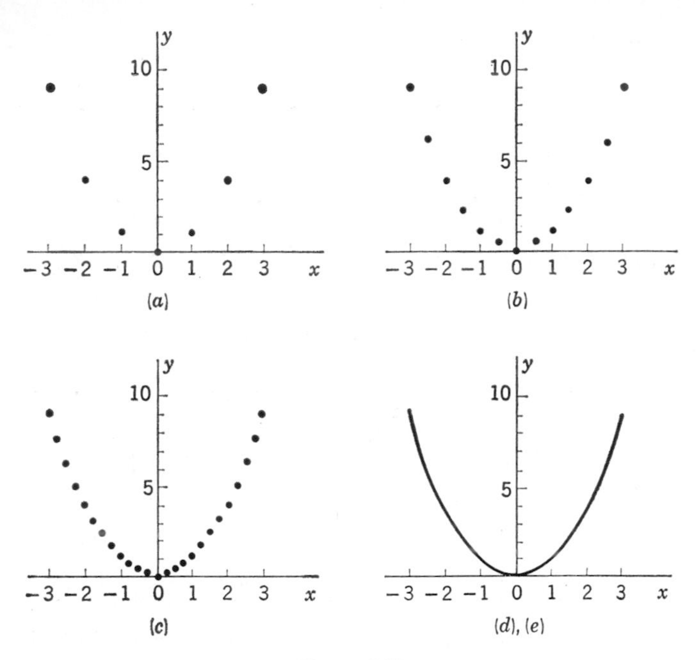

Figure 4–12

many elements as desired by making a table of ordered pairs and approximating its graph by the graph of these tabulated pairs. The complete graph may then be more closely approximated by drawing a smooth curve through these plotted points, being careful to avoid any points having abscissas not in the domain of the function or relation. If the domain is a discrete set of points, it would be incorrect to connect the plotted points with a curve, since this would imply an unauthorized extension of the domain.

ILLUSTRATION 2. Graph the function f defined by $f(x) = x^3 - 9x^2 + 24x - 7$ on the set $\{x \mid x \in R^{\#}, -1 \leq x \leq 6\}$.

Solution. A partial table of ordered pairs of f is given below.

x	-1	0	1	2	3	4	5	6
$f(x)$	-41	-7	9	13	11	9	13	29

These function elements are plotted on a graph and the points connected by a smooth curve, since we are told that every real number between -1 and 6 is in the domain of f. The result is shown in Figure 4–13.

ILLUSTRATION 3. Graph the relation in $R^{\#}$ defined by $9x^2 + 4y^2 = 36$.

Solution. If x is a real number that is larger in absolute value than 2, there is no corresponding real number y defined by the equation; but if $|x| \leq 2$, a corresponding real number y may be found that satisfies the

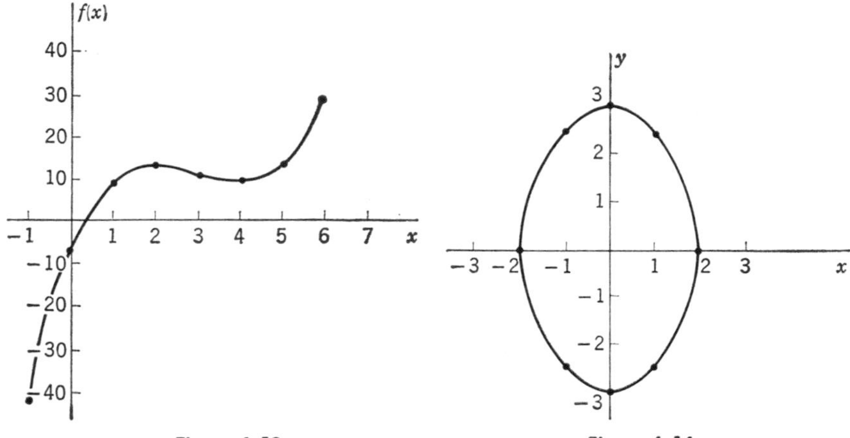

Figure 4–13

Figure 4–14

equation, and so $\{x \mid x \in R^{\#}, |x| \leq 2\}$ is the domain of the relation. It may also be observed that if $|y| > 3$, there is no real number x that may be associated with it, and so no point of the graph can have an ordinate larger in absolute value than 3. A partial table of ordered pairs of the relation is given below, and its associated graph is shown in Figure 4–14. It will be observed that for each non-zero real number of the domain, there are two real numbers of the range. The points that have been graphed are then joined by a smooth curve, as shown in the figure.

x	-2	-1	-1	0	0	1	1	2
y	0	$\frac{3\sqrt{3}}{2}$	$\frac{-3\sqrt{3}}{2}$	3	-3	$\frac{3\sqrt{3}}{2}$	$\frac{-3\sqrt{3}}{2}$	0

ILLUSTRATION 4. Graph the function f defined on the interval $[-3, 3]$ as follows: $f(x) = 2x - 3$, if $-3 \leq x < 1$; $f(x) = x^2$, if $1 < x \leq 3$; $f(x) = 2$, if $x = 1$.

Solution. A partial table of ordered pairs of this function is given below.

x	-3	-2	-1	0	1	3/2	2	5/2	3
$f(x)$	-9	-7	-5	-3	2	9/4	4	25/4	9

It should be noted that the rule for the definition of this function is not the same for all elements of the domain. The graph is shown in Figure 4–15, where we have joined the plotted points, except at $x = 1$, by a smooth curve. Why do we have the exception?

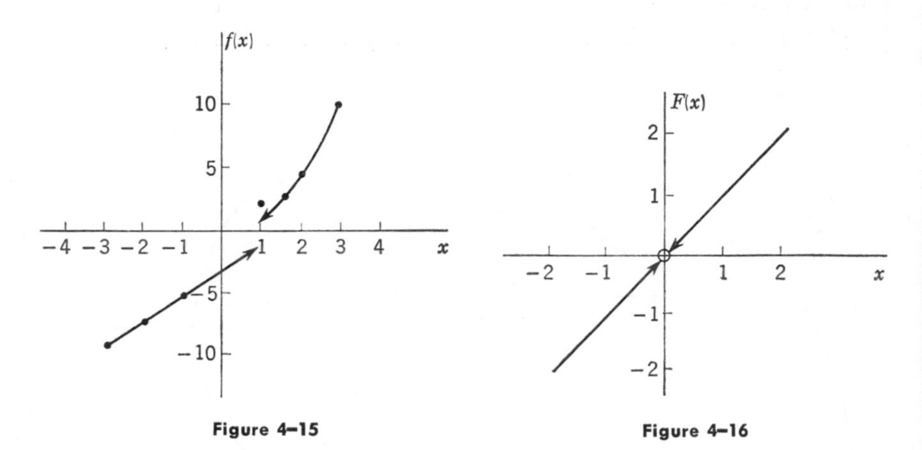

Figure 4–15

Figure 4–16

ILLUSTRATION 5. Graph the function F defined by $F(x) = x^2/x$ on the set of non-zero real numbers of the interval $[-2, 2]$.

Solution. A partial table of ordered pairs of F is given below.

x	-2	-1	1	2
$F(x)$	-2	-1	1	2

It should be observed that 0 is not in the domain of F. However, for each real number $x \neq 0$, $F(x) = x$; and the graph consists of what appears to be a straight line segment approaching the point $(0, 0)$ from both sides, but with this point missing from the graph. This is shown in Figure 4–16.

The functions defined in the last two illustrations have what are known as *discontinuities;* the graphical effect of this is the presence of breaks in what otherwise would be a smooth curve. The question of continuity will be more fully discussed in a later chapter.

PROBLEM SET 4.4

Each of the equations in Problems 1 through 10 may be regarded as the rule of correspondence for a relation in $R^{\#}$, with an unspecified domain of real numbers. Using the conventional symbolism, determine the largest possible domain for each relation.

1. $y^2 = x^2 - 5.$
2. $y^2 - 3x^2 = 9.$
3. $y = 4x^2 + 6.$
4. $x^2 = 12 - 2y^2.$
5. $y = \log (x^2 - 1).$
6. $x^2 + y^2 = 25.$
7. $y = \dfrac{2x + 1}{x}\cdot$
8. $y = \dfrac{x + 1}{x - 1}\cdot$
9. $y^2 = 1 - 2/x.$
10. $y = 4^x.$

In Problems 11 through 18, use the indicated domain D and graph each of the functions defined by the given equations.

11. $f(x) = 2x^2$: (*a*) $D = \{x \mid x \in N,\ x \leq 3\}$; (*b*) $D = \{x \mid x \in I,\ |x| \leq 4\}$; (*c*) $D = \{x \mid x \in R^\#,\ |x| \leq 4\}$.
12. $f(x) = 3x - 4$: (*a*) $D = \{x \mid x \in I,\ |x| \leq 5\}$; (*b*) $D = \{x \mid x \in R^\#,\ |x| \leq 5\}$.
13. $f(x) = 6 - 4x$: (*a*) $D = \{x \mid x \in N,\ x \leq 3\}$; (*b*) $D = \{x \mid x \in I,\ |x| \leq 3\}$; (*c*) $D = \{x \mid x \in R^\#,\ |x| \leq 3\}$.
14. $f(x) = 3x^2 + 2$: (*a*) $D = \{x \mid x \in N,\ x \leq 3\}$; (*b*) $D = \{x \mid x \in I,\ |x| \leq 3\}$; (*c*) $D = \{x \mid x \in R^\#,\ |x| \leq 3\}$.
15. $f(x) = 3 - 2x^2$: (*a*) $D = \{x \mid x \in I,\ |x| \leq 5\}$; (*b*) $D = \{x \mid x \in R^\#,\ |x| \leq 5\}$.
16. $f(x) = 3x^2 - 2x + 4$: (*a*) $D = \{x \mid x \in I,\ |x| \leq 5\}$; (*b*) $D = \{x \mid x \in R^\#,\ |x| \leq 5\}$.
17. $f(x) = x^3 + 4$: (*a*) $D = \{x \mid x \in I,\ |x| \leq 3\}$; (*b*) $\{x \mid x \in R^\#,\ |x| \leq 3\}$.
18. $f(x) = 2x^3 - x^2$: (*a*) $D = \{x \mid x \in I,\ |x| \leq 5\}$; (*b*) $D = \{x \mid x \in R^\#,\ |x| \leq 5\}$.
19. Graph the function F defined by $F(x) = |x|$, on the interval $[-5, 5]$.
20. Graph the function F defined by $F(x) = [x]$, on the interval $[-5, 5]$, where $[x]$ is the largest integer not larger than x.
21. If $D = \{x \mid x \in R^\#, |x| \leq 2\}$, graph the function f on D defined by $f(x) = x + [x]$. (See Problem 20.)

For Problems 22 to 24, x is an arbitrary real number in the domain of a function f defined as indicated by the given equation. In each case, graph the function f.

22. $f(x) = x + 1$, for $-3 \leq x \leq 1$; $f(x) = 2x^2$, for $1 < x \leq 3$.
23. $f(x) = -2x^2$, for $-3 \leq x < 0$; $f(x) = 1$, for $x = 0$; $f(x) = 5 + x$, for $0 < x \leq 3$.
24. $f(x) = -2x^2$, for $-5 \leq x \leq 0$; $f(x) = 3x$, for $0 < x \leq 2$; $f(x) = x^2$, for $2 < x \leq 5$.

In Problems 25 to 28, graph each of the relations defined on the set D by the given equation.

25. $x = 2y^2$, $D = \{x \mid x \in R^\#,\ 0 \leq x \leq 32\}$.
26. $x^2 + 4y^2 = 4$, $D = \{x \mid x \in R^\#,\ |x| \leq 2\}$.
27. $2x + 3 = y^2$, $D = \{x \mid x \in R^\#,\ -1 \leq x \leq 2\}$.
28. $x^2 - 4y^2 = 4$, $D = \{x \mid x \in R^\#,\ 4 \leq |x| \leq 8\}$.
29. If $D = \{x \mid x \in I,\ |x| \leq 5\}$, a function f on D to the set $\{0, 1\}$ is defined as follows: $f(x) = 0$, if x is even; $f(x) = 1$, if x is odd. Graph this function.
30. Graph the function F defined on the set D by $F(x) = 2$, if (*a*) $D = \{x \mid x \in I,\ |x| \leq 5\}$; (*b*) $D = \{x \mid x \in R^\#,\ |x| \leq 5\}$.

4.5 Special Relations

Let $U = \{1, 2, 3, 4\}$, and consider the relations in U depicted by the graphs of Figure 4–17. A close inspection of (*a*) and (*b*) reveals that the points of these graphs are mutually exclusive, but together they make up

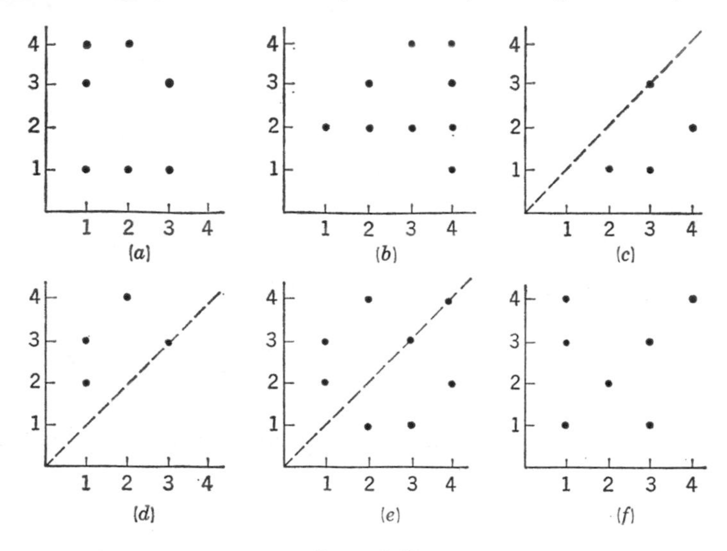

Figure 4–17

the whole set $U \times U$. That is, every point of $U \times U$ is on one of the graphs, but no point is on both. These are graphs of what are known as *complementary* relations. (See Chapter 1 for general complementary sets.) We can now formulate the following more formal definition.

DEFINITION. If R is a relation from a set A to a set B, the relation from A to B that is *complementary* to R is the set $\{(a, b) \mid (a, b) \in A \times B, (a, b) \notin R\}$.

ILLUSTRATION 1. The relations "is less than or equal to" and "is greater than" are complementary relations in any set U of real numbers. If $U = \{-2, -1, 0, 1, 2, 3\}$, the graph of Figure 4–18 portrays these two relations, with a heavy mark (•) indicating an element of the first relation and an asterisk (*) indicating an element of the second.

Let us now consider graphs (*c*) and (*d*) of Figure 4–17. If we imagine the indicated diagonal line as a mirror, the points of one graph are the images of the points of the other. Relations, having graphs with this "mirror" property are *inverses* to each other according to the following more precise definition.

DEFINITION. A relation R_1 is the *inverse* of a relation R_2 provided $(a, b) \in R_1$ if and only if $(b, a) \in R_2$.

The domain and the range must be the same set for any relation having an inverse.

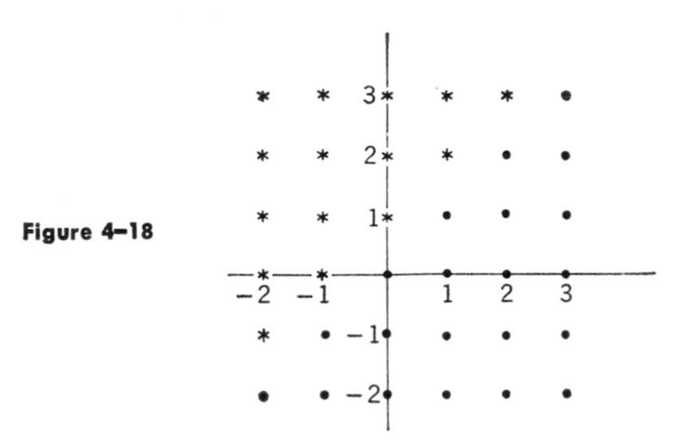

Figure 4–18

ILLUSTRATION 2. Let $U = \{x \mid x \in I, \ |x| \leq 10\}$. The sets $\{(x, y) \mid (x, y) \in U \times U, \ y = 2x\}$ and $\{(x, y) \mid (x, y) \in U \times U, \ x = 2y\}$ are relations that are inverse to each other, and portions of their graphs are shown in Figure 4–19. It should be observed that if a relation is defined by an equation in x and y, the inverse relation may be defined by the equation that results when x and y are interchanged.

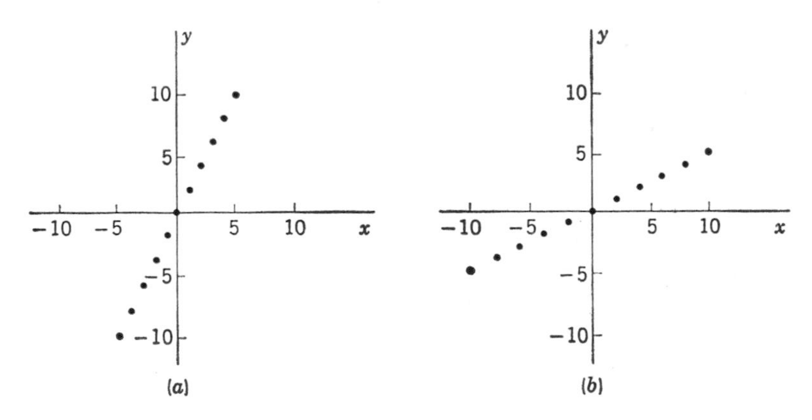

Figure 4–19

It sometimes happens that a relation is its own inverse, and is said to be *symmetric* according to the following definition.

DEFINITION. A relation is *symmetric* if (a, b) and (b, a) are either both present in or both absent from the relation.

Graph (*e*) of Figure 4–17 depicts a symmetric relation; the points of the graph form a figure that is geometrically symmetric with respect to the diagonal line shown.

ILLUSTRATION 3. Let $U = \{x \mid x \in I, |x| \leq 4\}$, and consider the relation in U defined as $\{(x, y) \mid (x, y) \in U \times U, x^2 + y^2 = 16\}$. It is apparent that if $a^2 + b^2 = 16$, then also $b^2 + a^2 = 16$. Thus (b, a) is a member of the relation whenever (a, b) is a member, and so the relation is symmetric. Its graph is shown in Figure 4–20.

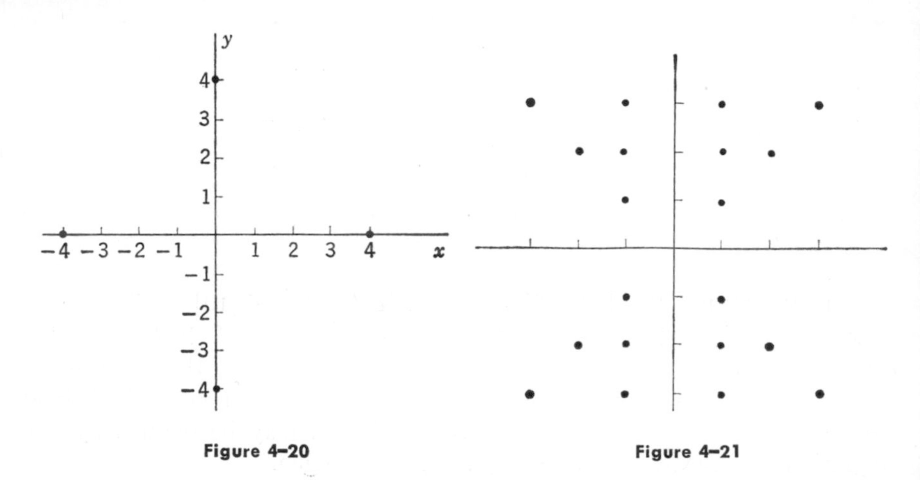

Figure 4–20 Figure 4–21

If we refer to graph (*f*) of Figure 4–17, we see that all the diagonal elements (1, 1), (2, 2), (3, 3), (4, 4) of $U \times U$ are present. This relation is then *reflexive* according to the following definition.

DEFINITION. A relation R in U is *reflexive* if $(x, x) \in R$, for every $x \in U$.

ILLUSTRATION 4. Let $U = \{-3, -2, -1, 1, 2, 3\}$, and consider the relation "is divisible by" in U. Since every non-zero number is divisible by itself, it follows that this relation contains all the elements of the form (x, x), with $x \in U$, and so the relation is symmetric. The graph is shown in Figure 4–21.

Inasmuch as a function is a special type of relation, all of the above definitions can be applied to functions; however, a few remarks should be made about these applications. While a relation that is complementary to an arbitrary function exists, this relation will be a function only in very special cases. Similarly, the relation that is *inverse* to a given function is not in general a function. For example, if U is any subset of real numbers, the function on U defined by $y = x^2$ has for its inverse a relation defined by $x = y^2$, and we have noted before that such a relation is not a function. The notion of *symmetry* carries over to functions, but a *reflexive* function in U must consist *only* of elements of the form (x, x), with $x \in U$, the graph of a reflexive function being merely a set of diagonal lattice points; the reflexive property as applied to functions is then not a very useful one. Several other characterizations of relations will be found in Problem Set 4.5.

PROBLEM SET 4.5

1. If $U = \{0, 1, 2, 3, 4, 5\}$, graph the relation in U defined by: (a) $y = x^2$; (b) $y = 2x - 1$; (c) $y = x + 1$.

2. Graph the relations that are complementary to the relations of Problem 1.

3. Graph the relations that are inverses to the relations of Problem 1.

4. A relation is defined in $R^{\#}$ by: (a) $y = 3x^2 + 1$; (b) $xy = 4$; (c) $y = x + 1$; (d) $2x^2 + 2y^2 = 5$; (e) $x^2y^2 + xy = 5$; (f) $x^2 - y^2 = 10$. Which of the above relations are symmetric?

5. If $U = \{1, 2, 3\}$, graph three relations in U that are reflexive.

6. If $U = \{x \mid x \in I, |x| \leq 6\}$, graph the relation on U that is defined by: (a) $y = x$; (b) $y = 2x$; (c) $y = x/2$.

7. Each of the following rules defines a relation in a suitable set. Classify each of these relations as symmetric, reflexive, both symmetric and reflexive, or neither symmetric nor reflexive. (a) "is a brother of"; (b) "is a relative of"; (c) "is two miles from"; (d) "is the same weight as"; (e) "is not more than two miles from."

8. What graphical characteristic is possessed by any function, the inverse of which is also a function?

9. If $U = \{x \mid x \in R^{\#}, 0 \leq x \leq 10\}$, which of the functions on U graphed below define one-to-one mappings of the set U onto itself?

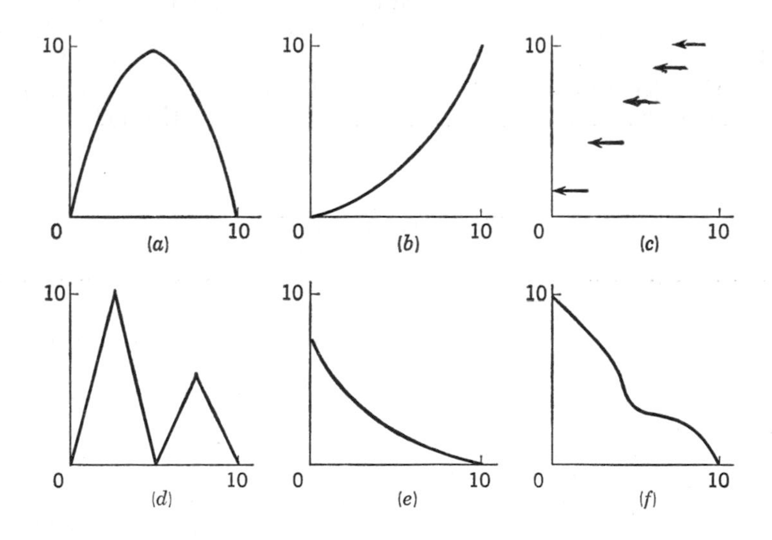

10. Let f_1 and f_2 be "constant" functions defined as follows:

$$f_1 = \{(x, y) \mid (x, y) \in I \times I, 0 \leq x \leq 10, y = 5\};$$

$$f_2 = \{(x, y) \mid (x, y) \in I \times I, 0 \leq x \leq 10, y = -2\}.$$

(a) Graph f_1 and f_2; (b) graph the inverses of f_1 and f_2.

11. A function in $R^{\#}$ is defined by (*a*) $y = x + 2$; (*b*) $y = 2x^2$; (*c*) $x^2 - 2y = 5$; (*d*) $xy = 4 + x$; (*e*) $y = \sqrt{x+1}$. Which of these functions have inverses that are also functions?

12. Is the complement of the inverse of a function the same as the inverse of its complement? Illustrate with a graph.

13*. A relation R is said to be *transitive* if $(c, b) \in R$ and $(b, a) \in R$ imply that $(c, a) \in R$. For example, the relation "is less than" if $R^{\#}$ is transitive, since $b < c$ and $a < b$ imply that $a < c$. Try to find a general characterization of the graphs of all transitive relations.

14*. Each of the following rules will define a relation in some suitable set. Classify each relation as symmetric, transitive, both symmetric and transitive, or neither symmetric nor transitive. (*a*) "is equal to"; (*b*) "is perpendicular to"; (*c*) "hates"; (*d*) "is greater than or equal to"; (*e*) "exceeds"; (*f*) "is faster than"; (*g*) "has the same remainder when divided by 5 as."

15*. Which of the relations in Problem 14 are reflexive?

16*. A relation that is reflexive, symmetric, and transitive is called an *equivalence* relation. Which of the relations in Problem 14 are equivalence relations?

17*. A relation R in U is called *tripartive* if it has the following properties: (*a*) $(a, a) \notin R$ for any $a \in U$; (*b*) either (a, b) or (b, a) but not both are members of R. If $U = \{1, 2, 3\}$, graph two tripartive relations in U.

18*. A relation which is tripartive and transitive is called an *order* relation. Show that "is less than" is an order relation on any set of real numbers.

19*. The operation of addition, applied to two integers, defines a function F on $I \times I$ to I by the rule $F(a, b) = a + b$, for any integers a and b. With this notation, what are $F(2, 3)$, $F(1, -2)$, $F(0, 4)$, and $F(5, -6)$?

20*. (See Problem 19.) If G is the function on $I \times I$ to I defined by $G(a, b) = ab$, what are $G(2, 3)$, $G(3, 5)$, $G(0, 3)$, $G(2, -8)$, and $G(-1, -1)$?

REVIEW TEST A

1. Which of the following ordered pairs satisfy the relation "is divisible by" in N? (*a*) (3, 2); (*b*) (10, 2); (*c*) (2, 10); (*d*) (3, 12).

2. A relation R consists of the set $\{(-2, 1), (3, 2), (-2, 4), (5, 0)\}$. List the members of (*a*) the domain of R; (*b*) the range of R.

3. Let the domain of a relation R be $\{1, 2, 3, 4, 5\}$. List the members of the relation, if $y = x^2 - 1$ for each member (x, y) of R.

4. Let $U = \{x \mid x \in I, |x| \leq 15\}$. List the members of the relation R in U defined by $R = \{(x, y) \mid (x, y) \in U \times U, y^2 = x + 2\}$.

5. Let $U = \{x \mid x \in I, |x| \leq 4\}$, and graph the function f defined in U by $f = \{(x, y) \mid (x, y) \in U \times U, y = x - 3\}$.

6. A function f is defined by $f(x) = (3x + 4)/(x + 3)$, for an element x of its domain. If 2 and -1 are elements of the domain of f, determine (*a*) $f(2)$; (*b*) $f(-1)$.

7. Let $A = \{1, 2, 3\}$ and $B = \{0, 1, 2\}$. How many different functions are possible from A to B, if each domain is to contain at least two elements?

8. Let functions f and g be defined by $f(x) = x^2 - 2x$ and $g(y) = (y^2 - 1)/y$, for x an element of the domain of f and y an element of the domain of g. Determine $[f(1)]/[g(2) + 2]$, assuming 2 is in the domain of g and 1 is in the domain of f.

9. Determine the domain and the range of the function f in I defined by: (*a*) $f(x) = 2 - x$; (*b*) $f(x) = 12/x$; (*c*) $f(x) = \sqrt{10 - x}$.

10. A right cone is inscribed in a sphere having a 10-inch radius. If the volume of such a cone is V cubic inches when the altitude is h inches, express V as a function of h.

11. Classify as symmetric, reflexive, both symmetric and reflexive, or neither symmetric nor reflexive, the relation on $R^{\#}$ defined by (*a*) $x^2y^2 = 4$; (*b*) $x^2 - 2y^2 = 4$; (*c*) $2x^2 + 2y^2 = 1$; (*d*) $y \leq |x| + 1$.

12. Compare the functions in $R^{\#}$ that are defined, respectively, by $y = 10^x$ and $y = \log x$.

REVIEW TEST B

1. Each of the following ordered pairs satisfies the relation "is less in absolute value than" in I. In each case, select the smallest positive integer which the letter may represent. (*a*) $(-3, a)$; (*b*) $(b, -4)$; (*c*) $(6, c)$; (*d*) $(d, -3)$.

2. Define all possible relations, the domains and ranges of which coincide, respectively, with the sets $\{1, 2\}$ and $\{0, 1\}$.

3. Let $\{x \mid x \in I, |x| \leq 3\}$ be the domain of a relation R. If $y = x - 2$, for each member (x, y) of R, list the members of R.

4. If $U = \{x \mid x \in I, 1 \leq x \leq 10\}$, graph the relation "is divisible by" in U.

5. If $A = \{1, 2, 3, 4, 5\}$, graph the function f on A to I, defined by $f(x) = 3x^2 - 1$.

6. The defining equation for a function F is $F(t) = t^2 - 4t + 2$. If 1/3 and -2 are in the domain of F, determine (*a*) $F(1/3)$; (*b*) $F(-2)$.

7. If $A = \{-1, 1, 2\}$ and $B = \{0, 1\}$, how many different functions may be defined on A to B?

8. The defining rule for a function f is $f(x) = 2x^2 - 3$, where x is an arbitrary element of its domain. If $x + h$ is also a member of the domain of f, find an expression for $[f(x + h) - f(x)]/h$.

9. Determine the domain and range of the function F defined in $\bar{R}$ by (*a*) $F(x) = 6 + x$; (*b*) $F(x) = 2/x$; (*c*) $F(x) = \sqrt{1 + x}$.

10. The radii of a circle are 20 inches in length. If the length of a chord, d inches from the center, is L inches, express L as a function of d.

11. A function f on the interval $[-3, 3]$ is defined by $f(x) = 2x^3 + 1$. Describe and graph the relation that is inverse to f.

12. The functions on $[-2, 2]$, defined respectively by $y = 2x^2$ and $y = -2x^2$, are subsets of the relation defined on $[-2, 2]$ by $y^2 = 4x^4$. Graph the two functions and the relation.

REFERENCES

Books

ALLENDOERFER, C. B. AND C. O. OAKLEY, *Principles of Mathematics*, New York, McGraw-Hill, 1955. (Chap. 6.)

DUBISCH, R., *Trigonometry*, New York, Ronald, 1955. (Pp. 5–16.)

THE COLLEGE MATHEMATICS STAFF, *Fundamental Mathematics*, Chicago, The University of Chicago Press, 1948. (Chaps. 4 and 5.)

American Mathematical Monthly

THIELMAN, H. P., "On the Definition of Functions," Vol. 60, p. 259 (1953).

5

THE BASIC ELEMENTARY FUNCTIONS

Obviousness is always the enemy to correctness.

BERTRAND RUSSELL

5.1 Introduction

In this chapter we introduce what are probably the most important basic functions of elementary mathematics. The student is urged to become thoroughly familiar with these functions, the equations that define them, and their graphs.

We have defined a *relation in a set A* as a subset of the Cartesian set of A, and a *relation from a set A to a set B* as a subset of $A \times B$. The graph of a relation was described as a set of points in one-to-one correspondence with the ordered pairs of the relation, and we have used a Cartesian coordinate system to establish this correspondence. Most of our relations will be in $R^{\#}$, and so will be subsets of ordered pairs of real numbers, the rule of correspondence between an element x of the domain and an element y of the range being given by an equation in x and y. We have agreed, moreover, to the following terminology: The *relation in* $R^{\#}$ *defined by an equation* is the set of *all* ordered pairs (x, y) of real numbers, with x and y satisfying the equation. There are, of course, many relations in $R^{\#}$ which have the same rule of correspondence, but their domains will be different and so will be subsets of the above relation. For example, the function in $R^{\#}$ defined by $y = x^2$ is the set $\{(x, y) \mid (x, y) \in R^{\#} \times R^{\#}, y = x^2\}$. However, the functions defined as the sets $\{(x, y) \mid (x, y) \in R^{\#} \times R^{\#}, y = x^2, x \geq 0\}$ and $\{(x, y) \mid (x, y) \in R^{\#} \times R^{\#}, y = x^2, |x| < 3\}$ have the same rule of correspondence as the above set, but are proper subsets of it.

We have already introduced the word "locus" to refer to the graph of a relation in $R^{\#}$; for example, the locus of an equation is the set of all points in a Cartesian plane having coordinates which satisfy the equation. It is this idea of a locus that is dominant in all of analytic geometry. As we noted in Section 4.4, the ordered pair (x, y) associated with a point, may be regarded as giving the *position* coordinates of the point, and so *locates* the point with respect to the coordinate axes. Thus, an equation in x and y determines both a relation in $R^\#$ and a geometric locus. The *relation* emphasizes the *correspondence* between an element x of its domain and an element y of its range, while analytic geometry emphasizes the relationship between the *equation* and its *locus* or *curve*. In fact, a large part of analytic geometry is a study of curves with the help of their equations. The notation $(x, f(x))$ for an ordered pair of the function f emphasizes the correspondence between x and $f(x)$, while the notation (x, y) for the *same* pair is more in harmony with the geometric aspects of the function. We shall use both notations, as the convenience of the situation warrants. Most of the relations with which we shall be concerned in this chapter will be *functions* in $R^\#$, frequently from a subset of $R^\#$ to $R^\#$.

5.2 The Basic Power Functions

There are probably more occurrences of what we are about to call *power functions* in applied mathematics and science than any other type of function. The equation $F = ks$ of Hooke's Law, stating that a measure F of the force necessary to stretch an elastic body is directly proportional to a measure s of its elongation, defines a very simple power function on an appropriate interval of real numbers. The measure s, in feet, of the distance traversed in t seconds by a body falling freely under gravity is given by $s = 16.1t^2$, an equation which defines a power function on an interval of real numbers. The measure T, in seconds, of the period of a simple pendulum of length L centimeters is given by $T = 2\pi\sqrt{L/g}$; the measure P, in pounds per square feet, of the air pressure on a flat surface perpendicular to the direction of an air current with a velocity of V miles per hour, is given by the equation $P = 0.003V^2$; the measure H, in horsepower, of the power transmissible by cold-rolled shafting of diameter d inches is given by $H = d^3N/50$, where N is the number of revolutions per minute of the shafting. Each of the preceding equations defines a power function on some suitable domain of real numbers.

DEFINITION. A *basic power* function is a function in $R^\#$ defined by an equation $y = x^n$, for some real number n. If $n \geq 0$, the domain of this function is either $R^\#$ or the set of all non-negative real numbers, while if $n < 0$, the domain is either the set of all positive or the set of all non-zero real numbers.

DEFINITION. A function f in $R^\#$ is said to be a *power* function if $f(x) = ax^n$ for some given real numbers a and n, and for each x in the domain of f. The domain may be any subset of the domain of the corresponding basic power function.

We shall always assume, in the present chapter, that $a = 1$, and so the power functions that will concern us here will be merely subsets of some basic power function. In all cases considered, moreover, n will be rational.

The simplest case of a power function occurs if $n = 0$, the function being then called a *constant* function. The domain of a basic constant function is $R^{\#}$, and since the defining equation of the basic constant function is $y = x^0 = 1$, the value of this function is 1 at every real number x. The locus of the equation $y = 1$ is the set of all points $(x, 1)$, and so is the straight line parallel to the x-axis, containing the point $(0, 1)$ on the y-axis. The graph of the constant function f defined by $f(x) = 1$ on the interval $[-2, 2]$ is shown in Figure 5–1.

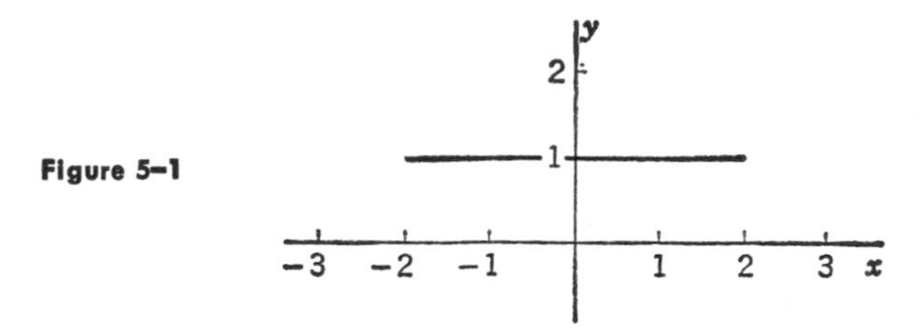

Figure 5–1

If $n > 0$, a power function is said to be *parabolic*, a special case being a *linear* function which occurs when $n = 1$. The defining equation for the basic linear function is $y = x$, and we shall show that the locus of this equation is the staight line through the points $(0, 0)$ and $(1, 1)$. The points $(0, 0)$ and $(1, 1)$ certainly lie on this locus, since their coor-

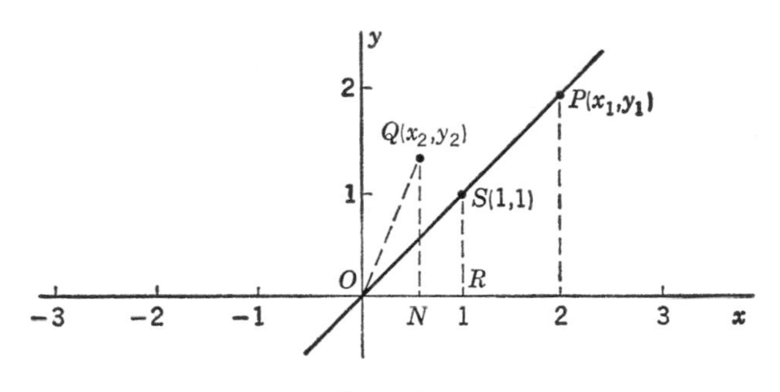

Figure 5–2

dinates satisfy the equation $y = x$. Suppose that $P(x_1, y_1)$ is any point on the line joining these two points, as shown in the diagram of Figure 5–2. [The notation indicates that the label of the point is P, and its coordinate pair is (x_1, y_1).] After dropping perpendiculars and using properties of similar triangles, it follows that $y_1/x_1 = 1/1$, i.e., $y_1 = x_1$. Thus, P, and so every point on the line, is on the locus. It remains to show that every point of the locus lies on the line. Let $Q(x_2, y_2)$ be any point of the locus, i.e., $y_2 = x_2$. The right triangles OQN and OSR are then similar, since the sides enclosing the right angles have lengths that are proportional, and so the angles at O are equal. It follows that Q must be on the line joining (0, 0) and (1, 1), and this line comprises the complete locus of the equation $y = x$, as asserted.

The domain of any basic parabolic function is either $R^{\#}$ or the set of all non-negative real numbers; its graph includes the points (0, 0) and (1, 1). Parabolic functions, in general, do not have this property, however; for, even if the rule of correspondence is $y = x^n$, the numbers 0 and 1 need not be in the domain of the function. The loci of the equations $y = x^2$, $y = x^3$, and $y^2 = x^3$ are called, respectively, the *basic parabola*, the *basic cubical parabola*, and the *basic semi-cubical parabola*. The table of Figure 5–3 shows how the number x^n changes with x for different exponents, and may be used in graphing power functions.

x	x^2	x^3	$x^{1/2}$	$x^{1/3}$	$x^{3/2}$	x^{-1}	x^{-2}
0.2	0.04	0.008	0.447	0.585	0.089	5.000	25.000
0.4	0.16	0.064	0.632	0.737	0.252	2.500	6.250
0.6	0.36	0.216	0.775	0.843	0.465	1.667	2.778
0.8	0.64	0.512	0.894	0.928	0.715	1.250	1.563
1.0	1.00	1.000	1.000	1.000	1.000	1.000	1.000
1.2	1.44	1.728	1.095	1.063	1.312	0.8333	0.6944
1,4	1.96	2.744	1.183	1.119	1.657	0.7143	0.5102
1.6	2.56	4.096	1.265	1.170	2.034	0.6250	0.3906
1.8	3.24	5.832	1.342	1.216	2.415	0.5556	0.3086
2.0	4.00	8.000	1.414	1.260	2.828	0.5000	0.2500
2.2	4.84	10.65	1.483	1.301	3.263	0.4545	0.2066
2.4	5.76	13.82	1.549	1.339	3.717	0.4167	0.1736
2.6	6.76	17.58	1.612	1.375	4.193	0.3846	0.1479
2.8	7.84	21.95	1.673	1.409	4.685	0.3571	0.1276
3.0	9.00	27.00	1.732	1.442	5.196	0.3333	0.1111
4.0	16.0	64.00	2.000	1.587	8.000	0.2500	0.0625
5.0	25.0	125.0	2.236	1.710	11.18	0.2000	0.0400

Figure 5–3

For any number $n > 1$, the number x^n is smaller than x if $0 < x < 1$, and larger than x if $x > 1$. It is for this reason that any portion of the graph of a parabolic function that lies in the first quadrant is "concave up" if $n > 1$ and "concave down" if $n < 1$. If the domain of the function includes negative numbers, the corresponding portion of the graph lies in either the second or third quadrant, depending on the number n. However, if x^n has been defined at all, it is clear that its absolute value is independent of the sign of x, and so the shape of the locus of $y = x^n$

is determined by the part that lies in the first quadrant. In Figure 5–4 we have shown sketches of several parabolic functions, defined on an interval containing the origin by $y = x^n$; a *sketch* is a rough graph with only a few points actually plotted, but which illustrates the important features of a graph.

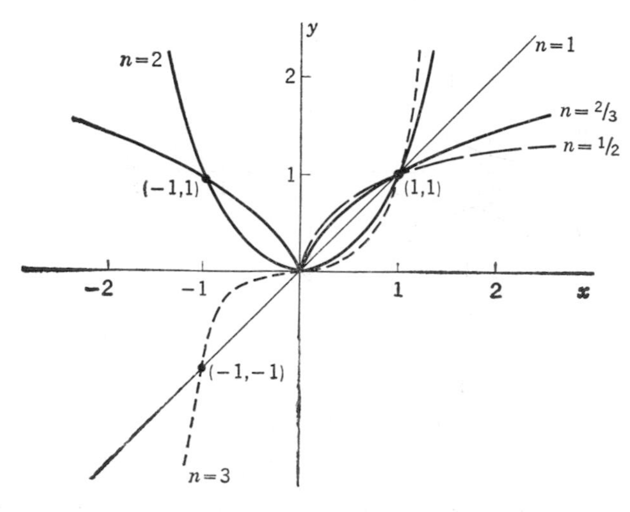

Figure 5–4

If $n < 0$, the corresponding power functions are *hyperbolic*, the domain of a basic hyperbolic function being either the set of all positive or the set of all non-zero real numbers. Since 0 is not in the domain of any hyperbolic function, the point $(0, 0)$ is not on the graph of any such function; the point $(1, 1)$ is on the graph of any *basic* hyperbolic function, however. For any real number $k > 0$, the number x^k exceeds any finite bound and the number $1/x^k$ is arbitrarily close to 0, if x is a sufficiently large positive number; furthermore, if x is a positive number sufficiently close to 0, the number x^k is arbitrarily close to 0 and $1/x^k$ is an arbitrarily large positive number. An inspection of the last two columns in the table of Figure 5–3 will further indicate the validity of these remarks. It follows that the graph of a basic hyperbolic function is "concave up" in the first quadrant, and gets arbitrarily close to both the x and y axes but never touches either of them. In view of this latter property, the axes are said to be *asymptotes* of the basic hyperbolic curves. As was the case with parabolic loci, a portion of a hyperbolic loci will lie in the second or third quadrant whenever the domain of such a function includes negative numbers. In Figure 5–5, we have sketched portions of the graphs of several basic hyperbolic functions; these sketches identify the quadrants in which the graph of such a function is located, as well as show the effect of n on the shape of the curve. The graph of a basic hyperbolic function is known as a basic *hyperbola*, or a basic *equilateral* hyperbola if $n = -1$ in its defining equation.

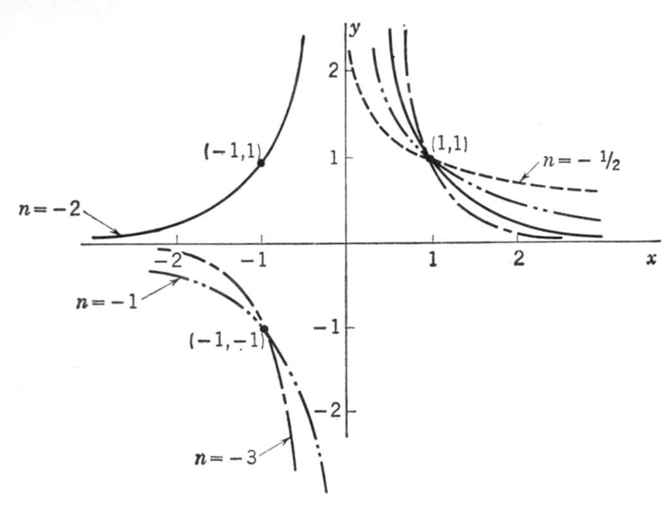

Figure 5–5

We have noted previously that the graphs of all basic parabolic functions, except for the constant ones, contain the points (0, 0) and (1, 1), and have no other first-quadrant points in common; the graphs of all basic

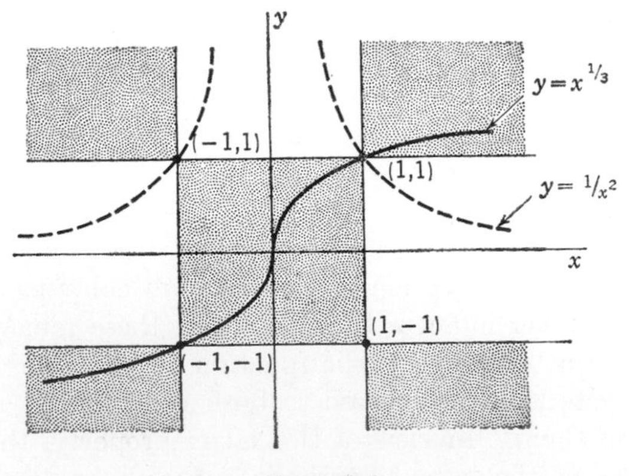

Figure 5–6

hyperbolic functions, on the other hand, contain the point (1, 1) as the only common point in the first quadrant. Moreover, the point (1, 1) is the only first-quadrant point common to the graphs of *all* basic power functions. In Figure 5–6, we have sketched portions of the graphs of a basic parabolic and a basic hyperbolic function, in order to illustrate these facts. The graphs of all basic parabolic functions lie in the cross-hatched regions, while the graphs of all basic hyperbolic functions lie entirely in the regions

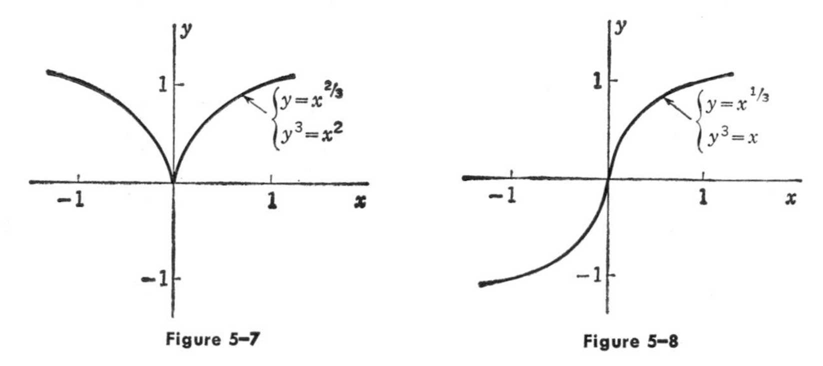

Figure 5–7

Figure 5–8

not cross-hatched. It may be observed that (1, 1) is the only point common to both regions, in the first quadrant.

It should be pointed out that a function which has its rule of correspondence given by an equation $y = x^{m/n}$ is not, in general, the same

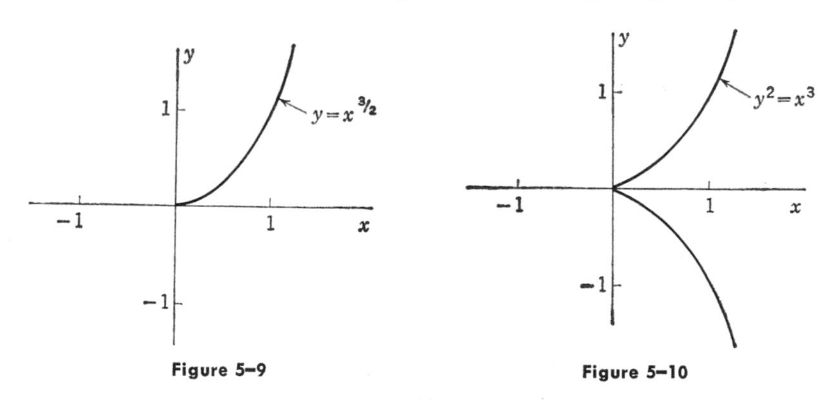

Figure 5–9

Figure 5–10

as a relation having $y^n = x^m$ for its rule of correspondence, even though the two domains may be the same. The function is in fact a possibly proper subset of the relation, and the graph of the former is a portion of the graph of the latter. If n is odd, however, the function and relation coincide provided their domains are the same. This is illustrated in Figures 5–7 and 5–8, where graphs are shown of a function and its associated relation on an interval containing the origin. However, if n is even and m is odd, the equation $y^n = x^m$ determines two real numbers, which we may designate y and $-y$, for each real number x of the domain of the relation. In this case the function and the relation are different, as illustrated in Figures 5–9 and 5–10.

PROBLEM SET 5.2

1. If x is any number between 0 and 1, arrange the following numbers in order of increasing magnitude: x^2; $x^{2/3}$; $x^{3/2}$; $x^{1/4}$; $x^{5/3}$; x^4; $x^{1/3}$.

2. If x is any number greater than 1, arrange the numbers of Problem 1 in order of increasing magnitude.

3. For any real number x between 0 and 1, x^3 is less than x^2. How is this shown on the graphs of the functions on the interval $[-1, 1]$ defined by $y = x^3$ and $y = x^2$? Sketch these graphs.

4. For any real number x between 0 and 1, $1/x^3$ is greater than $1/x^2$. How is this shown on the graphs of the functions on $[-1, 1] - \{0\}$, defined by $y = 1/x^3$ and $y = 1/x^2$? Sketch these graphs.

5. Identify the function in $R^{\#}$, defined by each of the following equations, as parabolic or hyperbolic: $y = x^3$; $yx^2 = 1$; $y = x^{1/2}$; $y = x^{-1/2}$; $xy = 1$; $y = x$; $yx^4 = 1$; $y = x^{1/3}$; $y = x^{2/3}$; $y = x^{-2}$; $y = x^{-6}$.

6. If x is a negative real number, which of the following symbols represent real numbers: $x^{1/2}$; $x^{2/3}$; $x^{1/3}$; x^4; $x^{-1/3}$; $x^{-3/2}$; $x^{3/5}$; $x^{-3/5}$; $x^{-1/4}$?

7. List the quadrants that contain points of the locus of each of the following equations: $y = x^3$; $y = x^{1/2}$; $y = x^{2/3}$; $y = x^{3/2}$; $y = x^{5/2}$; $y = x^{1/4}$; $y = x^{5/3}$; $y = x^4$.

8. List the quadrants that contain points of the locus of each of the following equations: $y^3 = x$; $y^3 = x^2$; $y^2 = x^3$; $y^2 = x^5$; $y^4 = x$; $y^3 = x^5$.

9. Which quadrants contain points of the graph of the function in $R^{\#}$, defined by each of the following equations? $y = x^{-2}$; $y = x^{-1/3}$; $y = 1/x^3$; $y = 1/x$; $y = x^{-3/4}$; $y = x^{-1/4}$.

10. Which quadrants contain points of the graph of the relation in $R^{\#}$, defined by each of the following equations? $y^3 = 1/x$; $y^2x^3 = 1$; $y^4 = 1/x^3$; $y^4x = 1$; $y^3 = 1/x^5$.

11. Use an enlarged scale to sketch, on a single diagram, graphs of the parabolic functions on the interval $[0, 2]$, defined by $y = x^n$ for $n = 1/10$; $n = 1/4$; $n = 1/3$; $n = 1/2$; $n = 2/3$; $n = 1$; $n = 3/2$; $n = 2$; $n = 3$; $n = 5$; $n = 10$.

12. Use an enlarged scale to sketch, on a single diagram, graphs of the hyperbolic functions defined on the set $[0, 2] - \{0\}$ by $y = x^n$ for $n = -1/3$; $n = -1/2$; $n = -1$; $n = -2$; $n = -3$; $n = -4$; $n = -10$.

13. Use the data of Figure 5–3 to graph the function on the interval $[0, 2]$, defined by (a) $y = x^2$; (b) $y = x^3$; (c) $y = x^{1/2}$; (d) $y = x^{1/3}$; (e) $y = x^{3/2}$.

14. Use the data of Figure 5–3 to graph the function on the set $[-2, 2] - \{0\}$, defined by (a) $y = 1/x$; (b) $y = 1/x^2$.

15. Are the relations in $R^{\#}$, defined separately by $y = x^{1/2}$ and $y^2 = x$, identical? Answer the same question for the equations $y = x^{1/3}$ and $y^3 = x$. Explain.

16. List the quadrants that contain points of the locus of each of the following equations: $x^{10}y = 1$; $y^4x^6 = 1$; $xy^3 = 1$; $x^{15}y^7 = 1$.

17. Use separate axes to sketch the two relations from $[-2, 2]$ to $R^{\#}$, defined by the equations: (a) $y = x^{1/2}$, $y^2 = x$; (b) $y = x^{-1/2}$, $y^2 = 1/x$; (c) $y = x^{-3/2}$, $y^2x^3 = 1$; (d) $y = x^{-3/5}$, $y^5x^3 = 1$.

18. Use separate axes to sketch the two relations from $[-2, 2]$ to $R^{\#}$, defined by the equations: (*a*) $y = x^{-2/3}$, $y^3 = 1/x^2$; (*b*) $y = x^{-3/2}$, $y^2x^3 = 1$; (*c*) $y = x^{-1/2}$, $y^2 = 1/x$; (*d*) $y = x^{-3/5}$, $y^5x^3 = 1$.

19. Using the same set of axes for each pair, sketch the two functions from $[-2, 2]$ to $R^{\#}$, which are defined by the equations: (*a*) $y = x^2$, $y = x^3$; (*b*) $y = x^3, y = x^5$; (*c*) $y = x^2, y = x^4$; (*d*) $y = x^{1/2}, y = x^{1/3}$; (*e*) $y = x^{2/3}, y = x^{3/5}$; (*f*) $y = x^{1/2}, y = x^{1/4}$; (*g*) $y = x^{3/2}, y = x^{5/2}$; (*h*) $y = x^{1/3}, y = x^{1/5}$.

20. Using the same set of axes for each pair, sketch the two functions from $[-2, 2]$ to $R^{\#}$, which are defined by the equations: (*a*) $y = 1/x^2$, $y = 1/x^4$; (*b*) $y = 1/x^3$, $y = 1/x^5$; (*c*) $yx^{1/2} = 1$, $yx^{2/3} = 1$; (*d*) $yx^{5/2} = 1$, $yx^{3/2} = 1$; (*e*) $yx = 1, yx^{1/2} = 1$; (*f*) $y = 1/x^5, y = 1/x^7$; (*g*) $y = 1/x, y = 1/x^{3/5}$.

5.3 The Basic Exponential and Logarithmic Functions

DEFINITION. A *basic exponential* function is a function in $R^{\#}$ defined by an equation $y = a^x$, for some real number $a(> 0)$. The domain of this function is the set $R^{\#}$ of all real numbers.

DEFINITION. A function f in $R^{\#}$ is said to be an *exponential* function if $f(x) = ka^x$, for some given real numbers k and $a(> 0)$, and for each x in the domain of f. The domain may be any subset of $R^{\#}$.

In this chapter, we shall assume that $k = 1$, so that the only exponential functions introduced here will be merely subsets of a basic exponential function. Let us now examine exponential functions for some of their characteristics.

The number a^x is positive for any real number x, and so all points of the graph of a basic exponential function will lie above the x-axis. Furthermore, since $a^0 = 1$ for every real number $a(> 0)$, the graph of any basic exponential function will include the point (0, 1) on the y-axis. If $a > 1$, the number a^x exceeds any finite bound if x is a sufficiently large positive number; and if x is a negative number, sufficiently large in absolute value, a^x will be arbitrarily close to 0. This trend is indicated in the table of Figure 5–11, with $a = 2$.

x	-4	-3	-2	-1	0	1	2	3	4
y	1/16	1/8	1/4	1/2	1	2	4	8	16

Figure 5–11

If $0 < a < 1$, the larger the number x, the smaller the number a^x, and if x is sufficiently large, a^x is arbitrarily close to 0; if x is negative, a^x is a large positive number if x is large in absolute value, and a^x exceeds any finite bound if the absolute value of x is sufficiently large. The table in Figure 5–12 indicates this, for $a = 1/2$.

Thus, the graph of any basic exponential function tends up to the right if $a > 1$ and down to the right if $0 < a < 1$, and has the x-axis as an

x	-4	-3	-2	-1	0	1	2	3	4
y	16	8	4	2	1	1/2	1/4	1/8	1/16

Figure 5–12

asymptote. This is shown in Figure 5–13, where graphs are sketched for functions on an interval containing the origin, defined by $y = a^x$ where $a = 2$ and $a = 1/2$. If $a = 1$, $y = 1^x = 1$ for every real number x, and

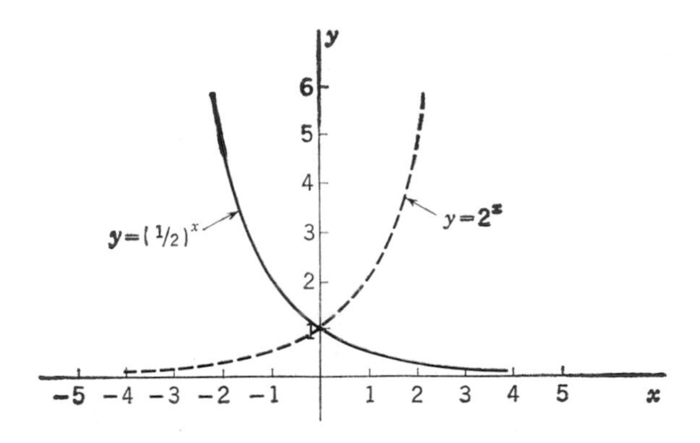

Figure 5–13

the graph of the basic exponential function defined by this equation is the straight line through the point (0, 1) parallel to the x-axis. This rather trivial exponential function may be seen to be identical with the basic power function for $n = 0$, as discussed in the preceding section.

DEFINITION. A *basic logarithmic* function is a function in $R^{\#}$ defined by an equation $y = \log_a x$, for some real number $a(> 0)$. The domain of such a function is the set of all positive real numbers.

DEFINITION. A function f in $R^{\#}$ is said to be a *logarithmic* function if $f(x) = k \log_a x$, for some given real numbers k and $a(> 0)$, and for each x in the domain of f. The domain may be any subset of positive real numbers.

We shall assume that $k = 1$, for the purposes of this chapter, so that the logarithmic functions concerning us here will be subsets of some basic logarithmic function. The equation $y = \log_a x$ is equivalent to the equation $a^y = x$, from the definition of a logarithm as given in Chapter 3; and the equation $a^y = x$ may be obtained from $y = a^x$ by an interchange of x and y. It then follows that $y = a^x$ and $y = \log_a x$ define functions in

$R^{\#}$, that are *inverse* to each other, as discussed in Chapter 4, their graphs being reflections of each other in the straight line locus of $y = x$. In Figure 5–14 we have sketched graphs of some exponential and logarithmic func-

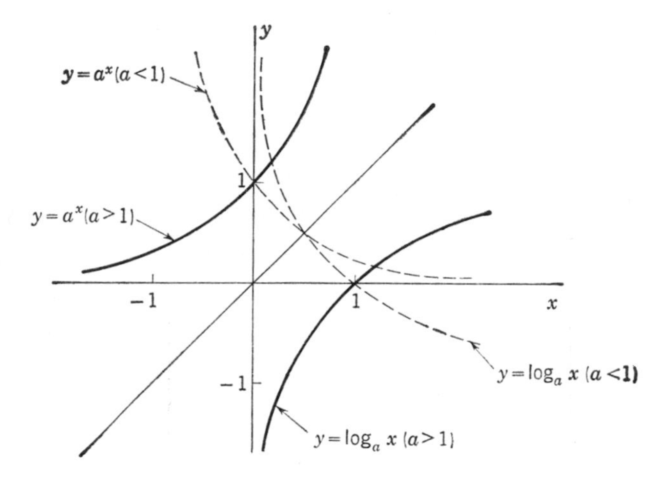

Figure 5–14

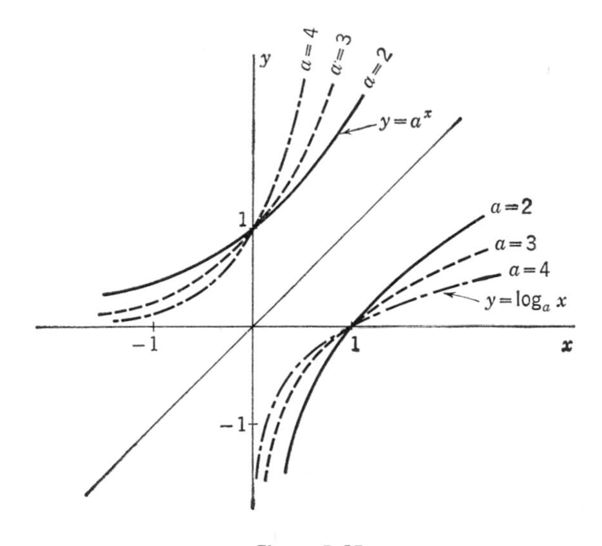

Figure 5–15

tions, defined from an interval containing the origin to $R^{\#}$, by equations of the form $y = a^x$ and $y = \log_a x$, including cases both where $a > 1$ and $a < 1$. The effect of a on the shape of an exponential or logarithmic graph is indicated in Figure 5–15, where graphs of such functions are sketched for several different base numbers.

5.4 An Important Special Case

If $P(x_1, y_1)$ and $Q(x_2, y_2)$ are any two points in the xy-plane, let us refer to the numbers $x_2 - x_1$ and $y_2 - y_1$ (or $x_1 - x_2$ and $y_1 - y_2$) as the respective *corresponding* differences in the abscissas and ordinates of the two points.

DEFINITION. The *slope* of a line with respect to a Cartesian coordinate system, is the quotient of the difference in the ordinates divided by the corresponding difference in the abscissas of any two points of the line.

The slope may be described as a measure of the "slant" of a line, and is quite independent of the particular points P and Q that have been selected on the line. This is evident from a consideration of similar triangles, as

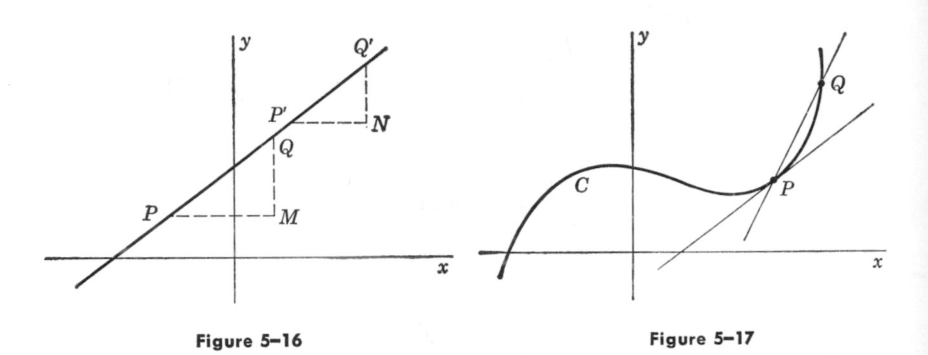

Figure 5–16

Figure 5–17

shown in Figure 5–16. Let us designate the *length* of a line segment by placing a bar over the indicated name of the segment. In the figure, P, Q, P', and Q' are arbitrary points on the line, and we see from similar triangles that $\overline{QM}: \overline{PM} = \overline{Q'N}: \overline{P'N}$. A proper interpretation of these lengths reveals that the slope of the line is the same, whether referred to the points P and Q or to the points P' and Q'. If we move from one point to another on the line, the slope may be considered a measure of the rate at which the ordinate changes as compared with the corresponding change in the abscissa. The slope of a line, that is parallel to the x-axis, is clearly 0, while the slope increases without finite bound as we consider lines more nearly vertical; the slope of a line parallel to the y-axis is *not defined.* It is evident that parallel lines have the same slope.

If P and Q are any two points of the curve C in Figure 5–17, the line segment joining P with Q is called a *secant line* or *secant* of C. Let P continue to designate the same point, but suppose Q indicates different points along the curve. It is *intuitively evident* for the point P of the figure, that as Q designates different points along C in the direction of P, the corresponding secant line will change, and will intersect a certain line through P

in an arbitrarily small angle, if Q designates a point sufficiently close to P. This certain line is called the *tangent line* to the curve at P. It is to be understood that Q may be any point on either side of P and, if the tangent line is to be defined, the secant lines on both sides must approach coincidence. There are many curves, of course, that have no well-defined tangent lines at some points. We shall make the above intuitive argument more rigorous in Chapter 8. By the *slope of a curve* at a point P, we shall now mean the slope of the tangent line to the curve at P. A positive slope indicates that the curve is rising upwards to the right, while a negative slope indicates a trend that is downward to the right.

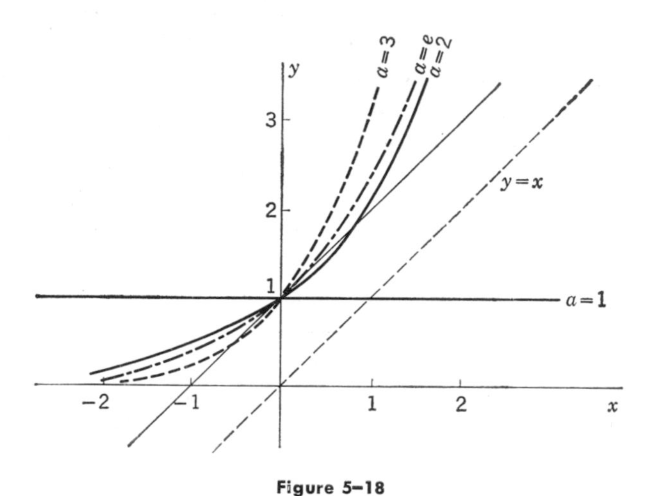

Figure 5–18

Now let us consider the graphs of basic exponential functions, for which the defining equations have different base numbers greater than 1, as shown in Figure 5–18. In particular, let us consider the slopes of these exponential curves at the point (0, 1) where they all cross the y-axis. If $a = 1$, this slope is 0, and as a designates successively larger numbers the slopes at this point increase beyond any finite bound. It is then *geometrically evident* that for some definite base number, the corresponding basic exponential curve will have a slope of 1 at its point of crossing the y-axis; in other words, the tangent line to this particular exponential curve at (0, 1) will be parallel to the straight line locus of the equation $y = x$. This special number is designated e, and it can be shown that e is an irrational number approximately equal to $2.7182818 \cdots$. If this number is used as a base for logarithms, the logarithms are called *natural* or *Napierian*. Although e may appear to be a very awkward number to consider using for a logarithmic base, we shall see later that it has many theoretical advantages. In the sequel, we shall indicate the natural logarithm of a number x by $\ln x$, the notation $\log x$ always implying the common (i.e., base 10) logarithm in this book.

It is sometimes necessary to change from one logarithmic base to another. Let a and b be any two logarithmic bases, and suppose that $x = \log_a N$ and $y = \log_b N$ for some positive number N. Then the definition of a logarithm implies that $N = a^x = b^y$. If we now take logarithms to base b of each member of the latter equation, we obtain $x \log_b a = y$ or its equivalent $\log_a N \log_b a = \log_b N$. This gives us $\log_a N = (\log_b N)/\log_b a$, and this equation enables us to determine logarithms to base a whenever logarithms to base b are known. In particular, if $a = e$ and $b = 10$, the above equation becomes $\log_e N = (\log N)/(\log e)$. The number $\log e$ is called the *modulus* of the common system, and is approximately equal to 0.4343. In the notation adopted earlier, we may now write $\ln N = (\log N)/0.4343 = 2.3026 \log N$.

ILLUSTRATION. Find the natural logarithm of 27.34, given that the common logarithm of the number is 1.43680.

Solution. $\ln 27.34 = 2.3026 \log 27.34 = (2.3026)(1.43680) = 3.3084$. The table of Figure 5–19 will be useful in sketching the graph of the basic exponential function with $a = e$, while a more comprehensive table (Table 4) may be found at the back of the book.

x	e^x	x	e^x	x	e^x	x	e^x
0.2	1.2214	1	2.7183	−0.2	0.8187	−1	0.3679
0.4	1.4918	2	7.3891	−0.4	0.6703	−2	0.1353
0.6	1.8221	3	20.0855	−0.6	0.5488	−3	0.0498
0.8	2.2255	4	54.5982	−0.8	0.4493	−4	0.0183

Figure 5–19

PROBLEM SET 5.4

1. Let $P(x_1, x_2)$ be the point $(2, -5)$ and $Q(x_2, y_2)$ be the point indicated below. In each case, determine $x_2 - x_1$ and $y_2 - y_1$. (*a*) $(3, -4)$; (*b*) $(1, -5)$; (*c*) $(-6, -4)$; (*d*) $(0, 1)$; (*e*) $(2, 5)$; (*f*) $(5, -5)$.

2. Find the slope (if defined) of the straight line containing the pair of points: (*a*) $(2, 4)$, $(-1, 6)$; (*b*) $(-1, 5)$, $(2, 7)$; (*c*) $(3, -4)$, $(5, 4)$; (*d*) $(2, -6)$, $(2, 8)$; (*e*) $(0, 0)$, $(-1, 8)$; (*f*) $(0, -5)$, $(2, 6)$; (*g*) $(4, -3)$, $(-1, 5)$; (*h*) $(1, 2)$, $(-2, -2)$.

3. Which of the lines, each determined by one of the following pairs of points, are parallel? (*a*) $(-1, 2)$, $(3, 4)$; (*b*) $(1, 3)$, $(4, 3)$; (*c*) $(2, -1)$, $(4, 0)$; (*d*) $(2, -1)$, $(3, 6)$; (*e*) $(2, -1)$, $(4, 7)$; (*f*) $(1, 4)$, $(3, 4)$.

4. Use a ruler to draw a straight line through the point (2, 3) having slope (*a*) 3; (*b*) −2; (*c*) 1; (*d*) −4; (*e*) 2; (*f*) 5; (*g*) −10.
5. Why does the locus of each logarithmic equation $y = \log_a x$ contain the point (1, 0)?
6. Using the same set of axes for each pair, sketch the two functions on [−2, 2] defined separately by: (*a*) $y = 3^x$, $y = 5^x$; (*b*) $y = e^x$, $y = 2^x$; (*c*) $y = (1/2)^x$, $y = (1/4)^x$; (*d*) $y = 5^x$, $y = 10^x$; (*e*) $y = (1/3)^x$, $y = (1/5)^x$.
7. Using the same set of axes for each pair, sketch the two functions on [0, 2] − {0} defined separately by: (*a*) $y = 3^x$, $y = \log_3 x$; (*b*) $y = e^x$, $y = \ln x$; (*c*) $y = 4^x$, $y = \log_4 x$; (*d*) $y = 5^x$, $y = \log_5 x$; (*e*) $y = 10^x$, $y = \log x$.
8. Using the same set of axes for each pair, sketch the two functions on [0, 3] − {0} defined separately by: (*a*) $y = \log_3 x$, $y = \log_5 x$; (*b*) $y = \log_4 x$, $y = \log x$; (*c*) $y = \log x$, $y = \ln x$; (*d*) $y = \log_{1/2} x$, $y = \log_{1/4} x$; (*e*) $y = \log_{1/5} x$, $y = \log_{1/7} x$.
9. Use Table 1 to compute the natural logarithms of the following numbers: 2.567; 1.543; 24.86; 15.49; 247.56; 0.0265; 0.001867; 1.1111.
10. Express each of the numbers $e^{0.001}$ and $10^{0.001}$, approximately, as rational numbers in decimal form.
11. Use the table of e^x in Figure 5–19 to make a careful sketch of the function on [−2, 2], defined by $y = e^x$.
12. The measure y of atmospheric pressure, in millimeters of mercury, is given by the formula $y = 760\, e^{-x/800}$, where x is the measure of altitude above sea level in meters. (*a*) Show that the above formula can be written as $x = 800(\ln 760 - \ln y)$; (*b*) show that the above formula can be written as $x = 1842(\log 760 - \log y)$; (*c*) at approximately what altitude would the pressure measure 700 millimeters of mercury?
13. If a and b are any two positive numbers, show that $\log_b a = 1/\log_a b$.
14. Distinguish between a single function defined by two equations, and two functions defined separately by each of two equations.
15. See Problem 14, and sketch the function on [−2, 2], defined by the inequalities $y \leq x$ and $y \geq x$.
16. See Problem 14, and sketch the function in [−3, 3], defined by the equations $y = |x|$ and $y = [x]$. (See Problem 20 of Problem Set 4.4.)

5.5 The Basic Circular Functions

The notion of length of arc of a curve is theoretically complicated, though intuitively simple. The reason for the theoretical difficulty is that all our units and subunits of length are linear, i.e., segments of a straight line, and no finite combination of them can be made to fit accurately an arc of a curve that is itself not linear. This problem is resolved in courses on the calculus, but for the present we shall accept the *intuitive* concept of arc length as satisfactory. In fact, we shall think of an arc of a circle as being measured by a flexible tape placed along the arc.

Suppose we have a circle, the radii of which measure 1 unit in length (a so-called *unit circle*), placed with its center at the origin of a Cartesian coordinate system, and intersecting the positive portion of the x-axis at the point P, as shown in Figure 5–20. Further, let us imagine an algebraic

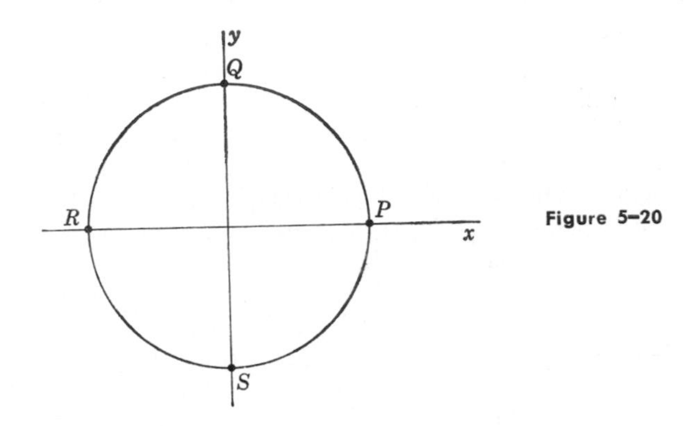

Figure 5–20

scale, having the same unit of length as the unit circle, as a flexible tape of infinite length but with otherwise negligible dimensions. If we now imagine that the point 0 of the tape is placed at the point P of the circle, and the tape is wrapped around the circle with the positive portion counter-clockwise and the negative portion clockwise, the points of the tape will be brought in contact with the points of the circle. It will be observed, however, that the correspondence established in this way between these two sets of points is not one-to-one; for each point of the tape is in contact with a unique point of the circle, but each point of the circle is in contact with infinitely many points of the tape. Let us now associate, with any given point on the circle, those real numbers that correspond to the points of the tape with which the given point is in contact. In other words, we associate with any point on the circle all those real numbers that measure the lengths of the various arcs of the circle, that start at P and terminate at the point; the positive numbers will be the measures of counterclockwise arcs, while the negative numbers will measure arcs in the clockwise direction. Since any number of complete circumferences can be included in an arc, there are infinitely many lengths of arcs that start at P and terminate at any given point. Thus, each point on the circle will be associated with infinitely many real numbers, as measures of arc length; and each real number will be associated with a unique point on the circle. In Figure 5–20, since the circumference of the circle measures 2π units, the point P will be associated with the real numbers 0, $\pm 2\pi$, $\pm 4\pi$, etc.; the point Q will be associated with the real numbers $\pi/2$, $5\pi/2$, $9\pi/2$, $\cdots$, $-3\pi/2$, $-7\pi/2$, $\cdots$; the point R will be associated with the real numbers $\pm\pi$, $\pm 3\pi$, $\pm 5\pi$, $\cdots$; and the point S will be associated with the real numbers

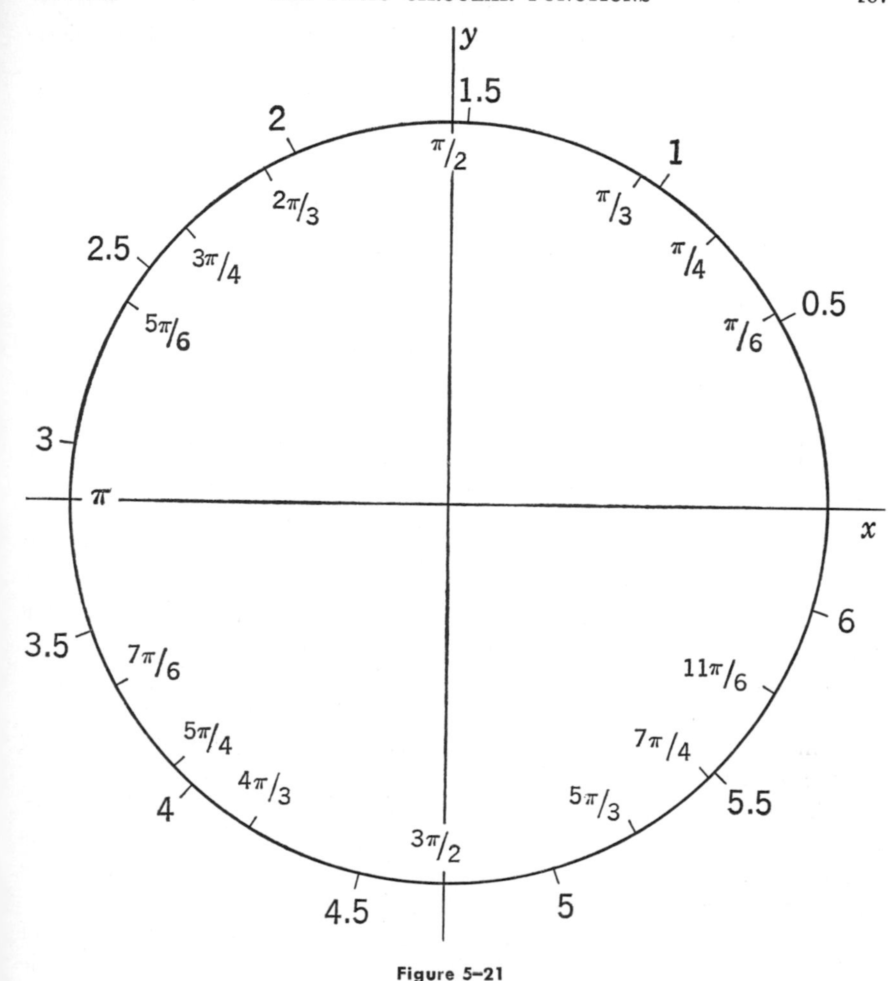

Figure 5–21

$3\pi/2,\ 7\pi/2,\ 11\pi/2,\ \cdots,\ -\pi/2,\ -5\pi/2,\ -9\pi/2,\ \cdots$. In Figure 5–21, we have indicated the location of the points associated with a scattering of real numbers between 0 and 2π, i.e., for a single wrapping of the circle by the tape in the positive direction. The student is urged to become familiar with this diagram, and to be able to visualize the approximate location of the point on such a circle, that is associated with any real number, whether it is expressed as a multiple of π or not.

It is customary to use the symbol θ to represent an arbitrary real number, when the latter is used as the measure of arc length on a unit circle, as in the preceding discussion. We have then shown that each real number θ has associated with it a unique point (x, y) on the circle. For example, θ is associated with the point $(1, 0)$ if $\theta = 0$, with the point $(0, 1)$ if $\theta = \pi/2$, with the point $(1/\sqrt{2}, 1/\sqrt{2})$ if $\theta = \pi/4$, etc. We now use this correspondence, which associates each real number θ with a unique point (x, y) on a unit circle, to define the *basic circular* functions.

DEFINITIONS. If the initial point of an arc of length θ units on a unit circle is $(1, 0)$, and the terminal point is (x, y), then:

1. The *basic sine* function is the function f on $R^\#$ defined by $f(\theta) = y$, for each θ in its domain $R^\#$. It is customary to write sine θ (or sin θ) instead of $f(\theta)$ in this case.

2. The *basic cosine* function is the function f on $R^\#$ defined by $f(\theta) = x$, for each θ in its domain $R^\#$. It is customary to write cosine θ (or cos θ) instead of $f(\theta)$ in this case.

3. The *basic tangent* function is the function f in $R^\#$ defined by $f(\theta) = y/x$, for each θ in its domain; the domain of this function is the set of all real numbers, except those which measure unit-circular arcs that start at $(1, 0)$ and terminate on the y-axis. It is customary to write tangent θ (or tan θ) instead of $f(\theta)$ in this case.

4. The *basic cosecant* function is the function in $R^\#$ defined by $f(\theta) = 1/y$, for each θ in its domain; the domain of this function is the set of all real numbers, except those which measure unit-circular arcs that start at $(1, 0)$ and terminate on the x-axis. It is customary to write cosecant θ (or csc θ) instead of $f(\theta)$ in this case.

5. The *basic secant* function is the function in $R^\#$ defined by $f(\theta) = 1/x$, for each θ in its domain; the domain of this function is the same as the domain of the basic tangent function. It is customary to write secant θ (or sec θ) instead of $f(\theta)$ in this case.

6. The *basic cotangent* function is the function in $R^\#$ defined by $f(\theta) = x/y$, for each θ in its domain; the domain of this function is the same as the domain of the basic cosecant function. It is customary to write cotangent θ (or cot θ) instead of $f(\theta)$ in this case.

The above functions are called the *basic circular* functions, in view of their close association with a unit circle; in fact, the values of these basic circular functions have been defined in terms of the coordinates of well-defined points on such a unit circle. It is apparent, from the above definitions, that the values of the basic cosecant, basic secant, and basic cotangent functions are the respective reciprocals of the values of the basic sine, basic cosine, and basic tangent functions, for any θ in the domain of each respective pair of functions. The basic cosine, cosecant, and cotangent functions are said to be *cofunctions* of the basic sine, secant, and tangent functions, respectively; the significance of this will appear later.

DEFINITION. A function f in $R^\#$, such that $f(x) = a \sin bx$, for some given real numbers a and b, and for each x in the domain of f, is said to be a *sine* function. A similar remark applies to the other basic circular functions, thereby completing the definitions of the *circular* functions.

In harmony with previous procedure in this chapter, we shall assume for the present that $a = b = 1$, so that the circular functions arising here will be subsets of the basic circular functions. In the next section, we shall discuss the ranges of the basic circular functions, and exhibit the graphs of a few restricted circular functions.

ILLUSTRATION 1. Use a ruler, marked in inches, on Figure 5–21 to compute an approximation to (*a*) cos 0.5; (*b*) cot 3.0.

Solution.

(*a*) The point associated with 0.5 on the unit circle is approximately 1.75 inches from the y-axis; and since $2'' = 1$ unit on the graph, the abscissa of the point is 0.88. Thus, $\cos 0.5 = 0.88$.

(*b*) The distance from the y-axis of the point on the unit circle associated with 3.0 is approximately 31/16 inches, while its distance from the x-axis is approximately 4.5/16 inches. The coordinate pair of the point, using the scale of the unit circle, is then $(-15.5/16, 2.25/16)$, and so $\cot \theta = -15.5/2.25 = -6.9$, approximately. (It is clear that it was really not necessary, in this case, to convert our measurements to the scale of the unit circle.)

ILLUSTRATION 2. Use a ruler, marked in inches, on Figure 5–21 to compute an approximation to (*a*) sin 3.75; (*b*) sec $8\pi/3$; (*c*) tan $8\pi/3$.

Solution.

(*a*) The distance from the y-axis of the point associated with 3.75 is estimated to be $30/16''$, while its distance from the x-axis is $19/16''$; the coordinate pair of the point, using the scale of the graph, is then $(-15/16, -9.5/16)$. Thus, $\sin 3.75 = -9.5/16 = -0.6$, approximately.

(*b*) The point associated with $8\pi/3$ coincides with the point associated with $2\pi/3$. By actual measurement, the coordinate pair of this point (reduced to the scale of the graph) is $(-0.5, 0.86)$. Thus, $\sec 8\pi/3 = 1/(-0.5) = -2$.

(*c*) From the data in (*b*) we find that $\tan 8\pi/3 = 0.86/(-0.5) = -1.7$, approximately.

PROBLEM SET 5.5

1. Make a cardboard "arc length" protractor of the same size and with the same markings as the one in Figure 5–21. Keep this in your book for ready use.
2. On a unit circle, mark the approximate locations of the points associated with the following real numbers: -3; -2; 6π; 12; -5π; 20; 8π.
3. Do the same as in Problem 2 for the following real numbers: -2π; 2π; 8; -3π; -10π; 15; 18.
4. Use a ruler, and either Figure 5–21 or the protractor that you made in Problem 1, to compute approximations to the following: (*a*) cos 2; (*b*) cos 4; (*c*) sin $\pi/4$; (*d*) sin $7\pi/4$; (*e*) sin π; (*f*) cos 0.

5. Do the same as in Problem 4 for the following: (*a*) $\tan \pi/6$; (*b*) $\cot \pi/6$; (*c*) $\tan 3$; (*d*) $\cot 4$; (*e*) $\tan 6$; (*f*) $\cot 5\pi/3$.
6. Do the same as in Problem 4 for the following: (*a*) $\sec 2.5$; (*b*) $\csc 5\pi/6$; (*c*) $\sec \pi/3$; (*d*) $\csc 11\pi/6$; (*e*) $\sec 2.5$; (*f*) $\csc 3$.
7. Do the same as in Problem 4 for the following: (*a*) $\sec(-5.5)$; (*b*) $\csc(-4\pi/3)$; (*c*) $\sin(-\pi/2)$; (*d*) $\cos(-3)$; (*e*) $\tan(-\pi/6)$; (*f*) $\cot(-5\pi/6)$.
8. Do the same as in Problem 4 for the following: (*a*) $\sin(-11\pi/6)$; (*b*) $\cot(-2)$; (*c*) $\cos(-4.5)$; (*d*) $\sec(-7\pi/3)$; (*e*) $\csc(-3.5)$; (*f*) $\cos(-3.5)$.
9. Use the cardboard protractor that you made in Problem 1 to draw a diagram similar to Figure 5–21, showing the locations of the points associated with the corresponding negative numbers.
10. If θ is a number in the domain of a circular function f, the algebraic sign of $f(\theta)$ is determined by the quadrant in which terminates a unit-circular arc that starts at $(1, 0)$ and is θ units in length. Choose a terminal point in each quadrant, assume that the associated θ is in the domain, and list the signs of the values of the six circular functions at each θ.
11. The following numbers are considered to measure the lengths of unit-circular arcs, that start at $(1, 0)$. Indicate the quadrant that contains the terminal point in each case: -6; -12; $-13\pi/4$; $7\pi/4$; 15; 13; $13\pi/6$; $-7\pi/3$; -10.
12. Indicate in which quadrants a unit-circular arc θ units in length, and starting at $(1, 0)$, may terminate if (*a*) $\sin\theta = -2/3$; (*b*) $\cos\theta = 4/5$; (*c*) $\cos\theta = -3/4$; (*d*) $\cot\theta = 4$; (*e*) $\tan\theta = 6$; (*f*) $\sec\theta = -12$; (*g*) $\sec\theta = 3$; (*h*) $\sin\theta = -0.23$; (*i*) $\cos\theta = -0.386$; (*j*) $\cos\theta = -4$.
13. Determine the smallest non-negative real number θ such that (*a*) $\cos\theta = 0$; (*b*) $\sin\theta = 0$; (*c*) $\sin\theta = -1$; (*d*) $\cos\theta = -1$; (*e*) $\tan\theta = 0$; (*f*) $\cot\theta = 0$.
14. Describe the domain of each of the following basic circular functions: (*a*) tangent; (*b*) cotangent; (*c*) secant; (*d*) cosecant.
15. Use the Pythagorean Theorem to prove each of the following, for any real number θ in the domains of the functions concerned: (*a*) $\sin^2\theta + \cos^2\theta = 1$; (*b*) $1 + \tan^2\theta = \sec^2\theta$; (*c*) $1 + \cot^2\theta = \csc^2\theta$. [Note: The notation $\sin^2\theta$ means $(\sin\theta)^2$, etc.]
16. Examine each of the equalities in Problem 15, and describe the set of real numbers θ, for which it is valid.
17. Prove for an arbitrary real number θ: (*a*) $\sin(-\theta) = -\sin\theta$; (*b*) $\cos(-\theta) = \cos\theta$. (Hint: Consider arcs that terminate in each quadrant.)
18. If θ is in the domain of the basic tangent function, so is $-\theta$; prove that $\tan(-\theta) = -\tan\theta$, for such a number θ. (See Problem 17.)
19. Prove for an arbitrary real number θ: (*a*) $\sin(\pi + \theta) = -\sin\theta$; (*b*) $\sin(2\pi + \theta) = \sin\theta$; (*c*) $\cos(\pi - \theta) = -\cos\theta$.

5.6 Ranges of the Basic Circular Functions

The circular functions have all been defined as functions in the set R^* of real numbers; in other words, the elements of the domain and the range of each such function are real numbers. The student who has had an introduction to these functions before, may be perplexed by the fact that we have not mentioned angles, which have always played a central role in the traditional approach to these functions. However, while the real numbers of the domains of these functions *may* be measures of angles, as we shall see in Chapter 7, there are many other applications in which angles are not involved; and we have preferred to relegate the study of trigonometry—a study of angles—to a place of secondary importance.

The values of each basic circular function f have been defined in terms of the coordinates of points on a unit circle. Since the circumference of such a circle measures 2π units in length, it is evident that if θ is any number in the domain of f, $f(\theta) = f(\theta_1)$ for some number θ_1 in the interval $[0, 2\pi]$. Accordingly, the range of any basic circular function will be completely determined if we examine the value of this function at each point in the above interval.

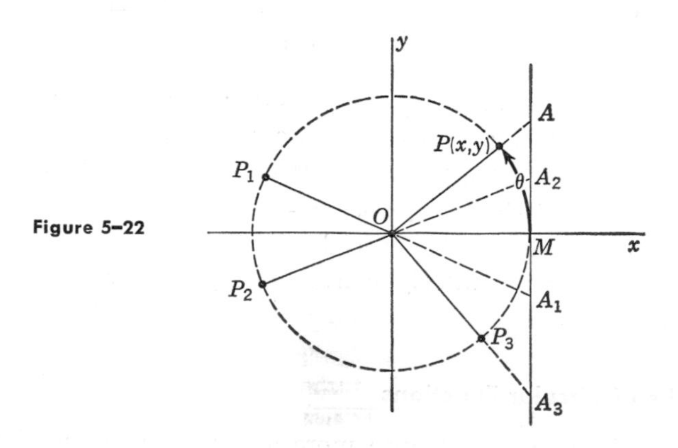

Figure 5–22

DEFINITION. A function f is said to be *periodic* if there exists a positive real number a such that $f(x + a) = f(x)$, for each x in its domain; the *period* of f is the smallest positive number a for which this is true.

It then appears that all the basic circular functions are periodic, with periods not greater than 2π. We shall see later that it is this periodic characteristic that makes circular functions so important. Let us now examine the range of each basic circular function f, which we have just seen is the set $\{f(\theta) \mid \theta \in [0, 2\pi], \theta \text{ in the domain of } f\}$.

In Figure 5–22, let $P(x, y)$ be a point on the unit circle, with θ the corresponding measure of length of arc MP. Let a vertical line be drawn tangent to the circle at M. If the radius OP is extended to intersect this vertical tangent line at A, a consideration of similar triangles shows that $|\tan \theta|$ is equal to the measure of length of the line segment MA, regardless of the position of P; this is, in fact, the reason for the name "tangent θ." The sine and cosine of θ are, respectively, the ordinate and abscissa of P, while the other three basic circular functional values are the reciprocals of those of the sine, cosine, and tangent. Several positions of P are shown in the figure, and if we observe the variation in length of MA, along with the abscissa and ordinate of P, as P designates different points on the circle, we shall get a mental picture of the variations of the values of the basic circular functions. In Figure 5–23, we have indicated these variations on

quadrant	θ	$\sin\theta$	$\cos\theta$	$\tan\theta$	$\csc\theta$	$\sec\theta$	$\cot\theta$
1	0 to $\pi/2$	0 to 1	1 to 0	0 to ∞	∞ to 1	1 to ∞	∞ to 0
2	$\pi/2$ to π	1 to 0	0 to -1	$-\infty$ to 0	1 to ∞	$-\infty$ to -1	0 to $-\infty$
3	π to $3\pi/2$	0 to -1	-1 to 0	0 to ∞	$-\infty$ to -1	-1 to $-\infty$	∞ to 0
4	$3\pi/2$ to 2π	-1 to 0	0 to 1	$-\infty$ to 0	-1 to $-\infty$	∞ to 1	0 to $-\infty$

Figure 5–23

the interval $[0, 2\pi]$. We are using the symbol ∞ in this table to indicate that the value of a function exceeds any finite bound, if θ is an element of the domain that is sufficiently close to the end-point of the given interval of real numbers; and similarly, we use $-\infty$ to indicate that the value is negative and its absolute value exceeds any finite bound. We emphasize, however, that these are merely convenient symbols and are not to be treated as numbers.

5.7 Graphs of Circular Functions

It would be necessary to use more advanced mathematics than we have developed so far, in order to obtain accurate values of the circular functions for arbitrary real numbers in their domains. However, there are certain special numbers for which we can obtain the circular functional values exactly, by geometric means, if they are defined. These values, along with the general survey contained in the table of Figure 5–23, will enable us to sketch the graph of any circular function with bounded domain, of the type being discussed in this chapter. The special real numbers, which we now consider, are $\pi/4$, $\pi/6$, and $\pi/3$.

(*a*) In Figure 5–24, let AP be an arc of length $\pi/4$ units, on the indicated unit circle. Arcs QA and AP are of equal lengths and, since equal arcs are subtended by equal angles, $\angle QOA = \angle AOP$. If AB is drawn parallel to OQ, it follows from simple geometry that triangle AOB is isosceles. Thus, segments OB and AB are equal in length, and so $x = y$; since $x^2 + y^2 = 1$, by the Pythagorean Theorem, we have $2x^2 = 1$, and hence $x = y = 1/\sqrt{2} = \sqrt{2}/2$. It then follows that $\sin \pi/4 = \cos \pi/4 = \sqrt{2}/2$ and $\tan \pi/4 = y/x = 1$.

(*b*) Let points A and B be located as shown in Figure 5–25, so that the arc AB is one-sixth of the circumference of the unit circle, with P the midpoint of this arc. Thus, arc PB measures $\pi/6$ units. Since $\angle BOA$ is

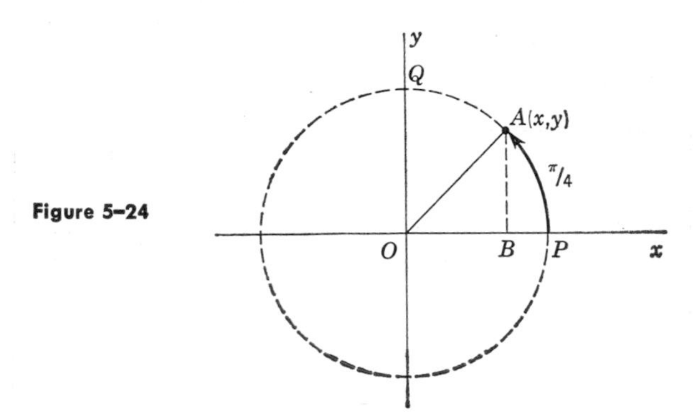

Figure 5–24

60°, it follows from simple geometry that triangle BOA is equilateral, and so each of the sides OB, OA, and AB is 1 unit in length. The measure of length of CB is then $1/2$, that of OC is $\sqrt{3}/2$, and B is the point $(\sqrt{3}/2, 1/2)$. The definitions of the basic circular functions then give: $\sin \pi/6 = 1/2$; $\cos \pi/6 = \sqrt{3}/2$; $\tan \pi/6 = \sqrt{3}/3$.

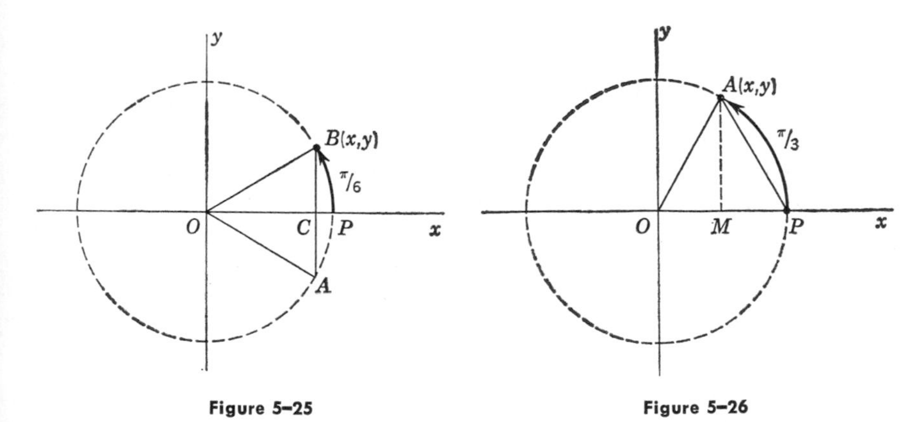

Figure 5–25 Figure 5–26

(*c*) In Figure 5–26, let point A be chosen so that the length of arc PA is $\pi/3$ units, i.e., arc PA comprises one-sixth of the circumference of the unit circle. If M is the midpoint of the segment OP, simple geometry shows that the line segment AM is a portion of the perpendicular bisector of the segment OP. If A is the point (x, y), it follows that $x = 1/2$ and $y = \sqrt{3}/2$. Hence, $\sin \pi/3 = \sqrt{3}/2$, $\cos \pi/3 = 1/2$, and $\tan \pi/3 = \sqrt{3}$.

In Figure 5–27, we have tabulated the values of the basic circular functions, for the important special real numbers on the interval $[0, \pi/2]$; this table includes the values for 0 and $\pi/2$, which we obtain immediately from the definitions of the functions. The student is urged to become thoroughly familiar with this table, as the data given there are used so frequently. The mark $\cdot\cdot$ indicates that no functional value is defined here, i.e., this number is not in the domain of the function.

θ	sin	cos	tan	csc	sec	cot
0	0	1	0	..	1	..
$\pi/6$	$1/2$	$\sqrt{3}/2$	$1/\sqrt{3}$	2	$2/\sqrt{3}$	$\sqrt{3}$
$\pi/4$	$\sqrt{2}/2$	$\sqrt{2}/2$	1	$\sqrt{2}$	$\sqrt{2}$	1
$\pi/3$	$\sqrt{3}/2$	$1/2$	$\sqrt{3}$	$2/\sqrt{3}$	2	$\sqrt{3}/3$
$\pi/2$	1	0	..	1	..	0

Figure 5–27

We are now about to state a very important principle, which reduces the problem of determining the circular functional values at any real number in the domains of these functions, to one in which the real number is non-negative and does not exceed $\pi/2$. We shall say that an arc of a unit circle is in *standard position*, if it is so located that its initial point coincides with the point $(1, 0)$ of a Cartesian coordinate system, which has its origin at the center of the circle. Furthermore, if θ is a real number that designates the signed length of an arc in standard position on a unit circle, let us define the associated *reference arc* to be that arc of length θ' units, $0 \leq \theta' \leq \pi/2$, that is intercepted between the terminal point of the given arc and the x-axis.

REDUCTION PRINCIPLE. Let θ be any real number, regarded as the measure of length of an arc in standard position on a unit circle, with θ' the measure of its associated reference arc. Then, if f is any basic circular function, $|f(\theta)| = f(\theta')$, i.e., the functional values $f(\theta)$ and $f(\theta')$ differ at most in sign.

The non-negative number θ' is not larger than $\pi/2$, by definition, and the sign of $f(\theta)$ can be determined by inspection of the quadrant in which the terminal point of the arc of length θ units lies. Thus, the values of any circular function are completely known, once we have determined the value at each number that is in the domain of the function and in the interval $[0, \pi/2]$.

The proof of the principle just stated follows from simple geometry and the definitions of the basic circular functions. Thus, in Figure 5–28, let P, P_1, P_2, and P_3 be four points symmetrically located with respect to the x and y axes on a unit circle. Let us suppose, further, that these

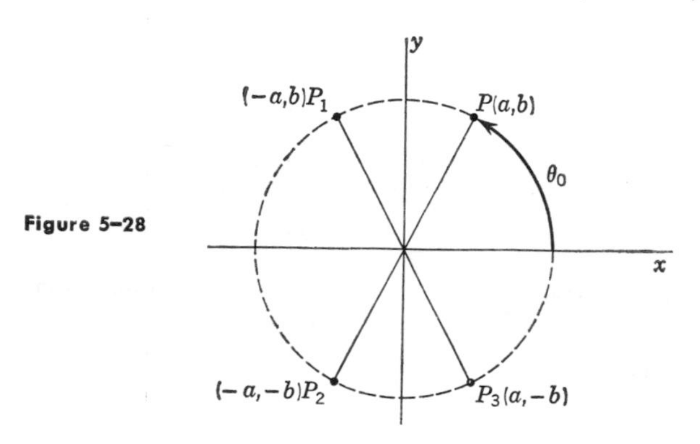

Figure 5–28

are the terminal points of four arcs in standard position on the circle, and having respective lengths of θ_0, θ_1, θ_2, and θ_3 units, where $0 \leq \theta_0 \leq \pi/2$. By elementary geometry, the coordinates of the four points differ only in sign and so, if f is any basic circular function, the values $f(\theta_1)$, $f(\theta_2)$, and $f(\theta_3)$ differ at most in sign from $f(\theta_0)$. The figure shows that the length of the reference arc associated with any of the above arcs is θ_0 units, and we have just shown that $|f(\theta_1)| = |f(\theta_2)| = |f(\theta_3)| = f(\theta_0)$. Thus, if θ is *any* real number (so that an arc of length θ units in standard position on a unit circle may terminate in *any* of the four quadrants), $|f(\theta)| = f(\theta')$, where θ' measures the length of the reference arc associated with the arc of length θ. This is the statement of the Reduction Principle.

ILLUSTRATION 1. Determine: (*a*) $\sin 5\pi/6$; (*b*) $\cos 4\pi/3$; (*c*) $\tan 17\pi/3$.

Solution.

(*a*) Using Figure 5–29 and the Reduction Principle, we have $|\sin 5\pi/6| = \sin \pi/6$. Since the arc in question terminates in the second quadrant, the sign of $\sin 5\pi/6$ is positive, and so $\sin 5\pi/6 = \sin \pi/6 = 1/2$.

(*b*) Using Figure 5–30 and the Reduction Principle, we have $|\cos 4\pi/3| = \cos \pi/3$. Since the terminal point of the arc is in the third quadrant, the sign of $\cos 4\pi/3$ is negative, and so $\cos 4\pi/3 = -\cos \pi/3 = -1/2$.

(*c*) An application of the Reduction Principle, with the aid of Figure 5–31, shows that $|\tan 17\pi/3| = \tan \pi/3$. Since the arc associated with $17\pi/3$ terminates in the fourth quadrant, the value of the tangent function is negative at $17\pi/3$, and so $\tan 17\pi/3 = -\tan \pi/3 = -\sqrt{3}$.

ILLUSTRATION 2. If $\pi/2 < \theta < \pi$ and $\sin \theta = 0.6$, determine $\cos \theta$ and $\tan \theta$.

Solution. In Figure 5–32, we have shown the approximate location

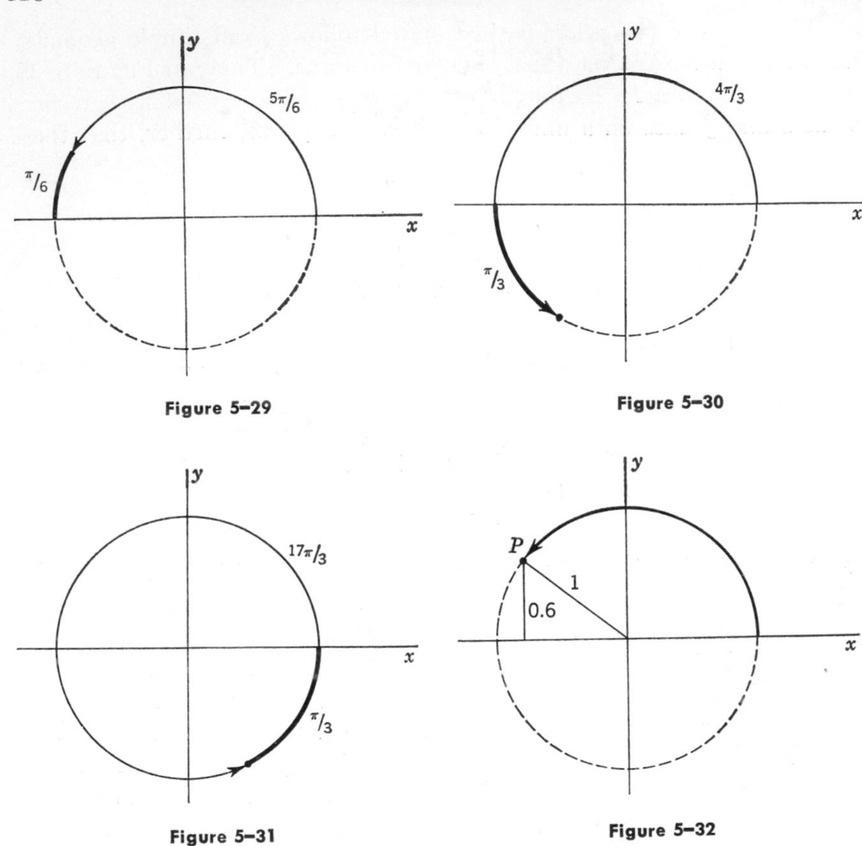

Figure 5–29

Figure 5–30

Figure 5–31

Figure 5–32

of the end point P of the arc in standard position of length θ units, as described. The ordinate of P is 0.6, while its abscissa may be obtained by using the Pythagorean Theorem. Thus, the absolute value of this abscissa is $\sqrt{1 - 0.36}$ or 0.8, and so P is the point $(-0.8, 0.6)$. It follows that $\cos \theta = -0.8$ and $\tan \theta = (0.6)/(-0.8) = -0.75$.

With the help of the Reduction Principle and the tables in Figure 5–23 and Figure 5–27, it is now easy to sketch the graph of an arbitrary circular function having a restricted domain. In Figures 5–33, 5–34, and 5–35, we have shown sketches of the functions from $[-\pi, 3\pi]$ to $R^{\#}$, defined separately by the equations $y = f(x)$, for each basic circular function f; reciprocal functions are sketched with the same axes. In our sketches, we have replaced the symbol θ, that we have been using, by the more usual "horizontal scale" symbol x, but this should not be confused with the x used in the definitions of some of the basic circular functions; in other words, *the* x *of our sketches is a real number which we regard, in this connection, as the measure of length of an arc in standard position on a unit circle.* An

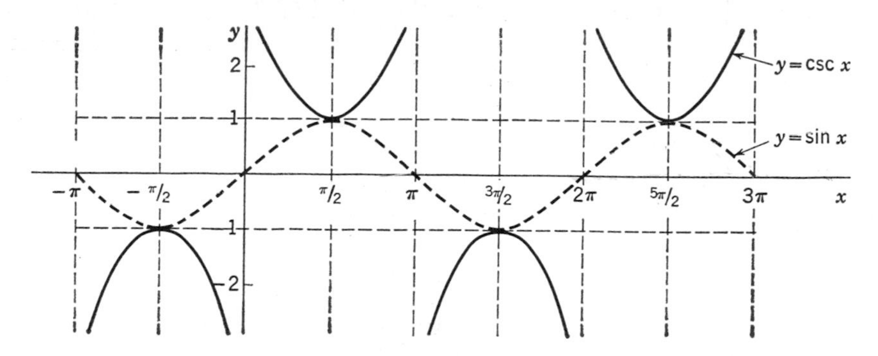

Figure 5–33

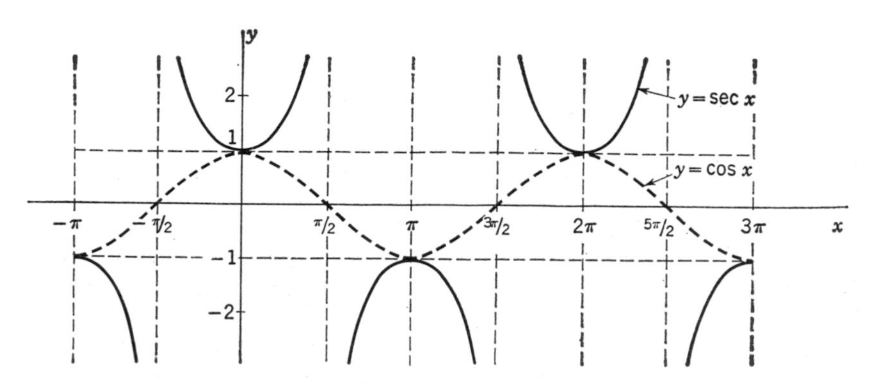

Figure 5–34

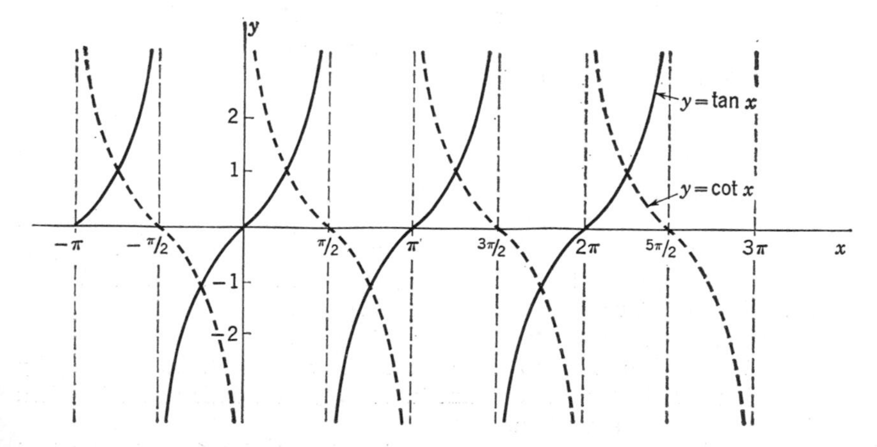

Figure 5–35

inspection of Figure 5–35 reveals that the period of the basic tangent function and of the basic cotangent function is π; the period of each of the other basic circular functions, however, may be seen to be 2π.

Note. We have stated that an entry $\cdot\cdot$ associated with a number θ, in the table of Figure 5–27, indicates that $f(\theta)$ is not defined, i.e., θ is not in the domain of the function. However, the domain of such a basic circular function does include all the numbers in a sufficiently small interval J containing θ, except θ itself. The table of Figure 5–23 then implies that the functional values, at numbers in J exceeding θ, are opposite in sign to those at numbers in J less than θ, and the absolute values of these functional values exceeds any finite bound. It is sometimes convenient to express this by saying that the functional values "become positively infinite" or "become negatively infinite" on the interval J.

PROBLEM SET 5.7

1. Prove the assertion with respect to Figure 5–22, that the length of segment MA is $\tan\theta$ units.
2. Prove that triangle AOB of Figure 5–24 is isosceles.
3. Prove that triangle BOA of Figure 5–25 is equilateral.
4. Prove that segment AM is perpendicular to the radius OP in Figure 5–26.
5. Give the range of each of the six basic circular functions.
6. Indicate which of the following are impossible for a real number θ: $\sin\theta = 2$; $\cot\theta = 0$; $\cos\theta = -1/2$; $\sec\theta = 2/3$; $\tan\theta = -57$; $\cos\theta = -5$.
7. Explain what is meant by the entry "$\tan\pi/2 = \cdot\cdot$" in the table of Figure 5–27.
8. Use the Reduction Principle and the table of Figure 5–27 to determine $\sin\theta$, $\cos\theta$, and $\tan\theta$, if θ is equal to (*a*) $-\pi/4$; (*b*) $-3\pi/4$; (*c*) $-7\pi/4$; (*d*) $-11\pi/4$; (*e*) $-\pi/6$; (*f*) $-\pi/3$.
9. Do the same as in Problem 8, if θ is equal to (*a*) $-5\pi/6$; (*b*) $-4\pi/3$; (*c*) $-5\pi/3$; (*d*) $14\pi/3$; (*e*) $11\pi/3$; (*f*) -7π.
10. Let us define the *co-reference arc* of a given arc of length θ units in standard position on a unit circle, to be the arc of length θ'' units, $0 \leq \theta'' \leq \pi/2$, intercepted between the terminal point of the given arc and the y-axis. Then, if f is any basic circular function and co-f is the corresponding basic co-function, prove that $|f(\theta)| = \text{co-}f(\theta'')$ for any θ in the domain of f.
11. Repeat Problem 8, using the result of Problem 10.
12. Repeat Problem 9, using the result of Problem 10.
13. Sketch the graph of the function on the interval $[-\pi/4, \pi/4]$, defined by $y = f(x)$ where f is (*a*) the basic sine function; (*b*) the basic secant function; (*c*) the basic tangent function.
14. Show on separate diagrams all arcs of length θ, $0 \leq \theta \leq 2\pi$, in standard position on a unit circle, such that (*a*) $\tan\theta$ does not exist; (*b*) $\cos\theta = -1/2$;

(*c*) $\sin \theta = -1$; (*d*) $\cos \theta = -1/2$; (*e*) $\cos \theta = -1/2$ and $\sin \theta$ is negative; (*f*) $\tan \theta = -\sqrt{3}$ and $\cos \theta$ is negative.

15. If $0 \leq \theta \leq \pi/2$ and $\cos \theta = 3/5$, determine $\sin \theta$.

16. If $\pi \leq \theta \leq 3\pi/2$ and $\sin \theta = 2/3$, determine $\cos \theta$.

17. If $0 \leq \theta \leq \pi/2$ and $\cos \theta = 1/3$, determine $\tan \theta$.

18. Determine $\tan \theta$, if $-\pi/2 \geq \theta \geq -3\pi/2$ and $\sin \theta = -0.3$.

19. Determine $\sin \theta$, if $-\pi/2 \leq \theta \leq 0$ and $\cos \theta = 2/3$.

20. Determine $\cot \theta$, if $7\pi \leq \theta \leq 15\pi/2$ and $\cos \theta = -0.54$.

21. If $0 < \theta < \pi/2$, use the result of Problem 10 to express the value of each basic circular function, at each of the following numbers, in the form $\pm f(\theta)$, where f is some basic circular function: (*a*) $\pi/2 - \theta$; (*b*) $\pi/2 + \theta$; (*c*) $3\pi/2 - \theta$; (*d*) $3\pi/2 + \theta$.

22. If $0 < \theta < \pi/2$, use the Reduction Principle to express the value of each basic circular function, at each of the following numbers, in the form $\pm f(\theta)$, where f is some basic circular function: (*a*) $\pi - \theta$; (*b*) $\pi + \theta$; (*c*) $-\theta$.

5.8 The Basic Inverse Circular Relations and Functions

In Chapter 4 we defined the inverse of any relation, by interchanging the roles played by the domain and the range. Thus, a relation, defined by the equation $y = x^2$, has an inverse defined by the equation $x = y^2$, obtained from the former by interchanging x and y. The basic circular functions are, of course, special relations and so have inverses which may be defined in this way. Hence, the relation inverse to the basic sine function is the relation in $R^\#$, defined by the equation $x = \sin y$. If we solve this equation for y, we must introduce a new notational device and write $y = \arcsin x$, which means that *y is a number such that $\sin y = x$.* In a similar manner, we may define the inverse relations of the other basic circular functions. Sometimes the notation $\sin^{-1} x$ is used instead of $\arcsin x$; however, we shall not use it, since the -1 could be easily confused with an exponent, and the other notation is more suggestive of "arc length" which is used in the definitions of the circular functions. The relation in $R^\#$, that is the inverse of any basic circular function, is called the corresponding *basic inverse* circular relation; the graphs of such inverse relations are the reflections of each other in the straight line locus of the equation $y = x$. In Figure 5–36, we have shown the graphs of the relations in the interval $[-2\pi, 2\pi]$, defined separately by the equations $y = \sin x$ and $y = \arcsin x$.

We have remarked before that the values of the circular functions depend only on the coordinates of the *end points* of arcs of a unit circle, and are independent of how many complete circumferences of the circle are included in the arc. Thus, there are infinitely many real numbers, at which the circular functional values are identical. For example, if $y = \arcsin 1$, y could be any of the numbers expressible as $\pi/2 + 2n\pi$, for an arbitrary integer n, as we can also infer from Figure 5–36. Accordingly, the inverse relations of the basic circular functions are not functions, because our definition of a function f allows only one functional value $f(x)$, at each element x of its domain. We now restrict the domains of the basic circular functions to define six new circular functions, the inverses of which are also functions.

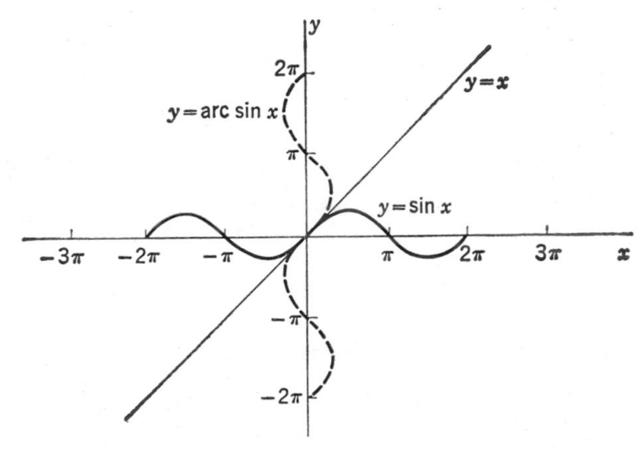

Figure 5–36

DEFINITION. The basic *Cap-sine* function, designated by Sine (or Sin), is the subset of the basic sine function with the domain of the latter restricted to the set of real numbers on the interval $[-\pi/2, \pi/2]$. In other words, the Cap-sine function is the function f on $[-\pi/2, \pi/2]$, defined by $f(x) = \sin x$.

The inverse of this function is called the *basic arc Cap-sine* function, designated by arc Sine (or arc Sin). Our definition states that $\text{Sin } x = \sin x$, for each real number x on the interval $[-\pi/2, \pi/2]$. The domain of the basic arc Sin function is the set of real numbers on the interval $[-1, 1]$ and, for each x in this domain, a real number arc Sin x is *uniquely* defined by the rule that arc Sin $x = y$ if $\text{Sin } y = \sin y = x$. The range of the basic arc Sin function is sometimes called a set of *principal values* for the arc sin relation.

In a similar manner, we can restrict the domains of the other basic circular functions and define new functions having inverses that are also functions, using the same "Cap" notation as above. The choice of the set of principal values, which constitutes the domain of a "Cap" function and the range of the associated inverse "Cap" function, is somewhat arbitrary, but must be a maximal set such that the associated "Cap" functional values are all distinct. The domain of the basic Cos function, which is also the set of principal values for the basic arc cos relation and the range of the basic arc Cos function, is usually chosen to be the set of real numbers on the interval $[0, \pi]$. While there is quite general agreement as to the domains of the basic Sine and basic Cosine functions, there is no such general agreement for the domains of the other basic

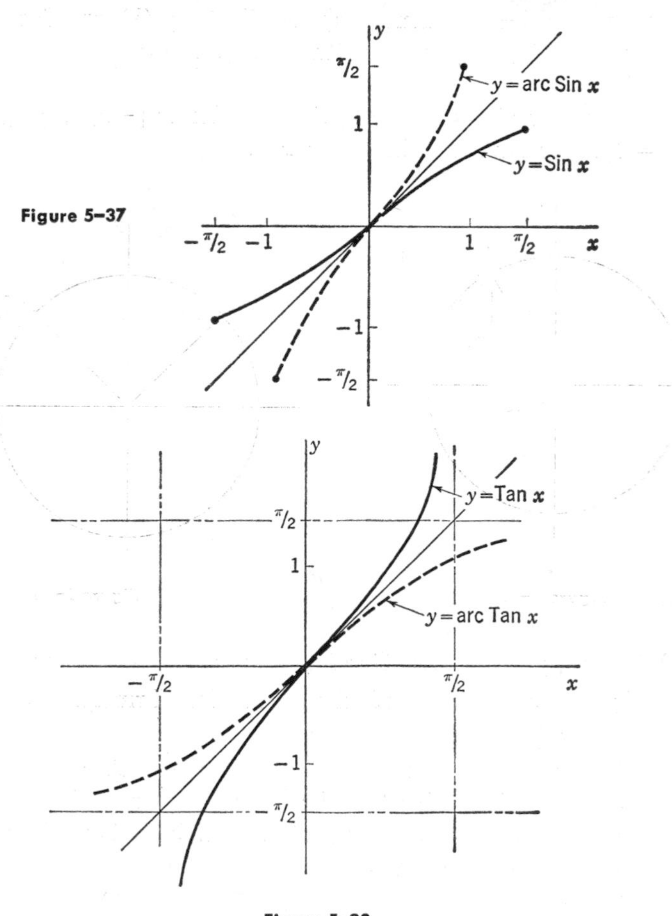

Figure 5–37

Figure 5–38

"Cap" functions. For our purposes here, however, we shall choose the domain of the basic Sec function to coincide with that of the basic Cosine function, and the domains of the other basic "Cap" functions to coincide with that of the basic Sine function except, of course, for those numbers for which a value of these functions is undefined. Thus, the principal values for all the basic inverse circular relations are in the interval $[-\pi/2, \pi/2]$ except for the basic arc cosine and arc secant relations, in which cases they have been chosen to be in the interval $[0, \pi]$. We again point out that there could have been many other choices of principal values, subject to the condition specified above, and we have merely made one such choice. In Figure 5–37, we have sketched graphs of the basic Sine and basic arc Sin functions, and in Figure 5–38 graphs of the basic Tan and arc Tan functions.

ILLUSTRATION. Determine: (*a*) arc Sin $1/2$; (*b*) arc Cos $(-\sqrt{3}/2)$; (*c*) Cos (arc Sin $2/3$); (*d*) arc Tan (tan $3\pi/4$).

Solution.

(*a*) The range of the basic arc Sin function is $[-\pi/2, \pi/2]$, and since $\sin \pi/6 = 1/2$, we have arc Sin $1/2 = \pi/6$.

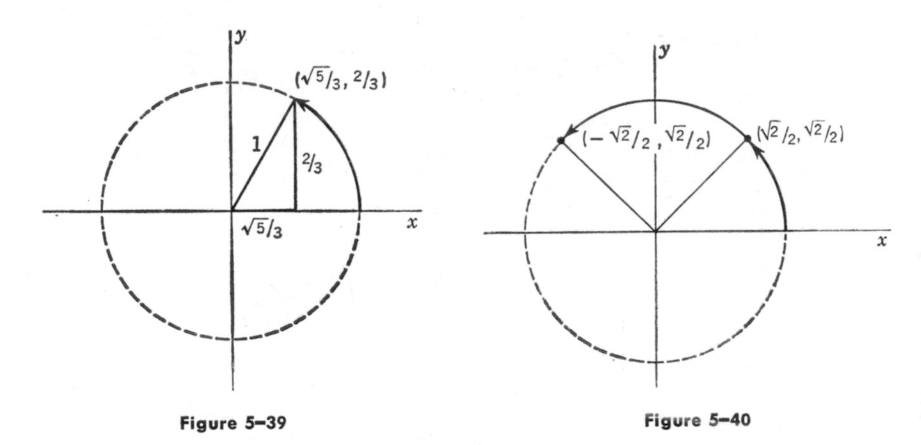

Figure 5–39

Figure 5–40

(*b*) The range of the arc Cos function is $[0, \pi]$, and since $\cos 5\pi/6 = -\sqrt{3}/2$ by an application of the Reduction Principle, we find that arc Cos $(-\sqrt{3}/2) = 5\pi/6$.

(*c*) The range of the arc Sin function is $[-\pi/2, \pi/2]$, and we need the value of the basic Cosine function at a number having a Sine of $2/3$. If we apply the Pythagorean Theorem to the triangle shown in Figure 5–39, we find that Cos (arc Sin $2/3$) $= \sqrt{5}/3$.

(*d*) Since $\tan 3\pi/4 = -\tan \pi/4$ (see Figure 5–40), which equals -1, our problem resolves itself into a determination of arc Tan (-1). Since the range of the basic arc Tan function is in $[-\pi/2, \pi/2]$, we find that arc Tan $(-1) = -\pi/4$. Thus, arc Tan (tan $3\pi/4$) $= -\pi/4$.

PROBLEM SET 5.8

1. Explain the difference between the basic cosine and basic Cosine functions.
2. Sketch graphs of the basic Cosine and basic arc Cosine functions.

3. Explain the difference between the relations in $R^{\#}$ defined separately by $y = \text{arc tan } x$ and $y = \text{arc Tan } x$.
4. Does the expression Sin $3\pi/4$ have any meaning? Explain.
5. Does the expression Cos $3\pi/4$ have any meaning? Explain the difference between the situation here and that in Problem 4.
6. Determine each of the following functional values: (*a*) $\sin 3\pi/4$; (*b*) arc Sin $(-1/2)$; (*c*) arc Tan $(-\sqrt{3})$; (*d*) Cot $(-\pi/4)$; (*e*) arc Sec (-2); (*f*) arc Cos $(-1/2)$.
7. Use the same axes to sketch graphs of the two functions in $R^{\#}$ defined separately by: (*a*) $y = \text{Cos } x$, $y = \text{arc Cos } x$; (*b*) $y = \text{Sec } x$, $y = \text{arc Sec } x$.
8. Use the same axes to sketch graphs of the two functions in $R^{\#}$ defined separately by: (*a*) $y = \text{Csc } x$, $y = \text{arc Csc } x$; (*b*) $y = \text{Cot } x$, $y = \text{arc Cot } x$.
9. Determine each of the following functional values: (*a*) arc Cos $1/2$; (*b*) arc Sin 0; (*c*) arc Tan (-1); (*d*) arc Cos (-1).
10. Determine each of the following:
    (*a*) sin (arc Cos $(-1/2)$); (*b*) cos (arc Sin $(-2/3)$);
    (*c*) tan (arc Sec $(-3/2)$); (*d*) cot (arc Csc (-3)).
11. Determine each of the following:
    (*a*) arc Sin (sin $5\pi/4$); (*b*) arc Cos (cos $(-\pi/3)$);
    (*c*) arc Sec (Csc $(-5\pi/6)$); (*d*) arc Cot (tan $5\pi/6$).
12. Show that (*a*) arc Sin $1/2$ + arc Sin $\sqrt{3}/2$ = − arc Sin (-1); (*b*) 3 arc Sin $\sqrt{3}/2 = \pi/2$ + arc Sin 1.

13*. A function f is defined by the indicated graph. Sketch the associated function with the same domain, defined by (*a*) $y = |f(x)|$; (*b*) $y = f(|x|)$; (*c*) $y = -f(x)$; (*d*) $y = e^{f(x)}$; (*e*) $y = \text{arc Sin } f(x)$.

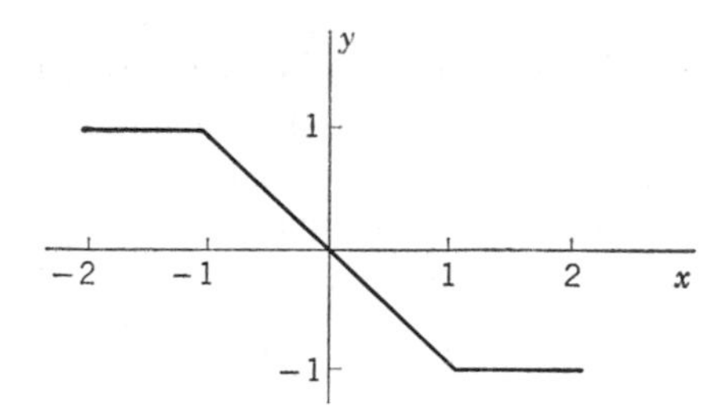

REVIEW TEST A

1. Each of the following equations defines a function from the interval $[-2, 2]$ to $R^{\#}$, which may be represented graphically. List the quadrants that contain points in each graphical representation, and also state whether the curve is "concave down" or "concave up" in the first quadrant. (*a*) $y = x^{2/3}$; (*b*) $y = x^{7/4}$; (*c*) $y = x^{6/5}$.
2. Sketch the three functions in Problem 1, using one pair of axes. Use another pair of axes to sketch the relations from $[-2, 2]$ to $R^{\#}$, defined by the equations $y^3 = x^2$, $y^4 = x^7$, and $y^5 = x^6$. Compare the graphs.

3. Use one pair of axes to sketch the relations from $[-3, 3]$ to $R^\#$, defined separately by (a) $y = x^{-1/2}$; (b) $y^4 = 1/x^3$; (c) $y = x^{-3/5}$.
4. Use one pair of axes to sketch the functions from $[-3, 3]$ to $R^\#$, defined separately by (a) $y = 2^x$; (b) $y = 5^x$; (c) $y = \log_5 x$.
5. Use one pair of axes to sketch the functions from $[-3, 3]$ to $R^\#$, defined separately by $y = (1/2)^x$ and $y = \log_{1/2} x$.
6. Determine the slope of the straight line through the point $(4, 6)$ and the point of intersection with the y-axis of the locus of the equation $y = e^x$.
7. A line L is drawn through the point $(3, -5)$ parallel to the line in Problem 6. Determine the abscissa of the point on L having ordinate 4.
8. If 2 grams of radium are left to decompose, the number y of grams remaining after t centuries is given by the formula $y = 2e^{-0.038t}$. Determine the "half-life" of the radium, i.e., the time required to decompose half of it, using (a) a table of natural logarithms; (b) a table of common logarithms.
9. Use the Reduction Principle to determine each of the following functional values: (a) $\sin(-13\pi/3)$; (b) $\csc(7\pi/4)$; (c) $\sec(-7\pi/6)$.
10. Determine the algebraic sign of each of the following: (a) $\sin 3.5$; (b) $\cos(-2.6)$; (c) $\tan 8$.
11. Determine both the smallest positive and the numerically smallest negative number x that satisfies: (a) $\cos x = -1$; (b) $\cot x = -1$; (c) $\sec x = -\sqrt{2}$.
12. Simplify: (a) $\text{arc Sin}(-\sqrt{2}/2) + \text{Tan}\,\pi/4$; (b) $\text{arc Sin}(\sin 5\pi/4)$.

REVIEW TEST B

1. Each of the following equations defines a function from $[-2, 2]$ to $R^\#$, which may be represented graphically. List the quadrants that contain points in each graphical representation, and also state whether the curve is "concave up" or "concave down" in the first quadrant: (a) $y = x^{4/3}$; (b) $y = x^{3/7}$; (c) $y = x^{7/4}$.
2. Using one pair of axes, sketch the three functions in Problem 1. Use another pair of axes to sketch the relations from $[-2, 2]$ to $R^\#$, defined separately by the equations: $y^3 = x^4$; $y^7 = x^3$; and $y^4 = x^7$. Compare the graphs.
3. Use one pair of axes to sketch the relations from $[-3, 3]$ to $R^\#$, defined separately by (a) $y = x^{-1/4}$; (b) $y^2 = 1/x$; (c) $y = x^{-5/3}$.
4. Use one pair of axes to sketch the functions from $[-3, 3]$ to $R^\#$, defined separately by $y = \log_3 x$; $y = \log_6 x$; and $y = 3^x$.
5. Use one pair of axes to sketch the functions from $[-1, 3]$ to $R^\#$, defined separately by $y = (1/3)^x$ and $y = \log_{1/3} x$.
6. A straight line L is drawn through the point $(-3, -2)$ and the point of intersection with the x-axis of the locus of the equation $y = \log_3 x$. Determine the slope of the line L.
7. The point $(3, y_1)$ lies on the line through $(-2, 4)$ parallel to the line in Problem 6. Determine the number y_1.

8. If 1000 bacteria in a certain culture are left to multiply, the number y present t hours later is given by $y = 1000\, e^{2.8t}$. Determine the time required for the number of bacteria to increase to 2000, by using (*a*) a table of natural logarithms; (*b*) a table of common logarithms.
9. Determine the algebraic sign of each of the following: (*a*) $\csc(-7\pi/8)$; (*b*) $\sec 7$; (*c*) $\cot(-2.6\pi)$.
10. Use the Reduction Principle to determine (*a*) $\cos 5\pi/4$; (*b*) $\cot(-10\pi/3)$; (*c*) $\tan 13\pi/6$.
11. Determine both the smallest positive and the numerically smallest negative number x that satisfies (*a*) $\sin x = -1/2$; (*b*) $\csc x = -2\sqrt{3}/3$; (*c*) $\tan x = 1$.
12. Simplify: (*a*) $\text{arc Cos}(-1/2) + \text{Tan}\, \pi/6$; (*b*) $\sin[\text{arc Sec}(-2\sqrt{3}/3)]$.

REFERENCES

Books

Allendoerfer, C. B. and C. O. Oakley, *Principles of Mathematics*, New York, McGraw-Hill, 1955. (Chaps. 6, 8, and 9.)

Dubisch, R., *Trigonometry*, New York, Ronald, 1955. (Chaps. 2, 3, 5, and 6.)

Slichter, C. S., *Elementary Analysis*, New York, McGraw-Hill, 1925. (Chaps. 2 and 8.)

American Mathematical Monthly

Cairns, W. D., "Napier's Logarithms as he Developed them," Vol. 35, p. 64 (1928).

Coolidge, J. L., "The Number *e*," Vol. 57, p. 591 (1950).

Huntington, E. V., "An Elementary Theory of the Exponential and Logarithmic Functions," Vol. 23, p. 241 (1916).

Ransom, W. R., "Introducing $e = 2.718+$," Vol. 55, p. 572 (1948).

Vance, E. P., "Teaching Trigonometry," Vol. 54, p. 36 (1947).

6

SOME BASIC PRINCIPLES OF GRAPHING

You boil it in sawdust; you salt it in glue:
You condense it with locusts and tape:
Still keeping one principal object in view—
To preserve its symmetrical shape.

LEWIS CARROLL

6.1 First Theorems on Graphing

A large portion of elementary mathematics is built around the functions introduced in the preceding chapter; their importance cannot be over-emphasized. In this chapter we study some functions and relations which are related in a simple way to those of the basic types already introduced; attention will be paid to their graphs, particularly to the effect on a graph of certain simple changes in its defining equation. There are several elementary results that we shall list as theorems; these will be of great assistance in sketching many graphs. We remind the student that the word "sketch" is used here to indicate a rough, free-hand drawing, with very few points accurately located, but which is neat and shows the characteristics of the graph.

We recall that the locus of an equation in x and y is the set of all points (x, y), such that x and y satisfy the equation. Thus, if we replace x by $-x$ in an equation, each point (a, b) of the original locus will be replaced by the point $(-a, b)$, as illustrated in Figure 6–1. This result is stated as our first theorem.

THEOREM 1 ON GRAPHING. If x is replaced by $-x$ in an equation of a locus, the locus of the resulting equation may be obtained from the original locus as follows: Replace each point (a, b) of the original locus by the point $(-a, b)$.

From a geometric point of view, the points (a, b) and $(-a, b)$ may be considered reflections of each other in the y-axis. Thus the new locus is the *reflection in the y-axis* of the original locus. A similar argument, using the point $(a, -b)$ of Figure 6–1, leads us to the next theorem.

THEOREM 2 ON GRAPHING. If y is replaced by $-y$ in an equation of a locus, the locus of the resulting equation may be obtained from the original locus as follows: Replace each point (a, b) of the original locus by the point $(a, -b)$.

In this case, the new locus may be seen to be the *reflection in the x-axis* of the original locus.

The next result is a combination of the two preceding theorems.

THEOREM 3 ON GRAPHING. If x is replaced by $-x$ *and* y is replaced by $-y$ in an equation of a locus, the locus of the resulting equation may

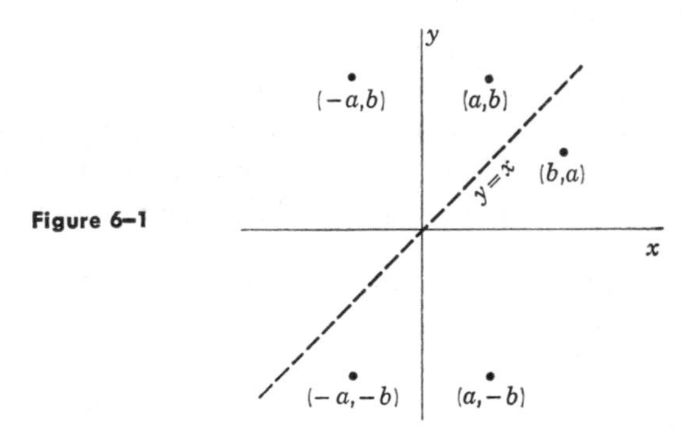

Figure 6–1

be obtained from the original locus as follows: Replace each point (a, b) of the original locus by the point $(-a, -b)$.

If we regard the points (a, b) and $(-a, -b)$ as reflections of each other in the origin, the new locus in this case may be seen to be the *reflection in the origin* of the original locus.

We have noted before, in connection with symmetric functions, that the points (a, b) and (b, a) are reflections of each other in the straight line locus of the equation $y = x$. This leads to our next theorem.

THEOREM 4 ON GRAPHING. If x and y are interchanged in an equation of a locus, the locus of the resulting equation may be obtained from the original locus as follows: Replace each point (a, b) of the original locus by the point (b, a).

We have already noted that the new locus will then be the *reflection* of the original locus *in the straight line locus of the equation* $y = x$.

If we obtain an equivalent equation (i.e., the same numbers x and y will satisfy it) after any of the above substitutions, the locus will evidently be its own reflection in the corresponding line or point and is said to be *symmetric* with respect to this line or point. If an equation contains only even powers of x, an application of Theorem 1 shows that the locus of this equation is symmetric with respect to the y-axis; and an application of Theorem 2 shows that the locus of an equation containing only even powers of y is symmetric with respect to the x-axis.

Since the graph of a relation that is defined by an equation is a portion of the locus of the equation, it will be a simple matter to sketch its graph if we are familiar with the locus of the defining equation. As a matter of fact, the graph of such a relation is the set of points (x, y) of the locus, such that x is in the domain of the relation. It should be observed, however, that the graph of a relation is not necessarily symmetric solely because the locus of its defining equation has this property. This may happen because the "image" of a point of the graph may have an abscissa that is not in the domain of the relation. For example, the locus of the equation $y = x^2$ is symmetric with respect to the y-axis, but the function defined on the interval $[0, 2]$ by the equation $y = x^2$ does not have this characteristic. Similarly, the locus of $y = 1/x$ is symmetric with respect to the diagonal line, but the function defined on the set $[0, 1] - \{0\}$ by the equation $y = 1/x$ does not have this type of symmetry: for instance, the point $(1/2, 2)$ lies on the graph but the point $(2, 1/2)$ does not, since 2 is not in the domain of the function.

It will be recalled from a discussion in Chapter 5 that the relation defined on a given domain by $y^n = x^m$ is not necessarily the same as the function defined on the same domain by $y = x^{m/n}$, with m/n a quotient of integers reduced to lowest terms. However, both equations determine the same *positive* real number y for a *positive* real number x in the given domain, which means that the first quadrant portion of the two graphs will be the same. If the equation $y^n = x^m$ determines an additional number $-y$ for some given x, these two numbers y and $-y$ will still have the same absolute value; thus, the complete graph of the relation defined by $y^n = x^m$ may be obtained from the graph of the function defined by $y = x^{m/n}$, along with a knowledge of the symmetry of the relation.

ILLUSTRATION 1. Graph the relation defined on the interval $[-2, 2]$ by the equation $y^4 = x^5$.

Solution. The equation $y^4 = x^5$ contains only even powers of y and so its locus is symmetric with respect to the x-axis; a relation that is defined on any domain by the same equation will then possess the same kind of symmetry. In the first quadrant, the graph is identical with that of the function defined by $y = x^{5/4}$, as shown in Figure 6–2*a*. A complete graph of the relation is then shown in Figure 6–2*b*.

ILLUSTRATION 2. Graph the relation on the interval $[-1, 2]$, defined by $y^2 = x^4$.

Solution. As the defining equation contains only even powers of both x and y, its locus is symmetric with respect to both the x and y axes. The first quadrant portion of this locus, moreover, is identical with that of the familiar parabola defined by $y = x^2$. The desired graph is then that part of the locus of $y^2 = x^4$, which comprises those points having abscissas in the interval $[-1, 2]$. Notice that this graph, which is illustrated in Figure 6–3, is not symmetric with respect to the y-axis.

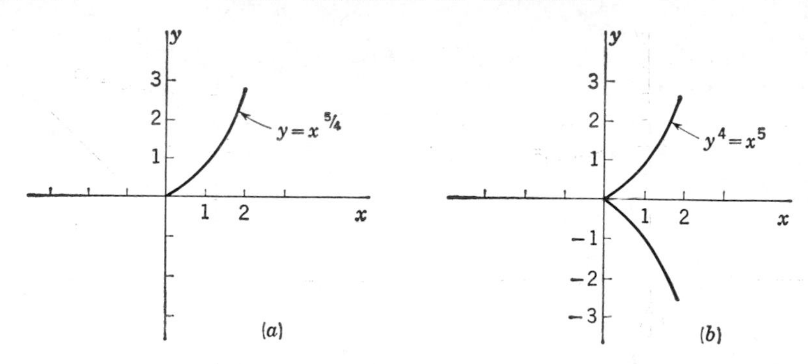

Figure 6–2

ILLUSTRATION 3. Compare graphs of the functions defined on the interval $[-2, 2]$ by the equations $y = e^x$ and $y = -e^x$.

Solution. The equation $y = -e^x$ may be obtained from $y = e^x$ by a replacement of y by $-y$, and so an application of Theorem 2 shows that the locus of the former equation is the reflection in the x-axis of the locus

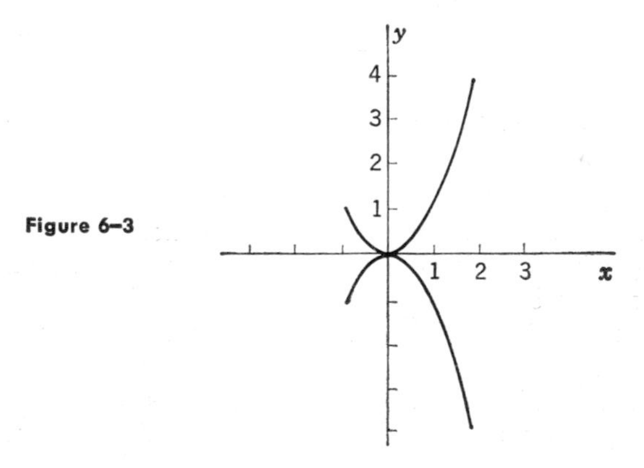

Figure 6–3

of the latter equation. The required graph is then that portion of the locus of $y = -e^x$ which consists of points having abscissas in the interval $[-2, 2]$, as shown in Figure 6–4.

ILLUSTRATION 4. Compare graphs of the functions on the interval $[-2, 2]$, defined by the equations $y = x^3$ and $x = y^3$.

Solution. The second equation is obtained from the first by an interchange of x and y. An application of Theorem 4 then shows that the locus of $x = y^3$ is the reflection of the locus of $y = x^3$ in the diagonal line locus of $y = x$. The portions of these two loci, consisting of points having abscissas in the interval $[-2, 2]$, are the desired graphs, as shown in Figure 6–5.

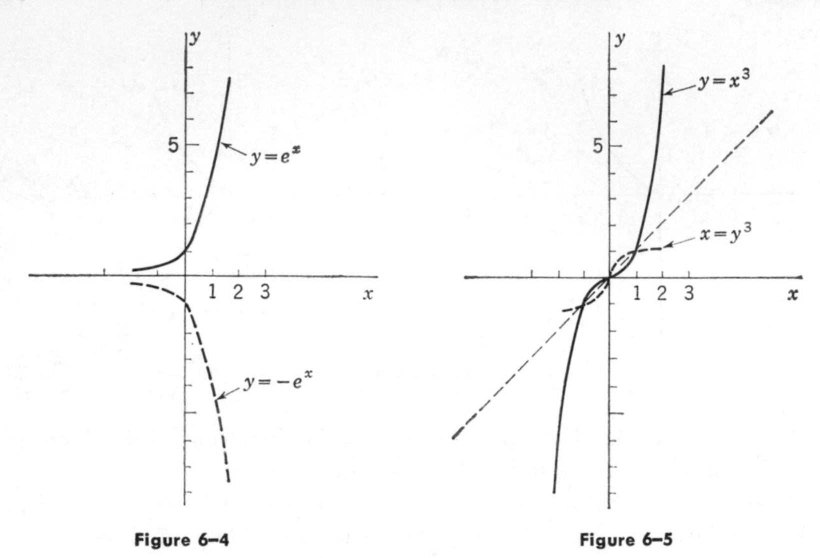

Figure 6–4

Figure 6–5

PROBLEM SET 6.1

1. Discuss the symmetry of the locus of each of the following equations. (*a*) $y^2 = x^5$; (*b*) $y^4 = x^6$; (*c*) $y^3 = x^5$; (*d*) $y^6 = x^8$; (*e*) $y = x^3$; (*f*) $y^3 = x^2$; (*g*) $y^2 = x^2$; (*h*) $y = x^4$. If the locus of an equation possesses a certain type of symmetry, does this also imply that any relation with this defining equation has a graph with this same type of symmetry? Explain.
2. The locus of each of the following equations is replaced by its reflection in the x-axis; write an equation of which this new curve is the locus: (*a*) $y = x^{2/3}$; (*b*) $y^3 = x^2$; (*c*) $y = x^4$; (*d*) $y^4 = x^3$; (*e*) $y = x$.
3. The locus of each of the following equations is replaced by its reflection in the y-axis; write an equation of which this new curve is the locus: (*a*) $y^2 = x$; (*b*) $y^3 = x^2$; (*c*) $y = x^4$; (*d*) $y = 1/x^3$; (*e*) $y^2 = 1/x^5$.
4. The locus of each of the following equations is replaced by its reflection in the diagonal line locus of $y = x$; write an equation of which this new curve is the locus: (*a*) $y = x^2$; (*b*) $y^2 = x^5$; (*c*) $y = x^{2/3}$; (*d*) $y = 1/x^3$; (*e*) $y^4 = 1/x^2$.
5. The locus of each of the following equations is replaced by its reflection in the origin; write an equation of which this new curve is the locus: (*a*) $y = x^2$; (*b*) $y^3 = x^5$; (*c*) $y^3 = 1/x^5$; (*d*) $y = 1/x^4$; (*e*) $y = 1/x^3$.
6. Using separate axes for each pair of functions, sketch graphs of the functions defined separately on the interval $[-3, 3]$ by (*a*) $y = 2^x$, $y = -2^x$; (*b*) $y = x^3$, $y = -x^3$; (*c*) $y = x^{2/3}$, $y = -x^{2/3}$; (*d*) $y = e^x$, $y = e^{-x}$.
7. Using separate axes for each pair of functions, sketch graphs of the functions defined separately on (*a*) $[-\pi/2, \pi/2]$ by $y = \text{Sin}\, x$ and $y = -\text{Sin}\, x$; (*b*) $[0, \pi]$ by $y = \text{Cos}\, x$ and $y = -\text{Cos}\, x$; (*c*) $[-\pi/4, \pi/4]$ by $y = \text{Tan}\, x$ and $y = -\text{Tan}\, x$.

8. Using separate axes for each pair of functions, sketch graphs of the functions defined separately on (*a*) $[0, 3] - \{0\}$ by $y = \ln x$ and $y = -\ln x$; (*b*) $[-3, 3] - \{0\}$ by $y = 1/x^2$ and $y = -1/x^2$; (*c*) $[-3, 3] - \{0\}$ by $y = 1/x^3$ and $y = -1/x^3$; (*d*) $[0, 3] - \{0\}$ by $y = \log_5 x$ and $y = -\log_5 x$; (*e*) $[-1, 1]$ by $y = \text{arc Sin } x$ and $y = -\text{arc Sin } x$.
9. The locus of each of the following equations is replaced by its reflection in the x-axis; write an equation of which this new curve is the locus: (*a*) $y = \text{Sin } x$; (*b*) $y = e^x$; (*c*) $y = \text{arc Cos } x$; (*d*) $y = \ln x$.
10. The locus of each of the following equations is replaced by its reflection in the diagonal line locus of $y = x$; write an equation of which this new curve is the locus: (*a*) $y = e^x$; (*b*) $y = \log_6 x$; (*c*) $y = \text{Sec } x$; (*d*) $y = \text{arc Cos } x$.
11. Sketch the graph of the relation defined on the interval $[0, 2]$ by (*a*) $y^2 = x^5$; (*b*) $y^4 = x^2$; (*c*) $y^4 = x^3$; (*d*) $y^3 = x^4$; (*e*) $y^5 = x^3$.
12. Sketch the graph of the relation defined on $[-2, 2] - \{0\}$ by (*a*) $y = 1/x^2$; (*b*) $y^3 = 1/x^4$; (*c*) $y^4 = 1/x^3$; (*d*) $y^4 = 1/x^6$.
13. Discuss the symmetry of the graph of the relation defined on the interval (*a*) $[-2, 2]$ by $y = x^2$; (*b*) $[0, 2]$ by $y = x^2$; (*c*) $[0, 3]$ by $y^2 = x$; (*d*) $[1, 3]$ by $y^2 = 1/x^2$.

6.2 More Theorems on Graphing

Let us consider, for a moment, the equations $y = x^2$ and $2y = x^2$, where x and y are real numbers. It is clear that $2y$ plays the same role in the second equation as y plays in the first; and so, for any given number x, the number y in the second equation must be just $1/2$ the number y in the first. For example, if $x = 2$, we have $y = 4$ in the first equation and $y = 2$ in the second. Thus, a replacement of y by $2y$ in the equation $y = x^2$ has required the "new" y to be only $1/2$ as large as the "old" y, *for the same number x.* A similar argument will show that a replacement of y by ay, where a is any real number, in any equation involving x and y, will require a number y that satisfies the new equation to be $1/a$ times as large as that which satisfies the original equation, for the *same* x. We may repeat the above argument in the case of a replacement of x by ax, and we state these two results in the form of theorems.

THEOREM 5 ON GRAPHING. If x is replaced by ax in an equation of a locus, the locus of the resulting equation may be obtained from the original locus as follows: Replace each point (x, y) of the original locus by the point $(x/a, y)$.

THEOREM 6 ON GRAPHING. If y is replaced by ay in an equation of a locus, the locus of the resulting equation may be obtained from the original locus as follows: Replace each point (x, y) of the original locus by the point $(x, y/a)$.

The new locus in Theorem 5 is then the set of points displaced in a direction parallel to the x-axis from the original locus, and having abscissas respectively $1/a$ times as large. The new locus in Theorem 6 is likewise the set of points displaced in a direction parallel to the y-axis from the original locus, and having ordinates respectively $1/a$ times as large. It is sometimes convenient to say that we have obtained the new locus by *dividing the abscissas* or *dividing the ordinates* of the original locus; the original locus has then been *stretched* or *compressed*, according as $a < 1$ or $a > 1$.

For some purposes, it is convenient to rephrase the two theorems above in an equivalent form.

THEOREM 5′ ON GRAPHING. If x is replaced by x/a in an equation of a locus, the locus of the resulting equation may be obtained from the original locus as follows: Replace each point (x, y) of the original locus by the point (ax, y).

THEOREM 6′ ON GRAPHING. If y is replaced by y/a in an equation of a locus, the locus of the resulting equation may be obtained from the original locus as follows: Replace each point (x, y) of the original locus by the point (x, ay).

In this case, we say that the abscissas or ordinates of the original locus have been *multiplied* by a; this will be a *stretching* or *compression* of the original locus according as $a > 1$ or $a < 1$.

As a result of the preceding theorems we may compare the graphs of general power functions, exponential functions, logarithmic functions, and circular functions with portions of the graphs of the corresponding basic functions. For the graph of a function defined on its domain by an equation is a portion of the locus of this equation; and the loci of the equations $y = ax^n$, $y = ka^x$, $y = k \log_a x$, $y = a \sin bx$, $y = a \cos bx$, $y = a \tan bx$, $y = a \csc bx$, $y = a \sec bx$, and $y = a \cot bx$ may now be compared with the corresponding basic loci, with the help of the above theorems.

ILLUSTRATION 1. Compare verbally and then sketch, using a single pair of axes, the functions on the interval $[-2, 2]$, defined by the equations: $y = x^2$; $y = 4x^2$; $2y = x^2$.

Solution. The function on $[-2, 2]$, defined by the equation $y = x^2$, is familiar from Chapter 5, its graph consisting of a portion of the basic parabola. The equation $y = 4x^2$ may be obtained from $y = x^2$, however, by a replacement of x by $2x$, and Theorem 5 now states that we may obtain the locus of $y = 4x^2$ by dividing the abscissas of all the points of the locus of $y = x^2$ by 2. It may be observed that the equation $y = 4x^2$ may also be obtained from $y = x^2$ by a replacement of y by $y/4$; and so the new locus may be obtained from the old by multiplying the ordinates of the original locus by 4. We may use whichever method we please to obtain the desired locus. Finally, the equation $2y = x^2$ may be most easily obtained from $y = x^2$ by a replacement of y by $2y$; and, according to Theorem 6, the locus of $2y = x^2$ may then be obtained from the locus of $y = x^2$ by dividing the ordinates of the latter locus by 2. The graphs of the desired functions are the portions of the loci of $y = x^2$, $y = 4x^2$, and $2y = x^2$, having points with abscissas in the interval $[-2, 2]$, as shown in Figure 6–6.

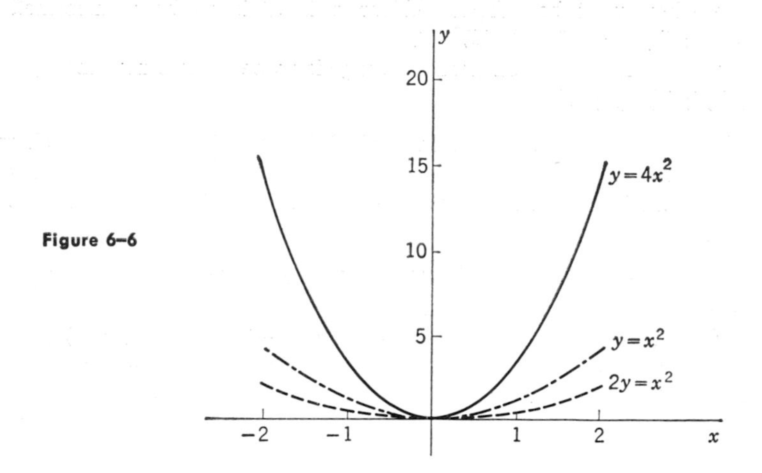

Figure 6–6

ILLUSTRATION 2. Compare verbally and then sketch, using a single pair of axes, the graphs of the functions on the interval $[-2\pi, 2\pi]$ defined by the equations $y = \sin x$ and $y = 3 \sin 2x$.

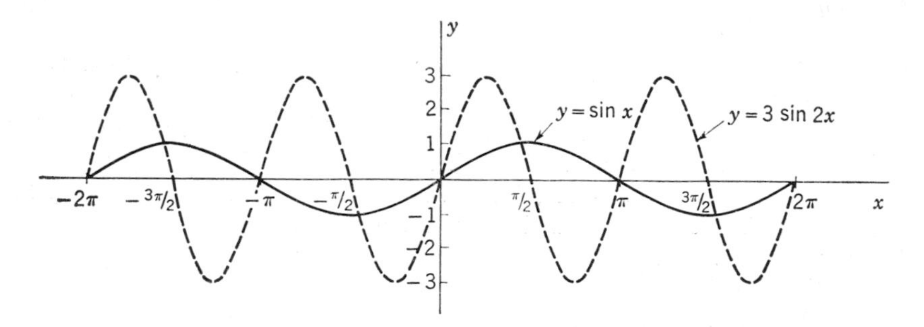

Figure 6–7

Solution. The function on $[-2\pi, 2\pi]$, defined by the equation $y = \sin x$, is familiar, and its graph is a portion of the graph of the basic sine function. However, the equation $y = 3 \sin 2x$ may be obtained from $y = \sin x$ by a replacement of y by $y/3$ and x by $2x$. This means that the locus of $y = 3 \sin 2x$ may be obtained from the locus of $y = \sin x$ by multiplying the ordinates by 3 and dividing the abscissas by 2. The desired graph is then that portion of this locus which has points with abscissas in the interval $[-2\pi, 2\pi]$, as shown in Figure 6–7.

PROBLEM SET 6.2

1. State what must be substituted for x if x^2 is to be transformed into (*a*) $4x^2$; (*b*) $3x^2$; (*c*) $9x^2$; (*d*) $2x^2$.

2. State what must be substituted for y if y^3 is to be transformed into (*a*) $27y^3$; (*b*) $9y^3$; (*c*) $4y^3$; (*d*) $8y^3$.

In Problems 3 through 9 compare the loci of the equations listed in each group, and sketch graphs of the functions defined separately by these equations on a convenient domain of real numbers; use a single pair of axes for each group of equations.

3. (*a*) $y = x^2$, $y = 4x^2$, $3y = x^2$; (*b*) $y = 1/x$, $y = 2/x$, $2y = 1/x$; (*c*) $y = x^{3/2}$, $y = -x^{3/2}$; (*d*) $y = x^{1/3}$, $x = y^{1/3}$.

4. (*a*) $y = e^x$, $y = e^{2x}$, $3y = e^x$; (*b*) $y = 2^x$, $y = -2^{4x}$, $y/3 = 2^x$; (*c*) $y = \sin x$, $y = \sin 2x$, $3y = \sin x$; (*d*) $y = \cos x$, $y = \cos x/2$, $4y = -\cos x$.

5. (*a*) $y = \ln x$, $y = \ln 3x$, $4y = -\ln x$; (*b*) $y = \log x$, $y = -\log x/2$, $6y = \log x$; (*c*) $y = \log_4 x$, $y = -\log_4 3x$, $3y = \log_4 3x$; (*d*) $y = \tan x$, $y = \tan 2x$, $y = \tan x/2$.

6. (*a*) $y = \text{Sin}\, x$, $x = \text{Sin}\, y$, $y = -\text{Sin}\, x$; (*b*) $y = \text{arc Sin}\, x$, $y = \text{arc Sin}\, x/2$, $y = \text{arc Sin}\, 3x$; (*c*) $y = \text{arc Tan}\, x$, $2y = \text{arc Tan}\, x$, $y = \text{arc Tan}\, 3x$; (*d*) $y = e^x$, $y = -e^{3x}$, $2y = -e^{3x}$.

7. (*a*) $y^2 = x^3$, $y^2 = 8x^3$, $2y^2 = x^3$; (*b*) $y^3 = x$, $y^3 = -2x$, $4y^3 = 3x$; (*c*) $y^2 = x$, $y^2 = 6x$, $4y^2 = x$; (*d*) $y^3 = x^2$, $4y^3 = 9x^2$, $y^3 = -2x^2$.

8. (*a*) $y = x$, $y = 3x$, $y = 10x$; (*b*) $y = x$, $3y = x$, $6y = x$; (*c*) $y = x$, $y = -2x$, $4y = -x$; (*d*) $y = x$, $y = -x$, $3y = 2x$.

9. (*a*) $y^2 = x^4$, $y^2 = 16x^4$, $y^2 = 9x^4$; (*b*) $y = 1/x^3$, $y = 2/x^3$, $3y = 1/x^3$; (*c*) $y = 1/x^2$, $y = 3/x^2$, $y = 1/(4x^2)$; (*d*) $y^3 = x^5$, $y^3 = 32x^5$, $8y^3 = x^5$.

10. Give an equation of the resulting locus, obtained from the locus of $y = 1/x^2$ by the following procedure: (*a*) divide abscissas by 2; (*b*) multiply ordinates by 4; (*c*) reflect in the x-axis; (*d*) divide abscissas by 2 and ordinates by 3; (*e*) reflect in the diagonal line locus of the equation $y = x$.

11. Use the directions of Problem 10 for the equation $y = \text{Sin}\, x$.

12. Use the directions of Problem 10 for the equation $y^4 = x^5$.

13. Use the directions of Problem 10 for the equation $y = e^x$.

6.3 Additional Theorems on Graphing

The theorems of the preceding section enable us to sketch the graph of any power, exponential, logarithmic, or circular function, as well as many other relations which are closely associated with these. In the present section we consider another class of relations which have graphs that are similar to those already studied; these graphs will involve a characteristic known as *translation*. For example, let us consider the loci of the equations $y = e^x$ and $y = e^{x-2}$. For a given y, it is evident that $x - 2$ in the second equation must equal x in the first, and this in turn implies that the x in the second equation must be *larger by 2* than the x of the first equation. This result may be generalized to give us the following theorem.

THEOREM 7 ON GRAPHING. If x is replaced by $x - a$ in an equation of a locus, the locus of the resulting equation may be obtained from the original locus as follows: Replace each point (x, y) of the original locus by the point $(x + a, y)$. A similar argument with respect to y gives a similar result.

THEOREM 8 ON GRAPHING. If y is replaced by $y - a$ in an equation of a locus, the locus of the resulting equation may be obtained from the original locus as follows: Replace each point (x, y) of the original locus by the point $(x, y + a)$.

The new locus of Theorem 7 is then the set of points displaced a units from those of the original locus in a direction parallel to the x-axis. In a similar way we may see that the new locus in Theorem 8 is the set of points displaced a units from those of the original locus in a direction parallel to the y-axis. Whether $x + a$ (or $y + a$) is actually larger or smaller than x (or y) depends on whether a is positive or negative. In any case, it is convenient to consider the new locus as having been obtained from the original locus by a process of *translation;* this translation will be parallel to the x-axis if Theorem 7 is used, and parallel to the y-axis if Theorem 8 is used.

We have implied that the number a in Theorems 7 and 8 may be either positive or negative, but it is sometimes desirable to have the following alternate statements of these theorems.

THEOREM 7′ ON GRAPHING. If x is replaced by $x + a$ in an equation of a locus, the locus of the resulting equation may be obtained from the original locus as follows: Replace each point (x, y) of the original locus by the point $(x - a, y)$.

THEOREM 8′ ON GRAPHING. If y is replaced by $y + a$ in an equation of a locus, the locus of the resulting equation may be obtained from the original locus as follows: Replace each point (x, y) of the original locus by the point $(x, y - a)$.

It now appears, as a result of these theorems, that if we can sketch the locus of a given equation in x and y, we can also sketch any relation defined by an equation obtainable from this equation by a substitution of any of the types discussed in the theorems. Thus, we have greatly enlarged our collection of elementary relations, which have graphs that can be readily sketched.

ILLUSTRATION 1. Compare verbally and graph the functions on the interval $[-2, 2]$, defined by the equations $y = e^x$ and $y = e^{x-2}$.

Solution. We have already noted that the locus of $y = e^{x-2}$ is the set of points translated 2 units in the positive direction of the x-axis from the points of the locus of $y = e^x$, the graph of one of the basic exponential functions. The portions of these two loci, having points with abscissas in the interval $[-2, 2]$, give us the desired graphs, as shown in Figure 6–8.

ILLUSTRATION 2. Compare verbally and graph the functions in the interval $[0, 3]$ defined by (*a*) $y = \ln x$; (*b*) $y = \ln 2x$; (*c*) $y = \ln 2(x - 1)$.

Solution. The locus of the equation in (*a*) is the graph of the basic natural logarithmic function, discussed in Chapter 5. The equation in (*b*) may be obtained from the equation in (*a*) by a replacement of x by $2x$; and

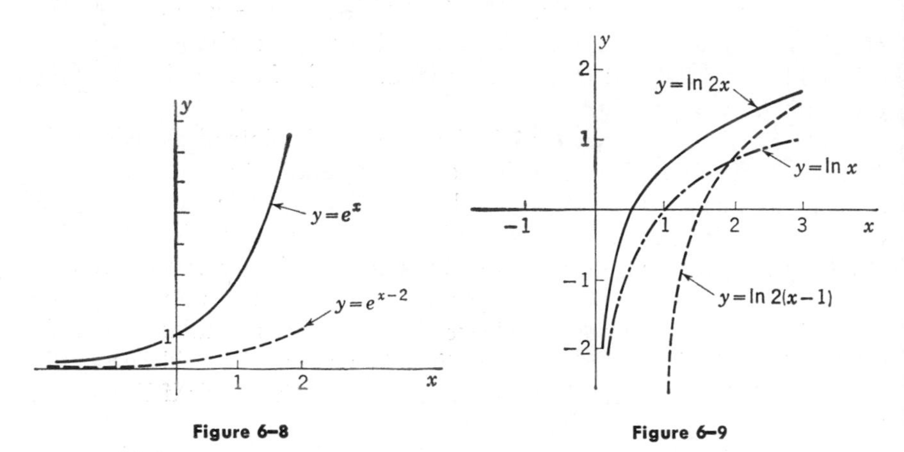

Figure 6–8

Figure 6–9

so Theorem 5 on Graphing tells us that the locus of the equation in (*b*) is the result of dividing the abscissas of the points of the locus of (*a*) by 2. We may now obtain the equation in (*c*) from that in (*b*) by replacing x in the latter equation by $x - 1$; and Theorem 7 on Graphing tells us that the locus of the equation in (*c*) is then the set of points that are translated 1 unit in the positive direction of the x-axis from the points of the locus of the equation in (*b*). The portions of these loci having points with abscissas in the interval $[0, 3]$ constitute the desired graphs, and are shown in Figure 6–9.

Note. The order in which the replacements of the theorems on graphing are made is very important. For example, referring to Illustration 2, if we had replaced x in $y = \ln x$ *first* by $x - 1$ and *then* replaced x by $2x$, the resulting equation would have been $y = \ln (2x - 1)$, which is different from the result in (*c*) of the illustration.

PROBLEM SET 6.3

In Problems 1 through 4 compare the loci of the equations given in each group, and sketch graphs of the functions or relations defined separately by these equations on a convenient domain of real numbers; use a single pair of axes for each group of equations.

1. (*a*) $y = x$, $y = 2x$, $y = 2(x - 1)$; (*b*) $y = x^2$, $y = 2x^2$, $y = 2(x - 2)^2$; (*c*) $y = x^3$, $2y = x^3$, $2y = (x - 3)^3$; (*d*) $y = e^x$, $3y = e^x$, $3y = e^{x-2}$; (*e*) $y = \ln x$, $y = 2 \ln x$, $y = 2 \ln (x - 2)$; (*f*) $y = x$, $y + 5 = x$, $y + 5 = 2x$.
2. (*a*) $y = \sin x$, $y = 3 \sin x$, $y + 2 = 3 \sin x$; (*b*) $y = \text{Tan}\, x$, $y + 2 = \text{Tan}\, x$, $y + 2 = \text{Tan}\, x/2$; (*c*) $y = 3^x$, $y = 3^{4x}$, $y + 1 = 3^{4x}$.
3. (*a*) $y = x^2$, $y = 4x^2$, $y - 4 = 4(x + 2)^2$; (*b*) $y = e^x$, $y = e^{x/2}$, $y + 2 = e^{x/2}$; (*c*) $y = x$, $y = 3x$, $y + 4 = 3(x - 2)$.
4. (*a*) $y = 1/x$, $y = 4/x$, $y + 1 = 4/(x - 2)$; (*b*) $y^2 = x^3$, $x^2 = y^3$, $(x - 1)^2 = (y + 2)^3$; (*c*) $y^2 = 1/x^3$, $y = 2/x^{3/2}$, $y = 2/(x = 2)^{3/2}$; (*d*) $y = x^{3/2}$, $y = 2x^{3/2}$, $y = 2(x - 2)^{3/2}$.
5. Write an equation of the locus of points related to the locus of the equation $y = 2x^3$ in the following way: (*a*) translated 2 units in the positive x direction; (*b*) translated 4 units in the negative y direction; (*c*) ordinates multiplied by 3; (*d*) abscissas divided by 2.
6. Write an equation of the locus of points related to the locus of the equation $y = \cos x$ in the following way: (*a*) translated 3 units in the negative x direction; (*b*) translated 2 units in the negative y direction; (*c*) ordinates divided by 4; (*d*) abscissas multiplied by 3.
7. Write an equation of the locus of points, described as the reflection in the x-axis of the locus of the equation $y = e^x$; write an equation of the locus resulting when the abscissas of the "reflected" locus are multiplied by 2; write an equation of the locus consisting of the points displaced 2 units in the positive direction of x from those of the "stretched" locus.
8. Write an equation of the locus of points resulting when the order of the procedure in Problem 7 is reversed.
9. The equations $y = \ln 2(x - 1)$ and $y = \ln (2x - 2)$ are equivalent. Use two different methods to compare the locus of these equations with the locus of $y = \ln x$.
10. Use two different methods to compare the locus of the equation $y = e^{2x-1}$ with the locus of $y = e^x$.

6.4 Some Useful Devices for Sketching

In most—though not all—of our sketches so far, we have used the same unit of length for both the x and y axes, the actual graphical picture thereby presenting a true portrayal of how the ordinates of points on the curve change with respect to the abscissas. As far as the graphical representation of a relation is concerned, it makes no theoretical difference whether the two units agree or not. But for practical reasons of reading a graph, it is sometimes desirable to have the "apparent" slope of the curve differ from ± 1 by as little as possible; and for this reason or for reasons of economy of space, it is often desirable to make the units of the two axes different. We can not, of course, change the actual slope of a curve, since this is fixed by the defining equation; it is only the "apparent" or "visual" slope which we are able to adjust by a change of units. This is illustrated in Figure 6–10, where we have sketched two graphs of the function defined on the interval $[-2, 2]$ by $y = x^4$.

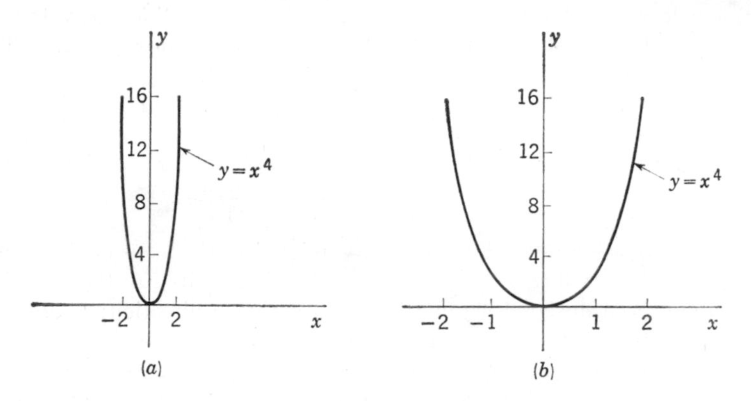

Figure 6–10

We have seen previously that the locus of the equation $y = 4x^2$ can be obtained from the locus of $y = x^2$, by multiplying the ordinates of all points of the latter locus by 4. However, this procedure of "stretching" the ordinates in the ratio 1:4 need not actually be carried out. For if we change the unit of the y-axis so that the scale reading of 4 occurs where the reading of 1 formerly occurred, the original graph of a function defined by $y = x^2$ may now be identified with the graph of the function defined on the same domain by $y = 4x^2$. The procedure of "stretching" the ordinates or abscissas of a locus may then be accomplished by the artifice of changing the units on the axes. But it must be emphasized that such a graph must be viewed with special attention paid to the scales, since the visual picture may otherwise be misleading. In Figure 6–11, we have sketched graphs for the functions defined on the interval $[-2, 2]$ by the equations $y = x^2$ and $y = 4x^2$; the same set of points represents both functions, the larger unit being assumed for the function defined by $y = x^2$.

It is also possible to eliminate the actual construction of a new graph, described as the set of points displaced a given distance parallel to either axis from some basic set, by merely choosing a new x or y axis. This is frequently much simpler than making a new drawing. Suppose, for example, that we wish a graph of the function defined on $[-2, 4] - \{1\}$ by the equation $y = 1/(x - 1)$. This equation may be obtained from the equation $y = 1/x$ by a replacement of x by $x - 1$; and so the locus of $y = 1/(x - 1)$ may be described as the set of points displaced 1 unit from those of the basic equilateral hyperbola in the positive direction of the

x-axis. However, if we replace the y-axis by a new parallel axis displaced 1 unit in the negative direction of the x-axis, the points comprising the basic equilateral hyperbola will now represent the locus of the given equation, with an appropriate relabeling of the x-axis. The desired graph is then the set of points of this locus which have abscissas in the given domain, as shown in Figure 6–12. It thus appears that the same set of points may

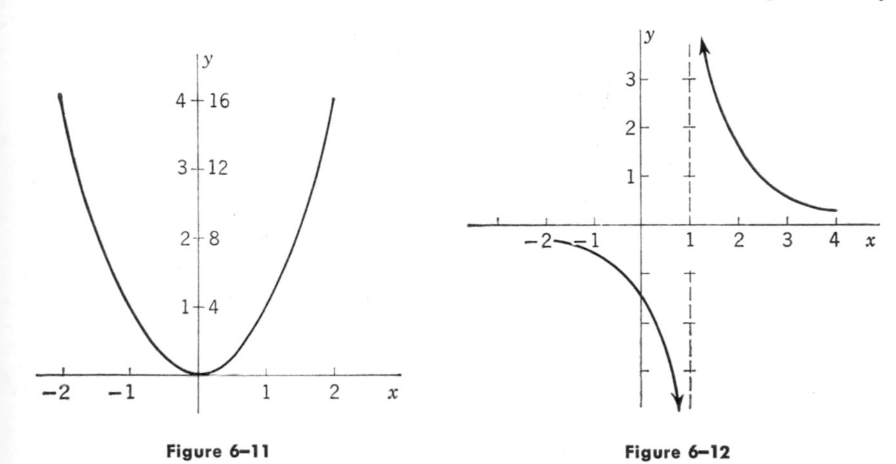

Figure 6–11

Figure 6–12

represent many different relations defined by equations, by merely changing the scale readings and by choosing new lines for axes. However, if we wish to keep the original graph for purposes of comparison, it is clear that these devices may not be used.

ILLUSTRATION 1. Graph the function defined on the interval $[-1, 5]$ by the equation $y + 4 = 2(x - 2)^2$.

Solution. The basic locus involved here is the familiar parabola, defined by $y = x^2$, while the locus of $y + 4 = 2(x - 2)^2$ may be obtained from this basic locus as follows:

1. Construct an intermediate locus by multiplying the ordinates of all points of the basic locus by 2.
2. Construct the desired locus as the set of points displaced 2 units in the *positive* direction of x and 4 units in the *negative* direction of y from those of the intermediate locus.

In view of the discussion of this section, however, the original basic parabola will represent the locus of $y + 4 = 2(x - 2)^2$ if we make the following changes:

1. Multiply each reading on the y-axis by 2.
2. Replace the y-axis by a new parallel axis displaced 2 units in the *negative* direction of x, with a corresponding relabeling of the x-axis.

3. Replace the x-axis by a new parallel axis displaced 4 units in the *positive* direction of y, with a corresponding relabeling of the y-axis.

The parabola, defined as the locus of the given equation, is now seen to have its vertex at the point $(2, -4)$, with reference to the final axes. The

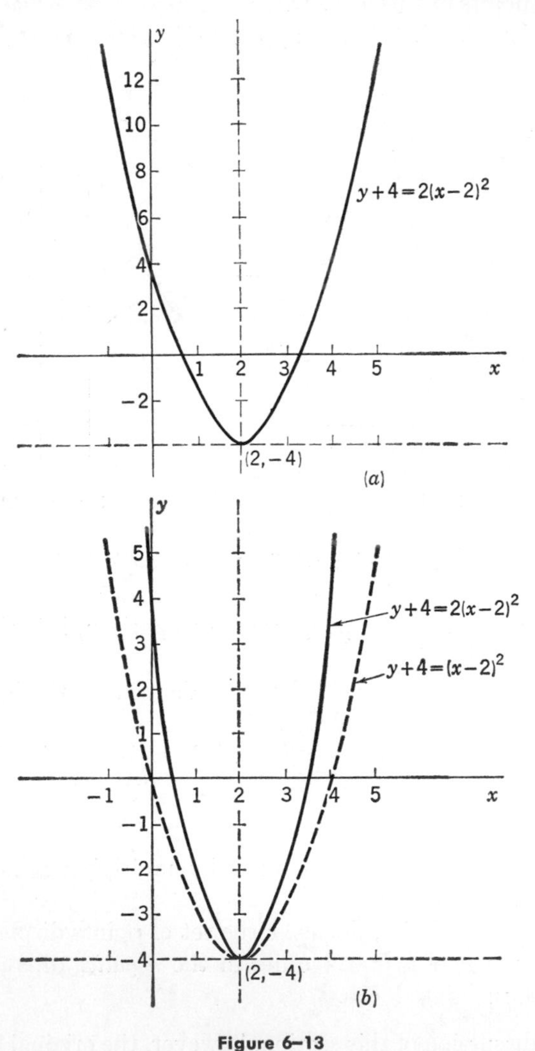

Figure 6–13

desired graph is that portion of the parabola which consists of those points that have abscissas, with reference to the final axes, in the interval $[-1, 5]$, as shown in Figure 6–13a. In Figure 6–13b, we have shown a graph of the same function, without any change of scale on the original graph; a part of the basic parabola is included here.

An expression $x^2 + bx$ can always be transformed into the square of a binomial by adding the square of half the coefficient of x, the new expression being $(x + b/2)^2$. We can use this device to show how the locus of an equation of the form $y = ax^2 + bx + c$, where a, b, and c are arbitrary numbers, may be constructed from a comparison with the locus of $y = x^2$. The following illustration shows the procedure for graphing a function defined by such an equation, a so-called *quadratic* function.

ILLUSTRATION 2. Sketch a graph of the function defined on the interval $[-2, 1]$ by the equation $y = 2x^2 + 3x - 1$.

Solution. We first use the above device for "completing the square" in order to put the equation in the desired form, as indicated by the following sequence of steps:

$$\begin{aligned} y &= 2x^2 + 3x - 1 = 2[x^2 + (3/2)x] - 1 \\ &= 2[x^2 + (3/2)x + 9/16 - 9/16] - 1 \\ &= 2[x^2 + (3/2)x + 9/16] - 9/8 - 1 = 2(x + 3/4)^2 - 17/8 \end{aligned}$$

and so

$$y + 17/8 = 2(x + 3/4)^2.$$

A comparison of this equation with $y = x^2$ shows that we can obtain the locus of the given equation from the basic parabola as follows:

1. Construct an intermediate graph by multiplying the ordinates of all points of the basic parabola by 2.
2. Construct the locus of the given equation as the set of points displaced $3/4$ of a unit in the negative direction of x and $17/8$ units in the negative direction of y from those of the intermediate locus.

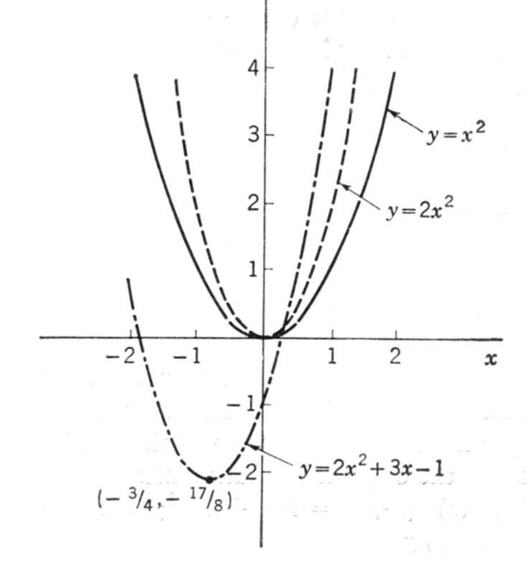

Figure 6–14

The desired graph consists of those points of this locus which have abscissas in the interval $[-2, 1]$, as shown in Figure 6–14. In this illustration we have not changed any scale readings nor replaced either of the axes, but have included a portion of the basic parabola for comparison purposes.

PROBLEM SET 6.4

1. Make on cardboard a careful graph of the parabolic function defined on the interval $[-2, 2]$ by $y = x^2$, using the same unit for both axes. Cut out a section of the cardboard, following the contour of the curve, to be used for tracing purposes.
2. Choose six pairs of axes, with the same unit for the x-axis as was used in Problem 1. Select a proper unit for the y-axis so that the cardboard "parabola" of that problem may be used to construct the graph of the function defined on the interval $[-2, 2]$ by (*a*) $y = 3x^2$; (*b*) $y = x^2/2$; (*c*) $y = 10x^2$; (*d*) $y = -4x^2$; (*e*) $y = -3x^2/4$; (*f*) $y = -x^2/2$.
3. Use the cardboard "parabola" of Problem 1 to construct the graph of the relation defined on some interval containing the origin by (*a*) $x = y^2$; (*b*) $x = 4y^2$; (*c*) $x = y^2/2$; (*d*) $x = -3y^2$; (*e*) $x = -2y^2$; (*f*) $x = -10y^2$.
4. Each of the equations that follow defines a function on some maximal subset of an interval containing the origin; use a pair of axes with a common unit, and graph each function without any replacement of either axis. (*a*) $y = 3(x - 2)^2$; (*b*) $y = 3e^{x+1}$; (*c*) $y = \sec (2x + 1)$; (*d*) $2y = \ln (x + 2)$; (*e*) $y = 2 \sin 2x$; (*f*) $y = 2 \cot (x + 2)$.
5. Each of the equations that follow defines a function on some maximal subset of a convenient interval containing the origin; sketch a graph of each of these functions, making a replacement of at least one of the axes in each case. (*a*) $y = 3 \cos 2x + 4$; (*b*) $y = 2e^{x-2}$; (*c*) $y + 1 = 3e^{x+2}$; (*d*) $2y = \ln (x + 5)$; (*e*) $y = e^{2x+1}$; (*f*) $y + 2 = 3(x - 4)^3$.
6. Determine the vertex of each of the parabolas, defined as the loci of the following equations, and sketch the graph of the relation defined on a convenient interval containing the origin by each equation: (*a*) $y = 3x^2 - x + 1$; (*b*) $y = -3x^2 + 6x + 2$; (*c*) $y = 6x^2 + 4x + 3$; (*d*) $x = 2y^2 - y + 1$; (*e*) $x = -3y^2 + 2y + 6$; (*f*) $x = 2y^2 + 4y + 10$.
7. Sketch the graph of the function defined on a maximal subset of $[-3, 3]$ by each of the following equations; axes may be replaced, but do not change the units adopted originally. (*a*) $y = 3/(x + 1)$; (*b*) $y + 2 = 2/(x - 2)$; (*c*) $y + 1 = 3/x^2$; (*d*) $y - 1 = 3/(x + 1)^3$; (*e*) $y + 4 = 2/(x + 2)^4$; (*f*) $(x + 2)(y - 2) = 3$.
8. Sketch the graph of the function defined on a maximal subset of some convenient interval containing the origin by each of the equations that follow; include graphical sketches of the basic and intermediate function in each case, keeping the original axes and units. (*a*) $y = 2(x - 2)^{3/2}$; (*b*) $y + 1 = 3(x + 1)^3$; (*c*) $y + 4 = 2(x + 1)^{1/2}$; (*d*) $y - 2 = 3e^{x-1}$; (*e*) $y + 3 = 2 \ln (x - 3)$; (*f*) $y = 3 \tan (x - \pi/4)$.

6.5 The Straight Line

We have previously observed that the locus of the equation $y = x$ is the straight line that bisects the first and third quadrants of a Cartesian graph. This line may be described as the set of points such that the abscissa of each point is equal to its ordinate. An application of Theorem 6′ on Graphing shows that the set of points, obtained from this locus by multiplying the ordinate of each of its points by m, is the locus of the equation $y/m = x$, i.e., $y = mx$. Since this new locus may be obtained by merely multiplying the original scale readings on the y-axis by m, it is evident that it is also a straight line. However, it is instructive to give a different proof.

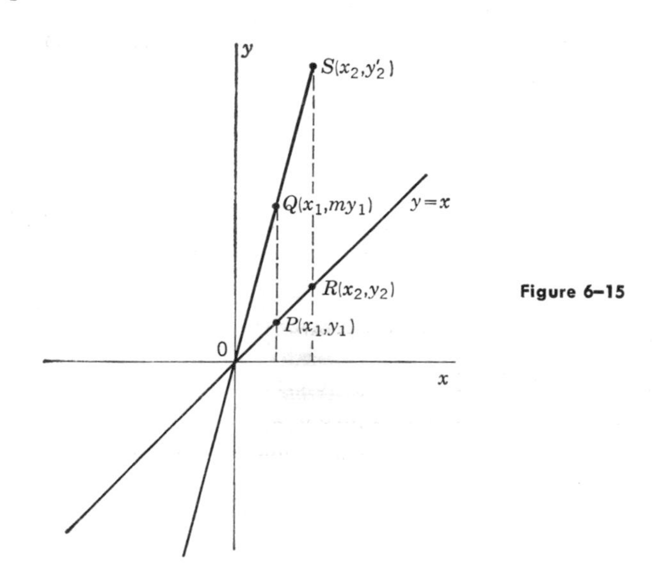

Figure 6–15

Referring to Figure 6–15, let $P(x_1, y_1)$ be an arbitrary point on the locus of $y = x$, with $Q(x_1, my_1)$ the corresponding point after all the ordinates have been multiplied by m. Let $R(x_2, y_2)$ be any other point on the locus of $y = x$ and let $S(x_2, y_2')$ be that point, on the line joining Q with the origin O, having the same abscissa as R. From a consideration of similar triangles, we then have $y_2'/y_2 = my_1/y_1 = m$, i.e., $y_2' = my_2$. Thus, S is the point corresponding to R, after the multiplication of ordinates, and since R was an arbitrary point on the locus of $y = x$, the *line* through O and Q is the locus of $y = mx$.

We have defined the slope of a straight line as the quotient of the difference in ordinates divided by the corresponding difference in abscissas of any two points of the line. The locus of the equation $y = x$ was seen to be a line with slope 1. If we select the origin (0, 0) and any other point (x_1, mx_1) on the line having the equation $y = mx$, the difference in ordinates is mx_1, while the corresponding difference in abscissas is x_1. The slope of the line is then m, and we have the following result:

> An equation of the straight line through the origin with slope m is $y = mx$.

The straight line, consisting of the points of the locus of $y = mx$ displaced b units in the positive direction of the y-axis, will intercept the

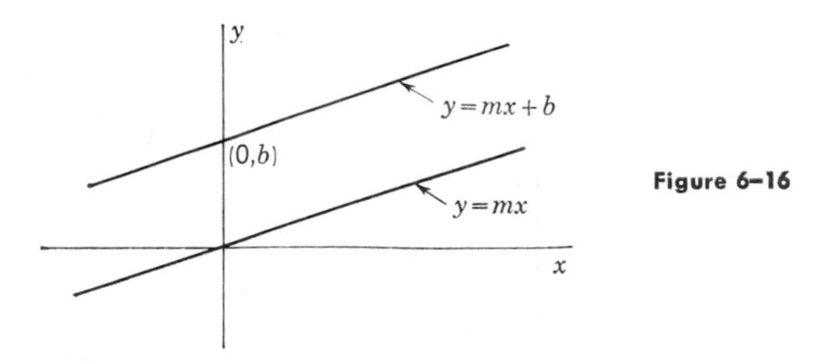

Figure 6–16

y-axis at the point $(0, b)$. If we designate b the *y-intercept* of the line, Theorem 8 on Graphing gives us the next result:

> An equation of the straight line with slope m and y-intercept b is $y - b = mx$ or $y = mx + b$.

The above equation is usually referred to as the "slope-y-intercept" equation of a straight line. In Figure 6–16 we have shown portions of the loci of the equations $y = mx$ and $y = mx + b$, for assumed numbers m and b.

The equation $y = mx + b$ is clearly a special case of the most general equation of the first degree in x and y, which we may write as $Ax + By + C = 0$. However, if $B \neq 0$, we can solve this equation for y in terms of x and obtain $y = (-A/B)x - C/B$, which has the form of $y = mx + b$ with $m = -A/B$ and $b = -C/B$; if $B = 0$, the general equation reduces to $Ax + C = 0$ or $x = -C/A$, where we may assume that $A \neq 0$, and the locus of this equation is clearly a straight line parallel to the y-axis. We have thus proved the validity of the following statement:

> The equation $Ax + By + C = 0$ is an equation of a straight line, provided not both A and B are 0.

This general equation is frequently called the *general linear equation.* The graph of a function, defined by a *linear equation* in x and y, is a subset of points of a straight line; however, we are not designating such a *function* as *linear* unless the term independent of x and y, i.e., C, is 0.

Suppose we wish to obtain an equation of the straight line with slope m, containing the point (x_1, y_1) as shown in Figure 6–17. The line through the origin with slope m has the equation $y = mx$; and the line in question is clearly the set of points displaced x_1 units in the positive direction of the x-axis and y_1 units in the positive direction of the y-axis from this other line. An application of Theorems 7 and 8 then gives us $y - y_1 = m(x - x_1)$ as an equation of the given line.

> An equation of the straight line with slope m containing the point (x_1, y_1) is $y - y_1 = m(x - x_1)$.

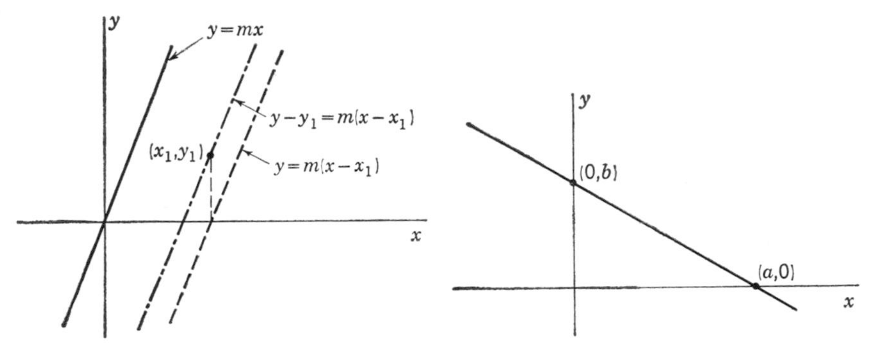

Figure 6–17

Figure 6–18

The above equation may be referred to as the "point-slope" equation of a straight line. Let us now suppose that the x-intercept of a line is a while its y-intercept is b, as shown in Figure 6–18. The slope of this line is seen to be $-b/a$ and, since it contains the point $(a, 0)$, its "point-slope" equation is $y - 0 = (-b/a)(x - a)$, which in turn may be written as $x/a + y/b = 1$.

> An equation of the straight line with x-intercept a and y-intercept b is $x/a + y/b = 1$.

This is called the "intercept" equation of a straight line.

ILLUSTRATION 1. The locus of the equation $2x - 3y + 5 = 0$ is a straight line. If we put the equation in the "slope- y-intercept" form we obtain $y = (2/3)x + 5/3$, and deduce that the slope of the line is 2/3 and its y-intercept is 5/3. If we put the same equation in the "intercept" form, we obtain $x/(-5/2) + y/(5/3) = 1$, and so the x-intercept is $-5/2$, while we again obtain 5/3 as the y-intercept. A sketch of a portion of this line in shown in Figure 6–19.

ILLUSTRATION 2. Determine an equation of the straight line which (a) has slope -2 and contains the point $(-1, 3)$; (b) contains the points $(1, 5)$ and $(-2, 4)$; (c) has x-intercept 4 and y-intercept -2.

Solution.

(*a*) We use the "point-slope" form directly to obtain an equation of this line. Thus, $m = -2$, $x_1 = -1$, and $y_1 = 3$, from which we obtain: $y - 3 = -2(x + 1) = -2x - 2$ or $2x + y - 1 = 0$.

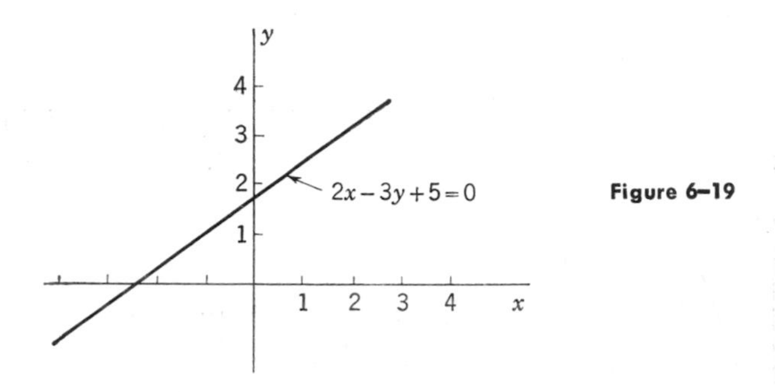

Figure 6–19

(*b*) We must first determine the slope of the line, and this is easily seen to be 1/3. If we now use the "point-slope" form with $m = 1/3$ and $x_1 = 1$, $y_1 = 5$, we obtain $y - 5 = (1/3)(x - 1)$, which becomes on simplification $x - 3y + 14 = 0$.

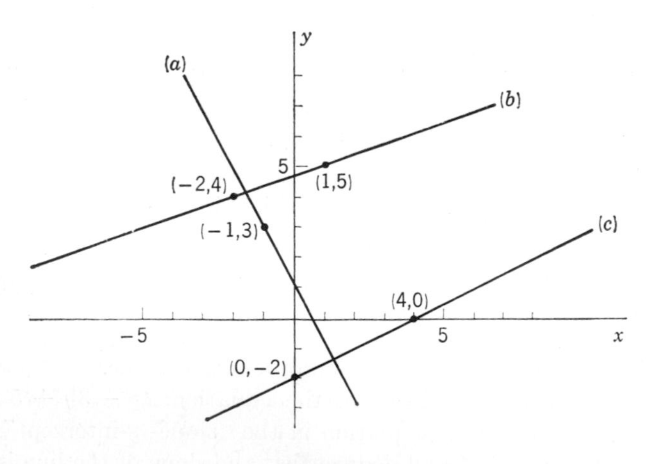

Figure 6–20

(*c*) In this case we may use the "intercept" form directly, with $a = 4$ and $b = -2$. The result is $x/4 + y/(-2) = 1$, which simplifies into $x - 2y - 4 = 0$.

In Figure 6–20, we have sketched portions of these straight lines.

PROBLEM SET 6.5

1. Use one pair of axes to sketch portions of the straight lines having the equations: (*a*) $y = x$; (*b*) $y = 2x$; (*c*) $y = 4x$; (*d*) $y = x/2$; (*e*) $y = 2x/3$; (*f*) $y = -3x$.
2. Use a single pair of axes to sketch portions of the straight lines having the equations: (*a*) $y = 2x + 3$; (*b*) $y = 2x + 5$; (*c*) $y = 2x - 1$; (*d*) $y = 2x - 2$.
3. Use a single pair of axes to sketch portions of the straight lines having the equations: (*a*) $x = 3$; (*b*) $x = -2$; (*c*) $x = -3$; (*d*) $y = 0$; (*e*) $x = 0$; (*f*) $y = 2$; (*g*) $y = -3$; (*h*) $y = 3$.
4. Determine the slope and y-intercept of each of the lines having the equations that follow, and sketch a portion of each line: (*a*) $y = x - 2$; (*b*) $y = 3x/2 + 2$; (*c*) $y = -x/2 + 2/3$; (*d*) $y = 4x - 2$.
5. Determine the x and y intercepts of each of the lines having the given equations, and sketch a portion of each line. (*a*) $x/2 - y/3 = 1$; (*b*) $x/5 + y/2 = 1$; (*c*) $2x/3 - 3y/4 = 1$; (*d*) $3x/5 + 2y/3 = 1$.
6. Put each of these equations in the form $y = mx + b$, and state the slope and y-intercept of each associated straight line. (*a*) $2x - 3y + 2 = 0$; (*b*) $4x + 2y - 5 = 0$; (*c*) $6x + 3y - 4 = 0$; (*d*) $3x - 7y + 2 = 0$.
7. Put each of the equations of Problem 6 in the "intercept" form, and state the x and y intercepts of each associated line.
8. Determine the equation of the straight line which (*a*) contains the points $(-2, 6)$ and $(5, -2)$; (*b*) contains the point $(-3, 5)$ and has slope -2; (*c*) has x-intercept 4 and y-intercept -6.
9. Determine equations of the three straight lines, segments of which are the sides of the triangle with vertices at $(-3, 7)$, $(5, 9)$, and $(6, -8)$.
10. Determine the number x if the points $(x, 5)$, $(7, -3)$, and $(-2, 6)$ are collinear. Do this by two different methods.
11. Determine an equation of the straight line which (*a*) has slope 3 and contains the point $(0, 0)$; (*b*) has slope -2 and y-intercept -3; (*c*) contains the point $(2, 2)$ and is parallel to the y-axis; (*d*) contains the points $(3, -6)$ and $(-4, 9)$.
12. Determine an equation of the straight line which (*a*) has y-intercept 4 and is parallel to the line having the equation $2x - 3y - 1 = 0$; (*b*) contains the point $(5, 8)$ and intersects on the y-axis the line having the equation $y = 3x + 2$; (*c*) has slope -2 and the same y-intercept as the line having the equation $x - 2y - 6 = 0$.
13. Determine an equation of the straight line through the point $(-4, -7)$, which has equal intercepts on the coordinate axes.
14. Graph the function defined by the equation $2x - 3y + 6 = 0$ (*a*) on the interval $[-2, 2]$; (*b*) on the set $\{x \mid x \in I, |x| \leq 5\}$; (*c*) on the set $\{-3, -1, 0, 2\}$.
15. Graph the function defined on the interval $[-3, 3]$ by $x - 2y = 0$ for $-3 \leq x < 0$, $y = x + 1$ for $0 \leq x < 2$, and $y = 3$ for $2 \leq x \leq 3$.

16. Sketch the graph of the function f defined on the interval $[-\pi, \pi]$ by $f(x) = \sin x$ for $-\pi \leq x \leq -1$, $f(x) = x$ for $-1 < x < 1$, and $f(x) = 2 \cos x$ for $1 \leq x \leq \pi$.

6.6 The Straight Line: A Different Approach

In the preceding section a straight line was considered to be the locus of an equation, closely related to the defining equation $y = x$ of one of the basic power functions; and the straight line was drawn from a comparison with this latter locus. In this discussion the *equation* has played the leading role. Many curves that are the loci of equations, however, may also be defined by means of certain geometric characteristics. For example, we have introduced the parabola and the hyperbola as curves which arise from the defining equations of certain power functions, but the theory of these curves can be based on sections of a cone; we shall refer again to this at a later time. A study of the straight line can also be based on its basic characteristic that the slope of the line segment joining any two points of the line does not depend on the points selected; we may then think of a straight line as a *curve of constant slope.* A straight line, from this point of view is a set of points such that if any two of its points are joined by a line segment, the slopes of all such segments are equal. We recall that an equation of a locus is an equation that must be satisfied by the coordinates x and y of *any* point (x, y) of the locus. Thus, to determine an equation of some particular line, we take an arbitrary point $P(x, y)$ of the line and impose the condition of constant slope. This procedure is outlined in the following illustrations.

ILLUSTRATION 1. Determine an equation of the straight line containing the points $(-3, 4)$ and $(5, -2)$.

Solution. Let $P(x, y)$ be any point of the line, as shown in Figure 6–21. The slope of the line segment RS is $-3/4$, while the slope of the segment PS is $(y + 2)/(x - 5)$. Equating these two slopes, we obtain an equation of the line as $(y + 2)/(x - 5) = -3/4$, which simplifies into $3x + 4y - 7 = 0$.

ILLUSTRATION 2. Determine an equation of the straight line with slope 4, containing the point $(3, -2)$.

Solution. Let $P(x, y)$ be any point on the straight line, with Q the point $(3, -2)$ as shown in Figure 6–22. The slope of the line segment PQ is $(y + 2)/(x - 3)$, and on equating this to 4 we obtain an equation of the line as $(y + 2)/(x - 3) = 4$. This equation may be easily simplified into $4x - y - 14 = 0$.

Each of the standard forms for an equation of a straight line, as discussed in the preceding section, has involved certain representative symbols in addition to the x and y of an arbitrary point on the line. These symbols, such as m and b in the equation $y = mx + b$ or a and b in the equation $x/a + y/b = 1$, are known as *parameters;* a particular line is identified if the numbers represented by these parameters are prescribed. If the numbers represented by the parameters are not prescribed, the equation will generate what is known as a *two-parameter family* of lines;

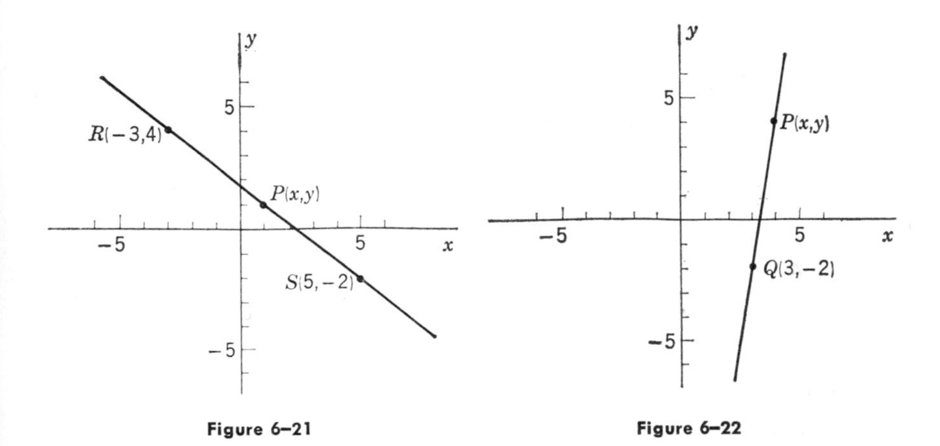

Figure 6–21

Figure 6–22

every line in the plane is included in the family generated by $y = mx + b$, except those lines that are parallel to the y-axis, while every line with finite non-zero intercepts is included in the family generated by $x/a + y/b = 1$. If the number represented by one parameter only is prescribed, the resulting equation generates a *one-parameter family* of lines. For example, the equation $y = 2x + b$ generates the one-parameter family of lines, consisting of all lines with slope 2; segments of a few of these lines are shown in Figure 6–23. The equation $y - 2 = m(x + 2)$ generates a one-parameter family of lines, consisting of all straight lines containing the point $(-2, 2)$ except the line that is parallel to the y-axis. In Figure 6–24, we have shown segments of some of the members of this family.

Now let $E_1 = 0$ and $E_2 = 0$ be any two equations in x and y. If the loci of these equations have any points in common, the coordinates of such points will satisfy both equations; in addition, they will satisfy the equation $k_1E_1 + k_2E_2 = 0$, for any given real numbers k_1 and k_2. The locus of this latter equation is then a curve which contains all the points of intersection of the loci of the original equations. If k_1 and k_2 are allowed to represent arbitrary real numbers, the equation will generate a family of curves through these points of intersection. In particular, if $E_1 = 0$ and $E_2 = 0$ are equations of straight lines, the equation $k_1E_1 + k_2E_2 = 0$ will also be of the first degree in x and y, and so will be an equation of a straight line for any k_1 and k_2, not both zero. If these symbols are allowed to represent arbitrary real numbers, the equation will generate the family of all straight lines through the point of intersection of the two given lines; the given lines are included in the family, with either k_1 or k_2 equal to 0 and the other equal to 1. Any particular member of this family may be identified by giving some other condition, as in the illustration below. We note in passing that, while the equation $k_1E_1 + k_2E_2 = 0$ appears to have two

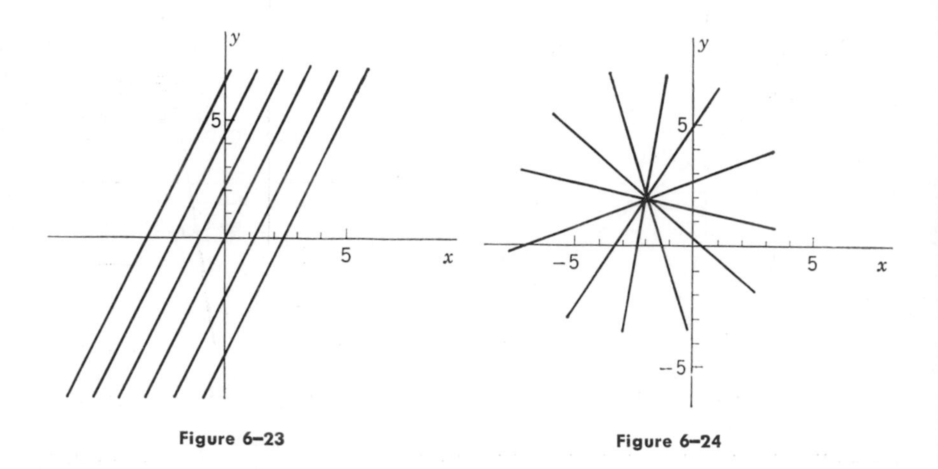

Figure 6-23

Figure 6-24

parameters, there is only one of significance: for at least one of k_1 and k_2 is not zero, and both sides of the equation may then be divided by this non-zero number, the only parameter remaining being *either* k_1/k_2 or k_2/k_1 which we may label k.

ILLUSTRATION 3. Determine an equation of the straight line through the point of intersection of the lines having the equations $2x - 3y + 4 = 0$ and $x + 5y - 6 = 0$, and containing the point $(2, -2)$.

Solution. The equation $k_1(2x - 3y + 4) + k_2(x + 5y - 6) = 0$ will generate the family of all straight lines through the point of intersection of the given lines, if k_1 and k_2 are allowed to be any real numbers. (Notice that we have not actually located the point of intersection.) If $k_1 = 0$, the corresponding member has the equation $x + 5y - 6 = 0$, and the point $(2, -2)$ does not lie on it. Thus, $k_1 \neq 0$, and we may divide both sides of the equation by k_1 obtaining $2x - 3y + 4 + k(x + 5y - 6) = 0$, where we have put $k = k_2/k_1$. Since the coordinates of the point $(2, -2)$ must satisfy any equation of the line in question, we must have $4 + 6 + 4 + k(2 - 10 - 6) = 0$, from which we obtain $k = 1$. It follows that an equation of the line is $2x - 3y + 4 + (x + 5y - 6) = 0$, which simplifies into $3x + 2y - 2 = 0$.

PROBLEM SET 6.6

1. Use the method of this section to determine an equation of the straight line that (*a*) contains the points $(4, -3)$ and $(2, 5)$; (*b*) has slope 4 and contains the point $(3, -6)$; (*c*) has x-intercept 4 and y-intercept -3; (*d*) is parallel to the locus of $2x - 4y + 5 = 0$, and contains the point $(-2, 6)$.
2. Use the method of this section to determine an equation of the straight line that (*a*) contains the points $(-3, 8)$ and $(2, 5)$; (*b*) is parallel to the locus of $3x + 5y - 6 = 0$, and has x-intercept 5; (*c*) has slope -4 and contains the point $(3, -5)$; (*d*) has y-intercept 5, and is parallel to the locus of $5x - 3y + 6 = 0$.
3. Determine an equation of the straight line that contains the point of intersection of the lines having the equations $3x + 4y - 3 = 0$ and $x + 2y - 4 = 0$, and has 5 for its x-intercept. Do not actually locate the point of intersection.
4. Determine an equation of the straight line with slope -1 that contains the point of intersection of the straight lines having the equations $3x - 5y + 2 = 0$ and $x - 2y = 0$. Do not actually locate the point of intersection.
5. Describe the family of lines generated by the equation $y = 3x + b$; sketch a few members of this family.
6. Describe the family of lines generated by the equation $y = mx + 5$; sketch a few members of this family.
7. Determine the member of the family of lines generated by the equation (*a*) $y = 3x + b$, that contains the point $(-2, 6)$; (*b*) $y = mx + 6$, that contains the point $(4, 8)$; (*c*) $2x + ky + 5 = 0$, that has slope -2.
8. Determine the member of the family of lines generated by the equation (*a*) $x/3 + y/k = 1$, that contains the point $(-2, 5)$; (*b*) $y = mx + 5$, that is parallel to the locus of $3x + 5y = 2$; (*c*) $y = mx - 3$, that has 2 for its x-intercept.
9. If $E_1 = 0$ and $E_2 = 0$ are equations of two straight lines, does the family of lines generated by the equation $E_1 + kE_2 = 0$ contain *all* the straight lines through the point of intersection of the two given lines? Compare this family with that generated by the equation $E_2 + kE_1 = 0$. Compare each of these families with that generated by $k_1E_1 + k_2E_2 = 0$.

6.7 Logarithmic Graph Paper

In Figure 6–25 we have shown portions of a pair of Cartesian coordinate axes, with two sets of scale readings marked on each axis. The outer scale is *uniform*, with readings shown from 0 to 1, while it is apparent that the inner scale is *non-uniform*, with readings from 1 to 10; the two scales on either axis are so related that at any point of the axis the outer scale reading is the common logarithm of the inner scale reading. For instance, 1 on the outer scale is opposite 10 on the inner scale, since $\log 10 = 1$; and since $\log 2 = 0.3$, approximately, the number 2 on the inner scale is approximately opposite 0.3 on the outer scale. Let x and y be the coordinates of an arbitrary point P, referred to the non-uniform or logarithmic scales,

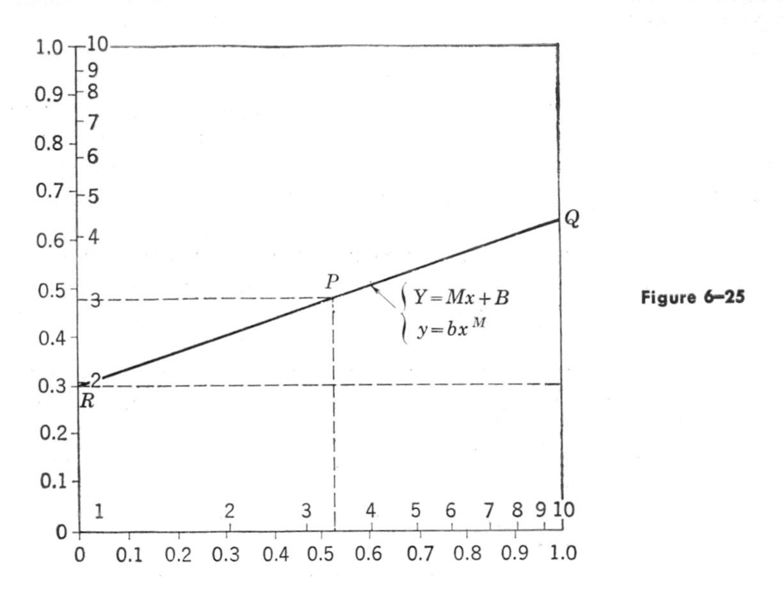

Figure 6–25

with X and Y the coordinates of the same point, referred to the uniform scales. For the point P in Figure 6–25, approximations for these coordinates are: $x = 3.4$, $y = 3.0$, $X = 0.53$, $Y = 0.48$.

Now consider a line containing the point P and intersecting the vertical axis at the point R. The "slope-y-intercept" equation of this line, referred to the uniform scales, is $Y = MX + B$, where M is the slope and B is the y-intercept. (For the line shown in Figure 6–25, $M = 0.34$ and $B = 0.3$, approximately.) By virtue of the relationship between the scales, $Y = \log y$, $X = \log x$, and $B = \log b$, where b is the reading on the non-uniform scale opposite B on the uniform scale. The above equation may now be written $\log y = M \log x + \log b = \log x^M + \log b = \log bx^M$, and so the corresponding equation of the line, referred to the logarithmic scales, is $y = bx^M$. The exponent M is the slope of the line, while the coefficient b is the logarithmic scale reading at the point where the line intersects the vertical axis. Since $x = 1$, rather than $x = 0$, defines the vertical axis, when the logarithmic scales are used, it might be misleading to refer to b as the y-intercept of the line.

The discussion of the preceding paragraph has shown that if the graph of a function is a straight line, when logarithmic scales are used, the function is a power function. In order to determine a defining equation, it is merely necessary to find the slope of the line and its point of crossing the vertical axis where $x = 1$. A sheet of paper with logarithmic scales, and rulings drawn through the points of division of the scales, is called a sheet of *logarithmic graph paper.* The uniform scale on such a sheet is usually omitted, but one uniform unit is always understood to correspond to one logarithmic cycle (i.e., 1 to 10, 10 to 100, etc.).

There are two principal uses for logarithmic graph paper. Since the graph of a power function is a portion of a straight line on such paper, it is clear that this paper will be very useful in graphing functions of this type. We now give a few illustrations of this.

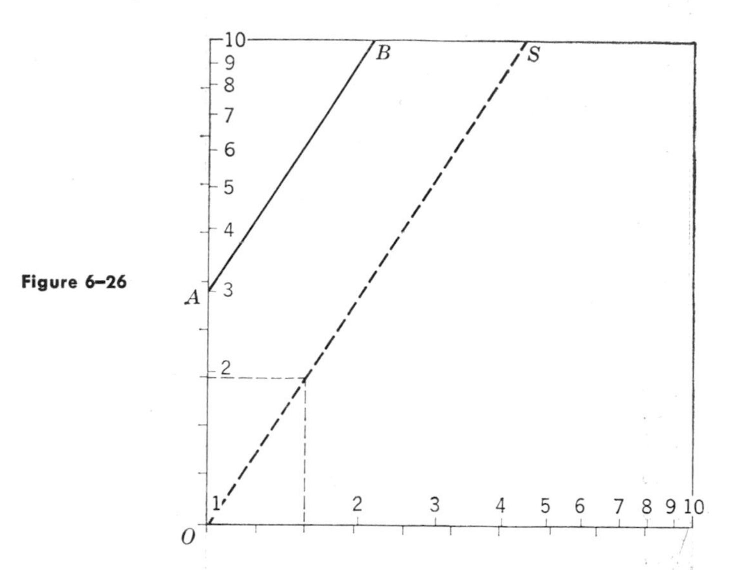

Figure 6–26

ILLUSTRATION 1. Construct the graph, using logarithmic graph paper, of the function defined in the interval [1, 10] by $y = 3x^{3/2}$.

Solution. The result is a straight line segment with slope 3/2, which intersects the left vertical scale at the point with scale reading 3. This is shown as the segment AB in Figure 6–26, with the auxiliary segment OS drawn as an aid in obtaining the correct slope.

ILLUSTRATION 2. Use logarithmic paper to construct the graph of the function defined in the interval [1, 10] by $y = 5/x$.

Solution. The result is a straight line segment with slope -1, which intersects the left vertical scale at the point with scale reading 5. In Figure 6–27, this graph is shown as the segment AB, the auxiliary line segment LM with slope -1 being included as a guide.

ILLUSTRATION 3. Use logarithmic paper to construct the graph of the function defined from the interval [1, 10] to the interval [0.01, 0.1] by $y = 0.05x^{-3}$.

Solution. In this case, the vertical scale must read from 0.01 to 0.1. The desired graph is a line segment with slope -3, intersecting the vertical axis at the point with scale reading 0.05. This is shown in Figure 6–28 as

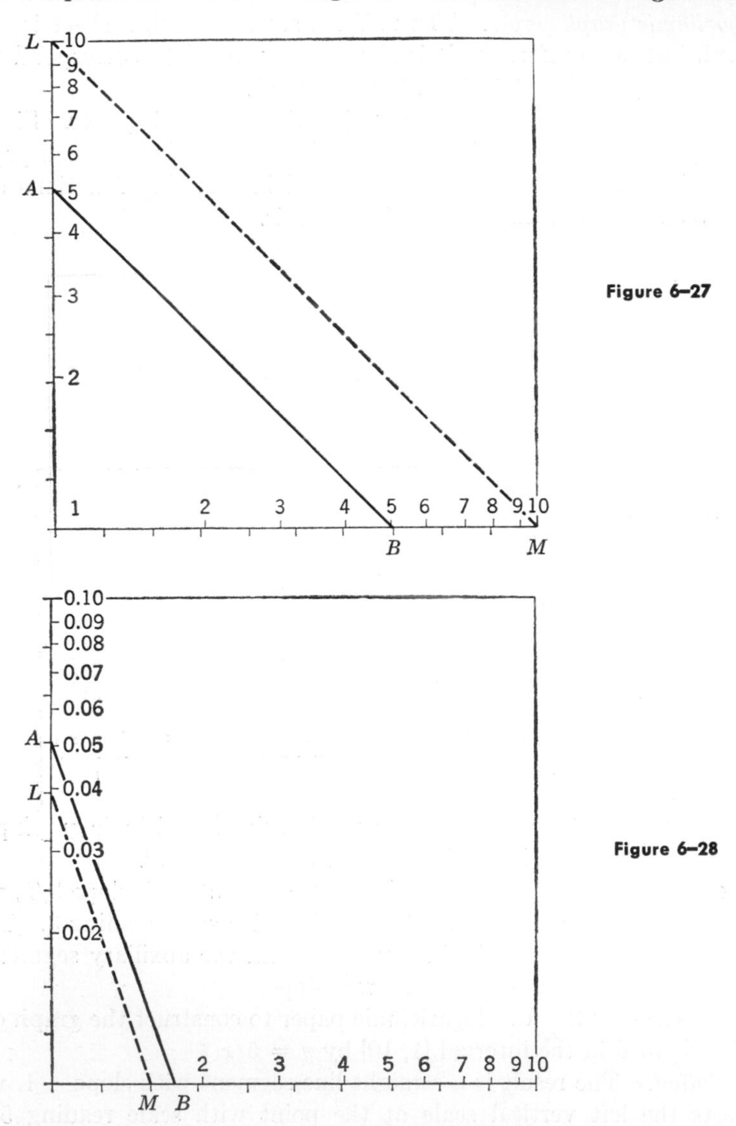

Figure 6–27

Figure 6–28

the segment AB, with the segment LM also shown as a guide line with slope -3.

Note. In the preceding illustration, the *uniform* vertical scale should read from -2 to -1. However, this scale is used only for the purpose of determining the slope of the line, and so the actual readings are of no importance. This scale is usually not even labeled.

The second and more important use for logarithmic paper is concerned with the determination of an empirical equation from some laboratory data. If two sets of associated data are plotted on logarithmic paper, as the graph of some function, and the result is a straight line segment, the function is now known to be a power function, and its defining equation can be easily found. Inasmuch as power function relationships occur very frequently in nature, this is a very important procedure.

ILLUSTRATION 4. Determine an empirical equation connecting x and y, from the following table of experimental data.

x	1.2	1.3	1.5	1.7	2.0	2.3	2.5
y	2.15	2.50	3.55	4.30	5.90	7.80	9.30

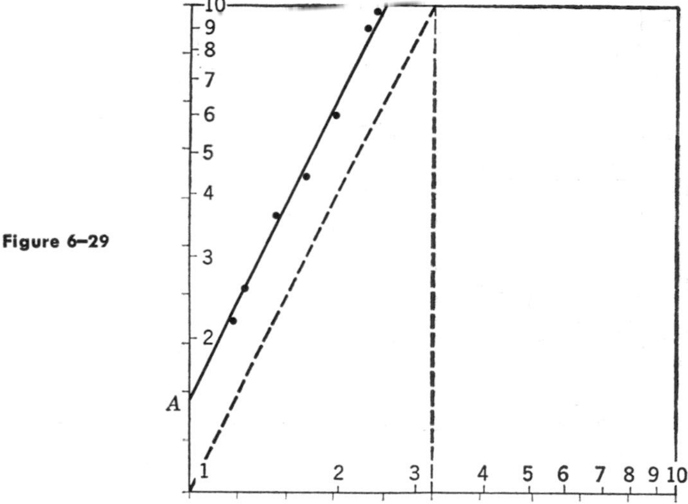

Figure 6–29

Solution. When the above data have been plotted on logarithmic paper, the result is the line segment AB, shown in Figure 6–29. The slope of AB is determined, with the aid of the dotted line segments, and found to be approximately 2. Since AB cuts the vertical axis approximately at the point with scale reading 1.5, an empirical equation connecting x and y is $y = 1.5x^2$.

If the extent of the data is such that 1 is not shown on the horizontal scale, the number b cannot be read from the graph, as in the preceding illustration. However, it is possible to determine b from the coordinates

x_0 and y_0 of any point on the line. Thus, if $y = bx^M$ is assumed to be an equation of such a line, with (x_0, y_0) one of its points, we have $y_0 = bx_0^M$ and from this we find that $b = y_0/x_0^M$.

ILLUSTRATION 5. Determine an empirical equation connecting x and y, from the following table of experimental data.

x	11	19	25	31	39	44	53	70
y	176	220	243	265	290	305	329	367

Solution. In this case the vertical scale, as shown, must read from 100 to 1000 while the horizontal scale must read from 10 to 100. The

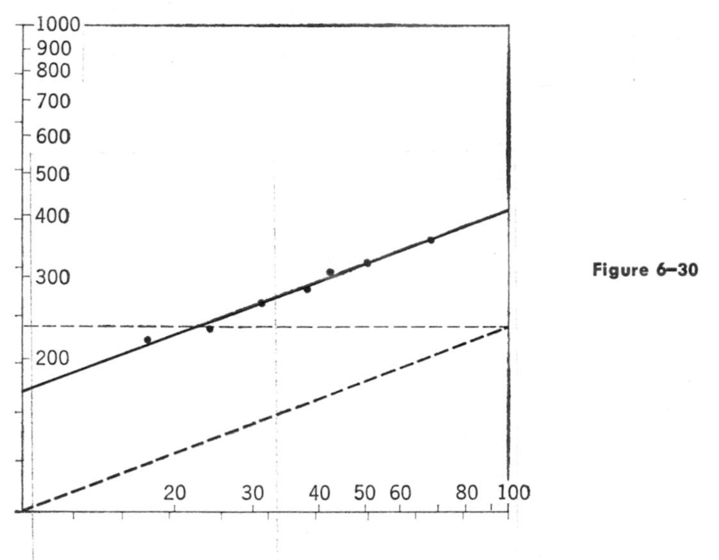

Figure 6–30

resulting graph is the line segment shown in Figure 6–30, and so we may assume that the desired empirical equation has the form $y = bx^M$. The dotted line segments have been shown to facilitate a determination of the slope M, and the graph shows that $M = 0.38$, approximately. If we use the fact that (31,265) is on the line, we find that $b = y_0/x_0^M = 265/(31)^{0.38} = 72$, approximately. An empirical equation connecting x and y is then seen to be $y = 72x^{0.38}$.

It should have been observed by now that, while the uniform scales associated with the logarithmic scales are frequently a convenience in a determination of the slope of a line, they are not essential. In fact, any uniform scale may be used for this purpose, such as a ruler marked off in inches or centimeters, and this is usually the better method for a graph constructed from experimental data. Since a slope is the quotient of two numbers, the actual size of the unit is of no importance, provided the same unit is used for both the horizontal and vertical measurements.

If the numbers in either set of data are found to lie in more than one logarithmic cycle, more than one sheet of logarithmic paper is needed. Sometimes combination sheets are provided, and these are called sheets of *multiple logarithmic paper*.

PROBLEM SET 6.7

1. Use simulated logarithmic paper to sketch the power function defined on the interval [1, 10] by (*a*) $y = 3x^3$; (*b*) $y = 8x^2$; (*c*) $y = 5/x$; (*d*) $y = 10/x^2$; (*e*) $y = 2x^{3/2}$; (*f*) $y = 7x^{1/3}$.

2. Use simulated logarithmic paper to sketch the power function defined on the interval [1, 10] by (*a*) $y = 25x^2$; (*b*) $y = 0.02x^{-2}$; (*c*) $y = 0.5x^{1/3}$; (*d*) $y = 150x^{1/4}$; (*e*) $y = 200/x^2$; (*f*) $y = 0.002/x$.

3. Use simulated logarithmic paper to sketch the power function defined on the interval [1, 10] by (*a*) $y = 0.037x^{2.1}$; (*b*) $y = 72x^{2.5}$; (*c*) $y = x^3$; (*d*) $y = x^{3/2}/4$; (*e*) $y = 420x^{-0.7}$; (*f*) $y = 2x^{10.1}$.

4. Write equations which define the power functions having the graphs shown below on simulated sheets of logarithmic paper.

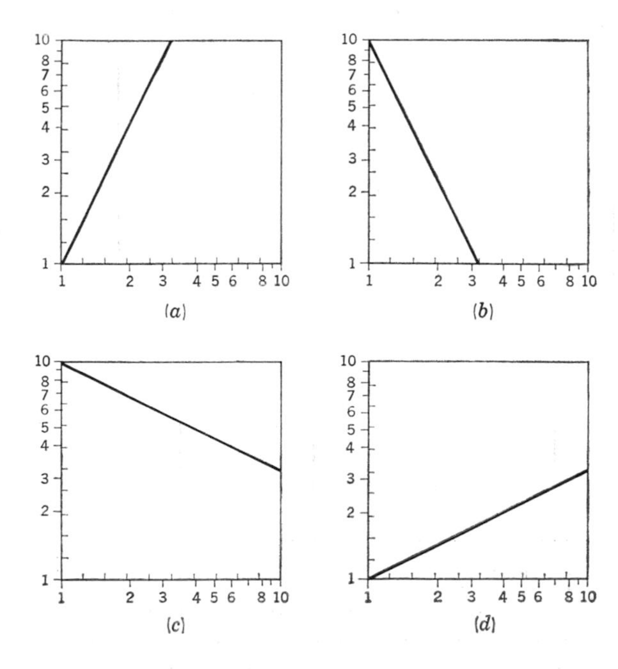

5. Do the same as in Problem 4 for each of the following sketches:

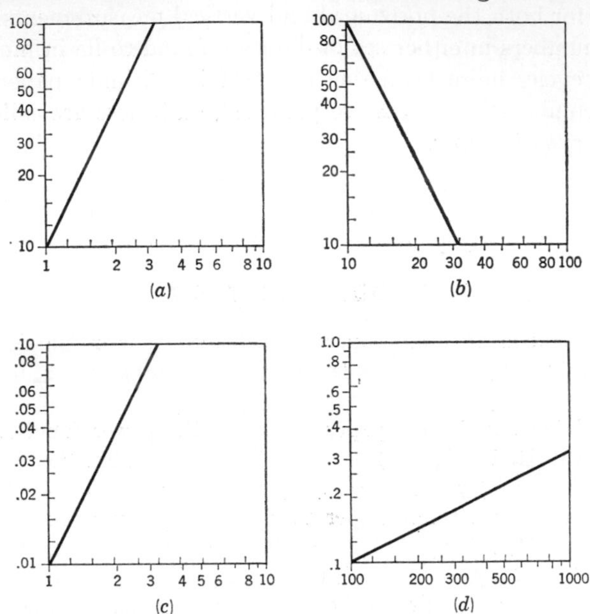

6. Do the same as in Problem 4 for each of the following sketches on simulated multiple logarithmic paper:

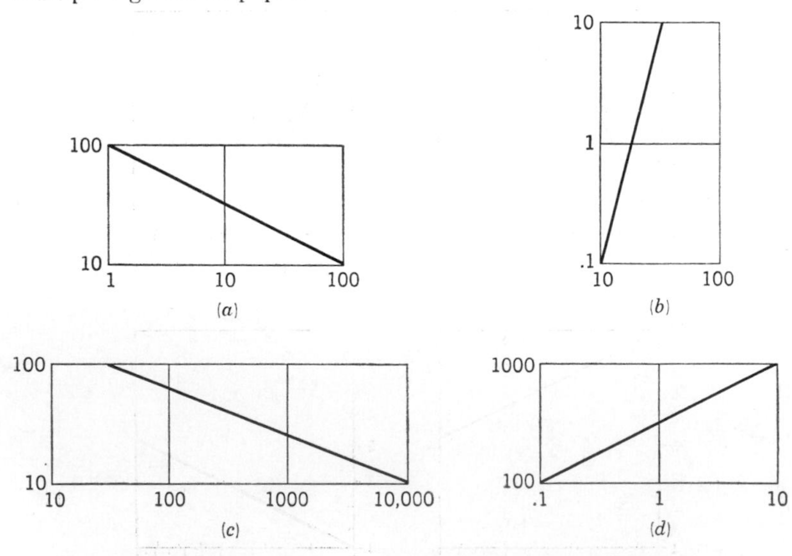

7. Determine an approximate equation of the straight line segment on logarithmic paper, that contains the points (0.25, 0.8) and (0.8, 5); use a ruler marked in inches or centimeters to approximate the slope.

8. Do the same as in Problem 7, using the points (15, 25) and (75, 50).

In each of Problems 9 through 13, graph the data on logarithmic paper, and if the graph approximates a straight line segment determine an empirical equation connecting x and y.

9.

x	1.0	1.5	2.5	3.0	4.5	5.0
y	1.3	2.1	4.0	5.0	8.2	9.5

10.

x	1.40	2.10	3.20	4.00	6.30	8.00	9.20
y	2.46	3.04	3.70	4.20	5.23	6.01	6.40

11.

x	1.6	2.1	3.0	3.3	3.7	4.3	5.5	7.2
y	0.0093	0.0069	0.0046	0.0041	0.0036	0.0031	0.0027	0.0017

12.

x	0.1	0.3	0.9	1.2	2.5	5.0	10
y	1.1	6.0	12.8	44.0	370	370	1000

13.

x	1.1	3.1	5.0	12.0	21.0	35.0	64.0	80.0
y	1.22	1.60	1.80	2.28	2.60	3.00	3.45	3.70

6.8 Semi-Logarithmic Graph Paper

In Figure 6–31 we have shown a pair of Cartesian coordinate axes, with a uniform scale indicated on the horizontal and both a uniform and corresponding non-uniform logarithmic scale on the vertical. The relationship between corresponding numbers on the vertical scale is then the same as it was with logarithmic paper. Let x be the abscissa of an arbitrary point P (referred, of course, to the uniform horizontal scale); and let y and Y be the ordinates of P referred, respectively, to the logarithmic and uniform vertical scales. If we now regard P as an arbitrary point on a straight line, the "slope-y-intercept" equation of the line referred to the uniform scales is $Y = Mx + B$, where M is its slope and B its Y-intercept. (In the figure M is approximately 1/3 and B is approximately 3.) Since $Y = \log y$ and $B = \log b$, for some real number b on the vertical logarithmic scale opposite B, the equation of the line becomes $\log y = Mx + \log b$ or $\log (y/b) = Mx$, from which we obtain $y = b(10)^{Mx}$. This is an equation of the line, referred to the uniform horizontal and logarithmic vertical scales.

When horizontal and vertical rulings are drawn through the points of division of the vertical logarithmic and horizontal uniform scales, the result is called a sheet of *semi-logarithmic* paper. We now have shown that if the graph of a function is a straight line segment on semi-logarithmic paper, the function is *exponential*, being defined by an equation of the form $y = b(10)^{Mx}$. It is also clear that the semi-logarithmic graph of any such exponential function is a portion of a straight line. Moreover, since any positive real number a can be written as 10^c, where $c = \log a$, any equation $y = ba^{Mx}$ can be written as $y = b(10)^{cMx}$; thus, the semi-loga-

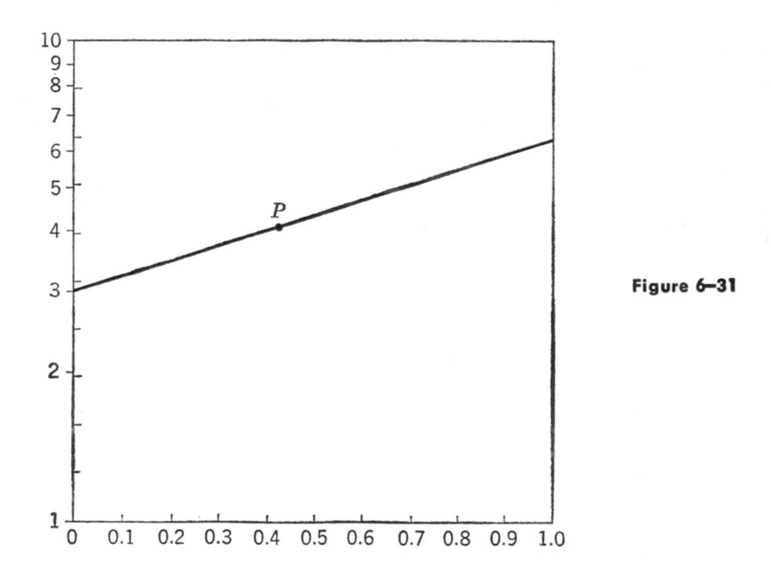

Figure 6–31

rithmic graph of an arbitrary exponential function will be a set of points on some straight line. A sheet of commercial semi-logarithmic paper frequently contains only a portion of the uniform scale shown in Figure 6–31. For example, a common type has "1 cycle × 70 divisions," the uniform scale reading from 0 to 0.7.

The uses of semi-logarithmic paper are similar to those of logarithmic paper: it may be used to graph an exponential function, or to determine an empirical equation connected with some experimental data. Thus, if the graph of experimental data is a straight line segment on logarithmic paper, the associated relation is a power function; on the other hand, if the graph of the data on a sheet of semi-logarithmic paper is a straight line segment, the associated relation is an exponential function. In either case, an empirical equation for the function may be determined from the graph.

The slope M of a straight line segment on semi-logarithmic paper can be determined as before, by using the two uniform scales of the paper. Any other uniform scale can be used for this purpose, provided the horizontal unit on the graph has the same length as one vertical logarithmic cycle; if this latter condition is not satisfied, the uniform scales of the graph must be used. The number b is the y-intercept; if the number 0 is not included on the portion of the horizontal scale used for the graph, it will be necessary to determine b algebraically. We now give a few illustrations.

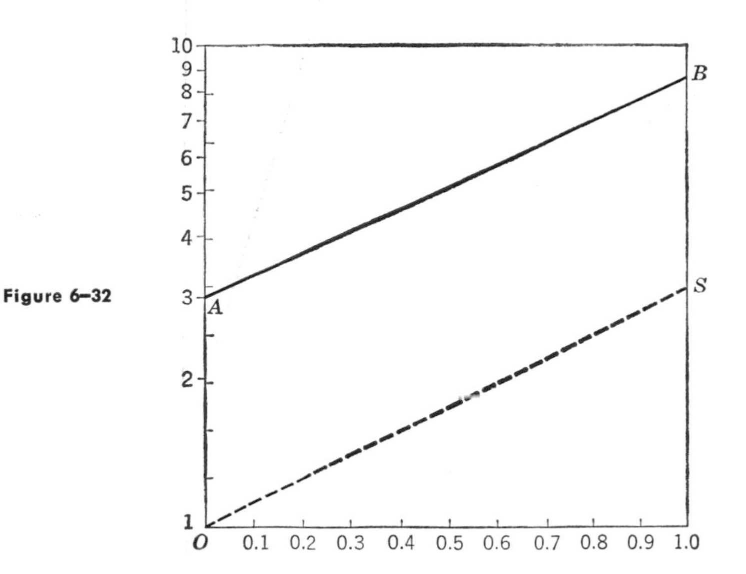

Figure 6–32

ILLUSTRATION 1. Make a semi-logarithmic graph of the function defined on the interval [0, 1] by $y = 3(10)^{x/2}$.

Solution. The desired graph is shown in Figure 6–32 as the line segment AB, with slope 1/2 and intersecting the vertical axis at the point 3. The line segment OS is drawn from O to the mid-point S of the right side of the graph paper, to be used as an aid in obtaining the correct slope for AB.

ILLUSTRATION 2. Make a semi-logarithmic graph of the function defined from the interval [0, 1] to the interval [10, 100] by $y = 50(10)^{-4x}$.

Solution. The vertical logarithmic scale must read from 10 to 100, and the vertical uniform scale would read from 1 to 2, but it is not necessary to label this latter scale. The result is the straight line segment AB, shown in Figure 6–33; this segment has slope -4 and intersects the vertical logarithmic scale at the point 50. The segment LM is an auxiliary line segment with slope -4, to be used as an aid in obtaining the correct slope for AB.

ILLUSTRATION 3. Pairs of numbers from two sets of experimental data have been plotted on semi-logarithmic paper, and have been found to lie on a straight line. If two of the plotted pairs are (0.3, 30) and (0.8, 70), determine an empirical equation of the associated function.

Solution. The vertical scale must read from 10 to 100, as shown in

Figure 6–34, with the horizontal scale reading from 0 to 1. The slope of the line segment can be computed to be 0.78, approximately, while an

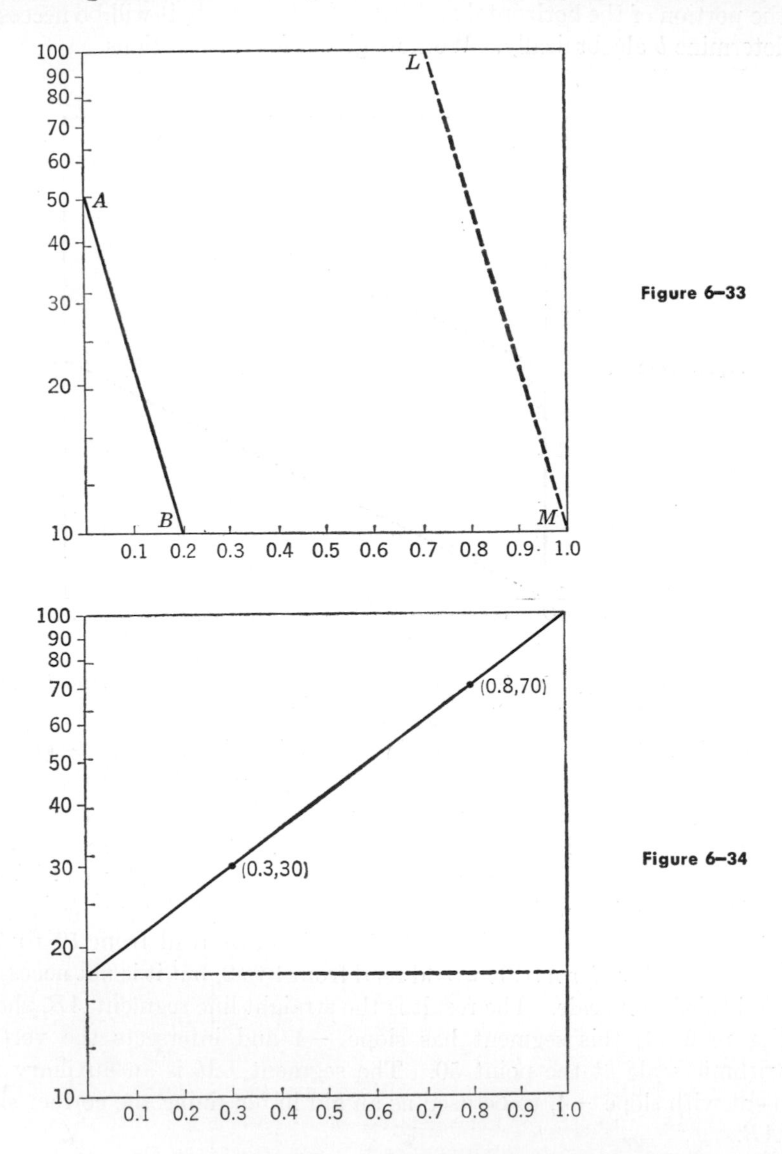

Figure 6–33

Figure 6–34

approximation to its intercept on the vertical axis may be seen to be 18. An empirical equation for the line is then $y = 18(10)^{0.78x}$.

ILLUSTRATION 4. Make a semi-logarithmic graph of the function defined on the interval [0, 1] by $y = 2e^{0.6x}$.

Solution. Since $e = 10^{0.4343}$, this equation may be written as

$y = 2(10)^{(0.4343)(0.6)x}$ or, approximately, as $y = 2(10)^{0.26x}$. The desired graph is the line segment AB, shown in Figure 6–35, with slope 0.26 and intersecting the vertical axis at the point 2.

ILLUSTRATION 5. Pairs of numbers from two sets of experimental data have been plotted on semi-logarithmic paper, and have been found to lie

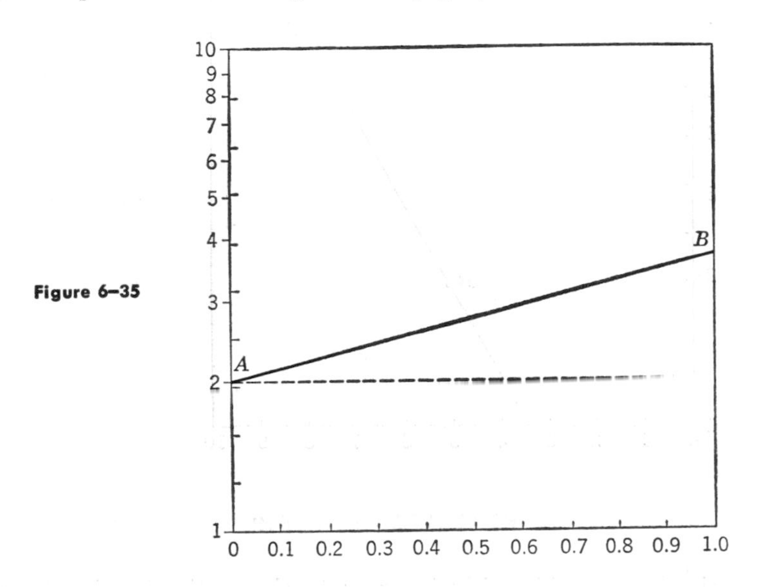

Figure 6–35

on a straight line. If horizontal scale readings from 0 to 10 and vertical scale readings from 1 to 10 are required for the graph, with (5, 2) and (8, 7) two of the plotted pairs, determine an empirical equation for the associated function.

Solution. The line segment of the graph is indicated as AB in Figure 6–36. There are two methods available for obtaining the slope M of AB. (*a*) An approximation for M can be found from the graph. Thus, the horizontal distance from B to A is approximately 5.6 horizontal units, while the corresponding vertical distance is 1.0 uniform units. The slope of AB is then 1.0/5.6 or 0.18. (*b*) A more accurate method is to compute the vertical distance between the two given points, using a uniform scale associated with the logarithmic scale. Since $\log 7 = 0.8451$ and $\log 2 = 0.3010$, the vertical "uniform scale" distance between the points is 0.5441 units, and so the desired slope is 0.5441/3 or 0.18, approximately. Since the line segment does not intersect the vertical axis, on the graph, we must determine b algebraically. If we assume an equation of the form $y = b(10)^{0.18x}$, with the point (5, 2) on the line, we must have $2 = b(10)^{(0.18)5} = b(10)^{0.90}$. Then, $\log 2 = \log b + 0.90$ and $\log b = 0.30 - 0.90 = -0.60 = 0.40 - 1$, from which we obtain $b = 0.25$, approximately. An empirical equation for the function associated with the graph is then $y = 0.25(10)^{0.18x}$.

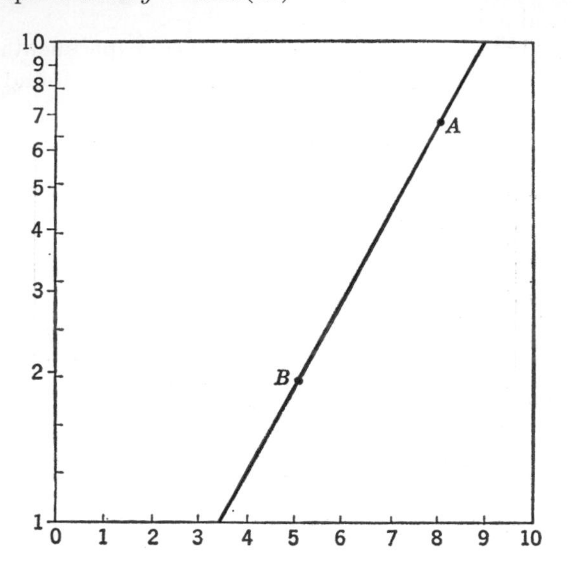

Figure 6–36

PROBLEM SET 6.8

1. Use simulated semi-logarithmic paper to sketch the function from the interval [0, 1] to the interval [1, 10], defined by (*a*) $y = 10^{2x}$; (*b*) $y = 10^{3x}$; (*c*) $y = 10^{8x}$; (*d*) $y = 10^{-x}$; (*e*) $y = 10^{-2x}$; (*f*) $y = 10^{-4x}$; (*g*) $y = e^{x}$; (*h*) $y = e^{3x}$; (*i*) $y = e^{-3x}$.
2. Use a sheet of simulated semi-logarithmic paper to sketch the function on the interval [0, 1], defined by (*a*) $y = 3(10)^{2x}$; (*b*) $y = 4(10)^{-5x}$; (*c*) $y = 3(10)^{-3x}$; (*d*) $y = 2e^{3x}$; (*e*) $y = 5e^{-3x}$; (*f*) $y = 4e^{-x/4}$; (*g*) $3x = \log y$; (*h*) $x/2 = \log y$; (*i*) $-x/3 = \log y$.
3. Determine equations which define the functions having the graphs shown below on simulated semi-logarithmic paper.

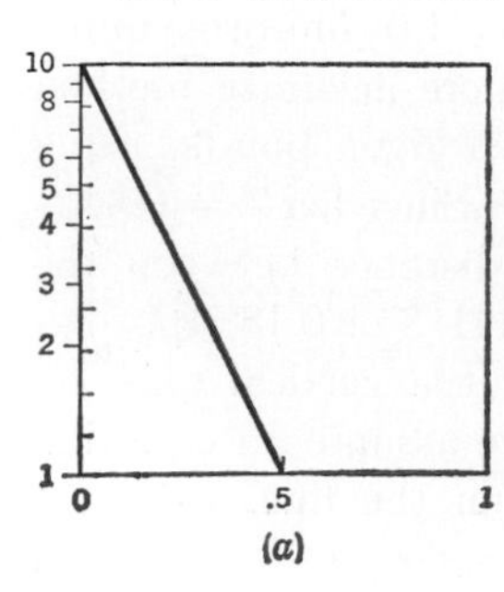

(*a*)

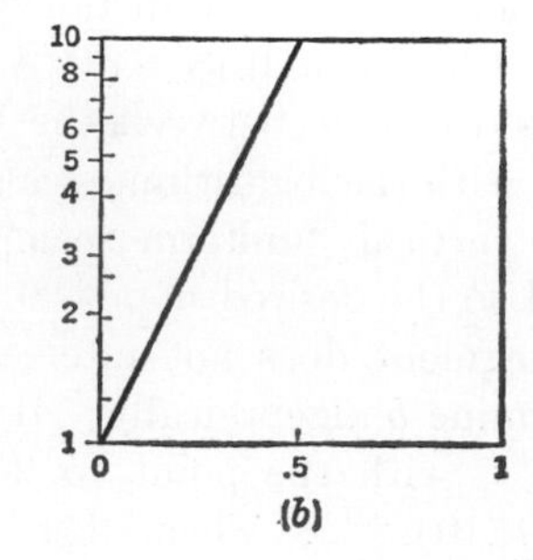

(*b*)

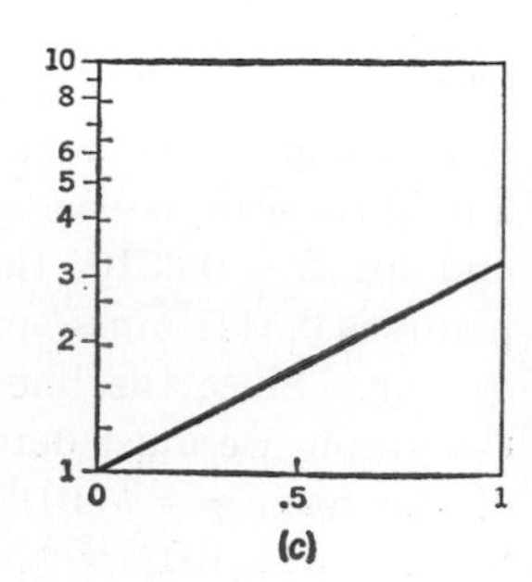

(*c*)

4. Determine equations which define the functions having the graphs shown below on simulated semi-logarithmic paper.

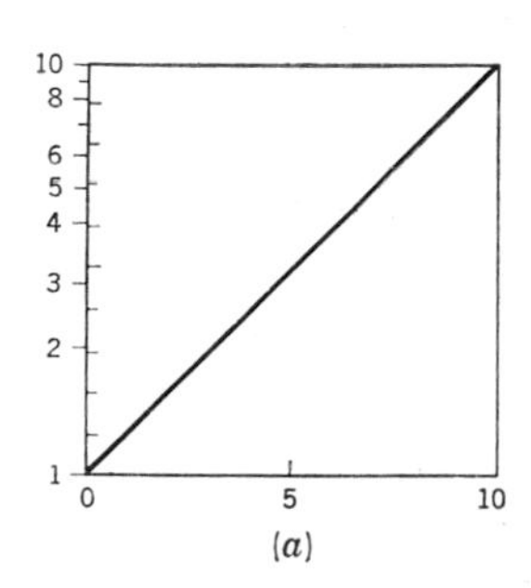

(a)

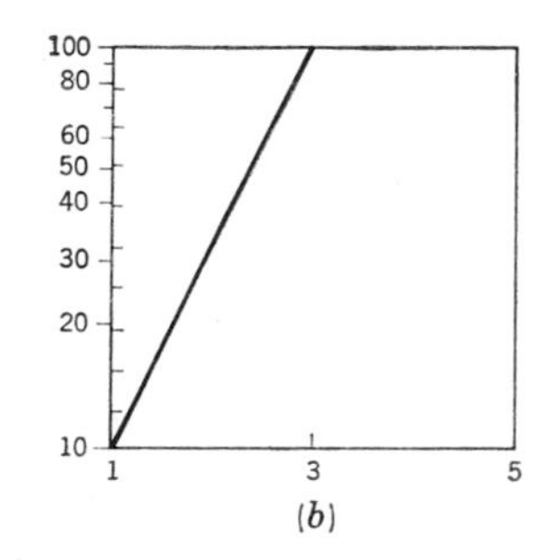

(b)

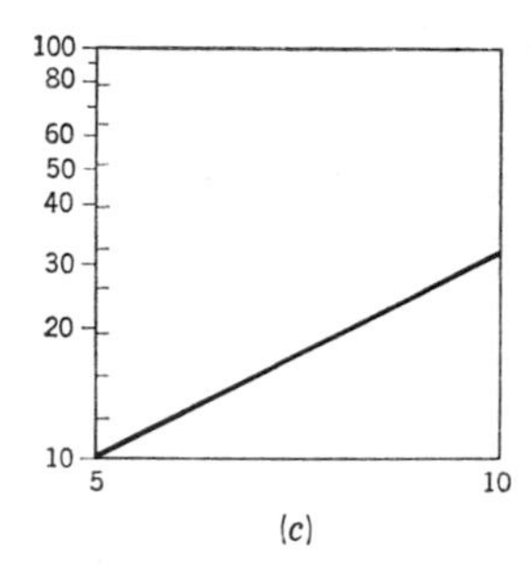

(c)

5. Determine equations which define the functions having the graphs shown below on simulated multiple semi-logarithmic paper.

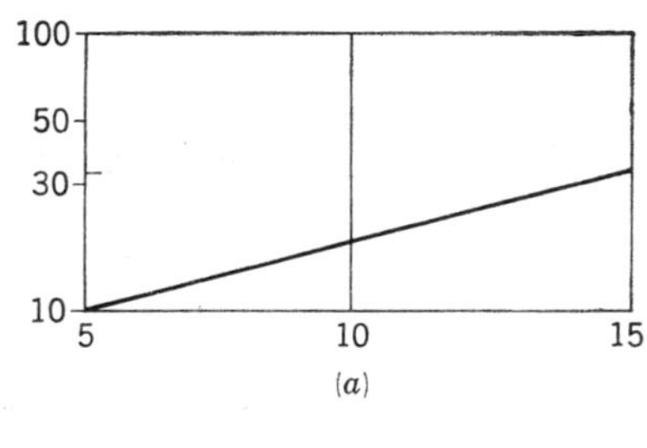

(a)

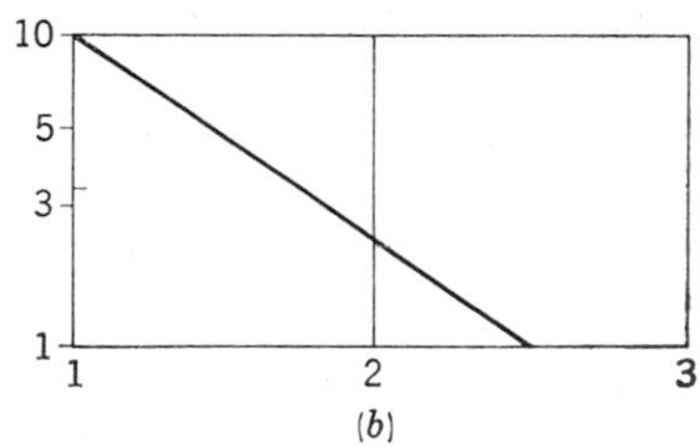

(b)

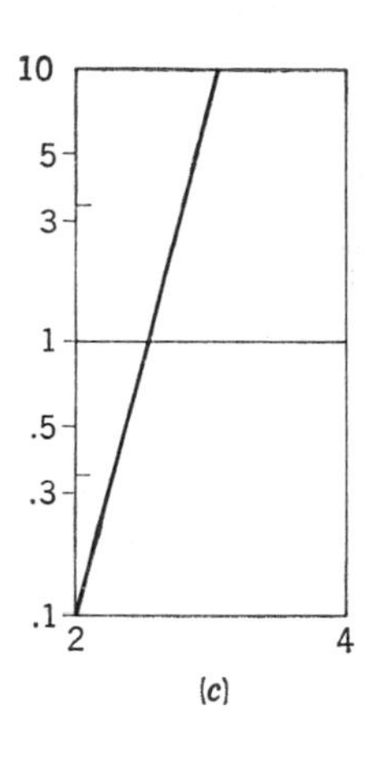

(c)

6. The semi-logarithmic graph of certain experimental data approximates a straight line segment. Use the graph to determine an approximate defining equation for the associated function if two of the plotted points are (*a*) (0.5, 4) and (0.8, 9); (*b*) (0.3, 6) and (0.7, 4).

7. Do the same as in Problem 6 for the points (*a*) (2, 0.05) and (8, 0.10); (*b*) (3, 12) and (8, 60).

8. Graph the data of the following table on semi-logarithmic paper, and determine an empirical equation which will define s as a function of r.

r	0.2	0.4	0.5	0.8	1.0	1.2
s	2.60	3.41	3.90	5.75	7.56	9.85

9. Graph the data of the following table on semi-logarithmic paper, and determine an empirical equation which will define y as a function of x.

x	0	1	2	3	4	5	6	7	8	9	10
y	80	66	56	44	35	28	24	19	15	13.5	10

10. Graph the data of the following table on semi-logarithmic paper, and determine an empirical equation which will define q as a function of p.

p	1	4	5	7	9
q	0.17	0.44	0.61	1.15	2.30

6.9 Analyses of the Elementary Functions, with Examples from Science

We have stated previously that the power functions, exponential functions, logarithmic functions, and circular functions form a foundation for the greater part of elementary mathematics. Let us now make a brief examination of these functions, to discover their essential distinguishing characteristics.

A power function f is defined by an equation $f(x) = ax^n$, for each x in its domain. Then, if mx is also in the domain of f, $f(mx)/f(x) = a(mx)^n/(ax^n) = m^n$, and we state this result as the

LAW OF THE POWER FUNCTION. If two numbers in the domain of a power function are selected so that one is a given multiple of the other, the corresponding functional values are in a ratio which is independent of the numbers selected.

For example, suppose x, $2x$, and $4x$ are in the domain of a power function defined by the equation $f(x) = 2x^3$. Then, $f(2x)/f(x) = 16x^3/(2x^3) = 8$, and also $f(4x)/f(2x) = 128x^3/(16x^3) = 8$, as the above law requires.

We have seen earlier that the Cartesian graph of a function, defined by an equation $y - a = c(x - b)^n$, is very similar to the corresponding graph of the function defined by $y = cx^n$. However, it may be seen by examples that a function of the former type does not obey the Law of the Power Function, and so cannot properly be considered a power function. Such a function belongs to the general class of *algebraic* functions, which we shall discuss later. The power function occurs in mathematical expressions of natural phenomena more frequently than any other kind of function.

An exponential function is defined on its domain by an equation of the type $f(x) = a^x$, and we have noted before that every logarithmic function is the inverse of some exponential function. In Chapter 8, we shall see that if an exponential function is defined on an interval, the slope of the Cartesian graph of this function at any point is proportional to the ordinate of that point. This is usually expressed in the following form of the

LAW OF THE EXPONENTIAL FUNCTION. Functional values increase or decrease at a rate proportional to themselves.

In other words, for this type of function, as the functional values increase (decrease), the rate of increase (decrease) increases (decreases), and eventually becomes very rapid (very slow). Again, graphs of functions defined by equations such as $y - d = ca^{x-b}$ and $y = ca^x$ may be very similar, but it may be shown that the Law of the Exponential Function does not hold for functions of the former type (and so these functions are not strictly exponential) except when $d = 0$.

The characteristic feature of a circular function is its periodicity, and we state this as the

LAW OF THE CIRCULAR FUNCTIONS. For each equation which defines a circular function f, there exists a positive real number k such that $f(x + nk) = f(x)$ for any integer n, provided x and $x + nk$ are in the domain of f.

The smallest such number k is, of course, the period of the circular function under consideration. If f is a subset of a basic circular function, this period is either π or 2π. We shall need these circular functions to express in mathematical terms all phenomena that are periodic or recurrent in character, such as all types of wave motion, vibrations, alternating currents, etc. Every machine, no matter how complicated its motions may be, repeats the motion after a certain cycle, and it is necessary to use circular functions to express the recurrent positions of the machine.

We shall now illustrate some applications of power functions and exponential functions, by listing a few formulas which express some laws of natural science. In a later chapter we shall discuss some of the applications of the circular functions.

1. If a particle, moving from a position of rest with a uniform acceleration of a feet per second, attains a velocity of v feet per second in t seconds, then $v = at$.

2. If a particle, falling freely under gravity, covers a distance of s feet in t seconds, then $s = 16.1t^2$, approximately.

3. If two objects of respective masses m_1 and m_2 units are separated by a distance of d linear units, a measure of the force of attraction between the two objects is F where $F = \gamma(m_1m_2)/d^2$, γ being a number dependent on the units adopted.

4. The radii of a circle are r centimeters in length. If a particle of mass m grams moves on the circumference of the circle, with a velocity of v centimeters per second, a centripetal force of F dynes is exerted on the particle, where $F = mv^2/r$.

5. A measure T of the period of a simple pendulum of length L units is given by $T = 2\pi\sqrt{L/g}$, where g is a measure of the acceleration due to gravity in units consistent with that adopted for the period.

6. If I amperes of current are passed through a resistance of R ohms, there will be an expenditure in heat of P watts with $P = RI^2$.

7. If I amperes of current pass along a long wire, a magnetic field of H gauss is established at a point r centimeters from the wire, with $H = 2I/r$.

8. The formula $M = M_0e^{-\alpha t}$ expresses the measure M of the amount of a radioactive material which remains from an original amount of M_0 units, after t units of time have elapsed, α being a "decay constant."

9. After t units of time, the measure A of a damped vibration, having an initial amplitude of a units, is given by $A = ae^{-bt}$, the number b depending on the unit of time and the vibrating material.

10. If H units of horse-power are required to give a speed of S knots to a steamship with D tons of displacement, then $H = S^3D^{2/3}/C$, where C is a number depending on the size and model of the ship.

11. The formula $N = 10 \log P_2/P_1$ expresses the gain in decibels for a repeater telephonic element having input and output powers of P_1 and P_2 units, respectively.

12. An alternating current of f cycles per second will develop a reactance of X_C ohms in a condenser of C farads capacity, where $X_C = 1/(2\pi fC)$.

13. If a particle falls from rest under gravity a distance of h linear units, a measure v of its terminal velocity is given by $v = \sqrt{2gh}$, where g is an appropriate measure of the acceleration due to gravity.

14. If H units of horse-power are transmissible by cold-rolled shafting, with d the length of a diameter of the shaft in inches and N the number of revolutions of the shaft per minute, then $H = d^3N/50$.

PROBLEM SET 6.9

1. Check the Law of the Power Function for a function defined by (*a*) $y = 4x^2$, using the numbers 2, 4, 8, and 16 of its domain; (*b*) $y = 5x^3$, using the numbers 3, 6, and 9 of its domain.
2. Check the Law of the Power Function for a function defined by (*a*) $y = 2/x$, using the numbers 1, 3, and 9 of its domain; (*b*) $y = 3/x^2$, using the numbers 2, 8, and 32 of its domain.
3. Check the Law of the Power Function for the function defined by (*a*) $y = 3x^{3/2}$, using the numbers 4, 16, and 64 of its domain; (*b*) $y = 6x$, using the numbers 5, 10, and 20 of its domain.
4. If a particle falls a total distance of 60 yards according to Formula **(13)**, what is the domain of the associated power function?

5. Compare the rise of the graph of a basic exponential function with a similar graph of a basic parabolic function.
6. Explain why the basic circular functions are periodic. Do these functions have the same period? Explain.
7. Indicate the type of natural phenomena, the descriptions of which make use of the circular functions.
8. Using the list of formulas given above, classify the power functions as parabolic, hyperbolic, or linear, considering one symbol on the right side of each formula as a reasonably representative element of the domain of the function in question.
9. Make a rough sketch of the graph of the function defined by Formula (**2**) on the interval [0, 4].
10. Make a rough sketch of the graph of the function on the interval [0, 10], defined by Formula (**13**); consider v in feet per minute, t in minutes and $g = 32.2$.
11. Make a rough sketch of the graph of the function on the interval [1, 5], defined by Formula (**14**) with $N = 50$.
12. Make a rough sketch of the graph of the function, defined on the interval [0, 10] by Formula (**6**), with $R = 100$.
13. Graph the function defined on the interval [0, 10] by Formula (**1**), assuming $a = 10$.
14. Compare graphs of the functions defined on the interval [0, 10] by Formulas (**5**) and (**13**).
15. If Formula (**10**) defines H as a function of D, what is the significance of the exponent 2/3 from a practical viewpoint?

REVIEW TEST A

1. Give a verbal comparison of the locus of the equation $y = e^x$ with that of (*a*) $y = 3e^x$; (*b*) $y = e^{2x}$; (*c*) $y = 2 + e^x$; (*d*) $y = 2 + e^{3x}$.
2. Consider each of the following pairs of equations, and give a verbal comparison of their loci: (*a*) $y = \sin x$, $y = -\sin x$; (*b*) $y = e^x$, $y = -2e^x$; (*c*) $y^3 = x^2$, $8y^3 = -x^2$.
3. Use the method of this chapter to find the coordinates of the vertex of the parabola having the given equation $y = 2x^2 - 5x + 4$.
4. The given equation of a parabola is $y = 2x^2 + 4x - 5$. Determine what translation of axes would be required in order that an equation of the parabola, referred to the new axes, would be $y = 2x^2$.
5. A parabolic mirror has the cross-section shown. If the segments OA, PB, and OC have respective lengths of 15, 20, and 5 inches, determine the length of RS.

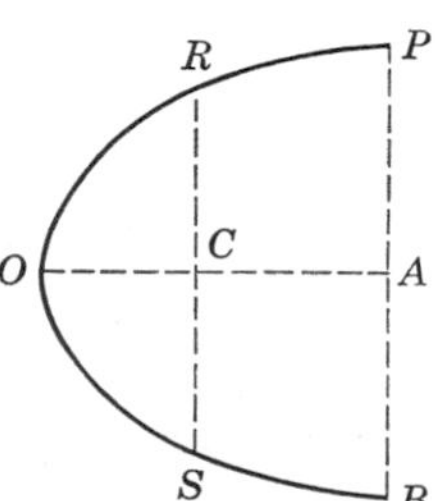

6. Determine an equation of the straight line containing the point $(-1, 2)$ and parallel to the line having the equation $3x - 2y + 1 = 0$.
7. Determine an equation of the straight line containing the points $(-2, 1)$ and $(3, -4)$.

8. Equations of a parabola and straight line are $y = x^2 - 2x$ and $3x + y - 2 = 0$, respectively. Determine the slope of the line segment that joins the vertex of the parabola with the point of intersection of the line with the y-axis.

9. Describe the common characteristic possessed by all members of the family of lines defined by the equation $y = (3/b)x + b$.

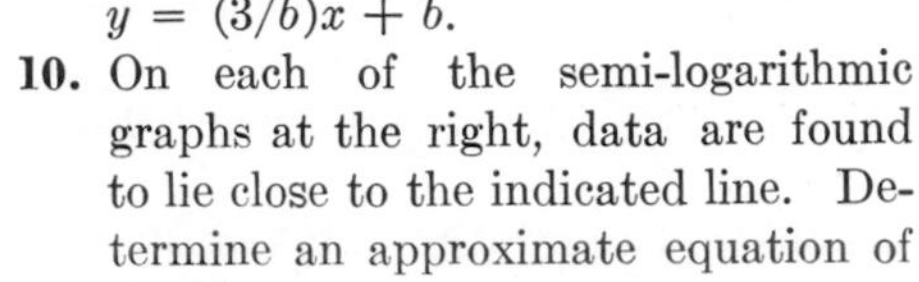

10. On each of the semi-logarithmic graphs at the right, data are found to lie close to the indicated line. Determine an approximate equation of the line.

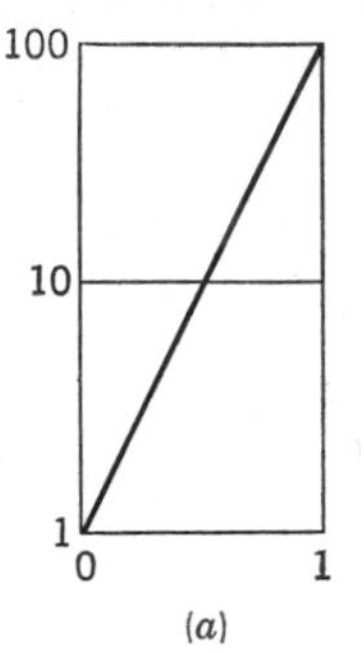

(a)

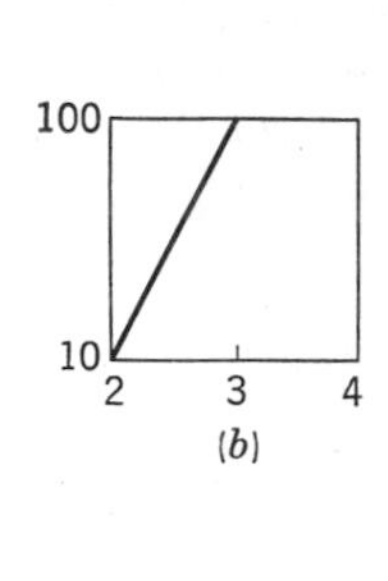

(b)

11. Determine an approximate defining equation for each of the functions, the graphs of which are shown below on logarithmic paper.

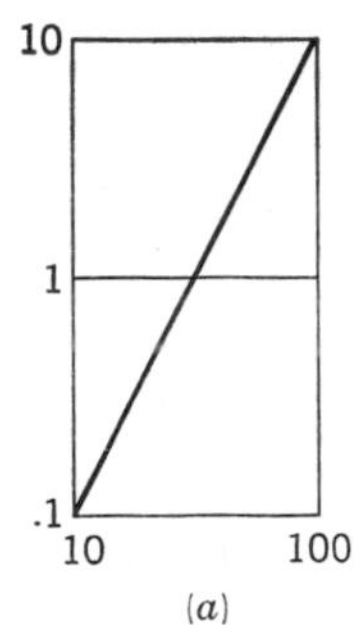

(a)

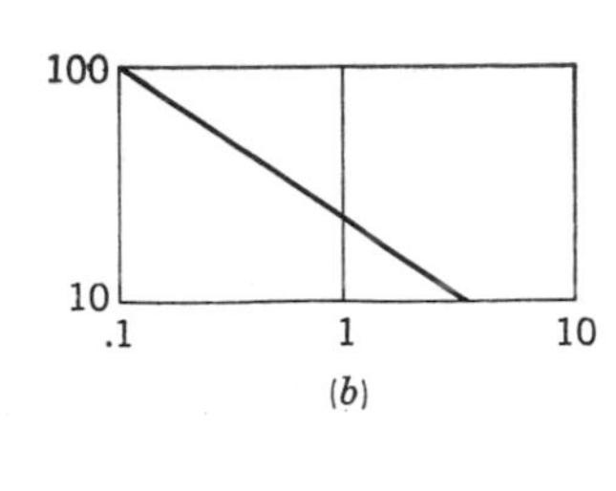

(b)

12. A straight line segment on semi-logarithmic paper contains the points (2, 7) and (5, 25). Determine the slope of the line without the aid of a graph.

REVIEW TEST B

1. Give a verbal comparison of the locus of the equation $y = x^2$ with that of (a) $y = 4x^2$; (b) $4y = x^2$; (c) $y = (x + 2)^2$; (d) $y + 1 = 3(x - 2)^2$.

2. Consider each of the following pairs of equations, and give a verbal comparison of their loci: (a) $y = \ln x$, $y = -2 \ln x$; (b) $y = \text{arc Sin}\, x$, $2y = -\text{arc Sin}\, x$; (c) $xy^2 = 1$, $xy^2 = 4$.

3. Use the method of this chapter to find the coordinates of the vertex of the parabola having the given equation $y = -4x^2 + 2x + 5$.

4. An equation of a parabola is $y = -4x^2 + 2x + 7$. Determine what translation of axes would be required in order that an equation of the parabola, referred to the new axes, would be $y = -4x^2$.

5. A tunnel on a roadway has the parabolic cross-section indicated. If the tunnel is to allow passage for a truck 8 feet wide, without the latter crossing the center-line, what is the maximum height of the truck?

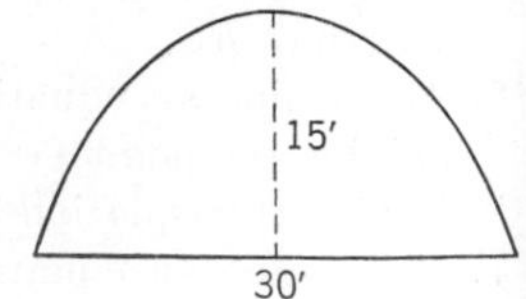

6. Determine an equation of the straight line, parallel to the line having the equation $3x + 4y + 2 = 0$, and having a y-intercept of -4.
7. Determine an equation of the straight line containing the points $(-2, -4)$ and $(4, 8)$.
8. The line having the equation $2x + 3y - 4 = 0$ intersects the y-axis at the point A, and the line having the equation $2x + 5y - 1 = 0$ intersects the x-axis at the point B. What is the slope of the line segment joining A with B?
9. What common characteristic is possessed by all members of the family of lines defined by the equation $y = kx - k$?
10. On each of the following semi-logarithmic graphs, data are found to lie close to the indicated line. Determine an approximate defining equation for each of the functions, determined by the graphs.

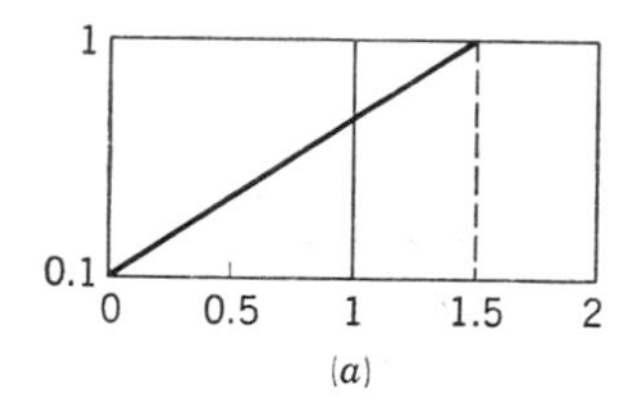

(a)

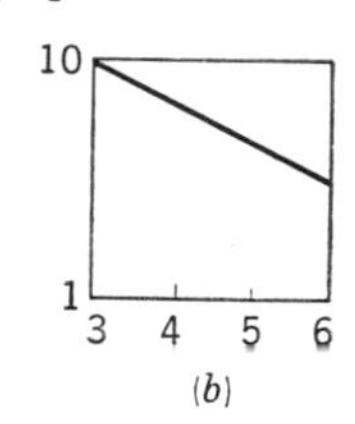

(b)

11. Determine approximate defining equations for each of the functions graphed below on simulated logarithmic paper.

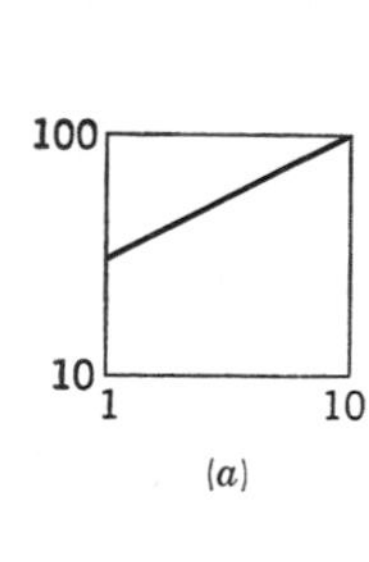

(a)

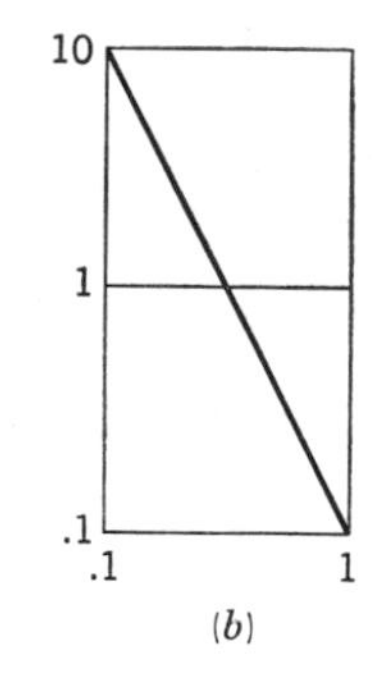

(b)

12. A straight line segment on logarithmic paper contains the points $(5, 21)$ and $(8, 75)$. Determine the slope of the line without the aid of a graph.

REFERENCES

Books

Brixey, John C. and Richard V. Andree, *Fundamentals of College Mathematics*, New York, Holt, 1954. (Chap. 23.)

Slichter, C. S., *Elementary Mathematical Analysis*, New York, McGraw-Hill, 1925. (Chaps. 2 and 8.)

7

FURTHER DEVELOPMENT AND APPLICATIONS OF CIRCULAR FUNCTIONS

I do not know.

J. L. LAGRANGE

7.1 The Distance Between Two Points

It is unfortunate that many students are introduced to the circular functions as functions on a set of angles, and are given the impression that their principal use is in connection with the solution of triangles. In this book, we have defined the circular functions as functions in the set of all real numbers, and have tried to emphasize that it is their periodic nature which makes them of particular importance for a description of natural phenomena. The objective of the present chapter is to derive some of the basic identities pertaining to the circular functions and others closely related to them, and include a few simple applications. But first we need an important formula.

There are two principal uses for a Cartesian coordinate system. One is for a graphical representation of a function or relation in $R^{\#}$, and as such, is a scheme for showing a *correspondence* between two sets of real numbers. For this purpose, it is of little importance whether the scales are uniform, whether the axes are perpendicular, or even whether they are straight; as we have emphasized before, the correspondence between the numbers is the only concern. However, when a Cartesian coordinate system is used for the location of points in a plane, the concept of *distance* enters, and it is necessary to have straight axes with uniform scales and equal units if this concept is to have its usual intuitive meaning; it is also convenient to follow the practice that we have already established of choosing our axes at right angles to each other, thereby making the coordinate system *rectangular*. We shall always assume that our axes have these characteristics, whenever we are concerned with a *distance*, and *all distances on the graph will be measured in the common units of the axes.*

The Fundamental Postulate of Analytic Geometry, enunciated in Chapter 2, states that there is a one-to-one correspondence between the set of points of a line and the set $R^{\#}$ of real numbers. Moreover, this correspondence was used in the construction of an algebraic scale in such a way that the absolute value of the number associated with any point was the measure of length of the segment from the origin to the point, in terms of the scale unit. It is then apparent that the length of the segment on an algebraic scale from the point marked a to the point marked b is $|b - a|$ units. Suppose, now, that $P(x_1, a)$ and $Q(x_2, a)$ are points on a line parallel

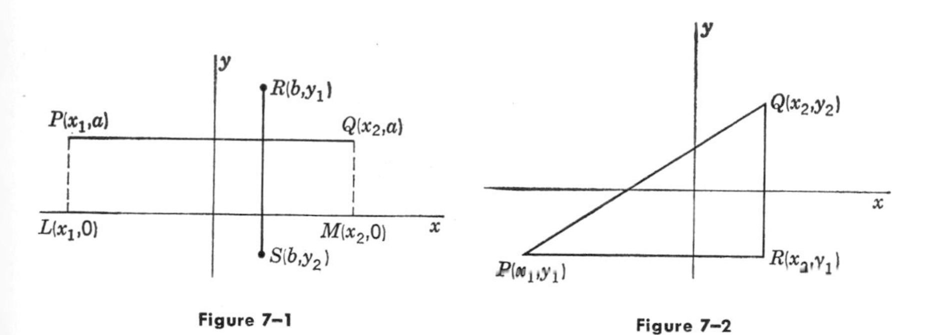

Figure 7–1

Figure 7–2

to the x-axis, as shown in Figure 7–1. If the indicated segments PL and QM are drawn parallel to the y-axis, the segments LM and PQ are of equal length since they are opposite sides of a parallelogram.

We have seen that the length of LM is $|x_2 - x_1|$ units, and so we have the *Lemma:* The length of the line segment joining two points $P(x_1, a)$ and $Q(x_2, a)$ is $|x_2 - x_1|$ units.

A similar discussion, applied to the points $R(b, y_1)$ and $S(b, y_2)$ on a line segment parallel to the y-axis, yields the *Lemma:* The length of the line segment joining two points $R(b, y_1)$ and $S(b, y_2)$ is $|y_2 - y_1|$ units.

We can now apply these two results, along with the Pythagorean Theorem, to obtain the distance between any two points of the xy-plane, where by *distance* we mean the length of the line segment joining the two points. Referring to Figure 7–2, let $P(x_1, y_1)$ and $Q(x_2, y_2)$ be any two such points. If QR and PR are line segments drawn parallel to the y and x axes, respectively, the results above give us the length of PR as $|x_2 - x_1|$ units and the length of QR as $|y_2 - y_1|$ units. With d the measure of distance between P and Q, the Pythagorean Theorem now yields $d^2 = (x_2 - x_1)^2 + (y_2 - y_1)^2$.

THEOREM. The distance between any two points $P(x_1, y_1)$ and $Q(x_2, y_2)$ in the xy-plane is d units, where $d = \sqrt{(x_2 - x_1)^2 + (y_2 - y_1)^2}$.

ILLUSTRATION. Determine the distance between the points $(3, -2)$ and $(-5, 3)$.

Solution. If d is the measure of distance in the given units, the above theorem asserts that $d^2 = (-5 - 3)^2 + (3 + 2)^2 = 64 + 25 = 89$. Thus, $d = \sqrt{89}$, and the desired distance is $\sqrt{89}$ units.

PROBLEM SET 7.1

1. Determine the distance between the indicated points: (*a*) $(-2, 6)$, $(3, 6)$; (*b*) $(3, -4)$, $(3, 8)$; (*c*) $(6, -3)$, $(-4, -3)$.
2. Determine the distance between the indicated points: (*a*) $(0, 0)$, $(-5, 0)$; (*b*) $(2, 3)$, $(-4, 1)$; (*c*) $(4, 8)$, $(-3, -2)$; (*d*) $(1, 2)$, $(2, 2)$.
3. Decide whether or not the triangle, with vertices at $(1, 1)$, $(6, 7)$, and $(-4, 5)$, is right angled.
4. Show that the triangle, with vertices at $(6, -2)$, $(-2, 2)$, and $(1, -2)$, is isosceles.
5. Prove that the diagonals of a rectangle bisect each other.
6. Determine the lengths of the sides of the triangle with vertices at $(1, 3)$, $(4, 7)$, and $(-1, -3)$.
7. Show that the triangle, with vertices at the following points, is right-angled: $(5, -1)$, $(1, -3)$, $(2, 5)$.

7.2 The Addition Theorems

The six basic circular functions, introduced in Chapter 5, are not independent of each other, for there exist many relationships between corresponding functional values. Reference was made in the problems of that chapter to some of these relationships, but we shall restate six of them now; these should be memorized by the student, because of their great importance.

1. $\csc\theta = 1/\sin\theta$.
2. $\sec\theta = 1/\cos\theta$.
3. $\tan\theta = 1/\cot\theta$.
4. $\sin^2\theta + \cos^2\theta = 1$.
5. $1 + \tan^2\theta = \sec^2\theta$.
6. $1 + \cot^2\theta = \csc^2\theta$.

The above equations are *identities* in the sense that they are valid on the nonempty set of real numbers for which both sides are defined. We shall refer to them as the *Fundamental Identities* of the circular functions. Identities (4), (5), and (6) are frequently useful in other forms: for example, $\sin^2\theta = 1 - \cos^2\theta$, $\tan^2\theta = \sec^2\theta - 1$, $\cot^2\theta = \csc^2\theta - 1$, etc.

If θ_1 and θ_2 are elements in the domain of a function f, it is not necessarily true that $\theta_1 + \theta_2$ and $\theta_1 - \theta_2$ are also in this domain. However, when this is the case, it is of interest to discover any relationship between the corresponding four functional values. A special type of function f, called a *linear* function, has the property that $f(\theta_1 + \theta_2) = f(\theta_1) + f(\theta_2)$, as for example the function f defined on $R^{\#}$ by $f(x) = mx$. We have seen before that the graph of this latter function is a straight line, but it should be observed that every function having a straight line graph does not have this linearity property; thus, if f is defined on $R^{\#}$ by $f(x) = 2x + 3$, $f(x_1 + x_2) = 2(x_1 + x_2) + 3 = 2x_1 + 2x_2 + 3$ while $f(x_1) + f(x_2) = 2x_1 + 3 + 2x_2 + 3 = 2x_1 + 2x_2 + 6$. The circular functions are certainly not linear, since we know, for example, that $\sin (\pi/4 + \pi/4) = \sin \pi/2 = 1$, while $\sin \pi/4 + \sin \pi/4 = \sqrt{2}/2 + \sqrt{2}/2 = \sqrt{2}$. It is the purpose of this section to discover what relationship does hold between $\sin \theta_1$, $\sin \theta_2$, and $\sin (\theta_1 \pm \theta_2)$, with a similar investigation for the cosine function.

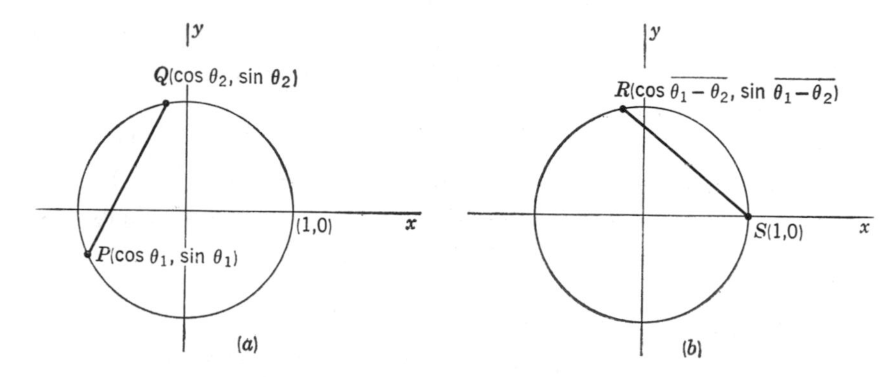

Figure 7–3

Referring to Figure 7–3*a*, let P terminate an arc of signed length θ_1 units and Q terminate an arc of signed length θ_2 units, both arcs in standard position on a unit circle. An arc of signed length $\theta_1 - \theta_2$ units is now considered in standard position on the unit circle of Figure 7–3*b*, with R the terminal point of the arc. The proof of our desired result depends upon the fact that equal arcs of unit circles subtend equal chords, so that the chords PQ and RS are equal in length. The coordinates of the points P, Q, and R are known from the definitions of the basic circular functions, and so using the result of the preceding section we have

$$(\cos \theta_1 - \cos \theta_2)^2 + (\sin \theta_1 - \sin \theta_2)^2 = (\cos \overline{\theta_1 - \theta_2} - 1)^2 + (\sin \overline{\theta_1 - \theta_2} - 0)^2.$$

An application of Fundamental Identity (4) gives us

$$2 - 2(\cos \theta_1 \cos \theta_2 + \sin \theta_1 \sin \theta_2) = 2 - 2 \cos (\theta_1 - \theta_2),$$

which leads to our result:

$$7. \quad \cos (\theta_1 - \theta_2) = \cos \theta_1 \cos \theta_2 + \sin \theta_1 \sin \theta_2.$$

We shall refer to an arc as first-, second-, third-, or fourth-*quadrantal* if, when considered in standard position on a unit circle, it terminates in the first, second, third, or fourth quadrant, respectively. From the definitions of the basic circular functions, applied to the measures of length of all four types of quadrantal arcs (see Problem 17 of Problem Set 5.5), we obtain immediately that $\sin(-\theta) = -\sin\theta$ and $\cos(-\theta) = \cos\theta$. We have established the validity of Formula (7) for all real numbers θ_1 and θ_2, and so let us replace θ_2 by $-\theta_2$ to obtain $\cos(\theta_1 + \theta_2) = \cos\theta_1 \cos(-\theta_2) + \sin\theta_1 \sin(-\theta_2)$. In view of the results immediately preceding, we now have:

$$8. \quad \cos(\theta_1 + \theta_2) = \cos\theta_1 \cos\theta_2 - \sin\theta_1 \sin\theta_2.$$

In Formula (7), if we put $\theta_1 = \pi/2$ and $\theta_2 = \theta$, we obtain $\cos(\pi/2 - \theta) = \sin\theta$. If we now replace θ in this equation by $\pi/2 - \theta$ we obtain $\sin(\pi/2 - \theta) = \cos\theta$.

We now use these two results to derive the other two addition formulas.

$$\begin{aligned}\sin(\theta_1 + \theta_2) &= \cos(\pi/2 - \overline{\theta_1 + \theta_2}) = \cos(\overline{\pi/2 - \theta_1} - \theta_2)\\ &= \cos(\pi/2 - \theta_1)\cos\theta_2 + \sin(\pi/2 - \theta_1)\sin\theta_2\\ &= \sin\theta_1\cos\theta_2 + \cos\theta_1\sin\theta_2.\end{aligned}$$

Similarly,

$$\begin{aligned}\sin(\theta_1 - \theta_2) &= \sin[\theta_1 + (-\theta_2)]\\ &= \sin\theta_1\cos(-\theta_2) + \cos\theta_1\sin(-\theta_2)\\ &= \sin\theta_1\cos\theta_2 - \cos\theta_1\sin\theta_2.\end{aligned}$$

Thus, we have obtained the two following results:

$$9. \quad \sin(\theta_1 - \theta_2) = \sin\theta_1\cos\theta_2 - \cos\theta_1\sin\theta_2.$$

$$10. \quad \sin(\theta_1 + \theta_2) = \sin\theta_1\cos\theta_2 + \cos\theta_1\sin\theta_2.$$

The identities (7), (8), (9), and (10) are the important addition formulas that we set out to derive, and they should be memorized by the student along with identities (1) through (6).

PROBLEM SET 7.2

1. Use Formulas (7) through (10) to prove the following identities: (*a*) $\tan(\theta_1 + \theta_2) = (\tan\theta_1 + \tan\theta_2)/(1 - \tan\theta_1\tan\theta_2)$; (*b*) $\tan(\theta_1 - \theta_2) = (\tan\theta_1 - \tan\theta_2)/(1 + \tan\theta_1\tan\theta_2)$.

2. Put $\theta_1 = \theta_2 = \theta$ in Identity (10) to obtain $\sin 2\theta = 2\sin\theta\cos\theta$.

3. Put $\theta_1 = \theta_2 = \theta$ in Identity (8) to obtain (*a*) $\cos 2\theta = \cos^2\theta - \sin^2\theta$; (*b*) $\cos 2\theta = 1 - 2\sin^2\theta$; (*c*) $\cos 2\theta = 2\cos^2\theta - 1$.

4. Use the results of Problem 3 to show that

(*a*) $\sin\theta = \sqrt{\dfrac{1-\cos 2\theta}{2}}$, if θ is the measure of length of a first- or second-quadrantal arc on a unit circle;

$\sin\theta = -\sqrt{\dfrac{1-\cos 2\theta}{2}}$, if θ is the measure of length of a third- or fourth-quadrantal arc on a unit circle.

(*b*) $\cos\theta = \sqrt{\dfrac{1+\cos 2\theta}{2}}$, if θ is the measure of length of a first- or fourth-quadrantal arc on a unit circle;

$\cos\theta = -\sqrt{\dfrac{1+\cos 2\theta}{2}}$, if θ is the measure of length of a second- or third-quadrantal arc on a unit circle.

5. Use the results of Problem 4 to prove that

(*a*) $\tan\theta = \sqrt{\dfrac{1-\cos 2\theta}{1+\cos 2\theta}}$, if θ is the measure of length of a first- or third-quadrantal arc on a unit circle;

$\tan\theta = -\sqrt{\dfrac{1-\cos 2\theta}{1+\cos 2\theta}}$, if θ is the measure of length of a second- or fourth-quadrantal arc on a unit circle.

6. If $\tan\theta$ is defined, prove that

(*a*) $\tan\theta = \dfrac{1-\cos 2\theta}{\sin 2\theta}$; (*b*) $\tan\theta = \dfrac{\sin 2\theta}{1+\cos 2\theta}$.

7. Use Identities (9) and (10) to show that $\sin\theta_1\cos\theta_2 = (1/2)[\sin(\theta_1-\theta_2) + \sin(\theta_1+\theta_2)]$.

8. Use Identities (7) and (8) to show that

(*a*) $\sin\theta_1\sin\theta_2 = (1/2)[\cos(\theta_1-\theta_2) - \cos(\theta_1+\theta_2)]$;

(*b*) $\cos\theta_1\cos\theta_2 = (1/2)[\cos(\theta_1-\theta_2) + \cos(\theta_1+\theta_2)]$.

9. Put $\theta_1+\theta_2 = X$ and $\theta_1-\theta_2 = Y$ in the results of Problems 7 and 8 to obtain

(*a*) $\sin X + \sin Y = 2\sin\dfrac{X+Y}{2}\cos\dfrac{X-Y}{2}$;

(*b*) $\sin X - \sin Y = 2\cos\dfrac{X+Y}{2}\sin\dfrac{X-Y}{2}$;

(*c*) $\cos X + \cos Y = 2\cos\dfrac{X+Y}{2}\cos\dfrac{X-Y}{2}$;

(*d*) $\cos X - \cos Y = -2\sin\dfrac{X+Y}{2}\sin\dfrac{X-Y}{2}$.

Note. In the following problems, use may be made of the results of Problems 1 through 9 as well as Identities (1) through (10).

10. Express each of the following as the value of a circular function at θ: (*a*) $\cos(\pi/2-\theta)$; (*b*) $\sin(\pi/3+\theta)$; (*c*) $\sin(2\pi/3-\theta)$; (*d*) $\tan(\pi/4+\theta)$; (*e*) $\tan(2\pi/3-\theta)$; (*f*) $\cos(\theta-3\pi/4)$.

11. Prove that the following are identities:

(*a*) $\sin(\pi/3+\theta) - \cos(\pi/6+\theta) = \sin\theta$;

(*b*) $\cos(\theta+\pi/6) - \cos(\theta-\pi/6) = -\sin\theta$;

(*c*) $\cos(\theta_1-\theta_2)\cos(\theta_1+\theta_2) = \cos^2\theta_1\cos^2\theta_2 - \sin^2\theta_1\sin^2\theta_2$.

12. Determine $\sin(\theta_1 + \theta_2)$ and $\cos(\theta_1 + \theta_2)$, given that (*a*) $\sin\theta_1 = 3/5$, $\cos\theta_2 = 5/13$, and both θ_1 and θ_2 are measures of length of a first-quadrantal arc on a unit circle; (*b*) $\tan\theta_1 = -5/12$, with θ_1 the measure of length of a second-quadrantal arc on a unit circle, and $\tan\theta_2 = -15/8$, with θ_2 the measure of length of a fourth-quadrantal arc on a unit circle.

13. Determine $\sin(\theta_1 - \theta_2)$ and $\cos(\theta_1 - \theta_2)$, given that (*a*) $\sin\theta_1 = 7/25$ and $\tan\theta_2 = -8/15$, with both θ_1 and θ_2 the measures of length of second-quadrantal arcs on a unit circle; (*b*) $\cos\theta_1 = 1/4$ and $\cot\theta_2 = 1/2$, with θ_1 and θ_2 the measures, respectively, of fourth- and third-quadrantal arcs on a unit circle.

14. Derive formulas, involving functional values at θ, for: (*a*) $\sin 3\theta$; (*b*) $\cos 3\theta$; (*c*) $\tan 3\theta$.

15. Use the results of Problem 4 to determine (*a*) $\sin\pi/8$; (*b*) $\cos\pi/12$; (*c*) $\sin 5\pi/12$.

16. Use the results of Problems 2 and 3 to determine (*a*) $\sin 2\theta$, if $\cos\theta = 1/2$ and θ is the measure of length of a fourth-quadrantal arc on a unit circle; (*b*) $\cos 2\theta$, if $\sin\theta = 2/3$ and θ is the measure of length of a second-quadrantal arc on a unit circle; (*c*) $\sin 2\theta$, if $\sin\theta = -1/3$ and θ is the measure of length of a third-quadrantal arc on a unit circle.

17. Use the results of Problem 5 to determine (*a*) $\tan\pi/12$; (*b*) $\tan\theta$ if $\sin 2\theta = 3/4$ and 2θ is the measure of length of a second-quadrantal arc on a unit circle; (*c*) $\tan\theta$ if $\cos 2\theta = -1/3$ and 2θ is the measure of length of a third-quadrantal arc on a unit circle.

18. Use the results of Problems 7 and 8 to express each product as a sum or difference: (*a*) $2\sin\pi/2\cos\pi/4$; (*b*) $2\cos\pi/3\cos\pi/6$; (*c*) $\sin 2x\sin 5x$; (*d*) $\cos 7x\sin 2x$; (*e*) $\cos 5x\cos 4x$; (*f*) $\sin 2\pi/3\sin 3\pi/4$.

19. Use the results of Problem 9 to express each sum or difference as a product: (*a*) $\sin\pi/3 + \sin 3\pi/4$; (*b*) $\cos\pi/3 - \cos\pi/4$; (*c*) $\sin 3\pi/4 - \sin\pi/3$; (*d*) $\sin 3x + \sin 5x$; (*e*) $\cos 10x - \cos 4x$; (*f*) $\cos 2x + \cos 6x$.

20. Using the known functional values derived in Chapter 5, determine the sine, cosine, and tangent of each of the following real numbers, leaving the answer in fractional or radical form: (*a*) $7\pi/12$; (*b*) $7\pi/8$; (*c*) $13\pi/8$; (*d*) $19\pi/12$.

7.3 The Important Identities

The identities established in Problems 1 through 9 of the preceding section are important in applications of the circular functions. No one can be proficient in such applications without a knowledge of these identities, and all of them should be memorized. However, a word of caution is added. These identities may be written in many different forms which should be recognized as equivalent. For example, the result of Problem 2, which we expressed as $\sin 2\theta = 2\sin\theta\cos\theta$, could also be written as $\sin\theta = 2\sin\theta/2\cos\theta/2$ or $\sin 4\theta = 2\sin 2\theta\cos 2\theta$—and in many other ways. The important point to notice, in connection with this identity, is that the number in the domain on the left side of the equality is *twice* that on the right, or alternatively, the number in the domain on the right side is *half* that on the left. The identity, in its most general form, could then be written in either of the following ways: (*a*) sin (number) = 2 sin (half number) cos (half number); (*b*) 2 sin (number) cos (number) = sin (twice number).

The purpose of this section is to enable the student to become more familiar with these basic identities, and to this end we are restating them in their customary form. They will be labeled from (11) on, since the first 10 basic identities were listed previously.

11. (*a*) $\tan(\theta_1 + \theta_2) = (\tan \theta_1 + \tan \theta_2)/(1 - \tan \theta_1 \tan \theta_2)$.
    (*b*) $\tan(\theta_1 - \theta_2) = (\tan \theta_1 - \tan \theta_2)/(1 + \tan \theta_1 \tan \theta_2)$.
12. $\sin 2\theta = 2 \sin \theta \cos \theta$.
13. $\cos 2\theta = \cos^2 \theta - \sin^2 \theta = 2 \cos^2 \theta - 1 = 1 - 2 \sin^2 \theta$.
14. $\sin \theta/2 = \sqrt{\frac{1 - \cos \theta}{2}}$, if $\theta/2$ is the measure of length of a first– or second-quadrantal arc on a unit circle;

$\sin \theta/2 = -\sqrt{\frac{1 - \cos \theta}{2}}$, if $\theta/2$ is the measure of length of a third– or fourth-quadrantal arc on a unit circle;

$\sin^2 \theta/2 = \frac{1 - \cos \theta}{2}$.

15. $\cos \theta/2 = \sqrt{\frac{1 + \cos \theta}{2}}$, if $\theta/2$ is the measure of length of a first– or fourth-quadrantal arc on a unit circle;

$\cos \theta/2 = -\sqrt{\frac{1 + \cos \theta}{2}}$, if $\theta/2$ is the measure of length of a second– or third-quadrantal arc on a unit circle;

$\cos^2 \theta/2 = \frac{1 + \cos \theta}{2}$.

16. $\tan \theta/2 = \sqrt{\frac{1 - \cos \theta}{1 + \cos \theta}}$, if $\theta/2$ is the measure of length of a first– or third-quadrantal arc on a unit circle.

$\tan \theta/2 = -\sqrt{\frac{1 - \cos \theta}{1 + \cos \theta}}$, if $\theta/2$ is the measure of length of a second– or fourth-quadrantal arc on a unit circle.

17. $\tan \theta/2 = \frac{1 - \cos \theta}{\sin \theta} = \frac{\sin \theta}{1 + \cos \theta}$. These identities are the rationalized forms of those in (16).
18. (*a*) $\sin \theta_1 \cos \theta_2 = (1/2)[\sin (\theta_1 - \theta_2) + \sin (\theta_1 + \theta_2)]$.
    (*b*) $\sin \theta_1 \sin \theta_2 = (1/2)[\cos (\theta_1 - \theta_2) - \cos (\theta_1 + \theta_2)]$.
    (*c*) $\cos \theta_1 \cos \theta_2 = (1/2)[\cos (\theta_1 - \theta_2) + \cos (\theta_1 + \theta_2)]$.

19. (a) $\sin \theta_1 + \sin \theta_2 = 2 \sin \frac{\theta_1 + \theta_2}{2} \cos \frac{\theta_1 - \theta_2}{2}.$

(b) $\sin \theta_1 - \sin \theta_2 = 2 \cos \frac{\theta_1 + \theta_2}{2} \sin \frac{\theta_1 - \theta_2}{2}.$

(c) $\cos \theta_1 + \cos \theta_2 = 2 \cos \frac{\theta_1 + \theta_2}{2} \cos \frac{\theta_1 - \theta_2}{2}.$

(d) $\cos \theta_1 - \cos \theta_2 = -2 \sin \frac{\theta_1 + \theta_2}{2} \sin \frac{\theta_1 - \theta_2}{2}.$

Our definition of an identity $f(\theta) = g(\theta)$ has stated that the set of elements θ, common to the domains of f and g, must not be empty. In general, this "identity" relation is not *transitive*: i.e., if f, g, and h are functions such that $f(\theta) = g(\theta)$ and $g(\theta) = h(\theta)$ are both identities, it is not necessarily true that the domains of f and h have any elements in common, and so $f(\theta) = h(\theta)$ may possibly not be an identity. In the case of identities involving circular functions, however, we may always assume this transitive characteristic, and the validity of an identity may be established by means of a "chain" of identities as illustrated below. One important purpose in such verifications is to enable the student to gain familiarity with the basic identities; but it is also frequently of interest to know whether or not two apparently different expressions are really equivalent, and to be able to transform one of them into the other.

ILLUSTRATION 1. Prove that $\tan \theta \csc \theta = \tan \theta \sin \theta + \cos \theta$ is an identity.

Proof.

$$\tan \theta \csc \theta = \frac{\sin \theta}{\cos \theta} \frac{1}{\sin \theta} = \frac{1}{\cos \theta} = \sec \theta.$$

$$\tan \theta \sin \theta + \cos \theta = \frac{\sin \theta}{\cos \theta} \sin \theta + \frac{\cos^2 \theta}{\cos \theta} = \frac{\sin^2 \theta + \cos^2 \theta}{\cos \theta}$$

$$= \frac{1}{\cos \theta} = \sec \theta.$$

Since both sides of the given equality are identically equal to $\sec \theta$, the identity is proved.

ILLUSTRATION 2. Prove that $\cos^6 \theta + \sin^6 \theta = 1 - (3/4) \sin^2 2\theta$ is an identity.

Proof.

$$\begin{aligned} \cos^6 \theta + \sin^6 \theta &= (\cos^2 \theta + \sin^2 \theta)(\cos^4 \theta - \cos^2 \theta \sin^2 \theta + \sin^4 \theta) \\ &= (1)(\cos^4 \theta - \cos^2 \theta \sin^2 \theta + \sin^4 \theta) \\ &= (\cos^2 \theta + \sin^2 \theta)^2 - 3 \cos^2 \theta \sin^2 \theta \\ &= 1 - (3/4)(4 \sin^2 \theta \cos^2 \theta) \\ &= 1 - (3/4) \sin^2 2\theta, \text{ as desired.} \end{aligned}$$

ILLUSTRATION 3. Prove that $\sin^2 5\theta - \sin^2 3\theta = \sin 8\theta \sin 2\theta$ is an identity.

Proof.

$$\begin{aligned}\sin^2 5\theta - \sin^2 3\theta &= (\sin 5\theta + \sin 3\theta)(\sin 5\theta - \sin 3\theta)\\ &= (2 \sin 4\theta \cos \theta)(2 \cos 4\theta \sin \theta)\\ &= (2 \sin 4\theta \cos 4\theta)(2 \sin \theta \cos \theta)\\ &= \sin 8\theta \sin 2\theta, \text{ as desired.}\end{aligned}$$

PROBLEM SET 7.3

1. Give a simple illustration of the fact that if $f(\theta) = g(\theta)$ and $g(\theta) = h(\theta)$ are identities, for functions f, g, and h, it is not necessarily true that $f(\theta) = h(\theta)$ is an identity.
2. One part of Identity (13) may be expressed as $\cos \theta = \cos^2 \theta/2 - \sin^2 \theta/2$. Express this same identity in another form.
3. Express Identity (14) in another form. (See Problem 2.)
4. Express Identity (17) in another form. (See Problem 2.)

Establish the validity of the identities in Problems 5 through 24.

5. $\dfrac{1 + \sin \theta}{\cos \theta} = \sec \theta + \tan \theta.$

6. $\csc \theta - \sin \theta = \sin \theta \cot^2 \theta.$

7. $\dfrac{1 - 2 \cos^2 \theta}{\sin \theta \cos \theta} = \tan \theta - \cot \theta.$

8. $(\tan^2 \theta)/(\sin^2 \theta) = 1 + \tan^2 \theta.$

9. $\dfrac{\cot \theta - \tan \theta}{\cot \theta + \tan \theta} = 1 - 2 \sin^2 \theta.$

10. $\dfrac{\sin 2\theta}{2} = \dfrac{\tan \theta}{1 + \tan^2 \theta}.$

11. $\sec 2\theta = \dfrac{\sec^2 \theta}{2 - \sec^2 \theta}.$

12. $2 \csc \theta = \tan \theta/2 + \cot \theta/2.$

13. $\dfrac{\cos 3\theta - \cos \theta}{\sin 3\theta - \sin \theta} = \dfrac{2 \tan \theta}{\tan^2 \theta - 1}.$

14. $\dfrac{\sin 2\theta + \sin \theta}{1 + \cos 2\theta + \cos \theta} = \tan \theta.$

15. $\dfrac{\sec \theta}{\sec \theta - \tan \theta} = \sec^2 \theta + \sec \theta \tan \theta.$

16. $\dfrac{1}{1 - \sin \theta} = \sec^2 \theta + \sec \theta \tan \theta.$

17. $\tan (\pi/4 + \theta) = \dfrac{1 + \tan \theta}{1 - \tan \theta}.$

18. $\cos 2\theta \cos \theta + \sin 2\theta \sin \theta = \cos \theta.$

19. $\dfrac{\cos 2\theta}{\sec \theta} - \dfrac{\sin 2\theta}{\csc \theta} = \cos 3\theta.$

20. $(\sin \theta/2 + \cos \theta/2)^2 = 1 + \sin \theta.$

21. $\dfrac{\sec \theta - 1}{\sec \theta} = 2 \sin^2 \theta/2.$

22. $\dfrac{\cot \theta - 1}{\cot \theta + 1} = \dfrac{1 - \sin 2\theta}{\cos 2\theta}.$

23. $\dfrac{\sin 2\theta + \sin 3\theta}{\cos 2\theta - \cos 3\theta} = \cot \theta/2.$ **24.** $\dfrac{\cos 2\theta - \cos 12\theta}{\sin 12\theta + \sin 2\theta} = \tan 5\theta.$

In Problems 25 through 32 change sums and differences into products, and products into sums or differences.

25. $\sin 8\theta + \sin 4\theta.$ **26.** $\sin 7\theta - \sin 5\theta.$
27. $\cos 3\theta + \cos 8\theta.$ **28.** $\cos 5\theta - \cos \theta.$
29. $2 \sin 3\theta \cos \theta.$ **30.** $2 \cos 5\theta \sin 4\theta.$
31. $\sin \theta/4 \sin 3\theta/4.$ **32.** $\cos 2\theta/3 \cos 5\theta/3.$

In Problems 33 through 40, use Identities (7) through (10) to express each of the indicated functional values as either $f(\theta)$ or $-f(\theta)$, where f is an appropriate circular function; check the results by using the Reduction Principle of Chapter 5, assuming $0 < \theta < \pi/2$.

33. $\sin (\pi + \theta).$ **34.** $\cos (\pi/2 + \theta).$
35. $\tan (\pi - \theta).$ **36.** $\sin (3\pi/2 - \theta).$
37. $\cos (\pi/2 + \theta).$ **38.** $\sin (\pi - \theta).$
39. $\tan (\pi/2 + \theta).$ **40.** $\sin (2\pi - \theta).$

7.4 Simple Harmonic Motion

We have defined the sine and cosine of a real number θ to be, respectively, the ordinate and abscissa of the terminal point of an arc of length θ units, placed in standard position on a unit circle. In Figure 7–4, DQ is

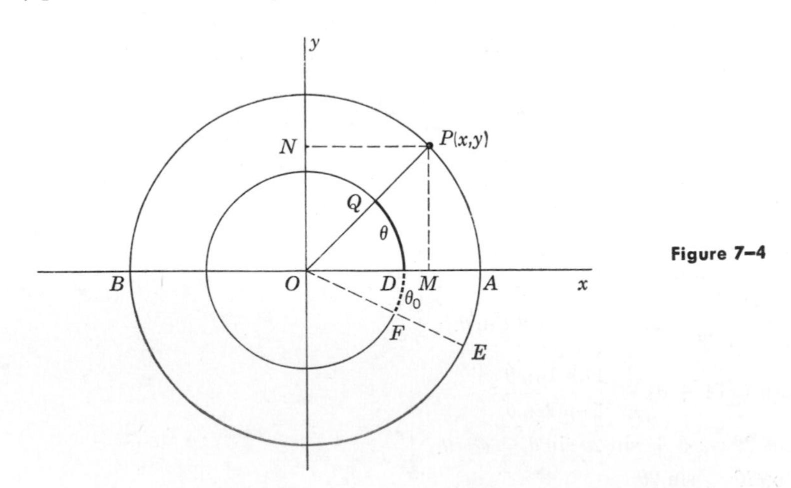

Figure 7–4

such an arc, with P the point at which the extended radius OQ meets a concentric circle that has radii r units in length. A consideration of similar triangles shows that the abscissa and ordinate of P are r times those of Q, and so if (x, y) are the coordinates of P, $x = r \cos \theta$ and $y = r \sin \theta$.

The points $M(x, 0)$ and $N(0, y)$, shown in the diagram, are called the *projections* of P on the x-axis and y-axis, respectively.

In the discussions of this chapter, we shall consider a *particle* to be a portion of matter so small that its position may always be approximated by a single point. Let us suppose that a particle p is moving in a counterclockwise direction around the circle having radii r units in length, at a uniform speed of kr units of distance per unit of time. We are going to be interested in the motions of two other particles p_x and p_y, located in such a way that when p is at P, p_x is at M and p_y is at N. Let us suppose first that the motion of p starts at A. Then as p moves around the circle, p_x moves from A to the left along the x-axis with increasing speed until it reaches O, and then with decreasing speed until it reaches B; p_x then reverses direction and moves to the right with increasing speed until it reaches O, and then with decreasing speed until it returns to A. The whole motion is then repeated, and a somewhat similar analysis applies to the motion of the particle p_y on the y-axis. In t units of time, the particle p will traverse an arc of length krt units; and if P is the position of the particle at this time, the corresponding arc DQ on the unit circle will be kt units in length, i.e., $\theta = kt$. It follows from the discussion of the preceding paragraph that if P is the point (x, y), $x = r \cos kt$ and $y = r \sin kt$, and these equations describe the respective positions of p_x and p_y in t units of time.

In the preceding description of the motions of p_x and p_y, we assumed that time was measured from some instant when p was at A, on the x-axis. However, if we measure time from an instant when p is at some other point E, so that the length of the indicated arc FD is θ_0 units, the measure of length of arc DQ—i.e., θ—will be $kt - \theta_0$. Thus, in t units of time, the positions of p_x and p_y will be given by $x = r \cos (kt - \theta_0)$ and $y = r \sin (kt - \theta_0)$, respectively.

DEFINITION. If a particle moves on a straight line in such a way that a measure x (or y) of its distance from some given point on the line is given by an expression of the form $x = r \cos (kt - \theta_0)$[or $y = r \sin (kt - \theta_0)$], with t a measure of time and r, k, and θ_0 given numbers, the motion of the particle is said to be *simple harmonic*.

We have then shown that if a particle moves with a uniform speed on the circumference of a circle, the motion of another particle, the position of which at any instant is the projection of the position of the original particle on any diameter of the circle, will be simple harmonic. It is clear that this type of motion is oscillatory and keeps repeating as time goes on. The time required for one cycle of the motion is called the *period* of the motion, and if we denote an appropriate measure of the period by T, we have $T = 2\pi/k$. The number of cycles of the motion per unit of time is called the *frequency*, and if we denote this by N, we have $N = 1/T = k/2\pi$. The number r is the measure of *amplitude* of the motion, which is the maximum displacement of the particle from its central position. When a simple harmonic motion is described by either of the equations given in the definition, $kt - \theta_0$ is the measure of *phase* of the motion in t units of time, while $-\theta_0$ is the measure of *initial phase;* it should be emphasized, however, that these numbers are not characteristics of the motion but rather of the equation that describes the motion.

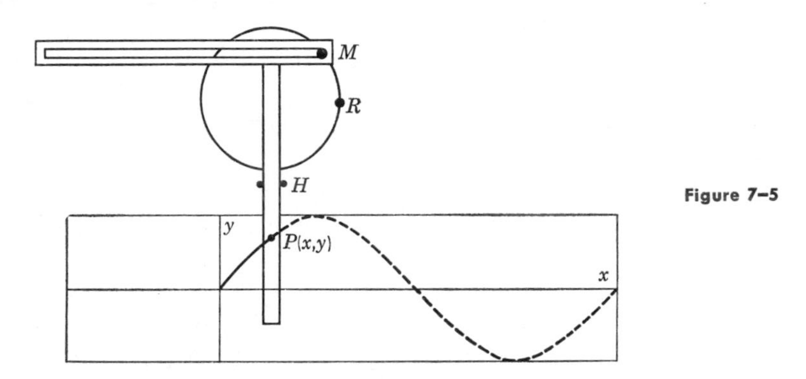

Figure 7–5

In Figure 7–5 we have shown a way in which simple harmonic motion can be generated by mechanical means. Suppose that the wheel, pictured in the diagram, is rotating uniformly in a counterclockwise direction, the wheel having a pin at M which fits into and is free to move in a slot of the indicated cross-arm. The vertical bar is restricted to vertical motion by the guides at H, so that any point P on this bar will execute simple harmonic motion.

If a tracing pencil is attached to the vertical bar at P, bearing upon a piece of paper moving with constant speed to the left, the pencil will trace out a distorted sine curve. Let us choose a system of Cartesian coordinate axes on the paper, so that P will be at the origin when the pin on the wheel is at R. If we measure time from this instant, in t units of time the position of P, with respect to this coordinate system, will be given by $x = Vt$ and $y = r \sin kt$, where V, r, and k are appropriate measures of the speed of the moving paper, the length of a radius of the wheel, and the speed of a particle on the rim of the wheel. These equations are known as *parametric equations* of the curve traced out by the pencil at P, with t the *parameter*, and by eliminating t we obtain the ordinary equation of the curve. Thus, since $t = x/V$, we have $y = r \sin kx/V$, an equation of a distorted sine curve.

Compound harmonic motion is the result of compounding simple harmonic motions, having frequencies that are multiples of a given first or *fundamental* frequency. Thus, $y = a \sin kt + b \sin 2kt$ describes a compound harmonic motion, obtained by the superposition of a simple harmonic motion with period and amplitude $2\pi/k$ and a units, respectively, upon a simple harmonic motion with respective measures of period and amplitude of π/k and b. If a trace of this motion were to be made, an equation of the resulting curve is $y = a \sin kx/V + b \sin 2kx/V$. It was shown by Fourier in 1822 that any periodic function f, satisfying certain conditions, can be represented in the form $f(x) = a_0 + a_1 \cos x + a_2 \cos 2x + a_3 \cos 3x + \cdots + b_1 \sin x + b_2 \sin 2x + b_3 \sin 3x + \cdots$. A study of the methods of determining the sine and cosine components of a periodic function is called *harmonic* analysis, and is studied in more advanced courses. Since the curve, associated with a periodic function, may be regarded as the trace of some periodic motion, it appears that most periodic motions can be resolved into simple harmonic components; this type of motion is then very important. It should be observed that since $\cos kt = \sin (kt + \pi/2)$, the motions defined by $y = \sin kt$ and $y = \cos kt$ differ only in phase, the phase difference being $\pi/2$.

PROBLEM SET 7.4

1. Determine the period and amplitude of each of the following simple harmonic motions: (*a*) $y = 2 \sin 3t$; (*b*) $x = 3 \cos 4t$; (*c*) $y = 3 \sin (10t - \pi/3)$; (*d*) $x = 4 \cos (2t/3 + \pi/4)$; (*e*) $y = 7 \cos 2\pi t$; (*f*) $x = 3 \sin \pi t$.
2. Determine the frequency and initial phase of each of the simple harmonic motions in Problem 1.
3. Explain the difference between the simple harmonic motion defined by $y = 3 \sin \pi t$ and that defined by $y = 3 \sin (\pi t - \pi/4)$.
4. A curve may be said to be an *undistorted* model of another curve if the points of the two curves may be made to correspond in such a way, that the ratios of the abscissas and the ratios of the ordinates of corresponding points are respectively equal. What would V need to be if the curve of Figure 7–5 is to be an undistorted model of the basic since curve? Compare this velocity of V units with that of the moving pin, shown in the figure at M.
5. Explain any differences between the simple harmonic motions defined by the equations $y = 3 \sin \pi t$, $y = 6 \sin \pi t$, and $y = 3 \sin (\pi t + \pi/3)$.
6. Referring to Figure 7–4, assume that the particle p is initially at A and moves counterclockwise around the circle with a speed of 2 centimeters per second. If the length of a radius of the circle is 10 centimeters, write the equations of motion for the particles p_x and p_y.
7. The period of a "seconds" pendulum is 2 seconds. If the bob swings a maximum of 3 centimeters on each side of its lowest position, write an equation for the motion of the bob; consider the motion to be approximately rectilinear and simple harmonic, and measure time from an instant when the bob is at the end of a swing.
8. Write an equation for the motion of the bob of a pendulum identical with

that in Problem 7, if the second pendulum is released 1/2 second after the release of the first pendulum.

9. An object moves on a straight line in such a way that a measure x of its distance from a given point on the line in t units of time is given by $x = 4\cos^2 t$. Show that the motion is simple harmonic, and determine its amplitude and period.
10. Compare the simple harmonic motions defined by $y = 2\sin 2t$ and $y = 3\cos(2t - 2)$.

7.5 Waves, Progressive and Stationary

Let us suppose that a progressive wave is present on the surface of a medium, and that the surface particles in a plane perpendicular to the crests are located at any instant on the points of a distorted sine curve. An example of such a wave is a ripple on the surface of a lake or pond, or the wave that travels down a rope when one end is rapidly shaken. The ordinary waves on an ocean or lake are not of this type, however, for they are not sinusoidal in form. We wish to find an equation which determines at each instant the position of any surface particle that lies in the plane mentioned above. This will be called an *equation of the wave.*

We may choose our Cartesian coordinate axes, so that at the moment from which we are measuring time, an equation of the instantaneous fixed wave can be assumed to be $y = a \sin hx$. We know from Theorem 7 on Graphing in Chapter 6, that a replacement of x by $x - b$ in the given equation of a curve replaces the curve by a similar one displaced b units from the original in the positive direction of x. A progressive wave may be regarded as a fixed wave which is being continually displaced; thus, if the measure of velocity of the wave is V, an equation of the wave form present in the plane in t units of time may be given by $y = a \sin h(x - Vt)$. This is an equation of the wave, and if we replace hV by k, we can write $y = a \sin(hx - kt)$ as an equivalent equation. The numbers x and y are the coordinates of a point in the xy-plane at which some particle on the surface of the medium is located in t units of time. We use a terminology similar to that of simple harmonic motion and refer to a as the measure of *amplitude* and $hx - kt$ as the measure of *phase* of the wave.

When a wave of the type just described passes through a medium, the individual particles of matter do not move in the direction of the wave; for we may examine the motion of such a particle by putting $x = c$ in the wave equation, the number c being the x-coordinate of the particle. The position of this particle is then given at any time by the equation $y = a \sin(hx - kt) = -a\sin(kt - hc) = a\sin(kt - hc - \pi)$, which shows that the motion is simple harmonic; the period is $2\pi/k$ and the initial phase is $-hc - \pi$, the latter varying with the particle under consideration. Thus, if a progressive wave passes through a medium having a horizontal surface, the surface particles will oscillate up and down in a motion which is simple harmonic of the same period as the wave.

The *wave length* of a progressive wave is the horizontal distance between corresponding points on successive cycles, and this distance is clearly the same as the corresponding distance on the initial sine curve, which has the assumed equation $y = a \sin hx$. Let us designate the measure of wave length of the progressive wave by L. Then, since the abscissa of each point of the curve defined by $y = a \sin hx$ is $1/h$ times as great as the abscissa of the corresponding point on the locus of $y = \sin x$ (Theorem 6 on Graphing in Chapter 6), and the period of this latter curve is 2π, it follows that $L = 2\pi/h$. Note that we refer to the *period* of a stationary sine curve and the *wave length* of the associated progressive wave, but the two are equal.

The *period* of a progressive wave is the time required for the wave to travel a distance of one wave length. Thus, if T and V are respective corresponding measures of period and velocity, $L = VT$ and so $T = L/V = 2\pi/hV = 2\pi/k$. The number N of periods per unit of time is called the *frequency* of the wave, and so $N = 1/T = k/2\pi$. Since $h = 2\pi/L$ and $k = 2\pi/T$, an equation of a progressive wave may be written as either $y = a \sin 2\pi(x/L - t/T)$ or $y = a \sin \dfrac{2\pi}{L}(x - Vt)$.

Consider now two progressive waves having the respective equations $y = a \sin \dfrac{2\pi}{L}(x - Vt)$ and $y = a \sin \dfrac{2\pi}{L}(x - Vt - E)$. These waves have the same amplitude, wave length, and velocity of propagation, but at any instant the second equation represents a sine curve which is E units beyond the position of that represented by the first equation, in the direction of motion of the wave. We refer to E as the *lead* or *lag* of the second wave over the first, according as E is positive or negative.

We have already referred to the high points of a wave as the *crests*, while the low points are called *troughs* and the midway points are the *nodes*. When a violin string is vibrated it assumes a sinusoidal form, but there is no progressive wave motion in evidence and the nodes, crests, and troughs appear to be stationary. Such a wave is known as a *stationary* wave. It is well known that when a violin string vibrates, it can do so in segments; thus, it may have many nodes if it is sounding a "harmonic." The surface of a lake may also vibrate in this way, in which case the stationary wave is called a *seiche*.

A stationary wave in a medium may always be considered to be the result of a progressive wave traveling in one direction and its reflection traveling in the opposite direction. If we assume no energy losses in the reflection, equations of such a pair of waves may be written: $y = a \sin (hx - kt)$; $y = a \sin (hx + kt)$. In this case, we are considering the waves to be moving in a direction parallel to the x-axis. Since the energy of each wave may be considered to be imparted simultaneously to the particles of the medium, the position (x, y) of an arbitrary particle on the surface of the medium in the plane under consideration will be given by the equation

$$\begin{aligned} y &= a \sin (hx - kt) + a \sin (hx + kt) \\ &= a[\sin (hx - kt) + \sin (hx + kt)] \\ &= 2a \cos kt \sin hx \text{ (Identity 19a of Section 7.3).} \end{aligned}$$

If we replace k and h by $2\pi/T$ and $2\pi/L$, respectively, we obtain $y = 2a \cos \frac{2\pi t}{T} \sin \frac{2\pi x}{L}$ as an alternate equation of a stationary wave.

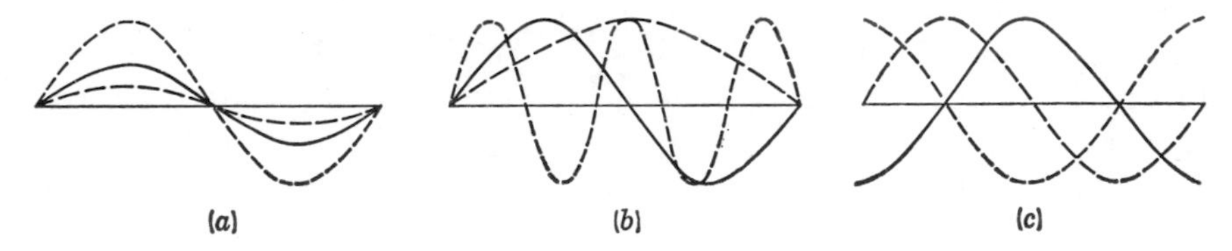

Figure 7–6

We may consider $|2a \cos 2\pi t/T|$ as measuring the ever-changing amplitude of the sine curve defined by $y = (2a \cos 2\pi t/T) \sin 2\pi x/L$. For example, as t changes from 0 to $T/2$, the amplitude changes from $2a$ units through 0 and back to $2a$ units in length, the curve being now reflected in

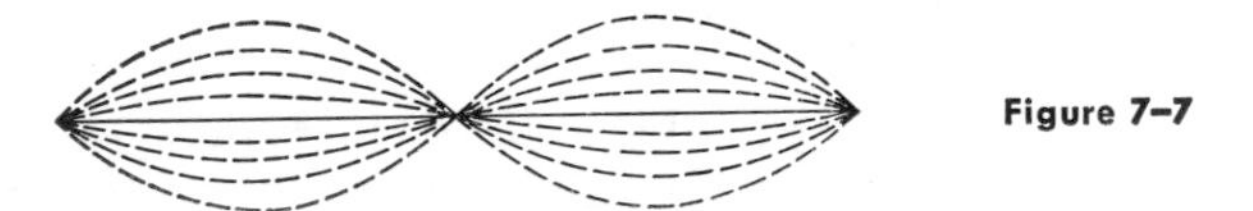

Figure 7–7

the x-axis. Thus, a stationary wave has the shape of a sine curve with fixed nodes and no forward motion, but with amplitude changing so rapidly that the wave appears to have a stationary solid form. In Figure 7–6 we have shown some wave forms with (a) different amplitudes, (b) different wave lengths, and (c) different phases. A stationary wave is illustrated in Figure 7–7.

PROBLEM SET 7.5

1. Give the amplitude and velocity of propagation of the wave having the equation

(a) $y = 2 \sin (5x - 3t)$; (b) $y = 10 \sin (x/3 - t/2)$;

(*c*) $y = 50 \sin \frac{2\pi}{30}(x - 15t - 3)$; (*d*) $y = 100 \sin (5x + 3t)$;

(*e*) $y = 0.25 \sin \frac{2\pi}{5} \frac{(x + 4t)}{3}$; (*f*) $y = 40 \sin (0.75x + 100t)$.

2. Determine the wave length and period of each of the waves having the equations given in Problem 1.
3. A sinusoidal wave is traveling with a velocity of 3 miles per hour, has a wave length of 15 feet and a maximum height of 3 feet. Write an equation of this progressive wave.
4. The velocity of sound in still air at 70° F is 1130 feet per second. Determine the wave lengths of sound waves with frequencies of 128, 200, 300, and 600 per second.
5. A string 20 centimeters long is vibrating in two segments with a frequency of 150 per second. Write an equation of the stationary wave if its amplitude is 1 centimeter.
6. Write an equation of the stationary wave described in Problem 5 if the string is vibrating in 3 segments.
7. Describe the wave motions defined by the following equations: (*a*) $y = 10 \cos 3\pi t \sin \pi x$; (*b*) $y = 2 \cos t/5 \sin x/6$.
8. When a seiche appears on a body of water, the shores are not nodes as are the end points of a vibrating string. A uninodal (i.e., one node) seiche with a period of 15 seconds is observed on a small pond 200 meters wide. Write an equation of the seiche if its amplitude is 10 centimeters.
9. Determine an equation of a binodal (i.e., two nodes) seiche on the pond in Problem 8, if the period is 10 seconds and the amplitude is 8 centimeters.
10. Draw rough sketches of the instantaneous appearances of two waves which are identical except that (*a*) amplitudes are in the ratio 1:2; (*b*) wave lengths are in the ratio 1:4; (*c*) phases differ by a quarter of a wave length.
11. An equation of a progressive wave is $y = 5 \sin (x/3 + 4t)$. Write the corresponding equation of a similar wave with (*a*) a lead of 10 units; (*b*) a lag of 5 units.

7.6 Angles and Degree-Circular Functions

The concepts of point, line, and plane are the undefined but intuitive elements of plane geometry. The only characteristic possessed by a point is *position,* but with any two distinct points there arises the notion of their *linear separation* or *distance apart.* This distance may be identified with the *length* of the line segment joining the points, and may be measured with the help of an algebraic scale, as indicated in Figure 7–8*a*. Moreover, if we designate one point as *initial* and the other as *terminal,* let the 0 of the scale coincide with the initial point and the terminal point fall on the positive portion of the scale, the distance so measured will be *positive* and *unique.*

The concept of linear separation is not meaningful, when an attempt is made to apply it to two arbitrary lines in space, but with any two intersecting lines in a plane we can associate the notion of *angular separation*. Probably the simplest way to conceive of the angular separation or *angle* between two lines is in terms of a physical rotation: If we think of a particle located at each point of one line, and this "line" of particles is rotated about the point of intersection of the lines until they fall on the points of the

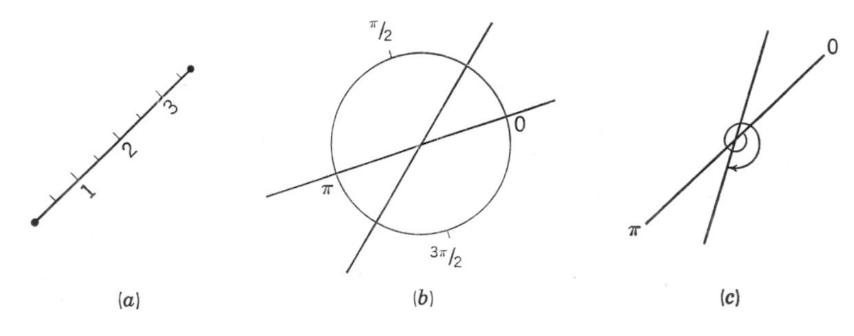

Figure 7–8

second line, the *amount of rotation* will be a physical interpretation of "the" angle between the lines. Just as we used an algebraic scale to measure the distance between two points, the natural way to measure this angle between two lines is to use a circular scale such as was used in the definition of the circular functions. Let us then identify one line as *initial* and the other line as *terminal*, and construct a circular scale with the center of the unit circle at the point of intersection of the lines and the 0 of the scale falling on the initial line. The angular separation of the terminal line from the initial line may now be read from the scale, *positive* angles corresponding to *counterclockwise* and *negative* angles to *clockwise* rotation, but we observe that this angle is not unique. For example, if the lines are perpendicular, the angle may be read as $\pi/2$, $-\pi/2$, $3\pi/2$, $-3\pi/2$, etc., units; each of these angles may be interpreted as different amounts of rotation associated with the lines. When an angle between two lines is measured by means of a unit-circular scale, the unit of measure is called a *radian*. Since the radian measure of an angle is also the measure of length of an arc on a unit circle, we eliminate the ambiguity of the angle associated with two lines by including in the diagram a curved arrow indicative of the arc which is used to measure it. In Figure 7–8*b*, we have shown a circular scale constructed so that the various angles associated with the indicated lines may be measured, while in Figure 7–8*c* we have designated a particular angle. In many cases, however, it will be clearly understood from the context which angle is meant; in problems of plane geometry, for example, the angle between two line segments will always be positive and will not exceed 2π radians.

If the circumference of a circle is divided into 360 equal parts, the angle between the radii to adjacent division points is one *degree*, indicated by 1°. Since the radian measure of an angle is the measure of length of the associated arc on a unit circle, and since the complete circumference corresponds to an angle of 360°, it is clear that 2π radians equal 360° or π radians equal 180°. The following approximations are frequently useful: 1 radian $= (180/\pi)° = 57.3°$; $1° = \pi/180$ radians $= 0.01745$ radians.

ILLUSTRATION 1. Express (*a*) 90° and 45° in radian measure; (*b*) 3 radians and $\pi/3$ radians in degree measure.

Solution.

(*a*) $90° = 90(\pi/180)$ radians $= \pi/2$ radians;
$45° = 45(\pi/180)$ radians $= \pi/4$ radians.

(*b*) 3 radians $= 3(180/\pi)° = 540/\pi° = 171.9°$, approximately;
$\pi/3$ radians $= (\pi/3)(180/\pi)° = 60°$.

Let us return to the notion of an angle as an amount of rotation of a "line" of particles located at the points of an "initial" line. As this "line" rotates, the circular arc traced out by any point of the line may be said to be *associated* with the angle of rotation. We have already referred

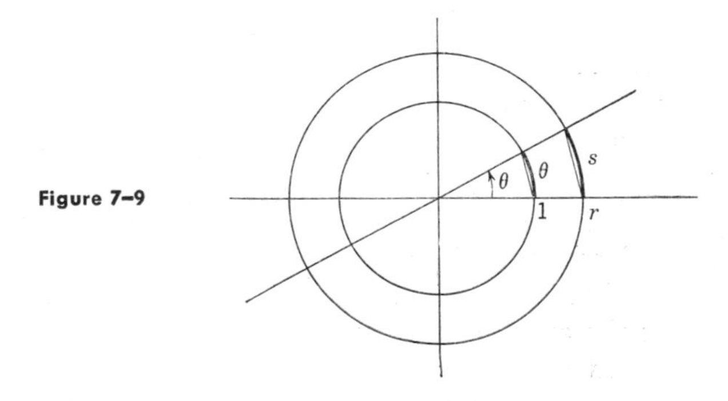

Figure 7–9

to this association between the angle and the unit-circular arc, the measure of length of which is the radian measure of the angle; but we now see that each circle, concentric with this unit circle, will also contain an arc associated with the angle. In problems of plane geometry, this arc associated with a given angle will be merely one of the arcs on the circle intercepted by the two lines defining the angle.

There is a very simple relationship between the *radian* measure of an angle and the measure of length of an associated arc. Thus, consider an angle formed by the two intersecting lines of Figure 7–9, and the associated arc on a circle having radii r units in length. If θ is the radian measure of the angle under consideration, let us first consider the case where $\theta < 2\pi$, with θ then also measuring the length of the associated arc on the unit circle; and let s be the measure of length of the associated arc on the given circle. If $\bar{\theta}$ and $\bar{s}$ are the measures of length of the respective chords that subtend these two arcs, it follows from a consideration of similar triangles that $\bar{s} = r\bar{\theta}$; and, since arc lengths are proportional to chord lengths, $s = r\theta$ for the case under consideration. However, an arbitrary arc on a circle is the union of an integral number of complete circumferences and an arc of the type just discussed. Hence, since the circumference of the given circle has a length r times that of the unit circle, it follows that the formula $s = r\theta$ is valid in general. It must be emphasized, however, that θ must be the *radian* measure of the angle. If $s = r$, the equation $s = r\theta$ shows that $\theta = 1$. Thus, the angle between two radii of a circle will be 1 radian if the associated arc and the radius of the circle are of equal length.

ILLUSTRATION 2. If the length of a radius of a circle is 3 inches, determine the length of arc associated with a central angle of (*a*) 2 radians; (*b*) 30°.

Solution.

(*a*) Since $\theta = 2$, the formula $s = r\theta$ gives $s = (3)(2) = 6$, and so the associated arc is 6 inches in length.

(*b*) The degree measure of the angle must first be converted to radian measure. Thus, $30° = 30(\pi/180)$ radians, and so $\theta = \pi/6$. The formula $s = r\theta$ now gives $s = 3(\pi/6) = \pi/2$, and the length of the associated arc is approximately 1.57 inches.

We have defined the six circular functions in the set $R^{\#}$ of all real numbers. The real numbers in the domains may, of course, be measures of arbitrary quantities; however, we have seen that if θ is a number in the domain of a circular function f, θ may be *interpreted* as the radian measure of the angle associated with the unit-circular arc used in the definition of $f(\theta)$. Since angles are most frequently measured in degrees, in practice it will be convenient to introduce six new functions, which have *values at* the *degree measure* of an angle that are *equal* to the *values of the corresponding circular functions, at the radian measure* of the angle.

DEFINITION. If f is a circular function, we define $f(\ °)$ to be an associated *degree-circular* function such that $f(x°) = f(\pi x/180)$. The domain of $f(\ °)$ is the set $\{x \mid x \in R^{\#}, \pi x/180 \text{ is in the domain of } f\}$.

Thus, for example, $\sin x° = \sin \pi x/180$, $\cos x° = \cos \pi x/180$, etc. The function $\sin (\ °)$ is known as the *degree-sign* function, but it will be convenient to read $\sin (x°)$ or $\sin x°$ as "the sine of x degrees," rather than "the degree-sign of x." A similar remark applies to the other degree-circular functions.

If x and θ are the respective degree and radian measures of an angle, with θ in the domain of a circular function f, we have defined $f(\ °)$ so that $f(x°) = f(\theta)$. Furthermore, it is apparent that in any identity involving $f(\theta)$, we may replace $f(\theta)$ by $f(x°)$, since these quantities are equal. Thus, for each identity involving values of circular functions, there is an equivalent identity involving values of degree-circular functions. For example, with the identity $\sin^2 \theta + \cos^2 \theta = 1$ we may associate the equivalent identity $\sin^2 x° + \cos^2 x° = 1$ (which is clearly the same as $\sin^2 \theta° + \cos^2 \theta° = 1$).

In applications of the degree-circular functions, it will be useful to have a reformulation of the Reduction Principle, given in Chapter 5 for circular functions. We shall say that an *angle* is in *standard position* if the unit-circular arc, that is used to measure the angle in radians, is in standard position as discussed in Chapter 5. We then define the *reference* angle of the given angle to be the angle, considered positive, associated with the reference arc of the given arc in standard position. For example, an

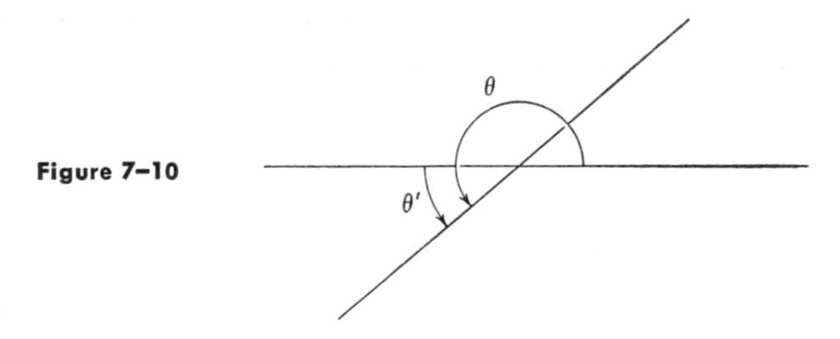

Figure 7–10

angle of $5\pi/4$ radians has a reference angle of $\pi/4$ radians, and an angle of 120° has a reference angle of 60°. In Figure 7–10 we have shown an angle of measure θ, with its reference angle of measure θ'. The Reduction Principle for degree-circular functions may now be stated in the form below.

REDUCTION PRINCIPLE. Let an angle of $x°$ have a reference angle of $x'°$. Then if $f(\ °)$ is a degree-circular function, $|f(x°)| = f(x'°)$ for each x in the domain of $f(\ °)$; the sign of $f(x°)$ may be determined by the quadrant that contains the terminal point of the unit-circular arc in standard position that measures the angle in radians.

ILLUSTRATION 3. Use the above form of the Reduction Principle to determine sin 600°.

Solution. The reference angle of 600° is 60°, and so $|\sin 600°| = \sin 60° = \sin \pi/3 = \sqrt{3}/2$. Since the terminal point of the associated unit-circular arc in standard position lies in the third quadrant, the sign is negative and so $\sin 600° = -\sqrt{3}/2$.

The actual computation of the values of circular functions for arbitrary real numbers is not simple, for there is no simple formula connecting the length of a circular arc with the length of its subtended chord. However, by means of calculus, it is possible to derive infinite series which represent $\sin \theta$ and $\cos \theta$ for an arbitrary real number θ. In the series below, the symbol $\underline{|n}$ (read "factorial n") stands for the product of all the positive integers from 1 to n, inclusive. For example, $\underline{|4} = 1 \cdot 2 \cdot 3 \cdot 4 = 24$.

$$\sin \theta = \theta - \theta^3/\underline{|3} + \theta^5/\underline{|5} - \theta^7/\underline{|7} + \cdots$$

$$\cos \theta = 1 - \theta^2/\underline{|2} + \theta^4/\underline{|4} - \theta^6/\underline{|6} + \cdots$$

The dots $(\cdots)$ indicate that the series is unending, but it can be shown that both series *converge* in the sense that as more terms are included in the sum, a closer approximation to $\sin \theta$ or $\cos \theta$ is obtained. The values of the other circular functions can be obtained from the values of the sine and cosine functions. In Table 2, we have given the values of the circular functions for real numbers in their domains from 0 to $\pi/2$; in the same table are included the values of the degree-circular functions for real numbers in their domains from 0 to 90. In view of the Reduction Principle, this table is quite adequate.

PROBLEM SET 7.6

1. Express each of the following angles in radians: (*a*) 150°; (*b*) 405°; (*c*) 270°; (*d*) 850°; (*e*) 240°; (*f*) 30°; (*g*) −150°; (*h*) −60°.

2. Express each of the following angles in degrees: (*a*) $\pi/4$ radians; (*b*) $\pi/8$ radians; (*c*) $\pi/6$ radians; (*d*) $3\pi/4$ radians; (*e*) $7\pi/8$ radians; (*f*) $11\pi/12$ radians; (*g*) $-5\pi/6$ radians.

3. Express each of the following angles in radians: (*a*) 200°; (*b*) −346°; (*c*) 72.6°; (*d*) −246.5°.

4. Express each of the following angles in degrees: (*a*) 4.5 radians; (*b*) 5 radians; (*c*) −2.4 radians; (*d*) −3.7 radians.

5. A circle has 6-inch radii. Determine the length of the arc intercepted by two radii, if the angle between them is (*a*) $\pi/3$ radians; (*b*) $7\pi/6$ radians; (*c*) $5\pi/6$ radians.

6. A circle has 12-inch radii. Determine the length of the arc intercepted by two radii, if the angle between them is (*a*) 15°; (*b*) 75°; (*c*) 245°; (*d*) 10°.

7. A circle has 10-inch radii. Determine, in degrees, the angle between two radii of this circle which intercept an arc of length (*a*) 2 inches; (*b*) 15 inches; (*c*) 20 inches.

8. From a point on the earth, the angle between two lines drawn to the opposite ends of a diameter of the sun is approximately 0.0093 radians. Determine the approximate length of a diameter of the sun, assuming 93,000,000 miles as the distance to the sun. (Assume that a diameter of the sun is an arc of a circle with center at the point on the earth.)

9. Use the corresponding circular functions to determine each of the following functional values: (*a*) sin 45°; (*b*) cos (−30°); (*c*) tan 45°; (*d*) sin 405°; (*e*) cos (−60°); (*f*) cot (−210°); (*g*) cos 225°; (*h*) sin 270°; (*i*) tan 150°; (*j*) cot 240°.

10. Use Table 2 and the Reduction Principle adapted to degrees, to determine each of the following functional values: (*a*) $\sin 37.2°$; (*b*) $\cos 148.6°$; (*c*) $\tan(-346.7°)$; (*d*) $\cot(-135.4°)$; (*e*) $\sin 164.8°$; (*f*) $\cos 306.4°$; (*g*) $\cos 120.3°$; (*h*) $\sin 238.8°$.
11. If we assume that the earth is a sphere with radii 4000 miles in length, determine the approximate distance between two points on the equator located at 60° West Longitude and 100° East Longitude, respectively.
12. A wheel with 10-foot radii is rotating at the rate of 300 revolutions per minute. (*a*) What is the angular velocity in radians per second, of a spoke of the wheel? (*b*) What is the speed in feet per second, of a particle on the circumference of the wheel?
13. Recall the corresponding values of the circular functions to confirm the entries of the following table, which may be regarded as a convenient memory device.

θ	0	30	45	60
$\sin\theta°$	$\sqrt{0}/2$	$\sqrt{1}/2$	$\sqrt{2}/2$	$\sqrt{3}/2$
$\cos\theta°$	$\sqrt{4}/2$	$\sqrt{3}/2$	$\sqrt{2}/2$	$\sqrt{1}/2$

14. A sector of a circle is the portion bounded by two radii and their intercepted arc. Use the fact that the area of a sector varies as its "central" angle, to show that $S = r^2\theta/2$ with r a measure of length of the radii, S the corresponding measure of area, and θ the radian measure of the angle between the radii.
15. Determine the angular velocity, in radians per second, of a 24-inch automobile tire, if the speed of the automobile is 20 miles per hour.
16. The speed of the turbine wheel of a 5-horse-power steam turbine is 20,000 revolutions per minute. Determine the angular velocity in radians per second.
17. Two radii intercept an arc of length 3 inches on a circle. If the associated angle between the radii is 2 radians, determine the length of a radius of the circle.
18. State the Reduction Principle for degree-circular functions, in terms of a *co-reference* angle. (See Problem 10 of Problem Set 5.7, and make an analogous definition.)
19. Repeat Problem 9, using the result of Problem 18.
20. Repeat Problem 10, using the result of Problem 18.

7.7 Trigonometry of the Right Triangle

Inasmuch as one of the important applications of the circular as well as of the degree-circular functions occurs when the elements of the domains are measures of angles, it will be useful to rephrase our definitions of these functions so that this application may be made a little easier. In this and the following sections of the present chapter, we shall be concerned principally with problems related to triangles, a study known as *trigonometry.*

An angle is determined by two intersecting lines and the unit-circular arc that is used to define its radian measure. Although, in reality, an angle is not a geometric entity, it is sometimes convenient to speak of the half-lines from the origin containing, respectively, the initial and terminal

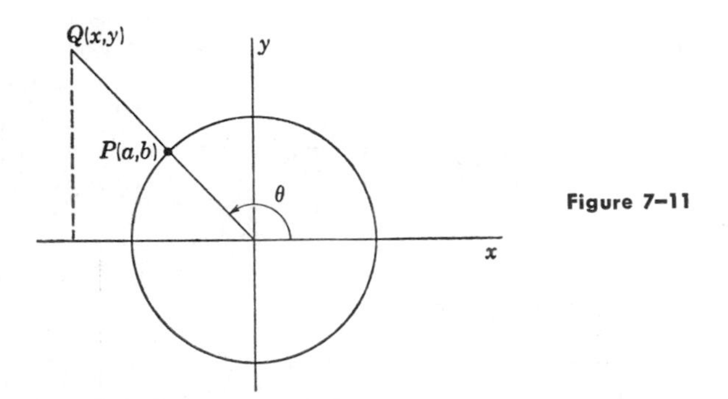

Figure 7–11

points of the measuring arc as the *initial* and *terminal sides* of the angle. Referring to Figure 7–11, let θ and $\bar{\theta}$ be the respective radian and degree measures of the indicated angle in standard position, with $P(a, b)$ the terminal point of the associated unit-circular arc. Our previous definitions then require that

$$\sin \theta = \sin \bar{\theta}^\circ = b, \csc \theta = \csc \bar{\theta}^\circ = 1/b,$$

$$\cos \theta = \cos \bar{\theta}^\circ = a, \sec \theta = \sec \bar{\theta}^\circ = 1/a,$$

$$\tan \theta = \tan \bar{\theta}^\circ = b/a, \cot \theta = \cot \bar{\theta}^\circ = a/b.$$

Now let $Q(x, y)$ be an *arbitrary* point on the terminal side of the angle, with $r(> 0)$ the measure of distance of Q from the origin. A consideration of similar triangles leads us to the following equalities: $b/1 = y/r$, $a/1 = x/r$, $b/a = y/x$. We may then make the following equivalent definitions for the circular and degree circular functions with reference to the point Q:

$$\sin \theta = \sin \bar{\theta}^\circ = y/r; \qquad \csc \theta = \csc \bar{\theta}^\circ = r/y;$$

$$\cos \theta = \cos \bar{\theta}^\circ = x/r; \qquad \sec \theta = \sec \bar{\theta}^\circ = r/x;$$

$$\tan \theta = \tan \bar{\theta}^\circ = y/x; \qquad \cot \theta = \cot \bar{\theta}^\circ = x/y.$$

If $f(\theta)$ is known for some basic circular function f, it is easy to apply these equivalent definitions to obtain the values at θ of the other basic circular functions, if they are defined; moreover, this method is usually simpler than a direct application of the original definitions, as in Illustration 2 of Section 5.7.

ILLUSTRATION 1. If $\sin\theta = 2/3$ and $\pi/2 < \theta < \pi$, determine $\cos\theta$ and $\tan\theta$.

Solution. We think of θ as the radian measure of an angle in standard position, similar to Figure 7–11. There will be some point Q on the terminal side of the angle with an ordinate of 2, and accordingly the coordinate pair of Q is $(-\sqrt{5}, 2)$, and $r = 3$. It then follows from the equivalent definitions that $\cos\theta = -\sqrt{5}/3$ and $\tan\theta = 2/(-\sqrt{5}) = -2/\sqrt{5}$.

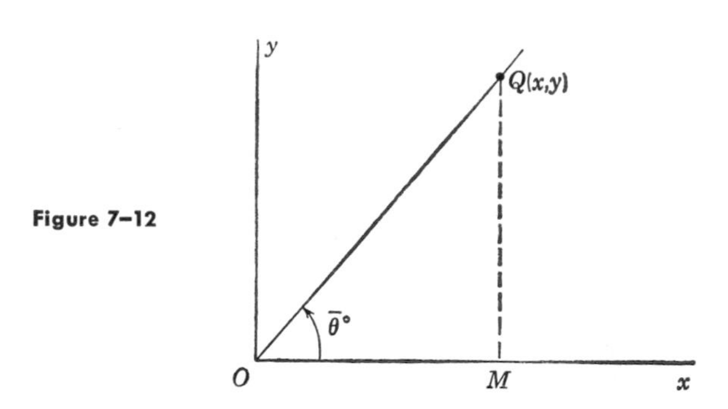

Figure 7–12

An angle of 90° or $\pi/2$ radians is frequently called a *right* angle, while a positive angle smaller than a right angle is said to be *acute*. It is possible to phrase the above definitions in even simpler terms, if the elements of the domains are measures of acute angles; in this case, the definitions may be made in terms of the sides of a right triangle, and independent of any coordinate system. Thus, consider the positive acute angle of radian measure θ and degree measure $\bar{\theta}$, shown in standard position in Figure 7–12. For this angle, the ordinate y and abscissa x of Q are positive numbers, as well as r. The "ordinate" segment QM, the "abscissa" segment OM, and the "radial" segment OQ then form the three sides of a right triangle; and if we refer to QM as the *side opposite* and OM as the *side adjacent* the angle, with OQ the *hypotenuse*, the above definitions become as follows:

$$\sin\theta = \sin\bar{\theta}° = \frac{\text{measure of length of side opposite}}{\text{measure of length of hypotenuse}};$$

$$\cos\theta = \cos\bar{\theta}° = \frac{\text{measure of length of side adjacent}}{\text{measure of length of hypotenuse}};$$

$$\tan\theta = \tan\bar{\theta}° = \frac{\text{measure of length of side opposite}}{\text{measure of length of side adjacent}};$$

$$\csc\theta = \csc\bar{\theta}° = \frac{\text{measure of length of hypotenuse}}{\text{measure of length of side opposite}};$$

$$\sec \theta = \sec \bar{\theta}^\circ = \frac{\text{measure of length of hypotenuse}}{\text{measure of length of side adjacent}};$$

$$\cot \theta = \cot \bar{\theta}^\circ = \frac{\text{measure of length of side adjacent}}{\text{measure of length of side opposite}}.$$

The advantage of these definitions is that, if the angle under consideration is one of the "interior" angles of a right triangle, we may apply them to the measures of such an angle without any reference to a coordinate system, for only geometric elements of the triangle are involved. It must be emphasized, however, that these simplified definitions are valid only if the elements of the domains are measures of acute angles, i.e., if $\theta < \pi/2$ or $\bar{\theta} < 90$.

A triangle has six basic dimensions—the lengths of the three sides and the magnitudes of the three "interior" angles formed by the sides. When some of the dimensions are given, a determination of the remaining ones is called a *solution* of the triangle. A right triangle can always be solved if, in addition to the right angle, the length of one side and any other dimension is given. The definitions just given are adapted to aid in the solution of a right triangle, and since it is customary to use degree measure for the angles of a triangle we shall use only degree-circular functions for this solution.

GENERAL PRINCIPLE FOR THE SOLUTION OF A RIGHT TRIANGLE. Use a degree-circular function to connect the measures of two known and one unknown dimension, and solve the resulting equation for the unknown measure. If the unknown dimension is the length of a side, choose a function that places the measure of this dimension in the numerator of a fraction, so that its solution will involve multiplication instead of division.

ILLUSTRATION 2. When the angle of elevation of the sun is 34.0°, the shadow of a building is 217 feet long. How high is the building?

Solution. The conditions of the problem are illustrated in Figure 7–13. Using the above General Principle, $\tan 34.0^\circ = h/217$ and so $h = 217 \tan 34.0^\circ = 217(0.6745) = 146$, approximately. An approximation to the height is then 146 feet.

ILLUSTRATION 3. A 24-foot pole is used to brace a vertical wall. If the bottom of the pole is 13 feet from the wall, what angle does the pole make with the wall?

Solution. The conditions of this problem are illustrated in Figure 7–14. An application of the General Principle then gives $\sin \theta^\circ = 13/24 = 0.5417$, and so $\theta = 33$, approximately. An approximation to the desired angle is then 33°.

While there is no inflexible rule with regard to consistency of measurements, we shall regard a linear measurement to 2 significant digits as consistent with an angle measurement correct to the nearest degree, a linear measurement to 3 significant digits as consistent with an angle measurement correct to the nearest tenth of a degree, etc. Furthermore,

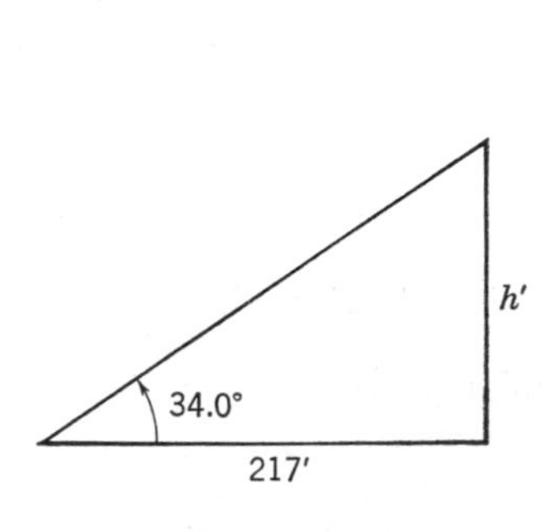

Figure 7–13

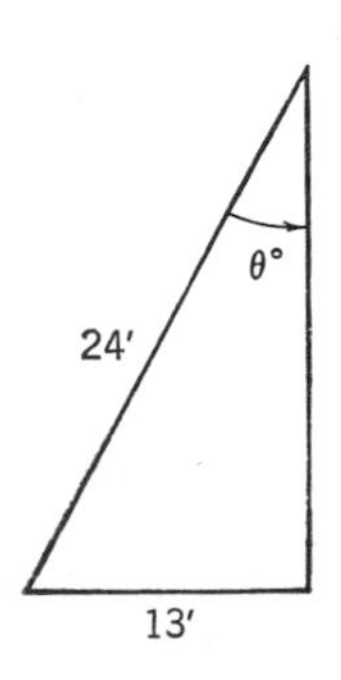

Figure 7–14

it has been found that better results are obtained, on the average, if one extra digit is retained in an intermediate result during the process of any further calculation.

PROBLEM SET 7.7

Note. In Problems 1 through 6, complete the solutions of the triangles, considering A, B, and C the degree measures of the angles of a right triangle, with a, b, and c respective measures of length of the corresponding "opposite" sides. Use the fact that $A + B + C = 180$.

1. $C = 90$, $A = 62$, $c = 40$.

2. $C = 90$, $B = 21.6$, $a = 73.4$.

3. $A = 90$, $b = 25$, $c = 57$.

4. $B = 90$, $C = 48.5$, $a = 15.0$.

5. $B = 90$, $a = 15$, $b = 35$.

6. $A = 90$, $a = 50$, $b = 36$.

Note. Use the method of Illustration 1 for the following two problems.

7. Problems 15–20 of Problem Set 5.7.

8. Problem 13 of Problem Set 7.2.

9. The angle of elevation of the top of a cliff, as seen from a boat, is found to be 17.3°. If the cliff is 120 feet high, how far is the boat from the foot of the cliff?

10. Determine the angle of elevation of the sun, if a tower 300 feet high casts a shadow 400 feet long.

11. When an object is below the observer, the angle of depression of the object is the acute angle between the line of sight to the object and the horizontal line in the same vertical plane. If the angle of depression of a boat at sea is 15°, as seen from the top of a 250-foot cliff, determine the distance of the boat from the foot of the cliff.

12. A pendulum 40 inches long is moved 20° from the vertical position. By how much is the lower end of the pendulum raised?
13. A 15-foot ladder, with its base fixed at one spot in an alley, will reach 9 feet up a building on one side of the alley and 12 feet up on the other side. How wide is the alley?
14. The fixed axis of a telescope mounting must point toward the north celestial pole, the angle of elevation of this point being the latitude of the observer. The fixed axis of a certain mounting is 9 feet long, with the lower end 6 feet above the floor. If the latitude of the spot is 33°, how far above the floor is the higher end?
15. From two successive milestones on a straight level road, a man observes the angles of elevation of the top of a hill directly ahead of him to be 6.2° and 37.8°. How high is the top of the hill above the level of the road?
16. A building is surmounted by a flagstaff. From a point on the ground, 125 feet from the building, the angle of elevation of the top of the building is 35.8°, while the angle of elevation of the top of the flagstaff is 39.5°. Determine the height of the building and of the flagstaff.
17. An airplane pilot notes that he is 8000 feet above the ocean as he approaches a small island. He estimates that the angle of depression (see Problem 11) of the farthermost point of the island is 40°, and that the angle of depression of the closest point is 55°. What is the approximate dimension of the island in the direction of flight?
18. A segment of a circle is the figure bounded by an arc and its subtended chord. If a radius of the circle is r units in length, and θ is the radian measure of the central angle between the radii to the two ends of the arc, show that the corresponding measure S of the area of the segment is given by $S = r^2(\theta - \sin\theta)/2$.
19. A radio tower stands on top of a building 200 feet high. From a point on the ground 500 feet from the base of the building, the angle between the lines of sight to the bottom and top of the tower is 10°. Determine the height of the tower.
20. Determine the acute angle between a diagonal and an adjacent edge of a cube.

7.8 Trigonometry of the General Triangle: The Law of Cosines

It frequently becomes necessary to solve triangles that are not right-angled, and so methods different from those of the preceding section must be devised. For example, if the distance and bearing of point A from point B are known, as well as the distance and bearing of point B from some other point C, a surveyor may wish to compute the distance and bearing of point A from point C. The triangle formed by the line segments joining the three points will usually not be right-angled, as indicated in Figure 7–15.

In an earlier chapter, we distinguished a vector quantity from a scalar quantity as one having a measure that involves both magnitude and direction. Quantities such as mass and volume are scalar quantities, but force, velocity, and acceleration are examples of vector quantities. The arithmetic associated with these quantities involves the solution

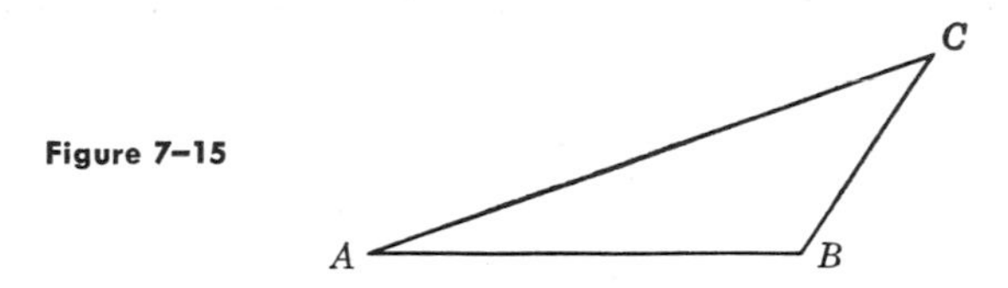

Figure 7–15

of general triangles. We may represent a vector quantity geometrically by a directed line segment which we called a *vector* in Chapter 2, or more properly a *geometric vector;* the measure of length of this segment represents the magnitude of the vector quantity, while the direction of this quantity is represented by the direction of the segment as indicated by an arrow. The sum of two vector quantities is, of course, not the sum of their magni-

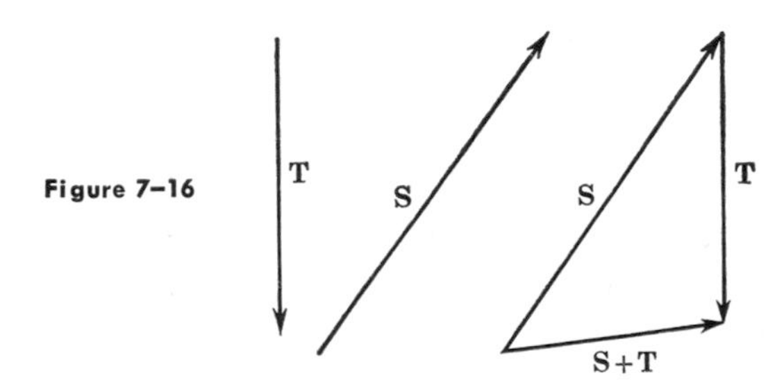

Figure 7–16

tudes, but we must add them according to the "triangle" or "parallelogram" law applied to their geometric vector representations. Thus, in Figure 7–16, let **S** and **T** be two geometric vectors representing vector quantities. If we place the tail of **T** on the head of **S**, the segment joining the tail of **S** with the head of **T** will be a geometric vector which will represent the sum of the vector quantities. The problem of determining the magnitude of this sum is again a problem of computing the length of a side of a triangle that is generally not right-angled. Let us then proceed with a solution of this problem.

In Figure 7–17 we have shown a general triangle with one side along the x-axis and one vertex at the origin. Following the notation introduced in the problems of the preceding section, we let A, B, and C be the degree measures of the angles of the triangle with a, b, and c measures of length of the corresponding "opposite" sides; we further let V_A, V_B, and V_C be the vertices of the triangle associated with the various angles. Using the symbolism of the figure, the definitions of the preceding section show that V_B has the coordinate pair $(c \cos A°, c \sin A°)$, while the coordinate pair of V_C is $(b, 0)$. An application of the distance formula applied to the line segment joining these two points, then gives us $a^2 = (c \cos A° - b)^2 + (c \sin A° - 0)^2 = c^2 \cos^2 A° - 2bc \cos A° + b^2 + c^2 \sin^2 A° = c^2(\sin^2 A° + \cos^2 A°) + b^2 - 2bc \cos A° = b^2 + c^2 - 2bc \cos A°$. This result is

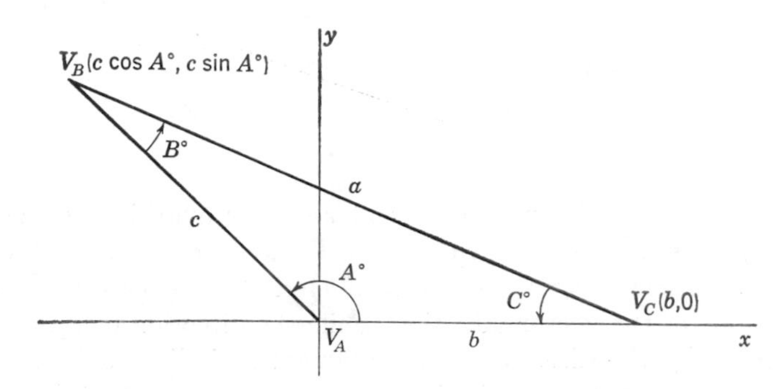

Figure 7–17

known as the Law of Cosines, and should be remembered in the following three equivalent forms:

$$a^2 = b^2 + c^2 - 2bc \cos A°;$$
$$b^2 = c^2 + a^2 - 2ac \cos B°;$$
$$c^2 = a^2 + b^2 - 2ab \cos C°.$$

If the angle, that is involved in one of these formulas, is a right angle, the Law of Cosines reduces to the Pythagorean Theorem, and so may be regarded as a generalization of this theorem. In the form given above, the Law of Cosines is useful in determining the length of the third side of a triangle when the lengths of two sides and the degree measure of the included angle are known.

If we solve for $\cos A°$, the first form of the Law of Cosines becomes $\cos A° = (b^2 + c^2 - a^2)/2bc$, and two similar formulas may be derived from the other forms. These formulas are useful in a determination of the angles of a triangle when the three sides are of known lengths. The formula for $\cos A°$ may be put in a more convenient form by the addition of 1 to the left side and $2bc/2bc$ to the right; with a simple algebraic manipulation, the result is $\cos A° = \dfrac{(b + c - a)(b + c + a)}{2bc} - 1$, which is simpler for purposes of calculation. A similar form may be obtained for the other two formulas.

At this point the student is reminded of the convention regarding the retention of significant digits in the solution of triangles, which was given at the end of the preceding section.

ILLUSTRATION 1. An airplane pilot is heading due north with an indicated air speed of 150 miles per hour. If a tail wind of 75 miles per hour is blowing in a direction N 32° E, determine the ground speed and direction of the plane.

Solution. In Figure 7–18 we have indicated the air velocity of the plane by the line segment **P**, the wind velocity by the segment **W**, with **P** + **W** representing the ground velocity of the plane in both magnitude and direction. If we designate the magnitude of this velocity as x miles per hour, we can indicate the measure of length of **P** + **W** by x. The Law of Cosines applied to the triangle then gives us

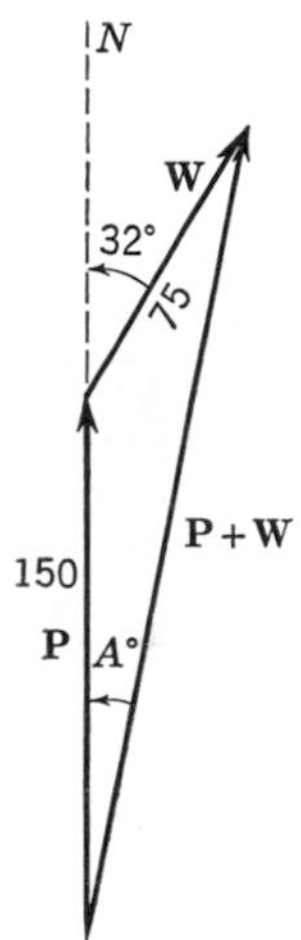

Figure 7–18

$$\begin{aligned} x^2 &= 150^2 + 75^2 - 2(150)(75)\cos 148° \\ &= 22500 + 5625 - (22500)(-0.8480) \\ &= 28125 + 19080 = 47205. \end{aligned}$$

Thus, $x = 217$, approximately, which is the ground speed of the plane in miles per hour, with one extra digit retained for the purposes of further calculation. Now let A be the degree measure of the angle between north and the resultant direction, and use the second form of the Law of Cosines to determine A. Thus,

$$\begin{aligned} \cos A° &= \frac{(b+c+a)(b+c-a)}{2bc} - 1 = \frac{(442)(292)}{(300)(217)} - 1 \\ &= 1.9825 - 1 = 0.9825, \end{aligned}$$

and so $A = 10.7$, approximately. Rounding off our computed figures, the speed of the plane is 220 miles per hour in a direction N 11° E.

PROBLEM SET 7.8

1. Solve the triangle completely with the Law of Cosines, using the symbolism of Problem Set 7.7: (*a*) $a = 23$, $b = 16$, $C = 38$; (*b*) $b = 15.0$, $c = 25.0$, $A = 28.7$; (*c*) $a = 26.0$, $c = 12.0$, $B = 130.5$.
2. Two planes leave the same airport at the same time in directions which differ by 40.3°. If the speed of one is 150 miles per hour, and the speed of the other is 180 miles per hour, determine their approximate distance apart in half an hour.
3. A body has two forces applied to it, one of magnitude 40 pounds and the other of magnitude 65 pounds. If the directions of the forces differ by 25°, determine the magnitude of the resultant force.

4. What is the length of a side of a regular pentagon inscribed in a circle, the radii of which are 10 inches in length?
5. The distance from point A to point B is desired but is impossible of direct measurement because of obstacles. However, the distance from A to another point C is found to be 450 yards, and the distance from C to B is found to be 205 yards. If all points lie in the same plane, and the angle between AC and CB is 70.2°, determine the distance from A to B.
6. The positions of two ships are reported to be 200 miles S 40° E and 378 miles S 61.5° W, respectively, from the same port. How far apart are the two ships?
7. A plane has a true air speed of 250 miles per hour in a direction N 45° E. If a head wind with velocity of 35 miles per hour is blowing from a direction N 25° W, determine the ground speed and actual direction of the plane.
8. A river is flowing at the rate of 2 miles per hour. A man sets out in a row boat for the bank opposite, at a still-water speed of 4 miles per hour. Determine the speed of the boat, and the direction in which he should head.
9. An airplane is climbing at the rate of 20 miles per hour. If the speed of the plane, as measured along the ground, is 135 miles per hour, determine the actual speed of the plane and its angle of climb.
10. The acute angle between two diagonals of a parallelogram is 35°. If the diagonals are 15 feet and 10 feet long, determine the lengths of the sides of the parallelogram.
11. Determine the magnitude and direction of a single force equivalent to the following two forces: (*a*) 20 pounds in a direction 25° East of North, 50 pounds in a direction E 33° S; (*b*) 35 pounds in a direction N 43° W, 150 pounds in a direction E 12° N.

7.9 Trigonometry of the General Triangle: The Law of Sines

The Law of cosines is not always adequate for the complete solution of a triangle, even though the triangle may be completely determined. For

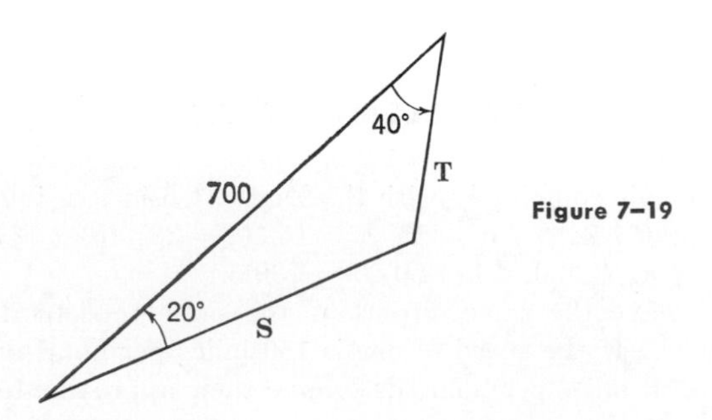

Figure 7–19

example, suppose we wish to resolve a force of 700 pounds into two components which make respective angles of 20° and 40° with the original force. Using the notation of Figure 7–19, the problem is to determine the indicated geometric vectors **S** and **T** such that **S** + **T** has magnitude 700. As this triangle of vectors has only one side given, the Law of Cosines cannot be applied, and so we have need of a different formula.

As usual, let A, B, and C be the degree measures of the interior angles of a triangle, with V_A, V_B, and V_C the associated vertices and a, b, and c measures of length of the corresponding opposite sides. In Figure 7–20, we have shown such a triangle with the side of length b units along the x-axis, and the vertex V_A at the origin. The definitions of Section 7.7 imply that

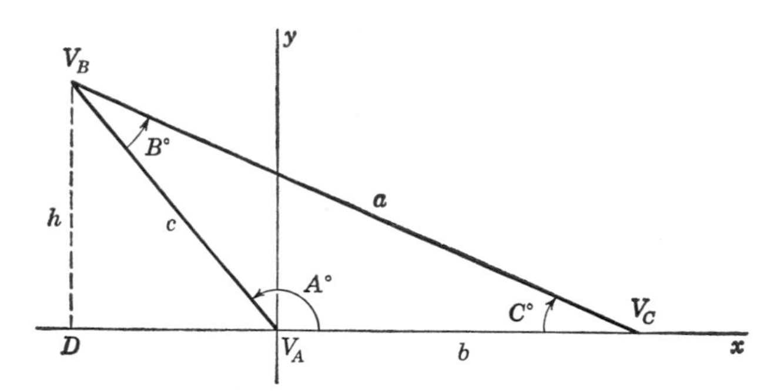

Figure 7–20

V_B has the coordinate pair $(c \cos A°, c \sin A°)$, and so $h = c \sin A°$, where h is the ordinate of V_B as indicated in the figure. If D is the projection of V_B on the x-axis, the triangle with vertices V_B, V_C, and D is right angled, and the simplified definition of the degree-sine function applied to this triangle gives $\sin C° = h/a$ or $h = a \sin C°$. On equating these two expressions for h we obtain $a \sin C° = c \sin A°$ or $\dfrac{a}{\sin A°} = \dfrac{c}{\sin C°}$. In a similar manner we can derive $\dfrac{c}{\sin C°} = \dfrac{b}{\sin B°}$ which, combined with the previous result gives

$$\frac{a}{\sin A°} = \frac{b}{\sin B°} = \frac{c}{\sin C°}.$$

This equation is known as the *Law of Sines* and may be stated in words as follows: The measures of length of the sides of a triangle are proportional to the degree sines of the degree measures of the opposite angles. It is clear, of course, that both the Law of Cosines and the Law of Sines have equivalent statements involving the circular functions in case the angles are measured in radians.

If the Law of Sines is to be used in the solution of a triangle, it is essential that at least one pair of "opposites" is known—i.e., one angle and the side opposite. For example, if A and a are known along with B, the formula $b = a \sin B°/\sin A°$ may be used to determine b; while if b is known in addition to A and a, the formula $\sin B^\circ = b \sin A^\circ / a$ may be used to determine B. In the latter case, however, an ambiguity may arise since $\sin B^\circ = \sin (180 - B)^\circ$. For example, if $\sin B^\circ = 1/2$, B may be either 30 or 150. If the problem involved is a practical one, the correct solution can usually be ascertained by common sense, but there are actually three possibilities that can arise in the solution of this so-called "ambiguous" case:

1. If $\sin B^\circ > 1$, there is no solution for B and the alleged triangle is non-existent.
2. While two solutions for B may be obtained from the equation, one of these may not be possible for a triangle. The impossible one may be eliminated by the fact that $A + B + C = 180$, or by the fact that in any triangle the larger side is opposite the larger angle.
3. There may be two valid solutions, as indicated in Figure 7–21 for the given dimensional measures A, a, and b.

If a triangle is determined by a set of given dimensions, repeated applications of the Law of Cosines or the Law of Sines will complete the solution. The solution of a triangle will usually not be an exact process,

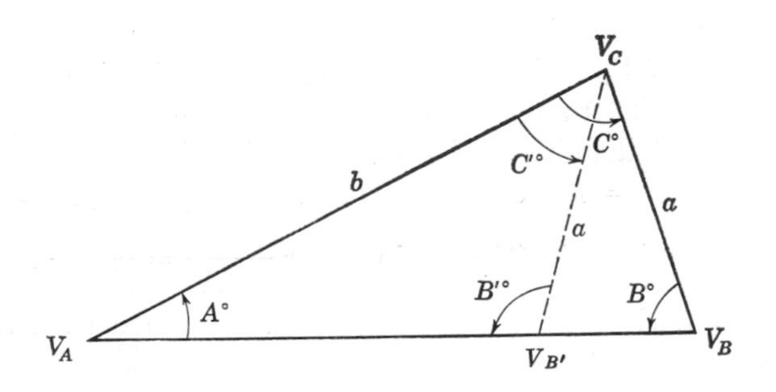

Figure 7–21

since the values of the circular and degree-circular functions given in Table 2 are only approximations. We repeat the advice given at the close of Section 7.7: when the result of an intermediate computation is to be used again, retain in this result one more significant digit than would be justified if this were an end result. In the problems, it will be expected that all final numerical results will be rounded off consistent with the original data.

ILLUSTRATION 1. Solve the triangle in the usual symbolism, given that $a = 38.0$, $b = 43.0$, $A = 57.7$.

Solution. The Law of Sines gives $\sin B° = \dfrac{b \sin A°}{a} = \dfrac{(43)(\sin 57.7°)}{38}$ $= 0.9565$, and so $B = 73.0$ or $B = 107.0$. The equation $A + B + C =$ 180 then yields $C = 49.3$ or $C = 15.3$ according to the respective solutions for B.

We note that $b > a$ and that both solutions for B exceed A, so that both solutions are possible. The two corresponding solutions for c can then be found with the use of the formula $c = a \sin C°/\sin A°$.

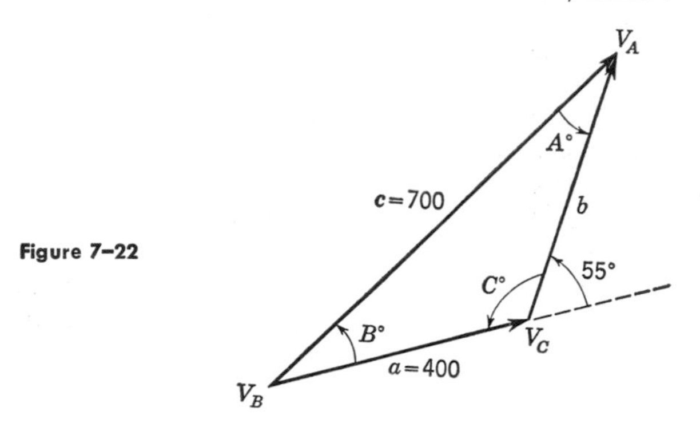

Figure 7–22

ILLUSTRATION 2. Resolve a 700 pound force into two components, as indicated in Figure 7–22, so that one component is 400 pounds and the directions of the components differ by 55°.

Solution. Using the notation indicated in the figure, an application of the Law of Sines gives us

$$\sin A° = \frac{a \sin C°}{c} = \frac{(400) \sin 125°}{700} = \frac{(400)(0.8192)}{700} = 0.4681,$$

so that $A = 27.9$ or $A = 152.1$. Since $c > a$, we must have $C > A$ and the only possible solution for A is 27.9. The other possible solution for A could also be discarded by the observation that $125 + 152 > 180$. Since $B = 27.1$, b can be determined: $b = \dfrac{c \sin B°}{\sin C°} = \dfrac{(700)(0.4555)}{0.8192} = 389.$ Rounding off this result, we see that the other component is approximately 390 pounds.

PROBLEM SET 7.9

Note. In Problems 1 through 6 use the Law of Sines to solve each triangle with the given parts, rounding off the solutions to obtain a consistent set of dimensions.

1. $a = 10$, $B = 30$, $C = 40$.
2. $b = 10$, $c = 9$, $C = 56$.
3. $a = 135$, $b = 149$, $B = 71.5$.
4. $a = 5.62$, $c = 9.28$, $A = 23.7$.
5. $a = 861$, $b = 579$, $A = 117.8$.
6. $c = 29.3$, $B = 58.5$, $A = 16.3$.
7. In surveying a straight path ABD, it is necessary to detour around an obstacle from B to a point C off the path, and then return to the path at D. If $\angle ABC$ is 147° and $\angle BCD$ is 69°, while the length of the segment BC is 647 feet, determine the lengths of the segments CD and BD.
8. From a ship, sailing on a straight course, a lighthouse is observed to be 17.6° to the left of the course. After sailing 12 miles, the same lighthouse is observed to be 43.3° to the left of the course. If the ship continues in the same direction, how close will it get to the lighthouse?
9. Resolve a force of 800 pounds into two components making angles of 20° and 45°, respectively, with the force.
10. The weight of an object is the vertical downward force due to gravity acting on the object. If a 3000 pound automobile is standing on a hill, inclined 10° with the horizontal, determine the components of the weight acting parallel and perpendicular to the hill.
11. A pilot, lost in a storm, radios his position at P to two stations known to be 200 miles apart and located at A and B. If the station at A reports that $\angle PAB$ is 48° and the station at B reports that $\angle PBA$ is 65°, determine the distance of the pilot from the closer station.
12. Prove the Law of Tangents for any triangle: $\dfrac{a-b}{a+b} = \dfrac{\tan (A - B)/2^\circ}{\tan (A + B)/2^\circ}$. (Hint: Let $a/\sin A^\circ = b/\sin B^\circ = K$, and substitute in the left member.)

REVIEW TEST A

1. Without the use of tables, determine the radian measure of the reference angle of 108°, correct to 4 significant digits.
2. If $\sin \theta = -3/5$, $-\pi/2 < \theta < 0$, determine the following functional values without the use of a table: (*a*) $\tan (\theta - \pi/4)$; (*b*) $\cos (\theta + \pi/2)$.
3. The loci of the equations $y = 2x^2 + 4x - 1$ and $2x - y - 5 = 0$ are, respectively, a parabola and a straight line. Determine the distance between the vertex of the parabola and the point on the line with abscissas equal to 3.
4. If $\cos \alpha = 1/3$ and $\tan \beta = 1$, where $\pi < \alpha < 2\pi$ and $-\pi/2 < \beta < \pi/2$, determine the following functional values: (*a*) $\tan (\alpha - \beta)$; (*b*) $\tan 2\alpha$; (*c*) $\cos \beta/2$.
5. Use Table 2 to determine the following functional values: (*a*) $\sin 7$; (*b*) $\cos (-5.5)$.
6. Use $\cos 150°$ to express $\sin 75°$ in radical form.
7. Show that $1 - \cos 4x = 8 \sin^2 x \cos^2 x$ is an identity.
8. If $\sqrt{3} \cos 2\pi t/3 + \sin 2\pi t/3$ is put in the form $A \cos (kt - \omega)$, where $0 \le \omega \le \pi$, determine ω.
9. An equation of a progressive wave is $y = 100 \sin (x/3 - 4t)$, with distance

measured in feet and time in minutes. What is the amplitude, wave length, period, and velocity of propagation of the wave?

10. An observer on a ship sailing on a straight course, observes a lighthouse bearing 27° to the left of its course. If this bearing is 39° after another four miles of sailing, determine the shortest distance from the course of the ship to the lighthouse.

11. It is difficult to measure the distance from one end A of a pond to the other end B. However, the distances from a point C to A and B are found to be 120 feet and 200 feet, respectively. If the angle between the line segments AC and BC is found to be 30°, compute the approximate distance between A and B.

12. Two military observation posts A and B are 500 feet apart, and the observer at each post takes note of a shell burst at a point C in enemy territory. If $\angle CAB$ is 65° and $\angle CBA$ is 70°, determine the approximate distance from each of the posts to point C.

REVIEW TEST B

1. Without the use of a table, determine the radian measure of the reference angle of 218°, correct to 4 significant digits.

2. If $\cos\theta = -3/5$, $\pi/2 < \theta < \pi$, determine the following functional values without the use of a table: (*a*) $\cot\theta$; (*b*) $\csc 2\theta$.

3. Determine the distance between the first maximum and the first minimum point to the right of the origin on the locus of the equation $y = \sin x$.

4. If $\cos\alpha = -1/2$ and $\tan\beta = -1$, where $0 < \alpha < \pi$ and $-\pi < \beta < 0$, determine the following functional values: (*a*) $\sin(\alpha - \beta)$; (*b*) $\cos(\alpha + \beta)$; (*c*) $\sin\beta/2$.

5. Use Table 2 to determine the ordinate of the point on the locus of the equation $y = 3\cos 2x$ that has -5 for its abscissa. Do the same for the point with an abscissa of 1.31.

6. Determine $\cos[\text{arc Sin } 2/3 - \text{arc Cos }(-4/5)]$.

7. Show that $1/(1 + \sin x) + 1/(1 - \sin x) = 2\sec^2 x$ is an identity.

8. The minute hand of a clock is 6 inches long. Determine the speed, in inches per minute, of the tip of the hand if the clock is running correctly.

9. A simple harmonic motion is represented by the equation $y = 10\sin(2t/3 - \pi/6)$. (*a*) Write down the amplitude and period. (*b*) What was the initial displacement from the neutral position?

10. Three points A, B, and C are located with respect to each other as follows: B is 1000 feet due north of A; the bearings of C from A and B are, respectively, N 30.0° E and N 40.0° E. Calculate the distance from C to the line containing A and B.

11. Three circles, having radii 6 inches, 8 inches, and 10 inches in length respectively, are drawn to touch each other externally. Determine the angles between the lines of centers.

12. Two warships are observed to fire simultaneously, the reports reaching an observer in 5 seconds and 8 seconds, respectively. If the angle between the lines of sight of the observer to the two ships is 47°, what is the distance between the ships, assuming that sound travels at the rate of 1100 feet per second? Determine the angle between the line of sight of the observer to the closer ship and the line segment through the positions of the two ships.

REFERENCES

Books

Dubisch, R., *Trigonometry*, New York, Ronald, 1955. (Chaps. 4–10.)

Sisam, Charles H., *College Mathematics*, New York, Holt, 1946. (Chaps. 13 and 18.)

Slichter, Charles S., *Elementary Mathematical Analysis*, New York, McGraw-Hill, 1925. (Chaps. 9 and 10.)

American Mathematical Monthly

Bettinger, A. K., "A Derivation of the Formula for Sin $(\alpha+\beta)$ and Cos $(\alpha+\beta)$," Vol. 60, p. 108 (1953).

Burton, L. J., "The Laws of Sines and Cosines," Vol. 56, p. 550 (1949).

Carver, W. B., "Trigonometric Functions — of What?" Vol. 26, p. 243 (1919).

Cohen, Carl, "Addition Theorems for the Sine and Cosine," Vol. 63, p. 248 (1956).

Pascual, M. J., "A Derivation of Sin (A − B) and Cos (A − B)," Vol. 61, p. 416 (1954).

Vaughn, H. E., "Characterization of the Sine and Cosine," Vol. 62, p. 707 (1955).

Wood, F. E., "Derivation of the Tangent Half-Angle Formula," Vol. 56, p. 103 (1949).

Zassenhaus, Hans, "What is an Angle?" Vol. 61, p. 369 (1954).

8

A GLIMPSE OF DIFFERENTIAL CALCULUS

The ghosts of departed quantities.

G. BERKELEY

8.1 Limits of Functions

In this chapter we introduce a concept which is basic in a development of what is known as the *calculus*. A real number x is an *interior point* of an interval $[a, b]$, if $x \in [a, b]$ and $x \neq a$ and $x \neq b$. Let 2 then be an interior point of an interval J, on which a function f has been defined by $f(x) = 2x^2 + 1$. If x is a number near 2, $f(x)$ is a number close to 9; and how close $f(x)$ is to 9 depends upon how near x is to 2. For example, if $1.9 < x < 2.1$, then $8.22 < f(x) < 9.82$. This could be stated in the form: if $-0.1 < x - 2 < 0.1$, then $-0.78 < f(x) - 9 < 0.82$; or, using absolute value signs, in the form: if $|x - 2| < 0.1$, then $|f(x) - 9| < 0.82$. If we choose a number x still nearer 2, so that $|x - 2| < 0.01$, we can show by a simple calculation that $-0.0798 < f(x) - 9 < 0.0802$, i.e., $|f(x) - 9| < 0.0802$. It would appear that $f(x)$, in this example, will be a number arbitrarily close to 9 if x is a number sufficiently close to 2. Notice also, in this case, that $f(2) = 9$.

Now consider the function g, defined on $J - \{2\}$ by $g(x) = (4x+1)(x-2)/x-2$. For any x in the domain of g, $g(x) = 4x+1$—in fact, we could have defined it this way; and it can be shown, as for the function f above, that $g(x)$ is a number which differs from 9 by an arbitrarily small amount, provided x is a number sufficiently close to 2. In the case of the function g, however, $g(2)$ is undefined. In *both* of these examples, we say that the *limit* of the function at x, as x "tends to 2," is 9 and write $\lim_{x \to 2} f(x) = 9$ and $\lim_{x \to 2} g(x) = 9$. It is important to notice that whether or not the number 2 is in the domain of the function, or what this functional value is if it is defined, are matters that are quite irrelevant as far as this particular limit is concerned.

Before giving an exact formulation of the concept illustrated above, we need some definitions. A *neighborhood* of a number c is a set of numbers, which can be described as $\{x \mid x \in R^{\#}, |x - c| < \delta, x \neq c\}$ for some $\delta > 0$, sometimes referred to as a *deleted open interval* of c.† Thus, if $0 < |x - c| < \delta$, it will be convenient to think of x as belonging to a *δ-neighborhood* of c. A number x, which *may or may not* belong to a set S of numbers, is called a *limit point* of S, if each δ-neighborhood of x contains infinitely many elements of S. The *closure* of S is the set consisting of the elements of S and its limit points. The closure of a set may or may not be the same as the original set. Thus, if S is the interval $[1, 2]$, each number in S is a limit point and there are no others. On the other hand, if S is the set $\{x \mid x \in R^{\#}, x^2 < 2\}$, the numbers 2 and -2 are in the closure of the set but not in S itself. As another example, 1 and 3 are members of the closure of $\{x \mid x \in R^{\#}, 0 < x - 1 < 2\}$, but are not members of this set. We are now in a position to give a precise definition of what we mean by $\lim_{x \to c} f(x)$.

DEFINITION. Let c be a limit point of the domain of a function f. The statement "The limit of $f(x)$, as x tends to c, equals L" $\left(\text{i.e., } \lim_{x \to c} f(x) = L\right)$ means that there exists a real number L which satisfies the following condition: for each real number $\epsilon > 0$, there exists a real number $\delta > 0$, such that $|f(x) - L| < \epsilon$ provided x is in the domain of f and $0 < |x - c| < \delta$.

In terms of neighborhoods, the above condition can be phrased as follows: For each positive real number ϵ, there exists a δ-neighborhood N_c of c, such that $|f(x) - L| < \epsilon$ if x is in the intersection of N_c and the domain of f.

There are several points which must be emphasized, in connection with the definition just given:

1. If no L exists which satisfies the condition of the definition, we say that $\lim_{x \to c} f(x)$ does not exist.

2. The actual number δ, associated with a given ϵ, is of no real interest; it is the *existence* of such a δ that is the important matter.

3. In applying the definition, the number ϵ must be considered chosen in advance of the determination of δ.

4. We consider $f(x)$, for x in a δ-neighborhood of c, only if x is also in the domain of f.

5. The number c is a limit point which may or may not be in the domain of f; in the former case, $f(c)$ is defined, while in the latter case it is not.

While a graph is not always reliable, it is often possible to use one to come to an intuitive decision as to whether or not a limit does exist. For example, consider the smooth graph without breaks shown in Figure 8–1. The number L is seen to satisfy the definition of $\lim_{x \to c} f(x)$, since $f(x)$

† This is sometimes known as a "deleted" neighborhood, as opposed to a "non-deleted" neighborhood which permits a number to be a member of its own neighborhoods.

will surely differ from L by less than ϵ if x is in any δ-neighborhood of c inside the interval $[A, B]$. We shall now consider a few illustrations of the ideas of this section, from an intuitive graphical viewpoint.

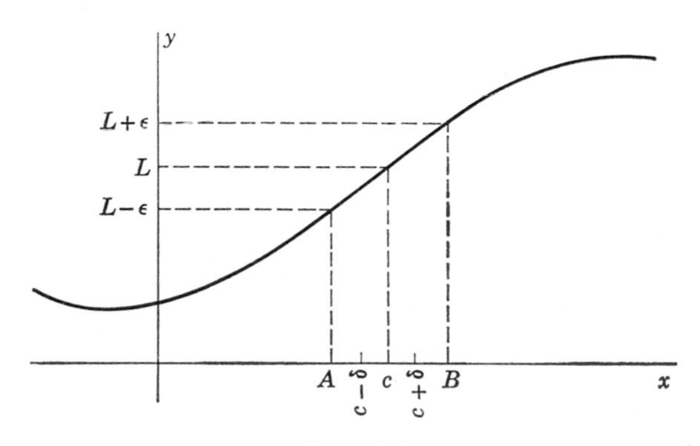

Figure 8–1

ILLUSTRATION 1. In Figure 8–2, we have shown the graph of the function f, defined by $f(x) = \tan x$ on the set $\{x \mid x \in R^{\#}, x \neq \pi/2, -\pi/2 < x \leq \pi\}$.

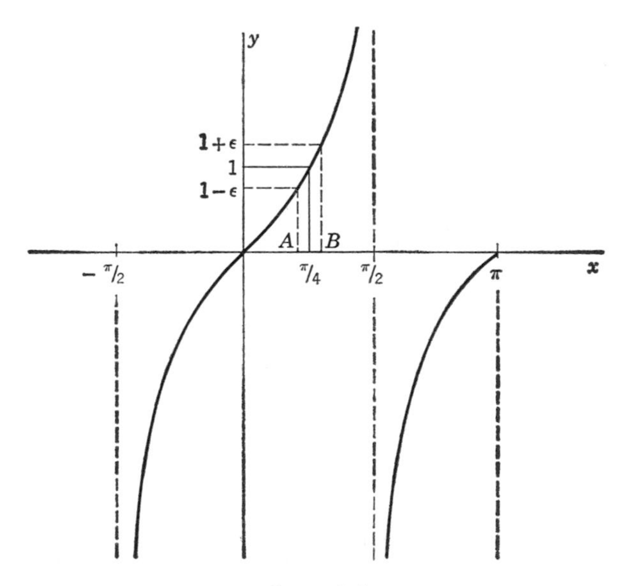

Figure 8–2

(*a*) First let us consider $\lim\limits_{x \to \pi/4} f(x)$. The graph indicates that $f(x)$ is close to 1, if x is close to $\pi/4$. Furthermore, in the symbolism of the diagram, $|f(x) - 1| < \epsilon$ provided x is in any δ-neighborhood of $\pi/4$ that lies inside the interval $[A, B]$. Thus, $\lim_{x \to \pi/4} f(x)$ exists and equals 1.

(*b*) Now let us consider $\lim_{x \to \pi/2} f(x)$. In this case $\pi/2$ is not in the domain of the function and the diagram does not suggest a possible limit number L. However, it is evident that every δ-neighborhood of $\pi/2$ will contain a number x such that $|f(x) - L|$ will be arbitrarily large for *any*

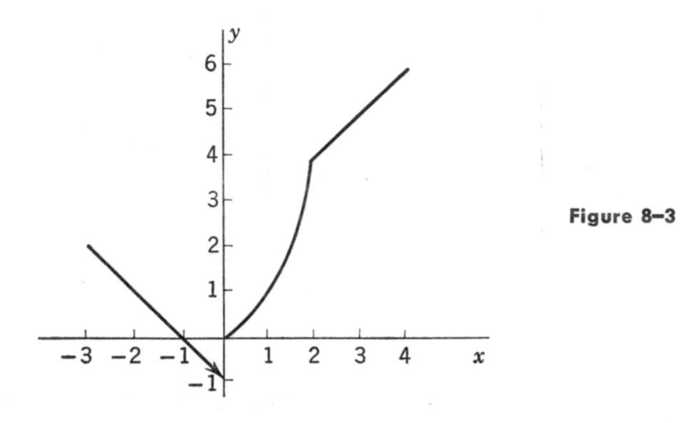

Figure 8–3

chosen L. Hence, if any positive ϵ is selected, it will be impossible to find a satisfactory δ-neighborhood of $\pi/2$, and so $\lim_{x \to \pi/2} f(x)$ does not exist. It may be seen that $\lim_{x \to c} f(x)$ exists, for each c in the domain of f, but not for $c = \pi/2$ in its closure.

ILLUSTRATION 2. In Figure 8–3, we have graphed the function f, defined on the interval $[-3, 4]$ by

$$\begin{aligned} f(x) &= x^2 \text{ if } 0 \leq x \leq 2; \\ &= x + 2 \text{ if } 2 < x \leq 4; \\ &= x - 1 \text{ if } -3 \leq x < 0. \end{aligned}$$

(*a*) Let us first consider $\lim_{x \to 2} f(x)$. The graph suggests $L = 4$, since $f(x)$ is close to 4 if x is close to 2. Indeed, for any positive ϵ, it is evident from the graph that a positive δ may be found, such that $|f(x) - 4| < \epsilon$ provided x is in the domain of f and in the δ-neighborhood of 2. This can be done, even though the function is defined by more than one equation in any neighborhood of 2. Thus, it appears that $\lim_{x \to 2} f(x)$ exists and equals 4.

(*b*) We now consider $\lim_{x \to 0} f(x)$. While 0 is in the domain of f, the graph shows a break to the left of this point. Moreover, it is clear that every δ-neighborhood of 0 will contain a number x such that $|f(x) - L| > 1/2$, regardless of the choice of L. Thus, if an $\epsilon < 1/2$ is selected, it is impossible to find a satisfactory δ-neighborhood of 0, and so $\lim_{x \to 0} f(x)$ does not exist.

(*c*) Finally, let us consider $\lim_{x \to 4} f(x)$. The graph indicates that $f(x)$ is close to 6, if x is close to 4, and that a satisfactory δ-neighborhood of 4 exists for any positive ϵ. Thus, $\lim_{x \to 4} f(x)$ appears to exist and equals 6. Notice that we do not consider a number x in a δ-interval of 4 with $x > 4$, since such a number is not in the domain of f.

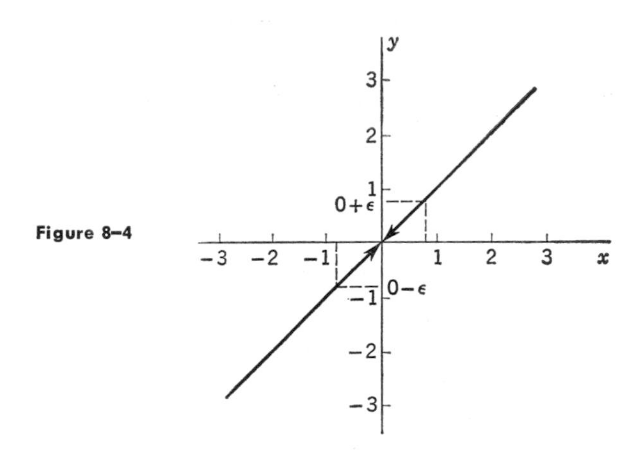

Figure 8–4

At the risk of being repetitious we wish to re-emphasize that the number c must be a limit point of the domain of f if the existence of $\lim_{x \to c} f(x)$ is even to be considered.

ILLUSTRATION 3. In Figure 8–4, we have shown the graph of the function f defined on $[-3, 3] - \{0\}$ by $f(x) = x^2/x$, and we wish to consider $\lim_{x \to 0} f(x)$. We notice that, while 0 is not in the domain of f, it is in the closure. The graph indicates that $f(x)$ is close to 0, if x is close to 0. Moreover, for any choice of $\epsilon > 0$, if we select $\delta = \epsilon$, a satisfactory δ-neighborhood of 0 exists, with $L = 0$. Thus, $\lim_{x \to 0} f(x) = 0$.

ILLUSTRATION 4. Let us now consider the function f, defined on the set of all real numbers by $f(x) = 1$ for x rational, $f(x) = 0$ for x irrational.

It would be misleading to try to graph this function, for any attempt at such a graph would be indistinguishable from the x-axis and the locus of the equation $y = 1$. This is the case because there is never a "next" rational number, and between any two rational numbers there are both rational and irrational numbers. Let us consider $\lim_{x \to c} f(x)$ for any real number c. Since each δ-neighborhood of c contains both rational and irrational numbers, it follows that the corresponding functional values differ by 1. Thus, if we assert that $\lim_{x \to c} f(x) = L$, for some real number L, and choose ϵ so that $0 < \epsilon < 1$, every δ-neighborhood of c contains a number x such that $|f(x) - L| > \epsilon$. Thus, no satisfactory δ-neighborhood exists, and $\lim_{x \to c} f(x)$ does not exist for *any* real number c.

PROBLEM SET 8.1

1. If x is a member of the subset of real numbers defined by the condition given below, list the members of the closure of the set which are not in the set: (*a*) $-2 \leq x < 5$; (*b*) $x > 3$; (*c*) $-3 < x \leq 3$; (*d*) $-2 < x < 1$; (*e*) $0 < x \leq 2$; (*f*) $x > 2$ or $x < -1$.

2. A function f is defined on the interval $[-2, 2]$ by the equation $f(x) = 2x^2$. Which of the following numbers could not be identified with c in the definition of $\lim_{x \to c} f(x)$, and give a reason for your answer: 0, 1, 3, -2, -4.

Note. Sketch the graph of each of the functions defined in Problems 3 through 14, and use the method of the illustrations to decide whether or not $\lim_{x \to c} f(x)$ exists for the given number c.

3. $f(x) = x^2$ on $[-2, 2]$; $c = 2$.
4. $f(x) = \sin x$ on $[-\pi, \pi]$; $c = \pi/2$.
5. $f(x) = \tan x$ on $[-\pi, 0] - \{-\pi/2\}$; $c = -\pi/2$.
6. $f(x) = e^x$ on $[0, 2]$; $c = 1$.
7. $f(x) = x^3/x$ on $[-1, 1] - \{0\}$; $c = 0$.
8. $f(x) = \ln x$ on $[1, 4]$; $c = 2$.
9. $f(x) = \sin x$ on $[0, \pi]$, $f(x) = \cos x$ on $[-\pi, 0] - \{0\}$; $c = 0$.
10. $f(x) = e^{2x}$ on $[0, 3]$, $f(x) = 1 - 3x$ on $[-3, 0] - \{0\}$; $c = 0$.
11. $f(x) = \ln 2x$ on $[0, 2] - \{0\}$, $f(x) = \tan x$ on $[-\pi/4, 0]$; $c = 0$.
12. $f(x) = [x]$ on $[0, 5]$; $c = 2$. (See Problem 20 of Problem Set 4.4.)
13. $f(x) = |x|$ on $[-3, 3]$; $c = 0$.
14. $f(x) = 1$ on $[0, 3]$, $f(x) = 0$ on $[-3, 0] - \{0\}$; $c = 0$; $c = 1$.
15. Consider the existence of $\lim_{x \to 0} f(x)$, for a function f defined on a neighborhood of 0 by $f(x) = \sin 1/x$, for each x in its domain.

8.2 Theorems on Limits

It is possible to establish an *arithmetic of functions* by defining operations of addition, subtraction, multiplication, and division on the members of a set of functions. Thus, if D is the common domain of two functions f and g, we can make the following definitions:

1. $f \pm g$ is the function on D defined by $(f \pm g)(x) = f(x) \pm g(x)$, for each x in D;

2. fg is the function on D defined by $(fg)(x) = f(x) \cdot g(x)$, for each x in D;

3. f/g is the function defined by $(f/g)(x) = f(x)/g(x)$, on the subset D' of D such that $g(x) \neq 0$, for each x in D'.

A special case of (2) arises if one of the functions is a constant function, i.e., all of its functional values are equal to some number C. We may list this as (2′):

Cf is the function, having the same domain as f, defined by $(Cf)(x) = Cf(x)$, for each x in its domain.

We now extend the notion of a limit of a function, introduced in the preceding section, to a composition of functions. The theorems which we state may be proven on the basis of the definition of Section 8.1, but we omit the proofs. In Theorems 2, 3, and 4, we assume that c is a limit point of the *common* domain D of the functions f and g.

THEOREM 1. If f is a constant function with $f(x) = C$, for each x in its domain, then $\lim_{x \to c} f(x) = C$ for any limit point c of the domain of f.

THEOREM 2. $\lim_{x \to c} (f \pm g)(x) = \lim_{x \to c} f(x) \pm \lim_{x \to c} g(x)$, provided $\lim_{x \to c} f(x)$ and $\lim_{x \to c} g(x)$ exist.

THEOREM 3. $\lim_{x \to c} (fg)(x) = \left[\lim_{x \to c} f(x)\right]\left[\lim_{x \to c} g(x)\right]$, provided $\lim_{x \to c} f(x)$ and $\lim_{x \to c} g(x)$ exists.

Corollary. $\lim_{x \to c} Cf(x) = C \lim_{x \to c} f(x)$, for any real number C, if $\lim_{x \to c} f(x)$ exists.

THEOREM 4. $\lim_{x \to c} (f/g)(x) = \left[\lim_{x \to c} f(x)\right] \Big/ \left[\lim_{x \to c} g(x)\right]$, provided $\lim_{x \to c} f(x)$ and $\lim_{x \to c} g(x)$ exist and $\lim_{x \to c} g(x) \neq 0$.

In Illustration 3 of Section 8.1, we considered the function f defined on $[-3, 3] - \{0\}$ by $f(x) = x^2/x$ for each x in its domain, and found that $\lim_{x \to 0} f(x) = 0$; and a similar argument would show that $\lim_{x \to c} f(x) = c$ for any c in the domain of f. We note, in passing, that the function f might have been defined on its domain by the more simple equation $f(x) = x$, since $x \neq 0$. Let us now consider the linear function F defined on some set S of real numbers by $F(x) = x$. If c is a limit point of S, we can show, as in the above illustration, that $\lim_{x \to c} F(x) = c$, but in view of the importance of this result in the sequel, we shall repeat the argument.

In Figure 8–5, we have shown a portion of the graph of the basic linear function, this graph then containing the points of F. We wish to consider $\lim_{x \to c} F(x)$, with x a point in the domain of F and c one of its limit points. In this case, since $F(x) = x$, it is clear that $|F(x) - c| < \epsilon$ whenever

$|x - c| < \epsilon$. Hence, for any chosen $\epsilon > 0$, if we select $\delta = \epsilon$, the corresponding δ-neighborhood of c is satisfactory; i.e., if we indicate this neighborhood by N_c, $|F(x) - c| < \epsilon$ provided $x \in N_c$. We have then proven that $\lim_{x \to c} F(x) = c$. It should be understood, of course, that a δ-neighborhood of c may contain points not in the domain of F, but on the other hand every such neighborhood does contain infinitely many points of this domain. We may now illustrate some consequences of this result and the above theorems.

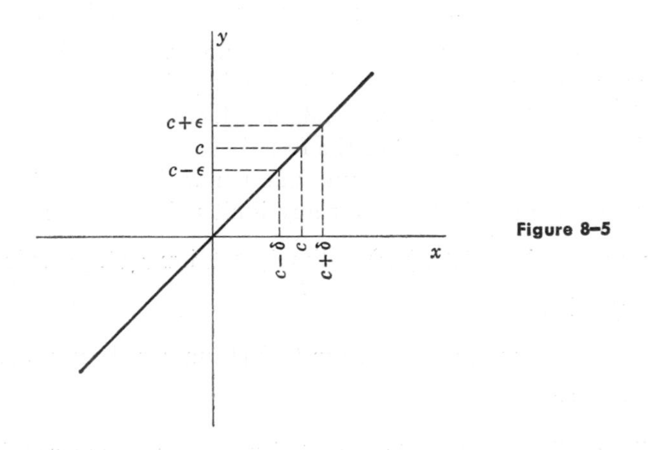

Figure 8–5

ILLUSTRATION 1. If c is a limit point of the domain of a function f defined by $f(x) = x^2$, for each x in its domain, then $\lim_{x \to c} f(x) = c^2$.

Proof. If F is the function defined on the same domain as f by $F(x) = x$, we may consider that $f = FF = F^2$. Since we have just shown that $\lim_{x \to c} F(x) = c$, it follows from Theorem 3 that $\lim_{x \to c} f(x) = \left[\lim_{x \to c} F(x)\right]\left[\lim_{x \to c} F(x)\right] = (c)(c) = c^2$.

ILLUSTRATION 2. If c is a limit point of the domain of a function f defined by $f(x) = x^n$, for a positive integer n, then $\lim_{x \to c} f(x) = c^n$.

Proof. With F defined as in Illustration 1, we may consider that $f = F^n$, and a repeated application of Theorem 3 shows that $\lim_{x \to c} f(x) = c^n$.

ILLUSTRATION 3. If c is a limit point of the domain of a function f defined by $f(x) = Cx^n$, for some real number C and a positive integer n, then $\lim_{x \to c} f(x) = Cc^n$.

Proof. With F defined as in Illustration 1, we may consider that $f = CF^n$. It then follows from the Corollary to Theorem 3 that $\lim_{x \to c} f(x) =$

$C \lim_{x \to c} F^n(x)$; the result of Illustration 2 now shows that $\lim_{x \to c} f(x) = Cc^n$.

A *polynomial* in x is an expression consisting of the sum of a finite number of terms of the form Cx^n, for some real number C and positive integer n. If $P[x]$ is such a polynomial, we shall indicate by $P[c]$ the result of replacing x by c in each term of the polynomial. A function f is said to be a *polynomial function* if its rule of correspondence has the form $f(x) = P[x]$, for each x in its domain. A power function is, of course, a special case of a polynomial function. A function f is known as a *rational function* if $f(x) = P[x]/Q[x]$ for each x in its domain, with $P[x]$ and $Q[x]$ polynomials in x. It is clear that a polynomial function is a special case of a rational function. The procedure used in the preceding illustrations can now be generalized to give us the following result, which may be considered a special case of Theorem 4.

THEOREM 5. If c is a limit point of the domain of a rational function f defined by $f(x) = P[x]/Q[x]$, for each x in its domain, then $\lim_{x \to c} f(x) = P[c]/Q[c]$, provided $Q[c] \neq 0$.

ILLUSTRATION 4. If f is the function defined on the interval $[3, 6]$ by $f(x) = (3x^2 + 4)/(2x - 5)$ for each x in its domain, determine $\lim_{x \to 3} f(x)$.

Solution. Since 3 is a limit point of the domain of f, the result follows from Theorem 5. Thus, $\lim_{x \to 3} f(x) = (3 \cdot 3^2 + 4)/(2 \cdot 3 - 5) = 31/1 = 31$.

ILLUSTRATION 5. If f is the function defined on $R^\# - \{2\}$ by $f(x) = (x^2 - 4)/(x - 2)$, for each x in its domain, determine $\lim_{x \to 2} f(x)$.

Solution. While 2 is not in the domain of f, it is a limit point of this domain, so we may consider $\lim_{x \to 2} f(x)$. Since $x \neq 2$, $f(x) = [(x - 2)(x + 2)]/(x - 2) = x + 2$, and so $\lim_{x \to 2} f(x) = 2 + 2 = 4$, by Theorem 5.

In addition to the five theorems on limits given above, there is another theorem which is very useful. We state it without proof, and refer to it as the "Domination Principle."

THEOREM 6 (DOMINATION PRINCIPLE). Let f, g, and h be functions on a set S of real numbers, such that $g(x) \leq f(x) \leq h(x)$, for each x in S. Then if c is a limit point of S, such that $\lim_{x \to c} g(x) = \lim_{x \to c} h(x) = L$, for some real number L, it follows that $\lim_{x \to c} f(x) = L$.

ILLUSTRATION 6. If 0 is a limit point of the domain of a circular function f, defined on its domain by $f(x) = \sin kx$ for some real number k, show that $\lim_{x \to 0} f(x) = 0$.

Proof. The result follows from Theorem 1 if $k = 0$, so let us assume that $k \neq 0$. With reference to the measure of length established by the unit circle of Figure 8–6, the definition of the sine function shows that $2\,|\sin kx|$ is equal to the measure of length of the chord PQ, while $2\,|kx|$ is the measure of length of the smaller arc PQ. Since the length of an arc is greater than the length of its subtended chord, it follows that $|\sin kx| < |kx|$, for $x \neq 0$. Thus, $-|kx| < |\sin kx| < |kx|$, for each x in a sufficiently small neighborhood of 0, and in particular for each such x that also lies in the domain of f. Let us now apply Theorem 6, with g and h functions defined, respectively, by $g(x) = -|kx|$ and $h(x) = |kx|$, the domains of these functions coinciding in some neighborhood of 0. Since $\lim_{x \to 0} g(x) = \lim_{x \to 0} h(x) = 0$, with a simple deduction on absolute values (see Problem 3), it follows from the Domination Principle that $\lim_{x \to 0} f(x) = 0$.

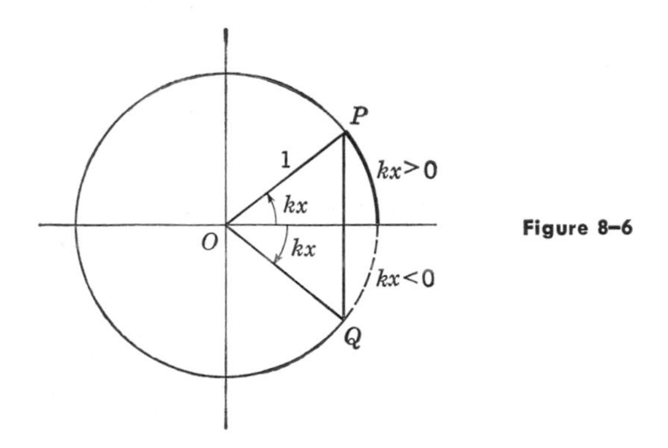

Figure 8–6

ILLUSTRATION 7. If 0 is a limit point of the domain of a circular function f, defined on its domain by $f(x) = \cos kx$ for some real number k, show that $\lim_{x \to 0} f(x) = 1$.

Proof. This result follows by Theorem 1 if $k = 0$, so let us assume $k \neq 0$. If x is a number sufficiently close to 0, $1 - \cos kx = \dfrac{(1 - \cos^2 kx)}{1 + \cos kx} \leq 1 - \cos^2 kx$, since $1 + \cos kx \geq 1$. For such an x, we then have the inequality $0 \leq 1 - \cos kx \leq \sin^2 kx$. The members of this inequality may be considered the respective values at x of three functions g, F, and h, having domains that coincide in some neighborhood of 0 with the domain of f. An application of the result of Illustration 6, along with the Domination Principle, now shows that $\lim_{x \to 0} F(x) = 0$. Since $f(x) = 1 - F(x)$, for each x in the above neighborhood, our desired result follows from Theorem 2, i.e., $\lim_{x \to 0} f(x) = 1$.

PROBLEM SET 8.2

1. Consider $\lim_{x \to 2} f(x)$ for the function f, defined on its domain D by $f(x) = x$ with (*a*) $D = R^{\#}$; (*b*) $D = [0, 3]$; (*c*) $D = [-1, 1]$; (*d*) $D = I$; (*e*) $D = \bar{R}$.
2. If c is an element in the *finite* domain (finite number of elements) of a function f, explain why our definition of a limit does not allow us to consider $\lim_{x \to c} f(x)$.
3. Let f and $\bar{f}$ be functions defined on $R^{\#}$, respectively, by $f(x) = \sin kx$ and $\bar{f}(x) = |\sin kx|$, for each real number k. If $\lim_{x \to 0} \bar{f}(x) = 0$, show that $\lim_{x \to 0} f(x) = 0$.
4. If f is the function defined on $R^{\#}$ by $f(x) = [x]$, with $[x]$ defined as in Problem 20 of Problem Set 4.4, use the definition of a limit to prove that $\lim_{x \to c} f(x)$ does not exist for any integer c.

Note. In Problems 5 through 16, determine $\lim_{x \to c} f(x)$, if it exists, for the given c and function f defined on D by $f(x)$ as indicated.

5. $f(x) = 5x^2 - 6$, $D = R^{\#}$, $c = 2$.
6. $f(x) = 2x^3 + 5x^2 - 3$, $D = R^{\#}$, $c = -4$.
7. $f(x) = x^5 - 6x^3 + 5$, $D = R^{\#}$, $c = 1$.
8. $f(x) = \dfrac{(4x^2 + 3x - 2)}{2x + 3}$, $D = [0, 5]$, $c = -1$.
9. $f(x) = \dfrac{x^2 - 1}{x - 1}$, $D = R^{\#} - \{1\}$, $c = 1$.
10. $f(x) = \dfrac{4x^2 + 5}{2x - 1}$, $D = [1, 3]$, $c = 3$.
11. $f(x) = x + \sin x$, $D = R^{\#}$, $c = 0$.
12. $f(x) = \tan 3x$, $D = [-\pi/4, \pi/4]$, $c = 0$.
13. $f(x) = 3x^2 + \cos 2x$, $D = R^{\#}$, $c = 0$.
14. $f(x) = 1 - \sec 3x$, $D = [0, \pi/4]$, $c = 0$.
15. $f(x) = \dfrac{x^2 + 2 \sin x}{\cos 2x}$, $D = [0, \pi/4]$, $c = 0$.
16. $f(x) = x$, $D = I$, $c = 2$.

17*. Use the definition of a limit to prove Theorem 2.

18*. Use the definition of a limit to prove Theorem 5.

8.3 Continuity

In all the illustrations of the preceding section except Illustration 5, we could have determined $\lim_{x \to c} f(x)$ by merely finding $f(c)$. In Illustration 5 we could not do this, however, for $f(c)$ was not defined; but even if $f(c)$

were defined, this would not necessarily be a valid procedure. For example, consider the function g defined on $R^{\#}$ by $g(x) = (x^2 - 4)/(x - 2)$ for $x \neq 2$, $g(x) = 6$ if $x = 2$. In this case, 2 is in the domain of the function with $f(2) = 6$; but since $\lim_{x \to 2} g(x)$ does not involve $x = 2$, we could find as in Illustration 5 that $\lim_{x \to 2} g(x) = 4$. Thus, $\lim_{x \to 2} g(x) \neq g(2)$. We shall see presently that $\lim_{x \to c} f(x) = f(c)$ only if the function f has a characteristic known as *continuity* at the point $x = c$. But first let us prove another result similar to that of Illustration 5, which will have many applications.

THEOREM 1. Let x be a point in the domain of a function f defined by $f(x) = \dfrac{\sin x}{x}$. Then, if 0 is a limit point of the domain of f, $\lim_{x \to 0} f(x) = 1$.

Proof. We may assume that x is a number with small absolute value, which measures the signed length of arc PA on the unit circle of Figure 8–7 if $x > 0$, and which measures the signed length of arc AP' if $x < 0$. More-

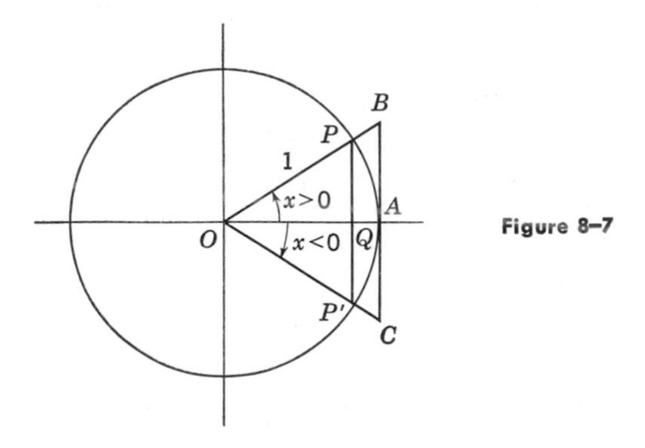

Figure 8–7

over, $\sin x$ will be the ordinate of point P or point P', according as $x > 0$ or $x < 0$. Since arcs of circles are longer than their subtended chords, it follows that $2\,|\sin x| < 2\,|x|$, i.e., $|\sin x| < |x|$. Also, the area of circular sector OPP' is $2(|x|/2)$ or $|x|$ square units, while the corresponding measure of area of the triangle OBC is $2(1/2 \cdot 1 \cdot |\tan x|)$ or $|\tan x|$. The figure shows that $|x| < |\tan x|$, and combining this with the previous result we obtain the inequality $|\sin x| < |x| < |\tan x|$; or dividing each member of the inequality by $|\sin x|$—which is not 0, since 0 is not in the domain of f—the result is $1 < |x/(\sin x)| < 1/\cos x$. Since $\sin x$ and x have the same sign for x sufficiently close to 0, $|x/(\sin x)| = x/(\sin x)$, and the above inequality may be written $1 < x/(\sin x) < 1/(\cos x)$. But $1/(\cos x)$ may be considered the value at x of another function, with a domain that coincides with that of f in a sufficiently small neighborhood of 0. Since 0 is a limit point of the domain of this function, Theorem 4 and the result of Illustration 7 of Section 8.2 imply that the limit of this function, as x tends to 0, is 1/1 or 1. The Domination Principle then requires that $\lim_{x \to 0} f(x) = 1$, as asserted. In connection with the last result, we note that if f had been so defined that $f(x) = \dfrac{\sin x^\circ}{x}$, we could not conclude that $\lim_{x \to 0} f(x) = 1$; for $\sin x^\circ = \sin (\pi x/180)$.

Our definition of $\lim_{x \to c} f(x)$ has required that c be a limit point of the domain of the function f, but c is not necessarily a member of the domain itself. Hence $f(c)$ may or may not be defined, and its existence is irrelevant as far as the existence of the above limit is concerned. However, we have seen from the illustrations of the preceding section that it happens very frequently that $\lim_{x \to c} f(x) = f(c)$, and in such instances we say that the function is continuous at the point $x = c$.

DEFINITION. Let c be a limit point *in* the domain of a function f. Then f is said to be *continuous* at the point c in case $\lim_{x \to c} f(x)$ exists and equals $f(c)$. If f is continuous at each point of a set S (possibly the whole domain), f is *continuous on* S.

If a function is not continuous at a point c *of its domain*, the function is said to be *discontinuous at* c and c will be a *point of discontinuity* of the function. Our definition has implied that at a point not in the domain, a function is neither continuous nor discontinuous. It is possible for a function to be continuous at each point of its domain as, for example, the function defined on $R^\#$ by $f(x) = x^2$; but a function may also be discontinuous at each point of its domain—or totally discontinuous—like the function of Illustration 4 of Section 8.1. Most of the functions, which will be of interest to us, will be either continuous or have a finite number of discontinuities.

The following theorem is a direct result of the definition of continuity and the theorems on limits in Section 8.2.

THEOREM 2. Let c be a point of continuity of functions f and g. Then the functions $f + g$, fg, and f/g are also continuous at c, provided $g(c) \neq 0$ in the case of f/g.

Corollary. If c is a point of continuity of a function f, the function Cf is also continuous at c, for any real number C.

The corollary follows from the theorem if, in the case of the function fg, g is a constant function with $g(x) = C$ for each x in its domain. A special case of this theorem follows from an application of Theorem 5 of Section 8.2 to a *polynomial function* or a *rational function* f defined on its domain, respectively, by $f(x) = P[x]$ or $f(x) = P[x]/Q[x]$, for polynomials $P[x]$ and $Q[x]$.

THEOREM 3. A polynomial or rational function is continuous at each limit point *in* its domain.

The power functions, as special polynomial functions, are included in Theorem 3, but we also have the following result which we state without proof.

THEOREM 4. An exponential, logarithmic, circular, or degree-circular function is continuous at each limit point *in* its domain.

We emphasize, in connection with Theorems 3 and 4, that the limit point must be *in* the domain of the function; otherwise the function would not have a value at this point.

The problem of determining limits is very simple, if the function is known to be continuous. For if c is a point of continuity of a function f, we can determine $\lim_{x \to c} f(x)$ by merely finding $f(c)$.

ILLUSTRATION 1. Let us consider the function f, defined on a set S of real numbers by $f(x) = \dfrac{\sin x}{x}$, for each x in S. An application of Theorems 2 and 4 shows that f is continuous at each limit point of S which is in S; and if c is such a point, $\lim_{x \to c} f(x) = \dfrac{\sin c}{c}$. It is clear that 0 can not lie in S; but let us suppose that 0 is a limit point of S and so is in its closure, and consider the function g defined on $S + \{0\}$ as follows: $g(x) = \dfrac{\sin x}{x}$, for each x in S; $g(x) = 1$, for $x = 0$. The function g is continuous at 0; for $\lim_{x \to 0} g(x) = 1$ by Theorem 1, and so $\lim_{x \to 0} g(x) = g(0)$.

ILLUSTRATION 3. Determine the real number k, if 1 is a point of continuity of a function f defined on its domain as follows:

$$f(x) = (x^2 - 1)/(x - 1), \text{ if } x \neq 1; f(x) = k, \text{ if } x = 1.$$

Solution. If $x \neq 1$, $f(x) = [(x + 1)(x - 1)]/(x - 1) = x + 1$. Then, the definition of continuity, applied to the point $x = 1$, shows that $k = \lim_{x \to 1} f(x) = 1 + 1 = 2$.

ILLUSTRATION 4. If 2 is known to be a point of continuity of a function g, defined on its domain by $g(x) = (x^2 - x + 2)/(x^2 + 1)$, determine $\lim_{x \to 2} g(x)$.

Solution. The definition of continuity implies that $\lim_{x \to 2} g(x) = g(2) = (2^2 - 2 + 2)/(2^2 + 1) = 4/5$.

ILLUSTRATION 5. If f is defined on the interval $[0, 5]$ by $f(x) = \dfrac{\sin x + e^x}{2x + 1}$, determine $\lim_{x \to 0} f(x)$.

Solution. Since 0 is a limit point in the domain of f, Theorems 3 and 4, along with the definition of continuity, imply that $\lim_{x \to 0} f(x) = f(0) = (0 + 1)/(0 + 1) = 1$.

The following theorem will be useful in the sequel. A proof may be based directly on the definition of continuity, though we leave the details to the student.

THEOREM 5. Let f be a function defined on the set D, g a function defined on the range of f, and F a function defined on D by $F(x) = g[f(x)]$ for each $x \in D$. Then, if f is continuous at a point $c \in D$, and g is continuous at $f(c)$ in its domain, the function F is also continuous at c.

For example, if F is a function defined on an interval $[a, b]$ by $F(x) = \sin(3x^2 + x - 2)$ for each $x \in [a, b]$, an application of Theorems 3, 4, and 5 shows that f is continuous at each point of its domain.

PROBLEM SET 8.3

1. A function f is defined on the interval $[-1, 1]$ by $f(x) = (x^2 - 4)/(x - 2)$, for each x in its domain. Decide whether the function is continuous, discontinuous, or undefined at each of the following points: (*a*) $x = 1$; (*b*) $x = 2$; (*c*) $x = 4$; (*d*) $x = 0$; (*e*) $x = -3$.
2. Without the use of a graph, discuss the continuity of the function f defined on the largest possible subset of the interval $[-2, 2]$ by
   (*a*) $f(x) = (3x^3 - 4x + 2)/(x^2 + 1)$; (*b*) $f(x) = 5x^4 - 3x^2 + 6$;
   (*c*) $f(x) = 3x^2 + \sin x$; (*d*) $f(x) = (\cos x)/(2 + x^2)$;
   (*e*) $f(x) = x^2, x \geq 0,$ $= 1 - x, x < 0$; (*f*) $f(x) = (\sin x)/x, x > 0,$ $= -x, x \leq 0$;
   (*g*) $f(x) = (1 + x)(\cos x)$; (*h*) $f(x) = e^x, x > 0,$ $= -x, x \leq 0$.
3. Assume that the function f is continuous at $x = c$, and use the definition of continuity to determine $\lim_{x \to c} f(x)$ in each of the following cases: (*a*) $f(x) = 3x^2 + 4x - 6$, $c = 1$; (*b*) $f(x) = (x^2 + 5)/(x + 1)$, $c = 2$; (*c*) $f(x) = (2x^3 - 4)/(x^2 - 2)$, $c = 5$; (*d*) $f(x) = \sin x/(2 - x)$, $c = 0$; (*e*) $f(x) = (2 + \cos x)/(2 - x)$, $c = \pi/2$; (*f*) $f(x) = (2 - \ln x)/(x - 2)$, $c = 1$.
4. A function f is defined on the interval $[0, 2]$ by the equation given below. Determine k so that the function is continuous on its domain.
   (*a*) $f(x) = 2 - x^2, x \neq 0;$ $= k, x = 0.$ (*b*) $f(x) = 1 - x^2, x \neq 2;$ $= k, x = 2.$
   (*c*) $f(x) = (1 - x^2)/(1 - x), x \neq 1;$ $= k, x = 1.$ (*d*) $f(x) = (x - 2)^2/(x - 2), x \neq 2;$ $= k, x = 2.$
   (*e*) $f(x) = x^2(x - 1)/(x^2 - 1), x \neq 1;$ $= k, x = 1.$
   (*f*) $f(x) = (\sin x)/(1 - \cos x), x \neq \pi/2;$ $= k, x = \pi/2.$
5. A function f is defined on the largest possible subset of the interval $[-6, 6]$ by the equations below; locate the points of discontinuity of the function. (*a*) $f(x) = x/x$. (*b*) $f(x) = [x]$ (See Problem 20 of Problem Set 4.4.) (*c*) $f(x) = \tan x$. (*d*) $f(x) = 2x + 1$, $x > 0$; $f(x) = 3x^2 + 1$, $x \leq 0$. (*e*) $f(x) = 1$, x rational; $f(x) = 0$, x irrational.

6. (*a*) If 3 is a point of continuity of two functions, g and h, of which the respective values at a point x of their domains are $4+\sqrt{5-x}$ and $x-2$, determine $\lim_{x\to 3} f(x)$ for a function f defined by $f = g/h$. (*b*) If 1 is a point of continuity of the function f, defined at each point x of its domain by $f(x) = \text{arc Sin } x$, determine $\lim_{x\to 1} f(x)$. (*c*) Two functions f and g are defined, respectively, by $f(x) = x$ and $g(x) = \text{Sin } x$ on a set S, while a function F is defined on S by $F(x) = x \text{ Sin } x$. If $\pi/2$ is a point of continuity of f and g, determine $\lim_{x\to\pi/2} F(x)$.

8.4 The Derivative of a Function

We now turn our attention to one of our two important applications of the limit idea, a study of which comprises the content of a course in *calculus.* The process of *integration* is historically very old. In fact, when the ancient Greeks were attempting to determine the area and circumference of a circle by considering, respectively, the areas and perimeters of circumscribed and inscribed polygons with a large number of sides, they were using a method that contained the germ of the *integral calculus.* The process of *differentiation,* on the other hand, is of much more recent origin. As we shall see, on the surface there does not appear to be any reason why these two processes should be related, and it was not until the time of Newton and Leibnitz in the seventeenth century that the relationship between them was recognized. The recognition that integration is, in a certain sense, the inverse of differentiation, marks the beginning of the development of what we now know as *calculus.* The process of integration is usually much more difficult to carry out, and for this reason we shall introduce differentiation first, and then take advantage of the inverse relationship that exists between them. It is to be understood, however, that this is not the historically correct order of development.

The notion of differentiation—as a process—arises in geometry, when we attempt to determine an equation of a tangent line to a curve. In Chapter 5 we gave an essentially intuitive idea of what we mean by the *slope of a curve* at one of its points, but let us review the idea. In Figure 8–8 we have shown the graph of a *continuous* function f on the interval $[a, b]$, with P and Q two points of the graph. If $(x, f(x))$ and $(x + h, f(x + h))$ are the respective coordinate pairs of P and Q, where h is a number so that $x + h \in [a, b]$, our earlier definition of the slope of a line gives us $[f(x + h) - f(x)]/h$ as the slope of the line containing P and Q. Let E be the set of non-zero real numbers such that $x + h$ is in the domain of f, if $h \in E$; in this case, E comprises the non-zero points in the interval $[a - x, b - x]$. We now associate with the point P a function E_x, defined on E by $E_x(h) = [f(x + h) - f(x)]/h$ for each $h \in E$. The values of this function are then the slopes of the various secant lines containing P and Q, as Q designates different points on the curve. We note that while 0 is not in the domain E of E_x, it is a limit point of E. The function E_x may be conveniently referred to as the *secant-slope* function associated with the point P.

ILLUSTRATION 1. If f is the continuous function defined on $[-2, 2]$ by $f(x) = 2x^2$, for each x in its domain, determine the secant-slope function associated with the point $(1, 2)$ on the graph of f.

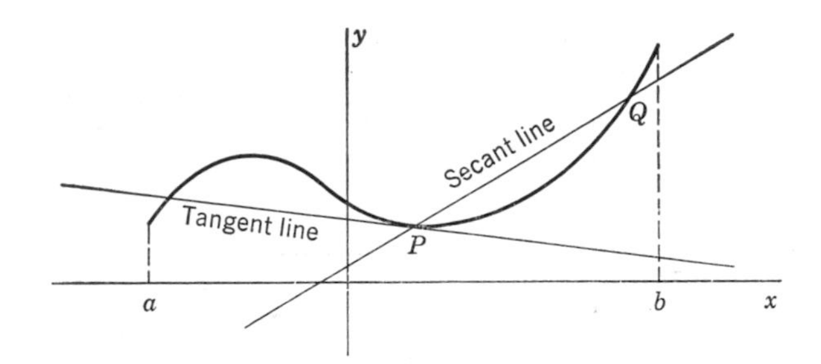

Figure 8–8

Solution. The domain E of this slope function is the set of non-zero points of $[-3, 1]$, and our definition of E_x implies that

$$E_1(h) = \frac{f(1+h) - f(1)}{h} = \frac{2(1+h)^2 - 2(1)^2}{h} = \frac{2(1 + 2h + h^2) - 2}{h}$$

$$= \frac{4h + 2h^2}{h} = 4 + 2h,$$

for each $h \in E$. (Why are we permitted to divide by h in the last step?) If we put $h = 1$, we find that $E_1(1) = 6$, which is the slope of the line containing $(1, 2)$ and the neighboring point with abscissa $1 + 1$—i.e., the point $(2, 8)$, as seen in Figure 8–9. Similarly, if $h = -1$ we obtain $E_1(-1) = 2$, which is the slope of the line containing $(1, 2)$ and $(1 - 1, 0)$—i.e., $(0, 0)$. It must be emphasized that there is a distinct secant-slope function associated with each point on the curve. For instance, the function associated with the point $(2, 8)$, in this illustration, will be different from the one which we considered.

The discussion of the secant-slope function could be easily generalized, but, of course, it is possible that the domain E is not the non-zero points of an interval. Let us then consider a function f, with x a limit point in its domain. It is clear that the set E of non-zero points, such that $x + h$ is in the domain of f if $h \in E$, contains infinitely many points in any neighborhood of 0, and so 0 is a limit point of E. We may then consider the existence of $\lim_{h \to 0} E_x(h)$, which brings us to the definition of the *derived function* or *derivative* of f.

DEFINITION. Let x be a limit point in the domain D of a function f, with E_x the associated secant-slope function. If D' is the subset of D such

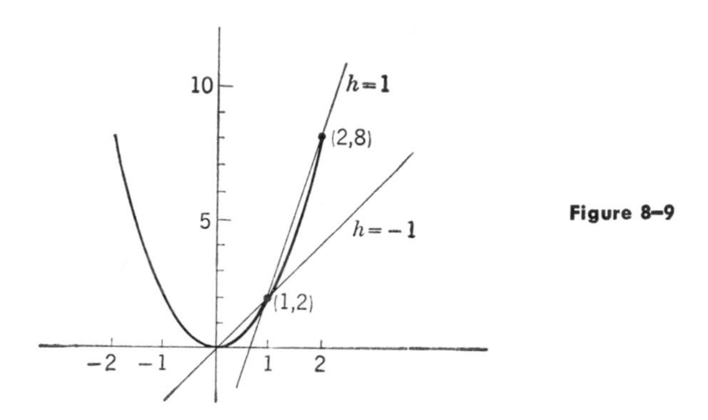

Figure 8-9

that $\lim_{h \to 0} E_x(h)$ exists, for each $x \in D'$, the *derivative* f' of f is the function on D' defined by $f'(x) = \lim_{h \to 0} E_x(h)$. The function f is said to be *differentiable* at a point x in D, if $x \in D'$; a function that is differentiable at each point of a set S is said to be *differentiable on* S.

It will be important for our applications to realize that each point of an interval is a limit point of the interval. Thus, if a function is defined on an interval, and is differentiable at each limit point of its domain, it is differentiable on the whole interval.

Let x be a point in the domain of a function f, defined on an interval. The graph of f is then a geometric curve, and the line containing the points $(x, f(x))$ and $(x + h, f(x + h))$ approximates what we intuitively call the *tangent line* to the curve at $(x, f(x))$, if h is a number near 0. The nearer h is to 0, the closer the agreement with our intuition, and so the following definition is natural.

DEFINITION. Let f be a function defined on an interval $[a, b]$. Then if $P(x, f(x))$ is a point on the graph of f at which f is differentiable, the tangent line to the curve at P is the line that contains P and has slope $f'(x)$.

It may be shown rather easily that a point at which a function is differentiable *must* be a point of continuity of the function, but the converse statement is not necessarily true. For it is clear geometrically that a tangent line could not be defined at a "sharp corner" of a curve, even though the defining function is continuous at such a point.

ILLUSTRATION 2. Determine the slope of the locus of $y = x^2$ at the point $(2, 4)$.

Solution. Our problem is to find the derivative f' of the function f

defined on $R^\#$ by $f(x) = x^2$. The secant-slope function associated with the point (2, 4) is given by

$$E_2(h) = \frac{f(2+h) - f(2)}{h} = \frac{(2+h)^2 - 2^2}{h} = \frac{4h + h^2}{h} = 4 + h.$$

Thus, $\lim_{h \to 0} E_2(h) = 4 + 0 = 4$, and the slope of the locus at (2, 4) is 4.

ILLUSTRATION 3. If x is a limit point in the domain of a function f, defined at each point t of its domain by $f(t) = 2/t$, show that f is differentiable at x and determine $f'(x)$.

Solution. The secant-slope function E_x is defined by

$$E_x(h) = \frac{f(x+h) - f(x)}{h} = \frac{2/(x+h) - 2/x}{h} = \frac{(2x - 2x - 2h)}{[x(x+h)h]}$$

$$= \frac{-2}{[x(x+h)]}.$$

Then $\lim_{h \to 0} E_x(h) = -2/x^2$, and so $f'(x) = -2/x^2$. We note that $x \neq 0$, since 0 is not in the domain of f.

ILLUSTRATION 4. Assume that the function g, defined at each point of an interval $[a, b]$ by $g(t) = \sqrt{t}$, is continuous on its domain, and determine $g'(x)$ for any x in the domain of g'.

Solution. The secant-slope function E_x, associated with such a point x, is defined on its domain by

$$E_x(h) = \frac{g(x+h) - g(x)}{h} = \frac{\sqrt{x+h} - \sqrt{x}}{h}$$

$$= \frac{(\sqrt{x+h} - \sqrt{x})(\sqrt{x+h} + \sqrt{x})}{(\sqrt{x+h} + \sqrt{x})} = \frac{x + h - x}{(\sqrt{x+h} + \sqrt{x})}$$

$$= \frac{h}{(\sqrt{x+h} + \sqrt{x})} = \frac{1}{(\sqrt{x+h} + \sqrt{x})}.$$

Then

$$\lim_{h \to 0} E_x(h) = 1/(2\sqrt{x}),$$

since g is assumed to be continuous and $x \neq 0$, and so $g'(x) = 1/(2\sqrt{x})$ for each x in the domain of g'.

PROBLEM SET 8.4

1. Describe the secant-slope function associated with the point $(-1, 1)$ on the locus of the equation $y = x^2$.

2. Describe the secant-slope function associated with the point (1, 3) on the locus of the equation $y = 2x^2 + 1$.
3. Use the secant-slope function of Problem 1 to determine the slope of the line containing the points (−1, 1) and (1, 1).
4. Use the secant-slope function of Problem 2 to determine the slope of the line containing the points (1, 3) and (3, 19).

In Problems 5 through 16, assume that the function f is differentiable at each point x in its domain, and determine $f'(x)$ from the given $f(x)$.

5. $f(x) = 5x^2$.
6. $f(x) = 5x^2 + 4$.
7. $f(x) = 3x - 6$.
8. $f(x) = 2x + 7$.
9. $f(x) = 1/(2x)$.
10. $f(x) = \sqrt{x + 2}$.
11. $f(x) = 1/\sqrt{x}$.
12. $f(x) = 1/(x + 2)$.
13. $f(x) = x^3 + 2x^2$.
14. $f(x) = x^3 - 3$.
15. $f(x) = 4x^3$.
16. $f(x) = 2x^4 - 3x^2$.
17. If x is a point at which a function is differentiable, why must x be also a point of continuity of the function?

8.5 Derivatives of Simple Polynomial Functions

The limit process outlined in the preceding section for finding the derivative f' of a function f is tedious, and it is desirable to develop some formulas of a general nature to assist us. In this section we shall develop some theorems and formulas necessary for a determination of the derivative of a polynomial function of low degree. A *theorem* will always be a result of wide general application, while a *formula* will refer to a special case.

THEOREM 1. If x is a point at which a function f is differentiable, the function Cf, with C an arbitrary real number, is also differentiable at x and $(Cf)'(x) = Cf'(x)$.

Proof. If $F = Cf$, the secant-slope function E_x of F, at the point x, is defined by

$$E_x(h) = \frac{F(x+h) - F(x)}{h} = \frac{Cf(x+h) - Cf(x)}{h} = C\left[\frac{f(x+h) - f(x)}{h}\right].$$

Then

$$\lim_{h\to 0} E_x(h) = C \lim_{h\to 0} \frac{f(x+h) - f(x)}{h} = Cf'(x),$$

by definition of f', and so $(Cf)'(x) = Cf'(x)$, as asserted in the theorem.

THEOREM 2. Let f_1 and f_2 be functions which are differentiable at the point x. Then, if $f = f_1 + f_2$, the function f is differentiable at x, and $f'(x) = f_1'(x) + f_2'(x)$.

Proof. Let us construct the secant-slope function E_x for f at the point x. Then

$$E_x(h) = \frac{f(x+h) - f(x)}{h} = \frac{[f_1(x+h) + f_2(x+h)] - [f_1(x) + f_2(x)]}{h}$$
$$= \frac{f_1(x+h) - f_1(x)}{h} + \frac{f_2(x+h) - f_2(x)}{h} = E_{x1}(h) + E_{x2}(h),$$

where we have written E_{x1} and E_{x2} for the respective secant-slope functions of f_1 and f_2, associated with the point x. Since both f_1 and f_2 are differentiable at the point x, it follows that $f'(x) = \lim_{h\to 0} E_x(h) = \lim_{h\to 0} E_{x1}(x) + \lim_{x\to 0} E_{x2}(x) = f_1'(x) + f_2'(x)$, as desired.

The significance of these two theorems in the *differentiation process* (i.e., finding $f'(x)$ from a given $f(x)$) is that the terms of a sum may be considered separately, and a factor independent of x in $f(x)$ may be factored out of any term before beginning the process.

FORMULA 1. If x is a limit point in the domain of a constant function f, then $f'(x) = 0$.

Proof. Let the constant value of f be C, and consider the secant-slope function E_x for f at the point x. Then

$$E_x(h) = \frac{f(x+h) - f(x)}{h} = \frac{C - C}{h} = 0,$$

and

$$f'(x) = \lim_{h\to 0} E_x(h) = 0.$$

FORMULA 2. If x is a limit point in the domain of the linear function f, defined on its domain by $f(t) = t$, then f is differentiable at x and $f'(x) = 1$.

Proof. If E_x is the secant-slope function for f at the point x, then

$$E_x(h) = \frac{f(x+h) - f(x)}{h} = \frac{(x+h) - x}{h} = \frac{h}{h} = 1,$$

and so

$$f'(x) = \lim_{h\to 0} E_x(h) = 1.$$

FORMULA 3. If x is a limit point in the domain of the parabolic function, defined on its domain by $f(t) = t^2$, then f is differentiable at x and $f'(x) = 2x$.

Proof. Let E_x be the secant-slope function for f at the point x. Then

$$E_x(h) = \frac{f(x+h) - f(x)}{h} = \frac{(x+h)^2 - x^2}{h} = \frac{x^2 + 2hx + h^2 - x^2}{h}$$
$$= \frac{2hx + h^2}{h} = 2x + h,$$

and so

$$f'(x) = \lim_{h \to 0} E_x(h) = 2x.$$

FORMULA 4. If x is a limit point in the domain of the power function f, defined on its domain by $f(t) = t^3$, then f is differentiable at x and $f'(x) = 3x^2$.

Proof. The proof of this result is similar to that of Formula 3, and is left as an exercise for the student. We assume that the following identity is known: $(a + b)^3 = a^3 + 3a^2b + 3ab^2 + b^3$.

ILLUSTRATION. If x is a limit point in the domain of a polynomial function f, defined on its domain by $f(t) = 2t^3 + 3t^2 - 5t + 4$, show that f is differentiable at x and determine $f'(x)$.

Solution. Let f_1, f_2, f_3, and f_4 be four functions defined on the domain of f, respectively, by $f_1(t) = t^3$, $f_2(t) = t^2$, $f_3(t) = t$, and $f_4(t) = 4$. It is clear that x is also a limit point in the domain of each of these functions, and so Formulas 1, 2, 3, and 4 imply that $f_1'(x) = 3x^2$, $f_2'(x) = 2x$, $f_3'(x) = 1$, and $f_4'(x) = 0$. Since x is then a point at which these functions are differentiable, it follows from Theorems 1 and 2 that f is differentiable at x and $f'(x) = 2(3x^2) + 3(2x) - 5 + 0 = 6x^2 + 6x - 5$.

PROBLEM SET 8.5

In Problems 1 through 10, the expression given is the value $f(x)$ of a function f at a point x of its domain. Assume that f is differentiable at x, and determine $f'(x)$ in each case.

1. $2x + 5$.
2. $3x^2 - 5x + 1$.
3. $4x^2 + 6x - 3$.
4. $x^2 - 16$.
5. $4x^3 - 3x - 5$.
6. $6x^3 + 35$.
7. $x^3 - 2x^2 + 2$.
8. $10x^2 - 6x - 1$.
9. $5x^2 + 13x$.
10. $5x - 1$.

In Problems 11 through 15, the expression given is the value $f(x)$ of a function f at a point x of its domain, the function being defined on an *interval* containing the indicated point. In each case, determine the slope of the tangent line to the graph of the function at this point.

11. $3x^2$; $(3, 27)$.
12. $2x^3 - 3x + 5$; $(1, 4)$.
13. $x^3 - 5$; $(2, 3)$.
14. $4x^2 + 1$; $(-1, 5)$.
15. $5x^3$; $(2, 40)$.
16. Determine an equation of the tangent line, at the point with abscissa 2 on the locus of the equation $y = -4x^3 - 2x$.
17. Determine an equation of the tangent line, at the point with abscissa 1 on the locus of the equation $y = -3x^2 + 2$.

18. Use a simple example to show that $(fg)'$ is not necessarily the same function as $f'g'$.

19. Use the same functions as were used in Problem 18, and test whether or not $(f/g)'$ is the same as f'/g', in this case.

20. Explain why continuity of a function f at a point x is necessary for the existence of $f'(x)$.

21. Define a continuous function, having at least one point x in its domain at which $f'(x)$ fails to exist.

8.6* Derivatives of Some Elementary Functions

Now that we have become somewhat familiar with the notion of a derivative, at least in connection with simple polynomial functions, let us generalize the notion to include some of the other elementary functions. But first it is desirable to establish a very important theorem.

THEOREM 1. Suppose f is a continuous and non-constant function on an interval $[a, b]$, and is differentiable at each point $x \in [a, b]$. Let us suppose further that a function g is defined *on the range* of f, and is differentiable at the point $f(x)$ which we shall indicate more simply by u, i.e., $f(x) = u$. Then the function F, defined on the interval $[a, b]$ by $F(x) = g(u)$, is also differentiable at x and $F'(x) = g'(u) \cdot f'(x)$.

Proof. Let E_x be the secant-slope function for F at the point x, so that

$$E_x(h) = \frac{F(x+h) - F(x)}{h} = \frac{g[f(x+h)] - g[f(x)]}{h},$$

for each h in the domain of E_x. Since f is differentiable at x, the definition of f' implies that $f(x+h) - f(x) = hf'(x) + h\epsilon_1$, where ϵ_1 is a real number which is arbitrarily close to 0, if h is sufficiently close to 0. In a similar manner, if we let $f(x+h) = u + k$, the differentiability of g at u implies that $g(u+k) - g(u) = kg'(u) + k\epsilon_2$, where ϵ_2 is a real number which is arbitrarily close to 0 if k is sufficiently close to 0. Moreover, the continuity of f at x, together with the equation $f(x+h) = u + k$, implies that ϵ_2, as well as ϵ_1, is arbitrarily close to 0 if h is sufficiently near 0. But now

$$g[f(x+h)] - g[f(x)] = g(u+k) - g(u) = g'(u)[hf'(x) + h\epsilon_1] \\ + \epsilon_2[hf'(x) + h\epsilon_1] = hg'(u)f'(x) + h[\epsilon_1 g'(u) + \epsilon_2 f'(x) + \epsilon_1\epsilon_2],$$

and so

$$\frac{g[f(x+h)] - g[f(x)]}{h} = g'(u)f'(x) + [\epsilon_1 g'(u) + \epsilon_2 f'(x) + \epsilon_1\epsilon_2].$$

The bracketed expression on the right is arbitrarily close to 0 if h is sufficiently near 0, and so

$$\lim_{h \to 0} \frac{g[f(x+h)] - g(x)}{h} = g'(u)f'(x).$$

But this means that

$$F'(x) = \lim_{h \to 0} E_x(h) = g'(u)f'(x),$$

as asserted in the theorem.

The result of Theorem 1 is frequently known as the *chain rule* for the process of differentiation.

ILLUSTRATION 1. If the function F is defined on an interval by $F(x) = (2x^2 + 1)^3$, for each x in its domain, determine $F'(x)$.

Solution. It is possible to expand $(2x^2 + 1)^3$ as a polynomial in x, and then use the results of Section 8.5, but it is simpler to apply the above theorem. In this case, f is defined on the interval by $f(x) = 2x^2 + 1$, while the function g of the theorem is defined on the range of f by $g(u) = u^3$. Since the range of f is also an interval—though a different interval from the domain of f—g is differentiable at u as well as f at x. We may then apply Theorem 1, along with the results of Section 8.5, to obtain $F'(x) = g'(u) \cdot f'(x) = (3u^2)(4x) = 3(2x^2 + 1)^2 4x = 12x(2x^2 + 1)^2$.

We now recall the rather intuitive definition which we gave for the number e, the base for natural logarithms; namely, e is that real number such that if a function g is defined on an interval containing the origin by $g(x) = e^x$, the slope of the graph is 1 at the point where it crosses the vertical axis. The existence of such a number was deduced from geometric considerations in Chapter 5. In terms of the derivative of g, this means that $g'(0) = 1$. We use this fact in the derivation of the next result.

THEOREM 2. Let f be a function which is continuous and differentiable at each point x of an interval $[a, b]$. Then if F is another function defined on $[a, b]$ by $F(x) = e^u$, where $u = f(x)$, the function F is differentiable at x and $F'(x) = e^u f'(x)$.

Proof. If f is a constant function, so is F, and the result follows from Formula 1 of Section 8.5: $F(x) = e^k$ where $f(x) = k$, and so $F'(x) = 0 = e^k f'(x) = e^k(0) = 0$. Hence we may assume that f is non-constant. Since f is continuous on its domain, it is intuitively evident that the range of f (i.e., the domain of g) is also an interval, though generally different from its domain. We shall assume this result, as we did in Illustration 1, though a proof of it may be found in more advanced books. If E_u is the secant-slope function of g at the point u, it follows in the usual symbolism that

$$E_u(h) = \frac{g(u+h) - g(u)}{h} = \frac{e^{u+h} - e^u}{h} = \frac{e^u(e^h - 1)}{h}.$$

Let us tentatively assume that 0 is in the domain of g, so that the preceding equation may be written in the form $E_u(h) = e^u E_0(h)$. But now, since u is a limit point in the domain of g, it follows from the Corollary to Theorem 3 of Section 8.2 that

$$\lim_{h \to 0} E_u(h) = e^u \cdot \left[\lim_{h \to 0} E_0(h)\right] = e^u g'(0) = e^u,$$

by definition of e. Thus, $\lim_{h \to 0} E_u(h)$ exists, and so $g'(u) = e^u$. It is clear that this result is independent of whether or not 0 is actually in the domain of g, and so this restriction may be removed. It now appears that the function F satisfies the hypotheses of Theorem 1, and so $F'(x) = g'(u)f'(x) = e^u f'(x)$, thereby completing the proof of the theorem.

It should not be overlooked that our proof of the existence of the derivative of the exponential function in Theorem 2 was based on the existence of the tangent line to the graph of this function at $x = 0$; and our assumption of the existence of this tangent line is equivalent to the assumption that the function is differentiable at this point. It is possible to give a different but equivalent definition of e, in which case the proof of Theorem 2 would be modified.

THEOREM 3. Let f be a function which is positive and continuous on an interval $[a, b]$, and differentiable at each point x of $[a, b]$. Then if F is another function defined on $[a, b]$ by $F(x) = \ln u$, where $u = f(x) > 0$, F is differentiable at x and $F'(x) = (1/u)f'(x)$.

Proof. If f is a constant function, so is F, and $0 = F'(x) = (1/u)0 = (1/u)f'(x)$, by Formula 1 of Section 8.5, and so the theorem is true for this case. Let us then assume, for the following proof, that f is not constant.

We have noted before that the basic exponential and the basic logarithmic functions are inverse functions. If we continue the somewhat geometric type of argument of the preceding theorem, we then see that the existence of a tangent line at each point of the basic exponential curve implies the existence of a tangent line at each point of the basic logarithmic curve, i.e., the logarithmic function is differentiable. It is now a simple matter to determine F', for the function F of the theorem. For we have just agreed that the function g, defined on the range of f by $g(u) = \ln u$, is differentiable; and so the function G, defined on the domain of g by $G(u) = e^{g(u)} = u$, is seen to satisfy the hypotheses of Theorem 2. Thus, $G'(u) = 1 = e^{g(u)}g'(u) = ug'(u)$, whence $g'(u) = 1/u$, and an application of Theorem 1 gives us the desired result: $F'(x) = g'(u) \cdot f'(x) = (1/u)f'(x)$.

THEOREM 4. Let f be a function which is continuous on an interval $[a, b]$, and differentiable at each point $x \in [a, b]$. Then, if F is another function defined on $[a, b]$ by $F(x) = u^n$, where $u = f(x)$ and n is a positive integer, F is differentiable at x and $F'(x) = nu^{n-1}f'(x)$.

Proof. If f is a constant function, the theorem is true by Formula 1 of Section 8.5. If f has a positive value at x, the continuity of f implies that it is positive on some interval containing x; on the other hand, if f has a negative value at x the function $(-1)f$ is positive at x, and the existence of $F'(x)$ may be seen to depend on the existence of $F'(x)$ with $f(x) > 0$. Let us then assume that $f(x) = u > 0$, so that $\ln F(x) = n \ln u$. If we think of $n \ln u$ and $\ln F(x)$ as equal values at x of a function G on the interval containing x mentioned above, an application of Theorem 3 of this section and Theorem 1 of Section 8.5 shows that $G'(x) = n(1/u)f'(x) = [1/F(x)]F'(x) = (1/u^n)F'(x)$. But then $F'(x) = nu^{n-1}f'(x)$, if $f(x) \neq 0$. If $f(x) = 0$, this result may be verified by an easy application of the definition of a derivative, and so the theorem is completely established. This theorem provides a generalization of the formulas of Section 8.5. It is possible to generalize the theorem still further to allow n to be an arbitrary rational number. We shall assume this result without proof. (See problem 19.)

ILLUSTRATION 2. If F is the function defined on an interval $[a, b]$ by $F(x) = e^{4x^2}$, for each $x \in [a, b]$, determine $F'(x)$.

Solution. This is an application of Theorem 2, with $F(x) = e^u$ and $u = f(x) = 4x^2$. But $f'(x) = 8x$ by Theorem 4, and so $F'(x) = 8xe^{4x^2}$.

ILLUSTRATION 3. If F is the function defined on a positive interval $[a, b]$ by $F(x) = \ln (3x^3 + 2x)$, for each $x \in [a, b]$, determine $F'(x)$.

Solution. This is an application of Theorem 3, with $F(x) = \ln u$ and $f(x) = 3x^3 + 2x$. But $f'(x) = 9x^2 + 2$ by Theorem 4 and the results of Section 8.5, and so $F'(x) = (9x^2 + 2)/(3x^3 + 2x)$.

ILLUSTRATION 4. If F is the function defined on an interval $[a, b]$ by $F(x) = (2x^2 + x)^5$, determine $F'(x)$.

Solution. In this case, we may apply Theorem 4 with $u = f(x) = 2x^2 + x$. The theorems of Section 8.5 imply that $f'(x) = 4x + 1$, and so $F'(x) = 5(2x^2 + x)^4(4x + 1) = 5(4x + 1)(2x^2 + x)^4$.

PROBLEM SET 8.6

1. Express each given $F(x)$ in the form $F(x) = g(u)$ where $u = f(x)$. (*a*) $F(x) = (x^2 + 1)^3$; (*b*) $F(x) = e^{x+1}$; (*c*) $F(x) = \cos (x^2 - 2)$.
2. Express each given $F(x)$ in the form $F(x) = g(u)$ where $u = f(x)$. (*a*) $F(x) = \sin 2(x - 1)$; (*b*) $F(x) = \sin (3x^2 + 2)$; (*c*) $F(x) = (1 + x + x^2)^2$

In Problems 3 through 16, the given quantity is the value $F(x)$ at a point x in the domain of a function F defined on an interval $[a, b]$. Determine $F'(x)$ in each case, assuming an interval of positive real numbers in case F is a logarithmic function.

3. $3x^4 - 2x + 1$.
4. $(2x^2 - 4)^4$.
5. $(x^2 + 1)^4$.
6. $e^{(x-1)^2}$.
7. e^{3x^4}.
8. $\ln(5x^4 - 2x)$.
9. $\ln(6x^2 + 5)^4$.
10. e^{2x+1}.
11. $(3x^3 + 2x - 5)^6$.
12. $(5x^4 - x + 2)^3$.
13. $5\ln(2x^2 - 3)$.
14. $10^{(3x-1)}$.
15. e^{3x^2}.
16. $e^{(x-1)^2}$.
17. A function f is defined on its domain D by $f(x) = x^2$, for each $x \in D$. Is f differentiable at the point x, if (*a*) $D = R^{\#}$; (*b*) $D = \bar{R}$; (*c*) $D = I$?
18. With reference to the theorems of this section, what simplification resulted from our stipulation that the domain of F was an interval in each case?
19. Prove Theorem 4, for n an arbitrary rational number.
20. Show that the assumption of differentiability of the basic logarithmic function at the point $x = 1$, implies that $\lim_{h \to 0} (1 + h)^{1/h} = e$.

8.7* More About Derivatives

In this section, we extend the notion of a derivative to include functions which are products or quotients of certain functions. In addition, we give a brief discussion of the derivatives of circular functions.

THEOREM 1. Let f and g be functions defined on an interval $[a, b]$, and which are differentiable at each point $x \in [a, b]$. Then the function fg is also differentiable at x and

$$(fg)'(x) = f'(x)g(x) + f(x)g'(x).$$

Proof. Let $F = fg$. Then, if E_x is the secant-slope function for F at the point x,

$$E_x(h) = \frac{F(x+h) - F(x)}{h} = \frac{f(x+h)g(x+h) - f(x)g(x)}{h}$$
$$= f(x+h)\left[\frac{g(x+h) - g(x)}{h}\right] + g(x)\left[\frac{f(x+h) - f(x)}{h}\right].$$

If we let E_{x1} and E_{x2} be, respectively, the secant-slope functions at x for f and g, we can write the last equation as

$$E_x(h) = f(x+h)E_{x2}(h) + g(x)E_{x1}(h).$$

Since
$$\lim_{h \to 0} E_{x1}(h) = f'(x)$$
and
$$\lim_{h \to 0} E_{x2}(h) = g'(x),$$
the theorems on limits in Section 8.2 imply that $\lim_{h \to 0} E_x(h)$ exists and equals $f(x)g'(x) + f'(x)g(x)$. But this means that

$$(fg)'(x) = f'(x)g(x) + f(x)g'(x),$$

as asserted in the theorem.

ILLUSTRATION 1. If F is a function defined on some interval by $F(x) = xe^x$, for each x in its domain, determine $F'(x)$.

Solution. If we define functions f and g on the interval by $f(x) = x$, and $g(x) = e^x$, we see that $F = fg$ with f and g both differentiable at any point x in the domain, by Theorems 2 and 4 of Section 8.6. We may then apply the above theorem, and so

$$F'(x) = xe^x + 1e^x = e^x(x + 1).$$

ILLUSTRATION 2. If F is a function defined on some interval by

$$F(x) = (1 + x^2)e^{2x^2},$$

for each x in its domain, determine $F'(x)$.

Solution. We may again apply the above theorem with $F = fg$, $f(x) = 1 + x^2$, and $g(x) = e^{2x^2}$. But $f'(x) = 2x$, by Formula 1 and Formula 2 of Section 8.5; and $g'(x) = 4xe^{2x^2}$, by Theorem 1 of Section 8.5 and Theorems 1 and 4 of Section 8.6. Theorem 1 then implies that

$$F'(x) = (1 + x^2)4xe^{2x^2} + e^{2x^2}(2x) = 2xe^{2x^2}(3 + 2x^2).$$

It is possible to derive a general result for the quotient of two functions which is comparable to Theorem 1. However, the following illustration shows how this same theorem may be used for the case of quotients.

ILLUSTRATION 3. If F is the function, defined on the interval $[2, 5]$ by $F(x) = (x + 1)/(x - 1)$ for each $x \in [2, 5]$, determine $F'(x)$.

Solution. If we write $F(x)$ in the form $(x + 1)(x - 1)^{-1}$, we may apply Theorem 1. Thus, $F = fg$ with $f(x) = x + 1$ and $g(x) = (x - 1)^{-1}$ for each $x \in [2, 5]$. But $f'(x) = 1$ and $g'(x) = -(x - 1)^{-2}$, so that

$$F'(x) = (x + 1)[-(x - 1)^{-2}] + (x - 1)^{-1}(1) = \frac{-x - 1}{(x - 1)^2} + \frac{1}{x - 1}$$
$$= \frac{-2}{(x - 1)^2}.$$

The derivative of any circular function may be based on the derivative of the circular function f, defined on the same domain by $f(x) = \sin x$. Let us then consider such a function.

THEOREM 2. If x is a limit point in the domain of a function f, defined on its domain by $f(t) = \sin t$, f is differentiable at x and $f'(x) = \cos x$.

Proof. Let E_x be the secant-slope function for f at the point x, so that

$$E_x(h) = \frac{f(x + h) - f(x)}{h} = \frac{\sin (x + h) - \sin x}{h}$$
$$= \frac{2 \cos (x + h/2) \sin h/2}{h} = \cos (x + h/2) \left[\frac{\sin h/2}{h/2}\right].$$

But then $E_x(h) = f_1(h) \cdot f_2(h)$, where f_1 and f_2 are functions defined on the domain of E_x by $f_1(h) = \cos(x + h/2)$ and $f_2(h) = \dfrac{\sin h/2}{h/2}$, respectively. Theorem 4 of Section 8.3 implies that f_1 is continuous on its domain, and so $\lim_{h \to 0} f_1(h) = \cos x$. By Theorem 1 of Section 8.3 and the definition of a limit, for an arbitrary $\epsilon > 0$ there exists $\delta_1 > 0$, such that $\left|\dfrac{\sin h}{h} - 1\right| < \epsilon$ if $|h| < \delta_1$. But this means that $\left|\dfrac{\sin h/2}{h/2} - 1\right| < \epsilon$ if $|h| < \delta$ where $\delta = 2\delta_1$, and the definition of a limit assures us that $\lim_{h \to 0} f_2(h) = 1$. We now apply Theorem 3 of Section 8.2 to obtain $f'(x) = \lim_{h \to 0} E_x(h) = (\cos x)(1) = \cos x$, as desired.

It is now possible to apply Theorems 1 and 2, with the aid of certain identities of Chapter 7, to obtain derivatives for other circular functions. The following theorem summarizes these results, without proof.

THEOREM 3. If x is a limit point in the domain of a circular function f, with $f(t)$ the value of f at any point t in its domain, f is differentiable at x and

1. $f'(x) = \cos x$, if $f(t) = \sin t$;
2. $f'(x) = -\sin x$, if $f(t) = \cos t$;
3. $f'(x) = \sec^2 x$, if $f(t) = \tan t$;
4. $f'(x) = -\csc x \cot x$, if $f(t) = \csc t$;
5. $f'(x) = \sec x \tan x$, if $f(t) = \sec t$;
6. $f'(x) = -\csc^2 x$, if $f(t) = \cot t$.

ILLUSTRATION 4. If f is the function, defined on the interval $[0, \pi]$ by $f(x) = \sin x$, determine $f'(\pi/6)$.

Solution. Since $\pi/6$ is a limit point in the domain of f, we may apply Theorem 3 and obtain $f'(\pi/6) = \cos \pi/6 = \sqrt{3}/2$.

ILLUSTRATION 5. If f is the function, defined on the interval $[0, \pi/3]$ by $f(x) = \sec 3x$, determine $f'(\pi/4)$.

Solution. Since $\pi/4$ is a limit point in the domain of f, we may apply Theorem 1 of Section 8.6 along with Theorem 3 of this section to obtain $f'(\pi/4) = [\sec \pi/4][\tan \pi/4]3 = 3(\sqrt{2})(1) = 3\sqrt{2}$.

PROBLEM SET 8.7

In Problems 1 through 21, let F be a function defined at each point x of an interval by the given $F(x)$, and determine $F'(x)$.

1. $3x^2 - 2$. **2.** $x(x + 1)$.

3. $4x^8 - 7x^2$. **4.** x^2e^x.

5. $x(x^5 - 1)$.
6. $(x - 1)(x + 1)^3$.
7. $x \ln (x + 1)$.
8. $(x + 4)/e^{2x}$.
9. $(x + 2) \ln (1 - x)$.
10. $(2 - x)/(x + 1)$.
11. $(x^2 + 1)(3 - x^3)$.
12. $\cos (1 - x)$.
13. $1/x + 1/x^2$.
14. $x \sin 2x$.
15. $x^2 \tan 3x$.
16. $2x/(\cos x)$.
17. $\cot (x^2 + 1)$.
18. $e^x \sin 2x$.
19. $(x^2 + 1)^5$.
20. $\sec^2 3x$.
21. $4 \ln (x^2 - 1)$.
22. Determine the slope of the locus of the equation $y = 3x^4 + x$ at the point with abscissa 1.
23. Determine the slope of the locus of the equation $y = xe^x$ at the origin.
24. Determine an equation of the tangent line to the locus of the equation $y = x(x^2 + 1)$, at the point where $x = 2$.
25. Determine an equation of the line which is tangent to the curve having the equation $y = xe^{2x}$, at the point where $x = 1$.
26. Determine an equation of the line with slope 4, which is tangent to the curve having the equation $y = 3x^2 + 4x - 7$.
27. Any real number $a > 0$ can be written in the form $e^{\ln a}$. Use Theorem 2 of Section 8.6 to derive an analogous result for $F(x) = a^u$, for any real number $a > 0$.
28. Since $N = a^u = e^{u \ln a}$, it follows that $\ln N = u \ln a = (\log_a N)(\ln a)$, and so $\log_a N = (\ln N)/(\ln a)$. Use Theorem 3 of Section 8.6 to derive an analogous result for $F(x) = \log_a u$, for any real positive logarithmic base a.

8.8 An Application of the Derivative

We have not by any means exhausted the subject of differentiation, but prefer to leave further developments for more extensive courses in the calculus. In this section, we present one of the most important and interesting applications of the derivative, in connection with the maximum and minimum values of a function. We shall consider for our present purposes, that each function is defined on an interval, and is continuous and differentiable at each point of this interval.

If we think of a function from a geometric point of view, it is intuitively *increasing* or *decreasing* on a subinterval of its domain, according as the graph of the function advances, respectively, upwards or downwards to the right, for points with abscissas in this subinterval. The following definition puts this notion in more precise mathematical terms.

DEFINITION. A function f, defined on an interval $[a, b]$, is said to be *increasing* or *decreasing* at a point $x \in [a, b]$, according as $f(x + h) - f(x)$ and h have like or unlike signs, for each $x + h$ in $[a, b]$ in a sufficiently small neighborhood of x. The function is increasing or decreasing on the *interval* according as it is increasing or decreasing at each point of the interval.

Thus, a function f, defined by $f(x) = x^2$, is increasing on any interval of non-negative real numbers in its domain and decreasing on any such interval of non-positive real numbers; on the other hand, a function g, defined by $g(x) = e^x$, is increasing on *any* interval in its domain. Since we are assuming that each function f is differentiable at any point x in its domain, we have seen that $f'(x)$ is the slope of the tangent line at the point $(x, f(x))$ on a graph of the function; and it is then intuitively evident that $f'(x) \geq 0$ for each x in an interval on which f is increasing, and $f'(x) \leq 0$ for each x in an interval on which f is decreasing. The following theorem, however, covers the situation more adequately.

THEOREM. Let x be a point in the domain of a differentiable function f defined on an interval $[a, b]$. Then f is *increasing* or *decreasing* at x according as $f'(x) > 0$ or $f'(x) < 0$; and $f'(x) \geq 0$ or $f'(x) \leq 0$ according as f is increasing or decreasing at the point x.

Proof. The first part of the theorem follows from the definition of f'. Thus, if E_x is the secant-slope function of f at the point x, $f'(x) = \lim_{h \to 0} E_x(h)$ where $E_x(h) = \dfrac{f(x + h) - f(x)}{h}$, and it is evident that if $f'(x) > 0$, $f(x + h) - f(x)$ and h have the same sign for $|h|$ sufficiently small; but this means that f is increasing at the point x. A similar argument

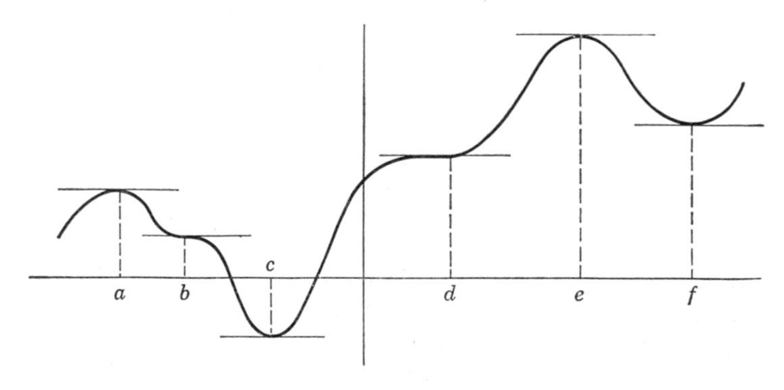

Figure 8–10

applies in case $f'(x) < 0$. Conversely, if f is increasing at x, the numerator and denominator of $E_x(h)$ have the same sign for $|h|$ sufficiently near 0, so that $\lim_{h \to 0} E_x(h)$—i.e., $f'(x)$—must be positive or 0. An analogous argument if f is decreasing will complete the proof. The above theorem gives no information about the function at a point x, in its domain, such that $f'(x) = 0$. At the corresponding point $(x, f(x))$ on the graph of f, the tangent line will be horizontal; but many different situations may prevail, some of which are illustrated in Figure 8–10 at the points where x equals a, b, c, d, e, and f, respectively.

In Figure 8–10, the points on the graph at $x = b$ or $x = d$ are known as *points of inflection* (or *inflection points*) with horizontal tangents; the points at $x = a$ or $x = e$ are *maximum* points, while those at $x = c$ and $x = f$ are *minimum* points. It is with maximum and minimum points that we are to be most concerned in the present section, and so we make a more precise mathematical definition.

DEFINITION. A continuous function f has a (relative) *maximum* value at a point x of its domain, if $f(x + h) < f(x)$ for each $x + h$ of the domain in a sufficiently small neighborhood of x. The corresponding point $(x, f(x))$ on the graph of f is a (relative) *maximum point* of the graph. A (relative) *minimum* value and a (relative) *minimum point* may be defined similarly, with $f(x + h) > f(x)$.

The word "relative" is often omitted in connection with the maximum or minimum values of a function, but it is usually understood. Thus, a function may have many different "maximum" and "minimum" values, and it is possible for a minimum value to be larger than some maximum value, since these concepts apply only in an immediate neighborhood of a point. In Figure 8–10, for example, the minimum value at $x = f$ is larger than the maximum value at $x = a$.

If a function f has a maximum value at the point x_0, f is increasing at $x < x_0$ and decreasing at $x > x_0$, for x in the domain of f and in a sufficiently small neighborhood of x_0. Since we are assuming that f is differentiable at each point x in its domain, $f'(x) > 0$ for $x < x_0$ and $f'(x) < 0$ for $x > x_0$, for x in such a neighborhood, and this gives a mathematical characterization of a maximum point. Similarly, if a minimum value of f occurs at x_0, $f'(x) < 0$ if $x < x_0$ and $f'(x) > 0$ if $x > x_0$, for x in a sufficiently small neighborhood of x_0 and in the domain of f. We abbreviate this result in the following form.

NECESSARY AND SUFFICIENT CONDITION FOR A MAXIMUM. A function f, defined on an interval $[a, b]$, and differentiable at each point in $[a, b]$, has a maximum value at a point x_0 if and only if: (1) $f'(x_0) = 0$; (2) $f'(x) > 0$ if $x < x_0$, and $f'(x) < 0$ if $x > x_0$, for each x in the domain of f and in a sufficiently small neighborhood of x_0.

NECESSARY AND SUFFICIENT CONDITION FOR A MINIMUM. A function f, defined on an interval $[a, b]$, and differentiable at each point in $[a, b]$, has a minimum value at a point x_0 if and only if: (1) $f'(x_0) = 0$; (2) $f'(x) < 0$ if $x < x_0$, and $f'(x) > 0$ if $x > x_0$, for each x in the domain of f and in a sufficiently small neighborhood of x_0.

Any solution of the equation $f'(x) = 0$ determines a *critical* point on the graph of f, at which point the tangent line is horizontal. The procedure for locating and identifying all the maximum and minimum points on the graph of f is then to find all the critical points, and examine the sign of $f'(x)$ for x in a sufficiently small neighborhood of each critical point. In this case, a "sufficiently" small neighborhood is one that does not include any other critical point. If the sign of $f'(x)$ is the same for $x > x_0$ as for $x < x_0$, the point x_0 is a point of inflection with a horizontal inflectional tangent.

ILLUSTRATION 1. Locate and classify the critical points on the graph of the function f, defined on the interval $[0, 5]$ by $f(x) = 2x^3 + 3x^2 - 12x + 10$, for each $x \in [0, 5]$.

Solution. We first solve the equation $f'(x) = 0 = 6x^2 + 6x - 12$, and observe that $6(x^2 + x - 2) = 6(x + 2)(x - 1) = 0$ has the numbers -2 and 1 as solutions. The only critical point on the graph of f is then $(1, 3)$, since $-2 \notin [0, 5]$. But $f'(x) < 0$ if $x < 1$, and $f'(x) > 0$ if $x > 1$, with x in any neighborhood of 1 in the domain of f, and so $(1, 3)$ is a minimum point.

The location and classification of the critical points of a graph is an invaluable aid in the sketching of the graph of a function, and this technique will be used in Chapter 12. However, our principal reason for introducing this topic now, is that it opens the way to solutions of some of the most interesting problems of the differential calculus. We now illustrate how this is accomplished.

ILLUSTRATION 2. A rectangular region is to be inclosed by a fence 500 feet long. Determine the dimensions of the rectangle, if the area of the region is to be a maximum.

Solution. If L and W are, respectively, the foot-measures of the length and width of such a region, the measure A of the area in square feet is given by $A = LW$. But $2L + 2W = 500$ or $W = 250 - L$, and so $A = L(250 - L) = 250L - L^2$. This equation expresses A as the value at L of a function f, defined on the interval $[0, 250]$ by $f(L) = 250L - L^2$, for each $L \in [0, 250]$. We may then use the above procedure to determine a maximum value for f, and so $f'(L) = 250 - 2L = 0$ if $L = 125$. If $L = 125$, $W = 125$ and the dimensions for maximum area are then 125 feet by 125 feet.

In the preceding illustration, the nature of the problem assured that $L = 125$ does make A or $f(L)$ a *maximum*. However, if there is any doubt about which type of critical point is involved, the complete test, as outlined above, must be applied.

ILLUSTRATION 3. Divide 16 into two parts, so that the sum of the squares of the two parts is a minimum.

Solution. Let the two parts be x and $16 - x$, so that we wish to determine the minimum value of the function f, defined on the interval $[0, 16]$ by $f(x) = x^2 + (16 - x)^2 = 2x^2 - 32x + 256$. But then $f'(x) = 4x - 32$, and the only solution of $f'(x) = 4x - 32 = 0$ is $x = 8$. The required division is then 8 for each part.

Again in this illustration, it was not necessary to actually test to determine which type of critical value was involved. The student should have noted that the procedure is precisely the same, whether we are attempting to maximize or minimize the values of a function, and common sense will usually identify the type in a problem. The following general directions may be helpful in applied problems.

GENERAL DIRECTIONS.

1. Express a symbolic measure of the quantity to be maximized or minimized in terms of convenient symbolic measures of the other quantities on which it depends.

2. Use the conditions of the problem to eliminate all but one of these other symbolic measures.

3. Consider that the remaining equation defines a function on some interval, and determine its maximum or minimum value as outlined above.

ILLUSTRATION 4. The strength of a beam with rectangular cross-section is jointly proportional to the breadth and the square of the depth. What are the dimensions of the strongest beam which can be sawed from a round log with a 3-foot diameter?

Solution. If the breadth of a rectangular beam is x feet and the depth is y feet, a measure S of the strength of the beam is given by $S = kxy^2$, with k a number depending on the unit of strength adopted, and on the type and quality of the wood. From the sketch in Figure 8–11, $x^2 + y^2 = 9$, and so $y^2 = 9 - x^2$ and $S = kx(9 - x^2) = 9kx - kx^3$. But this

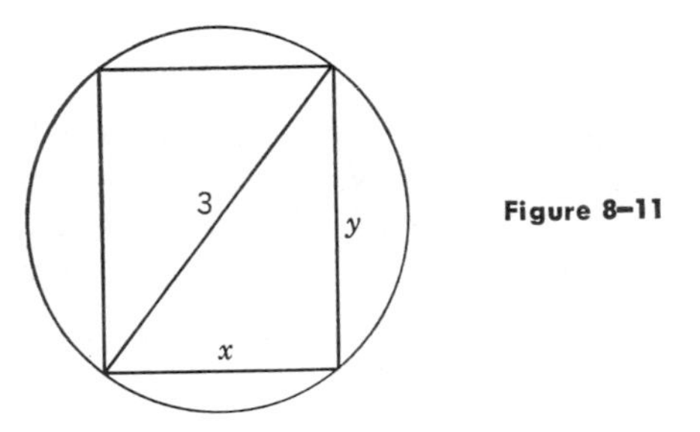

Figure 8–11

equation defines a function f on the interval $[0, 3]$ with $f(x) = 9kx - kx^3$, and $f'(x) = 9k - 3kx^2 = 3k(3 - x^2)$. The only solution of $f'(x) = 0$, in the domain of f, is $x = \sqrt{3}$, and so $x = \sqrt{3}$ and $y = \sqrt{9 - 3} = \sqrt{6}$ are the desired measures in feet of the dimensions of the beam of maximum strength.

PROBLEM SET 8.8

In each of Problems 1 through 10 is listed the value $f(x)$ of a function f at a point x in its domain. Determine the maximum and minimum points of a graph of each function, assuming a maximal domain in $R^{\#}$.

1. $x^3 - 6x^2 + 9x$.
2. $7 + 12x - 2x^2$.
3. $10 + 15x - 3x^2$.
4. $x^3 - 6x^2 + 12x + 1$.
5. $1 - x - x^2$.
6.* $x/(x + 1)$.
7.* $x^2/(1 + x)$.
8.* $x \ln x$.
9.* $(\ln x)/x$.
10.* xe^{-mx}.
11. A rectangular box with a square base and open top is to be made. Determine the volume of the largest box that can be made from 1200 square feet of lumber.
12. We wish to make an open-top box of maximum volume from a square piece of tin 12 inches to a side, by cutting out equal squares from the corners of the tin and then folding up the sides. What should be the dimensions of the squares which are cut out?
13. Use a derivative to locate the vertex of the parabola, which has for its equation (*a*) $y = ax^2 + bx + c$; (*b*) $y = 3x^2 + 2x - 3$; (*c*) $y = 4x^2 - 2x + 3$; (*d*) $y = -3x^2 - 2x + 4$.
14. Prove that the largest rectangle with a given perimeter is a square.
15. A man wishes to inclose two separate lots with 340 yards of fencing, one lot being a square and the other a rectangle twice as long as it is wide. Determine the dimensions of each lot, if the total area inclosed is to be a maximum.
16. Divide 36 into two parts so that the product of one part and the square of the other is a maximum.
17. Divide 64 into two parts so that the sum of the cubes of the two parts is a minimum.
18. If 110 volts is maintained at one end of a line having a resistance of 22 ohms, the power W in watts delivered to the load is given by the equation $W = 110I - 22I^2$ when I amperes of current are flowing. Find the maximum power that can be delivered to the load.
19. One ship A is 50 miles north of another ship B, and is sailing south at the rate of 10 miles per hour. If B is sailing west at the rate of 20 miles per hour, determine the minimum distance between the ships.
20. A window is to be designed in the form of a rectangle surmounted by a semicircle, the diameter of which coincides with the upper base of the rectangle. If the total perimeter of the window is to be 30 feet, determine its dimensions to admit the greatest amount of light.
21. It has been found in a certain locality that if 20 orange trees are planted per acre, the average yield will be 600 oranges per tree. If the average yield per tree is reduced by 15 oranges for each additional tree per acre, determine the best number of trees to plant on one acre of ground.
22. Find the dimensions of the right circular cylinder of maximum volume that can be inscribed in a sphere, having radii a units in length.
23. The cost of transmitting electrical energy is given by the formula $D = 2/A + 2A/3$, where D is the measure of cost in dollars and A a measure of cross-sectional area of the wire. Determine the cross-sectional area which results in the least cost.
24.* Determine x if $x^{1/x}$ is to be a maximum for a real number x.

8.9* A Special Interpretation of the Derivative

We have been giving the geometric interpretation of the derivative of a function defined on an interval, as a new function the values of which are the slopes of the tangent lines to the graph of the original function. A special case of this arises if the domain is a measure of an *interval of time* and the value of the function f at any measure t of time in this interval is a measure d of the distance of a particle from some fixed point, Thus, $d = f(t)$, and we wish to examine the corresponding interpretation for $f'(t)$, whenever this latter quantity exists. If E_t is the secant-slope function for the function f at the point t in its domain, $E_t(h) = [f(t+h) - f(t)]/h$; and since the numerator of this expression measures a change in distance of the particle and the denominator is a corresponding measure of time, we can interpret $E_t(h)$ as the corresponding measure of average velocity of the particle during the time interval $[t, t+h]$. Then it is natural to interpret $\lim_{h\to 0} E_t(h)$ or $f'(t)$ as the corresponding measure of *instantaneous* velocity of the particle at the instant when the measure of time is t. It is still true, of course, that if a graph of the function f is constructed, $f'(t)$ will be the slope of the tangent line to the graph at the point $(t, f(t))$; but the physical interpretation of this number will be that of the measure of instantaneous velocity of the particle having the motion described by the original equation $d = f(t)$. We now give a few illustrations of this type of application of the derivative.

ILLUSTRATION 1. The position of a particle on a straight line is described by the equation $d = t^2 - 4t + 2$, where d is a measure of distance of the particle from some fixed point in t units of time. Examine the motion during the time interval $[0, 5]$.

Solution. Let $d = f(t) = t^2 - 4t + 2$ define a function f on $[0, 5]$, so that $f'(t) = 2t - 4$. Then $f'(t) = 0$ if $t = 2$, so that our present interpretation of the derivative shows that the particle is at rest at this instant. Furthermore, $f'(t) < 0$ if $t < 2$, while $f'(t) > 0$ if $t > 2$. This means that the particle starts $(t = 0)$ at the point 2 units on the positive side of the given point, moves to the left $(f'(t) < 0)$ to the point 2 units on the negative side of the given point where it stops momentarily at $t = 2$ $(f'(2) = 0)$, and then moves in the positive direction again $(f'(t) > 0)$

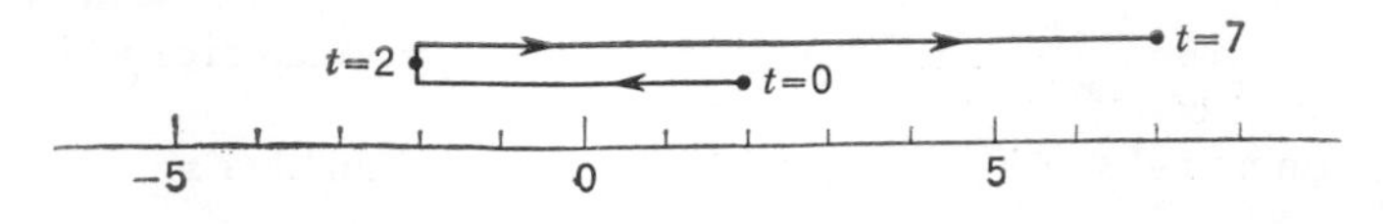

Figure 8-12

until it reaches the point 7 units on the positive side of the given point at time $t = 5$. The motion is illustrated in Figure 8–12.

If y is a value of a differentiable function, it is sometimes convenient to indicate the value of the derivative *at the same point* in the domain by y'. We do this in the next two illustrations.

ILLUSTRATION 2. A light is hung 12 feet directly above a straight horizontal path, along which a boy is walking. If the boy is 5 feet tall and he is walking away from the light with a horizontal speed of 168 feet per minute, how fast is the length of the boy's shadow increasing?

Solution. The situation *in* t *minutes* from some given instant, is illustrated in Figure 8–13, where x and y are the measures in feet of the the indicated distances. From similar triangles, we see that $5/12 = y/(x + y)$ or $y = (5/7)x$. Both x and y may be considered the values at t of functions on a time interval, and so, using the symbolism suggested above, $y' = (5/7)x'$. Since x' is the measure in feet per second of the

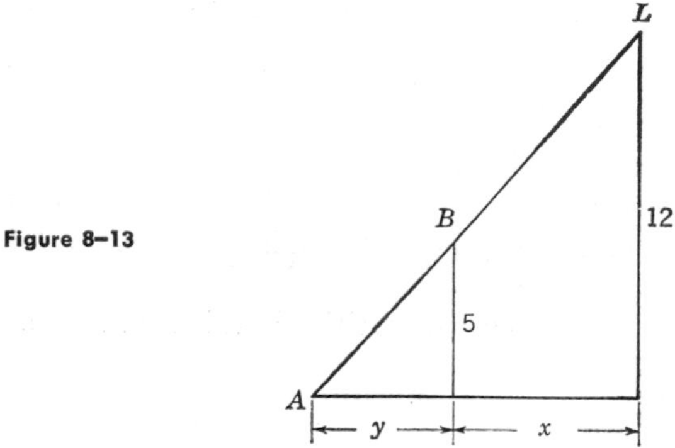

Figure 8–13

horizontal speed of the boy, $x' = 168$ and $y' = (5/7)(168) = 120$. The shadow is then increasing in length at the rate of 120 feet per minute.

ILLUSTRATION 3. Water is being poured into an inverted conical tank, as shown in Figure 8–14, at the rate of 2 cubic feet per minute. How fast is the water level rising when the water is 6 feet deep?

Solution. Suppose that V cubic feet of water have been poured into the tank in t minutes, with x and y the measures in feet of the distances indicated in the figure. Then, $V = \pi x^2 y/3$, and since $x/y = 5/10$ from a consideration of similar triangles, the formula for V may be written $V = \pi y^3/12$. As in Illustration 2, V and y may be considered the values at t of functions on a time interval, and so $V' = (3\pi y^2 y')/12 = (\pi y^2 y')/4$. But the problem states that $V' = 2$, so that $\pi y^2 y' = 8$, and when $y = 6$ $y' = 8/(36\pi) = 2/(9\pi) = 0.071$, approximately. Thus, the water is rising in the tank at the approximate rate of 0.071 feet per minute, when the depth of the water is 6 feet.

As a guide for the solution of general "time-rate" problems, we suggest the following procedure.

1. Draw a figure representing the situation of the problem in t units of time, indicating by $x, y, z, \cdots$, etc., corresponding measures of those quantities that change with time.

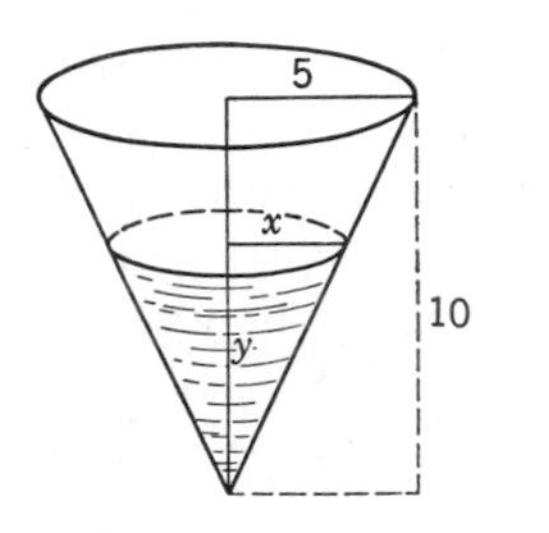

Figure 8–14

2. Obtain an equation connecting these symbols, including the one directly involved in the problem.

3. Eliminate as many as possible of these auxiliary symbols, using the conditions of the problem and the geometry of the figure.

4. Each of the remaining symbols may be considered the value at t of some function on an interval of time, and by a process of differentiation a corresponding equation may be obtained involving the values of the respective derivatives.

5. Substitute the known quantities in this equation, and solve for the unknown symbol.

PROBLEM SET 8.9

In each of problems 1 through 6, x is a measure of the distance, in t units of time, of a particle from some given point. In each case, assume that the particle remains on a straight line and describe the motion from the time when $t = 0$ to the time when $t = 5$.

1. $x = 4t - 12$. **2.** $x = 2t - t^2$.

3. $x = t^2 - 46t + 2$. **4.** $x = 4 - t^2$.

5. $x = 4t^2 - t^3$. **6.** $x = 2 + t^2$.

7. If the area of a circular plate is A square inches when a radius measures r inches, what is the relationship between A' and r' in the notation introduced in this section?

8. If the volume of a spherical globe is V cubic inches when a radius measures r inches, write an equation connecting V' and r' in the notation of this section.

9. A conical pile of sand is being poured at the rate of 10 cubic feet per minute, in such a way that a radius of the base of the conical pile is always equal in length to one half the altitude. How fast is the altitude of the pile increasing, when the pile is 5 feet high?
10. A circular plate of metal expands by heat so that the length of a radius increases at the rate of 0.01 inches per second. At what rate is the surface of the plate increasing, when the radii are 2 inches long?
11. A conical cistern is 12 feet across the top and 12 feet deep. If water is being poured into the cistern at the rate of 2 cubic feet per second, how fast is the area of the top surface of water increasing when the water is 6 feet deep?
12. A horizontal trough 10 feet long has a vertical section in the shape of an isosceles right triangle. If water is being poured into it at the rate of 8 cubic feet per minute, at what rate is the surface of the water rising when the water is 3 feet deep?
13. A boy is flying a kite at a height of 300 feet, the wind blowing it away from the boy at a horizontal rate of 25 feet per second. How fast must he be paying out the string, when the kite is 500 feet distant from him?
14. A 17-foot ladder leans against a vertical wall. If the lower end is pulled away from the wall at the rate of 4 feet per second, how fast will the top of the ladder be dropping when the lower end is 15 feet from the wall?
15. An object is dropped vertically downwards. If it is h feet above the ground in t seconds, with $h = 3600 - 16t^2$, with what speed will the object hit the ground?
16. Two highways intersect at an angle of 60°. One automobile leaves the intersection at 2:00 P.M. at a speed of 40 miles per hour, while another leaves the same intersection at 2:30 P.M. at a speed of 48 miles per hour. How fast are the automobiles separating at 3:30 P.M.?
17. A man is walking at a speed of 5 feet per second on a bridge, 80 feet directly over a boat traveling 10 feet per second at right angles to the bridge. How fast are the man and boat separating 8 seconds later?
18. How fast is the area of an equilateral triangle increasing, when each side is s inches long and increasing at the rate of k inches per hour?
19. A ball is dropped from a point 100 feet high, which is even with a light on the top of a pole 32 feet distant. If we assume that the ball will fall s feet in t seconds, according to the law $s = 16t^2$, how fast is the shadow of the ball moving along the ground, 2 seconds after the ball is dropped?
20. Determine x if x^3 is increasing 12 times as fast as x.

8.10* A Use for Higher Derivatives

If a function f is defined on an interval $[a, b]$ by $f(x) = 3x^3 - 2x^2 + 5$, for each $x \in [a, b]$, the derivative f' is defined on the same interval by $f'(x) = 9x^2 - 4x$. Since $f'(x)$ is a polynomial in x, the derivative f' is also differentiable at each point of the interval, and we can define this derivative f'' of f' by $f''(x) = 18x - 4$, for each $x \in [a, b]$, the function f'' being known as the *second derivative* of f. In a similar manner, the *third derivative*

f''' may be defined on $[a, b]$ by $f'''(x) = 18$, so that f''' is a constant function; in this case, it is clear that fourth and higher derivatives are zero functions, i.e., all functional values are 0. However, it is possible for derivatives of all orders to exist and be distinct from zero functions. For example, if a function f is defined at each point x in $[a, b]$ by $f(x) = e^x$, derivatives of every order exist for this function; in this case, the derivatives are indistinguishable from the original function f, since $f'(x) = e^x = f(x)$, for each x in the domain.

Now let us consider an arbitrary function f defined on an interval containing the point x. If both f and f' are differentiable at x, it is clear that f'' will bear the same relationship to f' as f' does to f. Thus, just as $f'(x)$ is the slope of the tangent line to the graph of f at the point $(x, f(x))$, so is $f''(x)$ the slope of the tangent line to the graph of f' at the point $(x, f'(x))$. If $f''(x) > 0$, the "slope function" f' of f is increasing at the point x in its domain, which implies that the graph of f is *concave up* at the point $(x, f(x))$. On the other hand, if $f''(x) < 0$, f' is decreasing at x and so the graph of f must be *concave down* at the point $(x, f(x))$. This gives us a convenient test for a maximum or minimum value of a function:

If $f'(x) = 0$ and $f''(x) < 0$, $f(x)$ is a *maximum* value of f;

If $f'(x) = 0$ and $f''(x) > 0$, $f(x)$ is a *minimum* value of f.

This test is frequently more convenient to use than the one given in Section 8.8. However, in some cases, it may be difficult to determine $f''(x)$.

If $f''(x_0) = 0$, and $f'(x)$ has the same sign for $x > x_0$ as for $x < x_0$, with x in a sufficiently small neighborhood of x_0, the point $(x_0, f(x_0))$ on the graph of f is a *point of inflection*. A special case of this was mentioned in Section 8.8. It may be seen, geometrically, that such a point separates a portion of the graph that is *concave down* from a portion that is *concave up*. If $f''(x_0) = 0$, but $f'(x_0) \neq 0$, the corresponding point on the graph is definitely a point of inflection; but if $f''(x_0) = f'(x_0) = 0$, the point may be either a maximum point, a minimum point or a point of inflection. In this latter case, the above test for a maximum or a minimum can not be used, and it is best to proceed as we did in Section 8.8.

If f is a function on an interval, interpreted as a measure of *time*, with the values of f interpreted as measures of *distance* of a particle from some given point, we have seen that f' is a function, the values of which may be interpreted as corresponding measures of velocity of the particle. In view of the relationship between the functions f' and f'', it is clear that if we apply the same type of analysis to f' as we previously did to f, we may regard f'' as a function, the values of which may be interpreted as measures of acceleration of the particle. Thus, if $f(t)$ is a measure of distance of the particle from a given point in t units of time, $f'(t)$ and $f''(t)$

will be, respectively, the corresponding measures of velocity and acceleration of the particle at the same instant. If the position of a particle is given by an equation in t, its motion can then be more fully analyzed with the help of the second derivative.

ILLUSTRATION 1. Classify the critical points on the graph of the function f, defined on $R^{\#}$ by $f(x) = 2x^3 + 3x^2 - 12x + 10$ for each $x \in R^{\#}$.

Solution. As in Illustration 1 of Section 8.8, we can find the critical points to be $(-2, 30)$ and $(1, 3)$. Since f is differentiable on its domain, we find that $f'(x) = 6x^2 + 6x - 12$, and similarly $f''(x) = 12x + 6 = 6(2x + 1)$. Thus, $f''(-2) = -18$, and so our preceding discussion shows that $(-2, 30)$ is a maximum point; also $f''(1) = 18$, and so $(1, 3)$ is a minimum point. The only solution of $f''(x) = 6(2x + 1) = 0$ is $x = -1/2$, and since $f'(-1/2) \neq 0$ the point $(-1/2, 33/2)$ is a point of inflection.

ILLUSTRATION 2. Discuss the acceleration of the particle, having the motion described in Illustration 1 of Section 8.9.

Solution. Since $d = f(t) = t^2 - 4t + 2$, it follows that $d' = f'(t) = 2t - 4$ and $d'' = f''(t) = 2$, expanding a system of notation introduced in Section 8.9. Thus, the acceleration of the particle is constant with a measure of 2.

Before closing this chapter, the student may be interested in the question of the existence of a function which will give us the slope of the tangent line at any point on the graph of a relation, just as the derivative f' has done for the function f. The answer is that such a function does exist under conditions somewhat similar to those for the derivative of a function. This will involve continuity and the existence of a certain limit at a point of a relation, but we leave this discussion for more advanced courses. It may happen, however, that a relation is the union of two or more functions, and in this case each function component may be considered separately. For example, the relation on the interval $[-1, 1]$, defined by the equation $x^2 + y^2 = 1$, may be considered the union of the two functions f and g defined on the same interval by $f(x) = \sqrt{1 - x^2}$ and $g(x) = -\sqrt{1 - x^2}$, respectively. The slope of the tangent line at any point of this relation, the graph of which is a unit circle, may then be found by considering the derivative of the appropriate function component. (See Problem 19 of Problem Set 8.6.) It is clear, however, that only simple relations can be treated in this manner.

PROBLEM SET 8.10

In Problems 1 through 6, use the method of this section to classify the critical points of the given function.

1. Problem 1 of Problem Set 8.8
2. Problem 2 of Problem Set 8.8
3. Problem 4 of Problem Set 8.8
4. Problem 5 of Problem Set 8.8
5. Problem 7 of Problem Set 8.8
6. Problem 8 of Problem Set 8.8

In Problems 7 through 12, discuss the acceleration of the particle, having the motion described in the indicated problem of Problem Set 8.9.

7. Problem 1
8. Problem 2
9. Problem 3
10. Problem 4
11. Problem 5
12. Problem 6
13. Show that the graph of the parabolic function f, defined on $R^{\#}$ by $f(x) = ax^2 + bx + c$ is concave up if $a > 0$, and concave down if $a < 0$.
14. Under certain conditions, a hockey puck is known to travel a distance of s feet in t seconds, where $s = 60t - 3t^2$. What is the acceleration of the puck, and how far will it travel before coming to rest?
15. From a point 50 feet above the surface of the earth, a stone is cast upward so that in t seconds it will be h feet above the ground with $h = -16t^2 + 155t + 50$. With what velocity will it strike the ground?
16. Determine the velocity of the stone in Problem 15 as it passes a window ledge 149 feet above ground level.
17. Determine the minimum value of the function f, defined on the set of positive real numbers by $f(x) = x + 1/x$, for each x in its domain.

REVIEW TEST A

1. Explain why $\lim_{x \to c} f(x) = c$ for any point c in the domain of a function f, defined on an interval $[a, b]$ by $f(x) = x$ for each $x \in [a, b]$.
2. (*a*) If a function f is defined on an interval containing 2 by $f(x) = (x + 2)/(x - 3)$, determine $\lim_{x \to 2} f(x)$. (*b*) If 1 is a limit point in the domain of a function f, defined by $f(x) = 3x^3 - x^2 + 1$ for each x in its domain, determine $\lim_{x \to 1} f(x)$. (*c*) Explain why the limits in (*a*) and (*b*) may be obtained by replacing x in $f(x)$ by appropriate numbers.
3. (*a*) A function f is defined by $f(x) = (x^2 + x - 6)/[x(x - 2)]$, for each x in its domain. If 2 is a limit point of the domain of f, determine $\lim_{x \to 2} f(x)$. (*b*) If the function f is defined on $[0, 2] - \{1\}$ by $f(x) = (x^2 - x)/(x - 1)$, for each x in its domain, determine $\lim_{x \to 1} f(x)$. (*c*) Why are we justified in "canceling out" the factor $x - 2$ in (*a*) and the factor $x - 1$ in (*b*)?
4. A function f is defined on the interval $[0, 3]$ by $f(x) = (x^2 - 1)(x - 2)$ for each $x \neq 2$ in $[0, 3]$, $f(x) = a$ for $x = 2$. Determine a if f is to be a continuous function on the interval.
5. If x is a point in the domain of a function f at which f is differentiable, determine $f'(x)$ from $f(x)$ given below: (*a*) $4x^3 - 3x + 2$; (*b*) $(2x - 1)^3$.

6.* Do the same as in Problem 5 for the following: (*a*) $(2x + 1)^2e^{2x}$; (*b*) $5x^3 \ln 3x$.

7. A straight line with slope 2 is tangent to the curve having the equation $y = -2x^2 - 10x$. Find the coordinates of the point of contact.

8. Use the derivative to find the coordinates of the vertex of the parabola, an equation of which is $y = 3 - 2x - x^2$.

9. If 400 rods of fencing are available for fencing a rectangular field, including one cross fence, determine the width of the largest such field.

10.* A function f is defined on $R^\#$ by $f(x) = 3x^4 - 4x^3 + 1$, for each $x \in R^\#$. Find the points of inflection of the graph of this function, and also determine the intervals of the domain for which the graph is (*a*) concave up; (*b*) concave down.

11.* A particle moves along a straight line, so that in t seconds it will be s feet from a given point, where $s = t^2/2 - 2t + 1$. At what time will the particle be momentarily at rest?

12.* A spherical balloon is being deflated at the rate of 1000 cubic feet per minute. At what rate are the radii decreasing in length at the moment when the surface area is 1000 square feet?

REVIEW TEST B

1. Explain why $\lim_{x \to c} f(x) = 2c$ for any point c in the domain of a function f, defined on an interval $[a, b]$ by $f(x) = 2x$ for each $x \in [a, b]$.

2. (*a*) If a function f is defined on an interval containing -1 by $f(x) = 2x^2 + x - 2$, determine $\lim_{x \to -1} f(x)$. (*b*) If 1/2 is a limit point in the domain of a function g, defined by $g(x) = (3x - 1)/(2x + 1)$ for each x in its domain, determine $\lim_{x \to 1/2} g(x)$. (*c*) Explain why the limits in (*a*) and (*b*) may be obtained by replacing x in $f(x)$ by appropriate numbers.

3. (*a*) A function f is defined by $f(x) = \dfrac{2x^2 - x - 1}{x(2x + 1)}$, for each x in its domain. If $-1/2$ is a limit point of the domain of f, determine $\lim_{x \to -1/2} f(x)$. (*b*) If the function g is defined on $[-1, 1] - \{0\}$ by $g(x) = \dfrac{x^2 + 2x}{x}$, for each x in its domain, determine $\lim_{x \to 0} g(x)$. (*c*) Why are we justified in "canceling out" the factor $2x + 1$ in (*a*) and the factor x in (*b*)?

4. The function f is defined on $[-2, 2]$ by $f(x) = \dfrac{xe^x - x}{x}$ for each $x \neq 0$ in $[-2, 2]$, $f(x) = a$ for $x = 0$. Determine a, if f is to be continuous on $[-2, 2]$.

5. If x is a point in the domain of a function f, at which f is differentiable, determine $f'(x)$ from $f(x)$ given below: (*a*) $(x - 2)(x^2 + 1)$; (*b*) $(3x - 1)^3$.

6.* Do the same as in Problem 5 for the following: (*a*) e^{3x}/x^2; (*b*) $(x + 1) \ln 3x$.

7. Determine an equation of the tangent line at the point (2, 7) on the curve having the equation $y = 3x^2 - 5$.
8. Determine the minimum value of the function f, defined on $R^\#$ by $f(x) = 2x^2 + 6x - 5$ for each x in $R^\#$.
9. A farmer wishes to fence a rectangular field, bordered on one side by a river. If he has 720 yards of fencing available, what would be the dimensions of the largest field which he could fence?
10. Examine the curve, described as the locus of $y = x^3 - 9x^2 + 24x - 7$, for maximum and minimum points, and points of inflection.
11.* A bullet is shot vertically upwards, so that it will be s feet high in t seconds, where $s = 6 + 352t - 16t^2$. Determine the muzzle velocity of the bullet, its maximum height, and the time when this maximum height is attained.
12.* If the length of each side of an equilateral triangle is increasing at the rate of 2 inches per second, how fast is the area of the triangle increasing when each side measures 30 inches?

REFERENCES

Books

ALLENDOERFER, C. B. AND C. O. OAKLEY, *Principles of Mathematics*, New York, McGraw-Hill, 1955. (Chaps. 11 and 12.)

COURANT, RICHARD, *Differential and Integral Calculus*, New York, Interscience Publishers Inc., 1937. (Vol. 1, pp. 88–96.)

COURANT, RICHARD AND HERBERT ROBBINS, *What is Mathematics?*, New York, Oxford, 1941. (Chap. 8.)

NEWSOM, CARROLL V. AND HOWARD EVES, *Introduction to College Mathematics*, New York, Prentice Hall, 1954. (Chap. 15.)

RANDOLPH, JOHN F., *Calculus*, New York, Macmillan, 1952. (Chap. 1.)

American Mathematical Monthly

BALLANTINE, J. P., "A Peculiar Function," Vol. 37, p. 250 (1930).

CAJORI, FLORIAN, "The History of Zeno's Arguments on Motion," Vol. 22, pp. 1, 39, 77, 109, 143, 179, 215, 253, 292 (1915).

KNEBELMAN, M. S., "An Elementary Limit," Vol. 50, p. 507 (1943).

SPIEGEL, M. R., "On the Derivatives of Trigonometric Functions," Vol. 63, p. 118 (1956).

9

SEQUENCES AND A GLIMPSE OF THE INTEGRAL CALCULUS

"And how many hours a day did you do lessons?" said Alice, in a hurry to change the subject. "Ten hours the first day," said the Mock Turtle; "nine the next, and so on." "What a curious plan!" exclaimed Alice. "That's the reason they're called lessons," the Gryphon remarked, "because they lesson from day to day."

LEWIS CARROLL

9.1 Arithmetic and Geometric Sequences

As we have noted before, the "process" of integration is much older than that of differentiation, for we first encounter it when we attempt to measure the area of a plane region bounded by curves. If the bounds of a plane region are straight line segments, it is always possible to subdivide it into a finite number of triangles and rectangles, and the area can be computed by methods of plane geometry. However, if some of the boundaries are curves, these methods are not applicable and the notion of the *limit of a sequence* arises in any attempt to determine the area of such a region. The principal topics of this chapter are then sequences and their limits.

In Chapter 2 we defined a sequence as a set, the members of which are arranged in some definite order. Thus, each element or *term* of a sequence occupies a unique *position* in the array of elements comprising the sequence. We shall be concerned here with *numerical* sequences, i.e., the terms will be real numbers. If a numerical sequence has the property that the *subtraction* of any term from the succeeding term results in the same number, regardless of which successive terms are selected, the sequence is said to be *arithmetic,* and the number, obtained as the difference, is known as the *common difference*. If the *quotient* of any term divided by the preceding term of a numerical sequence is independent of which pair of successive terms is chosen, the sequence is said to be *geometric*, and the number obtained as the quotient is known as the *common ratio*. For example, 1, 3, 5, 7, 9 and 5/2, 1, $-1/2$, -2 are finite arithmetic sequences with common differences of 2 and $-3/2$, respectively; while 2, 4, 8, 16 and 2, -1, 1/2, $-1/4$ are finite geometric sequences, with respective common ratios of 2 and $-1/2$.

Let us use the natural numbers as subscripts to index the terms of a general numerical sequence, and label the nth term of such a sequence a_n. If the sequence is arithmetic, and the common difference is d, it is clear that $a_2 = a_1 + d$, $a_3 = a_2 + d = a_1 + 2d$, $a_4 = a_3 + d = a_1 + 3d$, etc., and for the nth term, $a_n = a_1 + (n - 1)d$. If the sequence is geometric with common ratio r, $a_2 = a_1r$, $a_3 = a_2r = a_1r^2$, $a_4 = a_3r = a_1r^3$, etc., while for the nth term, $a_n = a_1r^{n-1}$. Thus, from a knowledge of the first term and the common difference or common ratio, we can determine any particular term of an arithmetic or geometric sequence without finding the intermediate terms.

ILLUSTRATION 1. Determine the 25th term of the arithmetic sequence, the first three terms of which, in order, are 39, 34, 29.

Solution. Since $29 - 34 = 34 - 39 = -5$, we find that $d = -5$. Thus, $a_{25} = a_1 + 24d = 39 + 24(-5) = 39 - 120 = -81$.

ILLUSTRATION 2. Determine the 8th term of the geometric sequence, the first three terms of which, in order, are 9, 3, 1.

Solution. Since $1/3 = 3/9 = 1/3$, it follows that $r = 1/3$. Thus, $a_8 = a_1r^7 = 9(1/3)^7 = 1/243$.

If terms are inserted between two numbers so that the resulting array of numbers is a finite arithmetic (or geometric) sequence, the terms that are added are known as *arithmetic* (or *geometric*) *means* of the original numbers. In case only one term is inserted, this number is known as *the* arithmetic (or geometric) mean of the numbers.

ILLUSTRATION 3. Insert 5 arithmetic means between 4 and 13.

Solution. Since 13 is now the 7th term of an arithmetic sequence, the first term of which is 4, we must have $13 = 4 + (7 - 1)d$, i.e., $9 = 6d$. Thus, $d = 3/2$, and the required means are $4 + 3/2$ or 11/2, $11/2 + 3/2$ or 7, $7 + 3/2$ or 17/2, $17/2 + 3/2$ or 10, and $10 + 3/2$ or 23/2.

ILLUSTRATION 4. Insert 3 geometric means between 31 and 496.

Solution. Since 496 is now the 5th term of a geometric sequence, the first term of which is 31, we must have $496 = 31r^4$, i.e., $r^4 = 16$ and $r = \pm 2$. Thus, the desired means are 62, 124, and 248 (with $r = 2$) or -62, 124, and -248 (with $r = -2$).

The yearly amounts of money which accumulate from some initial principal, under simple (or compound) interest, comprise the terms of an arithmetic (or geometric) sequence. Thus, if \$$P$ is invested at simple interest of $i\%$ per annum, the amount of the investment in dollars at the end of successive years will be $P + i/100$, $P + 2i/100$, $P + 3i/100$, etc., which are terms of an arithmetic sequence with $d = i/100$. If the interest is $i\%$, compounded annually, the corresponding amounts at the end of successive years will be $P(1 + i/100)$, $P(1 + i/100)^2$, $P(1 + i/100)^3$, etc., which are terms of a geometric sequence with $r = 1 + i/100$.

ILLUSTRATION 5. For how many years must \$1 accumulate at simple interest of $3\frac{1}{2}\%$ to exceed \$100?

Solution. If the money accumulates for n years, 100 is the $(n + 1)$th term of an arithmetic sequence that has 1 for its first term and has a common difference of 0.035. Thus, $100 = 1 + n(0.035)$, and so $n = 2829$, approximately, which is the required number of years.

PROBLEM SET 9.1

1. Determine the 20th term of an arithmetic sequence, the first 3 terms of which are -2, -5, -8.
2. Determine the 15th term of an arithmetic sequence, the first 3 terms of which are 3, 7, 11.
3. Determine the 8th term of a geometric sequence, the first 3 terms of which are 1/3, 1/9, 1/27.
4. Determine the 9th term of a geometric sequence, the first 3 terms of which are 1/6, 1/2, 3/2.
5. Determine the 9th term of a geometric sequence, having 1 for its 1st term and 3 for its common ratio.
6. Determine the 61st term of an arithmetic sequence, having 19 for its 1st term and -2 for its common difference.
7. Determine the 12th term of an arithmetic sequence, having 10 for its 1st term and 6 for its common difference.
8. Determine the 8th term of a geometric sequence, having 9/16 for its 1st term and 2/3 for its common difference.
9. Insert 2 geometric means between 56 and 875.
10. Insert 6 arithmetic means between 3 and -11.
11. Insert 3 arithmetic means between -6 and 6.
12. Insert 3 geometric means between 18 and 2/9.
13. Insert 5 arithmetic means between 2 and 1/4.
14. The common difference of an arithmetic sequence is 4; if the 15th term is 59, determine the 1st term.
15. The common difference of an arithmetic sequence is 1/2; if the 14th term is $-1/2$, determine the 1st term.
16. The common ratio of a geometric sequence is $-1/3$ and the 3rd term is 1/9. Determine the 1st term.

17. The common ratio of a geometric sequence is $-1/2$ and the 4th term is $1/32$. Determine the 1st and 2nd terms.

18. If \$500 is invested at 4% simple interest, determine the amount of the investment at the end of 10 years.

19. If \$500 is invested at 4% interest, compounded annually, determine the amount of the investment at the end of 4 years.

20. Determine the 31st term of an arithmetic progression, that has -1 for its 4th term and 3 for its 16th term.

21. A body, falling freely under gravity, travels 16 feet the first second, and during each second thereafter falls approximately 32 feet farther than it did the preceding second. How far would the body fall during the 10th second?

22. For how many years must \$10 accumulate at 5% simple interest to exceed \$50?

9.2 Sums of Sequences

It is frequently necessary to determine the sum of a specified number of terms of a sequence, and it will be convenient to introduce a notation for such a sum. If the nth term of a sequence is a_n, the notation we have adopted for S_n, the sum of n terms, is $\sum_{i=1}^{n} a_i$. Thus,

$$S_n = a_1 + a_2 + a_3 + \cdots + a_n = \sum_{i=1}^{n} a_i.$$

The Greek letter $\sum$ corresponds to the letter S, and may be considered to indicate the word SUM. The letter i is an index, and the complete symbol means that the sum is to be found of all terms of the sequence, having index numbers that lie, inclusively, between those integers written below and above the "summation sign" $\sum$. For example, the sum $x_1^2 + x_2^2 + x_3^2 + x_4^2 + x_5^2$ may be abbreviated by the symbol $\sum_{i=1}^{5} x_i^2$; and $\sum_{i=3}^{6} (1/2)^i$ may be considered an abbreviation for the sum $(1/2)^3 + (1/2)^4 + (1/2)^5 + (1/2)^6$. If the sequence is arithmetic or geometric, it is simple to develop a formula for S_n, as we are about to see.

ARITHMETIC SEQUENCE. In this case we can replace a_i by $a_1 + \overline{i-1}d$, for each positive integer i, and obtain $S_n = a_1 + (a_1 + d) + (a_1 + 2d) + \cdots + (a_1 + \overline{n-1}d)$. On reversing the order of the terms, this sum may be written as

$$S_n = a_n + (a_n - d) + (a_n - 2d) + \cdots + (a_n - \overline{n-1}d).$$

If we now add these two expressions for S_n, termwise, we obtain

$$2S_n = n(a_1 + a_n), \text{ i.e., } S_n = \frac{n}{2}(a_1 + a_n).$$

GEOMETRIC SEQUENCE. In the case of a geometric sequence, $a_i = a_1r^{i-1}$, for each positive integer i, and so $S_n = a_1 + a_1r + a_1r^2 + \cdots + a_1r^{n-1}$. If we multiply both members of this equality by r, the result is

$$rS_n = a_1r + a_1r^2 + \cdots + a_1r^{n-1} + a_1r^n.$$

Then $S_n - rS_n = a_1 - a_1r^n$ or $S_n(1 - r) = a_1(1 - r^n)$, whence

$$S_n = \frac{a_1(1 - r^n)}{1 - r} = \frac{a_1(r^n - 1)}{r - 1}.$$

It is convenient to use the latter formula if $r > 1$, and the former if $r < 1$.

Suppose that an imaginary frog of "point" size tries to jump across a 20-foot creek, by jumping half way to the opposite bank in each successive jump. It is clear that the total distance that the frog jumps will never quite equal 20 feet but nevertheless, as he keeps on jumping, the *total* distance jumped will differ from 20 feet by an arbitrarily small amount. Under these circumstances, we may think of the foot-measures of the total distance jumped, at the end of each successive jump, as the terms of an unending or infinite sequence: 10, 15, 17.5, 18.75, 19.375, 19.6875, 19.84375, 19.921875, $\cdots$. We now say that the *limit* of this sequence is 20. As another example of this notion of the limit of a sequence, consider the infinite sequence of rational numbers 1/2, 2/3, 3/4, 4/5, $\cdots$, in which the terms get arbitrarily close to 1. There is no positive number, however small, which does not exceed the difference between 1 and each term of this sequence after a certain term, the position of which in the sequence depending on the number that is chosen. For example, if we choose the positive number 0.001, it is clear that every term after 999/1000 will differ from 1 by less than 0.001. Again we say that the *limit* of this sequence is 1. With this introduction, we now proceed to a more formal definition.

DEFINITION. The real number L is the *limit* of the infinite numerical sequence $a_1, a_2, a_3, \cdots, a_n, \cdots$ if, for each $\epsilon > 0$, there exists a natural number N_ϵ (depending on ϵ) such that $|a_n - L| < \epsilon$ provided $n > N_\epsilon$. We then write $\lim a_n = L$, which may be read "the limit of a_n is L." If no such L can be found, we say that the limit of the sequence *does not exist.*

Associated with every infinite numerical sequence is another sequence which has for its nth term the sum of the first n terms of the original sequence. The nth term of this *sequence of partial sums* has already been denoted by S_n, and we shall continue to use this notation. Since the terms of the sequence of partial sums of an arithmetic sequence differ successively by the same number, it is evident that $\lim S_n$ does not exist for such a sequence. However, let us consider the situation with respect to a geometric sequence. In the notation adopted earlier, $S_n = [a_1(1 - r^n)]/(1 - r)$ and this may be written in the form $S_n = a_1/(1 - r) - a_1 r^n/(1 - r)$. If $r < 1$, the numerator of the second term of this expression is arbitrarily small for a sufficiently large n, and so S_n is arbitrarily close to $a_1/(1 - r)$ if a sufficient number of terms of the original sequence is taken. According to the definition above, it then follows that $\lim S_n = a_1/(1 - r)$, for this case, described as follows: If $S_n = \sum_{i=1}^{n} a_i$, with a_i the ith term of a geometric sequence, $\lim S_n = a_1/(1 - r)$, provided $r < 1$. It is clear that the sequence of partial sums of a geometric sequence will have no limit if $r > 1$. We emphasize that if $\lim S_n$ does exist, for a geometric sequence of non-zero terms, this limit is never attained as the sum of a finite number of terms of the original sequence, but is rather a bound which is approached indefinitely as more and more terms are taken.

ILLUSTRATION 1. Determine the sum of the first 50 terms of an arithmetic sequence, that has 5, 3, 1 for its first three terms.

Solution. Since $1 - 3 = 3 - 5 = -2$, it follows that $d = -2$, and so $a_{50} = 5 + 49(-2) = -93$. An application of the formula for S_n, for an arithmetic sequence, then gives $S_{50} = \frac{n}{2}(a_1 + a_{50}) = 25(5 - 93) = -2200$.

ILLUSTRATION 2. Determine the sum of 6 terms of a geometric sequence, having 3, 9, 27 for its first three terms.

Solution. Since $27/9 = 9/3 = 3$, it follows that $r = 3$. The formula for S_n, in the case of a geometric sequence, then gives

$$S_6 = \frac{a_1(r^6 - 1)}{r - 1} = \frac{3(728)}{2} = 1092.$$

ILLUSTRATION 3. Determine $\lim S_n$, if S_n is the sum of the first n terms of the infinite geometric sequence, that has 1/3, 1/9, 1/27 for its first three terms.

Solution. Since $(1/27)/(1/9) = (1/9)/(1/3) = 1/3$, it follows that $r = 1/3 < 1$. The above result then shows that $\lim S_n$ exists, and $\lim S_n = 1/3/(1 - 1/3) = (1/3)/(2/3) = 1/2$.

PROBLEM SET 9.2

1. For an arithmetic sequence, determine the following: (*a*) S_8, if $a_1 = 3$ and $d = -4$; (*b*) S_9, if $a_1 = -6$ and $d = 3$; (*c*) S_{12}, if $a_1 = 5$ and $d = 5$.

2. For a geometric sequence, determine the following: (*a*) S_6, if $a_1 = 8$ and $r = 1/2$; (*b*) S_6, if $a_1 = 1/8$ and $r = 2$; (*c*) S_8, if $a_1 = 4$ and $r = -1/2$.

3. For an arithmetic sequence, determine the following: (*a*) S_9, if $a_7 = 13$ and $a_{12} = 28$; (*b*) S_{10}, if $a_4 = 15$ and $d = 3$; (*c*) S_{14}, if $a_{14} = -1/2$ and $d = 1/2$.

4. For a geometric sequence, determine the following: (*a*) n, if $a_1 = 3$, $a_n = 48$, and $S_n = 93$; (*b*) S_8, if $a_1 = 6$ and $r = -2$; (*c*) S_5, if $r = 2/3$ and $a_5 = 2/15$.

5. Determine lim S_n for the infinite geometric sequence, that has the following first three terms: (*a*) 2/3, 1/3, 1/6; (*b*) 4, -3, 9/4; (*c*) 25, -20, 16; (*d*) 5, $-5\sqrt{3}/2$, 15/4.

6. Consider each of the following infinite repeating decimals as the limit of a sequence of partial sums of finite decimals, and express it as a rational fraction: (*a*) $0.\overline{36}$; (*b*) $0.3\overline{636}$; (*c*) $0.8\overline{3}$

7. The first swing of a pendulum is 15 inches in length, and each swing thereafter is 5/6 as long as the preceding. Determine the theoretical distance traveled by the pendulum, before coming to rest.

8. An elastic ball is dropped from a height of 30 feet, and after each fall it rebounds 1/5 of the height from which it falls. What is the total theoretical distance which the ball will travel before coming to rest?

9. Find a formula for the sum of the first n odd integers.

10. Find a formula for the sum of the first n even integers.

11. A sequence of equilateral triangles is constructed by starting with an equilateral triangle having sides 1 foot long, and using the midpoints of the sides of each triangle for the vertices of the next triangle. Determine the theoretical sum of the perimeters of all the triangles which may be so constructed.

12. Determine the theoretical sum of the areas of all the triangles in Problem 11.

9.3 Area as the Limit of a Sequence; the Definite Integral

We now return to a consideration of an arbitrary numerical sequence, the nth term of which we shall indicate by a_n. We have said that lim a_n exists and equals L if the absolute value of the difference between a_n and L is as small as we please, for n a sufficiently large integer. When such a number L exists, the sequence is also said to *converge* to L. There are several theorems on sequences, similar to the theorems on limits of functions given in Section 8.2; it would be easy to prove these theorems, directly from the definition of the limit of a sequence, but we shall merely state them without proof.

THEOREM 1. If a_n is the nth term of a sequence, with $a_n = a$ for every natural number n, then lim $a_n = a$.

THEOREM 2. If a_n and b_n are the respective nth terms of two sequences, with lim $a_n = a$ and lim $b_n = b$, the sequence having $a_n \pm b_n$ for its nth term also has a limit, and lim $(a_n \pm b_n) = a \pm b$.

THEOREM 3. If a_n and b_n are the respective nth terms of two sequences, with lim $a_n = a$ and lim $b_n = b$, the sequence having a_nb_n for its nth term also has a limit, and lim $a_nb_n = ab$.

Corollary. If a_n is the nth term of a sequence with lim $a_n = a$, the sequence having Ca_n for its nth term, where C is a real number, also has a limit, and $\lim Ca_n = Ca$.

THEOREM 4. If a_n and $b_n (\neq 0)$ are the respective nth terms of two sequences, with $\lim a_n = a$ and $\lim b_n = b$, the sequence having a_n/b_n for its nth term also has a limit, and $\lim a_n/b_n = a/b$, provided $b \neq 0$.

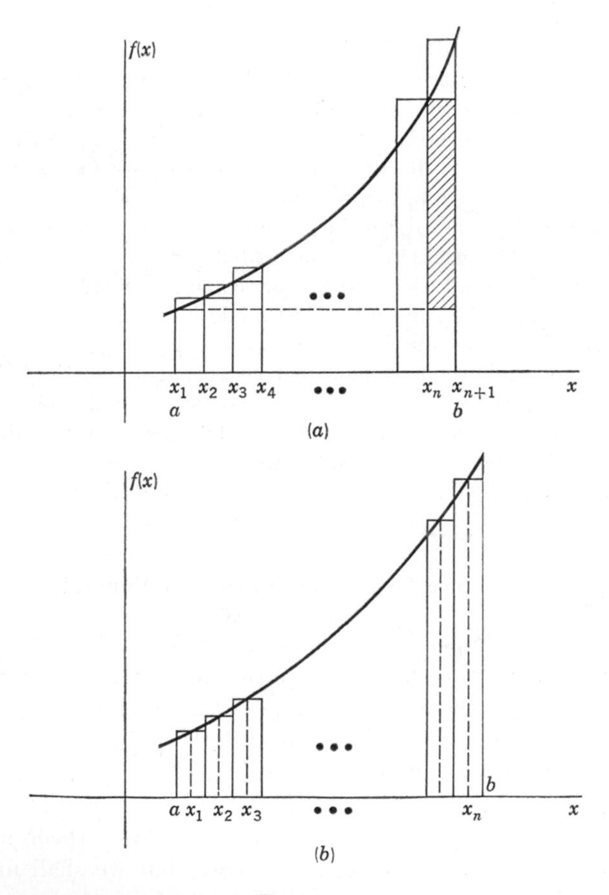

Figure 9–1

THEOREM 5 (DOMINATION PRINCIPLE). Let a_n, b_n, and c_n be the respective nth terms of three sequences, such that $a_n \leq b_n \leq c_n$ for each n exceeding some integer N. Then if $\lim a_n = \lim c_n = L$, $\lim b_n$ also exists and equals L.

Let us now consider a function f on the real number interval $[a, b]$, with f continuous, non-negative, and increasing on the whole interval. We are interested in the *area* of the plane region bounded by the graph of f, the x-axis, and the line segments drawn perpendicular to the x-axis from the end-points of the graph. In the future we shall refer to such an area as the area "under the graph of f and above the x-axis." Since the notion of *area* is, in general, complicated as is the notion of *length* in connection with a curve, we shall adopt a somewhat intuitive approach. In Figure 9–1, we have shown the graph of a function of the type under consideration. Let us subdivide the interval $[a, b]$ on the x-axis into n equal parts, and from each point of subdivision draw a line segment to the graph, each segment perpendicular to the x-axis. The region under consideration is now subdivided into n strips, but it is no simpler to determine the area of one of these strips than it is to determine the area of the original region. We now form two sets of rectangles, by drawing line segments parallel to the x-axis and through the points of intersection of the edges of the strips with the graph. The rectangles of one set lie completely inside the original region, while those of the other set lie partly outside, as shown in Figure 9–1a. Let $x_1(=a)$, x_2, x_3, $\cdots$ x_n, $x_{n+1}(=b)$ be the abscissas of the points of subdivision on the x-axis, with $h_n = (b - a)/n$, the common measure of width of each rectangle. If we let s_n be the associated measure of area for the totality of interior rectangles, with S_n the similar measure of area for the other rectangles, the following expressions for s_n and S_n may be seen to be valid:

$$s_n = f(x_1)h_n + f(x_2)h_n + f(x_3)h_n + \cdots + f(x_n)h_n = \sum_{i=1}^{n} f(x_i)h_n;$$

$$S_n = f(x_2)h_n + f(x_3)h_n + f(x_4)h_n + \cdots + f(x_{n+1})h_n = \sum_{i=2}^{n+1} f(x_i)h_n.$$

If A is to represent the associated measure of what we intuitively regard as the area of the region being considered, a glance at Figure 9–1a reveals the validity of the inequality $s_n \leq A \leq S_n$ which, on subtraction of s_n from each member, becomes $0 \leq A - s_n \leq S_n - s_n$. The quantity $S_n - s_n$ measures the *difference* in area of the two sets of rectangles and, by actual subtraction, $S_n - s_n = [f(b) - f(a)]h_n$; this region is shown cross-hatched in the figure.

We now let n, the number of subintervals, increase indefinitely so that h_n is arbitrarily close to 0; i.e., $\lim h_n = 0$. Since $f(b) - f(a)$ is a real number, fixed by the original region, an application of the Corollary to Theorem 3 shows that $\lim (S_n - s_n) = [f(b) - f(a)][\lim h_n] = 0$. The Domination Principle for sequences, applied to the above inequality, now shows that $\lim (A - s_n) = 0$; and, by Theorems 1 and 2, $A = \lim s_n$. But $S_n = (S_n - s_n) + s_n$ and, by Theorem 2, $\lim S_n = \lim (S_n - s_n) + \lim s_n = 0 + \lim s_n = \lim s_n$. Hence we may write $A = \lim s_n = \lim \sum_{i=1}^{n} f(x_i)h_n = \lim \sum_{i=2}^{n+1} f(x_i)h_n = \lim S_n$.

In the above expressions for A as the limit of a sequence, x_i is the abscissa of the left end-point of the ith subinterval of $[a, b]$ on the x-axis. If we now let x_i be an *arbitrary* point in the ith subinterval, it is clear from Figure 9-1*b* that $s_n \leq \sum_{i=1}^{n} f(x_i)h_n \leq S_n$. Since $\lim s_n = \lim S_n = A$, a further application of the Domination Principle for sequences shows that $A = \lim \sum_{i=1}^{n} f(x_i)h_n$.

We required, for the above argument, that the function f be increasing at each point of its domain, but it is clear that a similar argument could be given in case f is decreasing on $[a, b]$; moreover, the expression derived above for A is clearly valid for a constant function. If a function f is continuous on $[a, b]$, it is possible to subdivide this interval into subintervals, on each of which f is either increasing throughout, decreasing throughout, or constant. In view of the preceding remark, an application of Theorem 2 now shows that the expression $A = \lim \sum_{i=1}^{n} f(x_i)h_n$ remains valid, if we remove the condition that f is increasing on the whole interval $[a, b]$. If this limit is to give a measure for *area* that is intuitively satisfactory, however, we must insist that f is both non-negative and continuous on its domain.

The geometric notion of the slope of the tangent line at a point of a curve led us to the definition of the derivative of a function, in Chapter 8; and we now use the area under a curve to lead us to the concept of a definite integral.

DEFINITION. Let f be a continuous function on the interval $[a, b]$. Then, if $[a, b]$ is subdivided into n equal subintervals of length $h_n = (b - a)/n$, with x_i an arbitrary point in the ith subinterval, we define the *definite integral of f from a to b* to be $\lim \sum_{i=1}^{n} f(x_i)h_n$ and indicate it by $\int_a^b f(x)\,dx$, whenever this limit exists. We refer to $f(x)$ as the *integrand*, and a and b the *lower* and upper *limits*, respectively, of the integral.

The symbol $\int_a^b f(x)\,dx$ is a relic of early days of the calculus, and it does not appear feasible to attempt to completely justify it. However, we may regard $\int$ as an elongated S, indicative of a summation, while dx indicates the axis on which the interval $[a, b]$ is considered to be located.

It is clear that if f is continuous and non-negative on $[a, b]$, the definite integral represents the associated measure of area for the region under the graph of f and above the x-axis. In case the values of f are non-positive at each point of the interval, it is evident that the definite integral represents the *negative* of the measure of area for the region *above* the graph of f and *below* the x-axis. If f has both positive and negative values on $[a, b]$, the definite integral may be interpreted as the measure of area for the regions bounded by the curve above the x-axis minus the measure for the regions bounded by the curve below the x-axis. However, while it is always possible to *interpret* a definite integral as a measure of area, we must emphasize that the definition of a definite integral is quite independent of such an interpretation. In spite of this remark, we shall confine our applications to areas.

ILLUSTRATION 1. A function f is defined on the interval $[0, 2]$ by $f(x) = x^2 + 1$, for each x in $[0, 2]$. Determine the area under the graph of f and above the x-axis.

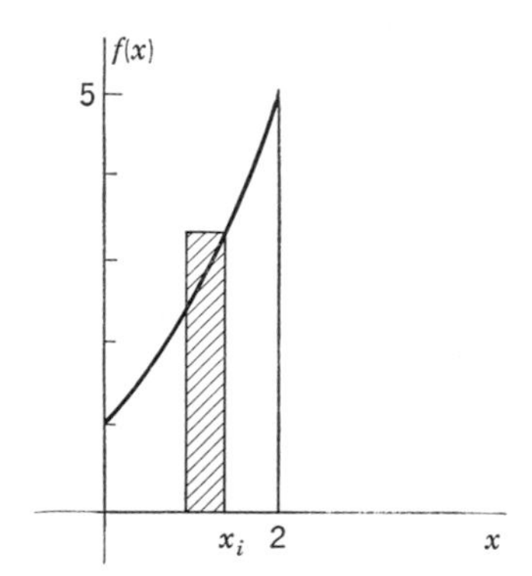

Figure 9–2

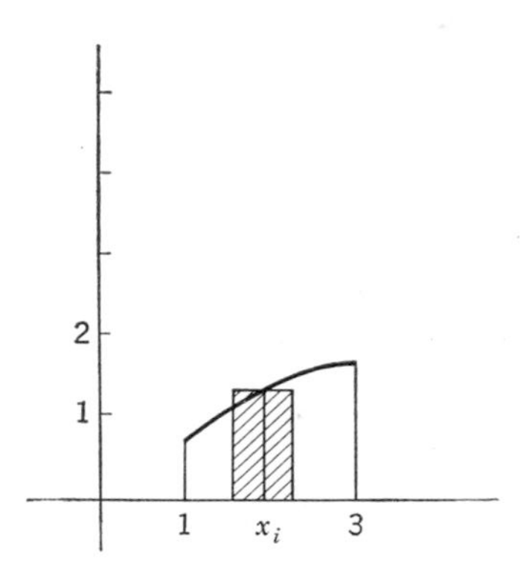

Figure 9–3

Solution. The graph of f is shown in Figure 9–2. If we subdivide the interval $[0, 2]$ into n equal parts, the width h_n of each subinterval is given by $h_n = 2/n$. Let us choose $x_i = ih_n$ in the ith subinterval, so that if we indicate the desired measure of area by A, $A = \lim S_n$ where

$$S_n = \sum_{i=1}^{n} f(x_i)h_n = \sum_{i=1}^{n} (i^2h_n^2 + 1)h_n = h_n^3 \sum_{i=1}^{n} i^2 + 2.$$

It is known that

$$\sum_{i=1}^{n} i^2 = 1^2 + 2^2 + 3^2 + \cdots + n^2 = \frac{n(n+1)(2n+1)}{6},$$

so that

$$S_n = (8/n^3)\frac{n(n+1)(2n+1)}{6} + 2 = 8/3 + 4/n + 4/(3n^2) + 2$$
$$= 14/3 + 4/n + 4/(3n^2).$$

It then follows that $A = \lim S_n = 14/3$.

This example has been worked out, not as a recommended procedure for problems of this type, but rather to illustrate the complexity of this method of solution. This may explain why very little progress was made with integration in ancient times. In the following sections we shall explain a more modern method, which will enable us to evaluate many definite integrals with great ease. For the present, we shall be concerned principally with "setting up" a few of these integrals.

ILLUSTRATION 2. A function f is defined on the interval $[1, 3]$ by $f(x) = \ln 2x$. Set up an expression for the associated measure of area of the region under the graph of f and above the x-axis.

Solution. The definition of the definite integral, adapted to Figure 9–3, shows that the associated measure A of the area may be expressed by

$$A = \lim \sum_{i=1}^{n} (\ln 2x_i)h_n = \int_1^3 \ln 2x\, dx.$$

PROBLEM SET 9.3

In each of Problems 1 through 12, set up an expression for the associated measure of area of the region under the graph of f and above the x-axis, using the indicated function and interval of definition.

1. $f(x) = x^3$ on $[0, 3]$.

2. $f(x) = x^2$ on $[0, 3]$.

3. $f(x) = x^2 + 2$ on $[1, 4]$.

4. $f(x) = x^{1/2}$ on $[1, 4]$.

5. $f(x) = e^{2x}$ on $[0, 3]$.

6. $f(x) = 3e^x$ on $[2, 5]$.

7. $f(x) = e^{-2x}$ on $[-1, 3]$.

8. $f(x) = \ln 3x$ on $[2, 5]$.

9. $f(x) = \sin x$ on $[0, \pi/2]$.

10. $f(x) = \cos x$ on $[0, \pi/2]$.

11. $f(x) = x^3 - 2$ on $[2, 5]$.

12. $f(x) = 2x + 3$ on $[-1, 3]$.

13.* Prove Theorem 2.

14.* Prove Theorem 3.

In Problems 15 through 18, take $h_n = 1/n$ and $x_i = i/n$.

15. Show that $\int_0^1 (1)\, dx = 1$.

16. Show that $\int_0^1 x\, dx = 1/2$, being given that $1 + 2 + 3 + \cdots + n = n(n + 1)/2$.

17. Show that $\int_0^1 x^2\, dx = 1/3$, being given that $1^2 + 2^2 + 3^2 + \cdots + n^2 = n(n + 1)(2n + 1)/6$.

18. Show that $\int_0^1 x^3\, dx = 1/4$, being given that $1^3 + 2^3 + 3^3 + \cdots + n^3 = n^2(n + 1)^2/4$.

9.4 Antiderivatives and Indefinite Integrals

It is sometimes easy to discover a function that has a given function for its derivative. For example, if f is the function defined on $[a, b]$ by $f(x) = 3x^2$, it is clear that the function F, defined on $[a, b]$ by $F(x) = x^3$, has the property that $F' = f$; we are led to the function F by our knowledge of the derivative of a polynomial function. The function F is an antiderivative of f, according to the following definition.

DEFINITION. Let f be a function on an interval $[a, b]$. Then a differentiable function F on $[a, b]$, such that $F' = f$, is known as an *antiderivative* or *primitive (function)* of f.

The above example may be easily generalized to an arbitrary polynomial function f on $[a, b]$. For, if $f(x) = cx^n$, for any x in $[a, b]$, it is clear† that $F(x) = \dfrac{cx^{n+1}}{n+1}$ will define a primitive F of f. If a primitive of a function exists, however, it is not unique. Thus, the function F_1, defined on $[a, b]$ by $F_1(x) = x^3 + 2$, is also a primitive of the function f in the example, and, in fact, the number 2 could be replaced by any real number C. The following theorem implies that any primitive of this function f must be of this type, however.

THEOREM 1. If f is a function on an interval $[a, b]$, the difference of any two primitives of f is a constant function.

Proof. Suppose that F_1 and F_2 are primitives of f. The definition of a primitive then implies that $F_1'(x) - F_2'(x) = f(x) - f(x) = 0$, for each x in $[a, b]$. It is possible, at this point, to give a rigorous proof that $F_1 - F_2$ must be a constant function, but we appeal to intuition: a graph of $F_1 - F_2$ has a tangent parallel to the x-axis at each of its points, and so must be a straight line segment with $(F_1 - F_2)(x) = C$, at each x in $[a, b]$, for some real number C. Thus, $F_1(x) - F_2(x) = C$, as asserted in the theorem.

The student may wonder why a discussion of primitives has been injected into a chapter on the Integral Calculus, but we are about to see that these functions play a very important role in the evaluation of definite integrals. At this time we should recall the definition of the definite integral $\int_a^b f(x)\,dx$ for a continuous function f on $[a, b]$. Since the definite integral depends only on the function f and the interval $[a, b]$, it is clearly irrelevant what symbol we use for an arbitrary element of the domain. Thus, $\int_a^b f(x)\,dx = \int_a^b f(t)\,dt = \int_a^b f(u)\,du$, etc., and it will sometimes be convenient to replace the customary x by some other symbol.

If $[\alpha, \beta]$ is any subinterval of $[a, b]$, we can imitate the procedure of

† If all of Chapter 8 has not been studied, see Theorem 4 of that chapter.

the preceding section to define the *definite integral of* f *from* α *to* β. Thus, let us subdivide $[\alpha, \beta]$ into n equal subintervals of length h_n, take an element x_i in the ith subinterval, for each i, and form $S_n = \sum_{i=1}^{n} f(x_i)h_n$. It can now be shown—though we omit the proof—that $\lim S_n$ exists if $\int_a^b f(x)\,dx$ exists, and we designate $\lim S_n$ by $\int_\alpha^\beta f(x)\,dx$. It is evident that if $\int_a^b f(x)\,dx$ measures the area of a region, the integral $\int_\alpha^\beta f(x)\,dx$ is the corresponding measure of area for a portion of this region.

In accordance with the above agreement on symbolism, the definite integral $\int_c^x f(t)\,dt$ has now been defined for c and x in $[a, b]$ with $c \leq x$. We now define a function G on the interval $[c, b]$ by $G(x) = \int_c^x f(t)\,dt$, for each x in $[c, b]$, and refer to G as an *indefinite integral* of f. It is clear that there is an indefinite integral of f, associated with each point c in the domain $[a, b]$ of f. In particular, if we let $c = a$, we obtain an indefinite integral of f with a most important property. It is this property which connects differential with integral calculus, and the following theorem may properly be referred to as the *Fundamental Theorem of the Differential and Integral Calculus.*

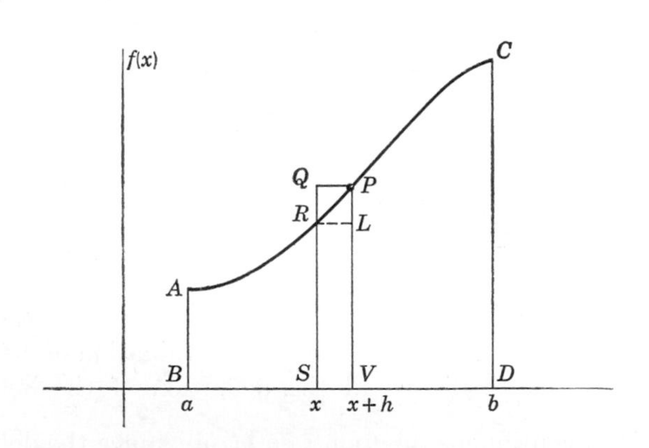

Figure 9-4

THEOREM 2. Let f be a continuous function on $[a, b]$. Then the indefinite integral G, defined on $[a, b]$ by $G(x) = \int_a^x f(t)\,dt$, is a primitive of f, i.e., $G'(x) = f(x)$ for each x in $[a, b]$.

Proof. We wish to show that G is differentiable at each point x of $[a, b]$, and that $G'(x) = f(x)$. In our proof we shall assume that f is non-negative and non-decreasing from a to b, so that we can use intuitive notions of area; a general proof may be found in many calculus books. Let us refer to Figure 9–4, so that the definite integral $\int_a^b f(x)\,dx$ measures the area of the region $ABDC$. With G defined in the statement of the theorem, it is clear that $G(x)$ measures the area of the region $ABSR$, where $(x, f(x))$ is the point R; in particular, $G(a) = 0$ and $G(b) = \int_a^b f(x)\,dx$. Let E_x be the secant-slope function for G at the point x, so that $E_x(h) = [G(x + h) - G(x)]/h$, for each h in the domain of E_x. The figure shows that $G(x + h) - G(x)$ measures the area of the region $RSVP$, which is intermediate between the areas of the rectangles $RSVL$ and $QSVP$. Thus, $hf(x) \leq G(x + h) - G(x) \leq hf(x + h)$ and $f(x) \leq \dfrac{G(x + h) - G(x)}{h} \leq f(x + h)$; and in view of our definition of E_x, this last inequality may be written in the form $f(x) \leq E_x(h) \leq f(x + h)$. The continuity of f implies that $\lim_{h \to 0} f(x + h) = f(x)$ and so, by the Domination Principle for functions, $\lim_{h \to 0} E_x(h) = G'(x) = f(x)$, as desired.

We can now use Theorem 2 to develop a simple method for evaluating definite integrals. If F is any primitive of f, we know by Theorem 1 that $F(x) = G(x) + C$, for some real number C. But $G(a) = 0$ and so $C = F(a)$, while $F(b) = G(b) + C = G(b) + F(a)$. We noted in the early part of the proof of Theorem 2 that $G(b) = \int_a^b f(x)\,dx$, so we have now proved that $\int_a^b f(x)\,dx = F(b) - F(a)$. This result is sometimes known as the *Fundamental Theorem of the Integral Calculus.*

THEOREM 3. Let f be a continuous function on $[a, b]$. Then, if F is any primitive of f, $\int_a^b f(x)\,dx = F(b) - F(a)$.

As a result of this theorem, the problem of evaluating a definite integral of a function f, has been changed into one of determining a primitive or antiderivative of f. We shall give more discussion to the question of primitives in the next section, but we have already described a primitive F for power functions: if $f(x) = cx^n$, $F(x) = \dfrac{cx^{n+1}}{n + 1}$. Since a polynomial function may be considered a sum of power functions, it is easy to find a primitive for any such function.

ILLUSTRATION 1. If f is the function defined on $[0, 2]$ by $f(x) = x^2 + 1$, evaluate the definite integral $\int_0^2 f(x)\,dx$.

Solution. (See Illustration 1 of Section 9.3.) The above rule, for determining a primitive of a power function, shows that the function F, defined on $[0, 2]$ by $F(x) = x^3/3 + x$, is a primitive of f. It then follows from Theorem 3 that $\int_0^2 f(x)\,dx = F(2) - F(0) = 8/3 + 2 - 0 = 14/3$.

ILLUSTRATION 2. A function f is defined on $[-1, 3]$ by $f(x) = x^2 - 2x + 1$. Determine the area under the graph of f and above the x-axis.

Solution. We note that $f(x) = (x - 1)^2$, and the graph of f, shown in Figure 9–5, lies entirely above the x-axis. We can then determine the associated measure of the area, by evaluating $\int_{-1}^{3} f(x)\,dx$. The function F, defined on $[-1, 3]$ by $F(x) = x^3/3 - x^2 + x$, is seen to be a primitive of f, and so $\int_{-1}^{3} f(x)\,dx = F(3) - F(-1) = (9 - 9 + 3) - (-1/3 - 1 - 1) = 16/3$.

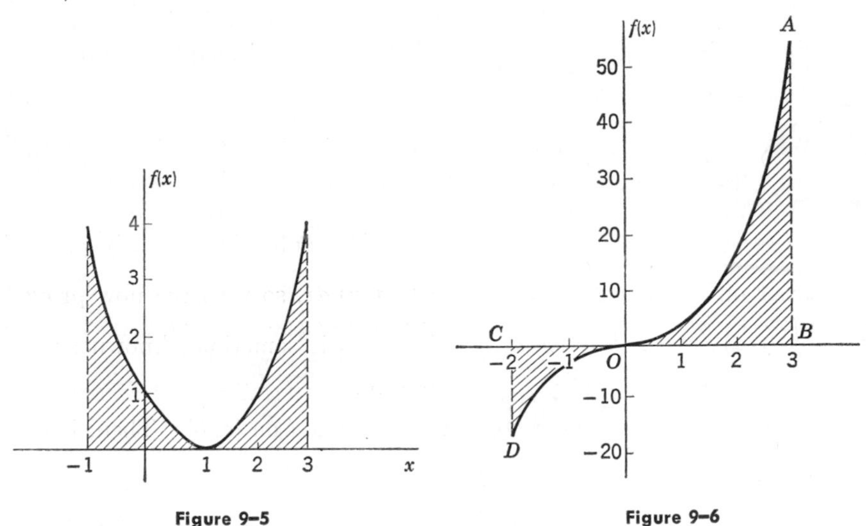

Figure 9–5

Figure 9–6

ILLUSTRATION 3. If f is the function defined on $[-2, 3]$ by $f(x) = 2x^3$, evaluate the definite integral $\int_{-2}^{3} f(x)\,dx$.

Solution. The graph of f is shown in Figure 9–6. The function F, defined on $[-2, 3]$ by $F(x) = x^4/2$, is a primitive of f, and so $\int_{-2}^{3} f(x)\,dx = F(3) - F(-2) = 81/2 - 8 = 65/2$. In this case, $65/2$ will be the associated measure of the area of the region AOB less that of the region DOC. If we wished to find the measure of area for the *sum* of these two regions, we would add the absolute value of $\int_{-2}^{0} f(x)\,dx$ to $\int_{0}^{3} f(x)\,dx$.

PROBLEM SET 9.4

1. Find the simplest primitive of a function f, with $f(x)$ defined below: (a) $x^3 + 2x^2 - 5x$; (b) $3x^4 - 4x^2 + 2x - 3$; (c) $2x^3 + 3x$; (d) $x^5 - 5x^3$.

2. Find the simplest primitive of a function f, with $f(x)$ defined below: (a)* $x + 1/x$; (b) $3x^2 - x + 2$; (c) $x^4 - 4x^3 - 1$; (d)* $3/x^2 - 1/x$.

3. If F is a primitive of a function f, determine $f(x)$ from $F(x)$ below: (a) $1/x^2 + 3x - 5$; (b) $2x^2 - 3x + 7$.

4. If F is a primitive of a function f, determine $f(x)$ from $F(x)$ below: (a) $3x^3 + 4x - 5$; (b)* $2x - 3/x$.

5. Evaluate $\int_a^b f(x)\,dx$, with f defined on $[a, b]$ by $f(x)$ below: (a) $x^2 + 3x - 1$, $a = -2, b = 3$; (b) $3x^3 + 4x + 2$, $a = 0, b = 2$; (c) $2x^3 - 4x + 5$, $a = -2$, $b = 2$; (d) $4x^4 + 3x^2 - 2$, $a = 0$, $b = 1$.

6. Evaluate $\int_a^b f(x)\,dx$, with f defined on $[a, b]$ by $f(x)$ below: (a) $x^2 - 3x$, $a = 1$, $b = 2$; (b) $2x^3 - 3x + 2$, $a = -1$, $b = 3$; (c) $2x^3 - 5$, $a = -3$, $b = 1$; (d) $3x^2 - 2/x$, $a = -3$, $b = -1$.

7. If f is the function defined on $[-5, 5]$ by $f(x) = 2x^3 - x + 2$, evaluate (a) $\int_{-2}^{3} f(x)\,dx$; (b) $\int_{0}^{3} f(x)\,dx$; (c) $\int_{-1}^{5} f(x)\,dx$; (d) $\int_{-4}^{0} f(x)\,dx$.

8. The function f is defined on $[0, 3]$ by $f(x) = 2x^2 + 5$. Determine the area of the region below the graph of x and above the x-axis.

9. Determine the area of the plane region bounded by the x-axis and the parabola, described as the locus of $y = x^2$, between $x = 2$ and $x = 5$.

10. Determine the total area of the plane regions bounded by the x-axis and the cubical parabola, described as the locus of $y = x^3$, between $x = -2$ and $x = 2$.

11. The function f is defined on $R^{\#}$ by $f(x) = 2x^4 + x^2 + 1$. Determine the area of the plane region bounded by the x-axis and the graph of f, between $x = -3$ and $x = 2$.

12. Use a definite integral to establish the formula $A = bh/2$, for the area of a triangle.

9.5* Primitives of the Elementary Functions

In the preceding section, we developed a very simple method for evaluating a definite integral of a continuous function, provided we could find a primitive of this function. Moreover, a formula for a primitive was given, in case the function is of the polynomial type. In view of the relationship between a function f and one of its primitives F, i.e., $F' = f$, a formula for a primitive can be checked by differentiation. Though the notation has questionable merit, it is customary to indicate the value at the point x of an arbitrary primitive of a function f by $\int f(x)\,dx$. Notice that there are no limits on the integral sign. The notation might lead one to suspect that, if F is any primitive of a function f, it is possible to express $F(x)$ in the form $\int_a^x f(t)\,dt$ for some real number a. However, it is easy to find a counter-example of this: the function G, defined on $R^\#$ by $G(x) = 1$, is a primitive of the function f, defined on $R^\#$ by $f(x) = 0$; but it is clear that $\int 0\,dt$ can not equal 1 for any number a.

For the following formulas, we assume that the function in the integrand is defined on some interval. The results of Chapter 8 may be used to check each formula, since $\int f(x)\,dx = F(x)$ provided $F'(x) = f(x)$. As in Chapter 8, the symbol $u = g(x)$ indicates the value at x of some differentiable function g.

1. $\displaystyle\int 0\,dx = C.$

2. $\displaystyle\int 1\,dx = x + C.$

3. $\displaystyle\int [f(x) + g(x)]\,dx = \int f(x)\,dx + \int g(x)\,dx.$

4. $\displaystyle\int cf(x)\,dx = c\int f(x)\,dx.$

5. $\displaystyle\int u^n u'\,dx = \frac{u^{n+1}}{n+1} + C, \text{ if } n \neq -1.$

6. $\displaystyle\int e^u u'\,dx = e^u + C.$

7. $\displaystyle\int \frac{u'}{u}\,dx = \ln u + C.$

8. $\displaystyle\int \cos u\, u'\,dx = \sin u + C.$

9. $\displaystyle\int \csc u \cot u\, u'\,dx = -\csc u + C.$

10. $\displaystyle\int \sin u\, u'\,dx = -\cos u + C.$

11. $\displaystyle\int \sec u \tan u\, u'\,dx = \sec u + C.$

12. $\displaystyle\int \sec^2 u\, u'\,dx = \tan u + C.$

13. $\int \csc^2 u\, u'\, dx = -\cot u + C.$

ILLUSTRATION 1. Determine $\int 2e^{3x}\, dx$.

Solution. This involves a use of Formulas 4 and 6, with $c = 2$ and $u = 3x$. Since $u' = 3$,

$$\int 2e^{3x}\, dx = 2(1/3) \int e^{3x}\, (3)\, dx = (2/3)e^{3x} + C.$$

ILLUSTRATION 2. Determine $\int \frac{3x\, dx}{x^2 + 1}$.

Solution. This involves a use of Formulas 4 and 7, with $c = 3$ and $u = x^2 + 1$. Since $u' = 2x$,

$$\int \frac{3x\, dx}{x^2 + 1} = \frac{3}{2} \int \frac{2x\, dx}{x^2 + 1} = \frac{3}{2} \ln (x^2 + 1) + C.$$

ILLUSTRATION 3. Determine $\int \sec^2 (3x + 1)\, dx$.

Solution. We use Formula 12, with $u = 3x + 1$. Since $u' = 3$,

$$\int \sec^2 (3x + 1)\, dx = (1/3) \int 3 \sec^2 (3x + 1)\, dx = (1/3) \tan (3x + 1) + C.$$

In the applications of the Fundamental Theorem of the Calculus, it is convenient to introduce the notation $F(x)|_a^b$ for $F(b) - F(a)$.

ILLUSTRATION 4. Evaluate the definite integral $\int_0^1 2e^{3x}\, dx$.

Solution. The result of Illustration 1 shows that

$$\int_0^1 2e^{3x}\, dx = (2/3)e^{3x}|_0^1 = (2/3)e^3 - (2/3)e^0 = (2/3)(e^3 - 1).$$

ILLUSTRATION 5. Let f be the function defined on $R^\#$ by $f(x) = 3 \sin 2x$. Determine the area enclosed by the x-axis and the graph of f between the origin and $(\pi/2, 0)$.

Solution. The desired measure of area will be given by the definite integral $\int_0^{\pi/2} 3 \sin 2x\, dx$. If $u = 2x$, $u' = 2$ and so

$$\int_0^{\pi/2} 3 \sin 2x\, dx = 3(1/2) \int_0^{\pi/2} 2 \sin 2x\, dx = (3/2)(-\cos 2x)|_0^{\pi/2}$$

$$= (3/2)(1) - (3/2)(-1) = 3/2 + 3/2 = 6/2 = 3.$$

PROBLEM SET 9.5

In Problems 1 through 6, find the indicated value of the primitive function.

1. $\int (x^2 - 2x + 3)\,dx$

2. $\int (e^{2x} - 3x^2)\,dx$

3. $\int x^2 \sin x^3\,dx$

4. $\int \sec 2x \tan 2x\,dx$

5. $\int \frac{5x}{x^2 + 3}\,dx$

6. $\int (3x^2 + 2)^4\,x\,dx$

In Problems 7 through 18, evaluate the indicated definite or indefinite integral, assuming that it exists.

7. $\int_0^2 (2x^2 + x - 1)\,dx$

8. $\int_0^1 (e^{2x} - x)\,dx$

9. $\int_1^x \cos 2x\,dx$

10. $\int_0^{\pi} (x - \sin 3x)\,dx$

11. $\int_0^{\pi/6} \sec^2 2x\,dx$

12. $\int_{-1}^0 (5x - 2)^5\,dx$

13. $\int_0^x e^{\sin x} \cos x\,dx$

14. $\int_0^1 \tan 2x\,dx$

15. $\int_{-1}^0 (x^2 + 2)^3\,x\,dx$

16. $\int_1^2 (x + 1/x)\,dx$

17. $\int_1^2 \frac{1}{(1 - 2x)^2}\,dx$

18. $\int_1^x \frac{2}{3 - x}\,dx$

19. The function f is defined on $[0, 3]$ by $f(x) = 2/(x + 1)$. Determine the area of the region in the first quadrant which lies under the graph of f.

20. Find the area bounded by the x-axis and the loci of the equations $y = 2e^{3x}$, $x = 1$, and $x = 3$.

REVIEW TEST A

1. Classify each of the sequences, the first three terms of which are given, as arithmetic or geometric, and include two more terms. (*a*) 2, 5, 8; (*b*) 16, 12, 8; (*c*) 1, $-\sqrt{3}$, 3; (*d*) 1/2, 2/3, 5/6.

2. If the nth term of a sequence is given by the formula $a_n = \frac{n + 2}{\lfloor n}$, find the first three terms.

3. The nth term of a sequence is given by the formula $b_n = \frac{a_{n+1} - 2}{2n}$, with a_n defined in Problem 2. Find the first three terms of the sequence.

4. Determine the 20th term and the sum of the first 20 terms of the arithmetic sequence, that has the following first three terms: (*a*) $-12, -9, -6$; (*b*) 50, 140/3, 130/3.
5. Find the sum of the first 10 terms of a geometric sequence, the first three terms of which are $9, -3, 1$.
6. With S_n indicating the sum of the first n terms, determine $\lim S_n$ for the infinite geometric sequence having $10, -4, 8/5$ for its first three terms.
7. A 31-rung ladder is to be built with the rungs tapering from 29 inches at the bottom to 14 inches at the top. By what amount should successive rungs differ in size, and what total length of material would be required for the rungs? (Neglect the material wasted in the cutting process.)
8. A man piles 204 bricks to form a tapering pile, one brick thick. If the top row contains 4 bricks and the number of bricks in successive rows differ by 1, how many bricks are there in the bottom row?
9. Determine a primitive of the function f, with $f(x)$ given below. (*a*) $3x^2 - 2x + 1$; (*b*)* $2x^3 - \sin 2x + x$; (*c*)* $e^{2x} - \cos 3x$.
10. Evaluate each of the following definite integrals, assuming that it exists. (*a*) $\int_{-1}^{0} (2x^4 + x^2 + 1)\,dx$; (*b*)* $\int_{1}^{2} (1/x - e^{3x} + x)\,dx$.
11. Determine the area of the plane region bounded by the x-axis, and the loci of the equations given below. (*a*) $y = 4x^2 + 2x + 2$, $x = 0$, $x = 4$; (*b*)* $y = 2xe^{x^2}$, $x = 0$, $x = 1$.
12. Use the *definition* of a definite integral to show that $\int_0^4 2x^2\,dx = 128/3$. (Assume that $1^2 + 2^2 + 3^2 + \cdots + n^2 = \dfrac{n(n+1)(2n+1)}{6}$.)

REVIEW TEST B

1. Classify each of the sequences, having the indicated first three terms, as arithmetic or geometric, and include two more terms. (*a*) $4, 1, -2$; (*b*) 1/3, 1/6, 1/12; (*c*) $1, \sqrt{2}/2, 1/2$; (*d*) $-2, -7/2, -5$.
2. If the nth term of a sequence is given by the formula $a_n = \dfrac{n^2 - n}{n+1}$, find the first three terms.
3. The nth term of a sequence is given by the formula $b_n = \dfrac{na_{n+1}}{2+n}$, with a_n defined in Problem 2. Find the first three terms of the sequence.
4. Determine the 15th term and the sum of 15 terms of the arithmetic sequence, having the following first three terms: (*a*) 2, 7, 12; (*b*) 5, 7/2, 2.
5. Find the sum of 12 terms of a geometric sequence, having 3, 2, 4/3 as its first three terms.
6. With S_n indicating the sum of the first n terms, determine $\lim S_n$ for the infinite geometric sequence, having 2, 4/3, 8/9 as its first three terms.

7. A slide of uniform grade is to be built on a level section of ground. If there are to be 10 equally spaced supports, the heights of the shortest and longest of which are 5 feet and 59 feet, respectively, determine the required height of each support.
8. A 256-gallon tank is full of pure alcohol. If 64 gallons are removed and replaced by pure water and thoroughly mixed, and this procedure is repeated 6 times, use a formula introduced in this section to determine how much alcohol remains in the solution.
9. Determine a primitive of the function f, with $f(x)$ given below: (*a*) $4x^2 + 2x + 5$; (*b*)* $\cos 2x - 3/x$; (*c*)* $x - e^{\sin x} \cos x$.
10. Evaluate each of the following definite integrals, assuming that it exists: (*a*) $\int_{-1}^{1} (3x^3 - 2x + 1)\, dx$; (*b*)* $\int_0^1 (e^t + 1)^2 e^t\, dt$.
11. Determine the area of the plane region bounded by the x-axis, and the loci of the equations given below. (*a*) $y = 2x^3 + 1$, $x = 1$, $x = 3$; (*b*)* $y = \cos 3x$, $x = 0$, $x = \pi/6$.
12. Use the *definition* of a definite integral to show that $\int_0^3 (x^2/2 + 1)\, dx = 15/2$. $\left[\text{Assume that } 1^2 + 2^2 + 3^2 + \cdots + n^2 = \frac{n(n+1)(2n+1)}{6}.\right]$

REFERENCES

Books

ALLENDOERFER, C. B. AND C. O. OAKLEY, *Principles of Mathematics*, New York, McGraw-Hill, 1955. (Chap. 12.)

COURANT, RICHARD, *Differential and Integral Calculus*, New York, Interscience Publishers, Inc., 1937. (Vol. 1, pp. 76–88, 109–117.)

COURANT, RICHARD AND HERBERT ROBBINS, *What is Mathematics?*, New York, Oxford, 1941. (Pp. 399–414, 436–441.)

American Mathematical Monthly

SCHILLO, PAUL, "On the Applications of the Fundamental Theorem of the Integral Calculus," Vol. 63, p. 340 (1956).

10

POLYNOMIAL (AND OTHER) EQUATIONS AND INEQUALITIES

$e^{i\pi} + 1 = 0$

L. EULER

10.1 Complex Numbers

We now pick up a thread of reasoning that we dropped at the end of Chapter 2. In that chapter we developed the real number system, by successively introducing new numbers which simplified the problem of making more accurate or comprehensive the measurement of physical quantities. We noted, also, that whenever a new type of number was introduced, we were able to solve a type of algebraic equation that was previously unsolvable. As a matter of fact, the number system may be developed with *either* the solution of equations *or* the problem of measurement as its prime motivation, for the two go hand-in-hand. Thus, with the positive integers of counting, we could solve the equation $3x = 9$, but not until we introduced rational numbers could we solve $3x = 5$. We could use rational numbers to solve $x + 2/3 = 7/3$, but we had to introduce signed numbers before it was possible to solve $x + 7/3 = 2/3$. Finally, the equation $x^2 = 4$ was solvable with signed numbers, but we were unable to solve $x^2 = 2$ until the introduction of irrational numbers; we recall that these latter numbers were a theoretical necessity, but were not required by the science of practical measurement. We are now about to make our final extension of the number system; these new numbers will be useful for the measurement of certain vector quantities, not measurable with real numbers, and will also enable us to solve previously unsolvable equations.

It is possible to use real numbers for a satisfactory measurement of all vector quantities that have either the same or opposite directions. We shall continue to use the word *vector*, introduced in Chapter 2, to refer to a line segment that represents a vector quantity in magnitude, direction, and sense. Thus, in Figure 10–1, a vector of length s units in the direction chosen as positive (along the positive x-axis) can be measured by the real number $+s$ or simply s; and a vector of length t units in the opposite direction (along the negative x-axis) can be measured by the real number $-t$. However, it would not be possible to use a real number to make a simultaneous measurement of a vector, such as OP, which is not parallel to the x-axis. A vector has the two basic qualities of magnitude and direction, but its actual position on a plane is unimportant. Thus, there will be no loss of generality if we assume that each vector emanates from the origin of a rectangular coordinate system. If we make O the origin of such a system, we notice that the vector OP is *completely determined* by the coordinates a and b of its end-point P. In view of the determination of the

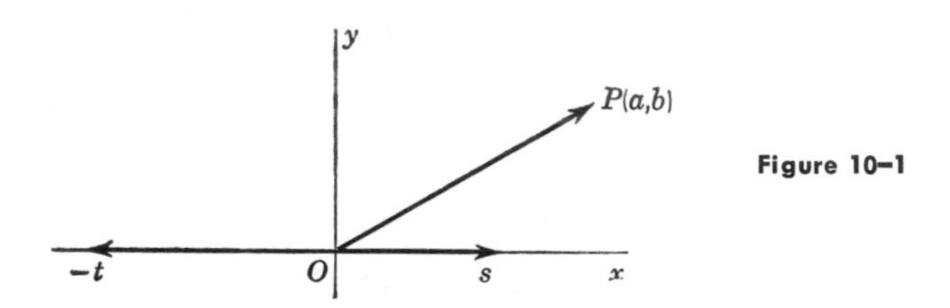

Figure 10–1

vector OP by the ordered pair (a, b), it is perhaps not too far-fetched to consider this *ordered pair* as a new kind of *number*, which in some sense measures the vector that is determined by it. In order to justify the use of the word *number* in connection with an ordered pair, we must show that we can define operations of addition and multiplication in the set of such pairs, in such a way that at least most of the Basic Laws of Arithmetic of Chapter 2 remain valid.

DEFINITION. A *complex number* is an ordered pair (a, b) of real numbers a and b, with the operations of addition and multiplication, and the relation of equality, defined as follows:

addition, $(a, b) + (c, d) = (a + c, b + d)$.

multiplication, $(a, b)(c, d) = (ac - bd, ad + bc)$.

equality, $(a, b) = (c, d)$ if and only if $a = c$ and $b = d$.

We do not define a relation of "less than" in the complex numbers; but we note that two complex numbers are equal if the vectors which are determined by them are identical. The rule for multiplication may seem a little strange, but it will lose some of this strangeness later on. For the present, it is sufficient to say that it is a matter of straightforward verification that all the Basic Laws of Arithmetic, save only for the monotonic law, are valid with these definitions. We leave this verification to the student, except for the commutative law of addition, which is verified in Illustration 1.

We can define *subtraction* and *division* in a manner analogous to the corresponding definitions for real numbers. Thus, to *subtract* b from a means to find a number x such that $b + x = a$. To *subtract* the number

(c, d) from the number (a, b) means to determine a complex number (x, y) such that $(c, d) + (x, y) = (a, b)$. It may be easily verified that $x = a - c$ and $y = b - d$ will satisfy this equation, and so subtraction is always possible. In particular, $(a, b) - (a, b) = (0, 0)$ and, since $(a, b) + (0, 0) = (a, b)$, the number $(0, 0)$ plays a role in complex number operations similar to that played by 0 in connection with real numbers. Similarly, to *divide* a by $b (\neq 0)$ means to find a number x such that $a = bx$. Thus, to *divide* the complex number (a, b) by the number $(c, d)[\neq (0, 0)]$, we must find a complex number (x, y) such that $(c, d)(x, y) = (a, b)$. It may be

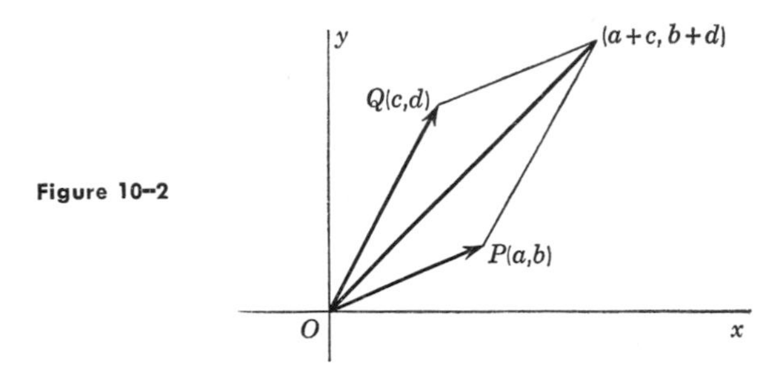

Figure 10–2

checked that $x = (ac + bd)/(c^2 + d^2)$ and $y = (bc - ad)/(c^2 + d^2)$ will satisfy the equation, so that division is always possible except when $c^2 + d^2 = 0$, i.e., when the divisor is $(0, 0)$. We thus see that the set of complex numbers is closed under the operations of addition, subtraction, multiplication, and division, except for division by $(0, 0)$. In the following section we shall see that the set of complex numbers contains a subset which operates just like the real numbers, and if we identify the real numbers with this subset we may regard the complex numbers as a satisfactory extension of $R^\#$.

Finally, we note that the rule, which we have given for the addition of two complex numbers, is the algebraic equivalent of the "parallelogram law" for the addition of two vectors. Thus, if we identify the vectors OP and OQ in Figure 10–2 with the complex numbers (a, b) and (c, d), respectively, the complex number $(a, b) + (c, d) = (a + c, b + d)$ may be identified with the diagonal of the parallelogram which has the vectors OP and OQ for two adjacent sides.

ILLUSTRATION 1. Verify the commutative law of addition for complex numbers.

Solution. We wish to show that $(a, b) + (c, d) = (c, d) + (a, b)$. The rule for addition gives $(a, b) + (c, d) = (a + c, b + d)$ and $(c, d) + (a, b) = (c + a, d + b)$. But $a + c = c + a$ and $b + d = d + b$, since real numbers satisfy the commutative law of addition, and so it follows from the definition of equality that the above sums are equal.

ILLUSTRATION 2. Subtract the complex number (2, 5) from the complex number (4, 1).

Solution. The rule, that we developed for subtraction, gives us the number $(4 - 2, 1 - 5)$ or $(2, -4)$. Since $(2, 5) + (2, -4) = (2 + 2, 5 - 4) = (4, 1)$, by the rule of addition, the subtraction is verified.

ILLUSTRATION 3. Divide the complex number (2, 5) by the complex number (4, 1).

Solution. If we put $(a, b) = (2, 5)$ and $(c, d) = (4, 1)$ in the rule for division that we developed, we find that the quotient is (x, y) where $x = (ac + bd)/(c^2 + d^2) = (8 + 5)/(16 + 1) = 13/17$ and $y = (bc - ad)/(c^2 + d^2) = (20 - 2)/17 = 18/17$. The desired quotient is then $(13/17, 18/17)$, which result may be immediately verified by multiplication as follows: $(4, 1)(13/17, 18/17) = (52/17 - 18/17, 72/17 + 13/17) = (34/17, 85/17) = (2, 5)$.

PROBLEM SET 10.1

1. Find the sum of the following complex numbers: (*a*) (2, 5), (4, 6), (7, 2), (8, 0); (*b*) (4, 2), (0, 5), (−4, −2), (4, −3); (*c*) (1, −1), (2, 3), (4, −5), (5, −5).
2. Subtract the first complex number from the second, in each of the following pairs of complex numbers: (*a*) (2, −4), (6, 8); (*b*) (−4, 9), (3, 4); (*c*) (−2, −6), (5, −5).
3. Find the product of the complex numbers, in each of the following pairs of complex numbers: (*a*) (3, 6), (−4, 5); (*b*) (3, 7), (−2, 4); (*c*) (3, −4), (−4, 5).
4. Use the formula for division to divide the first number by the second, in each of the following pairs of complex numbers: (*a*) (3, −5), (2, 7); (*b*) (5, −3), (−2, 7); (*c*) (4, −6), (2, 9).
5. Verify the commutative law of multiplication for complex numbers.
6. Verify the associative law of multiplication for complex numbers.
7. Verify the distributive law for complex numbers.
8. Represent each of the complex numbers in Problem 2 as a directed line segment, and use the parallelogram law to find the sum of each pair of numbers. Check your results by complex addition.

10.2 The Normal or Rectangular Form of a Complex Number

The student may be a little confused, at this point, by the fact that we have previously identified an ordered pair of real numbers with an *element of a relation* in $R^{\#}$, whereas we have now defined such an ordered pair as a *complex number*. Actually, there is no contradiction here, for we are merely using the geometry of the situation to extend the previously established correspondence between real numbers and the points of a line, considered as an algebraic scale. Thus, the arithmetic correspondent of a point on such a scale is a real number, designated by a familiar symbol, but it is only after we define the operations of addition and multiplication on these "numbers" that we obtain the *real number system.* In a similar way, we have set up a correspondence between the points of a plane and the set of all ordered pairs of real numbers, in such a way that the point with abscissa a and ordinate b will correspond to the ordered pair (a, b); but it is only after we have defined addition and multiplication in this set of pairs, that we may properly regard them as designating complex *numbers*, and members of the *complex number system.* Thus, a set of ordered pairs may define a relation in $R^{\#}$; but, at the same time, if we are to be concerned with arithmetic operations, we may regard these same ordered pairs as complex numbers. We are not concerned with any arithmetic structure in a study of relations, though this is very important in a study of a number system.

Returning now to the system of complex numbers, the definition of addition enables us to express a complex number (a, b) in the form $(a, 0) + (0, b)$. The definition of multiplication makes valid the equality $(0, b) = (b, 0)(0, 1)$, and so $(a, b) = (a, 0) + (b, 0)(0, 1)$; if we represent the complex number $(0, 1)$ by the symbol i, this equation becomes $(a, b) = (a, 0) + (b, 0)i$.

If we apply the four fundamental arithmetic operations—sometimes called *rational* operations—to complex numbers with second member 0, we obtain the following results:

$$(a, 0) + (b, 0) = (a + b, 0); \qquad (a, 0)(b, 0) = (ab, 0);$$

$$(a, 0) - (b, 0) = (a - b, 0); \qquad (a, 0)/(b, 0) = (a/b, 0),\ b \neq 0.$$

It then appears that these operations can be performed by merely effecting the corresponding operations on the first members; in other words, complex numbers with second members 0 behave, with respect to the rational operations, exactly as their first members. As a matter of fact, there would be no change except in symbolism, if we actually replaced each complex number $(a, 0)$ by the real number a; this would, of course, be in complete harmony with the geometric representations of real and complex numbers. We shall agree to do this, in the sequel, and so a complex number (a, b) may be represented in the form $a + bi$.

DEFINITION. The *normal* or *rectangular* form of a complex number (a, b) is $a + bi$. For historical reasons, a is sometimes called the *real* part and b the *imaginary* part of the number, but no significance should be attached to these words.

If we square i, by using the rule for multiplication, we obtain $i^2 = (0, 1)^2 = (0, 1)(0, 1) = (-1, 0)$ which, if we identify the number $(-1, 0)$

with the real number -1, becomes $i^2 = -1$. In performing rational operations on complex numbers in rectangular form, it is now clear that we may treat them as polynomials in i, replacing i^2 by -1 whenever it occurs. Some of the advantages, resulting from the rectangular form of a complex number, will be made apparent by the following illustrations.

ILLUSTRATION 1. Determine the cube of the complex number $(1, -1)$.

Solution. The rectangular form of $(1, -1)$ is $1 - i$. But

$$(1 - i)^2 = 1 - 2i + i^2 = 1 - 2i - 1 = -2i,$$

and so

$$\begin{aligned}(1 - i)^3 &= (-2i)(1 - i) = -2i + 2i^2 \\ &= -2i - 2 = -2 - 2i = (-2, -2).\end{aligned}$$

ILLUSTRATION 2. Reduce the expression $(1 - 3i)/(1 + 2i)$ to a complex number in rectangular form.

Solution. In order to determine the quotient, we multiply numerator and denominator by $1 - 2i$. Thus

$$\frac{(1 - 3i)}{(1 + 2i)} = \frac{(1 - 3i)(1 - 2i)}{(1 + 2i)(1 - 2i)} = \frac{1 - 5i + 6i^2}{1 - 4i^2} = \frac{-5 - 5i}{5} = -1 - i.$$

Two complex numbers of the form $a + bi$ and $a - bi$ are said to be *conjugates* of each other. The above illustration then shows the procedure for dividing one complex number in rectangular form by another: *multiply both numerator and denominator of the indicated quotient by the conjugate of the denominator, and simplify.* In general we shall find that rational operations on complex numbers are usually carried out with much greater ease, if the numbers are expressed in rectangular form, and so we shall usually write our numbers in this way.

The complex number, which we have labeled i, has the property that $i^2 = -1$, and so i may be considered to be a solution of the equation $x^2 + 1 = 0$. Since this equation was previously unsolvable, the complex numbers are seen to be a useful extension of the real numbers. One might expect that additional types of new numbers would need to be introduced in order to solve a general polynomial equation $ax^n + bx^{n-1} + \cdots + cx + d = 0$, with real coefficients and $a \neq 0$. That any such equation can be solved completely, with the use of complex numbers, follows from the *Fundamental* Theorem of Algebra, which we now state.

THEOREM. Any polynomial equation with real or complex coefficients, has a complex number for a solution.

This theorem was first proven by the great mathematician Gauss in 1799. Since that time, there have been other proofs of the theorem, but they are all quite difficult and beyond the scope of this book. Inasmuch as it is not necessary to introduce new numbers to solve any polynomial equation with complex coefficients, we say that the set of complex numbers is *algebraically closed.*

We make a final remark about the geometrical representation of complex numbers. We have used a Cartesian coordinate system in order to identify the set of complex numbers with the points of a plane; the axis, which contains the points identified with the numbers of the form $(a, 0)$ or a, is frequently referred to as the *axis of reals,* while the axis containing the points identified with the numbers of the form $(0, b)$ or bi is sometimes known as the *pure imaginary axis,* though this name should be used with caution.

PROBLEM SET 10.2

1. Write the following complex numbers in rectangular form: (a) $(2, -6)$; (b) $(-3, 4)$; (c) $(-1, -1)$; (d) $(0, 4)$; (e) $(-3, 0)$.
2. Find the sum of the following complex numbers: (a) $2 - 3i$, $-4 + 2i$; (b) $-4 - 2i$, $3 + 7i$; (c) i, $21 - 8i$; (d) 5, $2i + 4$.
3. In Problem 2, subtract the second number in each pair from the first.
4. Multiply the two numbers in each pair of numbers in Problem 2.
5. Express in the rectangular form of a complex number: (a) $(5 - i)/(2 + i)$; (b) $(3 + 2i)/(1 - 2i)$.
6. Express in the rectangular form of a complex number: (a) $(2 + 2i)(3 - i)/(1 - 3i)$; (b) $(1 - 5i)(2 + i)(5 - 2i)$.
7. Solve each of the following equations for x and y: (a) $(x + yi) + (2 - 2i) = 4 + 5i$; (b) $(x + yi) - (1 - 4i) = 6 - 2i$.
8. Verify that $x^3 = 1$, if $x = -1/2 - (\sqrt{3}/2)i$.
9. Reduce to the rectangular form of a complex number: (a) $\dfrac{(1 + i)}{i} + \dfrac{i}{1 - i}$; (b) $1/i$; (c) $[(1 + i)/\sqrt{2}]^4$.
10. Reduce $[1/2 + (\sqrt{3}/2)i]^3$ to rectangular form of a complex number. (Cf. Problem 8.)
11. Give a geometrical representation of the following complex numbers on a graph: $2 + 3i$, $-3 - 2i$, 5, $-5i$, $10i$, $3 - 4i$, -4, $1 - 2i$.
12. Give a representation of the vectors that are measured by the complex numbers of Problem 11.

10.3 De Moivre's Theorem and the Extraction of Roots

The Fundamental Theorem of Algebra states that every polynomial equation that has complex number coefficients has a complex number for a solution. For example, the equation $x^n - a = 0$, i.e., $x^n = a$, has a solution, which means that there now exists an nth root of any complex number, and in particular of any negative real number. In this section, we shall see how such a root can actually be found, with the help of a theorem due to de Moivre; but first we must describe the *polar* representation of a complex number.

In Figure 10–3, let P be the geometric representation of the complex number z, where $z = (a, b) = a + bi$. The non-negative real number r, where $r = \sqrt{a^2 + b^2}$, is known as the *absolute value* or *modulus* of z, and is sometimes indicated by $|a + bi|$. The measure θ, of any one of the angles between the vector OP and the positive axis of reals, is known as the *argument* or *amplitude* of z, sometimes indicated by arg z. While degree measure may be used, we shall always use radian measure for angles in this connection. If $\pi/4$ is the smallest positive argument of a complex number z, a more general argument could be written as $\pi/4 + 2k\pi$, for any integer k; however, unless there is some reason for doing otherwise, we shall select an argument for a complex number in the interval $[-2\pi, 2\pi]$. We see from the figure that $a = r \cos \theta$ and $b = r \sin \theta$, and so $z = a + bi = r \cos \theta + (r \sin \theta)i = r(\cos \theta + i \sin \theta)$. This is known as the *polar* representation of the complex number z, and emphasizes the fact that a complex number is a measure of both magnitude and direction.

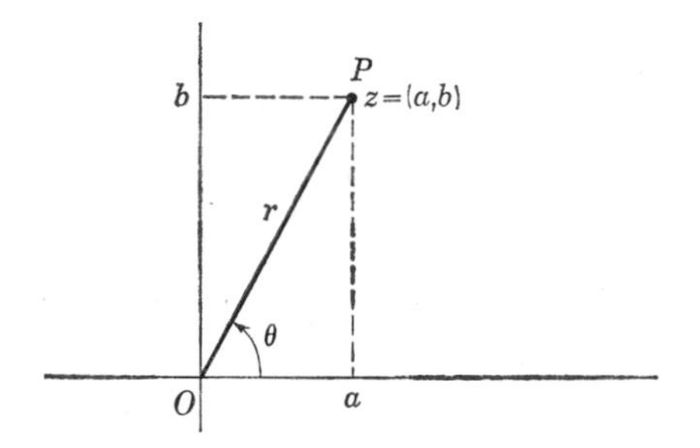

Figure 10–3

While most rational operations can be performed with greater ease, if the complex numbers are in rectangular form, the case of powers is one exception. It will be a notational convenience to abbreviate the polar form $r(\cos \theta + i \sin \theta)$ to r cis θ.

THEOREM 1. The product of two complex numbers, in polar form, may be effected by multiplying their moduli and adding their arguments, i.e., $(r_1 \operatorname{cis} \theta_1)(r_2 \operatorname{cis} \theta_2) = r_1 r_2 \operatorname{cis} (\theta_1 + \theta_2)$.

Proof. $(r_1 \operatorname{cis} \theta_1)(r_2 \operatorname{cis} \theta_2)$

$$= r_1 r_2 \operatorname{cis} \theta_1 \operatorname{cis} \theta_2$$
$$= r_1 r_2 (\cos \theta_1 + i \sin \theta_1)(\cos \theta_2 + i \sin \theta_2)$$
$$= r_1 r_2 (\cos \theta_1 \cos \theta_2 - \sin \theta_1 \sin \theta_2) + i(\sin \theta_1 \cos \theta_2 + \cos \theta_1 \sin \theta_2)$$
$$= r_1 r_2 [\cos (\theta_1 + \theta_2) + i \sin (\theta_1 + \theta_2)]$$
$$= r_1 r_2 \operatorname{cis} (\theta_1 + \theta_2), \text{ as desired.}$$

It follows from the above theorem that, if $z = r \text{ cis } \theta$, then $z^n = r^n \text{ cis } n\theta$, for any natural number n. Although the preceding study requires that n be a natural number, it can be shown that the result remains valid for *any real number* n, and this constitutes the theorem of de Moivre.

THEOREM 2 (DE MOIVRE). $(r \text{ cis } \theta)^n = r^n \text{ cis } n\theta$, for any real number n.

The proof which we gave for Theorem 1 remains valid if θ_2 is negative, and an application of the theorem to this case gives us the rule for division of complex numbers in polar form.

THEOREM 3. The quotient of two complex numbers, in polar form, may be effected by dividing their moduli and subtracting their arguments, i.e., $(r_1 \text{ cis } \theta_1)/(r_2 \text{ cis } \theta_2) = (r_1/r_2) \text{ cis } (\theta_1 - \theta_2)$.

Proof.

$$\frac{r_1 \text{ cis } \theta_1}{r_2 \text{ cis } \theta_2} = \frac{r_1 \text{ cis } \theta_1}{r_2 \text{ cis } \theta_2} \cdot \frac{\text{cis } (-\theta_2)}{\text{cis } (-\theta_2)} = \frac{r_1 \text{ cis } (\theta_1 - \theta_2)}{r_2 \text{ cis } 0}.$$

Since $\text{cis } 0 = \cos 0 + i \sin 0 = 1 + 0 = 1$, the above expression is equal to $(r_1/r_2) \text{ cis } (\theta_1 - \theta_2)$, as desired. In the statement and proof of this theorem, we are assuming, of course, that $r_2 \neq 0$.

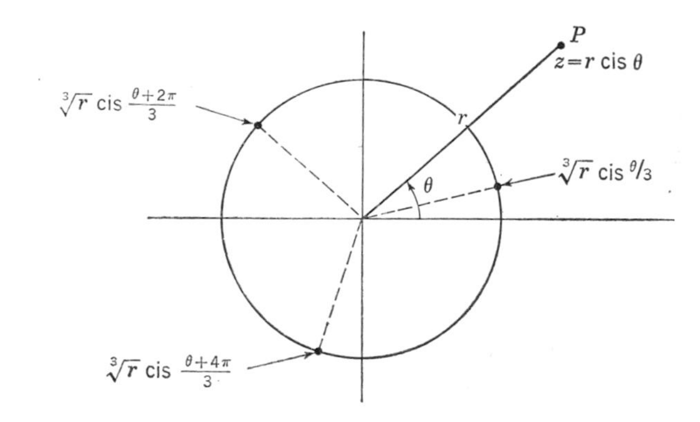

Figure 10–4

We now use de Moivre's theorem to find the nth roots of any complex number z. Suppose that a geometric representation of z, with $z = r \text{ cis } \theta$, be the point P in Figure 10–4. If $s \text{ cis } \alpha$ is an nth root of z, it follows that $(s \text{ cis } \alpha)^n = s^n \text{ cis } n\alpha = z$. By our earlier agreement, θ is in the interval $[-2\pi, 2\pi]$, and $\arg z$ could be $\theta + 2k\pi$, for any integer k. Thus, $s^n = r$ and $n\alpha = \theta + 2k\pi$, i.e., $s = \sqrt[n]{r}$ and $\alpha = \dfrac{\theta + 2k\pi}{n}$, for any integer k. The n complex numbers, obtained from $\sqrt[n]{r} \text{ cis } \dfrac{(\theta + 2k\pi)}{n}$ by putting $k = 0, 1, 2, \cdots, n - 1$ are all distinct, and are nth roots of z, but any other integer substituted for k will result in repetitions of those previously obtained. We shall see later that this set of solutions is the complete *solution set* of the equation $x^n - z = 0$, and so contains all the nth roots of z. From a point of view of geometry, these n nth roots correspond to n points equally spaced around a circle, the radii of which are $\sqrt[n]{r}$ units in length. This is illustrated in Figure 10–4, with $n = 3$.

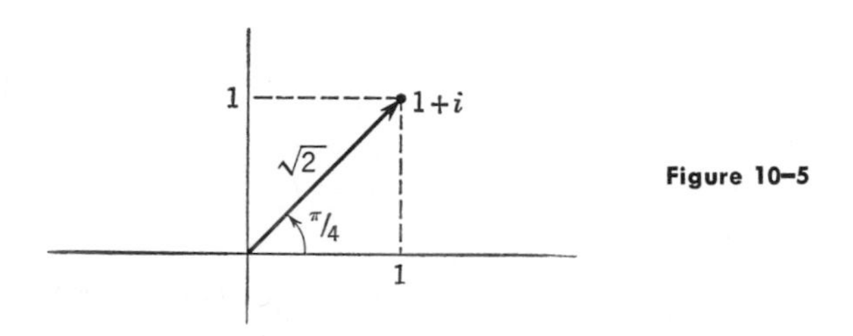

Figure 10–5

ILLUSTRATION 1. Determine the complex number $(1 + i)^5$.

Solution. The polar form of $1 + i$, as shown in Figure 10–5, is seen to be $\sqrt{2}\text{ cis }\pi/4$. Thus $(1 + i)^5 = (\sqrt{2}\text{ cis }\pi/4)^5 = 4\sqrt{2}\text{ cis }5\pi/4 = 4\sqrt{2}\,[-1/\sqrt{2} - (1/\sqrt{2})i] = -4 - 4i$.

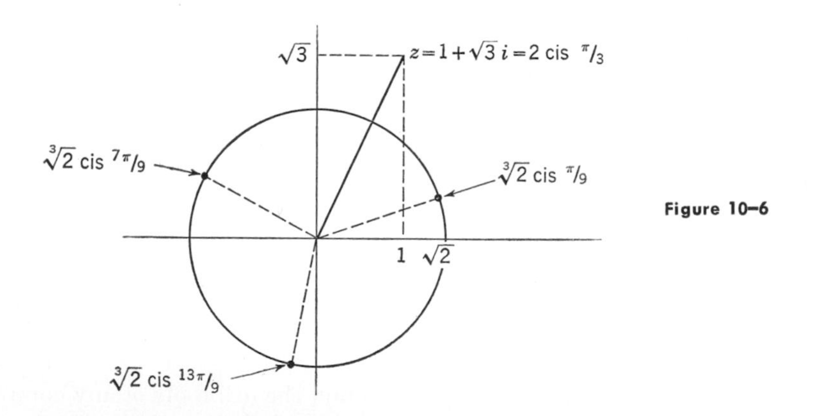

Figure 10–6

ILLUSTRATION 2. Find the three cube roots of $1 + \sqrt{3}\,i$.

Solution. The number $1 + \sqrt{3}\,i$ is represented geometrically in Figure 10–6, and its polar form is seen to be $2\text{ cis }\pi/3$ or, more generally, $2\text{ cis }(\pi/3 + 2k\pi)$ for any integer k. An application of de Moivre's theorem then gives the three cube roots of $1 + \sqrt{3}\,i$ as $\sqrt[3]{2}\text{ cis }\dfrac{(\pi/3 + 2k\pi)}{3}$, with $k = 0, 1, 2$, i.e., $\sqrt[3]{2}\text{ cis }\pi/9$, $\sqrt[3]{2}\text{ cis }7\pi/9$, and $\sqrt[3]{2}\text{ cis }13\pi/9$. With the help of Table 2, these roots may be approximated by $\sqrt[3]{2}\,(0.9397 + 0.3420i)$,

$\sqrt[3]{2}\,(-0.7660 + 0.6428i)$ and $\sqrt[3]{2}\,(-0.1736 - 0.9848i)$, i.e., by $1.1839 + 0.4309i$, $-0.9651 + 0.8099i$, and $-0.2187 - 1.2408i$. They are represented geometrically in Figure 10–6.

ILLUSTRATION 3. Find the cube roots of -1.

Solution. The number -1 can be written as a complex number in polar form as $1 \cdot \text{cis}\,\pi$ or, more generally, as $\text{cis}\,(\pi + 2k\pi)$, i.e., $\text{cis}\,(2k + 1)\pi$, for any integer k. An application of de Moivre's theorem then

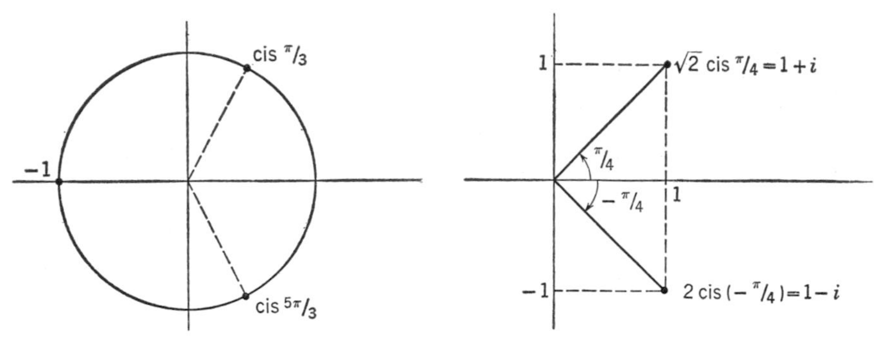

Figure 10–7

Figure 10–8

gives us the three desired cube roots: $\text{cis}\,\pi/3$, $\text{cis}\,\pi$, $\text{cis}\,5\pi/3$. The rectangular forms of the three cube roots of -1, as shown in Figure 10–7, are then $\sqrt{3}/2 + i/2$, -1, and $\sqrt{3}/2 - i/2$.

ILLUSTRATION 4. Simplify $(1 + i)^4/(1 - i)$.

Solution. With the help of Figure 10–8, this expression can be written as $(\sqrt{2}\,\text{cis}\,\pi/4)^4/(\sqrt{2}\,\text{cis}\,(-\pi/4))$, by using polar representations of the numbers. An application of de Moivre's theorem, and the rule for division given in Theorem 3, yields $(4\,\text{cis}\,\pi)/(\sqrt{2}\,\text{cis}\,(-\pi/4))$ or $2\sqrt{2}\,\text{cis}\,5\pi/4$ as a simple polar form of the expression. But then, $(1 + i)^4/(1 - i) = 2\sqrt{2}\,(-1/\sqrt{2} - i/\sqrt{2}) = -2 - 2i$, the simplest form of the expression.

PROBLEM SET 10.3

1. Express each of the following complex numbers in rectangular form: $(2, -5)$; $(-4, 5)$; $(-1, -1)$; $(4, -6)$; $(1, -1)$.
2. Express each of the following complex numbers in polar form: $(1, 1)$; $(-1, 1)$; $(1, \sqrt{3})$; $(-1, -\sqrt{3})$; $(\sqrt{3}, -1)$; $(-2, -2)$.
3. Use Table 2 to express each of the following complex numbers in polar form: $(2, 3)$; $(-3, -1)$; $(4, -2)$; $(-3, -3)$.

4. Simplify each of the following expressions to represent a complex number in polar form: (*a*) $(2 \text{ cis } 11\pi/36)(4 \text{ cis } 5\pi/12)$; (*b*) $\dfrac{(4 \text{ cis } 7\pi/12)(\text{cis } \pi/2)}{(2 \text{ cis } 5\pi/12)}$; (*c*) $(5 \text{ cis } 5\pi/4)/(10 \text{ cis } 4\pi/3)^2$; (*d*) $(2 \text{ cis } \pi/12)^4$.

5. Simplify each of the following expressions to represent a complex number in polar form: (*a*) $(5 \text{ cis } 3)^5$; (*b*) $(4 \text{ cis } 2.5)^3/(2 \text{ cis } 0.8)$; (*c*) $(10 \text{ cis } 0.78)^4$.

6. Simplify each of the following expressions to represent a complex number in polar form: (*a*) $(1 + i)^3/(2 - 2i)$; (*b*) $(\sqrt{3} + i)^2(1 - i)$; (*c*) $(2 - 2i)^5$.

7. Find the three cube roots of 1, and locate them on a graph.

8. Find the three cube roots of $8 \text{ cis } 3\pi/2$, and show this number and its cube roots on a graph.

9. Find four complex numbers that are solutions of the equation $x^4 - 1 = 0$.

10. Find the four 4th roots of i, and locate all five numbers on a graph.

11. Use de Moivre's theorem to simplify $(\sqrt{3} + i)^8$.

12. Simplify the following expression to represent a complex number in rectangular form: $(1 - 2i)^4/(1 - i)^{10}$.

Note. If Z_1 and Z_2 are the respective measures of impedance of the two branches of a parallel electric circuit, the corresponding measure Z of the total impedance is given by $Z = (Z_1Z_2)/(Z_1 + Z_2)$. The ohm-measure of impedance of a capacitance of C farads to an alternating current of frequency f cycles per second is $[1/(2\pi fC)] \text{ cis } (-\pi/2)$; the corresponding measure of impedance of an inductance of L henries is $2\pi fL \text{ cis } \pi/2$.

13.* Refer to the above note, and determine the impedance of the circuit shown in the diagram, assuming a current frequency of 995 kc.

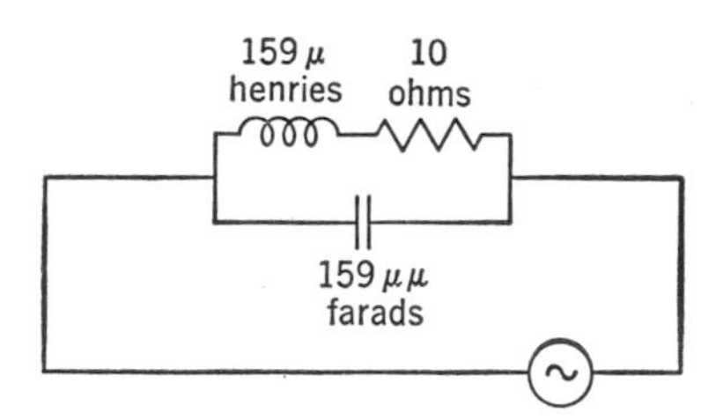

14.* Refer to the above note, and determine the impedance of the circuit shown in the diagram, assuming a current frequency of 92.5 kc.

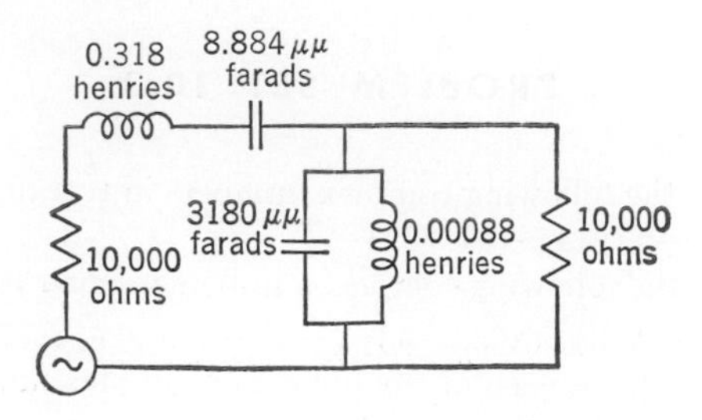

10.4 Polynomial Equations

If we include with the rational operations of addition, subtraction, multiplication, and division, the operation of root extraction, we have what are called the *algebraic operations* of a number system. We have seen that it is now possible to perform all of these operations in the set of complex numbers, except for division by 0. Sometimes it is necessary to perform some of these operations, with one of the complex numbers unspecified, and the result is an *algebraic expression.* The usual symbol for an unspecified complex number is x, and examples of algebraic expressions are then $1 + 2x$, $\sqrt{2 + x}$, $(1 - x)/(2 + x)$, and $[(1 - i)x^2 + 1]/(2 + ix^3)$; some examples of non-algebraic expressions are 2^{x+1}, $\sin(1 - x)$, and $\ln(2 + x)$, where we are assuming here, that x is a real number, though this restriction is removed in more advanced courses. A special type of algebraic expression is a polynomial in x, which was introduced in an earlier chapter; however, it should be understood that the coefficients and x are now permitted to be complex numbers and not necessarily real. A polynomial in x can always be written in the form $a_0x^n + a_1x^{n-1} + a_2x^{n-2} + \cdots + a_{n-1}x + a_n$, where we have made an obvious extension of indexing procedure for the coefficients, in order to conform with the usual practice. The *degree* of the polynomial is the highest exponent of x, which occurs among all the non-zero terms; the previous definition of a polynomial requires, of course, that the degree of any polynomial is a positive integer.

If two algebraic expressions involving x are equated, the number x is usually no longer arbitrary, but must be one of the members of the *solution set* of the equation. Under these circumstances, x is often referred to as the "unknown" of the equation, and a determination of the solution set of the equation is known as *solving* the equation. We have often had occasion to refer to simple cases of such solutions, in earlier portions of the book. It must be emphasized that we must know the nature of the "unknown" number x, before attempting a solution of an equation in x. For example, the equation $3x = 7$ has no solution if x is to be an integer, but it has one solution if x is rational. We shall continue to use the notation of $P[x]$, introduced in Chapter 8 for a polynomial in x, and the remainder of this chapter will be concerned, principally, with matters pertinent to a solution of a polynomial equation $P[x] = 0$, with complex number coefficients. We recall, in passing, that a polynomial function is a function f, defined on its domain by $f(x) = P[x]$, for some polynomial $P[x]$; and x is a solution of the polynomial equation $P[x] = 0$, if and only if $f(x) = 0$. We begin our study of the solution of polynomial equations in the complex number system, with a brief discussion of equations of the first and second degree.

FIRST DEGREE OR LINEAR EQUATIONS. Any linear equation may be written in the form $ax + b = 0$, where $a \neq 0$, and the only solution of this equation is $x = -b/a$.

SECOND DEGREE OR QUADRATIC EQUATIONS. Any quadratic equation may be written in the form $ax^2 + bx + c = 0$, with $a \neq 0$, and the general solution of this equation is probably familiar to the student. However, we review the procedure. On dividing each term of the left member by a $(\neq 0)$, and adding $-c/a$ to both members, the equation becomes $x^2 + (b/a)x = -c/a$. If we now add $b^2/(4a^2)$ to both members, so that the left member is a perfect square, we obtain $x^2 + (b/a)x + b^2/(4a^2) = -c/a + b^2/(4a^2)$, i.e., $[x + b/(2a)]^2 = (b^2 - 4ac)/(4a^2) = D/(4a^2)$, where $D = b^2 - 4ac$ is known as the *discriminant* of the equation. Any one of four possible cases can now arise.

(*a*) If $D = 0$, $[x + b/(2a)]^2 = 0$ and $x = -b/(2a)$. The solution set contains the single number $-b/(2a)$, in this case.

(*b*) If D is *real* and *positive*, the symbol $\sqrt{D}$ is defined, and so $x + b/(2a) = \pm\sqrt{D}/(2a)$, from which we obtain $x = (-b \pm \sqrt{D})/2a$. In this case, the solution set contains the two numbers $(-b + \sqrt{D})/2a$ and $(-b - \sqrt{D})/2a$, and no others.

(*c*) If D is real and negative, we can write $D = -d$ with $d > 0$. An application of de Moivre's theorem then yields the two square roots of D as $\sqrt{d}\,i$ and $-\sqrt{d}\,i$, and so $x + b/(2a) = \pm\sqrt{d}\,i/2a$, whence $x = (-b \pm \sqrt{d}\,i)/2a$. The solution set contains, in this case, the numbers $(-b + \sqrt{d}\,i)/2a$ and $(-b - \sqrt{d}\,i)/2a$.

(*d*) If D is a non-real complex number, the two square roots of D may be obtained by de Moivre's theorem, and the equation thereby solved. If we designate one of these roots by $\sqrt{D}$, the other root will be $-\sqrt{D}$, and so $x = (-b \pm \sqrt{D})/2a$, the two members of the solution set.

The type of quadratic equation of particular interest to us is that in which the coefficients are real numbers. For such an equation, the character of the solution set depends entirely on the nature of the discriminant, as follows: if $D = 0$, there is only one solution and this is real; if $D > 0$, there are two real solutions; if $D < 0$, there are two non-real solutions.

The above results show that, in the case of linear or quadratic equations, it is possible to exhibit a *formula* for the complete solution of such an equation, this formula involving only the coefficients of the original equation. It is also possible to exhibit this type of solution for any third (cubic) or fourth (quartic) degree equation, but we shall not discuss this matter further. The solution of equations of degree 5 and higher present new difficulties, and it can be shown by methods of more advanced mathematics that it is impossible to determine the solutions of such an equation, using only a finite number of algebraic operations; in other words, no solution formula exists. We shall see later, however, that it is possible to obtain *approximate* solutions of *any* polynomial equation, with any desired degree of accuracy. We now present three theorems which will be very useful in a determination of the solution sets of many polynomial equations.

THEOREM 1 (REMAINDER THEOREM). If a polynomial $P[x]$ is divided by $x - r$, for any complex number r, until a remainder R that is free of x is obtained, then $R = P[r]$.

Proof. The definition of division implies that $P[x] = (x - r)Q[x] + R$, for some polynomial $Q[x]$, and remainder R free of x. This equation is valid for any number x, and in particular it is valid if $x = r$. On substitution of r for x, we then obtain $P[r] = R$.

ILLUSTRATION 1. If $P[x] = 4x^4 + 2x^2 - 3x + 2$, use the Remainder Theorem to determine the remainder when $P[x]$ is divided by $x + 1$.

Solution. In this case, $r = -1$, and the Remainder Theorem yields the remainder as $P[-1]$, i.e., $4(1) + 2(1) - 3(-1) + 2$ or 11. This result may be verified by actual division.

THEOREM 2 (FACTOR THEOREM). If r is a solution of $P[x] = 0$, then $x - r$ is a factor of $P[x]$.

Proof. The statement that r is a solution of $P[x] = 0$ means that $P[r] = 0$; and the Remainder Theorem implies that the remainder is 0 if $P[x]$ is divided by $x - r$. Thus, $P[x] = (x - r)Q[x]$, for some polynomial $Q[x]$, and so $x - r$ is a factor of $P[x]$.

THEOREM 3. The solution set of a polynomial equation of degree n contains s complex numbers, with $s \leq n$; if n_i is the multiplicity of the solution r_i, $\sum_{i=1}^{s} n_i = n$.

Proof. The Fundamental Theorem of Algebra asserts that a polynomial equation $P[x] = 0$ has a complex number r_1 for a solution. If $P[x]$ has degree n, the Factor Theorem implies that $P[x] = (x - r_1)Q_1[x]$, with $Q_1[x]$ a polynomial of degree $n - 1$. The Fundamental Theorem, applied to the equation $Q_1[x] = 0$, asserts that some complex number r_2 is a solution of this equation and so $Q_1[x] = (x - r_2)Q_2[x]$, with $Q_2[x]$ a polynomial of degree $n - 2$. But then $P[x] = (x - r_1)(x - r_2)Q_2[x]$. We now continue this process as long as possible, but it must stop after we have produced n factors of $P[x]$, otherwise its degree would exceed n. Thus, $P[x] = (x - r_1)(x - r_2)\cdots(x - r_n)a_0$, for n complex numbers $r_1, r_2, \cdots, r_n$, while the number a_0 must be the leading coefficient of $P[x]$, i.e., the coefficient of x^n. Of course, the numbers $r_1, r_2, \cdots, r_n$ are possibly not all distinct, but if there are s distinct solutions, it is clear that $s \leq n$. Furthermore, the manner in which the solutions were produced requires that if n_i is the number of times that r_i occurred, i.e., its multiplicity, we must have $\sum_{i=1}^{s} n_i = n$.

ILLUSTRATION 2. Find a polynomial equation of degree 3, with solution set $\{1, -2, 3\}$.

Solution. The Factor Theorem implies that $x - 1$, $x + 2$, and $x - 3$ are factors of the desired $P[x]$, and Theorem 3 does not permit any more factors of the form $x - r$. Thus, $P[x] = a_0(x - 1)(x + 2)(x - 3)$, for any number $a_0 \neq 0$; in particular, if $a_0 = 1$, $(x - 1)(x + 2)(x - 3) = 0$ or $x^3 - 2x^2 - 5x + 6 = 0$ is a satisfactory equation.

It is an important result of one of the Cancellation Laws of our Basic Laws of Arithmetic, that the product of any two complex numbers is 0 *only if* at least one of them is 0. This leads to a converse of the Factor Theorem, and provides us with one of our principal tools for solving a polynomial equation. Thus, a solution of any equation, resulting from setting any one of the factors of $P[x]$ equal to 0, is a solution of $P[x] = 0$, and Theorem 3 asserts that there are no more. We thus have the following result: The solution set of a polynomial equation is the union of the solution sets of the equations resulting by setting the various factors of the original polynomial equal to 0.

ILLUSTRATION 3. Determine the solution set of $(x + 1)(x - 2)(x^2 + 1) = 0$.

Solution. The above result shows that the desired solution set is the union of the solution sets of $x + 1 = 0$, $x - 2 = 0$, and $x^2 + 1 = 0$, and so is the set $\{-1, 2, i, -i\}$.

PROBLEM SET 10.4

1. If x is any complex number, identify each of the following expressions as rational, algebraic, or non-algebraic: (*a*) $1/2$; (*b*) $3/\sqrt{x - 1}$; (*c*) 4^x; (*d*) $(x - 2)/(x + 1)$; (*e*) x^x; (*f*) $(3 + x)^{1/3}$; (*g*) $\tan 2/x$; (*h*) $(1 + x + x^2)/(x - 3)$.
2. Write each of the following expressions as a polynomial in x: (*a*) $(x - 2)(x^2 + x - 1)$; (*b*) $(ix + 2)(ix^2 - x + 2)$; (*c*) $(x + 2)[(1 + i)x^2 - ix + 4]$; (*d*) $(x^2 + 1)(x^3 - 2) + (1 - i)x^2 + 5$.
3. Give the degree of each of the following polynomials: (*a*) $3x^5 - 2x^2 + 5$; (*b*) $4x^2 - 3x + 1$; (*c*) $(1 - i)x^3 - ix + 2$.
4. If equations are formed by setting each of the polynomials in Problem 3 separately equal to 0, state the number of complex numbers in the solution set of each question, assuming no repeated solutions.
5. Determine the polynomial equation, with lowest degree and leading coefficient 1, having the following solution set: (*a*) $\{2, -5, 3\}$; (*b*) $\{0, -1, 1, 2\}$; (*c*) $\{1, i, -i\}$; (*d*) $\{0, 1 + i, 1 - i\}$; (*e*) $\{i, -1, 1 + i\}$; (*f*) $\{2 + i\}$.
6. Find the polynomial equation with leading coefficient 1, having solution set (*a*) $\{0, -2, 2\}$, with 0 a solution of multiplicity 2; (*b*) $\{1, -3\}$, with 1 a

solution of multiplicity 3; (*c*) $\{i, -1\}$, with i a solution of multiplicity 3; (*d*) $\{1 + i, i\}$, with $1 + i$ a solution of multiplicity 2.

7. If $P[x] = 3x^3 - 2x^2 + x - 1$, use the Remainder Theorem to find (*a*) $P[0]$; (*b*) $P[-1]$; (*c*) $P[2]$; (*d*) $P[-i]$; (*e*) $P[1 - i]$.
8. If $P[x] = 4x^4 + x^2 - 2$, use the Remainder Theorem to find (*a*) $P[-1]$; (*b*) $P[3]$; (*c*) $P[i]$; (*d*) $P[-i/2]$.
9. Determine the solution set of each of the following equations, assuming that x is either real or complex: (*a*) $(x - 2)(x + 4)(x - 3) = 0$; (*b*) $(x + 2)(x - 6)(x - 4)(x - 4) = 0$; (*c*) $x^2(x - 3)^2(x^2 + x - 1) = 0$; (*d*) $(x - 2)^3(x + 1)(x^2 - x + 2) = 0$.
10. Find the discriminant D of each of the following equations: (*a*) $3x^2 - 2x + 5 = 0$; (*b*) $2x^2 + 5x + 2 = 0$; (*c*) $2x^2 - 4x + 8 = 0$; (*d*) $ix^2 - (1 + i)x + 1 = 0$; (*e*) $x^2 + (2 + i)x - 1 = 0$; (*f*) $x^2 + 10x - 25 = 0$.
11. Use the discriminants in Problem 10 to determine the nature of the solutions of each quadratic equation listed there, assuming that x is either real or complex.
12. Determine the solution set of each of the following quadratic equations, expressing the non-real solutions in rectangular form: (*a*) $3x^2 - 2x + 5 = 0$; (*b*) $2x^2 + 5x - 1 = 0$; (*c*) $x^2 - 4x + 2 = 0$.
13. Determine the solution set of each of the following equations, expressing each non-real solution in rectangular form: (*a*) $x^2 - (1 + \sqrt{3}\, i) = 0$; (*b*) $2x^2 - ix + (2 - i) = 0$; (*c*) $ix^2 + (1 - 2i)x - (1 - i) = 0$; (*d*) $x^2 + (1 - 2i)x - i = 0$.

10.5 Real Polynomial Equations

We have already indicated that the problem of determining the solution set of a polynomial equation is, in general, quite complicated. For the remainder of this chapter, we shall confine our attention to polynomial equations with *real number* coefficients, i.e., real polynomial equations, though even this does not simplify the problem very much.

It is, of course, possible that every real number is a solution of an equation, and the equation is then an *identity*, as defined in Chapter 7. For example, the equation $(x + 1)^2 = x^2 + 2x + 1$ is an identity, since it is a valid equality regardless of the number x.

THEOREM 1. If a real polynomial equation of degree n has more than n solutions, the total coefficient of each power of x is 0.

Proof. Let the polynomial equation be denoted by $P[x] = a_0x^n + a_1x^{n-1} + a_2x^{n-2} + \cdots + a_{n-1}x + a_n = 0$. We know from a previous result that this equation has n solutions, which we may represent by $r_1, r_2, r_3, \cdots, r_n$, and the Factor Theorem allows us to express the equation in the form $a_0(x - r_1)(x - r_2)(x - r_3)\cdots(x - r_n) = 0$, where $a_0 \in R^{\#}$. If c is a solution of $P[x] = 0$, with $c \neq r_i$, $i = 1, 2, \cdots, n$, then $a_0(c - r_1)(c - r_2)(c - r_3)\cdots(c - r_n) = 0$ and so $a_0 = 0$. But then $P[x]$ has the form $a_1x^{n-1} + a_2x^{n-2} + \cdots + a_{n-1}x + a_n$, and our hypothesis is that $P[x] = 0$ has more than n—and so more than $n - 1$—solutions. A repetition of the previous argument would now require that $a_1 = 0$, and in a like manner we can show that $a_2 = a_3 = \cdots = a_n = 0$.

ILLUSTRATION 1. Prove that

$$\frac{(x-b)(x-c)}{(a-b)(a-c)} + \frac{(x-c)(x-a)}{(b-c)(b-a)} + \frac{(x-a)(x-b)}{(c-a)(c-b)} = 1$$

is an identity, for distinct but otherwise arbitrary numbers a, b, and c.

Proof. The above equation has degree 2, and it is clear that its solution set contains a, b, and c. It follows from Theorem 1 that each total coefficient in the equation is 0, and so the equation is an identity.

THEOREM 2. If the equation, formed by equating two polynomials of degree n, has more than n solutions, the two polynomials are identical.

Proof. Let the two polynomials be $a_0x^n + a_1x^{n-1} + \cdots + a_{n-1}x + a_n$ and $b_0x^n + b_1x^{n-1} + \cdots + b_{n-1}x + b_n$. Then any number which, when substituted for x reduces both polynomials to the same number, will also be a solution of the equation $(a_0 - b_0)x^n + (a_1 - b_1)x^{n-1} + \cdots + (a_{n-1} - b_{n-1})x + (a_n - b_n) = 0$. But this equation, of apparent degree n, will then have more than n solutions, and by Theorem 1 all of its coefficients must be 0. Thus, $a_0 = b_0, a_1 = b_1, \cdots, a_{n-1} = b_{n-1}, a_n = b_n$, and the polynomials are identical.

ILLUSTRATION 2. Show, without expanding, that the polynomials $(x-1)^2 + 8(x-4)^2$ and $6(x-3)^2 + 3(x-5)^2$ are identically equal.

Solution. If $x = 0$, both polynomials equal 129; if $x = 1$, both polynomials equal 72; and if $x = 2$, both polynomials equal 12. Since the degree of each polynomial is 2, an application of Theorem 2 shows that they are identically equal.

ILLUSTRATION 3. Determine A and B if $7x - 12 = A(4x + 1) + B(x + 3)$ is to be an identity.

Solution. We have seen, by Theorem 2, that the right and left members of this equation are identically equal if they are equal for two distinct substitutions for x. If $x = -3$, $-33 = -11A$ and so $A = 3$; if $x = 0$, $-12 = A + 3B$, i.e., $3B = -15$ and $B = -5$.

The problem of determining the solution set of an equation presents no difficulties if the equation is known to be an identity. However, let us now return to a consideration of equations which are not identities but *conditional* equations. Since we have already seen how to solve any linear or quadratic equation, the solution of any polynomial equation would be available if we could factor the polynomial into linear and quadratic factors. A result of some theoretical interest in this connection is the following theorem.

THEOREM 3. Any real polynomial can be written as the product of real linear and real quadratic factors.

Proof. If $P[x]$ is a real polynomial, we show that if $a + bi$ is a solution of $P[x] = 0$, so is $a - bi$. In order to show this, we first form the quadratic expression $g[x] = (x - a - bi)(x - a + bi) = x^2 - 2ax + a^2 + b^2$. We now divide $P[x]$ by $g[x]$ until a first-degree remainder appears, and we represent this remainder by $rx + s$, so that $P[x] = g[x]\,h[x] + rx + s$ for some real polynomial $h[x]$. Since $a + bi$ is a solution of $P[x] = 0$ and of $g[x] = 0$, replacing x in the preceding equation by $a + bi$ yields $0 = 0 + r(a + bi) + s = 0$, i.e., $ra + s + rbi = 0$. Thus, $ra + s = 0$ and $rb = 0$ whence, since $a + bi$ is a non-real solution with $b \neq 0$, it follows that $r = 0 = s$. The remainder $rx + s$ is then 0, and so $P[x] = g[x]\,h[x]$. We have just shown that the complex conjugate of each solution of a polynomial equation is also a solution, and that a quadratic factor with real coefficients, corresponding to these two solutions, may be factored out of the polynomial; this process can be continued until the remaining polynomial has only real solutions if equated to 0. If these real solutions are r_1, $r_2, \cdots, r_k$, the remaining polynomial may be written, according to the Factor Theorem, as $a_0(x - r_1)(x - r_2)\cdots(x - r_k)$ where $a_0 \in R^{\#}$; and this, combined with the previous result, gives us the complete factorization of $P[x]$ as $a_0(x - r_1)(x - r_2)\cdots(x - r_k)D_1[x]D_2[x]\cdots D_t[x]$, where $D_1[x]$, $D_2[x]$, $\cdots$, $D_t[x]$ are the real quadratic factors.

The above proof contains an important result, which may be conveniently expressed in the following form.

THEOREM 4. Non-real complex solutions occur in pairs in the solution of a real polynomial equation; with each non-real complex solution, there also appears its conjugate.

The above two theorems give us information about the nature of the solutions of a real polynomial equation, but it is clear that they do not help us in a determination of its solution set. Another result of this kind is known as *Descartes' Rule of Signs*. If the terms of a polynomial in x are arranged in order of descending powers of x, we say there is a *variation in sign* whenever two successive terms of the polynomial have opposite signs, all zero terms having been omitted. For example, $3x^5 - 2x^3 - 3x + 5$ has 2 variations in sign, while $2x^4 - 4x^3 - 5x - 1$ has only 1. In more advanced courses, it is then possible to establish the following rule.

DESCARTES' RULE OF SIGNS. The number of positive real solutions of a real polynomial equation $P[x] = 0$ is equal to the number of variations in sign of $P[x]$, or less than this number by a positive even integer.

It should be observed that this result, which we do not attempt to prove, gives information about the *positive* real solutions only, and not precise information even then. However, since $P[r] = P[-(-r)]$, it is clear that r is a negative solution of $P[x] = 0$ if and only if $-r$ is a positive solution of $P[-x] = 0$; thus, we can study the negative solutions of $P[x] = 0$ by an examination of the positive solutions of $P[-x] = 0$.

PROBLEM SET 10.5

1. Establish the identity

$$\frac{(x-b)(x-c)a^2}{(a-b)(a-c)} + \frac{(x-c)(x-a)b^2}{(b-c)(b-a)} + \frac{(x-a)(x-b)c^2}{(c-a)(c-b)} = x^2.$$

2. Establish the following identities, without expanding:
   (*a*) $(x-1)(x-3)(x-5) = (1-x)^3 + 2(x-2)^3 + 2x$;
   (*b*) $4x^2 - x - 39 = 3(x+2)(x-5) - (x-1)(x-5) + 2(x-1)(x+2)$.
3. Establish the following identities, without expanding:
   (*a*) $(1+x)^3 - 3(x+2)^2 = x(x-3)(x+3) - 11$;
   (*b*) $(x+2)(x+1) - (x-1)^2 = 5x + 1$.
4. Determine A, B, and C if the following equations are to be identities:
   (*a*) $(x-2)(x+1) + x^2 = A(x-2)^2 - B(x+2)^2$;
   (*b*) $x^2 + 12x + 2 = A(x-1)(x+1) + B(x+2)(x-1) + C(x-3)$.
5. Determine A, B, C, and D if the following equation is to be an identity:

$$(A-2)x^3 + (B+3)x^2 + Cx - D = 6x^3 + 4x + 5.$$

6. Determine A, B, C, and D if the following equation is to be an identity:

$$Ax^3 + (B-2)x^2 - Cx + D - 1 = 5x^2 + 4x + 2.$$

7. Write an equation having the same degree, the solutions of which are opposite in sign but numerically equal to those of the equation (*a*) $x^3 - 3x^2 + 2x - 1 = 0$; (*b*) $4x^4 + 3x^3 - 5x + 2 = 0$; (*c*) $2x^5 - 5x^2 + 4x - 1 = 0$; (*d*) $3x^3 - 2x^2 + 5x - 6 = 0$.
8. Try to find an equation with solutions numerically equal but opposite in sign to those of (*a*) $4x^4 + 3x^2 - 2 = 0$; (*b*) $x^6 - 3x^4 + 4x^2 - 5 = 0$. What can you say about the solution sets of these equations?
9. Use Descartes' Rule of Signs to obtain information about the real solutions of each equation in Problem 7.
10. Use Descartes' Rule of Signs to obtain information about the real solutions of the equation (*a*) $2x^4 + 3x^2 + 5x + 1 = 0$; (*b*) $x^3 - 2x^2 - 5x - 1 = 0$.
11. Write an equation of degree n, with real coefficients, and having the indicated solutions: (*a*) $n = 2$, $r_1 = 1 - i$; (*b*) $n = 3$, $r_1 = 2$, $r_2 = i$; (*c*) $n = 4$, $r_1 = i - 1$, $r_2 = 2i + 1$; (*d*) $n = 4$, $r_1 = i$, $r_2 = 2 - i$.
12. Write an equation of degree n, with real coefficients, and having the indicated solutions: (*a*) $n = 3$, $r_1 = 2$, $r_2 = 2 - 3i$; (*b*) $n = 5$, $r_1 = 2$, $r_2 = 3$, $r_3 = -1$, $r_4 = i$.
13. Factor $P[x]$ into linear and quadratic factors, with real coefficients, being given that (*a*) $P[x] = 2x^3 + 5x^2 - 2x - 15 = 0$ has $-2 + i$ as a solution; (*b*) $P[x] = x^4 - 20x^2 - 36x + 55 = 0$ has $-3 + \sqrt{2}\,i$ as a solution.

10.6 Synthetic Division

If a polynomial $P[x]$ is divided by a binomial $x - r$, where r is a complex number, the division continuing until a remainder R independent of x

is obtained, we can express the result in the form $P[x] = (x - r)g[x] + R$; the polynomial $g[x]$ has a degree one less than that of $P[x]$. We refer to $P[x]$ as the *dividend*, $(x - r)$ as the *divisor*, $g[x]$ as the *quotient*, and R as the *remainder*. It is possible to abbreviate the process of long division here by omitting all but the essential numbers, and we refer to this abbreviated process as *synthetic division.* While it is possible to apply synthetic division to complex polynomials, we shall restrict our examples to polynomials with integral coefficients. If we wish to divide $3x^5 - 4x^4 - 10x^2 - x + 1$ by $x - 2$, we have arranged the work of the long division below.

$$
\begin{array}{r|rrrrrr|l}
x - 2 & 3x^5 & -\,4x^4 & +\,0x^3 & -\,10x^2 & -\;\;x & +\;\;1 & 3x^4 + 2x^3 + 4x^2 - 2x - 5 \\
 & 3x^5 & -\,6x^4 & & & & & \\ \cline{2-3}
 & & 2x^4 & +\,0x^3 & & & & \\
 & & 2x^4 & -\,4x^3 & & & & \\ \cline{3-4}
 & & & 4x^3 & -\,10x^2 & & & \\
 & & & 4x^3 & -\;\;8x^2 & & & \\ \cline{4-5}
 & & & & -2x^2 & -\;\;x & & \\
 & & & & -2x^2 & +\,4x & & \\ \cline{5-6}
 & & & & & -5x & +\;\;1 & \\
 & & & & & -5x & +\,10 & \\ \cline{6-7}
 & & & & & & -9 &
\end{array}
$$

In the above process, the various powers of x play no important role, except to keep the coefficients in order. If we agree to keep the various coefficients in fixed vertical columns, we may then safely omit the powers of x from the computation. The array of numbers would look as follows.

$$
\begin{array}{r|rrrrrr|rrrrr}
1\ -2 & 3 & -4 & 0 & -10 & -1 & 1 & 3 & 2 & 4 & -2 & -5 \\
 & 3 & -6 & & & & & & & & & \\ \cline{2-3}
 & & 2 & 0 & & & & & & & & \\
 & & 2 & -4 & & & & & & & & \\ \cline{3-4}
 & & & 4 & -10 & & & & & & & \\
 & & & 4 & -8 & & & & & & & \\ \cline{4-5}
 & & & & -2 & -1 & & & & & & \\
 & & & & -2 & 4 & & & & & & \\ \cline{5-6}
 & & & & & -5 & 1 & & & & & \\
 & & & & & -5 & 10 & & & & & \\ \cline{6-7}
 & & & & & & -9 & & & & &
\end{array}
$$

The above array can still be simplified, for there are many needless duplications. For example, two 3's appear in the first column, and this same number also appears as the first entry of the quotient coefficients; there are two 2's in the second column below the first line of subtraction, and this number also appears as the second coefficient of the quotient; and similar remarks may be made of the numbers 4, -2, and -5. If we eliminate all these duplications, writing each of these numbers only once, and "project" the remaining numbers into three lines, the result will be the following:

$1-2$	3	-4	0	-10	-1	1
		-6	-4	-8	4	10
		2	4	-2	-5	-9

The coefficient 1, of the divisor, is always the same and may well be omitted. Also, if we copy down the leading 3 of the dividend to the third line, the numbers on the third line will now be the coefficients of the quotient, in their order of occurrence, followed by the remainder -9. With these two further changes, the computation will look like this:

-2	3	-4	0	-10	-1	1
		-6	-4	-8	4	10
	3	2	4	-2	-5	-9

We notice that any number on the second line may be obtained by multiplying the number immediately preceding it on the third line by -2; and the numbers on the third line may be obtained by subtracting the numbers on the second line from those on the first. Thus, by starting with the first number on the third line—which is merely carried down from the first line—we can alternately produce the successive numbers on the second and third lines. One final change gives us the final process known as *synthetic division:* We replace the coefficient -2 of the divisor by 2, and produce the third line by *adding* the first and second lines instead of subtracting; for it is clear that multiplying by 2 and adding is equivalent to multiplying by -2 and subtracting. The final computation would have the following appearance:

2	3	-4	0	-10	-1	1
		6	4	8	-4	-10
	3	2	4	-2	-5	-9

We must warn that this process of synthetic division requires that the coefficient 0 be assigned to each missing power of x.

ILLUSTRATION 1. Use synthetic division to divide $2x^4 + x - 5$ by $x + 1$.

Solution. In this case, $r = -1$, and the computation may be arranged as shown, wherein care has been taken to write the zero coefficients in their proper places.

-1	2	0	0	1	-5
		-2	2	-2	1
	2	-2	2	-1	-4

The quotient is then $2x^3 - 2x^2 + 2x - 1$, and the remainder is -4.

The synthetic division process gives us an easy method for checking a possible solution of a polynomial equation; for if r is a solution of $P[x] = 0$, the remainder which appears, when $P[x]$ is divided by $x - r$, is 0.

ILLUSTRATION 2. Use synthetic division to show that 3 is a solution of the equation $6x^4 - 23x^3 - 6x^2 + 53x + 30 = 0$.

Solution. The synthetic division process yields the following:

3	6	−23	−6	53	30
		18	−15	−63	−30
	6	−5	−21	−10	0

Since the remainder, the last number on the third line, is 0, the number 3 is a solution.

In our search for the solution set of an equation, it is often helpful if we can assign upper and lower bounds to the real solutions. Our synthetic division process gives us two results which are of value in this connection.

THEOREM 1 (UPPER BOUNDS). If r is a positive real number, such that when a real polynomial $P[x]$ is divided by $x - r$, synthetically, all the numbers on the third line have the same sign or are zero, the number r is an upper bound to the real solutions of the equation $P[x] = 0$, i.e., r exceeds all solutions of the equation.

Proof. Let us write $P[x]$ in the form $(x - r)g[x] + R$, where $g[x]$ is the quotient and R is the remainder when $P[x]$ is divided by $x - r$. The fact that the third line of the synthetic division process has numbers with only one sign implies that both R and $g[x]$ have the same sign for any positive number x. Moreover, if x exceeds r, the number $x - r$ is positive and $P[x]$ will exceed R in absolute value and can not be zero. Thus, each real positive solution must be less than r, and so r is an upper bound to these solutions.

THEOREM 2 (LOWER BOUNDS). If r is a negative real number, such that when a real polynomial $P[x]$ is divided by $x - r$, synthetically, the numbers on the third line alternate in sign, either sign being assigned to 0, the number r is a lower bound to the real solutions of the equation $P[x] = 0$, i.e., all solutions exceed r.

Proof. The proof resembles that of the previous theorem, and depends on the fact that the alternating signs in the third line imply that $g[x]$ and R have opposite signs for any negative number x. If we note that $x - r$ is negative for any number x less than r, it again appears that $|P[x]| > |R|$ and can not be zero. We leave the details of the proof to the student.

ILLUSTRATION 3. Show that -3 is a lower and 5 is an upper bound to the real solutions of the equation $2x^3 - 7x^2 - 10x + 20 = 0$.

Solution. We divide the polynomial, synthetically, by $x + 3$ and $x - 5$, as shown on page 300:

-3	2	-7	-10	20
		-6	39	-87
	2	-13	29	-67

5	2	-7	-10	20
		10	15	25
	2	3	5	45

Since the numbers on the third line of the first computation alternate in sign, and -3 is a negative number, Theorem 2 implies that -3 is a lower bound to the real solutions. Since the numbers on the third line of the second computation are all of the same sign, and we note that 5 is a positive number, Theorem 1 asserts that 5 is an upper bound to the real solutions. There is, of course, nothing unique about these upper and lower bounds, unless we require that they be integers; and even then, this procedure will not always determine them. It might be pointed out that Theorems 1 and 2 provide *sufficient* but *not necessary* conditions for the bounds in question.

PROBLEM SET 10.6

1. Use synthetic division to obtain the quotient and remainder if the polynomial $3x^4 - 2x^2 - 5x + 1$ is divided by (*a*) $x - 2$; (*b*) $x + 2$; (*c*) $x - 5$; (*d*) $x + 5$; (*e*) $x - 3$; (*f*) $x + 3$; (*g*) $x - 1/2$; (*h*) $x + 1/3$.
2. If $P[x] = x^5 - 2x^3 + x^2 - 2$, use synthetic division to determine (*a*) $P[-1]$; (*b*) $P[2]$; (*c*) $P[-3]$; (*d*) $P[1/2]$; (*e*) $P[1.2]$.
3. Show that 4 is greater than any real solution of $x^4 - 3x^3 - 4x^2 + 3x - 7 = 0$.
4. Show that -2 is less than any real solution of the equation in Problem 3.
5. Show that 2 and -3 are solutions of $x^4 + x^3 + 66x^2 + 72x - 432 = 0$, and determine the other solutions.
6. Show that the real solution set of the equation $x^4 - 2x^3 - 9x^2 + 2x + 8 = 0$ is $\{-2, -1, 1, 4\}$. Use synthetic division, and apply the process to *successive* quotients, instead of going back to the original equation each time. Why is this procedure proper?
7. A polynomial function f is defined by $f(x) = x^4 - 8x^2 + 18$, for each x in its domain $R^{\#}$. Use synthetic division to determine $f(a)$, for each integer a between an upper and lower bound of the solutions of the equation $f(x) = 0$. Plot these functional values on a graph, and join the points with a smooth curve.
8. Do the same as in Problem 7, for the function f defined on $R^{\#}$ by $f(x) = 2x - 3x^4 + x^2 - 15x^3$.
9. By trial and error, determine an integral upper and an integral lower bound to the real solutions of the equation (*a*) $x^3 - 3x^2 + 2x - 1 = 0$; (*b*) $3x^5 + 2x^2 - x - 2 = 0$; (*c*) $x^4 - 2x^2 + 4x - 2 = 0$.
10. If $x^2 - 3x + 2$ is divided by $x - r$, the remainder is 2. Determine the possible solutions for r.
11. Use synthetic division to show that if $ax^2 + bx + c$ is divided by $x - 1$ the remainder is $a + b + c$. Does this check with the Remainder Theorem?

12. Fill in the details of the proof of Theorem 2 on lower bounds.
13. Determine k if (*a*) the remainder is 7 when $x^3 + kx^2 - 3x + 7$ is divided by $x - 3$; (*b*) the remainder is -4 if $kx^5 + 9x^2 - 3x - 7$ is divided by $x + 1$.

10.7 Rational Solutions of Rational Polynomial Equations

We have seen in an earlier section, that the Fundamental Theorem of Algebra leads us to the theorem that a polynomial equation of degree n has at least one, but not more than n, distinct complex solutions. Of course, some of these numbers may be real, some may be rational, and some may be integral; if the degree of the equation is odd, however, we are assured of the existence of at least one real solution, since non-real solutions always occur as conjugate pairs. The Fundamental Theorem did not help us to locate any of the solutions of an equation, but we have developed some theorems and techniques in the previous sections which are useful, though not completely adequate for this purpose. The theorem on the factorization of any real polynomial into a product of real linear and quadratic factors might have appeared to have disposed of the problem of solving any polynomial equation, but unfortunately this theorem gave no clues on how this factoring could be accomplished. We now drop the general problem of determining the solution set of an arbitrary polynomial equation, and consider only polynomials with rational coefficients, i.e., rational polynomial equations.

The solution set of an equation is certainly unchanged if both members of the equation are multiplied by the same non-zero number. The coefficients may be expressed as quotients of integers, and if we multiply by the least common multiple of their denominators, the coefficients of the resulting equation will be integers. We may then assume, for the purposes of analysis, that our polynomial equations have integral coefficients. The following theorem is of importance in determining whether an equation has any *rational* solutions.

THEOREM. Let $P[x] = a_0x^n + a_1x^{n-1} + a_2x^{n-2} + \cdots + a_{n-1}x + a_n$, where $a_0, a_1, a_2, \cdots, a_n$ are integers. Then if p/q is a rational solution of $P[x] = 0$, with p/q reduced to lowest terms, p is an integral factor of a_n and q is an integral factor of a_0.

Proof. Since p/q is a solution, we must have $P[p/q] = 0$, i.e.,

$$a_0(p/q)^n + a_1(p/q)^{n-1} + a_2(p/q)^{n-2} + \cdots + a_{n-1}x + a_n = 0.$$

If we multiply both members of this equation by q^n, we obtain

$$a_0p^n + a_1p^{n-1}q + a_2p^{n-2}q^2 + \cdots + a_{n-1}pq^{n-1} + a_nq^n = 0,$$

and this equation may be written in the equivalent form

$$a_0p^n + a_1p^{n-1}q + a_2p^{n-2}q^2 + \cdots + a_{n-1}pq^{n-1} = -a_nq^n.$$

Now p is a factor of the left member of this equation, since it is a factor of each term, and so p must be a factor of the right member. Our assumption regarding the reduced form of p/q does not permit p and q^n to have any common factors, and so p must be a factor of a_n, as asserted. If we write the equation in the equivalent form

$$a_0p^n = -a_1p^{n-1}q - a_2p^{n-2}q^2 - \cdots - a_{n-1}pq^{n-1} - a_nq^n,$$

a similar argument shows that q must be a factor of a_0.

As a result of this theorem, it is possible to determine all numbers which might be rational solutions, from a mere inspection of the first and last coefficients of the equation.

ILLUSTRATION 1. From an inspection of the coefficients, determine a set of rational numbers which will contain all the rational solutions of $4x^5 - 3x^3 + 2x - 6 = 0$.

Solution. In view of the preceding theorem, each rational solution p/q must be such that p divides 6 and q divides 4. The numbers of this kind are: $\pm 6/1$, $\pm 6/2$, $\pm 6/4$, $\pm 3/1$, $\pm 3/2$, $\pm 3/4$, $\pm 2/1$, $\pm 2/2$, $\pm 2/4$, $\pm 1/1$, $\pm 1/2$, $\pm 1/4$. When duplicates are eliminated, the desired set is $\{\pm 1, \pm 2, \pm 3, \pm 6, \pm 1/4, \pm 1/2, \pm 3/4, \pm 3/2\}$.

After we have obtained a set of rational numbers, which contains all the rational solutions of an equation, there remains the problem of actually checking all these possible solutions. Of course, it is possible—and for an arbitrary equation extremely likely—that there will be *no* rational solutions, but each number in the set may be checked by synthetic division. It should be pointed out that if a fraction appears on the third line of the synthetic division process, when checking a rational number as a solution, this number may be rejected immediately.

ILLUSTRATION 2. Determine the rational solutions of the equation $2x^3 - 15x^2 + 10x + 12 = 0$.

Solution. If we use the above theorem, we see that the following set of numbers contains all the rational solutions of the equation:

$$\{\pm 1, \pm 1/2, \pm 3/2, \pm 2, \pm 3, \pm 4, \pm 6, \pm 12\}.$$

If we make a systematic check, we discover that 3/2 is the only rational solution, the computation being shown for this case:

$$\begin{array}{c|rrrr} 3/2 & 2 & -15 & 10 & 12 \\ & & 3 & -18 & -12 \\ \hline & 2 & -12 & -8 & 0 \end{array}$$

The synthetic division shows that $2x^3 - 15x^2 + 10x + 12$ may be written as $(x - 3/2)(2x^2 - 12x - 8)$. The "reduced" equation $2x^2 - 12x - 8 = 0$ is, in this case, quadratic, and the other solutions can be found by the quadratic formula:

$$x = (12 \pm \sqrt{144 + 64})/4 = (12 \pm \sqrt{208})/4 = 3 \pm \sqrt{13}.$$

PROBLEM SET 10.7

1. Determine a set of rational numbers which contains all the rational solutions of (*a*) $2x^4 - 3x^2 + 8 = 0$; (*b*) $3x^3 + 2x^2 - 5 = 0$; (*c*) $2x^5 - 5x^3 + x^2 - 3x + 10 = 0$; (*d*) $x^4 - 2x^2 + 5x - 10 = 0$.
2. What can be said about the rational solutions of an equation that has 1 for its leading coefficient?
3. Determine a set of rational numbers which contains all the rational solutions of (*a*) $2x^3 - 4x^2 + 5x + 1 = 0$; (*b*) $3x^4 + 2x^2 - x - 2 = 0$; (*c*) $5x^3 - 2x^2 + 4 = 0$; (*d*) $x - 2x^2 + x^5 = 0$.
4. (*a*) Determine a set of rational numbers which contains all the rational solutions of $2x^4 + 3x^3 + x^2 + x + 10 = 0$; (*b*) show how Descartes' Rule of Signs can be used to make the set in (*a*) smaller.
5. Use the method of this section to determine any rational solutions of the equation $x^2 - 2 = 0$. Since $\sqrt{2}$ is certainly a solution, comment on the nature of this number.
6. Determine the rational solutions of the following equations, and if the final reduced equation is quadratic, determine the complete solution set: (*a*) $x^3 + 3x^2 - 2 = 0$; (*b*) $x^4 - 9x^3 + 30x^2 - 44x + 24 = 0$; (*c*) $4x^4 - 23x^2 - 9x + 10 = 0$; (*d*) $3x^3 + 14x^2 + 2x - 4 = 0$.
7. Use the directions of Problem 6 for each of the following equations: (*a*) $6x^4 + 5x^3 + 7x^2 - 34x - 12 = 0$; (*b*) $2x^4 + 9x^3 + 15x^2 + 13x + 6 = 0$; (*c*) $6x^3 - 35x^2 + 19x + 30 = 0$; (*d*) $x^4 + 2x^3 - 13x^2 + 10x = 0$.
8. Write down an equation of the fourth degree, which will have (*a*) no positive roots; (*b*) no real roots.

10.8 Real Solutions of Polynomial Equations

In this section we discuss a method, known as *Newton's Method*, for determining the solutions of an equation which are real but not necessarily rational. While the method has much more general usage, as we shall see later, we shall confine our present remarks to polynomial equations. From the point of view of relative occurrence, the irrational solutions of an equation are of much more importance than the rational; for, outside of "text-book" problems, it very seldom happens that an equation will have a rational number as a solution.

The idea of Newton's Method is graphical, and depends on the fact that the x-intercepts of the graph of a function f on $R^{\#}$, are the solutions of the equation $f(x) = 0$; these solutions are also known as the *zeros* of the function. We then determine successive approximations to each of these intercepts, by replacing portions of the graph by tangent lines in smaller and smaller neighborhoods of the intercept. The only requirement on the nature of the equation $f(x) = 0$ is that the function f be differentiable in a neighborhood of each intercept; this is true, of course, if $f(x)$ is a polynomial $P[x]$.

We first locate a real solution r between two integers, using synthetic division. For if $f(a)$ and $f(b)$ differ in sign, the continuity of f implies that the graph of f intercepts the x-axis between $x = a$ and $x = b$, i.e., the equation $f(x) = 0$ has a real solution in the interval $[a, b]$. Of course, there may be more than one solution in this interval, and in this case we must determine a smaller interval which contains only one solution. We also

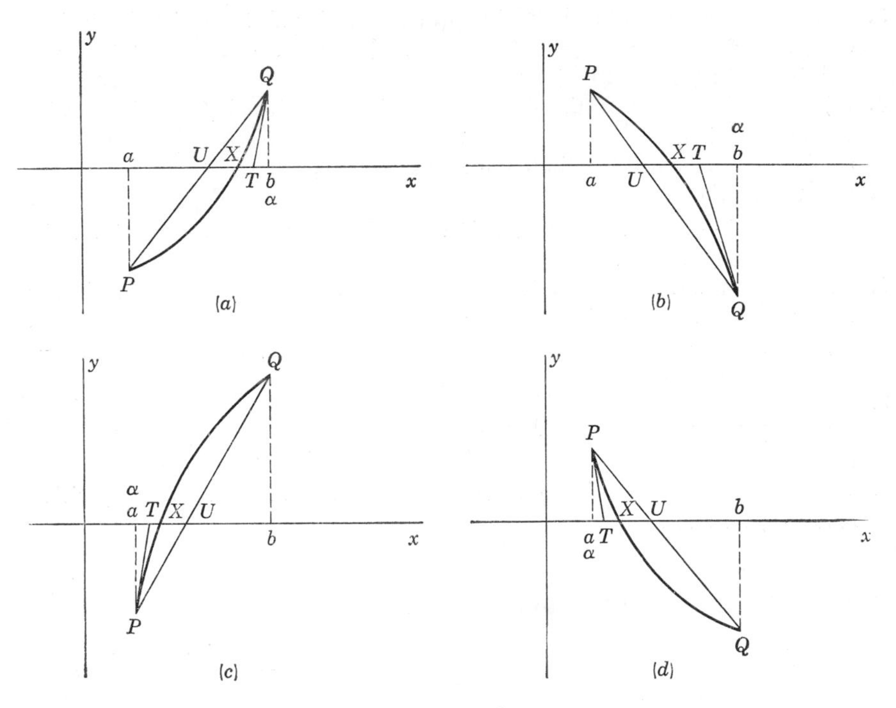

Figure 10–9

wish to avoid any points of inflection in the interval, and both requirements will be satisfied if we pick an interval so small that $f''(x)$ is positive throughout or negative throughout the interval.† In some small neighborhood of the real solution under discussion, the graph of f will then resemble one of the four graphs shown in Figure 10–9. In (*a*) and (*d*) $f''(x)$ is positive on the interval shown, while $f''(x)$ is negative on the interval shown in (*b*) and (*c*).

We now suppose that $[a, b]$ is an interval of the type required above, and let $\alpha = a$ or $\alpha = b$ according as $f(a) \cdot f''(a) > 0$ or $f(b) \cdot f''(b) > 0$.

† If sec. 8.10 was not studied, we remark that f'' is a function which bears the same relation to f' as f' does to f.

Thus, in the diagram of (*c*) or (*d*) above, $\alpha = a$, while in (*a*) or (*b*), $\alpha = b$. If we construct the tangent line to the graph at the point with abscissa α, the x-intercept of this line is nearer the desired solution than is α, and may be regarded as a first approximation to this solution. Since the slope of the tangent line is $f'(\alpha)$, the equation of the tangent line is seen to be $y - f(\alpha) = f'(\alpha)(x - \alpha)$, using the "point-slope" equation of a straight line. If we put $y = 0$ and solve for x, we obtain *Newton's Formula* for the first approximation α_1 of the solution: $\alpha_1 = \alpha - [f(\alpha)]/[f'(\alpha)]$.

The proper choice of a or b as α guarantees that α_1 is actually nearer the exact solution than is α. If we now draw the tangent line to the graph at the point where $x = \alpha_1$, the point of intersection of this new tangent line with the x-axis will determine a second approximation to the desired solution. It is clear that this second approximation α_2 may be obtained by replacing α by α_1 in the preceding formula, so that

$$\alpha_2 = \alpha_1 - \frac{f(\alpha_1)}{f'(\alpha_1)}.$$

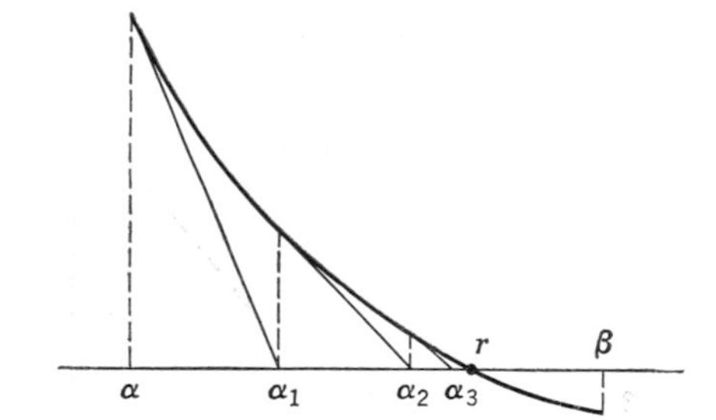

Figure 10–10

We can now continue this process indefinitely, obtaining a sequence of numbers $\alpha, \alpha_1, \alpha_2, \cdots$, which has the exact solution as a limit. In Figure 10–10, we have given an illustration of the first three stages of Newton's Method.

A glance at Figure 10–9 shows that the chord PQ and the tangent line at the point where $x = \alpha$, intercept the x-axis at points U and T, respectively, which are on opposite sides of the desired solution. Thus the abscissas of U and T will provide bounds for the solution—which is the abscissa of X—and will provide us with an estimate of our error in using Newton's Formula. The abscissa of T, which we have already represented by α_1, is given by this formula. If we designate by β whichever of a or b is not represented by α, the equation of the line containing P and Q is

$$y = f(\beta) + \frac{f(\beta) - f(\alpha)}{\beta - \alpha}(x - \alpha).$$

The abscissa of U will then be β_1, where

$$\beta_1 = \beta - \frac{f(\beta)}{f(\beta) - f(\alpha)} (\beta - \alpha).$$

The inequality $\alpha_1 < r < \beta_1$ if $\alpha = a$, or the inequality $\beta_1 < r < \alpha_1$ if $\alpha = b$, then gives us an estimate of the error involved in using the first approximation to the solution r, by Newton's Method.

If the possible error in the first approximation to the solution is considered too large, we must find a closer approximation. We have already shown how to obtain a second approximation α_2, but in order to obtain an estimate of the possible error associated with this approximation, we must find a number β_2 obtained from α_1 and β_1 just as β_1 was obtained from α and β. Thus

$$\beta_2 = \beta_1 - \frac{f(\beta_1)}{f(\beta_1) - f(\alpha_1)} (\beta_1 - \alpha_1).$$

The difference between β_2 and α_2 will then give us an estimate of the possible error in this second approximation to the solution r. This procedure may be continued indefinitely, as illustrated in Figure 10–11.

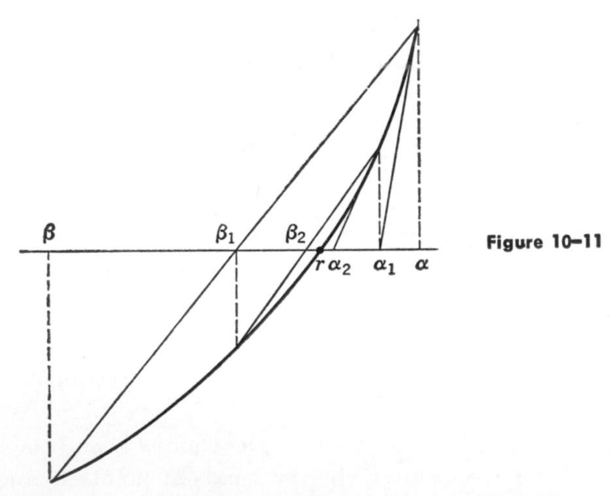

Figure 10–11

ILLUSTRATION. Determine, correct to three decimal places, the positive real solution of the equation $x^3 + 4x^2 - 7 = 0$.

Solution. We note that Descartes' Rule of Signs guarantees the existence of precisely one positive real solution of the equation. If we consider the function f, defined on $R^\#$ by $f(x) = x^3 + 4x^2 - 7$, we find by synthetic division that $f(1) = -2$ and $f(2) = 17$, and so the real solution lies on the interval $[1, 2]$. Since $f'(x) = 3x^2 + 8x$ and $f''(x) = 6x + 8$, we find that $f''(x)$ is positive throughout the interval $[1, 2]$, and the graph of f resembles that of Figure 10–9a. We then choose $\alpha = 2$ and $\beta = 1$.

The formulas above give us

$$\alpha_1 = \alpha - \frac{f(\alpha)}{f'(\alpha)} = 2 - \frac{f(2)}{f'(2)} = 2 - \frac{17}{28} = 1.39+$$

and

$$\beta_1 = \beta - \frac{f(\beta)}{f(\beta) - f(\alpha)}\,(\beta - \alpha) = 1 - \frac{f(1)}{f(1) - f(2)}\,(-1) = 1 + 2/19 = 1.10+.$$

Since $f(1.39) = 3.414019$ is positive, and $f(1.10) = -0.829$ is negative, we may round off the above numbers designated α_1 and β_1 to $\alpha_1 = 1.39$ and $\beta_1 = 1.10$, and be assured that the desired solution does lie in the interval [1.10, 1.39].

We now proceed to the second approximation.

$$\alpha_2 = \alpha_1 - \frac{f(\alpha_1)}{f'(\alpha_1)} = 1.39 - \frac{3.414019}{16.9163} = 1.39 - (0.2018+) = 1.1881+;$$

$$\begin{aligned}\beta_2 = \beta_1 - \frac{f(\beta_1)}{f(\beta_1) - f(\alpha_1)}\,(\beta_1 - \alpha_1) &= 1.10 - \frac{f(1.10)}{f(1.10) - f(1.39)}\,(-0.29) \\ = 1.10 - \frac{-0.829}{-0.829 - 3.414019}\,(-0.29) &= 1.10 + \frac{0.24041}{4.243019} \\ = 1.10 + (0.0567+) = 1.1567+. \end{aligned}$$

We now round off α_2 to 1.19 and β_2 to 1.16, after checking that $f(1.19) = 0.349559$ is positive, and $f(1.16) = -0.056704$ is negative, so that the desired solution lies in the interval [1.16, 1.19].

To obtain a third approximation, we determine α_3 and β_3. Thus

$$\alpha_3 = \alpha_2 - \frac{f(\alpha_2)}{f'(\alpha_2)} = 1.19 - \frac{0.349559}{13.7683} = 1.19 - 0.02538 = 1.16461+;$$

and

$$\begin{aligned}\beta_3 = \beta_2 - \frac{f(\beta_2)}{f(\beta_2) - f(\beta_2)}\,(\beta_2 - \alpha_2) &= 1.16 + \frac{0.056704}{0.406263}\,(0.03) \\ = 1.16 + (0.0041+) = 1.1641+. \end{aligned}$$

Since the solution lies in the interval [1.1641, 1.1646], a three-decimal approximation is 1.164.

It is frequently necessary in electrical engineering to determine the non-real solutions of a polynomial equation, and Newton's Method is not suitable for this job. The best procedure is one due to Graeffe, and may be used to find both the real and non-real solutions of the equation. The basic idea of the method is to form a new equation, the solutions of which are some high power of the solutions of the original equation. If the power is high enough, the solutions of the transformed equation will be widely separated, and may be obtained by a fairly simple but tedious process; the solutions of the original equation may then be readily obtained. We shall not discuss this method further, here, but refer the interested reader to more advanced books on the Theory of Equations.

PROBLEM SET 10.8

In Problems 1 through 5, use Newton's Method to determine the smallest positive real solution, correct to 3 decimal places.

1. $x^3 - 3x + 1 = 0$.
2. $x^3 - 4x^2 + 2x + 2 = 0$.
3. $x^3 + x - 3 = 0$.
4.* $x^4 + 3x^3 + x^2 - 4x - 6 = 0$.
5. $x^3 + 24x - 16 = 0$.

In Problems 6 through 8, use Newton's Method to determine the largest positive real solution, correct to 3 decimal places.

6. $x^3 - 3x + 1 = 0$.
7. $x^3 + 2x^2 - 6x + 3 = 0$.
8.* $x^4 - 3x^3 - 4x^2 + 10x + 6 = 0$.

10.9 Transcendental Equations

An expression that is not algebraic is said to be *transcendental*, and the result of equating a transcendental expression to 0 is known as a *transcendental equation*. For example, $\sin 2x - x^2 = 0$, and $2x + e^{3x} - 1 = 0$ are transcendental equations. A function, which has a transcendental expression for its value at a point x of its domain, is known as a *transcendental function;* the circular functions, exponential functions, and logarithmic functions all belong to this class. A determination of the real solution set of a transcendental equation may be regarded as equivalent to a determination of the zeros of the corresponding function in $R^\#$. The first three illustrations below involve circular functions. In the first illustration, we give a procedure which may be used if the left member of the equation is factorable.

ILLUSTRATION 1. Determine all solutions of the equation $2 \tan x \cos x + 2 \cos x - \tan x - 1 = 0$, which lie in the interval $[0, 2\pi]$.

Solution. On factoring the left member, the equation becomes $(\tan x + 1)(2 \cos x - 1) = 0$. Thus, $\tan x = -1$ or $\cos x = 1/2$, and the desired solution set of the equation is $\{3\pi/4, 7\pi/4, \pi/3, 5\pi/3\}$.

If the left member of the equation does not factor, and more than one circular function is involved, the best procedure is usually to make use of the appropriate identities and eliminate all but one circular function.

ILLUSTRATION 2. Determine all solutions of the equation $\cos x + 2 \sin x = 1$, which lie in the interval $[0, 2\pi]$.

Solution. $\cos x = 1 - 2 \sin x$, and on squaring both members, we obtain $\cos^2 x = 1 - 4 \sin x + 4 \sin^2 x$. Since $\cos^2 x = 1 - \sin^2 x$, this equation becomes $1 - \sin^2 x = 1 - 4 \sin x + 4 \sin^2 x$ or $5 \sin^2 x - 4 \sin x = 0$. Thus, $\sin x\ (5 \sin x - 4) = 0$ and $\sin x = 0$ or $\sin x = 4/5 = 0.8$. Hence, $x = 0, \pi, 2\pi, 0.6435$, or 2.2143; but a check reveals that π and 0.6435 are extraneous, so the desired solution set is $\{0, 2\pi, 2.2143\}$.

ILLUSTRATION 3. Determine all solutions of the equation $\cos x/2 - 1 = \cos x$, which lie in the interval $[0, 2\pi]$.

Solution. $\cos x/2 = 1 + \cos x$ and, on squaring both members, we obtain $\cos^2 x/2 = 1 + 2 \cos x + \cos^2 x$. But $\cos^2 x/2 = (1 + \cos x)/2$, and so $1 + \cos x = 2 + 4 \cos x + 2 \cos^2 x$ or $2 \cos^2 x + 3 \cos x + 1 = 0$. But then $(2 \cos x + 1)(\cos x + 1) = 0$, whence $\cos x = -1/2$ or $\cos x = -1$. It follows that $x = 2\pi/3, 4\pi/3$, or π; but $4\pi/3$ is found to be extraneous, and so the desired solution set is $\{2\pi/3, \pi\}$.

We noted earlier that Newton's Method is quite general in its application, so that we can use this technique in case the special methods of the preceding illustrations are not applicable. Since the process of synthetic division is not available for our use with transcendental equations, however, we must determine the approximate solutions by other means. One of the best of these is to graph the associated function in $R^{\#}$, and read the approximate zeros from the graph.

The method of *addition of ordinates* is useful, whenever a rough sketch of a non-elementary function is required. We illustrate the method for the function f, defined on its domain by $f(x) = 5 \ln x - x$. A sketch of the graph of this function may be obtained by *adding* the ordinates of corresponding points on the graphs of the functions f_1 and f_2 defined, respectively, on the same domain by $f_1(x) = 5 \ln x$ and $f_2(x) = -x$. This is illustrated in Figure 10–12, where we have assumed that the domain is $[0.5, 5]$.

ILLUSTRATION 4.† Use Newton's Method to approximate the real solution of the equation $5 \ln x - x = 0$.

Solution. The graph of Figure 10–12 shows that the function f has a zero—and the equation has a solution—in a small neighborhood of 1.3. This is further substantiated when we find that $f(1.29) = -0.0168$ and $f(1.3) = 0.0118$, with the help of Table 3. In this case $f(x) = 5 \ln x - x$, $f'(x) = 5/x - 1$, and $f''(x) = -5/x^2$. Since $f''(x) < 0$, for every x, we choose $\alpha = 1.29$ and $\beta = 1.30$, in the notation of the preceding section. Then

$$\alpha_1 = \alpha - \frac{f(\alpha)}{f'(\alpha)} = 1.29 - \frac{(-0.0168)}{2.8760} = 1.29 + 0.0058 = 1.2958;$$

† Since the solutions in Illustrations 4 and 5 involve derivatives of non-polynomial functions, these solutions may be omitted if sec. 8.6 and sec. 8.7 were not studied.

and

$$\beta_1 = \beta - \frac{f(\beta)}{f(\beta) - f(\alpha)} (\beta - \alpha) = 1.3 - \frac{(0.0118)(0.01)}{0.0118 + 0.0168}$$

$$= 1.3 - 0.004 = 1.296.$$

Since the solution lies in the interval $[\alpha_1, \beta_1]$, a 3-decimal approximation is seen to be 1.296.

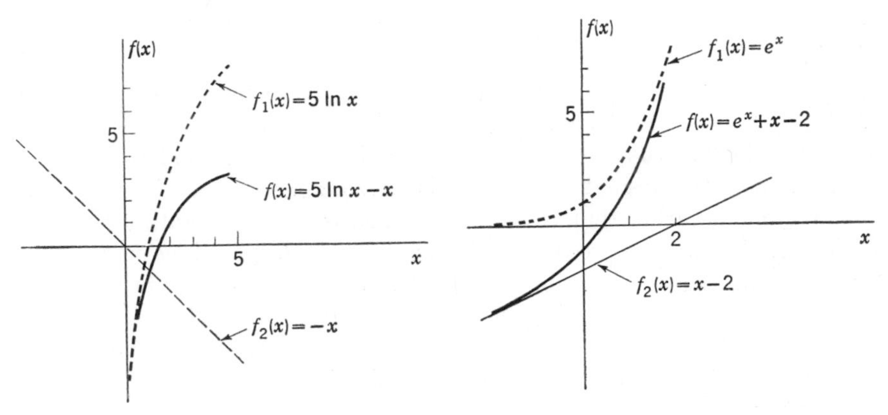

Figure 10–12

Figure 10–13

ILLUSTRATION 5. Determine the real solution of $e^x + x - 2 = 0$.

Solution. A rough graph of the function f, defined on a convenient interval by $f(x) = e^x + x - 2$, is shown in Figure 10–13. The method of addition of ordinates was used, with the auxiliary functions f_1 and f_2, defined by $f_1(x) = e^x$ and $f_2(x) = x - 2$, respectively. With the help of Table 4, we find that $f(0.4) = 1.4918 + 0.4 - 2 = -0.1082$, and $f(0.5) = 1.6487 + 0.5 - 2 = 0.1487$, so that a solution lies in the interval $[0.4, 0.5]$. Since $f'(x) = e^x + 1$ and $f''(x) = e^x > 0$, we choose $\alpha = 0.5$ and $\beta = 0.4$, in the notation of the preceding section. Then

$$\alpha_1 = \alpha - \frac{f(\alpha)}{f'(\alpha)} = 0.5 - \frac{0.1487}{2.6487} = 0.5 - 0.056 = 0.444;$$

and

$$\beta_1 = \beta - \frac{f(\beta)}{f(\beta) - f(\alpha)} (\beta - \alpha) = 0.4 - \frac{(-0.1082)(-0.1)}{-0.1082 - 0.1487}$$

$$= 0.4 + 0.42 = 0.442.$$

The desired solution is then 0.443, with an error of not more than 0.001. A more accurate result would require the use of a more elaborate table of powers of e.

PROBLEM SET 10.9

In Problems 1 through 24, determine the solutions of each equation in the interval $[0, 2\pi]$.

1. $\sin x + \sin x \tan x = \tan x + 1.$
2. $\cos x \tan 2x = 0.$
3. $\cot x\,(1 + \cos x) = 0.$
4. $1 - \cos t - 2\cos^2 t = 0.$
5. $\tan^2 x = 3.$
6. $\sec^2 \alpha = 4.$
7. $\cos x + \sin x = 0.$
8. $\sec x = 1 + \tan x.$
9. $\sin x - \cos x = 0.$
10. $3\cos^2 y + \cos y - 2 = 0.$
11. $\sin 2x + 2\sin^2 x = 0.$
12. $\cos 3x = \sin 2x.$
13. $\tan^2 x - 5\tan x + 4 = 0.$
14. $\cos^2 \alpha + \cos \alpha = 1/2.$
15. $\sec x + 1 = 2\cos x.$
16. $2\tan^2 \theta - \sec^2 \theta = 0.$
17. $6\tan^2 \theta + \sec \theta + 5 = 0.$
18. $4\cos^2 t = 3.$
19. $1 - \cos y = \sqrt{3}\sin y.$
20. $2\sin \alpha - \csc \alpha = 1.$
21. $1 - \tan x \tan 2x = 0.$
22. $\cos 2t - \sin 2t = 1.$
23. $\sin \beta = \cos 2\beta.$
24. $3\sec^2 t + \cot^2 t = 7.$

In Problems 25 through 30, use graphical means to determine the number of real solutions of each equation; compute the smallest positive solution, correct to 3 decimal places, if sec. 8.6 and sec. 8.7 were studied.

25. $\sin x + x = 1.$
26. $e^x - 4x = 0.$
27. $\tan x - x = 0.$
28. $\tan x + x - 1 = 0.$
29. $\ln x + 2x = 5.$
30. $\cos x - e^x + 1 = 0.$
31.* The equation $e^{-x} + x/5 - 1 = 0$ occurs in the quantum theory of radiation. Determine a 3-decimal approximation to the positive solution of this equation.
32.* If the central angle of a circular sector is x radians, while the length of a radius is r inches, the area of the sector is A square inches, where $A = (1/2)r^2(x - \sin x)$. Determine x if $r = 2$ and $A = 5$.

10.10 First and Second Degree Inequalities

An inequality resembles an equation in appearance, but instead of the "equality" sign $(=)$ it contains one or more of the well-known signs: $<, \leq, >, \geq$. The solution of an inequality in x is a determination of those numbers which satisfy the inequality, though, just as with equations, it is important to know the nature of x. Thus, if x is an integer, we may get one solution set and an entirely different one if x is only required to be real. The transformations which are permissible in the solution of an inequality are the same as those for equations, with *one notable exception:* if each member of an inequality is multiplied or divided by the same *negative* number, the *sense* of the inequality must be *reversed.*

ILLUSTRATION 1. Solve the inequality $2x + 3 < 5x - 4$, for $x \in R^*$.

Solution. $2x - 5x < -4 - 3$ (adding $-5x - 3$ to both members)

$$-3x < -7$$

$$x > 7/3 \qquad \text{(dividing both members by } -3)$$

The solution set consists of all real numbers exceeding 7/3.

If $x \leq b$ and $x \geq a$, it is customary to condense these two inequalities into the compact form $a \leq x \leq b$. This means, of course, that x is a number between a and b and so $x \in [a, b]$.

ILLUSTRATION 2. Solve the inequality $|3x + 1| \leq 2$, for x (*a*) an integer; (*b*) a real number.

Solution. The given inequality is equivalent to $-2 \leq 3x + 1 \leq 2$, or $-3 \leq 3x \leq 1$ (adding -1 to each member). On dividing each member by 3, we obtain $-1 \leq x \leq 1/3$.

(*a*) If x is an integer, the solution set is then $\{-1, 0\}$; (*b*) if x is a real number, the solution set is the interval $[-1, 1/3]$.

It is clear that any simple inequality may be transformed so that the right member is zero. If the left member is quadratic in x, the following illustration outlines a graphical method of solution.

ILLUSTRATION 3. Solve the inequality $x^2 - 2x < 1$, for $x \in R^{\#}$.

Solution. The above inequality is equivalent to $x^2 - 2x - 1 < 0$. Let us consider the function f, defined on $R^{\#}$ by $f(x) = x^2 - 2x - 1$, so

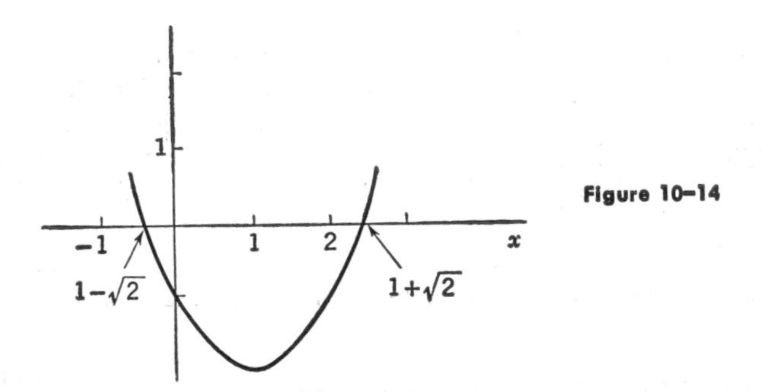

Figure 10–14

that the graph of f is a parabola opening upwards. We obtain the x-intercepts of the function by solving the equation $x^2 - 2x - 1 = 0$, and obtain the solutions $x = 1 + \sqrt{2}$ and $x = 1 - \sqrt{2}$. It is evident that the above inequality is satisfied by any x such that $f(x) < 0$, i.e., for which the corresponding graphed point lies below the x-axis. A glance at Figure 10–14 then shows that the desired solution is the interval $[1 - \sqrt{2}, 1 + \sqrt{2}]$ without the end points, i.e., $\{x \mid x \in R^{\#}, 1 - \sqrt{2} < x < 1 + \sqrt{2}\}$.

PROBLEM SET 10.10

Solve each of the following inequalities for $x \in R^{\#}$.

1. $3x - 2 < 1 + 2x$.
2. $x - 5 \leq 3 - 2x$.
3. $1 + 2x \leq 5x$.
4. $x + 2 > 5x - 2$.
5. $|2x + 1| < 6$.
6. $|x - 2| < 2$.
7. $|3x + 2| \leq 3$.
8. $\sqrt{x + 2} < 5$.
9. $\sqrt{2x + 1} \geq 4$.
10. $|2x| > -1$.
11. $|2x| < -1$.
12. $-2 < 13t + 2 \leq 100$.
13. $|y - 4| > 6$.
14. $|t - 1| > 2$.
15. $-3 < \dfrac{3x + 1}{4} \leq 5$.
16. $x^2 - 2x + 1 > 0$.
17. $x^2 - 4x + 2 \geq 0$.
18. $3x^2 - 2x + 1 \leq 0$.
19. $4x^2 + x \leq 5$.
20. $3x^2 + 4 \geq 2x$.
21. $-2x^2 + 3x < 2$.
22. $2x + 5 > -4x^2$.

10.11 More on Inequalities

Extreme care must be exercised in solving an inequality in x, in which x appears in a denominator. We illustrate with an example.

ILLUSTRATION 1. Solve the inequality $-1 < \dfrac{100}{100 + x} < 1$, for $x \in R^{\#}$.

Solution. If we multiply each member by $100 + x$, the result is $x > 0$ and $x > -200$, or simply $x > 0$, which is an incomplete answer. A correct solution involves a consideration of two cases.

(*a*) If $100 + x > 0$, we multiply each member by $100 + x$ and obtain $-100 - x < 100 < 100 + x$, which reduces to $x > 0$.

(*b*) If $100 + x < 0$, we multiply each member by $100 + x$, reverse the inequality signs, and obtain $-100 - x > 100 > 100 + x$. This reduces to $x < 0$ and $x < -200$, or simply $x < -200$.

It is possible to "clear fractions," without reversing the signs of the inequalities, by multiplying by the *square* of the least common denominator, but this will usually result in an inequality of higher order. However, this procedure may be used to simplify an inequality such as $-2/x < 1 < 3/x$ to $-2x < x^2 < 3x$, on multiplying each member by x^2.

We now illustrate a method for solving a more complex inequality. This method will be used in Chapter 12, in connection with general curve sketching.

ILLUSTRATION 2. Solve the inequality $\dfrac{(x - 2)(x + 3)}{(x - 1)(\log x)} < 0$, for $x \in R^{\#}$.

Solution. Draw four algebraic scales, one for each of the four components of the left member of the above inequality, and place the scales so that their readings line up vertically. This is shown in Figure 10–15. On each scale, mark with a heavy line those intervals for which the associated component is positive, leave unchanged those for which it is negative, and

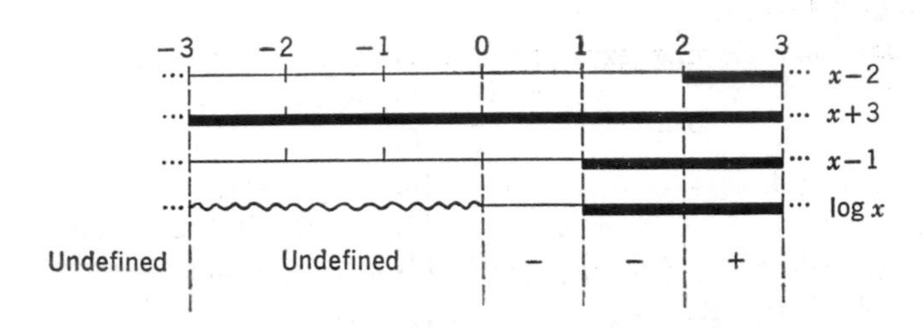

Figure 10–15

mark with a wavy line those intervals for which the associated component is undefined. It is then a simple matter to discover those intervals for which the original expression is positive, negative, or undefined. In particular, we see from the figure that $\dfrac{(x-2)(x+3)}{(x-1)(\log x)} < 0$, for $0 < x < 1$ and $1 < x < 2$. We must exclude $x = 1$, since the expression is undefined at this point.

PROBLEM SET 10.11

Solve each of the following inequalities, for $x \in R^{\#}$.

1. $|3x - 5| < 4.$

2. $|x + 4| > 3.$

3. $\left|\dfrac{x}{1+x}\right| < 2.$

4. $\left|\dfrac{2r}{r+5}\right| < 1.$

5. $-2 < \dfrac{5}{1+x} \leq 3.$

6. $-3 \leq \dfrac{20}{4-x} < 10.$

7. $(x + 1)(x - 2)(x - 3) < 0.$

8. $x(x - 1)(x + 1) \geq 0.$

9. $\dfrac{x^2 \log x}{x - 2} < 0.$

10. $\dfrac{(x+1)(x-2)}{(x-5)} \leq 0.$

11. $\dfrac{e^x(x-3)}{x^2} < 0.$

12. $\dfrac{x^2(x+1)(x-1)}{(x-3)} < 0.$

13. $x \sin x < 0.$

14. $-2 < \dfrac{5}{2x+1} < 3.$

REVIEW TEST A

1. If a, b, and c are complex numbers, prove that $a + (b + c) = (a + b) + c$.
2. Express the complex solutions of the equation $x^2 - 3x + 5 = 0$ in rectangular form.
3. Simplify the following expression, after having converted each complex number into polar form: $\dfrac{(2 + 2i)^4(\sqrt{3} + i)}{(2 - 2\sqrt{3}\, i)^3}$.
4. Determine the three complex cube roots of $1 - i$, and express each in the form $r \operatorname{cis} \theta$.
5. Use synthetic division to determine two integral solutions of the equation $x^4 + 2x^3 - 3x^2 - 4x - 12 = 0$, and then use the quadratic formula to find the remaining solutions.
6. Determine all the rational solutions of the equation
$$18x^4 + 9x^3 - 11x^2 + 20x - 6 = 0.$$
7. Determine all solutions of the equation $2 \sin \theta = \cos 2\theta$ that lie in the interval $[0, 2\pi]$.
8.* Use Newton's Method to compute a 2-decimal approximation to the real solutions of the equation $4x - 4 - e^{x-1} = 0$.
9. Solve the following inequalities, for $x \in R^{\#}$: (*a*) $x^2 - 7x + 12 > 0$; (*b*) $(x - 1)(2x + 1)(x + 2) \leq 0$.
10. Determine A, B, C, and D so that the following equation is an identity:
$$3x^3 - 2x + 1 = A(x - 1)^3 + B(x - 1)^2 + C(x - 1) + D.$$
11. Solve the following inequalities, for $x \in I$: (*a*) $(x - 3)^2 < 6$; (*b*) $-1 < x - 3 \leq 5$.
12. (*a*) Determine k so that the equation $x^2 + (k + 1)x + 4 = 0$ has only one real solution. (*b*) Express $1/(-1 - i\sqrt{3})$ in the form $a + bi$.

REVIEW TEST B

1. If a, b, and c are complex numbers, prove that $a(b + c) = ab + ac$.
2. Express the complex solutions of the equation $x^2 - 4x + 8 = 0$ in the form $r \operatorname{cis} \theta$.
3. Simplify the following expression, after having converted each complex number into polar form: $\dfrac{(1 - i)^3(2 + 2i)^4}{(\sqrt{3} - i)^3}$.
4. Express each of the four 4th roots of $4 + 4i$ in the form $r \operatorname{cis} \theta$.
5. Use synthetic division to determine the two integral solutions of the equation $x^4 + 6x^3 + 2x^2 - 28x - 16 = 0$, and then use the quadratic formula to find the remaining solutions.

6. Determine the rational solutions of the equation $12x^3 - 45x^2 + 43x - 12 = 0$.

7. Determine all solutions of the equation $2 \cos 2\theta = 3 \tan^2\theta$ that lie in the interval $[0, 2\pi]$.

8. Use Newton's Method to compute a 3-decimal approximation to the largest real solution of the equation $x^3 - x^2 - 11x + 14 = 0$.

9. Solve the following inequalities, for $x \in I$: (*a*) $|x - 2| < 3$; (*b*) $\sqrt{9 - x^2} > 0$.

10. Solve the following inequalities, for $x \in R^{\#}$: (*a*) $2x^2 + 3x - 2 < 0$; (*b*) $x(3x + 1)(x - 3) \geq 0$.

11. Determine A, B, and C so that $2x^2 - x + 4 = A(x + 2)^2 + B(x + 2) + C$ is an identity.

12. (*a*) If $s = 4t + (1/2)t^2$, express t in terms of s; (*b*) determine x and y so that the following equation is satisfied: $2x - 3i = 8 - 6yi + 2$.

REFERENCES

Books

JOHNSON, RICHARD E., NEAL H. MCCOY AND ANNE O'NEILL, *Fundamentals of College Mathematics*, New York, Rinehart, 1953. (Chap. 8.)

MACDUFFEE, C. C., *Theory of Equations*, New York, Wiley, 1953. (Chaps. 3, 4, and 5.)

USPENSKY, J. J., *Theory of Equations*, New York, McGraw-Hill, 1948.

American Mathematical Monthly

BALLANTINE, J. P., "Newton's Method for Trigonometry Students," Vol. 63, p. 722 (1956).

DINKINES, FLORA, "Simple Devices for Efficiency in the Elementary Theory of Equations," Vol. 62, p. 476 (1955).

HAMILTON, H. J., "A Type of Variation on Newton's Method," Vol. 57, p. 517 (1950).

MCGAUGHEY, A. W., "The Imaginary Number Problem," Vol. 64, p. 193 (1957).

OLDENBURGER, RUFUS, "Practical Computational Methods in the Solution of Equations," Vol. 55, p. 353 (1948).

RICHMOND, D. E., "Complex Numbers and Vector Algebra," Vol. 58, p. 622 (1951).

ROBINSON, R. M., "A Curious Trigonometric Identity," Vol. 64, p. 83 (1957).

STEWART, J. K., "Another Variation of Newton's Method," Vol. 58, p. 331 (1951).

TRIFAN, D., "Complex Roots of an Integral Rational Equation," Vol. 61, p. 640 (1954).

WAGNER, R. W., "A Substitution for Solving Trigonometric Equations," Vol. 54, p. 220 (1947).

WALL, H. S., "A Modification of Newton's Method," Vol. 55, p. 50 (1948).

11

SYSTEMS OF EQUATIONS

An equation is the most serious and important thing in mathematics.

SIR OLIVER LODGE

11.1 Two Linear Equations in Two Unknowns

If x and y are unspecified elements of a number system S, an equality $ax + by = c$, with a, b, and c in the system, is said to be a *linear* or *first-degree* equation in the two "unknowns" x and y. A *solution in S* of such an equation is an ordered pair (x_1, y_1), with x_1 and y_1 in S, such that $ax_1 + by_1 = c$. For example, if S is the set I of integers, the equation $2x + 5y = 1$ has $(3, -1)$ for a solution in I, since $2(3) + 5(-1) = 1$. The *solution set in I* of a linear equation in two unknowns, is the set of *all* ordered pairs of elements of S that are solutions of the equation. It is clear that the solution set in I of the equation $2x + 5y = 1$ contains infinitely many pairs. A determination of the solution set in S of an equation is known as *solving the equation in S*. In most instances, the equations of this chapter will be solved in $\bar{R}$, the set of rational numbers, though occasionally we shall only consider solutions that are in I. It is, of course, essential that we know the system in which we are solving an equation, for it is clear that the solution set in one system may be quite different from the solution set in another. Two equations are said to be *equivalent* in S, if they have the same solution set in S.

A *simultaneous* solution of two equations is a solution of both equations. For example, the equations $x + y = 3$ and $2x + y = 5$ have $(2, 1)$ as a simultaneous solution in I, since $2 + 1 = 3$ and $2(2) + 1 = 5$. The *solution set* of two equations is the set of all simultaneous solutions of the equations where, again, we must be cognizant of the number system in which we are solving the equations. We shall see that this solution set may be empty, or it may contain one or infinitely many ordered pairs.

Two *pairs* of equations may be said to be *equivalent* in S, if their solution sets in S coincide. The procedure for solving a pair of equations is to replace them by an equivalent pair, which have an obvious solution set. If any sequence of the following *elementary* operations is performed on a pair of equations, it is clear that the resulting pair is equivalent to the original:

1. eliminate any equation having 0 for each coefficient;
2. multiply both members of an equation by any non-zero number;
3. add any multiple of the members of one equation to the corresponding members of another equation.

We illustrate this procedure, which is the familiar "elimination" method for solving two linear equations in two unknowns.

ILLUSTRATION 1. Determine the simultaneous solution in I of the equations $2x + 3y = 2$ and $3x + 2y = -2$.

Solution. If we multiply both members of the first equation by 3, the resulting equivalent pair is:

$$6x + 9y = 6$$
$$3x + 2y = -2.$$

On subtraction of twice the members of the second equation from the corresponding members of the first, we obtain:

$$5y = 10$$
$$3x + 2y = -2.$$

It is now apparent that $y = 2$, and that the only solution of the two equations is $(-2, 2)$.

The above illustration is an example of the more general problem of determining the simultaneous solution of two equations of the form:

$$a_1x + b_1y = c_1$$
$$a_2x + b_2y = c_2.$$

Let us use the method of the illustration to find a solution of these equations in $\bar{R}$.

If we multiply the members of the first equation by b_2 and those of the second by b_1, we obtain the equivalent pair:

$$a_1b_2x + b_1b_2y = c_1b_2$$
$$a_2b_1x + b_2b_1y = c_2b_1.$$

On subtracting the members of the second equation from the corresponding members of the first, the result is:

$$(a_1b_2 - a_2b_1)x = c_1b_2 - c_2b_1$$
$$a_2b_1x + b_2b_1y = c_2b_1.$$

Hence, if $a_1b_2 \neq a_2b_1$, $x = (c_1b_2 - c_2b_1)/(a_1b_2 - a_2b_1)$; and in a similar manner we can obtain $y = (a_1c_2 - a_2c_1,)/(a_1b_2 - a_2b_1)$. In this case, there is a unique solution of the two equations. If $a_1b_2 - a_2b_1 = 0$, there are two possibilities: (1) $c_1b_2 - c_2b_1 = 0$, and the first equation may be eliminated, so there are infinitely many solutions of the equations; (2) $c_1b_2 - c_2b_1 \neq 0$, so that the equations are really *inconsistent*, i.e., there is no common solution.

At this point we introduce what we may regard now as a memory device for the general solution of the above pair of equations, if $a_1b_2 - a_2b_1 \neq 0$. Let us define the symbol $\begin{vmatrix} a & b \\ c & d \end{vmatrix}$ as a short notation for the expression $ad - bc$, so that the above solution may be expressed as

$$x = \frac{\begin{vmatrix} c_1 & b_1 \\ c_2 & b_2 \end{vmatrix}}{\begin{vmatrix} a_1 & b_1 \\ a_2 & b_2 \end{vmatrix}} \quad \text{and } y = \frac{\begin{vmatrix} a_1 & c_1 \\ a_2 & c_2 \end{vmatrix}}{\begin{vmatrix} a_1 & b_1 \\ a_2 & b_2 \end{vmatrix}}.$$

Three things should be noted concerning the above symbolic solution:

1. the numbers in the denominators comprise the array of coefficients of the left members of the equations, just as they appear;

2. the numerator of the solution for either unknown is obtained from the denominator, by replacing the coefficients of the unknown in question by the numbers in the right members of the equations;

3. this method fails to give a solution, in case $a_1b_2 - a_2b_1 = 0$.

ILLUSTRATION 2. Determine the solution in $\bar{R}$ of the equations

$$5x + 3y = 1$$
$$7x + 2y = 8.$$

Solution. Using the above memory device, we obtain

$$x = \frac{\begin{vmatrix} 1 & 3 \\ 8 & 2 \end{vmatrix}}{\begin{vmatrix} 5 & 3 \\ 7 & 2 \end{vmatrix}} = \frac{-22}{-11} = 2,$$

and

$$y = \frac{\begin{vmatrix} 5 & 1 \\ 7 & 8 \end{vmatrix}}{\begin{vmatrix} 5 & 3 \\ 7 & 2 \end{vmatrix}} = \frac{33}{-11} = -3.$$

The only solution in $\bar{R}$ of the above equations is then seen to be $(2, -3)$.

ILLUSTRATION 3. Determine the solution in $\bar{R}$ of the equations

$$5/x + 3/y = 4$$
$$3/x - 1/y = 1.$$

Solution. These equations are not linear, but if we replace x by $1/X$ and y by $1/Y$, we obtain a pair of linear equations, the solutions of which are related in a simple manner to those of the original pair. Thus, after making this substitution, the equations become

$$5X + 3Y = 4$$
$$3X - Y = 1.$$

The above method now gives

$$X = \frac{\begin{vmatrix} 4 & 3 \\ 1 & -1 \end{vmatrix}}{\begin{vmatrix} 5 & 3 \\ 3 & -1 \end{vmatrix}} = \frac{-7}{-14} = \frac{1}{2},$$

and

$$Y = \frac{\begin{vmatrix} 5 & 4 \\ 3 & 1 \end{vmatrix}}{\begin{vmatrix} 5 & 3 \\ 3 & -1 \end{vmatrix}} = \frac{-7}{-14} = \frac{1}{2}.$$

Since $x = 1/X$ and $y = 1/Y$, the pair $(2, 2)$ is seen to be the unique solution of the given equations. This illustration shows that a pair of non-linear equations may sometimes be solved by the methods employed for linear equations.

ILLUSTRATION 4. If we attempt to solve the pair of equations $x + y = 2$ and $3x + 3y = 6$, we see immediately that they are equivalent to the single equation $x + y = 2$. This equation has infinitely many solutions in either I or $\bar{R}$; three solutions in I are $(0, 2)$, $(2, 0)$, and $(1, 1)$, and it is easy to find many others. We notice that $a_1b_2 - a_2b_1 = 0$, in the previous notation.

PROBLEM SET 11.1

In each of Problems 1 through 6, use the memory device to determine the unique solution; check the solution in each equation.

1. $x + 2y = 8$
$x + 3y = 11.$

2. $5x + 6y = 8$
$x + 2y = 4.$

3. $2x + 7y = 13$
   $5x + 4y = 10.$

4. $y = (3/2)x - 5$
   $3x - 2y = 10.$

5. $1/x + 6/y = 3$
   $4/x - 1/y = 2.$

6. $(1/2)x + (1/3)y = 6$
   $(1/4)x + (1/5)y = 7/2.$

In each of Problems 7 through 12, use the memory device to determine one of the unknowns, and obtain the other by substitution in either equation; check the solution by substitution in the other equation.

7. $2x + 3y = 7$
   $3x + y = 7.$

8. $3x + 2y = 3$
   $5x + 4y = 7.$

9. $7x - 8y = 9$
   $3x - 4y = 5.$

10. $5x - 2y = 7$
    $2x + 3y = 26.$

11. $2/x + 6/y = 3$
    $4/x - 3/y = 1.$

12. $1.3x - 2.8y = 24.6$
    $9.4x + 3.5y = 7.2.$

13. Why does the memory device fail if we attempt to use it to solve the equations $4x + 14y = 11$?
    $12x + 42y = 7$

14. If $S = \{0, 1, 2, 3, 4, 5\}$, determine the elements of the function f, defined on S by the equation $x + 2y = 6$, considering x an arbitrary element of the domain.

11.2 Matrices and Determinants

A rectangular array of numbers, usually inclosed by curved lines, is called a *matrix*, the numbers being referred to as the *elements* of the matrix. Thus, for example, the following array is a matrix of integral elements:

$$\begin{pmatrix} 2 & 1 & 4 & 3 \\ 1 & -2 & 1 & -1 \\ 0 & 2 & 1 & 3 \end{pmatrix}.$$

The individual horizontal arrays are known as the *rows*, and the individual vertical arrays are known as the *columns*, of the matrix. A matrix is said to be "m by n" if it has m rows and n columns, so that the above example is a "3 by 4" matrix. If the number n of rows is equal to the number of columns, the matrix is *square* of order n; it is with this type of matrix that we are to be most concerned in this section.

It is convenient to represent the element in the ith row and jth column of a general matrix by a_{ij}, the first subscript then indicating the row and the second subscript the column to which the element belongs. The whole matrix may be represented then by $A = (a_{ij})$ which, if $n = 3$, takes the following form:

$$\begin{pmatrix} a_{11} & a_{12} & a_{13} \\ a_{21} & a_{22} & a_{23} \\ a_{31} & a_{32} & a_{33} \end{pmatrix}.$$

We now associate with every square matrix $A = (a_{ij})$ a number known as the *determinant* of A, indicated by $|A|$. We shall also write

$$|A| = \begin{vmatrix} a_{11} & a_{12} & a_{13} & \cdots & a_{1n} \\ a_{21} & a_{22} & a_{23} & \cdots & a_{2n} \\ a_{31} & a_{32} & a_{33} & \cdots & a_{3n} \\ \cdots & \cdots & \cdots & \cdots & \cdots \\ a_{n1} & a_{n2} & a_{n3} & \cdots & a_{nn} \end{vmatrix},$$

and shall refer to a determination of the number represented by this symbol as an *evaluation* of the determinant. We have implied that only square matrices have determinants. Our procedure will be to define the determinant of an n by n matrix recursively in terms of determinants of $n - 1$ by $n - 1$ matrices. Then, if we define the determinant of a 1 by 1 matrix $A = (a)$ to be the element a of the matrix, the determinant of any square matrix will have been defined.

If a row and column of a square matrix of order n are deleted, the remaining elements form a *submatrix* of order $n - 1$. The determinant of a submatrix is a *minor* of the matrix, and if the ith row and jth column are deleted, the resulting minor is indicated by M_{ij}. If we use the standard terminology and represent the element in the ith row and jth column by a_{ij}, the number $(-1)^{i+j}M_{ij}$ is called the *cofactor* of a_{ij} and is indicated by A_{ij}. If we select any row or column of the square matrix A, multiply the elements of this row or column by their respective cofactors and add the resulting products, we obtain a number *which can be shown to be independent of which row or column is selected.* We shall assume this result, without proof, and *define* this common number to be the *determinant* of the matrix. Using the notation introduced above, we can then make the following definition.

DEFINITION.

$$\begin{aligned} |A| &= a_{i1}A_{i1} + a_{i2}A_{i2} + a_{i3}A_{i3} + \cdots + a_{in}A_{in} \\ &= a_{1j}A_{1j} + a_{2j}A_{2j} + a_{3j}A_{3j} + \cdots + a_{nj}A_{nj}, \end{aligned}$$

the first evaluation being in terms of the elements of the ith row, and the second in terms of the elements of the jth column. In practice, it is customary to use $i = 1$ or $j = 1$, except in special cases.

ILLUSTRATION 1. Show that

$$\begin{vmatrix} a_{11} & a_{12} \\ a_{21} & a_{22} \end{vmatrix} = a_{11}a_{22} - a_{21}a_{12}.$$

Proof.

Since $A_{11} = (-1)^2a_{22} = a_{22}$ and $A_{12} = (-1)^3a_{21} = -a_{21}$,

$$\begin{vmatrix} a_{11} & a_{12} \\ a_{21} & a_{22} \end{vmatrix} = a_{11}a_{22} - a_{21}a_{12},$$

as desired. We now see that the "memory device" introduced in the preceding section was really the determinant of a 2 by 2 matrix.

ILLUSTRATION 2.

If

$$A = (a_{ij}) = \begin{pmatrix} 3 & -1 & 2 \\ 1 & 4 & -3 \\ 2 & 2 & 5 \end{pmatrix},$$

find the cofactors A_{23} and A_{12}.

Solution. If we delete the second row and third column of A, the determinant of the resulting submatrix is

$$M_{23} = \begin{vmatrix} 3 & -1 \\ 2 & 2 \end{vmatrix} = 6 - (-2) = 8;$$

thus

$$A_{23} = (-1)^5 M_{23} = (-1)(8) = -8.$$

If we delete the first row and second column of A, the determinant of the resulting submatrix is M_{12}, where

$$M_{12} = \begin{vmatrix} 1 & -3 \\ 2 & 5 \end{vmatrix} = 5 - (-6) = 11;$$

and so

$$A_{12} = (-1)^3 M_{12} = (-1)(11) = -11.$$

ILLUSTRATION 3. Use the elements of the first row and find the determinant of the matrix in Illustration 2.

Solution. We may determine A_{11}, A_{12}, and A_{13} and compute the sum $a_{11}A_{11} + a_{12}A_{12} + a_{13}A_{13}$.

$$A_{11} = (-1)^2 \begin{vmatrix} 4 & -3 \\ 2 & 5 \end{vmatrix} = 20 - (-6) = 20 + 6 = 26;$$

$$A_{12} = (-1)^3 \begin{vmatrix} 1 & -3 \\ 2 & 5 \end{vmatrix} = (-1)[5 - (-6)] = (-1)11 = -11;$$

$$A_{13} = (-1)^4 \begin{vmatrix} 1 & 4 \\ 2 & 2 \end{vmatrix} = 2 - 8 = -6.$$

Thus

$$|A| = 3(26) + (-1)(-11) + 2(-6) = 78 + 11 - 12 = 77.$$

We now state, without proof, several theorems on determinants. The proofs of these theorems may be found in more detailed treatises on determinants, but simple applications of the definition of $|A|$ may be used to establish their validity for matrices of low order.

THEOREM 1. If each element of any row or column of a square matrix is multiplied by a number c, the determinant of the matrix is multiplied by c.

THEOREM 2. If two rows or two columns of a square matrix are interchanged, the determinant of the matrix is changed only in sign.

Corollary. If two rows or two columns of a square matrix are identical, the determinant of the matrix is zero. For an interchange of these two rows or columns would leave the determinant invariant, and so by Theorem 2, $|A| = -|A| = 0$.

THEOREM 3. If any multiple of one row (or column) is added to another row (or column) of a square matrix, the determinant of the matrix is unchanged.

PROBLEM SET 11.2

1. If $A = (a_{ij}) = \begin{pmatrix} 2 & -3 & 4 & -5 \\ 3 & 4 & 1 & -2 \\ 1 & -1 & 0 & 4 \end{pmatrix}$ is an m by n matrix, identify (a) the numbers m and n; (b) a_{11}, a_{23}, a_{34}, and a_{14}.

2. Using the matrix A, of Problem 1, identify (a) the elements of the second row of A; (b) the elements of the third column of A; (c) the elements of A, indicated by a_{11}, a_{22}, and a_{33}.

3. If $A = \begin{pmatrix} 2 & -3 & 1 \\ 0 & 5 & 2 \\ -1 & -2 & 3 \end{pmatrix}$, determine the minor (a) M_{11}; (b) M_{23}; (c) M_{13}; (d) M_{33}.

4. Use the results of Problem 3 to determine the cofactor (a) A_{11}; (b) A_{23}; (c) A_{13}; (d) A_{33}.

5. Using the matrix A of Problem 3, evaluate $|A|$ in six different ways.

6. If $A = \begin{pmatrix} 3 & -4 & 6 \\ -1 & 5 & 9 \\ 0 & -2 & -3 \end{pmatrix}$, determine $|A|$ by an evaluation in terms of (a) the elements of the first row; (b) the elements of the first column; (c) the elements of the third row; (d) the elements of the second column.

7. If $A = \begin{vmatrix} -1 & 3 & 4 & 0 \\ 2 & -1 & 5 & 1 \\ 3 & 0 & -2 & 5 \\ -5 & -2 & 1 & 5 \end{vmatrix}$, find (*a*) A_{23}; (*b*) A_{14}; (*c*) A_{34}.

8. If A is the matrix of Problem 7, evaluate $|A|$ in terms of (*a*) the elements of the first row; (*b*) the elements of the second column; (*c*) the elements of the fourth column. Is there any preference for any of these methods of evaluation?

9. Use a general matrix of order 3 to prove Theorem 1.

10. Verify Theorem 2 for a general third-order matrix, by interchanging the second and third rows.

11. Check the truth of the Corollary to Theorem 2, by evaluating the determinant of a matrix of order 3, with two rows identical.

12. Verify Theorem 3 for a general matrix of order 3, by adding k times the third row to the first row.

13. Evaluate the following determinants:

(*a*) $\begin{vmatrix} 2-x & 3 \\ 5 & -5+x \end{vmatrix}$; (*b*) $\begin{vmatrix} 1+x & -2-x \\ 3-x & 5+x \end{vmatrix}$; (*c*) $\begin{vmatrix} 2-x & 3-x \\ 3+x & 2+x \end{vmatrix}$.

14. Evaluate the following determinants:

(*a*) $\begin{vmatrix} 1 & x & x^2 \\ 1 & y & y^2 \\ 1 & z & z^2 \end{vmatrix}$; (*b*) $\begin{vmatrix} 1 & 2 & 3 \\ x & -x & y \\ -x & 0 & -y \end{vmatrix}$; (*c*) $\begin{vmatrix} 1-x & -2 & 2+x \\ x & 1+x & 0 \\ 0 & 1-x & 2-x \end{vmatrix}$.

15. Prove that $\begin{vmatrix} x & y & 1 \\ x_1 & y_1 & 1 \\ x_2 & y_2 & 1 \end{vmatrix} = 0$ is an equation of the straight line containing the points (x_1, y_1) and (x_2, y_2).

16. Use the result of Problem 15 to determine an equation of the straight line containing the points $(-1, 3)$ and $(4, -5)$.

11.3 Determinants and Systems of Linear Equations

We now use the results of the preceding section to generalize the notions introduced in Section 11.1. Instead of a *pair* of equations, we consider a *system* of n linear equations in n unknowns:

$$\begin{aligned} a_{11}x_1 + a_{12}x_2 + a_{13}x_3 + \cdots + a_{1n}x_n &= k_1 \\ a_{21}x_1 + a_{22}x_2 + a_{23}x_3 + \cdots + a_{2n}x_n &= k_2 \\ a_{31}x_1 + a_{32}x_2 + a_{33}x_3 + \cdots + a_{3n}x_n &= k_3 \\ \cdots\cdots\cdots\cdots\cdots\cdots\cdots\cdots\cdots\cdots\cdots \\ a_{n1}x_1 + a_{n2}x_2 + a_{n3}x_3 + \cdots + a_{nn}x_n &= k_n \end{aligned}$$

By a *solution* of the system, we mean an ordered n-tuple $(c_1, c_2, c_3, \cdots, c_n)$, such that each of the equations of the system is satisfied, if $x_1 = c_1$, $x_2 = c_2$, $x_3 = c_3$, $\cdots$, $x_n = c_n$. The *solution set* of the system is the set of all solution n-tuples of the system.

THEOREM. If the elements of any row (or column) of a matrix are multiplied by the cofactors of the corresponding elements of another row (or column), the sum of the resulting products is zero.

Proof. Let us multiply the elements of the ith row by the respective cofactors of the elements of the jth row. It is clear that these products are identical with what we would obtain if we replaced the ith row by the jth and multiplied the respective elements of the jth row by their cofactors. But the sum of these products is the determinant of the matrix, and equal to 0, by the Corollary to Theorem 2, and so the former sum is also 0. We now apply this theorem to the problem of solving the given system of equations.

Let

$$D = \begin{vmatrix} a_{11} & a_{12} & \cdots & a_{1n} \\ a_{21} & a_{22} & \cdots & a_{2n} \\ \cdots & \cdots & \cdots & \cdots \\ a_{n1} & a_{n2} & \cdots & a_{nn} \end{vmatrix}, \qquad K_1 = \begin{vmatrix} k_1 & a_{12} & \cdots & a_{1n} \\ k_2 & a_{22} & \cdots & a_{2n} \\ \cdots & \cdots & \cdots & \cdots \\ k_n & a_{n2} & \cdots & a_{nn} \end{vmatrix},$$

$$K_2 = \begin{vmatrix} a_{11} & k_1 & \cdots & a_{1n} \\ a_{12} & k_2 & \cdots & a_{2n} \\ \cdots & \cdots & \cdots & \cdots \\ a_{1n} & k_n & \cdots & a_{nn} \end{vmatrix}, \qquad K_n = \begin{vmatrix} a_{11} & a_{12} & \cdots & k_1 \\ a_{21} & a_{22} & \cdots & k_2 \\ \cdots & \cdots & \cdots & \cdots \\ a_{n1} & a_{n2} & \cdots & k_n \end{vmatrix}.$$

Referring, of course, to the coefficient matrix

$$A = \begin{pmatrix} a_{11} & a_{12} & \cdots & a_{1n} \\ a_{21} & a_{22} & \cdots & a_{2n} \\ \cdots & \cdots & \cdots & \cdots \\ a_{n1} & a_{n2} & \cdots & a_{nn} \end{pmatrix},$$

we let A_{ij} be the cofactor of the element a_{ij}. If we now multiply both members of the first equation by A_{11}, both members of the second equation by A_{21}, $\cdots$, and both members of the nth equation by A_{n1}, and add the corresponding members of each new equation, the result is

$$\begin{aligned}(a_{11}A_{11} + a_{21}A_{21} + \cdots + a_{n1}A_{n1})x_1 + (a_{12}A_{11} + a_{22}A_{21} + \cdots \\ + a_{n2}A_{n1})x_2 + \cdots + (a_{1n}A_{11} + a_{2n}A_{21} + \cdots \\ + a_{nn}A_{n1})x_n = k_1A_{11} + k_2A_{21} + \cdots + k_nA_{n1}.\end{aligned}$$

But by the above theorem, the coefficients of x_2, x_3, $\cdots$, x_n are zero, while the coefficient of x_1 is the determinant D of the matrix A of coefficients.

Furthermore, the right member of this equation may be seen to be an evaluation of K_1, in terms of the elements of the first column of the associated matrix. The equation may then be written as $Dx_1 = K_1$, i.e., $x_1 = K_1/D$. In a similar manner we can obtain $x_2 = K_2/D, \cdots, x_n = K_n/D$. This result, usually known as *Cramer's Rule*, plays a role in the solution of n linear equations in n unknowns, which is comparable to that played by the quadratic formula in the solution of a quadratic equation. We notice that there is a *unique* solution of the system of equations, in case $D \neq 0$; if $D = 0$, it is evident that Cramer's Rule can not be used.

ILLUSTRATION. Use Cramer's Rule to determine the solution of the following system of linear equations:

$$\begin{aligned} 3x - y + 2z &= 9 \\ 2x + y - z &= 7 \\ x + 2y - 3z &= 4. \end{aligned}$$

Solution. In this case, we must find D, K_1, K_2, and K_3, where it is evident that we have replaced x_1, x_2, and x_3 by x, y, and z, respectively.

$$D = \begin{vmatrix} 3 & -1 & 2 \\ 2 & 1 & -1 \\ 1 & 2 & -3 \end{vmatrix} = -2; \qquad K_1 = \begin{vmatrix} 9 & -1 & 2 \\ 7 & 1 & -1 \\ 4 & 2 & -3 \end{vmatrix} = -6;$$

$$K_2 = \begin{vmatrix} 3 & 9 & 2 \\ 2 & 7 & -1 \\ 1 & 4 & -3 \end{vmatrix} = -4; \qquad K_3 = \begin{vmatrix} 3 & -1 & 9 \\ 2 & 1 & 7 \\ 1 & 2 & 4 \end{vmatrix} = -2.$$

It follows that $x = K_1/D = (-6)/(-2) = 3$, $y = K_2/D = (-4)/(-2) = 2$, $z = K_3/D = (-2)/(-2) = 1$, and it is a simple matter to check the solution $(3, 2, 1)$ in the system of equations.

Note. Instead of using Cramer's Rule to determine all the unknowns, as we did in the illustration, it is usually easier to find the third unknown by substitution, after we have determined the first two. For example, after we found $x = 3$ and $y = 2$ for the above system, a substitution in the first equation gives $9 - 2 + 2z = 9$, from which $2z = 2$ and $z = 1$; the second and third equations may then be used for checking purposes.

The procedure, which we have just given for the solution of n equations in n unknowns, is quite general in its application, but we must point out the following limitations:

1. If D, the determinant of the matrix of coefficients, is 0, this method may not be used.
2. If more than three equations are involved, the computation of the determinants becomes quite laborious.

3. The method may not be used, if the number of equations is not equal to the number of unknowns.

In the next section, we shall outline a method using only matrices, which can be used to advantage for these cases.

PROBLEM SET 11.3

Use Cramer's Rule to solve each of the systems of equations given in Problems 1 through 10.

1. $\begin{aligned} 2x_1 - 3x_2 + 8x_3 &= 19 \\ 3x_1 - x_2 + x_3 &= 6 \\ 2x_1 + 4x_2 - 3x_3 &= 7 \end{aligned}$

2. $\begin{aligned} x + 2y + z &= 7 \\ x + y - z &= 2 \\ 3x - y + 2z &= 12 \end{aligned}$

3. $\begin{aligned} A + B - C &= 7 \\ 2A - 3B - C &= 0 \\ 2A - 4B - 3C &= 0 \end{aligned}$

4. $\begin{aligned} u + v + w &= 8 \\ 5u - 5v + 4w &= 3 \\ u - 6v + 3w &= 1 \end{aligned}$

5. $\begin{aligned} 2x - 3y + 4z &= 8 \\ 3x + 4y - 5z &= -4 \\ 4x - 5y + 6z &= 12 \end{aligned}$

6. $\begin{aligned} r - 2s \qquad &= 7 \\ 3s + 5t &= 11 \\ 5r \qquad - 2t &= -3 \end{aligned}$

7. $\begin{aligned} 4/x + 5/y + 3/z &= -2 \\ 2/x - 1/y + 6/z &= 4 \\ 6/x - 4/y - 9/z &= 4 \end{aligned}$

8. $\begin{aligned} 1/x - 1/y - 1/z &= 0 \\ 3/x + 1/y + 3/z &= 1 \\ 2/x + 1/y + 1/z &= 1 \end{aligned}$

9. $\begin{aligned} x_1 - 3x_2 + 2x_3 &= 0 \\ x_1 - 2x_2 - x_3 &= 0 \\ 2x_1 - x_2 + 3x_3 &= 0 \end{aligned}$

10. $\begin{aligned} 2x + y + 2z + w &= 10 \\ 2x - 3y + z + w &= 18 \\ 5x + 2y + z - w &= 7 \\ 4x - y - 3z + 2w &= 1 \end{aligned}$

11. Check the truth of the theorem of this section, by assuming an arbitrary matrix of the third order, and applying the theorem to (*a*) the elements of the second row and the cofactors of the elements of the first row; (*b*) the elements of the third column and the cofactors of the elements of the second column.

12. If each of the right members $k_1, k_2, \cdots, k_n$ of a system of linear equations is 0, the system is said to be *homogeneous*. What does Cramer's Rule tell us about the solution of such a homogeneous system?

13. Carry out the necessary steps to establish Cramer's Rule for the determination of x_2 and x_n.

11.4 Matrices in Reduced Echelon Form

We now describe the reduction of a matrix into a form which will be extremely useful for the solution of a general system of linear equations. The three operations, called *elementary row* operations, which we shall use for this reduction may be listed as follows:

1. the interchange of any two rows of the matrix;

2. the multiplication of each element of any row of the matrix by a non-zero number;

3. the addition of any multiple of the elements of one row to the corresponding elements of another row.

A matrix, which is the result of applying any finite number of these elementary row operations to a given matrix, is said to be *row-equivalent* to the given matrix. For example, let us consider the matrix

$$\begin{pmatrix} 3 & -1 & 5 & 1 \\ 0 & 2 & -4 & 2 \\ 6 & -1 & 3 & 0 \end{pmatrix}.$$

If we interchange the first two rows, we obtain the row-equivalent matrix

$$\begin{pmatrix} 0 & 2 & -4 & 2 \\ 3 & -1 & 5 & 1 \\ 6 & -1 & 3 & 0 \end{pmatrix}.$$

If we now subtract twice the elements of the second row from the corresponding elements of the third row, leaving the second row in its present form, we obtain a matrix which is row-equivalent to each of the preceding matrices:

$$\begin{pmatrix} 0 & 2 & -4 & 2 \\ 3 & -1 & 5 & 1 \\ 0 & 1 & -7 & -2 \end{pmatrix}.$$

If we add the elements of the third row to the corresponding elements of the second row, leaving the third row unchanged, the result is the matrix

$$\begin{pmatrix} 0 & 2 & -4 & 2 \\ 3 & 0 & -2 & -1 \\ 0 & 1 & -7 & -2 \end{pmatrix},$$

which is also row-equivalent to each of the preceding matrices. It should be clear by now that row-equivalent matrices may not look alike. However, it is possible to apply elementary row operations to a matrix to produce a standard or *canonical* form, which will characterize the matrix. By this we mean that, while different operations may be used to put a matrix into this form, the final matrix will be invariant. We now give a description of one of these canonical forms.

Let us refer to the first non-zero entry of any row of a matrix as its *leading* entry. A matrix with integral elements is then said to be in *reduced echelon* form if it satisfies the following conditions:

1. the elements of any row are relatively prime, i.e., the only factor which is common to all is 1;

2. the column containing the leading entry of any row has 0 for all its other entries;

3. the leading entry of any non-zero row is positive;

4. if the leading entry of the ith row appears in the t_i th column, then $t_1 < t_2 < t_3 < \cdots < t_r$, where r is the number of non-zero rows;

5. all the zero rows appear below the non-zero rows.

The following are examples of matrices, with elements in reduced echelon form:

$$\begin{pmatrix} 1 & 0 & 0 \\ 0 & 1 & 0 \\ 0 & 0 & 2 \end{pmatrix}, \quad \begin{pmatrix} 1 & 0 & 0 & 1 \\ 0 & 3 & 2 & -1 \\ 0 & 0 & 0 & 0 \end{pmatrix}, \quad \begin{pmatrix} 2 & 2 & 0 & 0 & 1 \\ 0 & 0 & 1 & 0 & -1 \\ 0 & 0 & 0 & 1 & 2 \\ 0 & 0 & 0 & 0 & 0 \\ 0 & 0 & 0 & 0 & 0 \end{pmatrix}.$$

We now state the important result of this section.

THEOREM. Any matrix with integral elements is row-equivalent to a matrix with integral elements, in reduced echelon form.

We shall not give a formal proof of this theorem. Instead, we shall show by examples how such a reduction can be carried out, and then give a few suggestions as a guide.

ILLUSTRATION 1. Reduce the given matrix to reduced echelon form with integral elements:

$$\begin{pmatrix} 3 & -1 & 5 & 1 \\ 0 & 2 & -4 & 2 \\ 6 & -1 & 3 & 0 \end{pmatrix}.$$

Solution. We shall refer to the first, second, and third rows of the matrix by (1), (2), and (3), respectively.

$$\begin{pmatrix} 3 & -1 & 5 & 1 \\ 0 & 2 & -4 & 2 \\ 6 & -1 & 3 & 0 \end{pmatrix} \xrightarrow{\text{divide (2) by 2}} \begin{pmatrix} 3 & -1 & 5 & 1 \\ 0 & 1 & -2 & 1 \\ 6 & -1 & 3 & 0 \end{pmatrix} \xrightarrow{\text{subtract 2(1) from (3)}}$$

$$\begin{pmatrix} 3 & -1 & 5 & 1 \\ 0 & 1 & -2 & 1 \\ 0 & 1 & -7 & -2 \end{pmatrix} \xrightarrow{\text{add (2) to (1)}} \begin{pmatrix} 3 & 0 & 3 & 2 \\ 0 & 1 & -2 & 1 \\ 0 & 1 & -7 & -2 \end{pmatrix} \xrightarrow{\text{subtract (2) from (3)}}$$

$$\begin{pmatrix} 3 & 0 & 3 & 2 \\ 0 & 1 & -2 & 1 \\ 0 & 0 & -5 & -3 \end{pmatrix} \xrightarrow{\text{add 3(3) to 5(1)}} \begin{pmatrix} 15 & 0 & 0 & 1 \\ 0 & 1 & -2 & 1 \\ 0 & 0 & -5 & -3 \end{pmatrix} \xrightarrow{\text{subtract 2(3) from 5(2)}}$$

$$\begin{pmatrix} 15 & 0 & 0 & 1 \\ 0 & 5 & 0 & 11 \\ 0 & 0 & -5 & -3 \end{pmatrix} \xrightarrow{\text{multiply (3) by } -1} \begin{pmatrix} 15 & 0 & 0 & 1 \\ 0 & 5 & 0 & 11 \\ 0 & 0 & 5 & 3 \end{pmatrix}.$$

The final matrix has the desired reduced echelon form.

ILLUSTRATION 2. Reduce the following matrix to reduced echelon form, with integral elements:

$$\begin{pmatrix} 2 & 1 & 4 \\ 1 & -2 & 3 \\ 3 & 4 & 1 \end{pmatrix}.$$

Solution.

$$\begin{pmatrix} 2 & 1 & 4 \\ 1 & -2 & 3 \\ 3 & 4 & 1 \end{pmatrix} \xrightarrow{\text{interchange (1) and (2)}} \begin{pmatrix} 1 & -2 & 3 \\ 2 & 1 & 4 \\ 3 & 4 & 1 \end{pmatrix} \xrightarrow{\text{subtract 2(1) from (2)}}$$

$$\begin{pmatrix} 1 & -2 & 3 \\ 0 & 5 & -2 \\ 3 & 4 & 1 \end{pmatrix} \xrightarrow{\text{subtract 3(1) from (3)}} \begin{pmatrix} 1 & -2 & 3 \\ 0 & 5 & -2 \\ 0 & 10 & -8 \end{pmatrix} \xrightarrow{\text{divide (3) by 2}}$$

$$\begin{pmatrix} 1 & -2 & 3 \\ 0 & 5 & -2 \\ 0 & 5 & -4 \end{pmatrix} \xrightarrow{\text{subtract (2) from (3)}} \begin{pmatrix} 1 & -2 & 3 \\ 0 & 5 & -2 \\ 0 & 0 & -2 \end{pmatrix} \xrightarrow{\text{add 2(2) to 5(1)}}$$

$$\begin{pmatrix} 5 & 0 & 11 \\ 0 & 5 & -2 \\ 0 & 0 & -2 \end{pmatrix} \xrightarrow{\text{divide (3) by } -2} \begin{pmatrix} 5 & 0 & 11 \\ 0 & 5 & -2 \\ 0 & 0 & 1 \end{pmatrix} \xrightarrow{\text{subtract 11(3) from (1)}}$$

$$\begin{pmatrix} 5 & 0 & 0 \\ 0 & 5 & -2 \\ 0 & 0 & 1 \end{pmatrix} \xrightarrow{\text{add 2(3) to (2)}} \begin{pmatrix} 5 & 0 & 0 \\ 0 & 5 & 0 \\ 0 & 0 & 1 \end{pmatrix} \xrightarrow{\text{divide (1) and (2) by 5}}$$

$$\begin{pmatrix} 1 & 0 & 0 \\ 0 & 1 & 0 \\ 0 & 0 & 1 \end{pmatrix}.$$

The final matrix is in reduced echelon form.

There is no fixed procedure for reducing a matrix to reduced echelon form with integral elements. However, the following suggestions may be useful:

1. if the first column contains an entry 1, interchange the necessary rows to put 1 in the upper left corner of the matrix;

2. after the position of the leading entry of a given row has been established, reduce all the other entries of the column in which it occurs to 0;

3. proceed systematically with the reduction from the left side of the matrix to the right;

4. if at any stage of the reduction the elements of a row have a common factor, different from 1, divide the elements of this row by this common factor.

PROBLEM SET 11.4

Put each of the following matrices in reduced echelon form, with integral elements.

1. $\begin{pmatrix} 2 & 4 & -3 & 1 \\ 6 & -2 & 2 & -1 \\ 1 & 5 & 4 & 0 \end{pmatrix}$

2. $\begin{pmatrix} 5 & -4 & 6 & 1 \\ 2 & 7 & 3 & 0 \\ 1 & -3 & 1 & -2 \end{pmatrix}$

3. $\begin{pmatrix} 2 & 3 & 4 & 5 & 6 \\ 4 & -2 & 1 & -4 & 0 \\ 2 & -1 & -1 & 3 & 1 \end{pmatrix}$

4. $\begin{pmatrix} 4 & 5 & -6 \\ 2 & -4 & 3 \\ 7 & -1 & 0 \end{pmatrix}$

5. $\begin{pmatrix} 4 & -1 & 5 & 0 \\ 1 & -1 & 5 & 2 \\ 4 & -2 & 15 & 4 \\ 5 & -2 & 25 & 10 \end{pmatrix}$

6. $\begin{pmatrix} 3 & -5 & -2 & 1 & -6 \\ 2 & 1 & 2 & 0 & 5 \\ 8 & 2 & 4 & 0 & -6 \end{pmatrix}$

7. $\begin{pmatrix} 0 & -1 & -4 & 12 & 19 \\ 6 & 3 & 0 & 3 & 12 \\ 2 & 1 & 4 & 0 & 4 \\ -6 & -3 & 0 & 9 & 12 \end{pmatrix}$

8. $\begin{pmatrix} 3 & -6 & 6 & 1 \\ 2 & 5 & 0 & 2 \\ 5 & -2 & -3 & -1 \\ 4 & 10 & 0 & 4 \\ 6 & 15 & 0 & 6 \end{pmatrix}$

9. $$\begin{pmatrix} 6 & 2 & -8 & 5 & -3 \\ 9 & 4 & 0 & 5 & -9 \\ -3 & -2 & 8 & 0 & -2 \\ 15 & 12 & 0 & 10 & -25 \end{pmatrix}.$$

11.5 Solutions of Linear Systems with Matrices

We now return to the problem of solving a system of linear equations, i.e., of determining the unknowns of the equations so that all the equations will be satisfied simultaneously. As before, we shall assume that the unknowns are rational numbers, so that our solutions will be in $\bar{R}$. The method of solution, which we describe in this section, has none of the limitations of the determinant method discussed earlier.

We have already referred to the matrix of coefficients of the unknowns of a system of equations as the *coefficient matrix,* and if we include in this matrix an additional column consisting of the right members of the system, we have what is known as the *augmented matrix* of the system of equations. Every system of linear equations has associated with it an augmented matrix, and every matrix can be considered the augmented matrix of some system of linear equations. *Let us suppose that the augmented matrix of a system of linear equations is in reduced echelon form.* We can then classify the different possibilities into three categories:

1. The number of non-zero rows of the augmented matrix is equal to the number of unknowns of the equations.

Let us suppose, for example, that there are three unknowns x, y, and z, and that the augmented matrix is

$$\begin{pmatrix} 3 & 0 & 0 & 5 \\ 0 & 2 & 0 & 1 \\ 0 & 0 & 4 & -7 \end{pmatrix}.$$

In this case, the corresponding equations are

$$\begin{aligned} 3x \qquad\qquad &= 5 \\ 2y \qquad &= 1 \\ 4z &= -7, \end{aligned}$$

so that $x = 5/3$, $y = 1/2$, and $z = -7/4$, and the unique solution of the system is $(5/3, 1/2, -7/4)$. It is clear that there will always be a *unique* solution, if the augmented matrix has this form.

2. The number of non-zero rows is less than the number of unknowns of the equations.

Let us suppose, in this case, that there are four unknowns x, y, z, and w, and that the augmented matrix is

$$\begin{pmatrix} 4 & 0 & 0 & -1 & 6 \\ 0 & 3 & -3 & 1 & 3 \\ 0 & 0 & 0 & 0 & 0 \\ 0 & 0 & 0 & 0 & 0 \end{pmatrix}.$$

It is clear that the last two rows have no significance, as far as a solution of the equations is concerned, but the first two rows give us the corresponding equations

$$\begin{aligned} 4x \qquad\qquad\quad - w &= 6 \\ 3y - 3z + w &= 3. \end{aligned}$$

It is now possible to determine x and y from arbitrary choices for z and w. Thus, if $z = u$ and $w = v$, with u and v arbitrary rational numbers, we find that $4x = v + 6$ and $3y = 3 - v + 3u$, so that $x = 3/2 + (1/4)v$ and $y = 1 + u - (1/3)v$. The general solution of the equations may then be expressed in the form:

$$\begin{aligned} x &= 3/2 \qquad + (1/4)v \\ y &= 1 + u - (1/3)v \\ z &= \qquad u \\ w &= \qquad\qquad\quad v, \end{aligned}$$

and we emphasize again that u and v may be arbitrary rational numbers. For example, if $u = 0$ and $v = 0$, we obtain $(3/2, 1, 0, 0)$ as a solution of the system of equations, but there are infinitely many other solutions. It may be seen that there will always be infinitely many solutions, if the augmented matrix has the form described in this category.

3. The number of non-zero rows exceeds the number of unknowns of the equations.

Let us suppose, for example, that the unknowns are x, y, and z, and that the augmented matrix is

$$\begin{pmatrix} 5 & 0 & 0 & 0 \\ 0 & 2 & 0 & 0 \\ 0 & 0 & 2 & 0 \\ 0 & 0 & 0 & 1 \end{pmatrix}$$

The equations, corresponding to this augmented matrix, are easily seen to be

$$\begin{aligned} 5x \qquad\qquad\qquad &= 0 \\ 2y \qquad\quad &= 0 \\ 2z &= 0 \\ 0 &= 1. \end{aligned}$$

The last indicated equality is, of course, not satisfied for any choice of x, y, or z, and so the system of equations has no solution in this case. Whenever the augmented matrix has the form of this category, there will always be at least one indicated equality which has no solution, and so the system of equations will have no solution.

It is now apparent that if the augmented matrix of a system of linear equations is in reduced echelon form, we can tell by inspection whether the system has a unique solution, no solution, or infinitely many solutions; and furthermore, we can determine all existing solutions, immediately. Our principal problem, then, is to transform our system of equations so that its augmented matrix has reduced echelon form—*but without altering the simultaneous solutions of the equations.*

The question now before us is this: what changes may we make in a system of equations, without altering the solutions? A little reflection will reveal that the following changes are of this type:

1. the interchange of any two equations;
2. the multiplication of both members of an equation by a non-zero number;
3. the addition of any multiple of both members of one equation to the corresponding members of another equation.

If we check these allowable changes with the elementary row operations for matrices, given in the preceding section, we see that they are essentially the same, with the notion of a "row of a matrix" and an "equation" playing parallel roles. In view of the relationship between a system of equations and its augmented matrix, the following result is then evident:

THEOREM. If the augmented matrix of a system of linear equations is put in reduced echelon form, the simultaneous solutions of the equations associated with this form are the same as those of the original system of equations.

Since it is extremely easy to solve a system of equations, if its augmented matrix is in reduced echelon form, the procedure for solving an arbitrary system of linear equations in $\bar{R}$ is simply this:

> Put the augmented matrix of the system of equations in reduced echelon form, and solve the corresponding simplified equations.

We have already illustrated the three types of systems of linear equations, but we include one further example of the type that occurs most frequently —the one with a unique solution.

ILLUSTRATION. Determine the solution of the given system of equations:

$$\begin{aligned} 3x - y + 5z &= 1 \\ 2y - 4z &= 2 \\ 6x - y + 3z &= 0. \end{aligned}$$

Solution. The augmented matrix of the system of equations is

$$\begin{pmatrix} 3 & -1 & 5 & 1 \\ 0 & 2 & -4 & 2 \\ 6 & -1 & 3 & 0 \end{pmatrix}.$$

In Illustration 1 of the preceding section, the reduced echelon form of this matrix was found to be

$$\begin{pmatrix} 15 & 0 & 0 & 1 \\ 0 & 5 & 0 & 11 \\ 0 & 0 & 5 & 3 \end{pmatrix}.$$

The equations, associated with this reduced form, are

$$\begin{aligned} 15x &= 1 \\ 5y &= 11 \\ 5z &= 3, \end{aligned}$$

and from these we obtain $x = 1/15$, $y = 11/5$, and $z = 3/5$.

The unique solution of the given system is then $(1/15, 11/5, 3/5)$.

PROBLEM SET 11.5

1. The following is the reduced echelon form of the augmented matrix of a system of linear equations in three unknowns x, y, and z; solve the system of equations.

(a) $\begin{pmatrix} 3 & 0 & 0 & -4 \\ 0 & 3 & 0 & 2 \\ 0 & 0 & 5 & 6 \end{pmatrix}$; (b) $\begin{pmatrix} 6 & 0 & 0 & -5 \\ 0 & 2 & 0 & 9 \\ 0 & 0 & 1 & 0 \\ 0 & 0 & 0 & 0 \end{pmatrix}$;

(c) $\begin{pmatrix} 5 & 0 & 0 & 0 \\ 0 & 4 & 0 & 7 \\ 0 & 0 & 8 & 5 \\ 0 & 0 & 0 & 0 \\ 0 & 0 & 0 & 0 \end{pmatrix}$.

2. Solve the system of equations in three unknowns x, y, and z, the augmented matrix of which has the following reduced echelon form:

(a) $\begin{pmatrix} 5 & 0 & 0 & 6 \\ 0 & 4 & 2 & 1 \\ 0 & 0 & 0 & 0 \end{pmatrix}$; (b) $\begin{pmatrix} 4 & 0 & 0 & 9 \\ 0 & 0 & 5 & 6 \\ 0 & 0 & 0 & 0 \end{pmatrix}$;

(c) $\begin{pmatrix} 5 & 0 & 0 & 8 \\ 0 & 4 & 3 & -2 \\ 0 & 0 & 0 & 0 \\ 0 & 0 & 0 & 0 \end{pmatrix}$.

3. Solve the system of linear equations in four unknowns x, y, z, and w, the augmented matrix of which has the following reduced echelon form:

(a) $\begin{pmatrix} 2 & 0 & 0 & 0 & -5 \\ 0 & 5 & -1 & 0 & 8 \\ 0 & 0 & 0 & 4 & 7 \end{pmatrix}$; (b) $\begin{pmatrix} 6 & 5 & 0 & 0 & -2 \\ 0 & 0 & 4 & -2 & 3 \\ 0 & 0 & 0 & 0 & 0 \end{pmatrix}$.

If possible, use the matrix method to solve the systems of linear equations given in Problems 4 through 10.

4. $\begin{aligned} x - y + 2z &= -2 \\ 3x - 2y + 4z &= -5 \\ 2y - 3z &= 2 \end{aligned}$

5. $\begin{aligned} x + y - 5z &= 26 \\ x + 2y + z &= -4 \\ x + 3y + 7z &= -34 \end{aligned}$

6. $\begin{aligned} -4x + y + t &= -10 \\ -2x + 2z + t &= -4 \\ -7x + 2y + 2z &= -15 \end{aligned}$

7. $\begin{aligned} 3x - y + 2z &= 3 \\ 2x + 2y + z &= 2 \\ x - 3y + z &= 4 \end{aligned}$

8. $\begin{aligned} x - z &= 26 \\ x - y - 3z &= -6 \\ y + 2z &= 9 \end{aligned}$

9. $\begin{aligned} 2x + 3y + 4z &= 0 \\ 3x + 4y + 5z &= 0 \\ 5x + 7y + 9z &= 0 \end{aligned}$

10. $\begin{aligned} 2x + 3y - z - t &= 0 \\ x - y - 2z - 4t &= 0 \\ 3x + 3y - 7t &= 0 \end{aligned}$

11.6 Partial Fractions

In Chapter 8 we characterized a *rational* expression in x as the quotient of two rational polynomials, and we may assume, without loss of generality, that the coefficients of the polynomials are integers. We shall refer to such a rational expression $P[x]/Q[x]$ as a *proper fraction* if the degree of $P[x]$ is less than the degree of $Q[x]$. It is always possible to use long division to change a rational expression in x into either a rational polynomial, or the sum of a rational polynomial and a proper fraction. For certain purposes, especially in the calculus, it may be desirable to expand this proper fraction into a sum of simpler fractions, and this is possible if the denominator of the fraction is factorable. These simpler fractions are known as *partial fractions*, and we state the following theorem, without proof.

THEOREM. Any proper fraction, having rational polynomials for both its numerator and denominator, may be expressed as a sum of partial fractions, which are related to the factors of the denominator as follows:

1. for every linear factor $ax + b$, that appears to the rth power, there is a sum of r fractions of the form $A_1/(ax + b) + A_2/(ax + b)^2 + \cdots + A_r/(ax + b)^r$;

2. for every quadratic factor $ax^2 + bx + c$, that appears to the rth power, there is a sum of r fractions of the form $(D_1x + E_1)/(ax^2 + bx + c) + (D_2x + E_2)/(ax^2 + bx + c)^2 + \cdots + (D_rx + E_r)/(ax^2 + bx + c)^r$.

The numbers $A_1, A_2, \cdots, A_r, D_1, D_2, \cdots, D_r, E_1, E_2, \cdots, E_r$ are rational numbers, which may be determined by the methods of the illustrations below. The representation of a proper fraction as a sum of partial fractions will be understood to be an identity.

ILLUSTRATION 1. Resolve $(2x + 11)/[(x - 2)(x + 3)]$ into partial fractions.

Solution. The above theorem implies that there exist rational numbers A and B such that the equation

$$\frac{2x + 11}{(x - 2)(x + 3)} = \frac{A}{x - 2} + \frac{B}{x + 3}$$

is an identity. We are assuming that $x \neq 2$ and $x \neq -3$ (according to the definition of an identity), so we may multiply both members of this equality by $(x - 2)(x + 3)$ and obtain

$$2x + 11 = A(x + 3) + B(x - 2).$$

This polynomial identity is, of course, different from the identity assumed above, but the two are related in the following way: if A and B are chosen so that the latter equation is an identity (an equality for every real number x), the former equation will also be an identity (an equality for every real number x, except $x = 2$ and $x = -3$). We then consider the new identity, and notice that a simple equation results if we let $x = 2$ or $x = -3$. These equations are $15 = 5A$ and $5 = -5B$, from which we obtain $A = 3$ and $B = -1$. The desired resolution is then

$$\frac{2x + 11}{(x - 2)(x + 3)} = \frac{3}{x - 2} - \frac{1}{x + 3}.$$

Note. Our choices of substitutions for x are based on a matter of simplicity rather than of necessity. It is clear that any real number may be substituted for x, but if we select a number that makes at least one of the terms of the polynomial identity equal to zero, the resulting equations will be much easier to solve.

ILLUSTRATION 2. Resolve $(-2x^3 + 9x^2 - 10x + 9)/[(x - 1)^3(x + 2)]$ into partial fractions.

Solution. In this case, the theorem implies the existence of rational numbers A, B, C, and D, such that

$$\frac{-2x^3 + 9x^2 - 10x + 9}{(x - 1)^3(x + 2)} = \frac{A}{(x - 1)^3} + \frac{B}{(x - 1)^2} + \frac{C}{x - 1} + \frac{D}{x + 2}$$

is an identity. We assume, for this identity, that $x \neq 1$ and $x \neq -2$, so that $(x - 1)^3(x + 2) \neq 0$; and if we multiply both members of the equality by this quantity, the result is $-2x^3 + 9x^2 - 10x + 9 = A(x + 2) + B(x - 1)(x + 2) + C(x - 1)^2(x + 2) + D(x - 1)^3$.

We now use the same argument as was used in Illustration 1, and determine A, B, C, and D so that this new equation is an identity. As in the preceding illustration, we can let $x = 1$ and $x = -2$ to obtain A and D. Thus, if $x = 1$, $6 = 3A$ and so $A = 2$; if $x = -2$, $81 = -27D$ and so $D = -3$. In order to determine B and C it is now necessary to make respective replacements of x by two other numbers, say 0 and -1. Then $9 = 2A - 2B + 2C - D = 7 - 2B + 2C$ or $C - B = 1$; and $30 = A - 2B + 4C - 8D = 26 - 2B + 4C$ or $2C - B = 2$. The two equations

$$C - B = 1$$

$$2C - B = 2$$

may be readily solved, and we find that $B = 0$ and $C = 1$. The desired decomposition is then

$$\frac{2}{(x - 1)^3} + \frac{1}{x - 1} - \frac{3}{x + 2}.$$

Note. The procedure of this illustration is recommended, whenever the denominator of the original fraction contains linear factors that are repeated. Since it is necessary to make some substitutions for x which do not reduce any of the terms of the polynomial identity to zero, this method of solution will be more complicated than in the case of non-repeated factors.

ILLUSTRATION 3. Resolve $\dfrac{3x^3 - x^2 + 1}{(x^2 + 1)(x^2 + 2)}$ into partial fractions.

Solution. We must determine rational numbers A, B, C, and D, so that

$$\frac{3x^3 - x^2 + 1}{(x^2+1)(x^2+2)} = \frac{Ax+B}{x^2+1} + \frac{Cx+D}{x^2+2}$$

is an identity. The related polynomial identity is $3x^3 - x^2 + 1 = (Ax + B)(x^2 + 2) + (Cx + D)(x^2 + 1)$, which may also be written in the form $3x^3 - x^2 + 1 = (A + C)x^3 + (B + D)x^2 + (2A + C)x + 2B + D$.

We may now apply Theorem 2 of Section 10.5, and equate corresponding coefficients of x, obtaining the following equations:

$$\begin{aligned} A \quad\quad + C \quad\quad &= 3 \\ B \quad\quad + D &= -1 \\ 2A \quad\quad + C \quad\quad &= 0 \\ 2B \quad\quad + D &= 1 \end{aligned}$$

The augmented matrix of this system of equations is

$$\begin{pmatrix} 1 & 0 & 1 & 0 & 3 \\ 0 & 1 & 0 & 1 & -1 \\ 2 & 0 & 1 & 0 & 0 \\ 0 & 2 & 0 & 1 & 1 \end{pmatrix},$$

and the reduced echelon form of this matrix is easily found to be

$$\begin{pmatrix} 1 & 0 & 0 & 0 & -3 \\ 0 & 1 & 0 & 0 & 2 \\ 0 & 0 & 1 & 0 & 6 \\ 0 & 0 & 0 & 1 & -3 \end{pmatrix}.$$

We now see that $A = -3$, $B = 2$, $C = 6$, and $D = -3$, so that the desired decomposition is

$$\frac{-3x+2}{x^2+1} + \frac{6x-3}{x^2+2}.$$

Note. If the denominator of the original fraction contains no linear factors, there are no *convenient* substitutions for x, and so an application of Theorem 2 of Section 10.5 is recommended, as in the above illustration.

ILLUSTRATION 4. Resolve $\dfrac{49}{(x-2)(x^2+3)^2}$ into partial fractions.

Solution. We must determine A, B, C, D, and E, so that

$$\frac{49}{(x-2)(x^2+3)^2} = \frac{A}{x-2} + \frac{Bx+C}{x^2+3} + \frac{Dx+E}{(x^2+3)^2}$$

is an identity. The associated polynomial identity is $49 = A(x^2+3)^2 + (Bx+C)(x-2)(x^2+3) + (Dx+E)(x-2)$, which may also be written in the form $49 = (A+B)x^4 + (C-2B)x^3 + (6A+3B-2C+D)x^2 + (-6B+3C-2D+E)x + 9A - 6C - 2E$.

If we now apply Theorem 2 of Section 10.5, and equate corresponding coefficients of x, we obtain the following system of equations:

$$\begin{aligned} A + B \qquad\qquad\qquad &= 0 \\ -2B + C \qquad\qquad &= 0 \\ 6A + 3B - 2C + D \qquad &= 0 \\ 6B - 3C + 2D - E &= 0 \\ 9A - 6C - 2E &= 49. \end{aligned}$$

This system of equations can be solved by the matrix method, but it is simpler to take advantage of the special form of the system. Thus, if we let $x = 2$ in the first form of the polynomial identity above, we obtain $49 = 49A$ and so $A = 1$. If we now use the above equations, successively, as they appear, we obtain $B = -1$, $C = -2$, $D = -7$, and $E = -14$, and the desired decomposition is

$$\frac{49}{(x-2)(x^2+3)^2} = \frac{1}{x-2} - \frac{x+2}{x^2+3} - \frac{7x+14}{(x^2+3)^2}.$$

Note. This example illustrates the fact that no one procedure is always the best for a particular type of problem. However, whenever a linear factor $x - r$ appears in the denominator of the rational fraction which we wish to expand, a substitution of $x = r$ in the associated polynomial identity will always simplify the problem of solving the system of linear equations.

PROBLEM SET 11.6

In Problems 1 through 15, resolve the given rational expression into partial fractions.

1. $(x-2)/[(x+1)(x-1)]$.
2. $(2x+3)/[(2x+1)(x-1)]$.
3. $6/[(x+2)(2x-1)]$.
4. $3x/[(x-2)(3x+1)]$.
5. $(x-1)/[(x+2)^2(x+1)]$.
6. $(2x^2-1)/[x(3x-1)^3]$.
7. $(x^3+1)/(x^2+3)^3$.
8. $x/[(x-1)(x^2+4)^2]$.
9. $(6x^4+4x+1)/[x^3(x^2+x+1)^2]$.
10. $1/[x^3(1+x^2)]$.

11. $(x^4 - 3)/[(x - 1)(x^2 + 1)]$. **12.** $(12 + 6x^2)/(x^3 + 4x^2 + 3x)$.
13. $(x^4 + 1)/[(x^2 - 1)(x^2 + 1)]$.
14. $(7x^3 + 4x^2 + 2x - 4)/[x^3(x^2 + 2x + 2)]$.
15. $(2x^2 + 9x - 18)/(x^2 - 3x - 10)$.
16. Determine A, B, and C, if the polynomial function f, defined on $R^\#$ by $f(x) = Ax^2 + Bx + C$, contains the points $(-1, 2)$, $(3, -3)$, and $(-4, -1)$.
17. Determine the numbers A, B, C, and D, if the locus of the equation $y = Ax^3 + Bx^2 + Cx + D$ contains the points $(-2, 3)$, $(0, 3)$, $(1, 5)$, and $(3, -6)$.
18. Determine A, B, C, D, and E, if the polynomial function f, defined on $R^\#$ by $f(x) = Ax^4 + Bx^3 + Cx^2 + Dx + E$, contains the points $(-3, -4)$, $(-1, -6)$, $(1, 5)$, $(2, -4)$, and $(3, 3)$.

11.7 Simultaneous Linear and Quadratic Equations

The most general equation of the second degree in two unknowns x and y may be expressed as $Ax^2 + Bxy + Cy^2 + Dx + Ey + F = 0$, while the corresponding general equation of the first degree has the form $ax + by + c = 0$.

In this section we review the usual method of determining a solution set of a pair of such equations. The procedure is to use the linear equation to express one unknown in terms of the other, substitute this expression in the second-degree equation, and solve the resulting quadratic equation by one of the methods of Chapter 10. The solutions of the quadratic equation will determine the one unknown, while the other can now be found by substituting the solution just found in the *linear* equation and solving. If $x = x_1$ and $y = y_1$ are numbers which satisfy the equations, simultaneously, we shall continue the practice established earlier and refer to (x_1, y_1) as a solution of the system of equations. We illustrate this method with a couple of examples.

ILLUSTRATION 1. Determine the integral solution set of the following system of equations:

$$4x^2 + y^2 = 68$$

$$2x + y = 10.$$

Solution. We can use the linear equation to express y in terms of x, and write $y = 10 - 2x$. On substitution of this expression for y in the other equation, we obtain $4x^2 + (10 - 2x)^2 = 68$, which reduces to $x^2 - 5x + 4 = 0$. The left member may be factored into $(x - 4)(x - 1)$, so that $x = 4$ or $x = 1$. From the linear equation we obtain $y = 2$ if $x = 4$, and $y = 8$ if $x = 1$, and so the desired solution set is $\{(4, 2), (1, 8)\}$.

ILLUSTRATION 2. Determine the rational solution set of the following system of equations:

$$3x - 5y = 3$$
$$xy = 12.$$

Solution. In this case, it is more convenient to use the second-degree equation to express y in terms of x. Thus, $y = 12/x$, and on substitution of this expression for y in the linear equation, we obtain $3x - 60/x = 3$, which reduces to $x^2 - x - 20 = 0$. If we factor the left member, this equation becomes $(x - 5)(x + 4) = 0$, so that $x = 5$ or $x = -4$. Since $y = 12/x$, we find that $y = 12/5$ if $x = 5$, and $y = -3$ if $x = -4$, so that the desired solution set is $\{(5, 12/5), (-4, -3)\}$.

A quadratic equation always has either one or two complex (possibly real) solutions, and a pair of equations, one linear and one second-degree, will always have either one or two simultaneous solutions in the set of complex numbers. There is no guarantee, however, that these solutions will be rational or even real. There is one point which should always be emphasized, in connection with the solution of equations: regardless of the simplicity or complexity of the method of obtaining an alleged solution of an equation, the final test of the solution is that it satisfies the equation, and it it fails in this test, it should be rejected. Since extraneous "solutions" frequently arise in certain methods of solving equations, this test should be applied to each "solution" obtained, before it is to be accepted.

PROBLEM SET 11.7

Assume that x and y are real numbers, and determine the solution set of each of the following pairs of equations.

1. $x^2 + y^2 = 25$
$x - 7y + 25 = 0.$

2. $y^2 - 4x = 0$
$y + 4x = 0.$

3. $3x^2 + 2y^2 = 11$
$3x - 4y = 11.$

4. $x^2 + 3xy + y^2 = 4$
$x - y - 7 = 0.$

5. $3x - 2y - 6 = 0$
$xy - 12 = 0.$

6. $3x + 2y - 6 = 0$
$xy + 12 = 0.$

7. $x^2 + y^2 + 2x - 4y - 20 = 0$
$3x + 4y = 30.$

8. $2x^2 + 6x + 5y + 1 = 0$
$2x + y + 3 = 0.$

9. $x = ay$
$3x - 2y^2 = a^2.$

10. $xy + 1 = c^2$
$x - y = 2.$

11. Assume that x and y are complex numbers, not necessarily real, and determine the solution set of the following pair of equations:

$$x^2 + y^2 = 4$$
$$2y = x + 6.$$

12. Assume that x and y are complex numbers, not necessarily real, and determine the solution set of the following pair of equations:

$$xy = 1$$

$$x + y = 1.$$

11.8 Simultaneous Quadratic Systems

The problem of solving two arbitrary equations of the second degree in two unknowns is quite complicated, and we shall not discuss it. Instead, we shall indicate methods for solving some of the common, but special, second-degree or quadratic systems.

1. SYSTEMS OF EQUATIONS OF THE FORM $Ax^2 + By^2 = C$. A system of two equations in this form can be solved as a linear system, if we consider x^2 and y^2 to be auxiliary unknowns. The numbers x and y are then the respective square roots of the solutions for x^2 and y^2.

ILLUSTRATION 1. Determine the real solution set of the pair of equations:

$$4x^2 + y^2 = 61$$

$$2x^2 + 3y^2 = 93.$$

Solution. If we multiply both members of the first equation by 3, the resulting system is

$$12x^2 + 3y^2 = 183$$

$$2x^2 + 3y^2 = 93.$$

We may now subtract the members of the second equation from the corresponding members of the first, and obtain $10x^2 = 90$, $x^2 = 9$, and $x = 3$ or $x = -3$. If we substitute either of these solutions for x in the original first equation, the result is $36 + y^2 = 61$, $y^2 = 25$, and $y = 5$ or $y = -5$. The complete solution set of the system is then $\{(3, 5), (3, -5), (-3, 5), (-3, -5)\}$, as may be easily checked.

2. SYSTEMS OF EQUATIONS OF THE FORM $Ax^2 + Bxy + Cy^2 = D$. A system of two equations of this form can be solved by a method which eliminates the terms not involving x or y.

ILLUSTRATION 2. Determine the real solution set of the pair of equations:

$$9x^2 + 4y^2 = 10$$

$$3xy - 2y^2 = -2.$$

Solution. If we multiply both members of the second equation by 5, and add these members to the corresponding members of the first equation, the transformed first equation is $9x^2 + 15xy - 6y^2 = 0$ or $3x^2 + 5xy - 2y^2 = 0$. The left member of this equation can be factored, so that $(3x - y)(x + 2y) = 0$, and $y = 3x$ or $x = -2y$.

a. $y = 3x$. If we substitute $3x$ for y, the first equation becomes $9x^2 + 36x^2 = 10$, $45x^2 = 10$, $x^2 = 2/9$, and $x = \sqrt{2}/3$ or $x = -\sqrt{2}/3$. Since $y = 3x$, we obtain $y = \sqrt{2}$ if $x = \sqrt{2}/3$, and $y = -\sqrt{2}$ if $x = -\sqrt{2}/3$.

b. $x = -2y$. If we substitute $-2y$ for x in the first equation, the result is $36y^2 + 4y^2 = 10$ or $40y^2 = 10$, so that $y^2 = 1/4$ and $y = 1/2$ or $y = -1/2$. Since $x = -2y$, we obtain $x = 1$ if $y = -1/2$, and $x = -1$ if $y = 1/2$.

The complete set of solutions is now seen to be $\{(\sqrt{2}/3, \sqrt{2}), (-\sqrt{2}/3, -\sqrt{2}), (1, -1/2), (-1, 1/2)\}$, as may be easily verified by the second equation.

3. Some quadratic systems can be solved by some special device appropriate to the system at hand.

ILLUSTRATION 3. Determine the complex solution set of the system of equations:

$$y^2 - x^2 - 2x + 5 = 0$$
$$5y^2 + x^2 - x - 2 = 0.$$

Solution. If we multiply both members of the first equation by 5, and subtract them from the corresponding members of the second equation, the resulting second equation does not involve y: $6x^2 + 9x - 27 = 0$, i.e., $2x^2 + 3x - 9 = 0$. On factoring the left member of this equation, we obtain $(2x - 3)(x + 3) = 0$, so that $x = 3/2$ or $x = -3$. We now substitute each of these solutions, in turn, in the first equation and determine the corresponding solutions for y. Thus, if $x = 3/2$, $y^2 - 9/4 - 3 + 5 = 0$ or simply $y^2 = 1/4$, and $y = 1/2$ or $y = -1/2$; if $x = -3$, $y^2 - 9 + 6 + 5 = 0$, $y^2 = -2$, and so $y = \sqrt{2}\,i$ or $y = -\sqrt{2}\,i$. The complex solution set is then $\{(3/2, 1/2), (3/2, -1/2), (-3, \sqrt{2}\,i), (-3, -\sqrt{2}\,i)\}$.

Notice that there would be only two members of the *real* solution set of these equations.

4. SYMMETRIC SYSTEMS. An equation in x and y is *symmetric*, if it remains unaltered if x and y are interchanged. A system of two symmetric equations in x and y can be solved by substituting $x = u + v$ and $y = u - v$, followed by an elimination of v^2 from the resulting system of equations in u and v. After u and v have been determined, the unknowns x and y can be found readily. We shall not illustrate this type of system.

PROBLEM SET 11.8

Determine the complete solution set of each of the following systems of equations, allowing x and y to be complex if necessary.

1. $4x^2 + 3y^2 = 48$
$x^2 + y^2 = 13.$

2. $7x^2 - 3y^2 = 2$
$3x^2 + y^2 = 42.$

3. $4x^2 - 3y^2 = 9$
$5x^2 - 8y^2 = 41.$

4. $2x^2 - xy = 12$
$xy + y^2 = 6.$

5. $x^2 - y^2 = 18$
$2x^2 + xy - y^2 = 54.$

6. $x^2 + xy = 3$
$xy + 2y^2 = 2.$

7. $3x^2 + y^2 + 4y - 24 = 0$
$x^2 - y^2 - 4y + 20 = 0.$

8. $5x^2 - 6xy + 5y^2 = 8$
$x^2 + y^2 = 1.$

9. $2x^2 - xy = 24$
$y^2 + xy = 12.$

10. $x^2 + xy + y^2 = 39$
$xy - 3x - 3y = -11.$

11. $2x^2 + y^2 - 4y - 23 = 0$
$5x^2 - y^2 - 3y - 5 = 0.$

12. $2x^2 - 3xy = 5$
$2xy - 3y^2 = 2.$

REVIEW TEST A

1. Use Cramer's Rule to solve each of the following systems of equations, assuming the unknowns to be rational numbers:

(*a*) $3x - 4y = 11$
$4x + 3y = -2;$

(*b*) $2x - y + 4z = 10$
$4x + 2y - z = -2$
$4x - 3y + 2z = 9.$

2. Evaluate the indicated determinant, in terms of the elements of the third column. Check the result by reevaluating it in terms of the elements of the second row.

$$\begin{vmatrix} 2 & -1 & 1 \\ 0 & 1 & 4 \\ -2 & 4 & -3 \end{vmatrix}$$

3. A man invests \$4000, part of it at 4% interest and part of it at 6%. If his total interest earnings for one year amount to \$190, how much money does he have invested at each rate?

4. Use the matrix method to determine the solution set of the following system of equations, assuming the unknowns to be rational numbers:

$$3x + 2y - z = 1$$
$$4x + y + 2z = 13$$
$$x - 3y + 3z = 14.$$

5. Use the matrix method to solve the following system of equations, assuming the unknowns to be rational numbers:

$$\begin{aligned} 2x \quad\quad\; + z - \;\; w &= 6 \\ x + 2y - z - 3w &= 3 \\ 3x + 2y + z \quad\quad\; &= 3. \end{aligned}$$

6. Determine the rational numbers A and B, so that the following equation is an identity:

$$\frac{3x + 5}{x^2 + 4x + 3} = \frac{A}{x + 1} + \frac{B}{x + 3}.$$

7. Determine the rational numbers A, B, and C, so that the following equation is an identity:

$$\frac{x^2 + 2}{(x^2 + 1)(x - 1)} = \frac{Ax + B}{x^2 + 1} + \frac{C}{x - 1}.$$

8. Determine the solution set of the following pair of equations, allowing x and y to be non-real numbers, if necessary.

$$\begin{aligned} x^2 - y^2 &= 24 \\ 2x - y &= \;\; 9. \end{aligned}$$

9. Determine the complete solution set of the following pair of equations, allowing x and y to be non-real numbers, if necessary:

$$\begin{aligned} 4x^2 - 5xy + y^2 &= 10 \\ 3x^2 - 3xy - y^2 &= \;\; 5. \end{aligned}$$

10. Determine the rational solutions of the following homogeneous system of equations:

$$\begin{aligned} 3x - 4y + 5z &= 0 \\ 7x - 2y - \;\, z &= 0 \\ 2x + \;\, y - 3z &= 0. \end{aligned}$$

11. If the electrical resistance of two resistors is R_1 and R_2 ohms, respectively, their combined resistance in series is $R_1 + R_2$ ohms, while their combined resistance in parallel is R_p ohms where $1/R_p = 1/R_1 + 1/R_2$. Determine the approximate resistance of two resistors, which give a total resistance of 10 ohms in series and 2.0 ohms in parallel.

12. Assume x to be rational, and solve the following equation for x:

$$\begin{vmatrix} 1 - x & 2 & 0 \\ -2 & x + 1 & 2 \\ 0 & -2 & 1 - x \end{vmatrix} = 0.$$

REVIEW TEST B

1. Use Cramer's Rule to solve each of the following systems of equations, assuming the unknowns to be rational numbers:

(a) $$\begin{aligned} 3x + 4y &= 6 \\ 5x + 3y &= -1; \end{aligned}$$

(b) $$\begin{aligned} 2x - 2y + 3z &= 0 \\ x - y + 2z &= -1 \\ 3x + y - 2z &= 9. \end{aligned}$$

2. Evaluate the indicated determinant, in terms of the elements of the second column. Check the result by reevaluating it in terms of the elements of the third row.

$$\begin{vmatrix} -2 & 3 & -1 \\ 1 & 4 & 1 \\ 2 & 0 & -2 \end{vmatrix}.$$

3. The flight time from one city to another was recorded as 1 hour and 30 minutes, with a tail wind of 27 miles per hour. On the return trip against the wind, the time of flight was 2 hours. Determine the air speed of the plane, and the distance between the cities.
4. Use the matrix method to determine the solution set of the following system of equations, assuming the unknowns to be rational numbers:

$$\begin{aligned} 2x - 3y + z &= 7 \\ 3x + y - 2z &= -13 \\ 4x - 2y + 3z &= 4. \end{aligned}$$

5. Use the matrix method to solve the following system of equations, assuming the unknowns to be rational numbers:

$$\begin{aligned} 2x + 3y - z \qquad &= 1 \\ x + y + z - 2w &= 2 \\ 3x \qquad - 2z + 4w &= -5. \end{aligned}$$

6. Determine the rational numbers A and B, so that the following equation is an identity:

$$\frac{x + 1}{x^2 - 3x + 2} = \frac{A}{x - 1} + \frac{B}{x - 2}.$$

7. Determine the rational numbers A, B, and C, so that the following equation is an identity:

$$\frac{2x^2 - 2x + 1}{(x^2 + x + 1)(x + 2)} = \frac{Ax + B}{x^2 + x + 1} + \frac{C}{x + 2}.$$

8. Determine the solution set of the following pair of equations, allowing x and y to be non-real numbers, if necessary:

$$7x^2 - 4y^2 = 3$$
$$3x + 2y = 1.$$

9. Determine the solution set of the following pair of equations, allowing x and y to be non-real numbers, if necessary:

$$3x^2 + 2y^2 = 30$$
$$3y^2 - 5x^2 = 7.$$

10. Determine the rational solutions of the following system of homogeneous equations:

$$2x - 3y - 2z = 0$$
$$6x + y - z = 0$$
$$2x + 5y + 2z = 0.$$

11. Three numbers, forming an arithmetic sequence, have a sum of 25. If the difference between the smallest and largest is 2 less than twice the middle number, determine the three numbers.

12. Assume x to be rational, and solve the following equation for x:

$$\begin{vmatrix} x & -6 & 4 \\ -7 & 2 & 9 \\ 2 & 3 & 1 \end{vmatrix} = 0.$$

REFERENCES

Books

BRIXEY, JOHN C. AND RICHARD V. ANDREE, *Fundamentals of College Mathematics*, New York, Holt, 1954. (Pp. 364–379.)

SISAM, CHARLES H., *College Mathematics*, New York, Holt, 1946. (Chaps. 7 and 9.)

American Mathematical Monthly

WHITFORD, D. E. AND M. S. KLAMKIN, "On an Elementary Derivation of Cramer's Rule," Vol. 60, p. 186 (1953).

12

PLANE ANALYTIC GEOMETRY I: CURVE SKETCHING

"And they drew all manner of things—everything that begins with an M." "Why with an M?" said Alice. "Why not?" said the March Hare.

LEWIS CARROLL

12.1 Introduction

Geometry is one of the subjects studied intensively by Greek mathematicians of classical times. This Greek geometry was essentially a study of curves and figures, defined by certain physical properties. But the tremendous genius of the Greeks enabled them to make discoveries about these curves which, while easy with modern methods, are quite remarkable when we consider the theoretical equipment at their disposal. In fact, in spite of handicaps, a substantial part of the modern geometry of curves was known to the Greeks.

Three geometry problems arose at an early date in Greek history, and a large part of the work done in mathematics by the Greeks in classical times was due to attempts to solve these problems. These three famous problems are:

1. to construct a square, equal in area to a given circle, i.e., to "square the circle";

2. to divide a given angle into three equal parts, i.e., to "trisect an angle";

3. to construct an edge of a cube, the volume of which shall be twice that of a given cube, i.e., to "duplicate the cube."

By the time of Plato, it was generally considered a requirement, in the solution of these problems, that only a straight edge and compasses be used. It is now known that all three problems are incapable of solution under such requirements, but nevertheless a great deal of important mathematics was discovered in the many futile attempts to solve them.

The idea of a coordinate system dates back to Menaechmus and Apollonius in classical Greek times. However, the publication of *La*

Géométrie by René Descartes in 1637, made such an impact on subsequent mathematical thinking that this event is usually considered to mark the entry of analytic geometry into the history of mathematics. It was Descartes who first considered equations in two unknowns and their related graphs, and this brings us to the two central problems which underlie all plane analytic geometry: (*a*) given an equation in two unknowns x and y, to determine the plane graph of all solutions (x, y) of the equation, i.e., its locus; (*b*) given a set of points, defined on a plane by some geometric condition, to determine an equation which has the set of points for its locus.

It is with the first of these problems that we are going to be concerned, in this chapter; and since it is a geometric custom to refer to a plane locus as a *curve*, we shall then be considering the appearances of curves, from their known equations. The problem of determining the exact locus of an equation would, of course, involve the location of an endless number of points. However, for most purposes it is sufficient to obtain a rough approximation or *sketch* of the locus, usually in some finite neighborhood of the origin. We now proceed to a discussion of some of the techniques associated with the sketching of curves.

12.2 Review of Graphs of the Elementary Functions

We have previously referred to the set of all points (x, y), with real coordinates satisfying an equation, as the *locus* of the equation. This is the graph of the solution set of the equation, and it should not be overlooked by the student that this solution set constitutes the relation defined in $R^{\#}$ by the equation. Any relation, defined on its domain by one or more equations, may be considered the intersection of subsets of the solution sets in $R^{\#}$ of these equations. Thus, while the loci of equations are of geometric interest in themselves, some familiarity with these loci is necessary for the graphing of relations of this type. The basic functions, which were introduced in Chapter 5, may be considered the solution sets in $R^{\#}$ of certain equations, and so their graphs are the loci of these equations. This section is inserted as a review of these graphs. In connection with functions, we have always emphasized the correspondence between one set of real numbers, called the *domain*, and another set of real numbers, called the *range*. However, in this chapter we are adopting the point of view of geometry, and so it is the correspondence between the *points* of a graph and the *pairs* of real numbers (x, y), which is of prime interest. It is clear that we may emphasize either viewpoint. We now list the basic elementary functions, as discussed in Chapter 5.

1. *Power Function:* $y = x^n$, a special case of which is $y = x$.
2. *Exponential Function:* $y = b^x$, a special case of which is $y = e^x$.

3. *Logarithmic Function:* $y = \log_b x$, special cases of which are $y = \log x$, and $y = \ln x$.

4. *Circular Functions:*

(*a*) *infinite extent:* $y = \sin x$ $\quad y = \csc x$

$y = \cos x \quad y = \sec x$

$y = \tan x \quad y = \cot x.$

(*b*) *finite extent:* $y = \text{Sin } x$ $\quad y = \text{Csc } x$

$y = \text{Cos } x \quad y = \text{Sec } x$

$y = \text{Tan } x \quad y = \text{Cot } x.$

5. *Inverse Circular Functions:*

$y = \text{arc Sin } x \quad y = \text{arc Csc } x$

$y = \text{arc Cos } x \quad y = \text{arc Sec } x$

$y = \text{arc Tan } x \quad y = \text{arc Cot } x.$

If the graphs of any of these functions have been forgotten, the student is urged to review Chapter 5, where these basic functions were introduced.

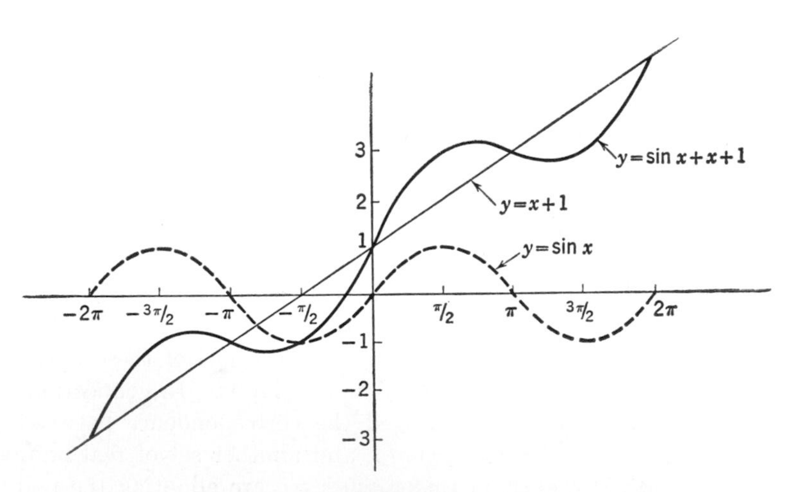

Figure 12–1

In addition to the above basic functions, familiarity is assumed with the graphs of the functions related to these by the Theorems on Graphing of Chapter 6. Thus, for example, the loci of such equations as $y = 3x - 2$, $y = 2e^{x+1}$, and $y = 3 \cos (x - 2)$ can be described readily with reference to the loci of $y = x$, $y = e^x$, and $y = \cos x$, respectively. The method of the *addition of ordinates*, introduced in Section 10.9, should also be recalled at this point; for this method allows us to sketch the locus of a somewhat complicated equation from a knowledge of the loci of its component parts. We review this method with the illustration of Figure 12–1, where we have sketched a portion of the locus of $y = \sin x + x + 1$, using the loci of $y = \sin x$ and $y = x + 1$.

PROBLEM SET 12.2

In Problems 1 through 5, make sketches, in a neighborhood of the origin, of the curves having the given equations; use a single pair of axes for each set of curves, and include a verbal comparison of each curve with the first one of the set to which it belongs.

1. (*a*) $y = x$, $y = 2x$, $y = 2x + 1$, $y = 2(x - 1)$.
(*b*) $y = e^x$, $y = -2e^x$, $2y = e^x$, $3y = e^{x-1}$.
(*c*) $y = x^2$, $4y = 3x^2$, $y = x^2$, $y + 1 = 3x^2$.
(*d*) $y = \sin x$, $y = \sin 2x$, $y = 2 \sin (x - 1)$, $2y = \sin 2x$.

2. (*a*) $y = x^3$, $y = (x - 2)^3$, $y = -3x^3$.
(*b*) $y = 1/x$, $y = 2/x$, $3y = 1/(x + 1)$.
(*c*) $y = \tan x$, $y = -\tan (x - \pi/4)$, $y = 2 \tan x/3$.
(*d*) $y = \text{arc} \cos x$, $y = \text{arc} \cos x/2$, $y = 2 \text{ arc} \cos 2x$.

3. (*a*) $y = \ln x$, $y = 2 \ln (x - 1)$.
(*b*) $y = \text{arc} \cos x$, $y = \text{arc} \cos 2x$.
(*c*) $y = \text{Sec } x$, $2y = \text{Sec } (x + \pi/2)$.
(*d*) $y = 1/x^2$, $y = -1/(x - 2)^2$.

4. (*a*) $y = e^x$, $x = e^y$, $3x = e^{y-1}$.
(*b*) $y = \text{Cot } x$, $x = \text{Cot } y$, $x - 1 = \text{Cot } y/2$.
(*c*) $y = \text{arc Tan } x$, $x = \text{arc Tan } y$, $x = 3 \text{ arc Tan } 2y$.
(*d*) $y = x$, $y = -x$, $y = -2x + 5$.

5. (*a*) $y = \cos x$, $y = -\cos x$, $y = \cos (-x)$.
(*b*) $y = \log x$, $y = -\log x$, $2y = -\log (x + 1)$.
(*c*) $y = 5^x$, $y = 5^{-x}$, $y = 5^{-x-1}$.
(*d*) $y = x^3$, $y = -x^3$, $y = (1 - x)^3$.

6. Use separate pairs of axes to sketch, in a neighborhood of the origin, the curves having the following equations:
(*a*) $y = x^{3/2}$ (*b*) $y = x^{1/2}$ (*c*) $y = x^{1/3}$ (*d*) $y = x^{2/3}$
$y^2 = x^3$; $y^2 = x$; $y^3 = x$; $y^3 = x^2$.

7. Use separate pairs of axes to sketch, in a neighborhood of the origin, the curves having the following equations:
(*a*) $y = 1/x^{1/2}$ (*b*) $y = 1/x^{1/3}$ (*c*) $y = x^{-1/4}$ (*d*) $y = x^{2/3}$
$y^2 = 1/x$; $y^3 = 1/x$; $y^4 = 1/x$; $y^3x^2 = 1$.

8. Use the method of addition of ordinates to sketch, in a neighborhood of the origin, the locus of the equation (*a*) $y = \cos x + x/2$; (*b*) $y = e^x - x + 1$; (*c*) $y = \ln x - 2x$.

9. Use the method of addition to ordinates to sketch, in a neighborhood of the origin, the curve having the equation (*a*) $y = -x/3 + \sin x$; (*b*) $y = \text{arc Sin } x + x$; (*c*) $y = x^2 + \ln x$.

10. Use the method of addition of ordinates to sketch, in a neighborhood of the origin, the curve having the equation (*a*) $y = 1/x + x^2$; (*b*) $y = e^x + \ln x$; (*c*) $y = e^{-x} + \text{Sin } x$.

12.3 Loci of Polynomial Equations of the Form $y = P[x]$

In this section we discuss several items which are of importance if a curve is to be sketched from its equation. If the equation has the form $y = P[x]$, with $P[x]$ a polynomial in x, an analysis based on these items will be quite sufficient for a complete description of the curve. We shall have a brief discussion of these five items, and then give some illustrations of the complete procedure for polynomial equations.

1. SYMMETRY. In Chapter 6 we discussed the notion of symmetry of a curve with respect to the x-axis, the y-axis, and the diagonal line locus of $y = x$, and obtained the following three tests:

(*a*) if the equation is replaced by an equivalent equation, when x is replaced by $-x$, the locus is *symmetric with respect to the* y-*axis;*

(*b*) if the equation is replaced by an equivalent equation, when y is replaced by $-y$, the locus is *symmetric with respect to the* x-*axis;*

(*c*) if the equation is replaced by an equivalent equation, when x and y are interchanged, the locus is *symmetric with respect to the line whose equation is* y = x.

In addition to the above three types of symmetry, we also have the notion of *symmetry with respect to the origin.* The point which is symmetric to the point (x, y) with respect to the origin is $(-x, -y)$, and so we have the following test for this type of symmetry:

(*d*) if the equation is replaced by an equivalent equation, when x is replaced by $-x$ and y is replaced by $-y$, the locus is symmetric with respect to the origin.

It should be pointed out that the actual *existence* of symmetrically placed points on a locus is not guaranteed by the fact that one of these tests is satisfied. All that is guaranteed is that if a test is satisfied, each point that *is* on the locus is accompanied by the corresponding symmetrically placed point. For example, all four tests of symmetry are satisfied for the locus of the equation $x^2 + y^2 + 5 = 0$, but since the solution set of this equation contains no pairs of real numbers, there are actually no points on the geometric locus.

The only two of the above tests which are of interest in connection with a polynomial equation $y = P[x]$ are (a) and (d). These tests may be rephrased for this type of equation as follows:

(a) if $P[x]$ contains only even powers of x, the locus of $y = P[x]$ is symmetric with respect to the y-axis;

(d) if $P[x]$ contains only odd powers of x, the locus of $y = P[x]$ is symmetric with respect to the origin.

2. INTERCEPTS. The *intercepts* of a curve are the respective abscissas and ordinates of the points where the curve intersects the x-axis and y-axis. To determine the x-intercepts of a curve, we replace y by 0 in its equation and determine the real solutions of the resulting equation in x; to determine the y-intercepts of a curve, we replace x by 0 in its equation and determine the real solutions of the resulting equation in y.

In the case of a curve which has an equation of the form $y = P[x]$, it is a simple matter to find the y-intercept, since $P[0]$ is merely the term independent of x. However, a determination of the x-intercepts of such a curve requires the solution of the equation $P[x] = 0$. If $P[x]$ is factorable into linear factors, this is simple; however, if $P[x]$ is not in factored form and has degree greater than 2, the exact x-intercepts are usually not found, though the theory of polynomial equations may be used to determine the number and signs of these intercepts.

For example, the locus of the equation $y = 2(x - 1)(x + 2)(x - 3)$ has a y-intercept of 12, and x-intercepts of 1, -2, and 3. On the other hand, it is easily seen that the locus of the equation $y = 3x^4 + 2x^2 + x + 1$ has a y-intercept of 1, but it is necessary to solve the equation $3x^4 + 2x^2 + x + 1 = 0$, in order to determine the x-intercepts. An application of Descartes' Rule of Signs to the latter equation reveals that there are no positive x-intercepts, while there are either two or no negative intercepts.

3. SLOPE OF THE TANGENT LINE; MAXIMA AND MINIMA. If the equation defines a function f, which is differentiable at some or all points of its domain, the derivative f' will give us very useful information for the sketching of the function. Thus, the slope of the curve at a point having an abscissa of x is positive or negative according as $f'(x)$ is positive or negative. The location of maximum and minimum points, as discussed in Chapter 8, will also be very useful. Since an equation $y = P[x]$ defines a

polynomial function on $R^{\#}$, which is differentiable at *every* real x, this item will be especially useful for this type of equation.

4. THE SECOND DERIVATIVE; CONCAVITY.† If the equation defines a function f, such that f'' exists, this second derivative may also be used to great advantage in curve sketching. This second derivative can be used, of course, in testing a critical point for maximum or minimum characteristics, as discussed in Chapter 8. However, the fact that $f''(x) > 0$ indicates that the curve is "concave up" at the point $(x, f(x))$, while $f''(x) < 0$ indicates that it is "concave down" at this point, is also very useful information. For example, consider the locus of $y = x^3 - 2x^2$. This equation defines a polynomial function f on $R^{\#}$, such that $f(x) = x^3 - 2x^2, f'(x) = 3x^2 - 4x$, and $f''(x) = 6x - 4$, for each real number x. The critical points are determined by $f'(x) = 0 = x(3x - 4)$, and so are $(0, 0)$ and $(4/3, -32/27)$. Since $f''(0) = -4 < 0$, the point $(0, 0)$ is a maximum; and since $f''(4/3) = 4 > 0$, the point $(4/3, -32/27)$ is a minimum. Furthermore, since $f''(x) > 0$ for any $x > 2/3$, the curve is "concave up" in this region; and since $f''(x) < 0$ for any $x < 2/3$, the curve is "concave down" in this region.

5. LIMITING NATURE. The question of the limiting nature of a curve (i.e., its nature for numerically large x) is especially applicable to a curve having a polynomial equation $y = P[x]$. The essential remark to make in this connection, which is stated without proof, is the following:

> For a real number x, of sufficiently large absolute value, a polynomial $P[x]$ is approximated to any desired degree of accuracy by its term of highest degree.

In the usual notation for a polynomial, $P[x]$ will be approximated by a_0x^n, and will lie outside any finite interval if x is of sufficiently large absolute value. Whether $P[x]$ is "ultimately" positive or negative depends on the sign of a_0 and the sign of x. For example, if $P[x] = 4x^4 - x^2 + 1$, $P[x]$ is approximated by $4x^4$ if x is numerically large, and will exceed any finite positive bound if x is either a positive or negative number, of sufficiently large absolute value. The graphical significance of this fact is that the points of the locus of this equation, outside some finite region containing the origin, lie above the x-axis, and there is no finite bound for the ordinates of these points. On the other hand, the polynomial $3x^5 - 2x^3 + 5x + 2$ is approximated by $3x^5$, if x is of sufficiently large absolute value. It may be readily seen that the points of the locus of this equation lie in the first and third quadrants, except possibly for those points in some finite region containing the origin.

ILLUSTRATION. Sketch, in a neighborhood of the origin, the locus of the equation $y = 2x^3 - 8x$.

† If sec. 8.10 was not studied, this analysis may be omitted.

Solution. We shall analyze the curve according to the above considerations.

1. The tests for symmetry show that the curve has symmetry with respect to the origin; this follows since the equations $y = 2x^3 - 8x$ and $-y = -2x^3 + 8x$ are equivalent.

2. By putting $x = 0$, we find that the y-intercept is 0. If we put $y = 0$, we find that $x(2x^2 - 8) = 0$, and so the x-intercepts are 0, 2, and -2.

3. The equation defines the function f on $R^{\#}$, with $f(x) = 2x^3 - 8x$ for each real x, so that $f'(x) = 6x^2 - 8$ and $f''(x) = 12x$. The equation $6x^2 - 8 = 0$ shows that the abscissas of the critical points are $2/\sqrt{3}$ and $-2/\sqrt{3}$. Since $f''(2/\sqrt{3}) > 0$, the point $(2/\sqrt{3}, -32\sqrt{3}/9)$ is a minimum; and since $f''(-2/\sqrt{3}) < 0$, the point $(-2/\sqrt{3}, 32\sqrt{3}/9)$ is a maximum.

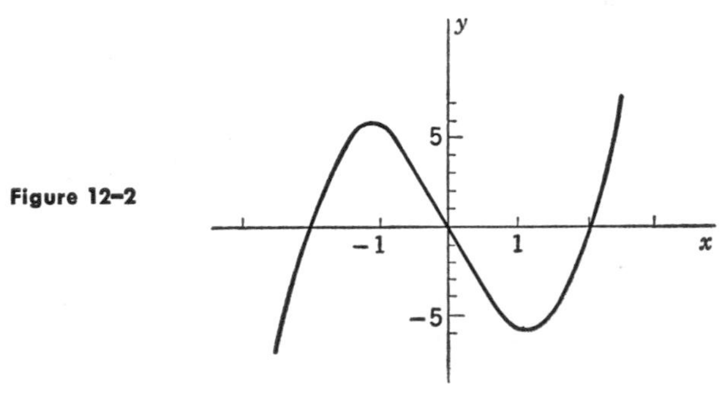

Figure 12–2

4. Since $f''(x) > 0$, for every positive number x, and $f''(x) < 0$, for every negative number x, the curve is "concave up" at all points to the right of the y-axis and "concave down" at all points to the left of the y-axis.

5. The polynomial $2x^3 - 8x$ is approximated by $2x^3$, for numerically large x. Thus, except for points with abscissas in a finite neighborhood of the origin, the curve will lie in quadrants 1 and 3; and the ordinates of these points will exceed in absolute value any finite bound, if the abscissas have sufficiently large absolute values.

If we give due consideration to all the above information, we shall see that the curve must resemble that shown in Figure 12–2, in a neighborhood of the origin.

PROBLEM SET 12.3

Examine each of the polynomial equations given in Problems 1 through 10, using the five headings discussed above, and sketch the locus of each equation in a neighborhood of the origin.

1. $y = x^2 - 4x + 3$. **2.** $y = 6 - 2x - x^2$.
3. $y = x^3 - 6x^2 + 9x$. **4.** $y = x(x + 1)^2$.
5. $y = x^4 - 32x + 48$. **6.** $y = x^2(9 - x^2)$.
7. $y = x^5 - 5x^4$. **8.** $y = 12 + 12x + x^3$.
9. $y = 2x^3 + 3x^2 + 12x - 4$. **10.** $y = (x - 1)^2(x - 2)^2$.

11.* Sketch the graph, in a neighborhood of the origin, of a function f having the following characteristics: $f(1) = 1, f''(x) < 0$ for $x < 1, f''(x) > 0$ for $x > 1$.

12.* Sketch the graph, in a neighborhood of the origin, of a function f having the following characteristics:

$$f(-3) = 6; \qquad f'(3) = f'(-3) = 0;$$
$$f(0) = 3; \qquad f'(x) < 0, \text{ if } |x| < 3;$$
$$f(3) = 0; \qquad f''(x) < 0, \text{ if } x < 0;$$
$$f'(x) > 0, \text{ if } |x| > 3; \qquad f''(x) > 0, \text{ if } x > 0.$$

13. If $P[x]$ is a real polynomial, what is the maximal domain of a function f defined in $R^{\#}$ by $f(x) = P[x]$?

14. Prove that, if an equation in x and y is replaced by an equivalent equation when x is replaced by $2m - x$, the locus of the equation is symmetric with respect to the line locus of the equation $x = m$.

15. Use the result of Problem 14 to devise a test for symmetry about the line locus of the equation $y = m$.

16. Use the result of Problem 14 to show that the locus of $y = x^2 - 6x + 9$ is symmetric with respect to the line having the equation $x = 3$.

17. Use the result of Problem 14 to show that the locus of $y = 300x - 2x^2$ is symmetric with respect to the line having the equation $x = 75$.

18. Use the result of Problem 14 to show that $x = -b/2a$ is an equation of the line of symmetry of the parabola having the equation $y = ax^2 + bx + c$.

19. Graph the function f, defined on the interval $[-3, 3]$ as follows:

$$\begin{aligned} f(x) &= -2x + 1, \text{ if } -3 \leq x < -1; \\ &= x^3 + 5, \text{ if } -1 \leq x < 1; \\ &= 2, \text{ if } 1 \leq x < 2; \\ &= -x^2 + 11, \text{ if } 2 \leq x \leq 3. \end{aligned}$$

20. Graph the function F, defined on the set $\{x \mid x \in I, -5 \leq x \leq 5\}$, as follows: $F(x) = -x^3 + 10x + 25$, if $x < -2$; $F(x) = 2x + 3$, if $-2 \leq x < 3$; $F(x) = x + x^2$, if $3 \leq x \leq 5$.

12.4 Asymptotes

We may say that a curve is *of infinite extent* if there are points of the curve which lie outside any finite region. It frequently happens that such curves have associated with them certain straight lines known as *asymptotes*, and these lines will prove to be very useful in sketching the curves. In this section we shall discuss methods which may frequently be used to discover the asymptotes of a curve.

Let (x, y) be an unspecified point of the curve under consideration. Then, if $|y|$ is arbitrarily large, provided either (at least one) $x - a$ or $a - x$ is sufficiently close to 0 but positive, the line locus of $x = a$ is said to be an *asymptote* of the curve. With the usual orientation of the x-axis as horizontal and the y-axis as vertical, this may be referred to as a *vertical* asymptote. For example, $x = 0$ is an equation of a vertical asymptote of the locus of $y = 1/x$, since $|y|$ is arbitrarily large if x is sufficiently close to 0. In an analogous way, we may define *horizontal* asymptotes. Thus, if we express the equation $y = 1/x$ in the form $x = 1/y$, we see that $y = 0$

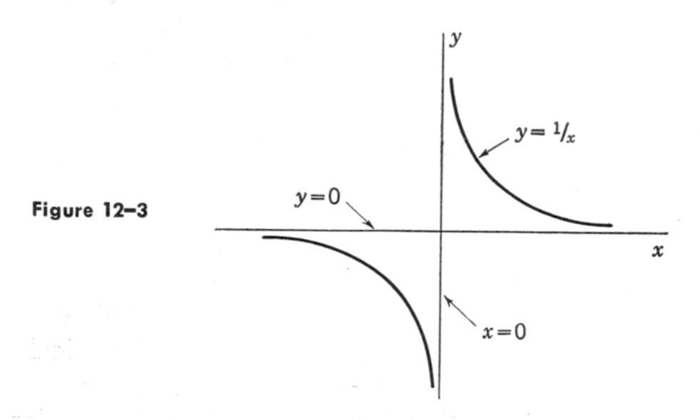

Figure 12–3

is an equation of a horizontal asymptote of the curve, since $|x|$ is arbitrarily large for y sufficiently close to 0. A portion of the locus of $y = 1/x$, an equilateral hyperbola, is shown in Figure 12–3, along with its horizontal and vertical asymptotes; the asymptotes, in this case are seen to be the x and y axes.

ILLUSTRATION 1. Determine the horizontal and vertical asymptotes of the curve having the equation $y = e^{-x}/(x - 2)$.

Solution. If (x, y) is an unspecified point on the locus of the above equation, the absolute value of y is arbitrarily large if x is sufficiently close to 2, so that $x = 2$ is an equation of a vertical asymptote. Furthermore, x must exceed any finite bound if y is sufficiently close to 0, so that $y = 0$ is an equation of a horizontal asymptote.

The above illustration shows that it is sometimes easy to discover the horizontal and vertical asymptotes of a curve, from a direct inspection of the equation. However, the following rule has much more general application.

HORIZONTAL AND VERTICAL ASYMPTOTES. If the given equation of a curve can be put in the form $P[y] = 0$, where $P[y]$ is a polynomial in y with coefficients involving x, the vertical asymptotes of the curve are defined by setting the leading coefficient of y equal to 0. Similarly, if it is possible to express the equation in the form $Q[x] = 0$, where $Q[x]$ is a polynomial in

x, with coefficients involving y, the horizontal asymptotes are defined by setting the leading coefficient of x equal to 0.

We do not give a rigorous proof of this rule, but offer an intuitive argument. Let us suppose that $x = c$ is an equation of a vertical asymptote of the curve having the equation $P[y] = 0$, with $P[y]$ described above. If x is suitably chosen close to c, our definition of a vertical asymptote implies that $|y|$ is very large, and so $P[y]$ can be approximated for such an x by its leading term, which we may indicate by a_0y^n. But if a_0y^n is close to 0 for a numerically large y, a_0 must be close to 0, which may be seen to imply that c is a solution of the equation $a_0 = 0$. A similar argument will give an intuitive verification of the other half of the rule.

ILLUSTRATION 2. Determine the horizontal and vertical asymptotes of the curve having the equation $(x - 2)^2 = 5/(y + 1)^3$.

Solution. The given equation may be written in the form $(x - 2)^2(y + 1)^3 - 5 = 0$, an equivalent equation having the same solution set as the original. If the left member is expressed as a polynomial in x, the leading coefficient is $(y + 1)^3$, while as a polynomial in y, the leading coefficient is $(x - 2)^2$. Hence $y = -1$ is an equation of a horizontal asymptote, and $x = 2$ is an equation of a vertical asymptote.

ILLUSTRATION 3. Determine the horizontal and vertical asymptotes of the curve having the equation $y^2 = x^2/(x + 4)$.

Solution. As in Illustration 1, we may write this equation as a polynomial, in this case taking the form $y^2(x + 4) - x^2 = 0$. The leading coefficient of y is seen to be $x + 4$, while the leading coefficient of x is -1. Thus, an equation of the only vertical asymptote is $x = -4$, while there are no horizontal asymptotes of this curve.

An expression involving x and y which is both a polynomial in x and a polynomial in y may be said to be a *polynomial in x and y*, and it will be convenient to designate such an expression by $P[x, y]$. The sum of the degrees in x and in y of any term is the *degree in x and y* of that term, while the largest degree in x and y among all the terms is the degree in x and y of the polynomial. For example, the polynomial $2y + 3xy + 5$ has degree 2 in x and y, but only degree 1 in x and degree 1 in y. We now give a more general definition for asymptotes of a curve, followed by a method for their determination, in case the given equation of the curve has the form $P[x, y] = 0$.

It will be convenient to think of a *simple branch* of a curve of infinite extent, as a portion which does not intersect itself, which contains points outside any finite region, but one end point of which is finite. Moreover, let us assume that there is a well-defined tangent line at each point of any simple branch of the curve under consideration. Let d_0 and d_L be the respective measures of distance of a point P in the plane from the origin and a given line L, where the latter notion is intuitively clear although we have not yet given it an analytic description.

DEFINITION. A line L is said to be an *asymptote* of a curve, if the following condition is satisfied for any one of its simple branches: for an arbitrary $\epsilon > 0$, there exists a number $N > 0$, such that $0 < d_L < \epsilon$, for any point P on the branch for which $d_0 > N$.

It should be noticed that this definition covers the special cases of horizontal and vertical asymptotes, which we have already discussed, but it will also include *oblique* asymptotes. Intuitively, we may think of an asymptote as the limiting position of a tangent line to the curve, as its point of tangency is considered to recede indefinitely along the curve. From a geometric point of view, a tangent line to a curve is a secant line which intersects the curve in two or more coincident points at its point of tangency. Thus, if $P[x, y] = 0$ is the polynomial equation of a curve, and $y = mx + b$ is the equation of any straight line, the points of intersection of the curve and line are determined by the simultaneous solutions of the equations $P[x, y] = 0$ and $y = mx + b$. If $mx + b$ is substituted for y in $P[x, y] = 0$, the resulting equation in x determines the abscissas of these points of intersection. If the degree in x and y of $P[x, y]$ is n, there will be, in general, n solutions of this equation corresponding to the n points of intersection, though some of these solutions may not be real. If the line is tangent to the curve, one of the solutions has multiplicity at least 2, this solution being the abscissa of this point of tangency. However, if we assume that the line is an asymptote, so that its point of tangency lies outside any finite region, there can be not more than $n - 2$ *finite* solutions of the equation. Hence the coefficients of the two highest powers of x must be 0, which leads us to the following rule for determining oblique asymptotes.

OBLIQUE ASYMPTOTES. Let $P[x, y] = 0$ be the given polynomial equation of a curve. Then if y is replaced in this equation by $mx + b$, any solution of the equations formed by setting the coefficients of the two highest powers of x equal to 0 will determine the equation $y = mx + b$ of an asymptote of the curve.

The leading coefficient set equal to 0 will, in fact, always determine the *slopes* of any non-vertical asymptotes, and these numbers, if substituted for m in the equation formed from the next coefficient, will usually determine the corresponding solutions for b. It sometimes happens, however, that this second equation is identically 0 and so will not determine b. In this case, it may be possible to determine b by equating to 0 the coefficient of the next highest power of x which is not identically 0, though we do not attempt to justify this remark. The rule which we have just given will, of course, determine the horizontal as well as the other oblique—but non-vertical—asymptotes.

ILLUSTRATION 4. Determine the asymptotes of the curve having the equation $x^2 - y^2 = 1$.

Solution. Replacing y by $mx + b$ yields the equation $(1 - m^2)x^2 - 2mbx - b^2 - 1 = 0$.

An application of the above rule now gives $m = 1$ or $m = -1$, and $b = 0$. The non-vertical asymptotes of the curve are then the line loci of the equations $y = x$ and $y = -x$. It may be seen that there are no vertical asymptotes.

ILLUSTRATION 5. Determine the asymptotes of the curve having the equation $y^3 = x^2(4 - x)$.

Solution. If we replace y in this equation by $mx + b$, the result is $(mx + b)^3 = x^2(4 - x)$, which may be written in the form $(m^3 + 1)x^3 + (3m^2b - 4)x^2 + 3mb^2x + k^3 = 0$.

An application of the above rule now gives us the equations $m^3 + 1 = 0$ and $3m^2b - 4 = 0$, from which we obtain $m = -1$ and $b = 4/3$. The only non-vertical asymptote is then the line having the equation $y = -x + 4/3$. It is clear that there are no vertical asymptotes of this curve.

PROBLEM SET 12.4

Determine the horizontal and vertical asymptotes of each of the curves having the equations given in Problems 1 through 6.

1. $y = x^2/(x^2 - 4)$.

2. $y = 1/[(x - 2)(x - 3)]$.

3. $y = (x^2 - 9)/[x(x^2 - 4)]$.

4. $y = \dfrac{e^{-x+1}}{x}$.

5. $y = (e^x \sin x)/(x - 2)$.

6. $y = e^{-x}/[(x - 1)(x - 2)]$.

Determine all the asymptotes of each curve, from its equation given in Problems 7 through 12.

7. $4x^2 - 9y^2 - 36 = 0$.

8. $x^3 + x^2y - 4 = 0$.

9. $x^2y - 4x^2 - xy^2 - 7 = 0$.

10. $x^4 + 20x^3 - y^4 = 0$.

11. $x^3 + x^2 - xy^2 + y^2 = 0$.

12. $3y^3 + xy^2 - 3xy + y^2 + 2x - 2y = 0$.

13. Write down an equation of a curve, which will have the line loci of the equations $y = 2$ and $y = -1$ for horizontal asymptotes.

14. Write down an equation of a curve, which has the line loci of the equations $y = -3$, $x = 1$, and $x = -2$ for asymptotes.

15. Write down the equation of a curve which has no asymptotes. Try to give a general description of the equation of a curve of this type.

12.5* Loci of Equations Which Express y Explicitly in Terms of x

The locus of any equation is, of course, the graph of its solution set, and it is notationally convenient, for the case to be discussed in this section, to consider this solution set as a function f. We may then write $y = f(x)$, for each x in its domain, with $f(x)$ an algebraic or transcendental expression involving x. We are going to apply the sketching techniques of the previous section to obtain a rough graph of f, but before doing this we include a discussion of two other items which are sometimes useful.

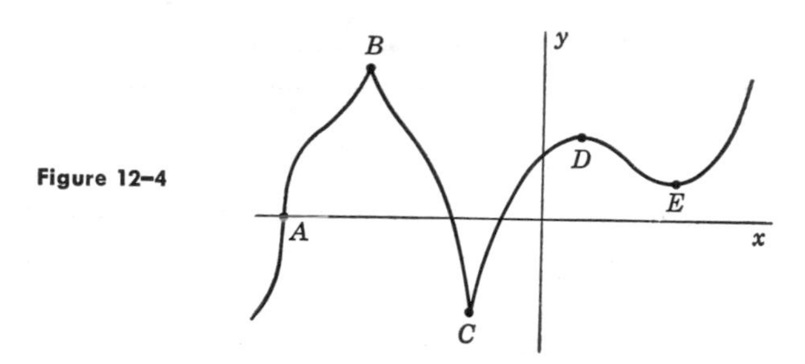

Figure 12–4

MAXIMUM AND MINIMUM POINTS DEFINED BY $1/f'(x) = 0$. We have previously used the fact that any solution of the equation $f'(x) = 0$ will determine a so-called *critical point* on the graph of f, and that this point is a maximum or minimum according as $f''(x) < 0$ or $f''(x) > 0$. However, if f is not a polynomial function, i.e., $f(x)$ is not a polynomial in x, it is possible to have maximum and minimum points (a, b) such that a is not a solution of the equation $f'(x) = 0$. For example, in Figure 12–4, the points B and C are clearly of this type, for their abscissas may be seen to be solutions of $1/f'(x) = 0$ rather than of $f'(x) = 0$. Point A would also appear as a critical point determined by the equation $1/f'(x) = 0$, and in order to identify the different kinds of critical points of this curve it would be necessary to examine the sign of $f'(x)$ on both sides of each point in question. It is clear that the "second derivative" test can not be used here, since $f''(x)$ does not exist at such a point. It follows from this discussion that if we are graphing non-polynomial functions, it is necessary to consider as critical points those which arise from solutions of $1/f'(x) = 0$ as well as $f'(x) = 0$.

ILLUSTRATION 1. Determine the maximum and minimum points of the curve having the equation $y = 5 - (x - 3)^{2/3}$.

Solution. If f is the function defined by the solution set of this equation, $f(x) = 5 - (x - 3)^{2/3}$ and $f'(x) = -2/[3(x - 3)^{-1/3}]$. Hence $f'(x) \neq 0$ for every x in the domain of f, but $1/f'(x) = 0$ if $x = 3$, so that $(3, 5)$ is a critical point on the graph. Since $f'(x) > 0$ for $x < 3$ and $f'(x) < 0$ for $x > 3$, this critical point is a maximum.

REGIONS OF THE PLANE WHICH CONTAIN POINTS OF THE CURVE. It is extremely helpful in sketching a curve to know which regions of the plane do and which regions do not contain points of the curve. If $f(x)$ is expressed as a quotient of products of simple factors, we can use the device of Illustration 2 of Section 10.11 for this purpose. We review this procedure with an illustration.

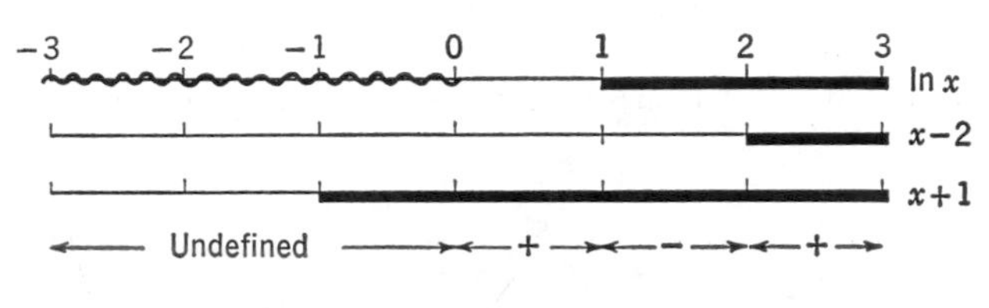

Figure 12–5

ILLUSTRATION 2. Determine the regions of a plane which contain points of the curve having the equation $y = \ln x/[(x - 2)(x + 1)]$.

Solution. The three number scales shown in Figure 12–5 correspond to the three distinct factors $\ln x$, $x - 2$, and $x + 1$. We draw a wavy line over that portion of each scale for which the associated factor is undefined,

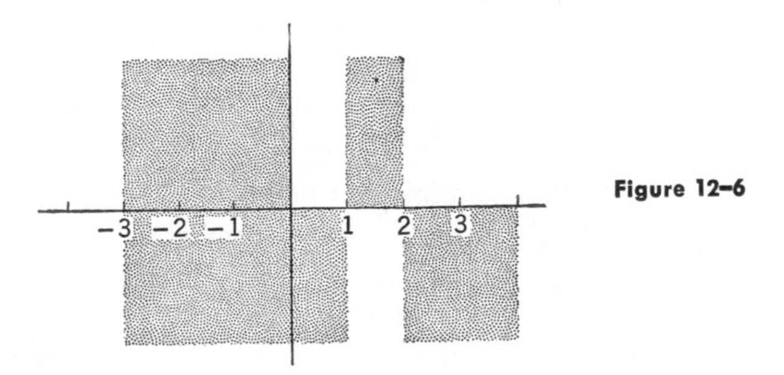

Figure 12–6

and draw an extra heavy line over those portions for which the factor is positive. A glance at the scales in unison shows that $y > 0$ if $0 < x < 1$ or $x > 2$, while $y < 0$ if $1 < x < 2$. Furthermore, y is undefined if $x \leq 0$ or $x = 2$. It follows from this analysis that there are no points of the curve in the regions shown cross-hatched in Figure 12–6.

We are now in a position to apply all the principles that we have discussed to the problem of sketching a curve having an equation of the form $y = f(x)$, with f as discussed in this section. It may not be practicable, of course, to apply all these principles, in which case a suitable selection should be made that is adequate for the sketching problem at hand. For instance, the expression $f(x)$ may be quite complex, and it would be difficult to determine the derivative f; the part of the analysis using the derivative should then be omitted.

ILLUSTRATION 3. Sketch the curve having the equation $y = x^2/(x^2 - 4)$.

Solution. We make an analysis of the equation, from the point of view of each of the items that has been discussed in this and previous sections.

1. *Region of Definition.* The scales indicate that there are points with positive ordinates for $x < -2$ and $x > 2$, negative ordinates for $-2 < x < 2$, while there are no points with $x = 2$ or $x = -2$.

2. *Symmetries.* The curve is symmetric with respect to the y-axis, but each of the other tests for symmetry fails.

3. *Intercepts.* The curve intercepts the axes only at the origin.

4. *Maximum and Minimum Points.* If f is the solution set of the equation, $f(x) = x^2/(x^2 - 4)$, and $f'(x) = -8x/(x^2 - 4)^2$, for each x in the domain of f. The equation $f'(x) = 0$ yields $x = 0$ as a solution and $(0, 0)$ as a critical point, but $1/f'(x) \neq 0$ for each x in the domain of f.

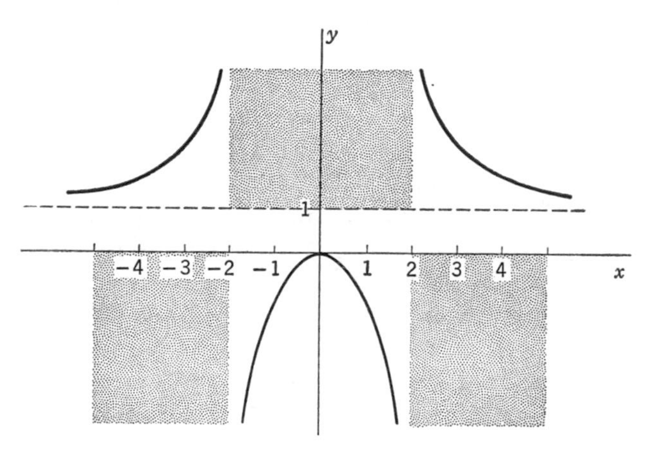

Figure 12–7

Note that $[-(x^2 - 4)^2]/8x = 0$ if $x = 2$ and $x = -2$, but these points are not in the domain of f. It is impracticable to determine $f''(x)$ in order to test the critical point $(0, 0)$, so we use the alternate method: $f'(x) > 0$, if $x < 0$; and $f'(x) < 0$, if $x > 0$. Hence the point $(0, 0)$ is a maximum point of the curve.

5. *Concavity.* This item is not practicable in view of the difficulty in determining f''.

6. *Limiting Nature of Curve.* For x of sufficiently large absolute value, the denominator of $f(x)$ is approximated by x^2, and so $f(x)$ is approximated by x^2/x^2 or 1. Thus, $f(x)$ is arbitrarily close to 1 if the absolute value of x is sufficiently large; this agrees with our next analysis, which lists $y = 1$ as an equation of a horizontal asymptote.

7. *Asymptotes.* If we express the equation in the form of a polynomial in x and y, the result is $y(x^2 - 4) - x^2 = 0$ or $x^2(y - 1) - 4y = 0$. Hence, there are two vertical asymptotes with equations $x = 2$ and $x = -2$, and one horizontal asymptote with equation $y = 1$. If we replace y in either form of the equation by $mx + b$, the result is $mx^3 + (b - 1)x^2 - 4mx - 4b = 0$, so that the only oblique asymptote is determined by $m = 0$ and $b = 1$; this is the horizontal asymptote with equation $y = 1$, that has already been determined.

The totality of information about the curve may now be used to obtain the sketch shown in Figure 12–7.

PROBLEM SET 12.5

Use the methods of this chapter to analyze the equations given in Problems 1 through 26, omitting those items which are not practicable or invalid. Use the information obtained in each case to sketch a portion of the associated curve.

1. $y = x^2/(x - 1)$.

2. $y = (x - 1)/(x + 1)$.

3. $y = (2x + 1)/(x - 2)$.

4. $y = (x - 1)/[(x + 2)(x - 2)]$.

5. $y = x(x - 2)(x + 1)$.

6. $y = x(x + 2)^2$.

7. $y = 1/(x + 3) + 1/(x - 3)$.

8. $y = x^4/(x^2 + 1)$.

9. $y = 8a^3/(x^2 + 4a^2)$.

10. $y = (x^2 - 2x + 1)/(x - 2)$.

11. $y = 1/[(x + 1)^2(x - 2)]$.

12. $y = 1/[(x - 1)(x - 4)]$.

13. $y = x^2/\sqrt{x + 1}$.

14. $y = \sqrt{x + 1}/x$.

15. $y = \sqrt{2 - x}/x$.

16. $y = \sqrt{8 + x^3}/x^2$.

17. $y = 2 - (x - 3)^{2/3}$.

18. $y = x + 1/\sqrt{x - 2}$.

19. $y = x^2 \ln x$.

20. $y = xe^{2x}$.

21. $y = e^{3x}/x$.

22. $y = \ln \sin x$.

23. $y = e^{-x^2}$.

24. $y = e^{-x^2}/(x - 2)$.

25. $y = \sqrt{(x - 1)(x - 2)(x - 3)}$.

26. $y = (\cos x)/x$.

27. Explain why $x = 0$ is an equation of a vertical asymptote of the curve having the equation $y = (\cos x)/x$, but not of the curve having the equation $y = (\sin x)/x$. Sketch the latter curve.

28. Explain why $x = 2$ is, while $x = -1$ is not, an equation of a vertical asymptote of the curve having the equation $y = (\ln x)/[(x - 2)(x + 1)]$. Complete the analysis of the curve from the equation, and sketch.

12.6 Loci of General Polynomial Equations

A complete discussion of polynomial equations of the form $P[x, y] = 0$ is beyond the scope of this book. However, it is sometimes possible to obtain a rough sketch of the locus of such an equation, using principally the methods that we have already discussed. This sketch will, of course, be an approximation to the graph of the relation consisting of the real solution set of the equation. Since we have not given a method for determining the slope of the tangent line at a point of the graph of a relation, except in simple cases including the functions, we must necessarily omit any graphical techniques that involve derivatives. The discussion on the limiting nature of a curve does not apply for general polynomial equations, and the method for determining the regions of a plane that contain points of the curve is valid only if either x or y is expressible explicitly in terms of the other. In the event that the equation may be written in the form $y = P[x]$, for some polynomial $P[x]$, the problem of sketching is, of course, covered in a preceding section. This means that in general our analysis of a polynomial equation will consist of the following items: symmetry, intercepts, asymptotes, and possibly, region of definition and limiting nature. If the curve contains the origin, however, it is sometimes possible to obtain another bit of useful information, which we now discuss.

TANGENT LINES AT ORIGIN. We have previously noted and used the fact that a polynomial in x may be approximated by its term of highest degree, if x is sufficiently large in absolute value. If x is a number close to 0, however, it is intuitively evident that it is the terms of lowest degree which are most significant. In the case of a polynomial in x and y, a similar intuitive argument will show that the polynomial may be approximated by the terms of lowest degree in x and y, provided both x and y are sufficiently close to 0. Since the geometric notion of a tangent line is a line which intersects the associated curve in two or more coincident points at its point of tangency—and so may be considered to approximate the curve in a small neighborhood of that point—the following result is plausible, though we do not attempt to prove it:

> If the locus of $P[x, y] = 0$ includes the origin, and a tangent line to the curve exists at this point, an equation of all such tangent lines is obtained by setting the terms of lowest degree in $P[x, y]$ equal to 0.

Before illustrating the remarks of this section, it is appropriate to take note of two special cases.

1. It may be possible to transform the polynomial equation into an equivalent form $y = P[x]$, to which case our analysis of the preceding section is applicable. For example, the equation $x^2y - 5x + 1 = 0$ may be written as $y = (5x - 1)/x^2$.

2. It may be possible to transform the equation into an equivalent form $y^n = P[x]$, for some positive integer n and polynomial $P[x]$. In this event, a portion of the graph is identical with either the first or third quadrant portions of the locus of $y = \sqrt[n]{P[x]}$, and considerations of symmetry will then describe the complete graph. In some cases, however, it

may be more desirable to use the original equation directly, as in the following illustration.

ILLUSTRATION 1. Sketch the locus of the equation $y^2 = x(x-1)(x-4)$.

Solution.

(*a*) Symmetry. The curve is symmetric with respect to the x-axis.

(*b*) Intercepts. The x-intercepts are 0, 1, and 4, while the y-intercept is 0.

(*c*) Asymptotes. It is clear that there are no horizontal or vertical asymptotes. A replacement of y in the equation by $mx + b$ yields $-x^3 + x^2(5 + m^2) + x(2mb - 4) + b^2 = 0$, from which it is evident that there are no oblique asymptotes.

(*d*) Limiting Nature. The right member of $y^2 = x(x-1)(x-4)$ may be written as a polynomial in x, and so may be approximated by x^3, if x has a sufficiently large absolute value. It then follows that for such an x, y^2 and so also y is arbitrarily large in absolute value and without any finite bound.

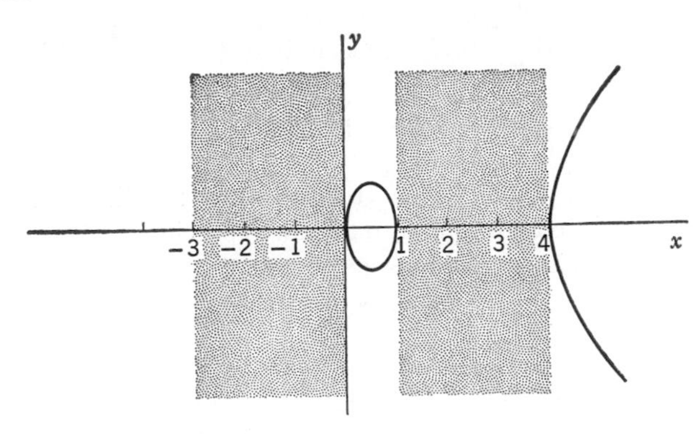

Figure 12–8

(*e*) Region of Definition. Since $y^2 = x(x-1)(x-4)$, the right member of this equation must be positive, so let us examine the factors.

x: −4 −3 −2 −1 0 1 2 3 4 5

$x-1$

$x-4$

− + − +

There is then no point (x, y) on the curve, with $x < 0$ or $1 < x < 4$.

(*f*) Tangent Lines at Origin. The given equation, in polynomial form is $y^2 - x^3 - 5x^2 + 4x = 0$, and so $x = 0$ is an equation of the only tangen line to the curve at the origin.

The above information can now be considered to produce the sketc in Figure 12–8. The portion of the sketch which lies above the x-axis i an approximation to a portion of the graph of the function f in $R^{\#}$, with $f(x) = \sqrt{x(x-1)(x-4)}$ for each x in its domain. If the exact location of the maximum point on the oval is desired, it will be necessary to determine $f'(x)$, but we do not do this.

We now consider a polynomial equation that does not fit either of the previously mentioned types.

ILLUSTRATION 2. Sketch the locus of the equation $xy^4 - y - 16x = 0$.

Solution.

(*a*) Symmetry. The curve is symmetric with respect to the origin.

(*b*) Intercepts. The curve intercepts the axes only at the origin.

(*c*) Tangent Lines at Origin. An equation of the tangent line at the origin is $16x + y = 0$.

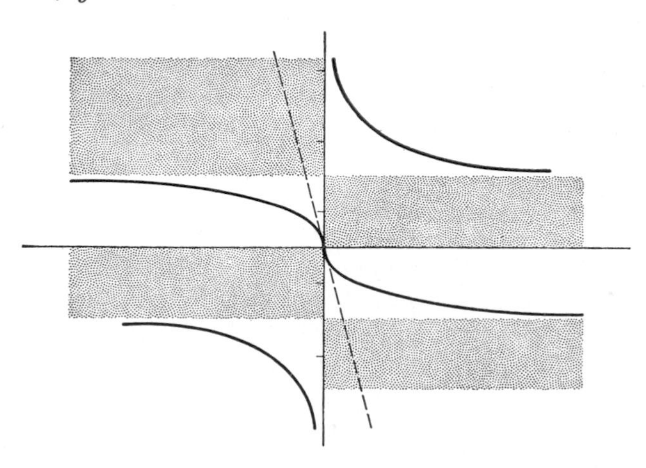

Figure 12–9

(*d*) Asymptotes. Equations of the vertical and horizontal asymptotes are $x = 0$, $y = 2$, and $y = -2$. It is clear that a substitution of $mx + b$ for y in the equation will not lead to any other oblique asymptotes.

(*e*) Region of Definition. While we cannot express y in terms of x, it is possible in this case to express x explicitly in terms of y: $x = y/(y^4 - 16)$. From an analysis of the component factors below, it is seen that a point (x, y) on the curve has a positive abscissa if $y > 2$ or $-2 < y < 0$, and a negative abscissa if $y < -2$ or $0 < y < 2$. The desired sketch is shown in Figure 12–9.

PROBLEM SET 12.6

Analyze each of the following equations according to the methods discussed in this section, and sketch a portion of the locus of each.

1. $y^2 = 25 - x^2$ (Circle).

2. $y^2 = (36 - 3x^2)/4$ (Ellipse).

3. $y^2 = (36 + 3x^2)/4$ (Hyperbola).
4. $y = 8/(4 + x^2)$ (Witch of Agnesi).
5. $y^2 = x^3/(2 - x)$ (Cissoid).
6. $y^2 = x^2(x - 1)$.
7. $y^3 = 3x/(x^3 - 2)$.
8. $y^3 = x^2(4 - x)$.
9. $y^2 = (x^2 + 1)/x^2$.
10. $y^2 = (2 - x)/x^2$.
11. $x^2 - xy - 2y^2 - 6 = 0$.
12. $3x^2 - 6xy + 4y^2 - 10 = 0$.
13. $(x^2 + y^2)^2 = 2(x^2 - y^2)$ (Lemniscate).
14. $x^2y - (x + 2)(y^2 - 4)$.
15. $x^3 - y^2(3 - y) = 0$.
16. $x^2y^2 = (y + 1)^2(4 - y^2)$ (Conchoid).
17. $xy^2 - x + 1 = 0$.
18. $x^3 + y^3 - 2x^2y = 0$.
19. Use the methods of this chapter, that are applicable, to sketch the locus of the equation $x^{2/3} + y^{2/3} = a^{2/3}$ for $a > 0$. This curve is called a *hypocycloid.*
20. Use the methods of this chapter, that are applicable, to sketch the locus of the equation $x^{1/2} + y^{1/2} = a^{1/2}$ for $a > 0$.

12.7 Loci of Second-Degree Polynomial Equations

Before leaving the subject of polynomial equations, we wish to have a brief discussion of the loci of polynomial equations of the second degree. The general form of an equation in x and y of this type is $Ax^2 + Bxy + Cy^2 + Dx + Ey + F = 0$. The analysis of the preceding section applies, of course, to these equations, but since the loci of these equations have special geometric significance, we devote a separate section to them.

The problem of sketching the locus of an equation is always simplified if we recognize the equation as being a member of a class which we have already studied. We have had this fact in mind during the course of this chapter, where we have studied graphical techniques associated with various general classes of equations. However, while the techniques may be similar for each member of one of these classes, it must have been noticed that the graphs may differ widely. On the other hand there are certain classes of equations, the loci of the members of which bear a close similarity to each other. The classifications which we have in mind are related to the Theorems on Graphing of Chapter 6, for it is easy to sketch the locus of an equation in one of these classes, once the basic equation of the class is identified. For example, the loci of the equations $y = 4x^2$, $y - 1 = (x + 2)^2$, and $y - 1 = 4(x + 2)^2$ or $y = 4x^2 + 16x + 17$ have a simple relationship to the locus of the basic equation $y = x^2$. For the locus of $y = 4x^2$ is the set of points obtained from the locus of $y = x^2$ by multiplying the ordinates of each point of the latter locus by 4 (or dividing the abscissas by 2); the locus of $y - 1 = (x + 2)^2$ is the set of points obtained from the locus of $y = x^2$ by decreasing by 2 the abscissa and increasing by 1 the ordinate of each point of the latter locus; and the locus of $y = 4x^2 + 16x + 17$, when written in the form $y - 1 = 4(x + 2)^2$, may be seen to be obtainable from the locus of $y = x^2$ by first multiplying the ordinate of each point of the latter locus by 4, and *then* decreasing by 2 the abscissa and increasing by 1 the ordinate of each point of this new curve. In Figure 12–10 we have shown sketches of these three loci, the similarities of which are apparent.

It was convenient in Chapter 6 to refer to the process of multiplying the abscissas or ordinates of the points of a curve as a *stretching* or *compression* of the curve, while a uniform increase or decrease of the abscissas or ordinates was known as a *translation*. In the next chapter, we shall introduce a third transformation known as *rotation*, which replaces each

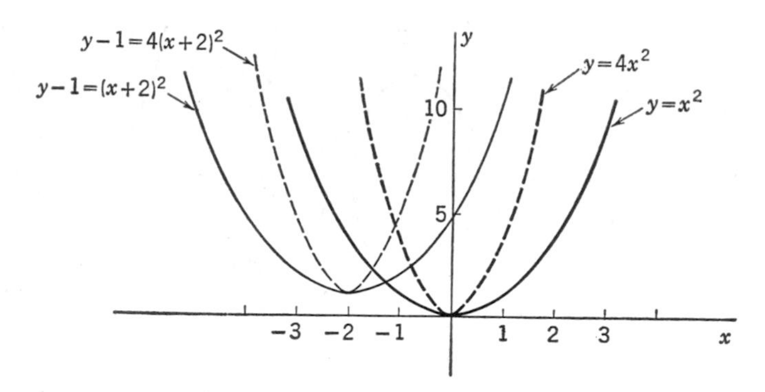

Figure 12–10

point of a curve by another point, by means of a uniform angular displacement about the origin. It is clear that neither a translation nor a rotation will alter the shape of a curve, since we are merely changing its position with respect to the coordinate axes; and while a stretching may effect some changes, even this transformation preserves the essential features of a curve, as was illustrated in Figure 12–10. It can be shown that the locus of any second-degree equation is the result of applying one or more of these three transformations to one of three very simple basic curves or their degenerate analogs. Hence the essential features of all such curves are known, after they are identified and the basic curves are known.

Though we make no attempt to justify this remark, the general shape of the locus of a second-degree polynomial equation in x and y depends on two considerations: the existence of asymptotes; and the existence of finite bounds for the regions containing points of the curve. Special names have been given to these curves, all of which have geometric significance, since they are the various possible curves in which a plane can intersect a right circular cone of infinite extent. These curves have been familiarly known as *conic sections* or *conics*. If the left member of the polynomial equation $P[x, y]$ factors into two linear factors with real coefficients, the locus of the equation is a *degenerate* conic, as described below. We now give a classification of conic sections, according to the characteristics mentioned at the beginning of the paragraph.

1. If asymptotes are present, the curve is a *hyperbola*, such as was introduced in Chapter 4. It can be shown that every hyperbola is the result of applying certain transformations of stretching, translation, or rotation to the equilateral hyperbola, defined as the locus of the equation $y = 1/x$. Thus, every hyperbola has the general appearance of the curve shown in Figure 12–11a. A degenerate hyperbola may be identified with its asymptotes, as is the case with the degenerate hyperbola having the equation $x^2 - y^2 = 0$.

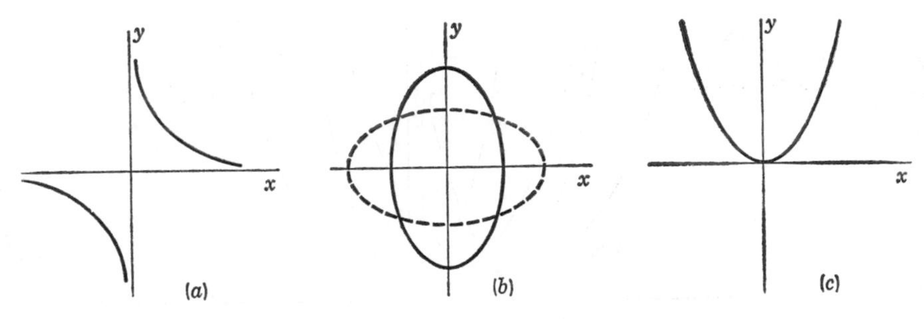

Figure 12–11

2. If asymptotes are not present and the region of definition of the curve has finite bounds, the curve is known as an *ellipse*. The basic curve of this class is the locus of $x^2 + y^2 = 1$, which may be easily recognized as the unit circle with center at the origin of the coordinate system. Every ellipse is the result of applying certain transformations of stretching, translation, or rotation to this unit circle, and has an oval appearance as shown in Figure 12–11b. A degenerate ellipse is a single point, an example of which is the locus of $x^2 + 3y^2 = 0$.

3. If asymptotes are not present, but the region of definition of the curve has no finite bounds, the conic section is a *parabola*, such as was first introduced in Chapter 4. Every parabola is the result of applying certain transformations of stretching, translation, or rotation to the basic parabola, defined as the locus of $y = x^2$. Hence every parabola has the general appearance of the curve shown in Figure 12–11c. A degenerate parabola is either one or two (parallel) straight lines as, for example, the loci of $x^2 - 4 = 0$ or $y = 5$.

If we replace y by $mx + b$ in the general second-degree equation, in an attempt to discover asymptotes of the curve, the leading coefficient of the resulting equation is $Cm^2 + Bm + A$. The slopes of any asymptotes, which may exist, are solutions of the equation $Cm^2 + Bm + A = 0$, and this equation has a real solution if and only if $B^2 - 4AC \geq 0$. However, if $B^2 - 4AC = 0$, a further analysis shows that no solution can exist for b. This is a partial justification of the following criterion: a conic section, which possibly is degenerate, is an ellipse, if $B^2 - 4AC < 0$; a hyperbola if $B^2 - 4AC > 0$; a parabola if $B^2 - 4AC = 0$. This is a very convenient test to apply to a second-degree equation.

The ellipse and hyperbola are *central* conics, and are symmetric with respect to two lines, and one point called the *center* of the conic. The segments of the two lines of symmetry intercepted by the ellipse are its *major* and *minor* axes, these being, respectively, the longest and shortest of the diameters of the ellipse. A parabola has only one axis of symmetry, and the point of intersection of this line with the conic is the *vertex*, a familiar name. It can be shown that an equation of the simplest form can be obtained for a central conic, if the center is at the origin of the coordinate system, and the axes of symmetry coincide with the coordinate axes. Such an equation has the form $Ax^2 + By^2 + F = 0$, the term in xy and the first-degree terms in x and y being absent. In the case of a parabola, the simplest type of equation can be found, if its axis of symmetry coincides with one of the coordinate axes, and its vertex is at the origin. The simplest equation of the parabola will then have the form $y + Ax^2 = 0$ or $x + By^2 = 0$.

Whole books have been written on the subject of conic sections, and so it would be presumptuous of us to try to give more than a mere glimpse of it here. We have pointed out, however, that the locus of every second-degree equation in x and y is either an ellipse, hyperbola, or parabola, which possibly is degenerate or has no real points; an example of an equation of this latter type is $x^2 + y^2 + 5 = 0$. A complete analysis of a conic section would involve a description of the various transformations which would be necessary to produce it from the basic conic, and we leave this for more detailed treatises on conic sections. We do state, however, that the absence of the xy term in the equation implies that each axis of symmetry is parallel to a coordinate axis; and in the case of a central conic, the absence of terms in x and in y implies that the center is at the origin. With this remark, we pass to some illustrations.

ILLUSTRATION 1. Sketch the conic having the equation $3x^2 - 4y^2 = 12$.

Solution. Since $B^2 - 4AC = 48 > 0$, the conic is a hyperbola.

(*a*) Symmetry. The curve is symmetric with respect to both axes and the origin.

(*b*) Intercepts. The x-intercepts are 2 and -2, but the curve has no y-intercepts.

(*c*) Asymptotes. A replacement of y by $mx + b$ in the equation gives us $(3 - 4m^2)x^2 - 8mbx - 4b^2 - 12 = 0$. Thus, $m = \pm\sqrt{3}/2$, and $b = 0$, so the asymptotes have the equations $y = \sqrt{3}\,x/2$ and $y = -\sqrt{3}\,x/2$.

(*d*) Region of Definition. Expressing y in terms of x, we obtain $y = \pm\sqrt{3x^2 - 12}/2$, so that we must have $|x| \geq 2$. If we express x in terms of y, we obtain $x = \pm\sqrt{4y^2 + 12}/3$, so there are no restrictions on y.

A sketch of a portion of the hyperbola having the given equation appears in Figure 12–12.

ILLUSTRATION 2. Sketch the locus of the equation $3x^2 + 4y^2 = 12$.

Solution. In this case, $B^2 - 4AC = -48 < 0$, so the conic is an ellipse.

(*a*) Symmetry. It is symmetric with respect to both axes and the origin.

(*b*) Intercepts. The x-intercepts are 2 and -2, while the y-intercepts are $\sqrt{3}$ and $-\sqrt{3}$.

(*c*) Asymptotes. There are no asymptotes.

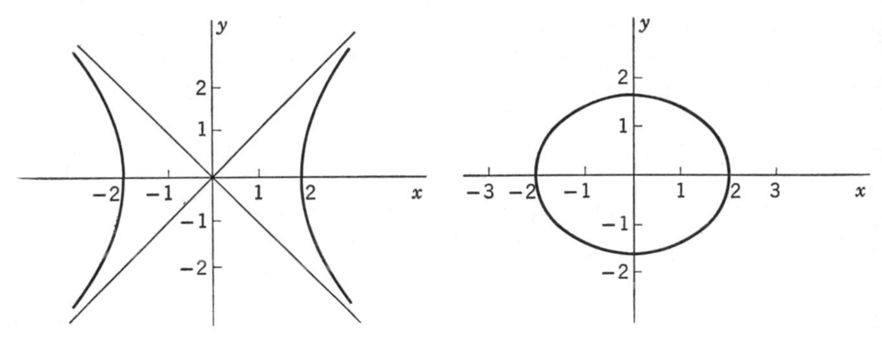

Figure 12–12

Figure 12–13

(*d*) Region of Definition. Expressing y in terms of x gives us $y = \pm\sqrt{(12 - 3x^2)}/2$, so that we must have $|x| \leq 2$. If we express x in terms of y, we obtain $x = \pm\sqrt{(12 - 4y^2)}/3$, so that we must have $|y| \leq 3$. A sketch of this ellipse is shown in Figure 12–13.

ILLUSTRATION 3. Sketch the conic having the equation $4x^2 - 4x - y - 1 = 0$.

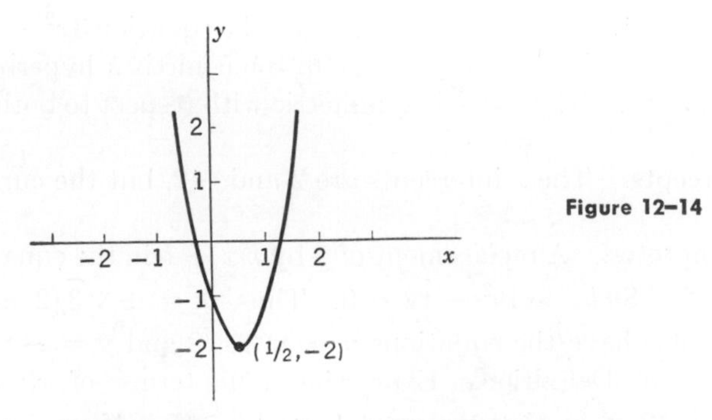

Figure 12–14

Solution. Since $B^2 - 4AC = 0$, this conic is a parabola. The recommended procedure for sketching is somewhat different in this case. If we write y in terms of x so that $y = 4x^2 - 4x - 1$, the solution set in $R^{\#}$ of this equation defines a function f, with $f(x) = 4x^2 - 4x - 1$ for each real number x. The vertex of the parabola will then be either a maximum or minimum point, and it may be easily located and identified with the use of f' and f''.† Thus, $f'(x) = 8x - 4 = 0$ if $x = 1/2$, and since $f''(x) = 8 > 0$, the curve is concave up. It follows that the vertex of the parabola is the minimum point $(1/2, -2)$. The y-intercept of the curve is -1, while the x-intercepts are the solutions of the equation $4x^2 - 4x - 1 = 0$. A sketch of a portion of the parabola is given in Figure 12–14.

PROBLEM SET 12.7

1. Identify the conics, defined as the loci of the following equations: (*a*) $x^2 + 4xy + 2y^2 - 6x + 4y - 6 = 0$; (*b*) $8x^2 - 4xy + y^2 - 5x + 7y - 14 = 0$; (*c*) $7x^2 - 4xy + y^2 - 5x + 7y - 7 = 0$; (*d*) $3x^2 + 12xy + 12y^2 - 6x - 9y - 12 = 0$.
2. Identify the conics, defined as the loci of the following equations: (*a*) $3x^2 - 4xy + 2x - 3y = 0$; (*b*) $xy - 3x + 2y - 1 = 0$; (*c*) $4x^2 + 9y^2 + 4x + 1 = 0$; (*d*) $x^2 - 2x + 5y - 6 = 0$.
3. Determine the equations of the asymptotes of each of the hyperbolas having the given equations: (*a*) $x^2 - xy - 2y^2 = 5$; (*b*) $2x^2 - 3xy - 2y^2 = 10$; (*c*) $3x^2 + 2xy - y^2 = 6$; (*d*) $4x^2 + 3xy - y^2 = 2$.
4. Analyze the following equations, and sketch a portion of the locus of each: (*a*) $x^2 + 4y^2 = 16$; (*b*) $x^2 - 4y^2 = 16$; (*c*) $2x^2 - 8y^2 = 21$; (*d*) $3x^2 + 5y^2 = 48$.
5. Analyze the following equations and sketch a portion of the locus of each: (*a*) $3y^2 - 2y + 5x - 10 = 0$; (*b*) $x^2 - 3x + 2y + 10 = 0$; (*c*) $9x^2 + 36y^2 - 36 = 0$; (*d*) $9x^2 - 36y^2 - 36 = 0$.
6. Analyze the following equations, and sketch a portion of the locus of each: (*a*) $2x^2 + 2y^2 = 5$; (*b*) $9x^2 - 81y^2 - 81 = 0$; (*c*) $9y^2 - 81x^2 - 81 = 0$; (*d*) $x = 2y^2 - 3y + 5$.
7. Discuss the nature of the degenerate conics having the following equations: (*a*) $3x^2 + 4y^2 = 0$; (*b*) $3y^2 - 5 = 0$; (*c*) $9x^2 - 4y^2 = 0$; (*d*) $x^2 + 2x + 1 = 0$.
8. Determine an equation of the ellipse obtained from the unit circle by first dividing the abscissas of each point on the latter by 2, and then translating the resulting locus 3 units to the right and 1 unit down.
9. Perform the transformations of Problem 8 on the (*a*) basic parabola; (*b*) basic hyperbola.

12.8 A Special Form of Second-Degree Equation: The Circle

If $A = B$ and $C = O$, in a second-degree equation, as discussed in the preceding section, the locus is a simple curve which we can investigate

† If sec. 8.10 was not studied, the test for maximum or minimum that does not involve f'' may be used.

fully. It is easy to show, in fact, that this curve is a circle, and the length of its radii and the location of its center can be readily found. The algebra involved makes use of the familiar technique of changing an expression $x^2 + bx$ into the square of a binomial, by the addition of $(b/2)^2$, i.e., the square of half the coefficient of the linear term. For example, if we add $(3/2)^2$ or $9/4$ to $x^2 + 3x$, the resulting expression $x^2 + 3x + 9/4$ is equal to $(x + 3/2)^2$. It is important to notice that the coefficient of x^2 is 1, if this rule is to hold.

It was noted previously that $x^2 + y^2 = 1$ is an equation of a unit circle with center at the origin. It is clear geometrically that a *uniform stretching* of the abscissas and ordinates of the points of this curve will result in a circle with center at the origin, but having radii that are no longer 1 unit in length. Thus, if we multiply both the abscissa and ordinate of each point on a unit circle by r, the result is a circle having radii r units in length, and an equation of this circle is $(x/r)^2 + (y/r)^2 = 1$ or $x^2 + y^2 = r^2$. It is clear that any equation $x^2 + y^2 = r^2$ may be written in the form $(x/r)^2 + (y/r)^2 = 1$, and so we have the following result:

> The locus of $x^2 + y^2 = r^2$ is a circle with center at the origin and having radii r units in length.

ILLUSTRATION 1. Discuss the locus of $3x^2 + 3y^2 = 4$.

Solution. This equation may be written as $x^2 + y^2 = 4/3$, and in this form we see that its locus is a circle with center at the origin, and having radii which are $2\sqrt{3}/3$ units in length.

If we replace x by $x - h$ and y by $y - k$ in the equation $x^2 + y^2 = r$, an application of Theorems 7 and 8 of Chapter 6 shows that the locus of the new equation $(x - h)^2 + (y - k)^2 = r^2$ is a circle with center at the point (h, k) and having radii r units in length. We shall show by an illustration that any second-degree equation which satisfies the conditions $A = C$ and $B = O$ can be put into this latter form and so, if there is any real locus at all, it will be a circle. (Notice that if r^2 is negative, no real locus is defined.) This gives us the following result:

> The locus of every second-degree equation of the form $Ax^2 + Ay^2 + Dx + Ey + F = 0$ is a circle, if a real locus is defined; and if the equation is written in the form $(x - h)^2 + (y - k)^2 = r^2$, it may be seen that the center is at (h, k) and the length of a radius is r units.

ILLUSTRATION 2. Discuss the locus of the equation $2x^2 + 2y^2 - 4x + 8y = 25$.

Solution. Since $A = C$ and $B = O$, this equation falls into the category under discussion. We first divide both members of the equation by 2, and obtain $x^2 + y^2 - 2x + 4y = 25/2$ or $x^2 - 2x + y^2 + 4y = 25/2$. If we now "complete the squares" of the quantities involving x and y, respectively, by adding the appropriate numbers to both members of the equation, the result is $(x^2 - 2x + 1) + (y^2 + 4y + 4) = 25/2 + 1 + 4 = 35/2$ or $(x - 1)^2 + (y + 2)^2 = 35/2$.

It may now be seen that the center of the circle is at $(1, -2)$, and the length of a radius is $\sqrt{35/2}$ or $\sqrt{70}/2$ units.

ILLUSTRATION 3. Write an equation of the circle with center at the point $(-3, 2)$, and having radii 2 units in length.

Solution. An equation of the circle is $(x + 3)^2 + (y - 2)^2 = 4$, which may be written as $x^2 + y^2 + 6x - 4y + 9 = 0$.

PROBLEM SET 12.8

1. Give a simple geometric proof of the fact that if the abscissa and ordinate of each point on a unit circle are multiplied by the positive number r, the result is a circle having radii r units in length.
2. Write an equation of the resulting circle, after the abscissa and ordinate of each point on the unit circle with center at the origin have been multiplied by (*a*) 5; (*b*) 2; (*c*) 10.
3. Discuss the locus of each of the following equations: (*a*) $x^2 + y^2 = 4$; (*b*) $x^2 + y^2 = 12$; (*c*) $x^2 + y^2 = 10$; (*d*) $3x^2 + 3y^2 = 2$; (*e*) $4x^2 + 4y^2 = 0$; (*f*) $5x^2 + 5y^2 = 14$.
4. Discuss the locus of the equation $2x^2 + 2y^2 + 5 = 0$.
5. Write down equations of the circles described as follows: (*a*) center $(2, -4)$, radii 10 units in length; (*b*) center $(3, -4)$, radii 5 units in length; (*c*) center $(-1, -3)$, radii 4 units in length; (*d*) center $(1, 5)$, radii 6 units in length.
6. Draw the circles described as the loci of the following equations: (*a*) $x^2 + y^2 - 4x + 2y = 5$; (*b*) $x^2 + y^2 - 5x + 2y = 6$; (*c*) $x^2 + y^2 + 8x + 4y - 10 = 0$; (*d*) $2x^2 + 2y^2 - 3x + 8y - 12 = 0$.
7. Describe and draw the locus of each of the following equations: (*a*) $3x^2 + 3y^2 - 9x - 5 = 0$; (*b*) $x^2 + y^2 + 8y - 8 = 0$; (*c*) $2x^2 + 2y^2 + 5x = 0$; (*d*) $x^2 + y^2 - 4y = 0$.
8. Describe how each of the ellipses, having the following equations, could be geometrically developed from a unit circle: (*a*) $x^2 + 4y^2 = 1$; (*b*) $2x^2 + 4y^2 = 1$; (*c*) $2x^2 + 4y^2 = 5$.

REVIEW TEST A

1. Sketch, in a neighborhood of the origin, portions of the loci of each of the following pairs of equations: (*a*) $y = x^2$, $y = (x + 2)^2$; (*b*) $y = e^x$, $y = e^{x/3}$; (*c*) $y^3 = x$, $8y^3 = x$.
2. Use the directions of Problem 1 for the following pairs of equations (*a*) $y = \sin x$, $y = 2 \sin 2x$; (*b*) $y = \tan x$, $y = \tan x/2$.

3. Use the methods of this chapter to analyze the following equation, and use the information to sketch a portion of its locus in a neighborhood of the origin: $y = x^4 - 4x^2 + 1$.
4. Use the directions of Problem 3 for the equation $y = x^2 \ln x$.
5. Find equations of the horizontal and vertical asymptotes of the curve having the equation $xy^2 + xy - 2x + 5y = 4$.
6. Find equations of any oblique asymptotes of the curve having the equation $x^4 + x^3y - 5x^2 - y^3 - 6 = 0$.
7. Sketch a portion of the curve in Problem 5 in some neighborhood of the origin.
8. Identify the (possibly degenerate) conic section having the equation (*a*) $2x^2 - 3xy + 4y^2 - x - y + 2 = 0$; (*b*) $4x^2 + 5xy - y^2 + 2x - 3y + 1 = 0$; (*c*) $2xy - 3x + y + 10 = 0$.
9. Determine the center, and length of a radius, of the circle having the equation $2x^2 + 2y^2 - 4x + 8y - 15 = 0$.
10. Determine an equation of the circle with center at the vertex of the parabolic locus of $y = x^2 - 4x + 5$, if the circle contains the origin as one of its points.
11. The equation of a curve is $y = x^3/(x^2 - 1)$. Discuss the nature of the curve at points having abscissas which (*a*) are slightly larger than 1; (*b*) are slightly less than 1; (*c*) exceed any finite positive bound; (*d*) are negative and their absolute values exceed any finite positive bound.
12. Determine an equation of the family of circles which contain the origin as one of their points, and which have their centers on the locus of $y = x$.

REVIEW TEST B

1. Sketch, in a neighborhood of the origin, portions of the loci of each of the following pairs of equations: (*a*) $y^2 = x$, $4y^2 = x$; (*b*) $y = 1/x^2$, $y = 3/x^2$; (*c*) $y = \ln x$, $y = \ln 2x$.
2. Use the directions of Problem 1 for the following pairs of equations: (*a*) $y = \text{arc Sin } x$, $2y = \text{arc Sin } x$; (*b*) $y = \cos x$, $3y = \cos x/2$.
3. Use the methods of this chapter to analyze the following equation, and use the information to sketch a portion of its locus in a neighborhood of the origin: $y = 2x^3 - 2x^2 - 2x + 4$.
4. Use the directions of Problem 3 for the equation $y = x^2e^{-x^2}$.
5. Find equations of any horizontal and vertical asymptotes of the curve having the equation $x^2y - 5xy - 2x + 6y = 0$.
6. Find equations of any oblique asymptotes of the curve having the equation $x^3 - 3x^2y + 2xy^2 - xy - 5 = 0$.
7. Sketch a portion of the curve in Problem 5 in some neighborhood of the origin.
8. Identify the (possibly degenerate) conic section having the equation (*a*) $2x^2 + 5x + 4y - 6 = 0$; (*b*) $3x^2 + 6xy + 3y^2 - 2x + y = 0$; (*c*) $x^2 + 2xy + 2y^2 - 12 = 0$.

9. Determine the center, and length of a radius, of the circle having the equation $3x^2 + 6x + 3y^2 = 13$.
10. Determine the equation of the circle with center at the point $(3, -4)$, and containing $(-2, -1)$ as one of its points.
11. The given equation of a curve is $y = x^2/(x - 3)$. Discuss the nature of the curve at points having abscissas which (*a*) are slightly less than 3; (*b*) are slightly larger than 3; (*c*) exceed any finite positive bound; (*d*) are negative and their absolute values exceed any finite positive bound.
12. State the results of applying the usual tests of symmetry to the locus of each of the following equations: (*a*) $xy^2 + 3x + 1 = 0$; (*b*) $2x^2y^2 = 4xy + 1$; (*c*) $y \ln x^2 = 4x$.

REFERENCES

Books

JOHNSON, RICHARD E., NEAL H. MCCOY AND ANNE F. O'NEILL, *Fundamentals of College Mathematics,* New York, Rinehart, 1953. (Chaps. 12 and 13.)

SMITH, EDWARD STAPLES, *et al., Unified Calculus,* New York, Wiley, 1947. (Pp. 192–197.)

American Mathematical Monthly

KARST, O. J., "Two Methods for Finding the Angle of Rotation," Vol. 63, p. 416 (1956).

LANGE, LUISE, "Deriving the Equations of the Sections of a Cone," Vol. 63, p. 488 (1956).

PORGES, ARTHUR, "Rapid Sketching of a Conic," Vol. 64, p. 41 (1957).

13

PLANE ANALYTIC GEOMETRY II: POLAR COORDINATES

Eadem mutata resurgo.

JACOB BERNOULLI

13.1 Polar Coordinates

Up to this point in the text, all graphs have been constructed with reference to a Cartesian coordinate system, based on two intersecting number scales. We introduced this coordinate system in order to obtain, in a unique way, a graphical respresentation of an ordered pair of real numbers, and we have frequently identified a geometric point with its coordinate pair. It is possible to use other systems for this representation, and in this chapter we describe what is known as the *polar* coordinate system. One of the earliest general users of this system was Jacob Bernoulli (1645–1705). A class of curves known as spirals is especially adapted for study with this system, and one of these spirals—the logarithmic—is reproduced after each of several geometric transformations. This fact was so fascinating to Jacob Bernoulli, that he directed that a spiral be engraved on his tombstone with the inscription "Eadem mutata resurgo" ("Though changed, I shall arise the same").

The basis of a polar coordinate system in the plane is a single number scale, known as the *polar axis*, the point 0 on this scale being referred to as the *pole*. It will be convenient to conceive of the polar axis as capable of rotation about the pole, with counterclockwise rotation considered to be positive. Then if we conceive of the polar axis as having been rotated about the pole through an angle of b radians, the point with scale reading a on the "rotated axis" will be the graphical representation, in this polar system, of the ordered pair (a, b). This is shown in Figure 13–1, while in Figure 13–2, are shown graphs of the pairs $(1, 1)$, $(-2, 9\pi/4)$, $(-2, -2)$, and $(3, 7\pi/4)$, with reference to the indicated polar system.

If we follow the analogy of a Cartesian system, and refer to the members of an ordered pair as *polar coordinates* of the point represented by the pair, it is clear that a geometric point may have many different coordinates. For example, the ordered pairs $(1, \pi/2)$, $(-1, 3\pi/2)$, and $(1, -3\pi/2)$ are represented by the same point in any given polar coordinate system, and there are infinitely many other coordinate pairs for this point. The fact that the correspondence between ordered pairs of real numbers and the points of a plane is not one-to-one in a polar system is responsible

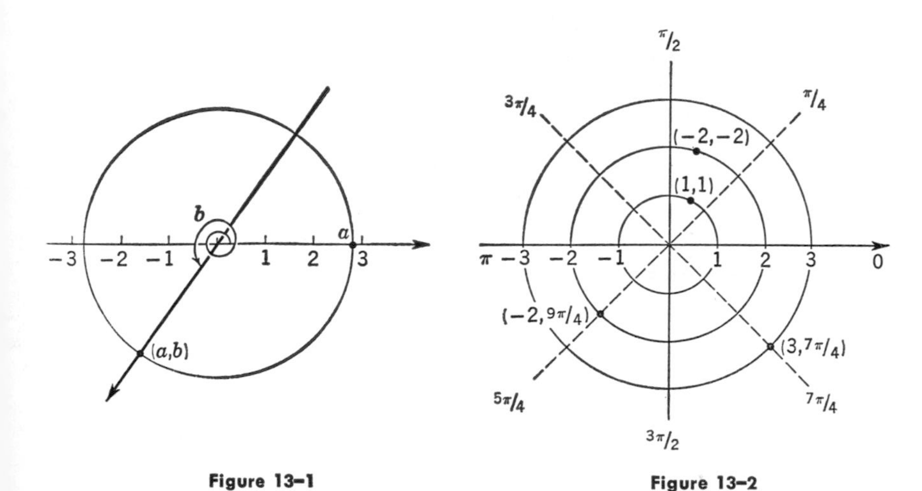

Figure 13-1 **Figure 13-2**

for certain complications which do not arise if a Cartesian system is used. On the other hand, we shall see that there are some curves which have much simpler polar than Cartesian equations, and so problems involving such curves are usually simplified if referred to a polar coordinate system.

The student must have noticed the close resemblance between a polar coordinate pair associated with a point, and a polar form of the complex number geometrically identified with the point. It may be seen that this latter pair is, in fact, merely a special coordinate pair of the point, in which the first member, the modulus or absolute value, is required to be positive. It is customary to use the notation of complex numbers, and designate polar coordinates of an arbitrary point as r and θ; as described above, $|r|$ is the distance of the point from the pole, while θ is the radian measure of one of the angles between the polar axis and the line containing the pole and the given point. Whether r is positive or negative for the point depends on the choice for the number θ. We shall continue the practice of identifying an ordered pair with the point represented by it, and so shall refer to the point representing the ordered pair (r, θ) on a polar graph as *the point* (r, θ).

ILLUSTRATION 1. Locate the following points on a polar graph: $(2, \pi/4)$; $(-2, \pi/4)$; $(-3, \pi)$; $(-2, -\pi/4)$; $(1, -3\pi/2)$.

Solution.

ILLUSTRATION 2. Find six other ordered pairs of real numbers which are represented on a polar graph by the same point as $(2, -\pi/4)$.

Solution. Six other pairs of numbers with the required characteristic are: $(-2, 3\pi/4)$; $(2, 7\pi/4)$; $(2, -9\pi/4)$; $(-2, -5\pi/4)$; $(2, -15\pi/4)$; $(-2, 11\pi/4)$. There are, of course, infinitely many others.

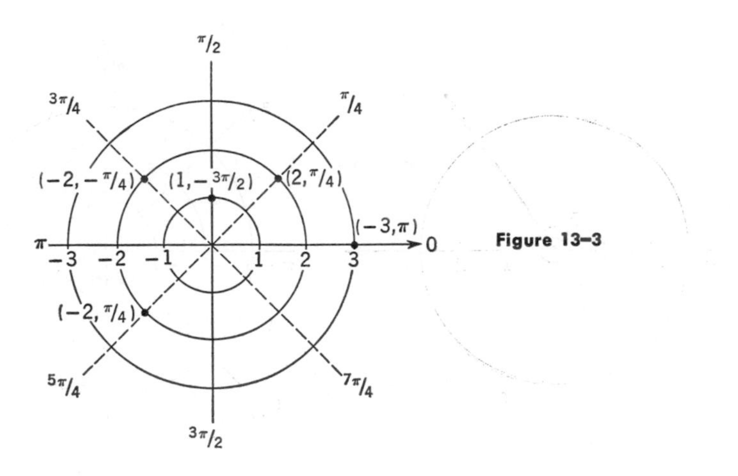

Figure 13–3

PROBLEM SET 13.1

1. List the six numerically smallest choices for θ, if (r, θ) is to be represented on a polar graph by the same point as $(5, \pi/6)$.
2. List the six numerically smallest choices for θ, if (r, θ) is to be represented on a polar graph by the same point as $(2, -\pi/3)$.
3. Plot the following points on a polar graph: $(2, \pi/6)$; $(3, 2\pi/3)$; $(-2, -\pi)$; $(3, 13\pi/6)$; $(-1, 25\pi/6)$.
4. Plot the following points on a polar graph: $(-2, 2\pi)$; $(3, 5\pi/2)$; $(-3, -9\pi/2)$; $(2, \pi/3)$; $(1, \pi/2)$; $(-2, \pi/6)$.
5. Find three additional polar coordinate pairs for each of the following points: $(3, \pi/2)$; $(-3, \pi/6)$; $(4, -\pi/3)$.
6. Find three additional polar coordinate pairs for each of the following points: $(6, 12)$; $(-3, -1)$; $(0, 0)$.
7. Find a polar coordinate pair for the point $(1, 2)$, having second member a negative number in the interval $[-\pi, 0]$.
8. Locate the following points on a polar graph: $(2, 5\pi/2)$; $(-3, -3)$; $(3, 10)$; $(-2, -4)$; $(5, -5)$.
9. Locate the following points on a polar graph: $(0, 0)$; $(4, \pi/2)$; $(6, \pi/6)$. Join the points with line segments and use the Law of Cosines to determine the distance between the last two points.
10. Determine the distance between the points $(3, -\pi/4)$ and $(-4, \pi)$ on a polar graph.

13.2 Polar Graphs

The procedure for constructing the graph of a relation is essentially the same, whether we use a Cartesian or a polar coordinate system: i.e., the ordered pairs of numbers, as elements of the relation, are coordinate pairs for points in the plane, and the set of all such points is the graph of the relation. However, the following notational difference is noteworthy. If an equation in r and θ is the defining rule of correspondence for a relation, θ is usually an arbitrary element of the domain, while r is the corresponding element of the range. If we were consistent with earlier practice, we would designate an arbitrary element of the relation by (θ, r), but the order in (r, θ) is firmly established by custom. We then refer to (r, θ) as a solution of the so-called *polar equation*, and the polar locus of the equation is the polar graph of its solution set. The polar graph of a relation, defined on its domain by one or more equations, is the polar graph of the intersection of certain subsets of the solution sets of the equations.

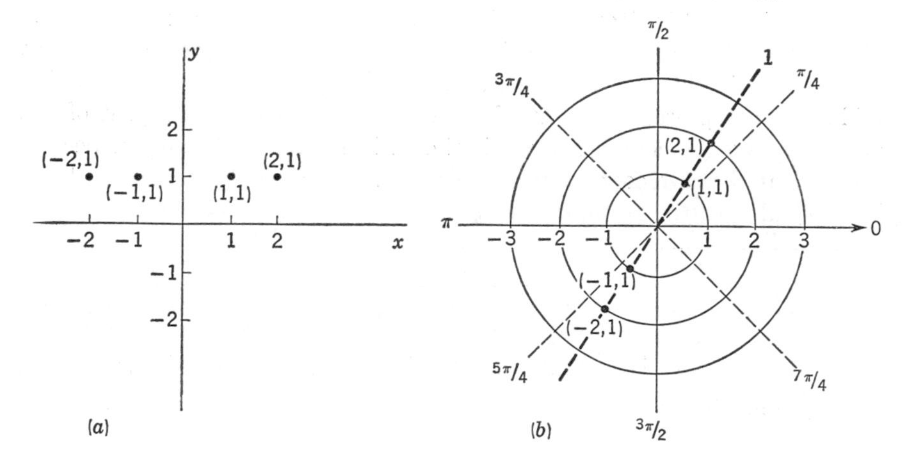

Figure 13–4

ILLUSTRATION 1. Graph the following four ordered pairs, using first a Cartesian and then a polar coordinate system: $(-2, 1)$, $(-1, 1)$, $(1, 1)$, $(2, 1)$.

Solution. The two graphs are shown in Figure 13–4.

If the locus of an equation is desired with reference to a polar coordinate system, we follow the procedure for Cartesian graphs and locate a representative set of points of the solution set, and join them with a smooth curve as the nature of the equation dictates. Care must be taken, of course, not to include on the graph points which are not in the solution set of the equation. The number of points actually plotted for such a

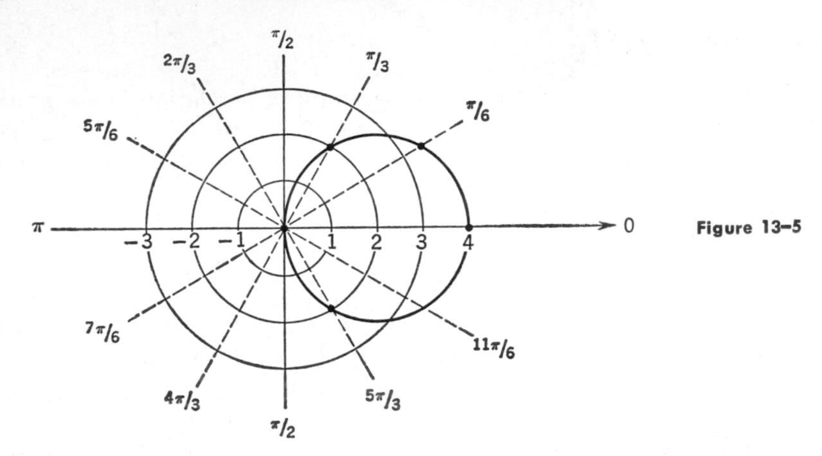

Figure 13–5

sketch depends on the complexity of the equation and the desired accuracy.

ILLUSTRATION 2. Use a polar coordinate system to sketch the locus of the equation $r = 4 \cos \theta$.

Solution. It is clear that while the second member of a solution (r, θ) of this equation may be an arbitrary real number, each geometric point of the locus is obtained for some θ in the interval $[0, 2\pi]$. The following table lists a representative set of ordered pairs of the solution set of the equation, and the complete locus is shown in Figure 13–5, with respect to the indicated polar coordinate system. In this case the geometric locus is identical with the graph of the associated function on the interval $[0, \pi]$.

θ	0	$\pi/6$	$\pi/3$	$\pi/2$	$2\pi/3$	$5\pi/6$	π	$7\pi/6$	$4\pi/3$	$3\pi/2$	$5\pi/3$	$11\pi/6$	2π
r	4	$2\sqrt{3}$	2	0	-2	$-2\sqrt{3}$	-4	$-2\sqrt{3}$	-2	0	2	$2\sqrt{3}$	4

We shall prove later that the locus in Figure 13–5 actually is a circle, which it appears to be.

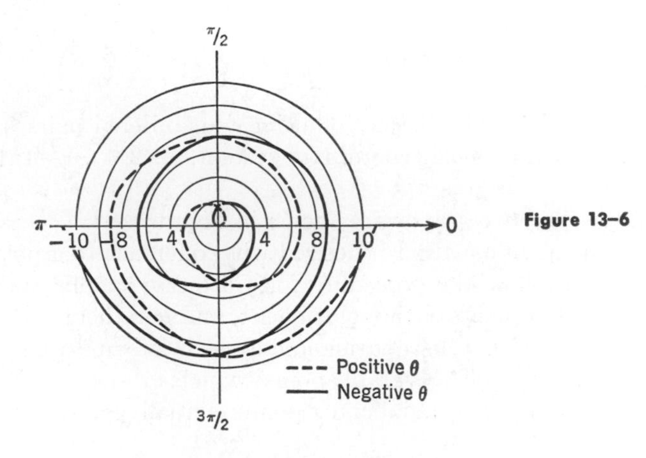

Figure 13–6

ILLUSTRATION 3. Sketch the polar graph of the function f, defined on $[-4\pi, 4\pi]$ by $f(\theta) = \theta$.

Solution. A representative set of ordered pairs of f is given in the table below, while a sketch of the function is shown in Figure 13–6.

θ	-4π	$-7\pi/2$	-3π	$-5\pi/2$	-2π	$-3\pi/2$	$-\pi$	$-\pi/2$	0	$\pi/2$	π	$3\pi/2$	2π	$5\pi/2$	3π	$7\pi/2$	4π
r	−12.6	−11.0	−9.4	−7.9	−6.3	−4.7	−3.1	−1.5	0	1.5	3.1	4.7	6.3	7.9	9.4	11.0	12.6

PROBLEM SET 13.2

In Problems 1 through 8, use a polar coordinate system to sketch the locus of each of given equations, plotting at least 10 points on each graph.

1. $r = 2 \sin \theta$.
2. $r = 3 \sin \theta$.
3. $r = 2 + \cos \theta$.
4. $r = 1 - \cos \theta$.
5. $r = 1 + \sin \theta$.
6. $r = 1 + \cos \theta$.
7. $r = -2 \sin \theta$.
8. $r = 5$.
9. Sketch the polar graph of the function defined on the interval $[-\pi, \pi]$ by $r = 2 + \theta$, for each θ in the domain of the function.
10. Sketch the polar graph of the function defined on the interval $[\pi/4, 2\pi]$ by $r = 10/\theta$, for each θ in the domain of the function.
11. Use a polar coordinate system to sketch a portion of the locus of the equation $\theta = 3$ in some neighborhood of the pole.
12. A function f is defined on the interval $[0, 5]$ by the equation $f(x) = 1 - x$, for each x in the domain of f. Sketch the graph of f using (a) a Cartesian coordinate system; (b) a polar coordinate system.
13. Compare the loci of $r = 5$ and $r = -5$, using a polar coordinate system. Make a similar comparison of the loci of $\theta = \pi/4$ and $\theta = -\pi/4$.
14. Make a careful sketch of the locus of $r = 2 \cos 2\theta$, using a polar coordinate system.
15. Make a careful sketch of a portion of the locus of $r \sin(\theta - \pi/3) = 2$, using a polar coordinate system.
16. Discuss the nature of the polar locus of (a) $r = 0$; (b) $\theta = 0$.

13.3 Some Simple Curves and Their Polar Equations

It is probable that straight lines and circles are most generally considered to be the simplest curves of plane geometry. However, it should not be assumed that these curves necessarily have the simplest equations; for it must be kept constantly in mind that the equation of a curve depends not only on its geometric nature but also on the *coordinate system* used. For example, $y = x^2$ and $y = x^2 + 4x + 1$ may be equations of the *same* parabola, considered as a set of points, merely referred to different Cartesian coordinate systems. The spiral, a portion of which was shown in Illustration 3 of the preceding section, has a very simple equation $r = \theta$, if referred to the coordinate system used in the illustration, but the curve has considerable geometric complexity. In this section we shall consider equations of straight lines and circles, with reference to a polar coordinate system.

Inasmuch as a single geometric point may have many different pairs of coordinates, even if referred to the same polar coordinate system, it should come as no surprise that under the same circumstances a curve may have many different equations, *which are not even equivalent;* for it is possible that the solution sets of these equations are not the same. As a simple example of this, we may consider the solution sets of the equations $r = 5$ and $r = -5$. Since $r = 5$ for any solution (r, θ) of the first equation, while $r = -5$ for any solution of the second equation, their solution sets are seen to be disjoint; in spite of this, however, their geometric loci are the same—a circle with center at the pole and radii 5 units in length.

In relating a curve to a polar equation, we must always remember that the curve is the polar graph of the set—and only this set—of ordered pairs (r, θ) which satisfy the equation. In order to find an equation of a curve which has been defined geometrically, we usually look for some geometric property which may be expressed as a condition on the coordinates of an arbitrary point (r, θ) on the curve. If the curve is a circle with center at the pole and radii C units in length, it is clear that this condition is $r = \pm C$, which are two possible equations of the circle. If the curve is a straight line through the pole, the coordinate θ of an arbitrary point (r, θ) on the line may be considered to satisfy a condition $\theta = C$, for some real number C, and this condition is an equation of the line. For example, an equation of the line shown in Figure 13–7 is $\theta = \pi/4$, though other equations of the same line are $\theta = -3\pi/4$, $\theta = 5\pi/4$, etc.

The locus of the equation $r = 4 \cos \theta$ appeared to be a circle in Figure 13–5, and we now prove that this is, in fact, the case. In Figure 13–8, we have shown a circle passing through the pole O, with a diameter of length a units lying along the positive portion of the polar axis. Let $P(r, \theta)$ be an arbitrary point on the circle, with M the outer extremity of the above-mentioned diameter. In line with the general procedure, we now observe the following geometric property: the points M, P, and O form the vertices of a right-angled triangle, with OP the projection of OM on the line through O and P. It then follows that $r = a \cos \theta$, and we have obtained an equation of the circle. It is now clear that the locus of $r = 4 \cos \theta$ is also a circle through the pole, with its diameters 4 units in length. The general result may be phrased in the following form:

> The equation $r = a \cos \theta$, $a > 0$, is a polar equation of a circle passing through the pole, with a diameter of length a units lying along the positive portion of the polar axis.

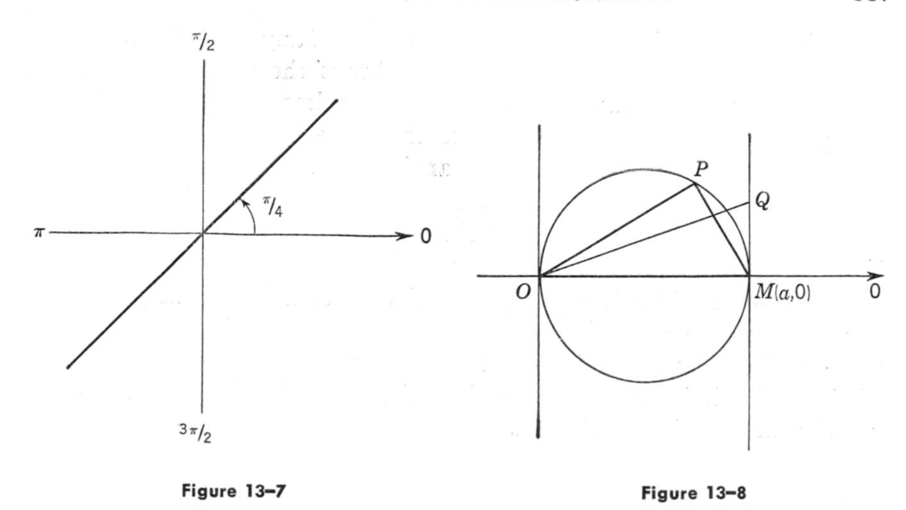

Figure 13–7

Figure 13–8

It is convenient at this time to determine an equation for the straight line perpendicular to the polar axis, and containing the point M of Figure 13–8; this line will, of course, be the tangent line to the circle at M. As before, we select an arbitrary point $Q(r, \theta)$ on the line and again observe that points O, Q, and M are vertices of a right-angled triangle. Since OM is the projection of OQ on the polar axis, an equation of the line is seen to be $r \cos \theta = a$. We now have established the following result:

> The equation $r \cos \theta = a$, $a > 0$, is a polar equation of the straight line perpendicular to the polar axis and intersecting it at the point $(a, 0)$, on the positive portion of the axis.

We now wish to present a theorem which, when applied to the special cases already considered, will enable us to find a polar equation of any straight line, and any circle passing through the pole. The Theorems on Graphing of Chapter 6 were given there with Cartesian coordinates in mind, but they also have interpretations when polar coordinates are used. At present, we are most concerned with Theorems 7 and 8 on translations, and the effect on the polar locus of an equation if θ is replaced in the equation by $\theta - \alpha$. It is evident that if θ is replaced by $\theta - \alpha$ in any equation in r and θ, with $\alpha > 0$, the "new" θ must be α units larger than the "old" θ, for the same r. The geometric result of this is to effect an apparent rotation of the original curve about the pole through an angle of α radians in the positive direction of θ, i.e., in the counter-clockwise direction. It is clear that the rotation will be clockwise if θ is replaced by $\theta + \alpha$, and we have the following general result:

THEOREM. A replacement of θ by $\theta - \alpha$ in a polar equation of a curve effects an apparent rotation of the curve about the pole through an angle of α radians.

We are now able to write a polar equation of any straight line, and of any circle passing through the pole, for either of these may be considered the result of rotating one of the lines or circles already considered through an appropriate angle. Thus, consider the circle in Figure 13–9, with diameter through the pole making an angle of ω radians with the positive polar axis. We have just seen that an equation of a circle of the same size, with a diameter lying along the positive polar axis, is $r = a \cos \theta$, if a is the common measure of length of the diameters of both circles. In view of the theorem it is now apparent that an equation of the given circle is $r = a \cos (\theta - \omega)$, and an alternate equation would be $r = a \cos (\theta + 2\pi - \omega)$; in order to obtain the first equation, we considered the rotation of the basic circle to be counter-clockwise, while in the second case the rotation was considered clockwise.

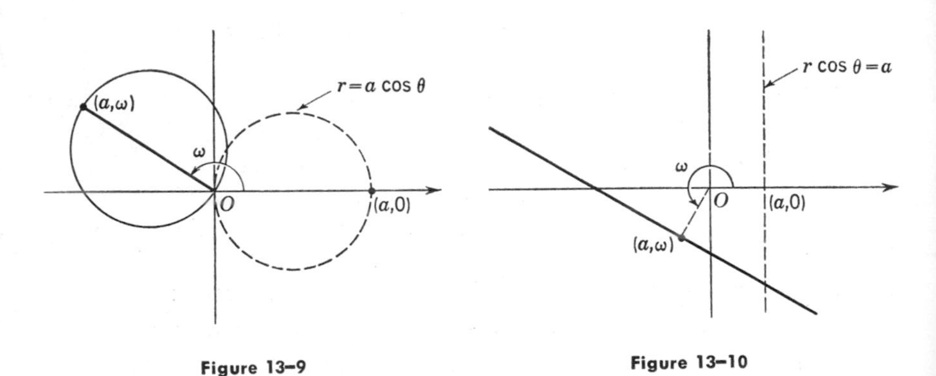

Figure 13–9 **Figure 13–10**

In a similar way we can obtain an equation of any straight line. For any straight line can be considered the result of rotating a straight line which is perpendicular to and intersects the positive portion of the polar axis. It will be convenient to refer to the perpendicular line segment from the pole to a line as its *normal*, and it is apparent that a line is determined by the length of its normal and the angle made by the normal and the positive portion of the polar axis. Thus, consider the line in Figure 13–10, with a normal of length a units making an angle of ω radians with the positive portion of the polar axis. It is now clear that we can consider this line the result of rotating the line locus of $r \cos \theta = a$ through an angle of ω radians, and so an equation of the given line is $r \cos (\theta - \omega) = a$. It is evident that an alternate equation is $r \cos (\theta + 2\pi - \omega) = a$.

It is sometimes helpful to recognize the simplified equations which arise from four special cases of the lines and circles just discussed. These cases occur when $\omega = 0$, $\omega = \pi/2$, $\omega = \pi$, and $\omega = 3\pi/2$, the special case with $\omega = 0$ having already been discussed. We have shown these special cases

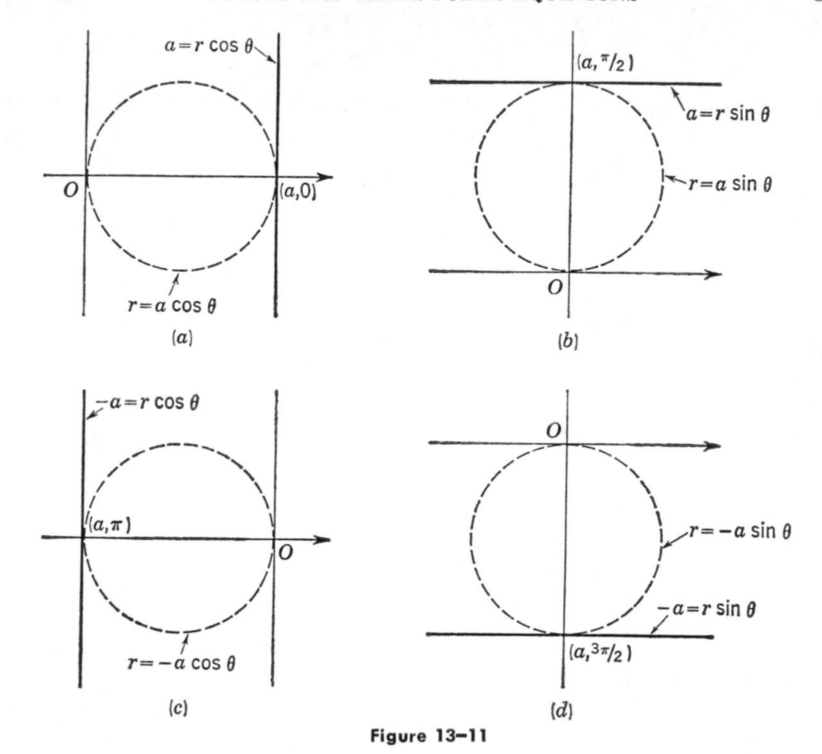

Figure 13–11

in Figure 13–11, along with the simplified equations which the student is urged to check from the general result.

ILLUSTRATION 1. Describe the locus of $r = -5 \sin (\theta - \pi/6)$.

Solution. An application of the theorem shows that this locus is the result of rotating a circle with diameters 5 units in length about the pole, through an angle of $\pi/6$ radians from the position of the circle in Figure 13–11*d*. The locus is shown in Figure 13–12.

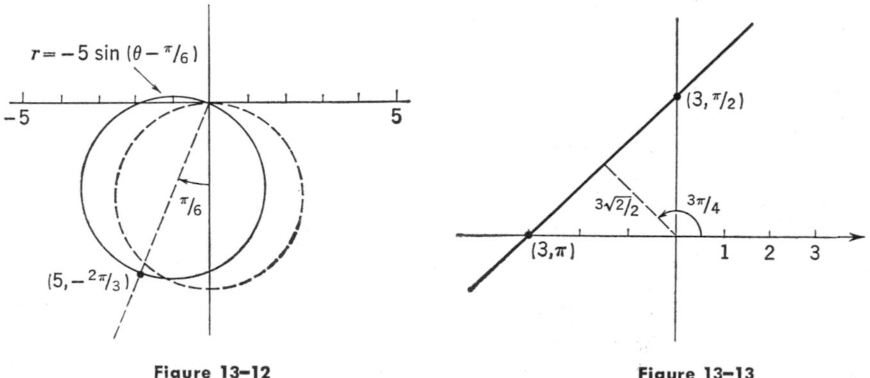

Figure 13–12

Figure 13–13

ILLUSTRATION 2. Find a polar equation of the line through the points $(3, \pi/2)$ and $(3, \pi)$.

Solution. The line is shown in Figure 13–13, from which it is seen that $a = 3\sqrt{2}/2$ and ω may be taken to be $3\pi/4$. The corresponding equation of the line is then $3\sqrt{2}/2 = r \cos(\theta - 3\pi/4)$, though we may give an alternate equation as $-3\sqrt{2}/2 = r \cos(\theta + \pi/4)$.

PROBLEM SET 13.3

Note. We shall refer to the *simplest* polar equation of a circle (line) as one expressed either as $r = \pm a \cos(\theta - \omega)$ $[\pm a = r \cos(\theta - \omega)]$ or as $r = \pm a \sin(\theta - \omega)$ $[\pm a = r \sin(\theta - \omega)]$, and involving the smallest numerical ω.

1. List six ordered pairs of the solution set of (*a*) $r = 5$; (*b*) $\theta = \pi/3$.
2. Give a verbal comparison of the polar loci of each of the following pairs of polar equations: (*a*) $r = 4\cos\theta$, $r = 4\cos(\theta - \pi/3)$; (*b*) $r\cos\theta = 3$, $r\cos(\theta + \pi/6) = 3$; (*c*) $r\sin\theta = 4$, $r\sin(\theta + 2\pi/3) = 4$.
3. Construct the polar locus of each of the following equations: (*a*) $r = 6\cos\theta$; (*b*) $r = 4\cos(\theta - 3\pi/4)$; (*c*) $r\cos\theta = 2$; (*d*) $r\cos(\theta + 2\pi/3) = 8$; (*e*) $r\cos(\theta + \pi/6) = 3$; (*f*) $r = 4\cos(\theta - 5\pi/6)$.
4. Construct the polar locus of each of the following equations, using only points in a neighborhood of the origin if the locus is of infinite extent: (*a*) $r = -5$; (*b*) $r = 10$; (*c*) $\theta = -3\pi/4$; (*d*) $\theta = 7\pi/3$; (*e*) $r\sin\theta = -5$; (*f*) $r = -6\sin\theta$.
5. Find the simplest polar equation of the circle passing through the pole with center at (*a*) $(5, \pi/3)$; (*b*) $(4, -3\pi/4)$; (*c*) $(10, 2\pi/3)$.
6. Find the simplest polar equation of the straight line having a normal satisfying the following conditions: (*a*) $a = 5, \omega = \pi/6$; (*b*) $a = 2, \omega = -2\pi/3$; (*c*) $a = 10, \omega = 4\pi/3$.
7. Find the simplest polar equation of the straight line, the normal of which intersects it at the point (*a*) $(4, 3\pi/4)$; (*b*) $(2, -4\pi/5)$; (*c*) $(6, -2\pi/3)$; (*d*) $(5, -\pi)$.
8. Find the simplest polar equation of the circle which contains the pole, and intersects its own polar diameter at the point (*a*) $(6, 2\pi/3)$; (*b*) $(5, -4\pi/5)$; (*c*) $(8, \pi/6)$; (*d*) $(10, 2\pi/3)$; (*e*) $(4, -7\pi/4)$.
9. Use the Law of Cosines to derive a polar equation for the circle with center at the point (c, γ) and with radii R units in length.
10. Find the simplest polar equation of the straight line (*a*) which may be considered the result of rotating the polar axis about the pole through $3\pi/4$ radians; (*b*) through the point $(-4, 0)$ and perpendicular to the polar axis; (*c*) through the point $(-5, \pi/6)$ and perpendicular to the line with equation $\theta = \pi/6$.
11. Refer to the result of Problem 9 and write a polar equation of the circle with center at the point $(12, 2\pi/3)$, having radii 10 units in length.
12. Since $\cos(\theta - \omega) = \cos\omega\cos\theta + \sin\omega\sin\theta$, the expression $a\cos(\theta - \omega)$

can be written $(a \cos \omega) \cos \theta + (a \sin \omega) \sin \theta$. Use this result to show that $r = b \cos \theta + c \sin \theta$ is a polar equation of the circle which contains the pole and the points $(b, 0)$ and $(c, \pi/2)$.

13. Use the result of Problem 12 to graph the locus of (*a*) $r = 2 \cos \theta + 5 \sin \theta$; (*b*) $r = 2 \cos \theta - 4 \sin \theta$; (*c*) $r = -3 \cos \theta + 2 \sin \theta$.
14. Write the simplest polar equation of the straight line, which is tangent to the locus of $r = 5 \cos (\theta - \pi/6)$ at the outer end of the polar diameter of this circle.
15. Use the result of Problem 12 to write a polar equation of the circle containing the pole, and with center at the point (*a*) $(2, \pi/3)$; (*b*) $(3, \pi/4)$; (*c*) $(4, 5\pi/6)$; (*d*) $(4, -\pi/3)$; (*e*) $(-6, -2\pi/3)$.
16. Graph the function f, defined on $[0, \pi]$ by $f(t) = 2 \cos t$, for each t in its domain, using (*a*) Cartesian coordinates; (*b*) polar coordinates.
17. Apply the directions of Problem 16 to the function F, defined on $[\pi, 2\pi]$ by $F(t) = 2 \sin (t + \pi/6)$ for each t in its domain.
18. Apply the directions of Problem 16 to the function f, defined on $[\pi/4, 3\pi/4]$ by $f(t) = 3 \csc t$, for each t in its domain.

13.4 Cartesian and Polar Coordinates

We have tried to emphasize before, that the shape of a geometric curve is quite independent of the coordinate system to which it may be referred. A circle is always the same circle, regardless of whether Cartesian or polar coordinates are used, or whether the origin is taken at the center of the circle. However, the *equations* of a curve may vary greatly in appearance, as different coordinate systems are used. In this section we are to be concerned with the changes in such equations due to the replacement of a polar system by a special Cartesian system, and vice versa.

The Cartesian system, with which we are to be concerned in this section, is so related to a polar system that the x-axis coincides with the polar axis. It is to be understood, moreover, that the scale units on the x and y axes are the same. Since a curve is a set of points, the problem resolves itself into a study of the changes in the coordinates of an arbitrary point in the plane. Hence, let P be a point in the plane, representing the pair (x, y) in the Cartesian system and the pair (r, θ) in the polar system as shown in Figure 13–14. It follows from the definitions of the circular functions that $x = r \cos \theta$ and $y = r \sin \theta$, and these two equations form the basis for the transformation of coordinates. It is also frequently useful to recall, however, that $x^2 + y^2 = r^2$, if the expression $x^2 + y^2$ happens to occur in an equation.

Strictly speaking, an equation is neither polar nor Cartesian, for these terms apply to the graphing procedure. However, it will be convenient to use these words to refer to equations of curves, with respect to the two types of coordinate systems. Thus, in harmony with the usual symbolism, a *polar equation* of a curve will usually be an equation in r and θ, while a *Cartesian equation* will regularly involve x and y. The polar and Cartesian equations of a curve, discussed in this section, will be *corresponding,* in the sense that they refer to the *same* curve.

ILLUSTRATION 1. Determine a polar equation corresponding to the Cartesian equation $x^2 + y^2 + 8x - 4y = 0$.

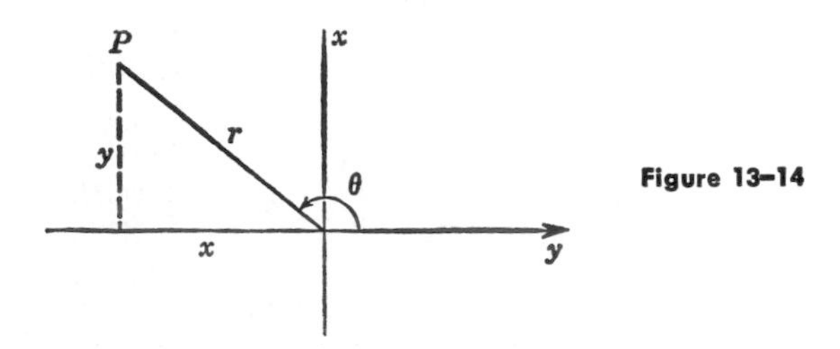

Figure 13–14

Solution. Using the substitutions above, we obtain $r^2 + 8r \cos \theta - 4r \sin \theta = 0$, which can be expressed as $r(r + 8 \cos \theta - 4 \sin \theta) = 0$. The only point on the graph, with polar coordinates satisfying $r = 0$, is the pole, and this point is also on the locus of $r + 8 \cos \theta - 4 \sin \theta = 0$ (see Problem 12 of Problem Set 13.3). The factor r may then be removed, and the resulting polar equation is $r + 8 \cos \theta - 4 \sin \theta = 0$.

ILLUSTRATION 2. Determine the Cartesian coordinates of the point having the polar coordinate pair $(2, -3\pi/4)$.

Solution. If (x, y) is the Cartesian coordinate pair of the given point, we must have $x = 2 \cos (-3\pi/4) = 2(-1/\sqrt{2}) = -\sqrt{2}$, and $y = 2 \sin (-3\pi/4) = 2(-1/\sqrt{2}) = -\sqrt{2}$.

The equations necessary for obtaining a Cartesian equation corresponding to a given polar equation, may be obtained from Figure 13–14. For it is clear that $r = \pm\sqrt{x^2 + y^2}$, and $\theta = \arctan y/x$. If polar coordinates of a point are desired, a sketch will help in choosing the proper sign for r, after θ has been selected; for it must be remembered that there are infinitely many solutions of this latter equation for θ, and the sign of r is related to the choice of this solution. These substitutions may also be used to obtain a Cartesian equation corresponding to a given polar equation, but it is sometimes necessary to examine the graph to obtain the correct sign of r. In order to avoid this question of sign, it is desirable to use the equivalent substitutions $r \cos \theta = x$ and $r \sin \theta = y$, if possible, rather than the basic substitutions for r and θ.

ILLUSTRATION 3. Determine polar coordinates for the point having the Cartesian coordinate pair $(-1, \sqrt{3})$.

Solution. Since $\theta = \arctan \sqrt{3}/(-1) = \arctan (-\sqrt{3})$, we can choose $\theta = 2\pi/3$. But $r = \pm\sqrt{3 + 1} = \pm\sqrt{4} = \pm 2$, and the point is in the second quadrant, so the correct choice of r to associate with $\theta = 2\pi/3$ is 2.

ILLUSTRATION 4. Determine a Cartesian equation that corresponds to the polar equation $r = 2 \cos \theta - 4 \sin \theta$.

Solution. Since the polar locus of this equation contains the pole (see Problem 12 of Problem Set 13.3), both members of this equation may be multiplied by r without introducing any new points on the locus. The new equation is $r^2 = 2r \cos \theta - 4r \sin \theta$ which, on using the above substitutions, becomes $x^2 + y^2 = 2x - 4y$.

ILLUSTRATION 5. Determine a Cartesian equation that corresponds to the polar equation $3r - 4 \tan \theta = 0$.

Solution. If we write the given equation as $3r = 4 \tan \theta$ and square both members, we obtain $9r^2 = 16 \tan^2 \theta = 16y^2/x^2$, or $9x^2(x^2 + y^2) = 16y^2$. It is conceivable that the locus of this latter equation contains points not present on the original locus, due to the squaring process. However, we may be assured that the Cartesian locus of $9x^2(x^2 + y^2) = 16y^2$ does *include* all points of the polar locus of $3r - 4 \tan \theta = 0$. A graphical check will reveal, however, that these two loci are the same, in this instance.

PROBLEM SET 13.4

Note. While there are infinitely many Cartesian systems which might be related to a given polar coordinate system, we shall assume for the purposes of the following problems that the Cartesian system is the one discussed in this section.

1. Obtain polar coordinates for each of the following points in the Cartesian system: (*a*) $(1, -1)$; (*b*) $(2, 4)$; (*c*) $(-\sqrt{3}, -1)$; (*d*) $(-2, 3)$; (*e*) $(-1, -1)$.
2. Obtain the Cartesian coordinates of each of the following points in a polar system: (*a*) $(2, -\pi/3)$; (*b*) $(-2, -3\pi/4)$; (*c*) $(3, -7\pi/4)$; (*d*) $(-2, 3\pi/2)$.
3. Determine a polar equation corresponding to each of the following Cartesian equations: (*a*) $x^2 + y^2 + 8x = 0$; (*b*) $x^2 + y^2 - 6x - 4y = 0$.
4. Determine a Cartesian equation corresponding to each of the following polar equations: (*a*) $r \cos \theta - 3r \sin \theta = 6$; (*b*) $r \cos \theta + 2r \sin \theta = 10$.
5. Determine a polar equation corresponding to each of the following Cartesian equations: (*a*) $3xy = x^2 + y^2$; (*b*) $2x^4 = x^2 + y^2$; (*c*) $x^2 + (y + 1)^2 = 9$.
6. Determine a Cartesian equation corresponding to each of the following polar equations: (*a*) $r \sin \theta = 10$; (*b*) $r \cos \theta = \sin 2\theta$; (*c*) $r(1 + \cos \theta) = 6$.
7. Determine a Cartesian equation corresponding to each of the following polar equations: (*a*) $r = 2 \cos \theta - 4 \sin \theta$; (*b*) $2r = 5 \cos 2\theta$; (*c*) $2r \sec \theta = 5$.
8. Determine a Cartesian equation corresponding to the polar equation $r \cos (\theta - \omega) = a$, and show that the Cartesian locus of this new equation is a straight line.

9. Determine a Cartesian equation corresponding to the polar equation $r = a \cos(\theta - \omega)$, and show that the Cartesian locus of this new equation is a circle.

10. Determine the center and length of the radii of the circle, described as the polar locus of $r = a \cos\theta + b \sin\theta$, by first finding a corresponding Cartesian equation.

11. Give simple Cartesian equations which correspond to the polar equations $r = C$ and $\theta = C$.

12. Determine the length of the radii and the Cartesian coordinates of the center of the circle, described as the polar locus of $r = 4 \cos\theta - 8 \sin\theta$.

13.5 The Sketching of Polar Loci

We now come to the problem of sketching the polar locus of an equation. Just as was the case with Cartesian graphs, it frequently happens that a polar locus can be sketched more easily if an analysis is made from the equation. In this section, we consider some of the items of analysis which may be useful for sketching purposes, and give a few illustrations of their application.

SYMMETRY. The geometric notion of symmetry of a curve with respect to a line or point has been introduced earlier in the text. Thus, a curve is symmetric with respect to the polar axis if, whenever (r, θ) is on the curve, so is the point $(r, -\theta)$. Since this means that $(r, -\theta)$ satisfies the equation whenever (r, θ) does, we have the following test:

> If the replacement of θ by $-\theta$ in the given equation of a curve results in an equivalent equation, the curve is symmetric with respect to the polar axis.

A similar argument leads to the following further test for symmetry:

> If the replacement of θ by $\pi - \theta$ in the given equation of a curve results in an equivalent equation, the curve is symmetric with respect to the line that is perpendicular to the polar axis and contains the pole.

The geometric notion of symmetry with respect to a point shows the validity of the following test:

> If the replacement of r by $-r$ in the given equation of a curve results in an equivalent equation, the curve is symmetric with respect to the pole.

For example, the locus of $r = 4 \cos\theta$ is symmetric with respect to the polar axis, since $\cos(-\theta) = \cos\theta$, and this symmetry was observed before. Also $\sin(\pi - \theta) = \sin\theta$, and so the polar locus of $r = 2 \sin\theta$ is symmetric with respect to the line through the pole perpendicular to the polar axis, a fact which we have observed earlier for this circle. Any curve, with a polar equation containing only even powers of r, will be symmetric with respect to the pole; for example, the locus of $r^2 = 3 \cos \theta$ has this type of symmetry.

We must warn the student that the above tests are *sufficient* but not necessary for geometric symmetry of a locus. By this remark we mean that, even though the tests fail, the curve may still possess some or all the types of symmetry mentioned above. This is due to the multiplicity of polar coordinates of any point, so that two points may be "geometrically" symmetric, even though this fact is not detected by the algebraic tests that we have given. For example, it may happen that $(2, \pi/4)$ and $(-2, 3\pi/4)$ are in the solution set of an equation, while $(2, -\pi/4)$ is not. The above test of the polar locus for symmetry with respect to the polar axis would fail, but inasmuch as the polar graph of $(-2, 3\pi/4)$ is the same geometric point as the graph of $(2, -\pi/4)$, the point symmetric to $(2, \pi/4)$ with respect to the polar axis is actually on the graph. It would be easy, of course, to include other tests, which would take care of any particular type of symmetry, but we prefer not to increase the number of these tests.

INTERCEPTS. The intercepts of a polar graph, which are of most interest to us, are the r-coordinates of the points of intersection of the curve with the polar axis and the line through the pole perpendicular to the polar axis. It is clear that any θ-coordinate of such a point will be some multiple of $\pi/2$. For example, if we are sketching the polar locus of $r = 1 + 2 \cos \theta$, the following intercepts will be useful: $\theta = 0$, $r = 3$; $\theta = \pi/2$, $r = 1$; $\theta = \pi$, $r = -1$; $\theta = 3\pi/2$, $r = 1$.

MAXIMUM AND MINIMUM r. If we can discover the points (r, θ), for which r is a maximum or a minimum, these will be extremely useful guide-points in a sketch of any locus. For example, consider the locus of $r = 2 \sin 2\theta$. It is clear that r $(=2)$ is a maximum if $\sin 2\theta = 1$, and this occurs if $2\theta = \pi/2$, $2\theta = 5\pi/2$, $2\theta = 9\pi/2$, etc.; i.e., if $\theta = \pi/4$, $\theta = 5\pi/4$, $\theta = 9\pi/4$, etc. Also, r $(= -2)$ is a minimum if $\sin 2\theta = -1$, and this occurs if $2\theta = 3\pi/2$, $2\theta = 7\pi/2$, $2\theta = 11\pi/2$, etc.; i.e., if $\theta = 3\pi/4$, $\theta = 7\pi/4$, $\theta = 11\pi/4$, etc.

TANGENT LINES AT POLE. If $(0, \alpha)$ is in the solution set of an equation, for some real number α, the polar locus of the equation includes the pole, and $\theta = \alpha$ is a polar equation of a line which is tangent to the locus at the pole. For example, if $r = 2 \sin 2\theta$, the number α may be any solution of the equation $\sin 2\theta = 0$; and equations of the two distinct tangent lines at the pole are $\theta = 0$ and $\theta = \pi/2$.

ILLUSTRATION 1. Make a sketch of the polar locus of $r = 1 + 2 \cos \theta$.

Solution.

(*a*) Symmetry. Since $\cos(-\theta) = \cos \theta$, the locus is symmetric with respect to the polar axis.

(*b*) Intercepts. $\theta = 0,\ r = 3;\ \theta = \pi/2,\ r = 1;\ \theta = \pi,\ r = -1;$ $\theta = 2\pi,\ r = 3$. Since the cosine function is periodic of period 2π, the points of the graph are repeated if $\theta \geq 2\pi$.

(*c*) Maximum and Minimum *r*. $r\ (=3)$ is a maximum if $\cos\theta = 1$, i.e., if $\theta = 0,\ \theta = 2\pi$, etc.; and $r\ (= -1)$ is a minimum if $\cos\theta = -1$, i.e., if $\theta = \pi,\ \theta = 3\pi$, etc.

(*d*) Tangent Lines at Pole. $r = 0$ if $\cos\theta = -1/2$, i.e., if $\theta = 2\pi/3$, $\theta = 4\pi/3$, etc., and so equations of tangent lines at the pole are $\theta = 2\pi/3$, $\theta = 4\pi/3$, etc.

After the above information has been put on a graph, a table should be made which shows the changes in *r* that accompany changes in θ.

θ	0 to $\pi/2$	$\pi/2$ to $2\pi/3$	$2\pi/3$ to π	π to $4\pi/3$	$4\pi/3$ to $3\pi/2$	$3\pi/2$ to 2π
$\cos\theta$	1 to 0	0 to $-1/2$	$-1/2$ to -1	-1 to $-1/2$	$-1/2$ to 0	0 to 1
r	3 to 1	1 to 0	0 to -1	-1 to 0	0 to 1	1 to 3

The final sketch is given in Figure 13–15, with the arrows indicating the correspondence between *r* and θ, for θ in the interval $[0, 2\pi]$, after which the points are repeated.

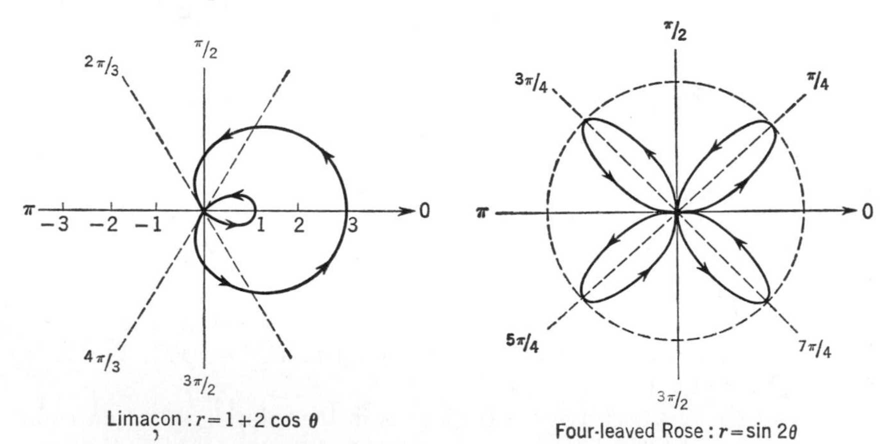

Limaçon : $r = 1 + 2\cos\theta$

Figure 13–15

Four-leaved Rose : $r = \sin 2\theta$

Figure 13–16

ILLUSTRATION 2. Make a sketch of the polar locus of $r = \sin 2\theta$.
Solution.

(*a*) Symmetry. All three tests for symmetry fail. (But notice the the final sketch!)

(*b*) Intercepts. The only intercept point is the pole.

(*c*) Maximum and Minimum *r*. $r\ (= 1)$ is a maximum if $2\theta = \pi/2$,

$5\pi/2$, $9\pi/2$, etc.; i.e., if $\theta = \pi/4$, $5\pi/4$, $9\pi/4$, etc. Also r $(= -1)$ is a minimum if $2\theta = 3\pi/2$, $7\pi/2$, etc.; i.e., if $\theta = 3\pi/4$, $7\pi/4$, etc.

(*d*) Tangent Lines at Pole. $r = 0$ if $\sin 2\theta = 0$, and this occurs if $2\theta = 0$, π, 2π, 3π, 4π, etc.; i.e., if $\theta = 0$, $\pi/2$, π, $3\pi/2$, 2π, etc., which are equations of tangent lines to the curve at the pole.

The following table shows the changes in the value r of the function, as the representative element θ of the domain changes. It should be noted that while the period of the function defined by $r = \sin 2\theta$ is π, the points of the graph do not repeat until $\theta \geq 2\pi$. The complete graph is shown in Figure 13–16, where the arrows indicate the correspondence between r and θ.

θ	0 to $\pi/4$	$\pi/4$ to $\pi/2$	$\pi/2$ to $3\pi/4$	$3\pi/4$ to π	π to $5\pi/4$	$5\pi/4$ to $3\pi/2$
2θ	0 to $\pi/2$	$\pi/2$ to π	π to $3\pi/2$	$3\pi/2$ to 2π	2π to $5\pi/2$	$5\pi/2$ to 3π
$\sin 2\theta$	0 to 1	1 to 0	0 to -1	-1 to 0	0 to 1	1 to 0

θ	$3\pi/2$ to $7\pi/4$	$7\pi/4$ to 2π
2θ	3π to $7\pi/2$	$7\pi/2$ to 4π
$\sin 2\theta$	0 to -1	-1 to 0

PROBLEM SET 13.5

Use the methods of this section to analyze the polar locus of each of the following equations; if the locus is of finite extent, sketch it; otherwise sketch a portion which lies in some convenient neighborhood of the pole.

1. $r = \cos 2\theta$.
2. $r = 3 \sin 2\theta$.
3. $r = 4 \cos 3\theta$.
4. $r = e^{\theta}$ (Logarithmic Spiral).
5. $r = c/\theta$ (Hyperbolic Spiral).
6. $r = 2 \sec \theta$.
7. $r = 4 \cos^3 \theta$.
8. $r^2 = 4 \sin \theta$.
9. $r^2 = 4 \tan^2 \theta$.
10. $r = 1 - 2 \cos \theta$ (Limaçon).
11. $r = 3(1 - \cos \theta)$ (Cardioid).
12. $r^2 = a^2 \cos 2\theta$ (Lemniscate).
13. $r = 6 \tan \theta$.
14. $r^2(2 - \cos^2 \theta) = 8$.
15. $r^2\theta = 4$ (Lituus).
16. $r = 6 \cos \theta/2$.
17. $r^2 = 9 \sin 2\theta$ (Lemniscate).
18. $r = 1 + \cos \theta/3$.

13.6 Further Remarks on Polar Graphs

It sometimes happens that the characteristics of a polar locus are more easily recognized if a Cartesian equation, corresponding to the given polar equation, is obtained. For example, the polar locus of $r^2(3 - \sin^2 \theta) = 5$ may not be identified, immediately, but the corresponding Cartesian equation $3x^2 + 2y^2 = 5$ reveals that the locus is an ellipse. It may happen, however, that the Cartesian equation is more complicated than the polar, in which case this transformation will be of no benefit.

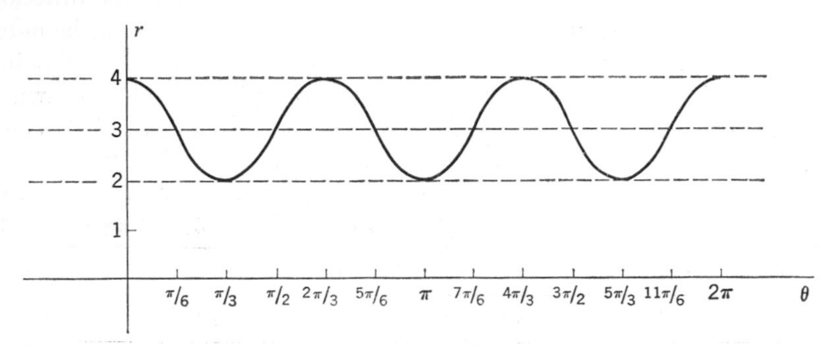

Figure 13–17

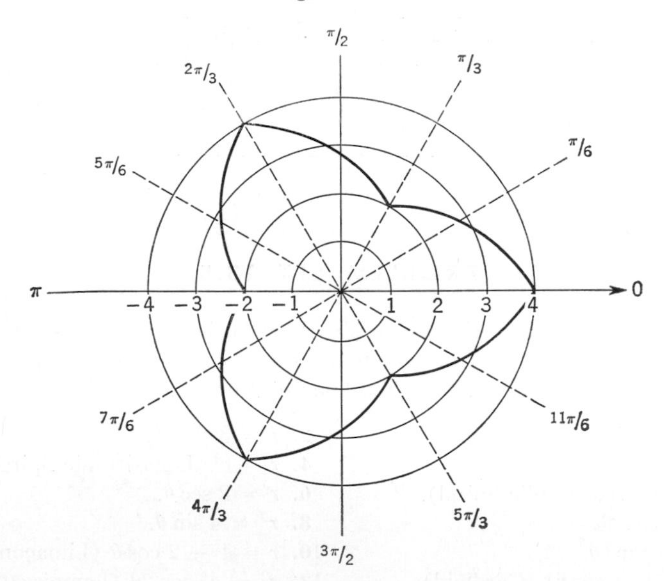

Figure 13–18

In some cases it is of help in sketching the polar locus of an equation to first make a Cartesian sketch of the *same* solution set; i.e., if the equation involves r and θ, we consider a solution (r, θ) to be a point on a Cartesian graph. For example, if we wish a sketch of the polar locus of $r = 3 + \cos 3\theta$, an inspection of the Cartesian graph in Figure 13–17 will be helpful. (Think of the equation $y - 3 = \cos 3x$.) It is now easy to sketch the polar locus, shown in Figure 13–18, by referring to the auxiliary Cartesian graph and reinterpreting the coordinates of the points as polar instead of Cartesian. We note, for example, that one cycle of the Cartesian graph is completed with θ in the interval $[0, 2\pi/3]$; also, r changes from 4 to 3 as θ increases from 0 to $\pi/6$, while r changes from 3 to 2 as θ increases from $\pi/6$ to $\pi/3$. This technique is especially useful in sketching the polar locus of an equation of the form $r = \sin n\theta$ or $r = \cos n\theta$, for a postive integer n.

If a polar locus is of infinite extent, it is sometimes necessary to use special devices to determine the nature of the locus, even in a finite region. For example, let us consider the locus of $r = \tan \theta/2$. It is clear that r is without a finite bound if θ is sufficiently close to π, but does this mean that the polar axis is an asymptote of the locus? In order to obtain an answer to this question, we examine the *ordinate* y $(= r \sin \theta)$ of an arbitrary point (r, θ) on the curve. But then $y = r[2 \sin (\theta/2) \cos (\theta/2)] = \dfrac{2 \sin (\theta/2) \cos (\theta/2) \sin (\theta/2)}{\cos (\theta/2)} = 2 \sin^2 \theta/2$, and if θ is sufficiently close to π, it is clear that y is arbitrarily close to 2. It may then be concluded that the locus is asymptotic to the line parallel to the polar axis, and

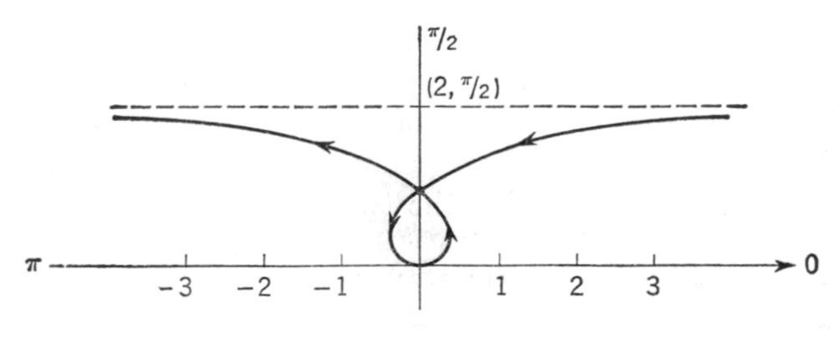

Figure 13–19

passing through the point $(2, \pi/2)$. A sketch of a portion of the locus is shown in Figure 13–19. It is worthy of note that the first-quadrant portion of the loop is a sketch of elements (r, θ) of the solution set of the equation, with θ in the interval $[0, \pi/2]$, while the second-quadrant portion is a sketch of elements with θ in $[3\pi/2, 2\pi]$. This type of information is sometimes useful in the solution of certain calculus problems, and the example illustrates the fact that we can not obtain this information from a mere inspection of the *curve*.

Problems frequently arise which require a knowledge of the points of intersection of two curves, equations of which are given in polar form. There is an inherent difficulty in this problem which is not present in the corresponding problem involving Cartesian coordinates. For while the points of intersection of two Cartesian loci are in one-to-one correspondence with the ordered pairs of the intersection of the solution sets of the equations, this is not necessarily the case, if polar coordinates are used; for there may be points of "geometric" intersection, which correspond to different ordered pairs in the two solution sets. If we are interested only in those points of intersection which correspond to common solutions of the two equations, the equations may be solved simultaneously, and the points thereby determined. On the other hand, if we wish to determine all points of intersection of the geometric loci, the best procedure is to accompany any algebraic solution of the equations with a sketch of their loci, and so be assured of *all* intersections.

ILLUSTRATION. Determine the points of intersection of the curves, described as the polar loci of the equations $r = \tan \theta/2$ and $\theta = 3\pi/4$.

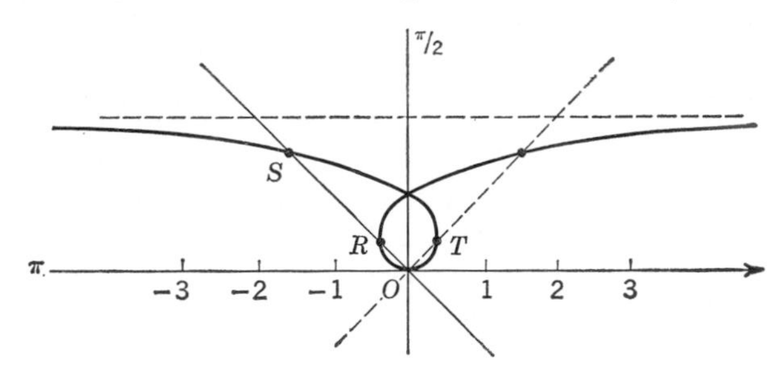

Figure 13–20

Solution. A sketch of portions of the loci is shown in Figure 13–20, and it is clear that there are three points of intersection, which we have labeled O, R, and S. If we solve the two equations, simultaneously, the only common solution is (r, θ) with $r = \tan 3\pi/8$ and $\theta = 3\pi/4$, and we may list an approximation to this solution as $(2.4, 3\pi/4)$. The second-quadrant portion of the loop corresponds to ordered pairs (r, θ) with θ in the interval $[3\pi/2, 2\pi]$, and so the solution which we obtained above must correspond to the point S. In order to obtain polar coordinates of the point R, we must use the fact observed from the figure that $|r|$ for this point is the same as r for the symmetrically placed point T on the first-quadrant portion of the loop. Since T is the point (r, θ) with $\theta = \pi/4$ and $r = \tan \pi/8 = 0.4$, approximately, it appears that an approximation for R is the point $(0.4, 3\pi/4)$; the point O is, of course, the pole, which we may designate as $(0, 0)$. It must be emphasized, however, that $(0.4, 3\pi/4)$ and $(0, 0)$ are not in the intersection of the solution sets of the equations.

PROBLEM SET 13.6

In Problems 1 through 9, sketch the polar locus of each of the given equations, if the locus is finite; if the locus is of infinite extent sketch a portion of it in some convenient neighborhood of the pole.

1. $r = 2 \sin 3\theta$.
2. $r = 4 \cos 2\theta$.
3. $r = 2 + \cos \theta$.
4. $r = 2 + \sin 2\theta$.
5. $r = 3 - 2 \cos 2\theta$.
6. $r^2 = 9 \cos 2\theta$.
7. $r^2 = 4 \sin 2\theta$.
8. $r = 5 - 5 \cos \theta$.
9. $r = \ln \theta$.
10. Sketch polar loci of the equations $r = 2$ and $r = 2(1 + \cos \theta)$, and determine a pair of coordinates for each point of geometric intersection. Do these points of intersection correspond to common solutions of the two equations?
11. Determine the elements of the intersection of the two functions, defined separately on the interval $[-\pi/2, \pi/2]$ by $r = 10 \cos \theta$ and $r \cos \theta = 2$.
12. Determine the elements in the intersection of the two functions, defined separately on the interval $[0, 2\pi]$ by the equations $r = 6 \cos \theta$ and $r = 6(1 - \cos \theta)$. Are there any other points of geometric intersection of the polar graphs of the functions?
13. Determine the elements in the intersection of the function defined on $[0, 2\pi]$ by $r = 2 + 3 \cos \theta$, and the relation described as the solution set of the equation $\theta = \pi/4$. If (r, θ) is any point on the small loop of the polar graph of the function, in what smallest real number interval is θ located?
14. Compare the polar loci of $r = 2 + \cos \theta$ and $r = 2 + \cos (\theta - \pi/3)$.
15. Compare the polar loci of $r = \theta$, $r = 2\theta$, and $2r = \theta$.
16. Determine the elements in the intersection of the functions, defined separately on $[0, \pi]$ by $r = \sin \theta$ and $r = \cos \theta$. Do these correspond to the points of geometric intersection of the polar graphs?
17. Make a sketch of a portion of the polar locus of $r = \tan \theta$ which lies in some neighborhood of the pole. Determine polar equations of the lines to which the locus is asymptotic. [Consider the abscissa x $(= r \cos \theta)$ of a point (r, θ), with θ in a small neighborhood of $\pi/2$, etc.]
18. Sketch the polar locus of each of the following equations, by sketching the Cartesian locus of the *same* equation; i.e., consider r and θ to be Cartesian coordinates of a point: (*a*) $r = 2 \csc \theta$; (*b*) $r^2(1 + 3 \sin^2 \theta) = 8$; (*c*) $r^2(2 - \cos^2 \theta) = 1$; (*d*) $\sin \theta = r \cos^2 \theta$.

REVIEW TEST A

1. Write down the Cartesian coordinates of the points that are the polar representations of $(2, -\pi/4)$ and $(-2, 3)$. Determine the approximate distance between these two points.
2. Write down the polar coordinates, with the smallest positive θ, of the points that are the Cartesian representations of $(-2, -2)$ and $(1, -2)$.
3. Sketch the polar locus of each of the following equations: (*a*) $r = 2 \cos (\theta - 3\pi/4)$; (*b*) $3 = r \sin (\theta + \pi/3)$.
4. Determine the polar equation of the line, a portion of which is shown in Figure 13-21, in the form $a = r \sin (\theta - \omega)$ with $0 < \omega < \pi/2$, $a > 0$.
5. Determine the polar equation of the circle in Figure 13-22, in the form $r = a \cos (\theta + \omega)$ with $0 < \omega < \pi/2$, $a > 0$.

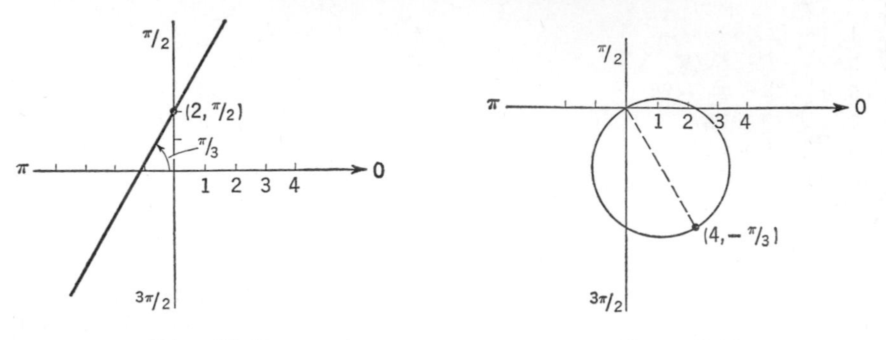

Figure 13–21

Figure 13–22

6. Draw the circle having $r = 2 \cos \theta - 3 \sin \theta$ as a polar equation, and express this equation in the form $r = a \cos (\theta + \omega)$ with $0 < \omega < \pi/2$, $a > 0$.
7. Determine a Cartesian equation corresponding to each of the following equations in polar form: (*a*) $r = 2 \cos \theta + 3 \sin \theta$; (*b*) $r = 4/(1 - \sin \theta)$.
8. Determine a polar equation corresponding to each of the following equations in Cartesian form: (*a*) $4x^2 - 9y^2 = 36$; (*b*) $2xy = x^2 + y^2$.
9. Sketch the polar locus of the equation $r = 1 - 2 \cos \theta$. Do the tests for symmetry give any information about the locus?
10. Use an auxiliary Cartesian graph to sketch the polar locus of the equation $r = 1 + \cos 2\theta$.
11. Make a polar sketch of the function f, defined on $[0, 2\pi]$ by $f(\theta) = 1 + 2 \cos \theta$, for each θ in the domain of f. If (r_1, θ_1) is an arbitrary element of f that is represented by a point on the smaller loop of the graph, what is the smallest real number interval containing all choices of θ_1?
12. Determine the polar coordinates involving the smallest positive θ, of the points of intersection of the curves, defined as the polar loci of the equations $r = 4 \cos \theta$ and $r = 2 \sin \theta$. Do these points represent the intersection of the solution sets of the equations?

REVIEW TEST B

1. Write down the Cartesian coordinates of the points that are the polar representations of $(-3, 5\pi/6)$ and $(1, -2)$. Determine the approximate distance between these two points.
2. Write down the polar coordinates, with the smallest positive θ, of the points that are the Cartesian representations of $(-\sqrt{3}, 1)$ and $(3, 1)$.
3. Sketch the polar locus of each of the following equations: (*a*) $3 = -r \cos (\theta + \pi/4)$; (*b*) $r = 2 \sin (\theta - \pi/6)$.
4. Determine the polar equation of the line, a portion of which is shown in Figure 13-23, in the form $a = r \cos (\theta + \omega)$ with $0 < \omega < \pi/2$, $a > 0$.
5. Determine the polar equation of the circle in Figure 13-24, in the form $r = a \sin (\theta + \omega)$ with $0 < \omega < \pi/2$, $a > 0$.

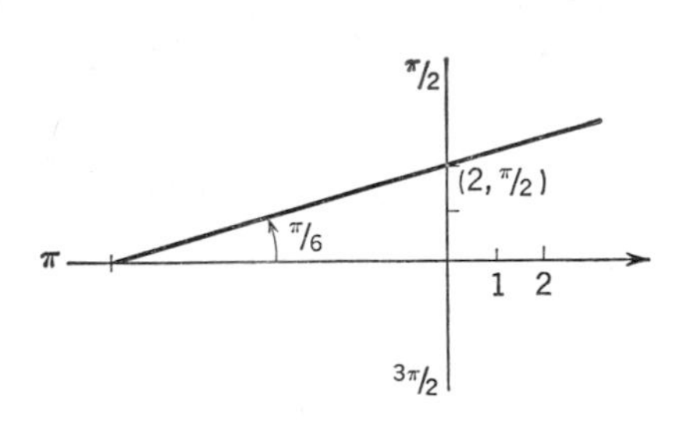

Figure 13–23

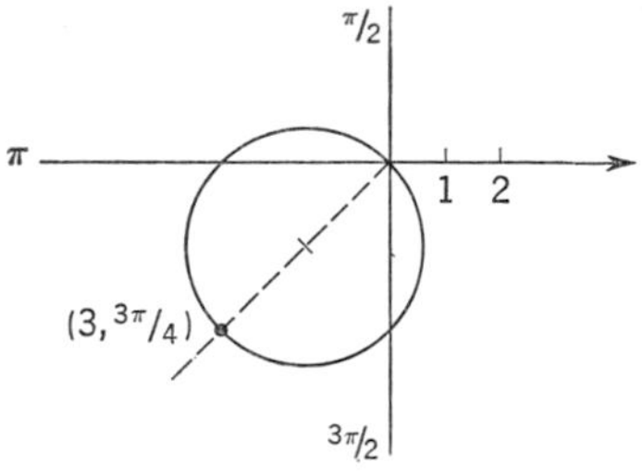

Figure 13–24

6. Draw the circle having $r = -3\cos\theta + \sin\theta$ as a polar equation, and express this equation in the form $r = a\sin(\theta - \omega)$ with $0 < \omega < \pi/2$, $a > 0$.
7. Determine a Cartesian equation corresponding to each of the following equations in polar form: (*a*) $r = -3\sin\theta + 2\cos\theta$; (*b*) $r = 3/(\cos\theta + 2\sin\theta)$.
8. Determine a polar equation corresponding to each of the following equations in Cartesian form: (*a*) $x^2 + y^2 - 4y = 0$; (*b*) $2x - 3y = 1$.
9. Sketch the polar locus of the equation $r = 1 + 2\sin\theta$. Do the tests for symmetry give any information about the locus?
10. Use an auxiliary Cartesian graph to sketch the polar locus of the equation $r = 3 + \sin 2\theta$.
11. Make a polar sketch of the function f, defined on $[0, \pi]$ by $f(\theta) = 3\sin 3\theta$, for each θ in the domain of f. If (r_1, θ_1) is an arbitrary element of f that is represented by a point on the lower loop of the graph, what is the smallest real number interval containing all choices of θ_1?
12. Determine the elements of the intersection of the two functions f and g defined, respectively, on $[0, \pi]$ by $f(\theta) = 3 - 3\cos\theta$ and $g(\theta) = 5\sin\theta$, for each θ in their domains. Are there any additional points of geometric intersection of the polar graphs of these two functions?

REFERENCES

Books

LENNES, N. J. AND MERRILL, A. S., *Plane Analytic Geometry,* New York, Harper, 1929. (Chap. 9.)

SLICHTER, CHARLES S., *Elementary Mathematical Analysis,* New York, McGraw-Hill, 1925. (Pp. 120–136.)

American Mathematical Monthly

BOYER, C. B., "Newton as an Originator of Polar Coordinates," Vol. 56, p. 73 (1949.)

LARIVIERE, R., "The Period of Polar Curves," Vol. 62, p. 254 (1955).

WAGNER, R. W., "Equations and Loci in Polar Coordinates," Vol. 55, p. 360 (1948).

14

PLANE ANALYTIC GEOMETRY III: LOCUS PROBLEMS

Descartes did not revise geometry; he created it.

E. T. BELL

14.1 The Point Dividing a Line Segment in a Given Ratio

In this chapter, we consider the second of the two principal problems of analytic geometry stated at the beginning of Chapter 12: to determine an equation of a plane curve that has been defined by some geometric condition. More generally, we are interested in determining a defining equation of a relation, a graph of which is some given set of points; since a set of points is a locus, we can refer to this equation as an *equation of the locus*, and the problem of its determination as the general *locus problem*. It should be clear, however, that the complete locus of this equation, while containing the above locus, may contain many additional points. For example, a Cartesian equation of a line segment may be $y = 2x + 1$, with x restricted to some interval, but the complete locus of this equation contains all points of the line containing the given segment. An interesting result of a study of locus problems is that a vast array of problems of plane geometry can be attacked by the analytic method. These problems usually involve points, line segments, simple curves, and geometric figures bounded by them, and we must first make a preliminary study of some topics related to line segments and angles. In this section, we consider one of these topics. It will be understood that, unless the contrary is stated, the coordinate system used is *Cartesian*.

Let $A(x_1, y_1)$ and $B(x_2, y_2)$ be the end points of a given line segment, as shown in Figure 14–1, with $P(\bar{x}, \bar{y})$ a point between A and B. If the ratio of the length of segment AP to the length of segment PB is $m:n$, we wish to determine the coordinates of P in terms of the coordinates of A and B. We first draw the segments BN and PM parallel to the y-axis, and the segments AN and PQ parallel to the x-axis, forming the similar triangles AMP and PQB. The length of segment AM is $\bar{x} - x_1$ units, while PQ is $x_2 - \bar{x}$ units in length, so that the similarity of the triangles gives us $(\bar{x} - x_1):(x_2 - \bar{x}) = m:n$. In a similar manner we obtain $(\bar{y} - y_1):(y_2 - \bar{y}) = m:n$, and if the two equations are solved, the solution is $(\bar{x}, \bar{y})$ with $\bar{x} = (mx_2 + nx_1)/(m + n)$ and $\bar{y} = (my_2 + ny_1)/(m + n)$. A special case of this result occurs if P is the mid-point of the segment; in this case $m = n$ so that $\bar{x} = (x_1 + x_2)/2$ and $\bar{y} = (y_1 + y_2)/2$. The last result shows that the coordinates of the mid-point of a line segment are the arithmetic means of the corresponding coordinates of the end points.

ILLUSTRATION 1. Determine the point which is two thirds of the distance on the line segment from $(-3, 1)$ to $(4, 10)$.

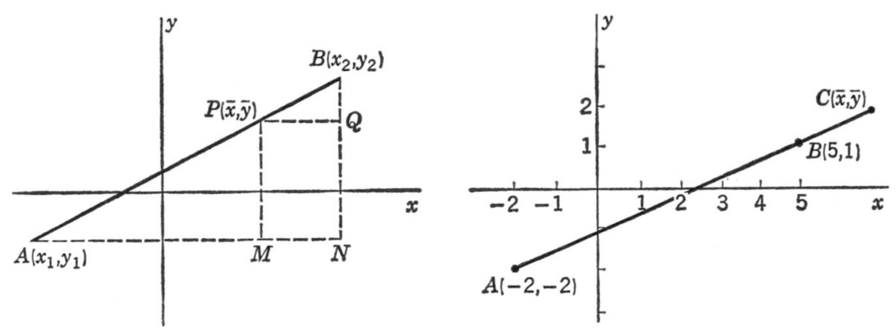

Figure 14–1

Figure 14–2

Solution. If we think of $A(x_1, y_1)$ as the point $(-3, 1)$ and $B(x_2, y_2)$ as the point $(4, 10)$, we have: $x_1 = -3$, $y_1 = 1$; $x_2 = 4$, $y_2 = 10$. Since $m:n = 2:1$, in this case, an application of the above result gives $\bar{x} = [2(4) + 1(-3)]/3 = 5/3$ and $\bar{y} = [2(10) + 1(1)]/3 = 21/3 = 7$. The desired point of division is then seen to be $(5/3, 7)$. In the following illustration, we see how the same formulas can be used to determine a point which divides a line segment *externally* in a given ratio.

ILLUSTRATION 2. If the line segment joining $A(-2, -2)$ to $B(5, 1)$ is extended to the point C such that the ratio of the length of AC to the length of BC is $5:1$, determine the coordinates of C.

Solution. The segment ABC is shown in Figure 14–2, and it is clear that we can regard B as the point dividing AC *internally* in the ratio $4:1$. But we can now use the above formulas and write $5 = (4\bar{x} - 2)/5$, $1 = (4\bar{y} - 2)/5$. From these equations we obtain $\bar{x} = 27/4$ and $\bar{y} = 7/4$ as the desired coordinates of C.

If the distance between two points (x_1, y_1) and (x_2, y_2) is d units, the formula for d was given earlier in the book, but we restate it for reference: $d = \sqrt{(x_2 - x_1)^2 + (y_2 - y_1)^2}$.

PROBLEM SET 14.1

1. Find the coordinates of the mid-point of the line segment joining (*a*) $(4, -3)$ to $(-10, 7)$; (*b*) $(-2, 4)$ to $(8, 10)$; (*c*) $(-3, -5)$ to $(6, -7)$.

2. Find the coordinates of the two points which trisect the segment joining $(-5, 3)$ to $(7, -6)$.
3. If the mid-point of a line segment is $(4, -6)$ and one end point is $(6, 4)$, determine the other end point.
4. The line segment from $A(x_1, 4)$ to $B(2, y_2)$ is divided by $C(4, 6)$, so that the ratio of the length of AC to the length of CB is 2:5. Determine x_1 and y_2.
5. The point $C(x, y)$ divides the line segment joining $A(-3, -6)$ to $B(4, 10)$, so that the ratio of the length of AC to the length of CB is 3:2. Determine the coordinates of C.
6. The segment AB of Problem 5 is extended to the point $D(x, y)$, so that the ratio of the length of AD to the length of BD is 3:1. Determine the coordinates of the point D.
7. In what ratio does the point $(4, -2)$ divide the segment joining $(-1, 8)$ with $(13, -20)$?
8. Determine the mid-points of the sides of the triangle with vertices $(4, 7)$, $(-2, 8)$, and $(6, -12)$.
9. The points $(6, -3)$, $(4, 8)$, and $(-4, 5)$ are joined by line segments to form a triangle. Find the lengths of the three medians of the triangle.
10. The line segment joining $A(4, 8)$ to $B(-3, -10)$ is extended to the point C, so that the ratio of the length of CA to the length of CB is 4:1. Determine the coordinates of C.
11. A straight line intercepts the x-axis at the point $A(3, 0)$ and the y-axis at the point $B(0, -4)$. Find an equation of the line that contains the origin and bisects the segment AB.
12. With reference to Problem 11, determine equations of the two lines that contain the origin and a point of trisection of AB.

14.2 Angles of Intersection of Two Lines

It is sometimes desirable to associate with a straight line or line segment the notion of *sense*, i.e., to designate which direction on the line is to be considered positive; this is always the case, when the line segment is regarded as a vector. The x and y axes are examples of so-called *sensed* lines, their positive directions coinciding with their directions of increasing scale readings. Unless the positive sense of a line is clearly understood, we shall usually indicate it by an arrow; if the direction is unimportant, the arrow will be omitted.

It is extremely ambiguous to speak of *the* angle between two lines in a plane. For if we regard an angle as an amount of rotation of a line about one of its points, and "the" angle between two intersecting lines as the amount of rotation required of one line about the point of intersection, so that it may coincide with the other line, we have seen before that there is nothing unique about "this" angle. However, for the purposes of plane geometry, it is usually possible to restrict all angles to be positive and less than 2π radians.

DEFINITION. Let L be a *sensed* line intersecting the x-axis at the point R. The smallest positive (counter-clockwise) angle through which one must conceive the x-axis to be rotated about R in order that it might coincide with L in both position and sense, is called the *inclination* of the line. If L is parallel to the x-axis, its inclination is 0 or π radians, according as its sense is the same or opposite to that of the x-axis.

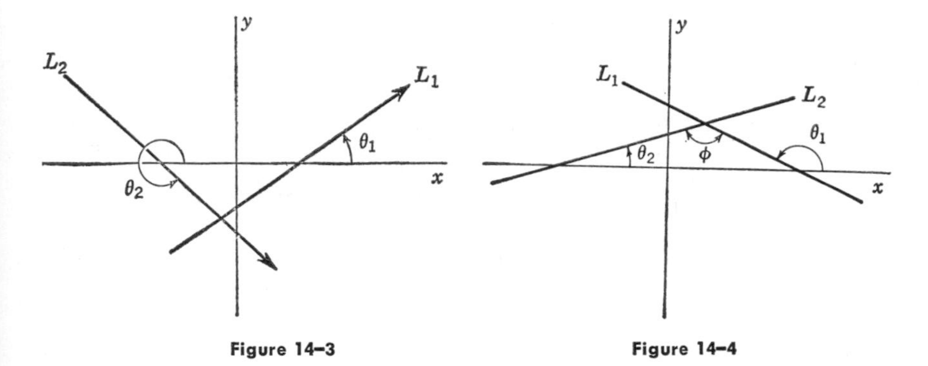

Figure 14–3

Figure 14–4

Two illustrations of inclination are shown in Figure 14–3. It is clear that if the inclination of a sensed line is θ radians, θ must lie in the interval $[0, 2\pi]$.

An unsensed line may be considered to have two different inclinations, differing by π radians, corresponding to the two possible senses of the line. However, the following definition removes the ambiguity.

DEFINITION. The inclination of an *unsensed* line is the smaller of the two possible inclinations of the corresponding sensed lines.

Hence we are requiring that the radian measure θ of the inclination of an unsensed line be a number in the interval $[0, \pi]$.

The definitions that we have given for the notion of inclination have been phrased with reference to *lines*, but it is evident that we shall wish to identify the *inclination of a line segment* with the inclination of the line of which it is a part. In the sequel, we shall have little occasion to deal with sensed lines, inasmuch as most of the problems of plane geometry are concerned with unsensed line segments. We shall then assume that a line or line segment is unsensed unless otherwise specified.

One of the important characteristics of a line, introduced earlier in this book, is the concept of *slope*, the definition of which implies the truth of the following theorem.

THEOREM 1. If the inclination of a line is θ radians and its slope is m, then $\tan \theta = m$.

If we follow the practice of plane geometry, and consider only positive angles less than 2π radians, there are two pairs of equal angles formed by any two intersecting straight lines. The two unequal angles—or two equal angles if the lines are perpendicular—are said to be *supplementary*, their sum being π radians or 180°. In Figure 14–4, we have shown two intersecting line segments L_1 and L_2, with respective inclinations of θ_1 and θ_2 radians, labeled so that $\theta_1 > \theta_2$. The angle of radian measure ϕ, with $\phi = \theta_1 - \theta_2$, is then one of the angles of intersection, and we shall now see how ϕ can be readily determined.

If m_1 and m_2 are the respective slopes of L_1 and L_2, our above definitions imply that $m_1 = \tan\theta_1$ and $m_2 = \tan\theta_2$. Since $\phi = \theta_1 - \theta_2$, we have $\tan\phi = \tan(\theta_1 - \theta_2) = (\tan\theta_1 - \tan\theta_2)/(1 + \tan\theta_1\tan\theta_2)$, so that $\tan\phi = (m_1 - m_2)/(1 + m_1m_2)$. If $\tan\phi$ is positive, ϕ is the acute angle of intersection, while ϕ is the obtuse angle if $\tan\phi$ is negative. Since these two angles are supplementary, either one can be determined immediately from the other.

ILLUSTRATION 1. Find the acute angle of intersection of the lines, defined as the loci of $x + 2y - 4 = 0$ and $5x - 6y + 5 = 0$.

Solution. A negative slope indicates an obtuse angle of inclination, and so in harmony with the above symbolism we set $m_1 = -1/2$ and $m_2 = 5/6$, as the slopes of the two lines. An application of the above formula then yields $\tan\phi = (-1/2 - 5/6)/[1 + (-1/2)(5/6)] = -16/7 = -2.2857$, so that $\phi = 1.984$. If follows that the acute angle of inclination is $3.142 - 1.984$ or 1.158 radians, approximately.

The definition of parallel lines implies that such lines have the same slope. If two lines are mutually perpendicular, the one angle of intersection is $\pi/2$ radians, and it is recalled that $\tan\pi/2$ is undefined. The only case in which the above formula for $\tan\phi$ is undefined is when $m_1m_2 = -1$, and so this must be the condition for two lines to be mutually perpendicular.

THEOREM 2. Two lines with respective slopes m_1 and m_2 are mutually perpendicular, if and only if $m_1m_2 = -1$, i.e., each slope is the negative reciprocal of the other.

ILLUSTRATION 2. Determine an equation of the line containing the point $(-1, 2)$ and perpendicular to the line having the equation $3x - 4y + 2 = 0$.

Solution. Since the slope of the given line is 3/4, the slope of the line perpendicular to it is $-4/3$. The "point-slope" equation of a general straight line then gives $y - 2 = (-4/3)(x + 1)$ or $4x + 3y - 2 = 0$ as one of the desired equations.

ILLUSTRATION 3. Determine an equation of the straight line containing the point $(3, -2)$ and perpendicular to the line having the equation $x + 3y - 5 = 0$.

Solution. An equation of any line perpendicular to the given line may be given as $3x - y + k = 0$ for some real number k. Since the line in question contains the point $(3, -2)$ we must have $9 + 2 + k = 0$, from which we obtain $k = -11$. It follows that one of the desired equations is $3x - y - 11 = 0$. The last two illustrations show alternate methods of solving the same type of problem.

PROBLEM SET 14.2

1. On a single diagram sketch lines through the origin having the following inclinations: (*a*) $\pi/6$ radians; (*b*) 2 radians; (*c*) $2\pi/3$ radians; (*d*) 3 radians; (*e*) 1 radian.
2. On a single diagram sketch sensed lines through the origin having the following inclinations: (*a*) $5\pi/6$ radians; (*b*) $7\pi/6$ radians; (*c*) $3\pi/2$ radians; (*d*) $11\pi/6$ radians.
3. Use Table 2, if necessary, to determine the slope of each of the lines described in Problem 1.
4. Find the slope of the line, described as the locus of (*a*) $3x - 2y + 5 = 0$; (*b*) $x + 3y - 4 = 0$; (*c*) $2x - 5y + 7 = 0$; (*d*) $2x + y = 0$.
5. Determine the slopes of the lines perpendicular to the lines given in Problem 4.
6. Find the acute angle of intersection of the lines having the equations:

   (*a*) $3x - y - 4 = 0$, $x + 2y + 5 = 0$; (*b*) $4x - 5y = 0$, $x - 2y = 0$.
7. Find the obtuse angle of intersection of the lines having the equations:

   (*a*) $5x - 3y + 4 = 0$, $x - 2y - 4 = 0$; (*b*) $x + y + 4 = 0$, $2x - y + 1 = 0$.
8. Determine an equation of the line containing the point $(3, -4)$ and perpendicular to the line having the equation $x - 3y + 4 = 0$.
9. Determine an equation of the line containing the point $(3, -4)$ and parallel to the line having the equation $x - 3y + 4 = 0$.
10. Find equations of the two lines containing the point $(2, -3)$, which intersect the locus of $4x - 3y - 6 = 0$ at an angle of $\pi/4$ radians.
11. The *normal* to a curve at one of its points, is the line through the point which is perpendicular to the tangent to the curve at this point. Determine equations of the normal and tangent lines at the point $(1, 3)$ on the locus of $y = 3x^2$.
12. Determine equations of the normal and tangent lines at the point $(2, 11)$ on the locus of $y = 3x^2 - x + 1$. (See Problem 11.)
13. Let us tentatively define an angle of intersection of two curves as the acute angle of intersection of the tangent lines to the curves at any point of intersection. Determine the angle of intersection of the loci of $y = 3x$ and $y = 6x^2$, at their point of intersection different from the origin.
14. Determine the angle of intersection of the loci of $y = x - 2$ and $y = x^2 - 2x - 3$. (See Problem 13.)
15. Determine an equation of the perpendicular bisector of the line segment joining $(4, -2)$ with $(6, 10)$.

16. Find equations of the two tangent lines to the locus of $y = x^2$, one of which is parallel and the other perpendicular to the line having the equation $3x + 4y = 0$.

14.3 The Normal Equation of a Straight Line

It will be recalled from Chapter 13, that a replacement of θ by $\theta - \omega$ in an equation in r and θ, has the effect of rotating the polar locus of the equation about the pole through an angle of ω radians. We know, however, that the Cartesian coordinates x and y of any point are related to polar coordinates r and θ of the point by the equations $x = r \cos \theta$ and $y = r \sin \theta$, and so the transforms of x and y, after such a rotation, are:

$$\begin{aligned} r \cos (\theta - \omega) &= r(\cos \theta \cos \omega + \sin \theta \sin \omega) \\ &= r \cos \theta \cos \omega + r \sin \theta \sin \omega \\ &= x \cos \omega + y \sin \omega; \\ r \sin (\theta - \omega) &= r(\sin \theta \cos \omega - \cos \theta \sin \omega) \\ &= r \sin \theta \cos \omega - r \cos \theta \sin \omega \\ &= y \cos \omega - x \sin \omega. \end{aligned}$$

THEOREM 1. If x is replaced by $x \cos \omega + y \sin \omega$ and y is replaced by $y \cos \omega - x \sin \omega$ in an equation of a curve, its Cartesian locus is rotated about the origin through an angle of ω radians.

ILLUSTRATION 1. The Cartesian locus of $y = a^2/x$ is considered to be rotated about the origin through an angle of $-\pi/4$ radians. Determine an equation of the resulting curve.

Solution. In this case, $\omega = -\pi/4$, and so we must replace x by $x/\sqrt{2} - y/\sqrt{2}$ and y by $y/\sqrt{2} + x/\sqrt{2}$. An equation of the new locus is then $(x/\sqrt{2} - y/\sqrt{2})(x/\sqrt{2} + y/\sqrt{2}) = a^2$, which may be simplified to $x^2 - y^2 = 2a^2$. It should be remarked that an apparent rotation of a curve about the origin through an angle of ω radians, may be considered equivalent to a similar rotation of the coordinate axes through an angle of $-\omega$ radians. Thus, any problem involving a curve, which is phrased in terms of a rotation of the axes, can be easily rephrased in terms of a rotation of the curve. In Figure 14–5, we have shown sketches of both loci in the above illustration.

Let us now apply Theorem 1 to the equation $x = p$ $(p \geq 0)$ of a straight line parallel to and displaced p units to the right of the y-axis. If we consider this line to be rotated about the origin through an angle of ω radians, an equation of the new line is seen to be $x \cos \omega + y \sin \omega = p$. Since an *arbitrary* straight line, p units distant from the origin, can be considered the result of a rotation of this type, this equation is adopted as a new standard form. We note that p is non-negative and ω can be chosen so that $0 \leq \omega < 2\pi$. In case $p = 0$, i.e., the line contains the origin, we shall agree to choose ω so that $0 \leq \omega < \pi$. If we think of the directed line segment, perpendicular to a line from the origin, as its *normal*, it is clear that p and ω measure, respectively, the length and inclination of this normal. Furthermore, it may be observed that p and ω constitute a special set of polar coordinates of the point of intersection of the line with its normal. The preceding discussion is illustrated by Figure 14–6.

THEOREM 2. Any straight line has a *normal* equation which can be written in the form $x \cos \omega + y \sin \omega = p$, in which p measures the length of the normal of the line, and ω is the radian measure of the inclination of this normal.

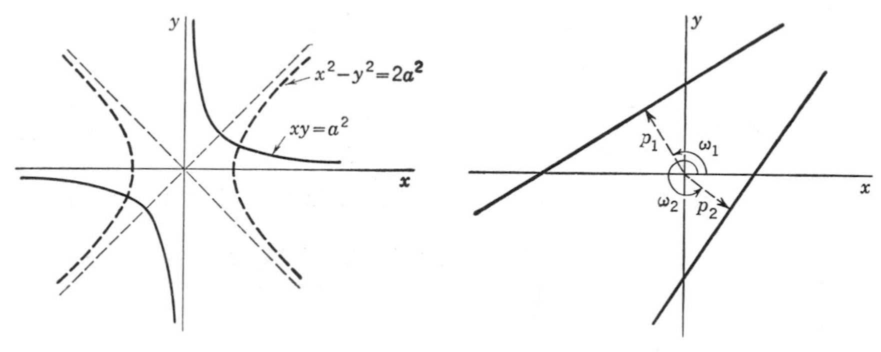

Figure 14–5

Figure 14–6

We now consider the problem of putting the standard equation $ax + by + c = 0$ of a straight line into normal form. Both members of this equation may be multiplied by any non-zero number k, but, in order to obtain the desired normal form, k must be chosen so that $ka = \cos \omega$ and $kb = \sin \omega$, for some ω such that $0 \leq \omega < 2\pi$. But then $k^2a^2 + k^2b^2 = \cos^2 \omega + \sin^2 \omega = 1$, and $k^2 = 1/(a^2 + b^2)$, so that $k = \pm 1/(\sqrt{a^2 + b^2})$. The normal form requires that p be non-negative, and so the sign of k must be chosen opposite to that of c.

ILLUSTRATION 2. Put the linear equation $3x - 4y + 2 = 0$ into normal form.

Solution. In this case, $k = \pm 1/(\sqrt{9 + 16}) = \pm 1/5$, and since c is positive we choose $k = -1/5$. The desired normal form is then seen to be $(-3/5)x + (4/5)y = 2/5$. The length of the normal is $2/5$ or 0.4 units, while $\cos \omega = -0.6$ and $\sin \omega = 0.8$, so that the inclination of the normal is approximately 2.2148 radians.

PROBLEM SET 14.3

1. Determine an equation of the curve, considered the result of rotating the locus of $y = 2x^2$ about the origin through an angle of $\pi/4$ radians.

2. Determine an equation of the curve, considered the result of rotating the locus of $x^2 - xy + y^2$ about the origin through an angle of $-\pi/4$ radians.

3. Determine an equation of the curve, considered the result of rotating the locus of $2x^2 + 3y^2 = 1$ about the origin through an angle of $2\pi/3$ radians.

4. The given equation of a hyperbola is $xy = 1$. If new axes are introduced, which may be considered the result of rotating the original axes about the origin through an angle of $\pi/4$ radians, determine an equation of the hyperbola with reference to the new axes.

5. The given equation of an ellipse is $3x^2 - 4y^2 = 1$. If new axes are introduced, which may be considered the result of rotating the original axes about the origin through an angle of $-\pi/3$ radians, determine an equation of the ellipse with reference to the new axes.

6. Write the normal equations of the straight lines having the following characteristics: (*a*) $p = 2, \omega = \pi/6$; (*b*) $p = 5, \omega = 2\pi/3$; (*c*) $p = 6, \omega = 5\pi/4$.

7. A straight line is 5 units distant from the origin. Write its normal equation if the inclination of its normal is (*a*) $2\pi/3$ radians; (*b*) $5\pi/6$ radians; (*c*) $7\pi/4$.

8. Write each of the following linear equations in normal form: (*a*) $3x + 4y - 6 = 0$; (*b*) $x - 3y + 5 = 0$; (*c*) $2x - 5y + 1 = 0$; (*d*) $x + y - 1 = 0$.

9. Write each of the following linear equations in normal form: (*a*) $x = 5$; (*b*) $x = -6$; (*c*) $y = 2$; (*d*) $y = -2$.

10. Find the length of the normal of the line having the equation (*a*) $3x - 5y + 2 = 0$; (*b*) $x - 2y - 6 = 0$; (*c*) $x + y = 5$; (*d*) $4y - x = 3$.

11. A straight line, 5 units distant from the origin, has an inclination of $\pi/3$ radians. Write its normal equation. (There are two possibilities.)

12. A straight line lies below the origin and has an inclination of $\pi/6$ radians. Write its normal equation, if the length of its normal is 2 units.

13. Determine the normal equation of the straight line having slope $-5/12$ and y-intercept 4.

14.* The general equation of a conic is $Ax^2 + Bxy + Cy^2 + Dx + Ey + F = 0$. Show that the xy-term is missing from an equation of the curve, considered the result of rotating the locus of the above equation about the origin through an angle of 1/2 arc Tan $[B/(C - A)]$ radians. Rephrase this result in terms of an equivalent rotation of axes.

15.* Referring to the equation of Problem 14, show that $B^2 - 4AC$ is invariant under any rotation of axes. (If A', B', and C' are the corresponding coefficients after the rotation, show that $B'^2 - 4A'C' = B^2 - 4AC$.) Is this result consistent with the rule given in Chapter 12 for the identification of a conic section from its equation?

16.* The given equation of an ellipse is $3x^2 - 2xy + y^2 = 1$. If this locus is considered rotated about the origin, through what angle must it be considered rotated, if an equation of the new locus is to contain no xy-term? (See Problem 14.) What is the new equation?

17.* Repeat the directions of Problem 16 for the hyperbola having the equation $2x^2 - 3xy - y^2 = 1$.

18.* The given equation of a conic section is $9x^2 + 4xy + 6y^2 + 10x - 20y + 5 = 0$. Determine an equation of the same curve, with reference to a new set of rectangular axes through the same origin and such that the new equation contains no xy-term. Now consider the axes translated to a new position so that an equation, with reference to these axes, contains no x or y terms. Give a final equation and sketch the curve, showing the three sets of axes.

19.* Repeat Problem 18 for the hyperbola having the equation

$$x^2 - 4xy - 2y^2 - 14x + 4y + 30 = 0.$$

20.* The given equation of a parabola is $4x^2 + 4xy + y^2 - 18x + 26y + 64 = 0$. Consider the original axes to be suitably rotated and translated, so that an equation of the curve, with reference to the final set of axes, may be as simple as possible. Give a final equation and sketch the curve, showing the three sets of axes. (In this case, both the x-term and the y-term can not be eliminated.)

14.4 Distance from a Point to a Line

We have regularly considered "distance" to be a scalar quantity, i.e., its measure has no sign attached. For example, the formula for the measure of distance between two points of a plane gives a measure which is scalar. In addition, we have just developed the normal equation of a straight line so that p, the length of the normal, is always positive or zero; and this is equivalent to an agreement that the distance of any line from the origin is to be considered a scalar quantity. Circumstances arise, of course, when it is necessary to attach a sign to a measure of distance, and in such instances positive and negative measures will indicate distances measured in opposite directions. An important example of this is when we wish to locate a point in a plane with the use of a Cartesian coordinate system, for it is essential here to consider the *signed* distance of the point from the coordinate axes. In spite of this, however, it is still true that we are free to choose any particular direction to have positive measure of distance, and the principal problem is always a determination of the numerical or absolute value of this measure. For this reason we shall continue to use the word "distance" in the scalar sense; if a direction is involved, we shall speak of a "signed distance."

The problem in this section is a determination of the distance of a given point $P(x_1, y_1)$ from an arbitrary straight line L, an equation of which is known. Two cases arise, as shown in Figure 14–7: in the one, the point and line are on the same side of the origin; and in the other, the point and line are on opposite sides of the origin.

With reference to Figure 14–7a, let us suppose that the normal equation of L is $x \cos \omega + y \sin \omega = p$. If L' is a straight line through P and parallel to L, it is clear that the normal equation of L' can be written as $x \cos \omega + y \sin \omega = p'$, where p' measures the length of the normal of L'. If the distance from P to L is d units, the figure shows that $d = p - p'$ or $d = p' - p$, according as L or L' is the farther from the origin, but in either case $d = |p' - p|$. Inasmuch as $P(x_1, y_1)$ is a point on L_1, we must have $x_1 \cos \omega + y_1 \sin \omega = p'$, and so $d = |x_1 \cos \omega + y_1 \sin \omega - p|$.

If we refer to Figure 14–7*b*, the equation of L' has the form $x \cos (\omega + \pi) + y \sin (\omega + \pi) - p' = 0$, and it is evident that $d = p' + p$, for this case. However, $\cos (\omega + \pi) = -\cos \omega$ and $\sin (\omega + \pi) = -\sin \omega$, and so the equation of L' may be written as $-x \cos \omega - y \sin \omega = p'$.

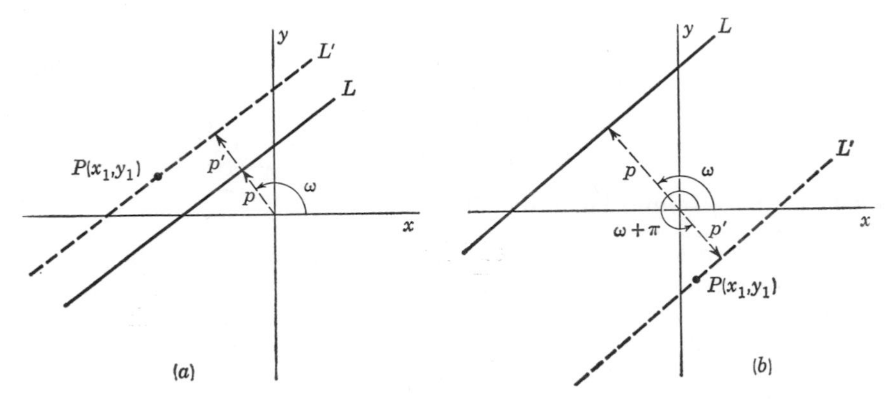

Figure 14–7

Hence, $d = p' + p = p - x_1 \cos \omega - y_1 \sin \omega$, with a similar analysis if L and L' are interchanged in position. An inspection of these results shows that in all instances $d = |x_1 \cos \omega + y_1 \sin \omega - p|$, which leads us to the following rule for determining the distance from a point to a straight line:

> Determine the normal equation of the line, and add $-p$ to both members, obtaining a new equation with right member 0. The measure of distance from a point (x_1, y_1) to the line is the absolute value of the left side of this new equation, if x and y are replaced, respectively, by x_1 and y_1.

ILLUSTRATION 1. Find the distance from the point $(-2, 3)$ to the line having the equation $3x + 4y - 10 = 0$.

Solution. The normal equation of the line is seen to be $(3/5)x + (4/5)y = 2$. An application of the above result now gives the desired measure d of distance to be $d = |(3/5)(-2) + (4/5)(3) - 2| = |-4/5| = 4/5$.

ILLUSTRATION 2. Find the distance between the two lines having the equations $x - 2y + 5 = 0$ and $x - 2y + 2 = 0$.

Solution. The desired distance is clearly the same as the distance between either line and any convenient point on the other. A point on the second line, with integral coordinates, is easily found, for instance the point (2, 2), and we must now find the distance from this point to the first line. Proceeding as in Illustration 1, the normal form of the first equation is $(-1/\sqrt{5})x + (2/\sqrt{5})y = 5/\sqrt{5}$, and if d is the desired measure of distance $d = |(-1/\sqrt{5})(2) + (2/\sqrt{5})(2) - 5/\sqrt{5}| = |-3/\sqrt{5}| = 3/\sqrt{5}$.

PROBLEM SET 14.4

In each of Problems 1 through 6, determine the distance between the point and the straight line having the given equation.

1. $3x - 4y + 5 = 0$, $(-3, -5)$.
2. $2x + 3y - 6 = 0$, $(3, -4)$.
3. $x + 2y + 3 = 0$, $(1, 2)$.
4. $3x + y - 5 = 0$, $(-1, -1)$.
5. $3x + 5y = 0$, $(3, -1)$.
6. $2x - 5y + 4 = 0$, $(0, 0)$.

In each of Problems 7 through 10, determine the distance between the two lines having the given equations.

7. $3x - 4y - 5 = 0$, $3x - 4y + 7 = 0$.
8. $x + 2y - 5 = 0$, $2x + 4y - 12 = 0$.
9. $x - 3y + 5 = 0$, $x - 3y - 10 = 0$.
10. $4x - 3y = 0$, $4x - 3y - 6 = 0$.
11. An equation of a straight line is $8x - 3y + 12 = 0$. Determine the distance from this line to the point of intersection of the lines having the equations $3x - y + 8 = 0$ and $x - 3y - 8 = 0$.
12. An equation of a straight line is $4x + 3y + 5 = 0$. Find equations of the two lines which are 6 units distant from this line.
13. The given equations of two lines are $x + 7y - 22 = 0$ and $3x - 4y + 9 = 0$. Determine two points on the first line which are 5 units distant from the second line.
14. The given equation of a line is $3x - 4y + 10 = 0$. Show that this line is tangent to the circle which has its center at the origin and its radii 2 units in length.

14.5 Applications to Plane Geometry

The characteristics of geometric figures, which are studied in Euclidean plane geometry, are entirely independent of any orientation of the figures. Such a study makes no use of any coordinate system; as a matter of fact, most proofs of the theorems date back to classical times, long before any effective use of coordinate systems. However, it happens frequently that a proposition pertaining to a geometric figure may be more easily proven, if a coordinate system and the methods of analytic geometry are used.

If a coordinate system is introduced for the purposes of a proof, there is a very basic principle to observe:

> Choose a coordinate system in such a way that equations of the pertinent lines and curves, when referred to this system are as simple as possible, *but with no loss of generality.*

We shall give two illustrations of this procedure.

ILLUSTRATION 1. Prove that the diagonals of a parallelogram bisect each other.

Proof. There is no loss of generality, if we choose the origin of a Cartesian coordinate system at one vertex of the parallelogram, with the x–axis along one side as shown in Figure 14–8. If we label the vertices as illustrated, it is clear that C is the point $(x_1 + a, y_1)$. The mid-point of OC is now found, using the result of Section 14.1, to be $[(x_1 + a)/2, y_1/2]$, and the mid-point of AB is found to be the same point. Hence the two diagonals AB and OC must bisect each other at this common point, as asserted.

Note. It has not been overlooked that the assignment of coordinates to C involved a geometric property of parallelograms which we did not establish here. However, unless we make a complete development of plane geometry from the analytic point of view, it is inevitable that some such assumptions be made. The only guide along this line, which we can give, is to say that our assumptions should be of a more basic nature than the proposition that we are attempting to prove.

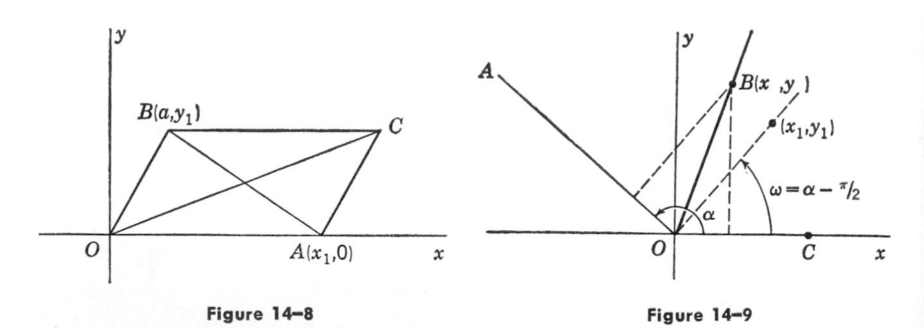

Figure 14–8 Figure 14–9

ILLUSTRATION 2. Prove that any point on the bisector of an angle is equidistant from the two lines that bound the angle.

Solution. We may assume that the given angle is less than π radians. Let us select the point of intersection of the lines as the origin of a Cartesian coordinate system, with one line OC along the x-axis as shown in Figure 14–9; the other line along OA and the bisector along OB may then be considered to extend upwards.

If $\angle AOC$ is α radians, we are assuming that $\angle BOC$ is $\alpha/2$ radians.

Since $\alpha/2$ radians is the inclination of the segment OB, the slope of this segment is $\tan \alpha/2$ or $\frac{(1 - \cos \alpha)}{\sin \alpha}$, and so an equation of the bisector is $y = \frac{(1 - \cos \alpha)x}{\sin \alpha}$. If (x_1, y_1) is an arbitrary point on the bisector, it then follows that $y_1 = \frac{(1 - \cos \alpha)x_1}{\sin \alpha}$. Since the inclination of its normal is $\alpha - \pi/2$ radians, the normal equation of the line through O and A is $x \cos (\alpha - \pi/2) + y \sin (\alpha - \pi/2) = 0$, which reduces to $x \sin \alpha - y \cos \alpha = 0$. The point (x_1, y_1) is then seen to be d units distant from the line through O and A, where

$$d = |x_1 \sin \alpha - y_1 \cos \alpha| = \left| x_1 \sin \alpha - x_1 \cos \alpha \frac{(1 - \cos \alpha)}{\sin \alpha} \right|$$

$$= \left| \frac{x_1 \sin^2 \alpha - x_1 \cos \alpha (1 - \cos \alpha)}{\sin \alpha} \right| = \left| \frac{x_1 - x_1 \cos \alpha}{\sin \alpha} \right| = y_1,$$

which proves the proposition.

Note. Our argument has been phrased with the assumption that the given angle is obtuse. The argument is similar in case the angle is acute, the only difference in the proof being that ω is now $\alpha + \pi/2$. It is noteworthy that $\frac{(1 - \cos \alpha)}{\sin \alpha}$ is non-negative, whether α is the radian measure of an acute or obtuse angle.

PROBLEM SET 14.5

Prove each of the following propositions of Euclidean plane geometry, making any necessary *basic* assumptions.

1. The proposition of Illustration 2, assuming that the angle is acute.
2. The mid-point of the hypotenuse of a right triangle is equidistant from all the vertices.
3. The segments joining the mid-points of opposite sides of a plane quadrilateral bisect each other.
4. The diagonals of an isosceles trapezoid are equal in length. (The non-parallel sides of an isosceles trapezoid are equal in length.)
5. The sum of the squares of measures of length of the sides of a parallelogram is equal to the sum of the squares of the corresponding measures of length of the diagonals.
6. In any triangle, the sum of the distances of any interior point from the three sides is constant. (Hint: choose a coordinate system so that each vertex has one coordinate zero.)

7. The segment joining the mid-points of two sides of a triangle is equal in length to one-half the third side.
8. A chord of a circle is perpendicular to any radius that bisects it. (Hint: choose the origin at the center of the circle, with the x-axis along the given radius.)
9. The three altitudes of a triangle meet in a point. This common point is known as the *orthocenter*.
10. The three medians of a triangle meet in a point, which is two-thirds the distance from a vertex to the mid-point of the opposite side. This common point is known as the *centroid*. (Hint: show that the point which divides one median in the ratio 2:1, also divides the other medians in the same ratio.)
11. The perpendicular bisectors of the sides of a triangle meet in a common point. This point is known as the *circumcenter*.
12. The centroid, circumcenter, and orthocenter of a triangle are collinear.

14.6 Locus Problems

We now discuss the problem of determining an equation of a curve, that has been defined by some geometric condition. We have already referred to this *locus* problem, the classical notion of a curve being a "locus" or "path" traced out by a "moving" point. We shall not use this classical language, but shall continue to use the word "locus" to refer to the set of points satisfying some condition on a plane. For example, we can describe a circle as the locus consisting of all points of a plane that are an invariant distance from a given point. The procedure for determining an equation of a locus is always the same: establish a coordinate system, unless one is assumed, select an *arbitrary* point on the locus and determine the condition that is imposed on its coordinates. This condition is usually an equation and, after its solution set is suitably restricted if necessary, is the desired equation of the locus with respect to the coordinate system adopted. It is usually a matter of judgment whether to use a Cartesian or polar coordinate system, unless one has been specified; but if neither has been specified, one should select the type and properly orient it so that the desired equation will be as simple as possible. We shall assume that a Cartesian system is to be chosen for all problems of this section, however. We now illustrate the application of the procedure given above.

ILLUSTRATION 1. Determine an equation of the locus consisting of all points 5 units distant from the point $(4, -2)$.

Solution. The locus is clearly a circle, having its center at $(4, -2)$ and its radii 5 units in length, but we ignore this observation and solve the problem from the point of view of a locus.

With reference to Figure 14–10, we select an arbitrary point $P(x, y)$, that is 5 units distant from the point $(4, -2)$. (Notice that the coordinate system is assumed in the statement of the problem.) The geometric condition is that the distance between (x, y) and $(4, -2)$ is 5 units, and so $\sqrt{(x-4)^2 + (y+2)^2} = 5$. This equation may be simplified to $(x-4)^2 + (y+2)^2 = 25$, or $x^2 - y^2 - 8x + 4y - 5 = 0$, as desired.

ILLUSTRATION 2. Determine an equation of the locus comprising all points equidistant from the points $(3, 4)$ and $(-5, -4)$.

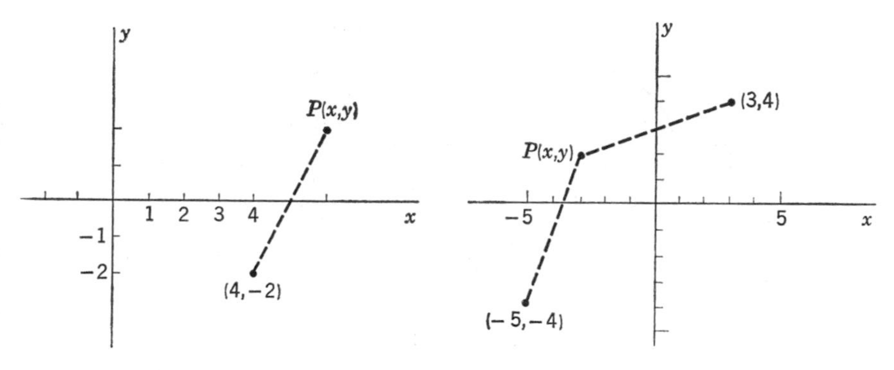

Figure 14–10

Figure 14–11

Solution. The sketch is shown in Figure 14–11, including an arbitrary point $P(x, y)$ on the locus. Since the distance from P to $(3, 4)$ is the same as the distance from P to $(-5, -4)$, we must have $\sqrt{(x-3)^2 + (y-4)^2} = \sqrt{(x+5)^2 + (y+4)^2}$ which becomes, on squaring both members, $x^2 - 6x + 9 + y^2 - 8y + 16 = x^2 + 10x + 25 + y^2 + 8y + 16$. A simplified form of an equation of the locus is then seen to be $x + y + 1 = 0$. The locus, a straight line, is evidently the right bisector of the line segment joining the two given points.

ILLUSTRATION 3. If the sum of the distances of a point P from two given points is prescribed, find an equation of the locus consisting of all possible positions of P.

Solution. The locus is illustrated in Figure 14–12, where we have chosen a coordinate system with origin midway between the two given points F_1 and F_2, and x-axis along the segment joining these points. We may assume the abscissas of F_1 and F_2 to be $-c$ and c, respectively, with $c > 0$. If $P(x, y)$ is an arbitrary point on the locus, the condition requires that $\sqrt{(x+c)^2 + y^2} + \sqrt{(x-c)^2 + y^2} = 2a$, where we have selected $2a$ units of length as the prescribed distance. If we add $-\sqrt{(x-c)^2 + y^2}$ to both members of this equation, and then square each member, the result may be written as $\sqrt{(x-c)^2 + y^2} = a - (c/a)x$. If we now square both members of this new equation and simplify, $x^2/a^2 + y^2/(a^2 - c^2) = 1$ is the result. Since the sum of the lengths of two sides of a triangle always exceeds the length of the third side, the figure shows that $2a \geq 2c$

or $a \geq c$. Hence $a^2 - c^2 \geq 0$, and if we represent this number by b^2, the above equation may be written as $x^2/a^2 + y^2/b^2 = 1$ or $b^2x^2 + a^2y^2 = a^2b^2$. The form of this equation shows that the locus is an ellipse, the development actually using one of the characteristic properties of this conic. The two

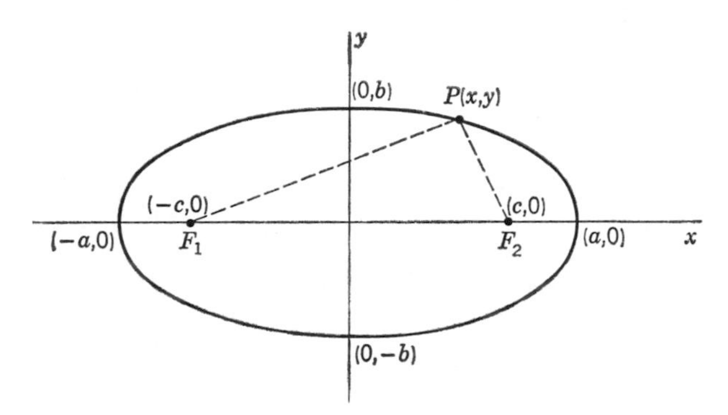

Figure 14–12

fixed points are the *foci*, while $2a$ and $2b$ measure the lengths of the *axes* of the ellipse in the units of the diagram. In Problem 5 we ask for a corresponding development of the hyperbola, and in Problems 6 and 7 for a development of both conics, using a different characteristic property.

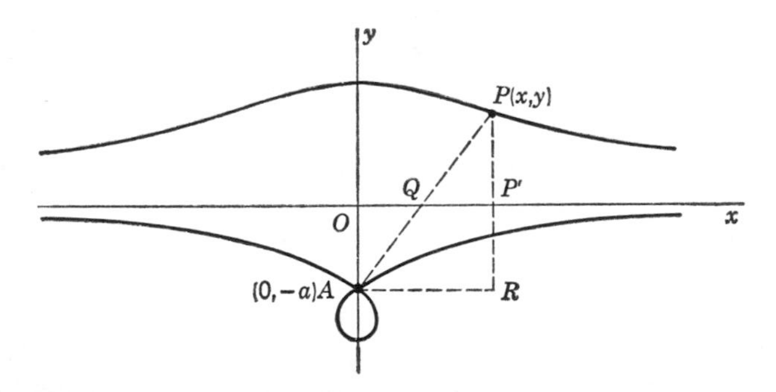

Figure 14–13

ILLUSTRATION 4. Let A be a point on the y-axis, below the origin of a Cartesian coordinate system, and through A draw a line meeting the x-axis at a point Q. If P is a point on this line, a prescribed distance (either way) from Q, determine an equation of the locus of all positions of P.

A representation of the locus is shown in Figure 14–13, where we have identified A with the point $(0, -a)$ and P, as usual, with (x, y). If we let b units be the given distance of P from Q, the similarity of triangles PAR and $QP'P$ yields $x/(y + a) = \sqrt{b^2 - y^2}/y$. This equation, after simplification, becomes $x^2y^2 = (a + y)^2(b^2 - y^2)$. The derivation of this equation has been made with the assumption that P is in the first quadrant, but only slight changes would be required in the argument for P in any other quadrant. The complete locus is known as the *Conchoid of Nicomedes*, the figure showing a portion of such a locus with $a < b$.

PROBLEM SET 14.6

In Problems 1–6 and 11–13, determine an equation of the locus consisting of all possible positions of a point P subject to the stated condition.

1. The sum of the coordinates of P is 3.

2. The sum of the squares of the coordinates of P is 9.

3. (*a*) P is 2 units to the left of the y-axis; (*b*) P is equidistant from the points $(-4, 7)$ and $(-1, 0)$; (*c*) P is 6 units distant from $(-1, -3)$.

4. (*a*) P is twice as distant from the origin as from the point $(1, 4)$; (*b*) P is on either the locus of $3x + y - 5 = 0$ or the locus of $2x - 4y + 1 = 0$; (*c*) the sum of the distances of P from $(2, 0)$ and $(-2, 0)$ is 4 units; (*d*) the product of the measures of distance of P from $(0, 1)$ and the locus of $y = -2$ is equal to 2.

5. The difference of the distances of P from two given points is prescribed; show that the locus is a hyperbola. (Use a figure similar to Figure 14–12; put $b^2 = c^2 - a^2$, and show that an equation of the locus is $b^2x^2 - a^2y^2 = a^2b^2$.)

6. The ratio of the distance of P from a given point to its distance from a given line is $e < 1$; show that the locus is an ellipse. The given point is a *focus*, the given line is a *directrix*, while e is the *eccentricity* of the ellipse. (Hint: put the x-axis through the focus and perpendicular to the directrix.)

7. Show that the locus of Problem 6 is a hyperbola if $e > 1$, and a parabola if $e = 1$.

8. Use the property of Problem 6 to determine an equation of a hyperbola, if one focus is at the point $(2, 3)$, an equation of the corresponding directrix is $3x - 4y + 2 = 0$, and its eccentricity is 5.

9. Use the property of Problem 6 to determine an equation of an ellipse, if one focus is at the point $(-4, 0)$, an equation of the corresponding directrix is $x + y - 5 = 0$, and its eccentricity is $1/2$.

10. Use the property of Problem 6 to determine an equation of a hyperbola, if one focus is at the point $(-4, 0)$, an equation of the corresponding directrix is $x = -6$, and its eccentricity is $3/2$.

11. The product of the measures of the distance of P from each of two given points is prescribed. This locus is known as an *Oval of Cassini*. (Hint: let $(-a, 0)$ and $(a, 0)$ be the given points, with c^2 the prescribed product.) What is the form of the equation if $c^2 = a^2$?

12. A line segment AB, with its end points on the positive portions of a pair of rectangular coordinate axes, forms with these axes a triangle of given area; P is a point on AB such that the ratio of its distances from A and B is $m{:}n$.

13. A line segment of given length has its end points on the axes of a rectangular coordinate system, while P divides the segment in a prescribed ratio.

14.7 Polar Equations of Loci

We tried to emphasize in the preceding section that sometimes one type of coordinate system is more suitable for a given locus problem than another. For example, if we use the characteristic property of a conic, described in Problems 6 and 7 of Problem Set 14.6, an equation of the locus can be obtained much more easily with the use of polar coordinates. Thus, referring to Figure 14–14, let us choose the focus F for the polar origin

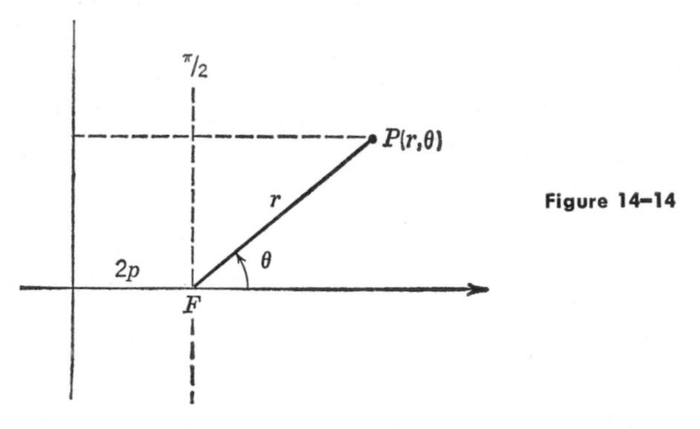

Figure 14–14

and the line through F perpendicular to the directrix for the polar axis, with F on its positive side. If $P(r, \theta)$ is any point on the locus, the figure shows that the distances from P to the directrix and the focus are, respectively, $2p + r \cos \theta$ and r units, where we are taking $2p$ units as the

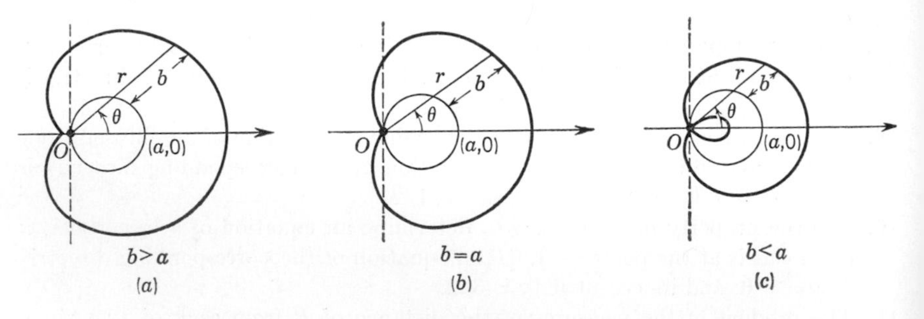

Figure 14–15

distance between the focus and the directrix. The property of a conic now requires that $r/(2p + r \cos \theta) = e$, and if we solve this equation for r we obtain $r = 2ep/(1 - e \cos \theta)$. This is an equation of the conic, referred to the polar coordinate system described above, and we note the simplicity of its derivation. For an ellipse, $e < 1$, and for a hyperbola, $e > 1$; for a parabola, $e = 1$ and the equation reduces to $r = 2p/(1 - \cos\theta)$.

ILLUSTRATION. A circle with center on the polar axis passes through the pole of a polar coordinate system. If chords of the circle are drawn from the pole, and extended a given distance beyond the circle, determine a polar equation of the locus consisting of the end points of these extended chords.

Solution. In Figure 14–15, we have shown the given circle, with its center on the positive portion of the polar axis. An equation of this circle is $r = a\cos\theta$ while, if each chord has been extended b units, the corresponding equation of the locus is easily seen to be $r = a\cos\theta + b$. It should be observed that $\cos\theta \leq 0$ if $\theta \in [\pi/2, 3\pi/2]$, and that $a\cos\theta + b \leq b$ for each θ in this interval. The figure shows the cases with (*a*) $b > a$, (*b*) $b = a$, and (*c*) $b < a$; the locus in (*b*) is known as a *cardioid*, while the other two are *limaçons*.

PROBLEM SET 14.7

1. Determine a polar equation of an ellipse, having eccentricity 1/2, one focus at the pole, and the associated directrix 4 units distant from the focus and perpendicular to the polar axis.
2. Determine a polar equation of a parabola, having its focus at the pole, and its directrix 6 units distant from the focus and perpendicular to the polar axis.
3. Determine a polar equation of a hyperbola, having eccentricity 3/2, one focus at the pole, and the associated directrix 8 units distant from the focus and perpendicular to the polar axis.
4. Through a given point O on a circle, a chord OP' is drawn, while P is the point which divides this chord in a given ratio. If all possible chords are drawn through O, find an equation of the locus comprising all positions of P. (Hint: use polar coordinates, select O for the pole, and have the polar axis pass through the center of the circle.)
5. A *focal radius* of a conic is the line segment joining any point on the curve to a focus. Show that the set of mid-points of all focal radii of a conic is another conic of the same type.
6. Find an equation of the locus consisting of all points which divide the focal radii of a conic in a given ratio. (See Problem 5.)
7. Sketch the ellipse which has the polar equation $r = 10/(2 - \cos\theta)$, after determining at least 10 solutions (r, θ) of the equation.
8. Sketch a portion of the hyperbola which has the polar equation $r = 10/(1 - 2\cos\theta)$, after determining at least 10 solutions (r, θ) of the equation.
9. Sketch a portion of the parabola which has the polar equation $r = 10/(1 - \cos\theta)$, after determining at least 10 solutions (r, θ) of the equation. What is the distance between the focus and directrix of this parabola?
10. If all possible line segments are drawn from a given point to intersect a given

line, determine an equation of the locus consisting of the points which divide these segments in a given ratio. (Hint: use polar coordinates, with the pole at the given point and polar axis perpendicular to the given line.)

14.8 Parametric Equations

Let us suppose that an airplane is headed due north, with an air speed of 300 miles per hour. If there is a steady wind, blowing due east at 50 miles per hour, what is the actual track of the plane? It is clear that the course will be somewhat east of north, but we can make a more careful analysis. If we assume a condition of level flight and a small lapse of time, the track will lie approximately in one geometric plane on which we can imagine a coordinate system. Let us measure time from a certain instant, and assume that the origin of a Cartesian coordinate system, scaled in miles, coincides with the position of the plane at this instant, with the positive x-axis directed due east. It is then clear that the position (x, y) of the plane t hours later is given by the equations $x = 50t$ and $y = 300t$, and the set of all such positions, under our restrictive time assumption, constitutes the track of the plane during this time. The equations just given are known as *parametric equations*, with t the *parameter*. If an ordinary Cartesian equation of the track is desired, we can eliminate the parameter, and obtain $y = 300x/50$ or $y = 6x$. The flight course is now seen to be a straight line with slope 3.

With reference to the preceding discussion, let us assume that the period of level flight is T hours, so that $t \in [0, T]$ for the track under consideration. It should be noted that each number t in $[0, T]$ determines a unique point (x, y) of the track, and so a function is defined on $[0, T]$ to $R^\# \times R^\#$, consisting of a set of ordered pairs of the type $(t, (x, y))$. This is the function defined on $[0, T]$ by the parametric equations, and which gives us the position of the plane at any instant. The actual track of the plane, for the T hours under consideration, is the set of *values* of this function, i.e., its *range;* we have seen above that this is a subset of the solution set of $y = 6x$. If we are interested in the position of the plane *at a certain time*, we must keep the parametric equations; if, on the other hand, we are interested only in the track, without reference to time, the parameter may be eliminated.

More generally, let us suppose that f and g are functions on D to $R^\#$, with D a set of real numbers, such that $x = f(u)$ and $y = g(u)$ for each u in D. These equations define a function F on D, such that $F(u) = (x, y)$ for each u in D. It is not feasible to make a graph of F on a plane, but the range of F may be easily graphed since this is a subset of $R^\# \times R^\#$. In harmony with what has gone before, if D is the maximal subset of $R^\#$ for which x and y may be defined by the above equations, this graph is the *locus of the parametric equations* $x = f(u)$ and $y = g(u)$. Furthermore, these equations may be considered *parametric equations* of this locus or any subset thereof, with u suitably restricted in the latter case.

There is no *unique* set of parametric equations for a given curve, and there are frequently even several choices for the same *type* of parameter. In the above example, we could have measured time from some other instant, or we could have placed the coordinate axes in some other position. In searching for a parameter one should search for a quantity, certain measures of which determine points on the curve, and each point on the portion of the curve in which we are interested is determined by one such measure. We have implied that it is possible for parametric equations to determine only a portion of a geometric locus, even without artificial restriction on u.

ILLUSTRATION 1. Find parametric equations for the straight line which contains the points (2, 3) and has an inclination of $\pi/4$ radians.

Solution. A segment of the line, with $P(x, y)$ an arbitrary point on it, is shown in Figure 14–16. Since the *signed* distance of any point on the line from (2, 3) determines its position, let us select d for the param-

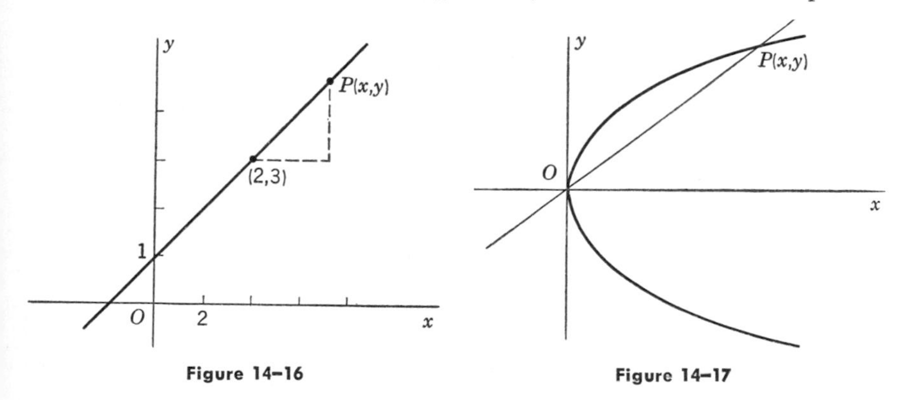

Figure 14–16

Figure 14–17

eter, with d the measure of signed distance of P from (2, 3), a positive d indicating that P is to the right of (2, 3). The figure now shows that $x = 2 + d \cos \pi/4 = 2 + d/\sqrt{2}$ and $y = 3 + d \sin \pi/4 = 3 + d/\sqrt{2}$, which constitute the corresponding parametric equations of the line. If we wish the ordinary equation of the line, we can eliminate d by a substitution of $(x - 2)\sqrt{2}$ for d in the expression for y, and obtain $y = 3 + (x - 2)$ or more simply $x - y + 1 = 0$.

ILLUSTRATION 2. Let us consider parametric equations for the parabola, defined as the locus of $y^2 = 4x$, a portion of which is shown in Figure 14–17. Any straight line through the origin has a unique slope m, and every point of the parabola, except the point at the origin O, can be considered the unique intersection point, different from O, of one of these lines.

In other words, each number $m \neq 0$ determines a point of the parabola, and each point of the parabola, except O, can be considered determined in this way. It is then reasonable to regard m as a parameter, with $y = mx$ as an equation of the line OP through an arbitrary point $P(x, y)$ distinct from O on the curve. Since P is a point of intersection of the line and the parabola, (x, y) must be a simultaneous solution of $y = mx$ and $y^2 = 4x$. It follows that $x = 4/m^2$ and $y = 4/m$, which constitute parametric equations for the locus consisting of all points of the parabola *except the origin.* A point (x, y) on the upper branch is determined by a positive m, while each point on the lower branch is determined by a negative m; it is clear from the equations that $m \neq 0$.

ILLUSTRATION 3. Suppose that a straight rod of indefinite length rotates in a counterclockwise direction about one of its end points, with an angular velocity of 20 revolutions per minute. If a particle, initially at the center of rotation, moves out along the rod with a velocity of 2 inches per minute as the rod rotates, determine the path of the moving particle.

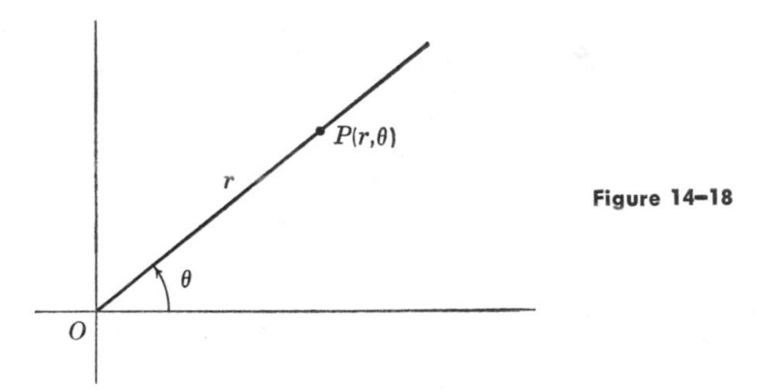

Figure 14–18

Solution. We shall simulate the path on a plane diagram and study it with the help of a polar coordinate system, with pole at the center of rotation and positive portion of the polar axis along the initial position of the rod. This is illustrated in Figure 14–18. If $P(r, \theta)$ is the position of the moving particle after t minutes, we must have $r = 2t$ and $\theta = 20(2\pi t) = 40\pi t$, $t \geq 0$. These two equations are polar parametric equations of the path, with the parameter t the measure of time in minutes after the rotation started. If we wish an ordinary polar equation of the path, we can eliminate t by substituting $t = \theta/(40\pi)$ in the equation $r = 2t$, and obtain $r = 2\theta/(40\pi) = \theta/(20\pi)$. This is a polar equation of a Spiral of Archimedes.

While the physical interpretation of the quantity measured by a parameter is always known, when a pair of parametric equations of a curve are derived, it is possible to determine the nature of the curve from parametric equations without this information on the parameter.

ILLUSTRATION 4. Determine the nature of the curve, defined as the locus of the parametric equations $x = 2 + 3 \cos \phi$ and $y = -1 + 4 \sin \phi$.

Solution. If we write the equations in the form $(x - 2)/3 = \cos\phi$ and $(y + 1)/4 = \sin\phi$, the parameter ϕ may be easily eliminated by squaring and then adding respective members of these equations. The result is $(x - 2)^2/9 + (y + 1)^2/16 = 1$, and from this equation the curve may be identified as an ellipse which has its center at the point $(2, -1)$.

PROBLEM SET 14.8

1. Each of the following pairs of parametric equations defines a function F on D to $R^\# \times R^\#$, with D some interval of real numbers. Assume a reasonable D and sketch the values of F on a graph, after an actual plot of ten of these values. (*a*) $x = 3t$, $y = 2 + t$; (*b*) $x = t^2$, $y = 2t^2 + t$; (*c*) $x = 2\sec\theta$, $y = 5\tan\theta$; (*d*) $x = t + 1/t$, $y = t - 1/t$.
2. Determine an ordinary Cartesian equation of the locus of each of the pairs of parametric equations in Problem 1.
3. Show that $x = 2 - 5t$ and $y = 3 + 2t$ are parametric equations of a straight line, and determine its slope.
4. Determine parametric equations of a circle, which has its center at the origin, using the radian measure of the inclination of a *sensed* line segment from the origin for parameter. (Hint: if $P(x, y)$ is any point of the circle, and θ radians is the inclination of the line segment from the origin to P, express x and y in terms of θ.)
5. Use a different parameter from that suggested in Problem 4, and try to find parametric equations of the circle, which has its center at the origin and radii 5 units in length. (Hint: use the method of Illustration 2, with the point $(-5, 0)$ playing the role of O in the illustration.) Is every point of the circle on the locus of the parametric equations?
6. Rework Problem 5, using the slope of a line through the point $(5, 0)$ for parameter.
7. A ship is heading due west, at a speed of 18 knots, in water flowing due north at a speed of 5 knots. Determine parametric equations of the track of the ship, using the measure t of time in hours as parameter. (1 knot is 1 nautical mile per hour.)
8. Determine parametric equations of the line *segment* joining the points $(1, 3)$ and $(4, 7)$. If the segment is the graph of a function F from $R^\#$ to $R^\# \times R^\#$, what is the domain of F?
9. With reference to the function F of Problem 1, determine the element of the domain of F which corresponds to the following point: (*a*) $(6, 4)$; (*b*) $(1, 1)$; (*c*) $(2\sqrt{2}, 5)$; (*d*) $(5/2, -3/2)$.
10. An object is dropped from an airplane, traveling in level flight at a speed of 200 miles per hour. Neglecting any effect of air resistance, write down parametric equations of the path of the object as it falls, using the measure t of time in seconds from the instant the object was dropped as parameter. (A body falls approximately s feet in t seconds under gravity, with $s = 16t^2$.)

11. Use a different coordinate system and determine a new pair of parametric equations of the path described in Problem 10.
12. Show that $x = \sin^2 t$ and $y = 3 \cos t$ are parametric equations of only a portion of the parabola, described as the locus of $y^2 = 9(1 - x)$.
13. A curve is described as the locus of the parametric equations $x = t/(1 + t^3)$ and $y = t^2/(1 + t^3)$. Plot at least ten points of the locus and sketch this curve, known as the *folium of Descartes*. Show that $x^3 + y^3 = xy$ is an ordinary equation of the curve.
14. Find parametric equations of the parabola, defined as the locus of $y^2 = 10x$.
15. The ends A and B of a line segment lie, respectively, on the x and y axes of a Cartesian coordinate system. Use parametric equations to show that the locus, comprising all positions of the midpoint of AB, is a circle.
16. A gun is mounted on the top of a cliff 200 feet above a section of level land. If a projectile is fired over this territory in a horizontal direction, with a muzzle velocity of 300 feet per second, write down parametric equations of the path of the projectile, neglecting all forces except gravity after the firing. How far from the base of the cliff will the projectile land?

14.9 Parametric Equations of Some Special Curves

By this time it will have been understood that what we are calling a *parameter* is merely a representative number in the domain of a function, the values of which constitute a subset of $R^{\#} \times R^{\#}$. The equations defining this function are *parametric equations* of the graph of the *values* of the function, this graph being a portion of the locus of the equations. We now consider some special curves which can be studied most easily if their equations are given in parametric form.

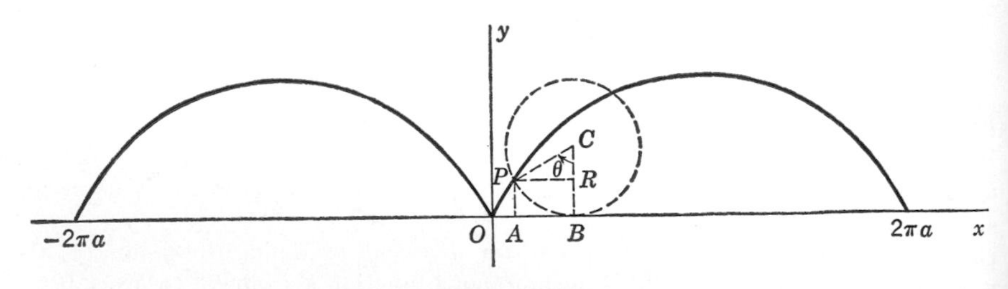

Figure 14–19

If a circular wheel rolls along a straight path, the track of a particle on its circumference is a curve with some interesting characteristics. The situation is illustrated in Figure 14–19, with point $P(x, y)$, on a circle having radii a units in length, depicting a representative position of the particle.

A Cartesian coordinate system has been selected so that the x-axis lies along the simulated path of the rolling wheel, the origin being chosen to coincide with one of the points of contact of the moving particle under observation with the path. As the wheel rolls to the right, the radian measure of $\angle RCP$ increases from 0, when the particle is at the origin, to θ when the particle is in the position of P shown in the figure. We shall consider this to be the positive direction of the motion, while any position of the particle to the left of the origin will correspond to a negative measure of the angle. Since every real number θ, positive, negative, or zero, determines a unique point on the track of the particle, and every point on the track can be so determined, it is evident that θ is a suitable choice for parameter.

We are assuming that the wheel rolls without any slipping, so that in the figure the length of the *segment* OB is the same as the length of the *arc* PB, with both equal to $a\theta$ units. It is clear from the figure that the length of PR is $a \sin \theta$ units, while the length of CR is $a \cos \theta$ units. Since P is the point (x, y), it then follows that $x = a\theta - a \sin \theta = a(\theta - \sin \theta)$ and $y = a - a \cos \theta = a(1 - \cos \theta)$. These are the desired parametric equations of the track of the moving particle, the complete locus of these equations being a curve of infinite extent known as a *cycloid*. If θ is restricted to lie in a finite interval, of course, the graph associated with these equations will be a cycloidal arc.

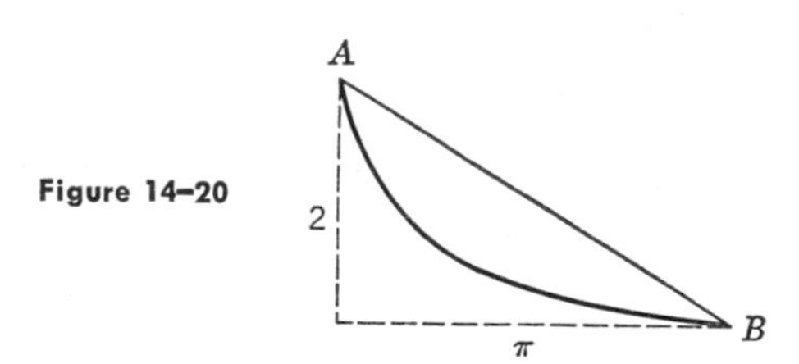

Figure 14–20

A cycloid has some interesting characteristics. Let A and B be two points above the surface of the earth, in a common gravitational field, with B below but not directly below A. Then it is always possible to fit a "least time" curve through these points, in the sense that a particle sliding from A to B along a frictionless path will do so in the least possible time if the path has the shape of this curve. This "least time" curve is known as a *brachistochrone*, and is a portion of an inverted cycloid if the ratio of the vertical to the horizontal distance from B to A is $2/\pi$. Point A will be at a cusp of the cycloid, with B at a low point, as shown in Figure 14–20. If this ratio is less than or equal to $2/\pi$, it is also possible to fit a "constant time" curve between A and B, in the sense that the time required for a sliding particle to reach B along a path of this shape, is independent of the point at which it is released along the path between A and B. Such a curve is called a *tautachrone* and is again a cycloid if the above ratio is equal to $2/\pi$. For this case, an arc of an inverted cycloid is both a "least time" and a "constant time" curve.

If we are interested in the ordinary Cartesian equation of a cycloid, the parameter θ can be eliminated, and the resulting equation is $x = a \text{ arc cos } (1 - y/a) \pm \sqrt{2ay - y^2}$. As this is a complicated equation, it is often more convenient to use the parametric equations, even when our interest lies only in the curve itself.

There are several other interesting curves which may be generated by methods similar to that used for the cycloid. The track of a particle that is located at either an interior or exterior point of a radius of a wheel as it rolls along a straight level path is known as a *trochoid;* the path is also known as a *curtate* or *prolate* cycloid, according to whether the point is

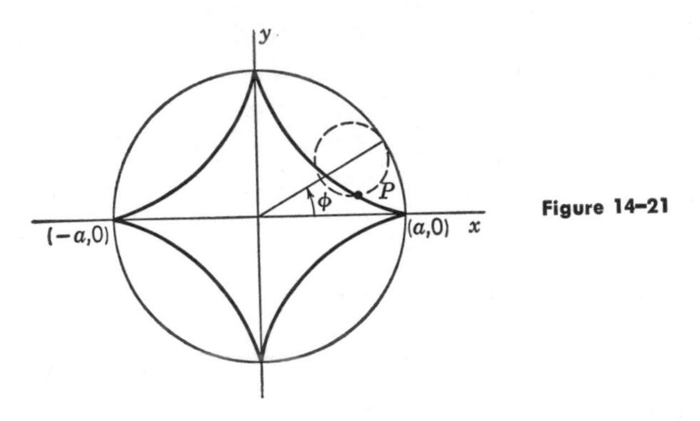

Figure 14–21

an interior or exterior point of the radius. If the wheel rolls internally on another circular but stationary wheel, a particle on the circumference of the rolling wheel traces out a curve known as a *hypocycloid.* In case a radius of the rolling wheel is one fourth as long as a radius of the stationary wheel, the path of the particle is a hypocycloid with four cusps, as shown in Figure 14–21. A hypocycloid of this type can be shown to have parametric equations of the form $x = a \cos^3 \phi$, $y = a \sin^3 \phi$. In these equations, a is the measure of length of a radius of the stationary wheel, while ϕ is the radian measure of the angle between the x-axis and the line drawn from the origin to the point of contact of the rolling wheel, as indicated in the figure. If ϕ is eliminated, the ordinary equation of the curve is $x^{2/3} + y^{2/3} = a^{2/3}$. If the rolling wheel rolls externally on the stationary one, the corresponding curves are known as *epicycloids.*

We conclude this section with a method for determining the slope of the tangent line at a point on a curve, if its parametric equations are given. We have seen before that if a function F on D to $R^\# \times R^\#$ is defined by a pair of parametric equations, with $F(\theta) = (x, y)$ for each θ in D, two other functions are also defined on D to $R^\#$. These are the functions f and g, with $f(\theta) = x$ and $g(\theta) = y$. Let us suppose that θ is a point in D at which f and g are differentiable, i.e., both $f'(\theta)$ and $g'(\theta)$ exist. Then θ

is a point of continuity of both f and g, and $(f(\theta + h), g(\theta + h))$ is a point on the curve arbitrarily close to (x, y) if $\theta + h$ is properly chosen in D. The slope of the line segment joining these two points is $\dfrac{g(\theta + h) - g(\theta)}{f(\theta + h) - f(\theta)}$, which we may consider the value at h of the slope function associated with the point (x, y), i.e., the point $(f(\theta), g(\theta))$. If we designate this slope function by E_h, in harmony with the procedure of Chapter 8, we see that the slope of the tangent line to the curve at (x, y) is

$$\begin{aligned}\lim_{h\to 0} E_h(\theta) &= \lim_{h\to 0} \frac{g(\theta + h) - g(\theta)}{f(\theta + h) - f(\theta)}\\ &= \lim_{h\to 0} \left[\frac{g(\theta + h) - g(\theta)}{h} \Big/ \frac{f(\theta + h) - f(\theta)}{h}\right]\\ &= \left[\lim_{h\to 0} \frac{g(\theta + h) - g(\theta)}{h}\right] \Big/ \left[\lim_{h\to 0} \frac{f(\theta + h) - f(\theta)}{h}\right] = g'(\theta)/f'(\theta),\end{aligned}$$

provided $f'(\theta) \neq 0$. This is our desired result.

ILLUSTRATION. A curve is defined as the locus of the parametric equations $x = t^2$ and $y = 1 - t$. Determine the slope of the tangent line at the point on this curve corresponding to $t = 2$.

Solution. In this case $f(t) = t^2$ and $g(t) = 1 - t$, and so $f'(t) = 2t$ and $g'(t) = -1$ for each real t. The slope of the tangent line at the point (x, y) is then $-1/(2t)$, and if $t = 2$, the required slope is $-1/4$. This may be seen to be the slope of the tangent line at the point $(4, -1)$.

PROBLEM SET 14.9

1. Make a table of ordered pairs (x, y), corresponding to elements θ which differ by multiples of $\pi/6$, and sketch one arch of the cycloid using $a = 1$.
2. What is the length of the base of one arch of a cycloid? Determine the coordinates of the highest point of the first arch of a cycloid, to the right of the origin.
3. Make a rough sketch of a prolate and a curtate cycloid, using merely geometric intuition.
4. Make a rough intuitive sketch of an epicycloid, if a radius of the rolling wheel is five times as long as a radius of the one that is stationary.
5. Determine the slope of the tangent line at a point (x, y) on the locus of the parametric equations: (*a*) $x = 1 + t^2$, $y = 4t^3$; (*b*) $x = 2 + t$, $y = 1/t$; (*c*) $x = 3\theta^2$, $y = 2(1 - 2\theta)$; (*d*) $x = 5t^3$, $y = 3t$.
6. Find the slope of the tangent line at the indicated point on the locus of the parametric equations: (*a*) $x = 2t^2$, $y = 1 + 2t$; $t = 1$; (*b*) $x = 1 + 1/t$, $y = 3t^2 - 1$; $t = 2$.

7. Determine an equation of the tangent line, at the point associated with $t = -2$, on the locus of the equations $x = 1 - 3t$ and $y = 2t^2$.
8. Determine an equation of the tangent line, at the point associated with $t = 1$, on the locus of the equations $x = t^2 + 3t$ and $y = t^2 + t$.
9. Find the point of the curve in Problem 7, at which the tangent line is parallel to the line having the equation $8x + 2y - 5 = 0$.
10. A circular wheel rolls along a straight path which may be simulated by the line locus of $y = x$ in the plane of the wheel. Determine a set of parametric equations for the track of a particle on the circumference of the wheel, if we assume that the track contains the origin of our coordinate system.
11. An *involute* of a plane curve is the locus described by the end point of a piece of thread, which is kept taut as it is imagined unwound from the given curve. Find parametric equations for the involute of the unit circle, having its center at the origin, if the end of the thread is considered initially on the x-axis. (Hint: let P be a representative point on the locus, and draw a line segment PB tangent to the circle at B. With O the center of the circle, choose as parameter the radian measure θ of the angle between segment OB and the x-axis.
12. Determine the slope of the tangent line at an arbitrary point of a cycloid. Determine equations of the tangent and normal lines to the cycloid at the point corresponding to $\theta = \pi/2$.

14.10 Assorted Problems of Geometry

We have previously referred to the fact that the subject matter of classical plane geometry is a study of the characteristics of curves, which have been defined by some geometric condition. The most important class of these curves, in the classical study, was the conic sections, including the special cases of the straight line and the circle. With the advent of analytic geometry, new and simpler methods of solving the associated problems were discovered, but even in modern times many courses in "analytic geometry" are largely studies of conic sections. In our presentation we have not given special consideration to these curves, but have tried rather to emphasize the relationship between *any* locus and its equation. However, in spite of this, it is hoped that the general methods which we have developed may be applied to a solution of most of the problems of classical geometry. In this section, we outline several techniques not previously discussed, and devote the remainder of the section to a collection of problems.

Among the problems of geometry, the problem of determining a tangent line to a curve is of frequent occurrence. If the line is to be tangent at a given point on the curve, the method of the calculus makes a solution of this problem quite easy provided the curve is the graph of a differentiable function; we have, in fact, already considered problems of this kind. We now illustrate two general methods which may be used to find the equations of the tangent lines to a curve, these lines containing a given point not on the curve. The illustration uses a circle, but the method is clearly of more general application.

ILLUSTRATION 1. Determine equations of the lines through the point $(7, -1)$, which are tangent to the circle having the equation $x^2 + y^2 = 25$.

Solution.

(*a*) First Method. An equation of the line through $(7, -1)$ with slope m is $y + 1 = m(x - 7)$. If this equation is put in normal form, its distance from the origin is seen to be $(7m + 1)/\sqrt{1 + m^2}$, and so the condition of tangency imposed on the line requires that $(7m + 1)/\sqrt{1 + m^2} = 5$. Hence $49m^2 + 14m + 1 = 25 + 25m^2$, and $m = 3/4$ or $m = -4/3$. It follows that equations of the tangent lines are $4x + 3y = 25$ and $3x - 4y = 25$, sketches of which are shown in Figure 14–22.

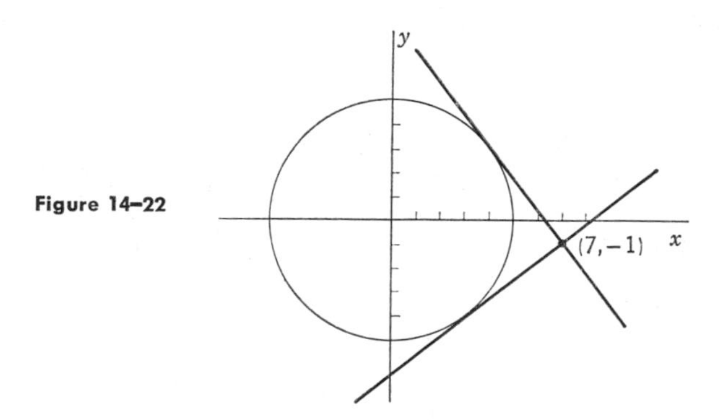

Figure 14–22

(*b*) Second Method. If the slope of a line is m and its y-intercept is b, an equation of the line may be written in the form $y = mx + b$. If we substitute $mx + b$ for y in the given equation of the circle, we obtain $x^2 + (mx + b)^2 = 25$ for the condition which must be satisfied by the abscissas of the points of intersection of the line and circle. The line will be tangent to the circle if and only if there is only one point of intersection, in which case the discriminant of the above equation in x must be zero. This gives the following condition on b: $b = \pm 5\sqrt{1 + m^2}$. If the line which has the equation $y = mx + 5\sqrt{1 + m^2}$ is to contain the point $(7, -1)$, we must have $-1 = 7m + 5\sqrt{1 + m^2}$, whence $m = -4/3$. In a similar manner the other equation yields $m = 3/4$. The two equations are then $y = -4x/3 + 25/3$ and $y = 3x/4 - 25/4$, which can be simplified to $4x + 3y = 25$ and $3x - 4y = 25$, as before.

A comparison of the two methods used in the solution of the above problem reveals that the first is the shorter. However, it should be noted that this method is applicable only to circles, whereas the second may be used to find the tangent lines to any conic section and many other algebraic curves.

Let us suppose that the respective loci of two equations $E = 0$ and $F = 0$ in x and y are the curves C_1 and C_2. Since any solution (x, y) of each of these equations is also a solution of the equation $k_1E + k_2F = 0$, for arbitrary numbers k_1 and k_2, the locus of the latter equation must include all points of intersection (if any) of C_1 and C_2. In particular, if C_1 and C_2 are circles, it is clear that the locus of $k_1E + k_2F = 0$ is a circle if $k_1 + k_2 \neq 0$, and the circle has this intersection characteristic. A special case arises if $k_1 + k_2 = 0$, in which case the locus is a straight line perpendicular to the line of centers of the given circles C_1 and C_2. This line, known as the *radical axis* of the circles, can be shown to contain all points from which tangents of equal length can be drawn to the circles. In case the circles intersect, the radical axis is the line containing their common chord as a segment. Various instances of radical axes are shown in Figure 14–23.

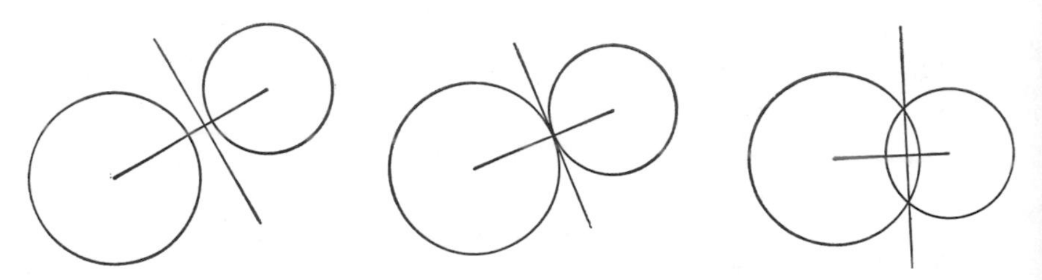

Figure 14–23

If we wish to determine the points of intersection of two circles, it is sometimes more convenient to find the points at which the radical axis intersects either circle, rather than to proceed directly. It is clear, incidentally, that if the coefficients of x^2 and y^2 are unity in the given equations of both circles, an equation of the radical axis is obtained by merely subtracting corresponding members of these equations, and equating the results.

ILLUSTRATION 2. Let $x^2 + y^2 + 12x + 2y - 16 = 0$ and $x^2 + y^2 + 3x - y - 7 = 0$ be the given equations of two circles.

(*a*) Determine an equation of the circle through the point $(-1, 4)$ and the points of intersection (if any) of the above circles.

(*b*) Determine an equation of the radical axis of the above circles.

Solution. An equation of an arbitrary circle through all points of intersection of the given circles is

$$k_1(x^2 + y^2 + 12x + 2y - 16) + k_2(x^2 + y^2 + 3x - y - 7) = 0.$$

The point $(-1, 4)$ is included on the circle if $(-1, 4)$ is a solution of this equation, i.e., if

$$k_1(1 + 16 - 12 + 8 - 16) + k_2(1 + 16 - 3 - 4 - 7) = 0,$$

which reduces to $k_1 = k_2$. If we now select k_1 and k_2 equal, for example $k_1 = k_2 = 1$, an equation of the circle described in (*a*) is $2x^2 + 2y^2 + 15x + y - 23 = 0$. In order to obtain an equation of the radical axis, desired in (*b*), we subtract corresponding members of the given equations, equate the results, and obtain $3x + y - 3 = 0$ after simplification.

We close this section with the solution of a locus problem involving the tangent lines of a parabola.

ILLUSTRATION 3. A tangent to the locus of $y^2 = 4x$ intersects a perpendicular line through the origin at the point P. Determine an equation of the locus of all possible positions of P.

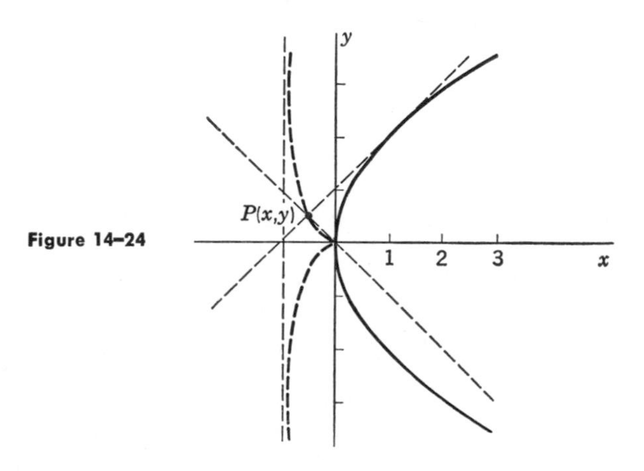

Figure 14–24

Solution. The problem is illustrated in Figure 14–24, with P in an arbitrary position on the locus. An equation of any line with slope m is $y = mx + b$, and this line will be tangent to the parabola if there is a single point of intersection, $m \neq 0$. This means algebraically that the equation $(mx + b)^2 = 4x$ has a single solution, which is true provided its discriminant is 0. From this condition, we find that $b = 1/m$, and an equation of the tangent line with slope m is $y = mx + 1/m$. An equation of the line through the origin and perpendicular to this tangent line is easily seen to be $y = -x/m$. For each real number $m \neq 0$, these two equations have a unique solution (x, y) which is a point of the desired locus, and each point of the locus can be considered to be a solution of these equations for some real number m. Hence we can regard these equations as parametric equations of the locus under consideration, its ordinary equation being obtained upon elimination of m. Thus, $m = -x/y$, and $y = (-x/y)x - y/x$ or $y^2 = -x^3/(x + 1)$ is an equation of the locus.

PROBLEM SET 14.10

1. Determine the solution set of the equations $y = mx$ and $y^2 = 4x - 4$. What is the restriction on m if the loci of these two equations are to intersect?

2. The loci of $x^2 + y^2 = 100$ and $2y = x + 10$ are a circle and a line, respectively. Determine the distance between their points of intersection.

3. Find the distance between the points of intersection with the coordinate axes of the line which has the equation $3x + 4y = 12$.

4. The given equations of a line and a circle are $x + y = c$ and $x^2 + y^2 = 25$, respectively. What is the restriction on c if these loci intersect in (*a*) only one point; (*b*) two points; (*c*) no points?

5. What is an equation of a locus consisting of all positions of a point P, if the sum of the squares of the coordinates of P is equal to 10? Describe this locus.

6. Determine an equation of the line through the origin and the point of intersection of the lines which have the equations $x + 3y = 8$ and $2x - y = 9$. Do not find the solution of these equations.

7. Determine an equation of the line with inclination $\pi/3$ radians, which includes the point of intersection of the lines in Problem 6 as one of its points.

8. A straight line through the point $(5, 0)$ is perpendicular to the locus of $5x + 2y = 0$. Determine the distance from the origin to the point of intersection of these two lines.

9. Find an equation of the line through the point $(5, -7)$ and parallel to the line having the equation $2x - 9y + 12 = 0$.

10. If the locus of $y = mx + 7$ is the bisector of the line segment joining the points $(-3, -7)$ and $(5, 2)$, determine the number m.

11. Determine an equation of the non-horizontal line through the point $(1, 2)$ and 2 units distant from the origin.

12. The center of a circle is the point $(4, -9)$. Find the length of a radius, if the given equation of one of its tangent lines is $7x - 4y - 12 = 0$.

13. The center of a circle is on the locus of $y = 2x$. Find an equation for the circle if it is tangent to the y-axis and the length of a radius is 10 units.

14. The center of a circle is on the locus of the equation $x - y = 1$. Determine an equation of the circle, if the origin is one of its points and the length of a radius is 5 units.

15. The given equation of a circle is $x^2 + y^2 = 16$. Find equations of its tangent lines which are perpendicular to the line having the equation $x - 2y + 8 = 0$.

16. The given equation of a circle is $x^2 + y^2 = 100$. Determine equations of its tangent lines which intersect at the point $(6, 8)$.

17. The given equation of a circle is $x^2 + y^2 = 25$. Find an equation of the line which is tangent to this circle at the point $(3, -4)$.

18. The center of a circle is on the locus of $5x - 3y + 12 = 0$. If $(-2, -4)$ and $(8, 2)$ are points on the circle, determine an equation of the circle.

19. If the given equations of two circles are $x^2 + y^2 = 25$ and $x^2 + y^2 - 3x + 2y - 5 = 0$, find an equation of their radical axis.

20. Find an equation of a circle, if $(3, -3)$ and the points of intersection of the circles in Problem 19 are among its points.

21. The given equation of a parabola is $y^2 = 10x$. Find an equation of the line which is tangent to this parabola and parallel to the line having the equation $3x - 5y - 5 = 0$.
22. If the given equation of a parabola is $y = x^2/8$, determine that one of its points at which the slope of the tangent line is $-3/4$.
23. The respective given equations of a line and parabola are $x + y = 6$ and $y^2 = 10x$. Determine the length of the segment of the line intercepted by the parabola.
24. The given equation of a parabola is $y = 4x^2$. Determine an equation of the line, which is perpendicular to the line having the equation $x + y = 5$, and is normal to the parabola at one of its points.
25. If the equation of a parabola is $y^2 = 5x$, find equations of its tangent lines that intersect at the point $(-5, 0)$.
26. The given equation of an ellipse is $4x^2 + 9y^2 - 36 = 0$. Determine equations of its tangent lines which (*a*) have slopes equal to 2/3; (*b*) are parallel to the line having the equation $x - 3y + 2 = 0$; (*c*) are perpendicular to the line having the equation $4x + 2y + 1 = 0$.
27. If the given equation of a hyperbola is $8x^2 - 3y^2 = 72$, find equations of its tangent lines which are perpendicular to the locus of $5x - 12y + 5 = 0$.
28. The given equation of a hyperbola is $16x^2 - 9y^2 = 144$. Determine equations of its tangent lines which intersect at the point $(2, 0)$.
29. The given equations of two circles are $x^2 + y^2 = 4$ and $x^2 + y^2 - 2x - 4 = 0$. Find an equation of the circle which includes $(6, 8)$ and the points of intersection of the given circles among its points.

Note. The respective given equations of circles A and B, referred to in the following 5 problems, are $x^2 + y^2 - 4x - 6y + 2 = 0$ and $x^2 + y^2 - 2x + 4y + 1 = 0$.

30. Does the center of circle A lie inside circle B? Does the center of circle B lie inside circle A?
31. Find the distance between the centers of circles A and B.
32. Find an equation of the radical axis of circles A and B. Does this line intersect the circles?
33. Determine an equation of the circle which includes among its points the origin and the points of intersection of circles A and B.
34. Determine an equation of the circle if the point $(2, 3)$ and the points of intersection of circles A and B are included among its points.
35. Give an analytical proof that an angle inscribed in a semicircle is a right angle.
36. The given equation of a circle is $x^2 + y^2 = 36$. If the tangent lines to this circle from a point P are perpendicular to each other, determine an equation of the locus comprising all positions of P.
37. If P is the center of a circle, which includes the intersection points of two given circles among its points, determine an equation of the locus comprising all positions of P.
38. The given equation of a parabola is $y^2 = ax$. Prove that the slope of the line, joining the vertex of the parabola to the point of intersection of any two of its tangents, is equal to the sum of the slopes of the tangents.

39. The given equation of a rectangular hyperbola is $x^2 - y^2 = a^2$. If P is the point of intersection of a tangent to the hyperbola with the perpendicular line through the origin, determine an equation of the locus of all positions of P. [The locus is known as the *Lemniscate of Bernoulli:* $(x^2 + y^2)^2 = a^2(x^2 - y^2)$.]

40. Let O be the origin of a Cartesian coordinate system. With the segment OT on the x-axis as a diameter, construct a circle and a segment of its tangent line at T. An arbitrary line segment OR intersects the circle at Q and the tangent line at R. If P is a point on OR such that the lengths of the segments OP and QR are equal, determine an equation of the locus comprising all positions of P. [If the length of OT is $2r$ units, with T on the positive x-axis, an equation is $y^2 = x^3/(2r - x)$: the *Cissoid of Diocles.*]

41. With O the origin of a Cartesian coordinate system, let OQ be a segment of the y-axis $2r$ units in length. Construct a circle, having OQ as a diameter, and include a segment of its tangent line at Q. An arbitrary line through the origin intersects the circle at K and the above tangent line at R. If P is the point of intersection of the lines through K and L, that are respectively parallel to the x and y axes, determine an equation of the locus comprising all positions of P. [The locus is known as the *Witch of Agnesi:* $x^2y = 4r^2(2r - y)$.]

42. The given equation of a hyperbola is $b^2x^2 - a^2y^2 = a^2b^2$, while equations of its asymptotes are $y = bx/a$ and $y = -bx/a$. Prove that the product of the measures of the distances of any point on the hyperbola from its two asymptotes is independent of the point selected.

REVIEW TEST A

1. Let $A(3, 5)$, $B(-1, -2)$, and $C(3, -8)$ be the vertices of a triangle, with D the midpoint of the side BC. Find the point on the segment AD, such that the ratio of its distances from D and A is 2:3.

2. The given equation of a parabola is $y = 4 - x^2$. Determine the acute angle between its tangent lines at the points $(1, 3)$ and $(-1, 3)$.

3. The respective given equations of a parabola and straight line are $y = 4x^2 - 2x + 1$ and $3x - 4y + 6 = 0$. Find an equation of a line, which is parallel to the given line and includes the vertex of the parabola as one of its points.

4. Prove analytically that the bisector of an angle of a triangle divides the opposite side into two segments, the lengths of which bear the same ratio to each other as the lengths of the other two sides of the triangle.

5. Show that $x = 2at/(1 + t^2)$ and $y = a(1 - t^2)/(1 + t^2)$ are parametric equations of a circle with t the parameter. Determine the center and the length of a radius.

6. If the sum of the squares of the measures of distance from a point P to the three sides of a given equilateral triangle is prescribed, show that the locus comprising all positions of P is a circle.

7. A thread of negligible thickness is conceived to be unwound from a spool of circular cross section, having radii a units in length. If the thread is kept taut and in the same plane, as shown in the figure, determine parametric equations of the locus comprising all positions of its end point; use the radian measure θ of the indicated angle for the parameter.

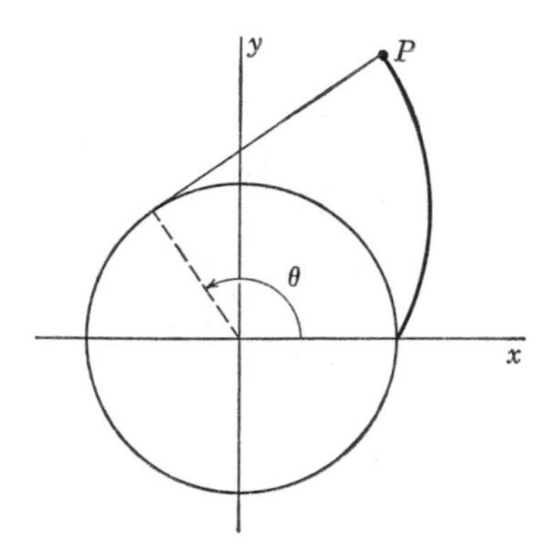

8. The given equations of two lines are $3x - y + 1 = 0$ and $2x + 3y - 6 = 0$. Determine an equation of the line having slope 1/2, which includes the point of intersection of these lines as one of its points.
9. If the given equation of a curve is $y = (3x^2 - 2)^4$, determine an equation of the line which is normal to this curve at the point (1, 1).
10. The given equations of three lines are $2x + y + 5 = 0$, $3x - 4y + 2 = 0$, and $2x + 4y - 3 = 0$. Determine an equation of the line which is perpendicular to the third line, and which includes the point of intersection of the first two as one of its points.
11. If $2x + 3y - 12 = 0$ is the given equation of the tangent line to a circle at the point (3, 2), with (6, −1) an additional point on the circle, determine an equation of the circle.
12. Find the area of the plane region inclosed by three lines, if their given equations are $2x + y - 6 = 0$, $x - y + 3 = 0$, and $x - 2y - 8 = 0$.

REVIEW TEST B

1. A line segment is drawn from the point $A(-3, -4)$ to the point $B(2, 8)$ and extended to the point C, so that the ratio of the lengths of AC to BC is 3:2. Determine the coordinates of point C.
2. The given equation of a parabola is $y = 2x^2$. If (1, 2) and (−2, 8) are the points of tangency of two of its tangents, determine the acute angle between the two tangents.
3. The point P is the relative maximum point on the locus of $y = x^3 - 3x$. Find an equation of the line through P and perpendicular to the line having

the equation $2x - y + 1 = 0$. Determine the distance from P to the latter line.

4. Show that 3 times the difference of the squares of the measures of length of two sides of a triangle is numerically equal to 4 times the difference of the squares of the measures of length of the medians upon these sides.
5. Show that $x = 3t/(1 + t^3)$ and $y = 3t^2/(1 + t^3)$ are parametric equations of the locus of $x^3 + y^3 - 3xy$, where $t(\neq -1)$ is the parameter.
6. If the sum of the measures of distances of a point P from the points $(2, 0)$ and $(-2, 0)$ is equal to 8, determine an equation of the locus comprising all positions of P.
7. With reference to the adjacent figure, OB is an arbitrary radius of the circle, with A the point on the x-axis having the same abscissa as B. If P is the point on OB such that the lengths of segments PB and AB are equal, determine the locus comprising all positions of P.

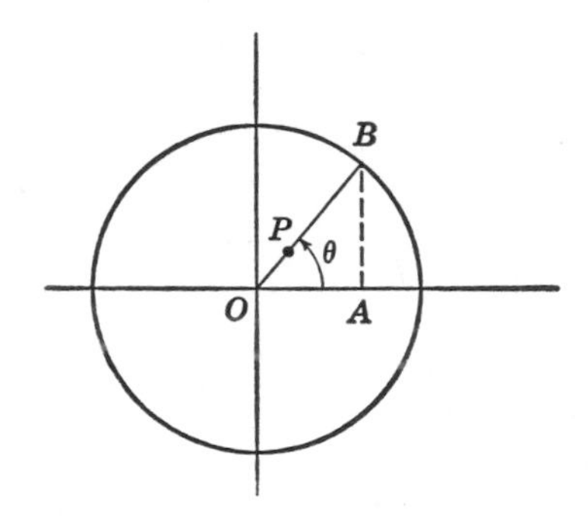

8. Determine equations of the two lines which are 8 units distant from the line having the equation $3x - 4y + 9 = 0$.
9. Determine the angle of intersection of two parabolic arcs, if the given equations of the arcs are $y = 4x^2 + 2$ and $y = -4x^2 + 4$, with $x \in [0, 1]$.
10. If parametric equations of a curve are $x = e^t$ and $y = e^{-t^2}$, where t is the parameter, determine an ordinary equation of the curve.
11. An equation of a given line is $x - 2y - 4 = 0$. Determine an equation of the line having positive slope which makes an angle of $\pi/4$ radians with the given line, and which includes $(3, 1)$ as one of its points.
12. If the given equation of a parabola is $x^2 = 4py$, its axis of symmetry is the y-axis and its focus is the point $(0, p)$. Show that a normal line to the parabola bisects the angle formed by two lines drawn from the point of tangency, one to the focus and one parallel to the axis of the parabola.

REFERENCES

Book

LENNES, N. J. AND A. S. MERRILL, *Plane Analytic Geometry*, New York, Harper, 1929.

American Mathematical Monthly

BALLANTINE, J. P. AND A. R. JERBERT, "Distance from a Line or Plane to a Point," Vol. 59, p. 242 (1952).

15

SOLID ANALYTIC GEOMETRY

Let no one ignorant of geometry enter here.

PLATO

15.1 Coordinates in Space

In this chapter we consider some simple relations from $R^{\#} \times R^{\#}$ to $R^{\#}$, i.e., the elements of the domain of such a relation are ordered pairs of real numbers while the elements of the range are real numbers. A relation of this type is then a set of ordered pairs $((x, y), z)$, where x, y, and z are real numbers, but it is customary to replace the pairs by ordered triples (x, y, z). When this simplified notation is used, it is understood that the first two members of the triple constitute an ordered pair in the domain, while the last member is the corresponding element of the range. If the relation is a function f, our customary notation then implies that $(x, y, z) \in f$ if and only if $f(x, y) = z$. In order to graph such a relation, we must associate each triple of real numbers with a point in 3-dimensional space, just as we associated each pair (x, y) with a point in a plane. The set of all such points, each associated with an element of the relation, is the graph of the relation. If the rule of mapping of a relation is an equation in x, y and z, the relation is a subset of solutions of this equation. The *locus* of such an equation is the graph of all the solutions (x, y, z) of the equation, and these graphs are the *surfaces* of solid geometry; it is clear that the graph of any relation, of the type under consideration, is a portion of one of these surfaces. The equation will be referred to as an *equation of the surface* or an *equation of the graph* of the relation under consideration. We now discuss the procedure for graphing.

The basis of a Cartesian coordinate system in 3-space is a set of three mutually perpendicular planes, intersecting in a common point known as the *origin*. These planes have pair-wise intersections consisting of three straight lines intersecting at the origin; two of these lines we may identify with the former x and y axes, while the third line may be referred to as the z-axis. We have implied that these axes are algebraic scales, having the origin as their common zero point. The planes will be known by the axes that lie in them, i.e., we shall refer to the xy-plane, the xz-plane, or the yz-plane, and the xy-plane may be identified with the xy-plane of plane analytic geometry. These three planes are the *coordinate planes,* and they are seen to divide the space about the origin into eight regions known as *octants.* The *coordinates* of any point are three numbers x_1, y_1, and z_1, with x_1 measuring the directed distance of the point from the yz-plane on the scale of the x-axis, y_1 measuring its directed distance from the xz-plane on the scale of the y-axis, and z_1 measuring its directed distance from the xy-plane on the scale of the z-axis. Our basic principle of graphing is then to associate the ordered triple (x_1, y_1, z_1) with the point having x_1, y_1, and

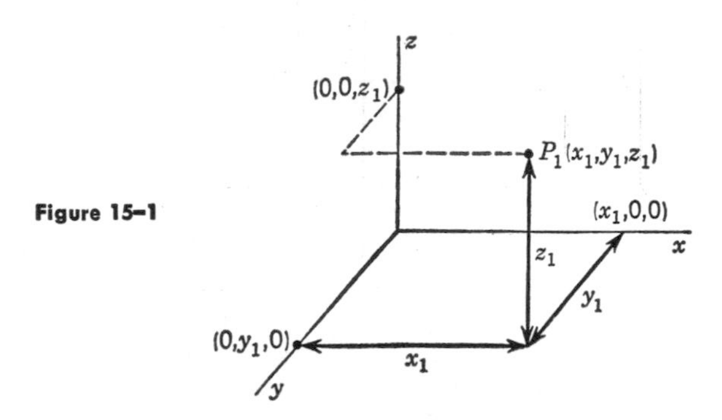

Figure 15–1

z_1 as its coordinates. In harmony with earlier practice we shall frequently identify the point in space with its ordered triple (x_1, y_1, z_1) of coordinates. The eight octants of space, formed by a system of rectangular coordinate planes, may be identified by the coordinates of their points according to the following scheme: first $(x \geq 0, y \geq 0, z \geq 0)$, second $(x \geq 0, y \leq 0, z \geq 0)$, third $(x \leq 0, y \leq 0, z \geq 0)$, fourth $(x \leq 0, y \geq 0, z \geq 0)$, fifth $(x \geq 0, y \geq 0, z \leq 0)$, sixth $(x \geq 0, y \leq 0, z \leq 0)$, seventh $(x \leq 0, y \leq 0, z \leq 0)$, eighth $(x \leq 0, y \geq 0, z \leq 0)$.

We have shown, in Figure 15–1, a coordinate system of the type that has just been described. One of the difficulties of solid geometry is to represent a 3-dimensional figure on a plane diagram, since such a figure must necessarily be distorted. However, it is essential to have such diagrams if a successful study of this type of geometry is to be made. It is sometimes helpful, when trying to visualize a 3-dimensional graph, to consider two adjacent walls and the floor of a room as portions of the coordinate planes, with the observer in the first octant.

If the same scale is used on each coordinate axis, the corresponding distance between any two points $P_1(x_1, y_1, z_1)$ and $P_2(x_2, y_2, z_2)$ can be determined by means of a 3-dimensional extension of the Pythagorean Theorem. We construct a rectangular parallelopiped, with faces parallel to the coordinate planes and containing P_1 and P_2 as diagonally opposite corners, as shown in Figure 15–2. The figure shows that segment P_1P_2 is the hypotenuse of right triangle P_1P_2A, while P_1A is the hypotenuse of right triangle P_1AB. Since the lengths of segments P_1B, AB, and P_2A are $|x_2 - x_1|$, $|y_2 - y_1|$, and $|z_2 - z_1|$ units, respectively, it follows that P_1P_2 is D units in length where

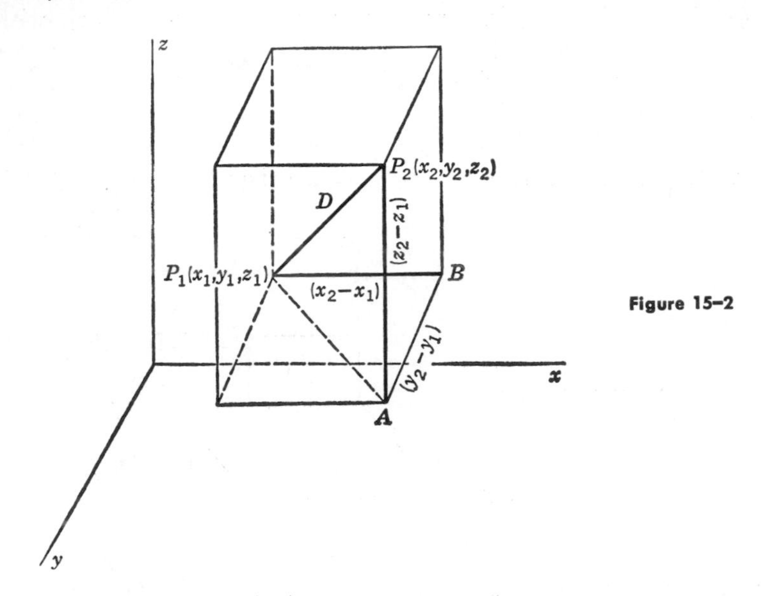

Figure 15–2

$D^2 = (x_2 - x_1)^2 + (y_2 - y_1)^2 + (z_2 - z_1)^2$. From this we obtain the desired distance formula: $D = \sqrt{(x_2 - x_1)^2 + (y_2 - y_1)^2 + (z_2 - z_1)^2}$. It will be understood that, whenever the length of a line segment or the distance between two points is involved, the three coordinate axes must have a common unit of distance on their scales, if the result is to have geometric meaning.

ILLUSTRATION. Determine the distance between the two points $(-2, 1, -5)$ and $(1, 3, -1)$.

Solution. If D units is the desired distance, we must have $D^2 = 3^2 + 2^2 + 4^2 = 9 + 4 + 16 = 29$, and so $D = \sqrt{29}$.

PROBLEM SET 15.1

1. Identify the octant in which each of the following points lies: (*a*) $(1, -3, -5)$; (*b*) $(-2, 4, -5)$; (*c*) $(3, -5, 7)$; (*d*) $(3, 4, -6)$.
2. Use a figure similar to Figure 15–1 to graph each of the following points: (*a*) $(-2, 1, 5)$; (*b*) $(4, -3, 6)$; (*c*) $(5, -3, -2)$; (*d*) $(3, -4, 6)$.
3. Determine the distance between each of the following pairs of points:

(*a*) $(2, -3, 4)$, $(-3, 5, 6)$; (*b*) $(-2, -4, 5)$, $(4, 3, 0)$; (*c*) $(0, 0, -5)$, $(-3, 2, -6)$; (*d*) $(3, 0, 0)$, $(4, 2, 1)$.

4. Show that $(3, 2, -3)$, $(5, 8, 6)$, and $(-3, -5, 3)$ are the vertices of an isosceles right triangle.
5. Show that $(6, 1, 3)$, $(4, 5, 5)$, and $(2, 3, 1)$ are the vertices of an equilateral triangle, and determine the common length of the equal sides.
6. Give the coordinates of three points having (*a*) x-coordinate -3; (*b*) y-coordinate 2.
7. What characterizes all points in the yz-plane?
8. What characterizes all points on the z-axis?
9. Use the distance formula to show that the points $(1, 2, -1)$, $(4, 14, 8)$, and $(2, 6, 2)$ are collinear.
10. Describe the location of a point having (*a*) z-coordinate 5; (*b*) x-coordinate -2.
11. If (a, b, c) is a solution of the equation $x^2 + y^2 + z^2 = 4$, where is (a, b, c) located on a graph?
12. If (a, b, c) is a solution of the equation $(x - 2)^2 + (y + 1)^2 + (z - 3)^2 = 9$, where is (a, b, c) located on a graph?
13. Write an equation of the sphere having radii 4 units in length, and its center at the point $(-2, 5, 3)$.
14. Write an equation of the sphere having radii 10 units in length, and its center at the point $(0, -4, 0)$.

15.2 Direction of a Line in 3-Space

The direction of a line in a plane, with reference to some Cartesian coordinate system, is usually described by stating its slope; or, if the line is sensed, its direction and sense can be given by its inclination. It is clear, however, that it is not so simple to describe the direction of a line in 3-space.

Let us suppose that $P_1(x_1, y_1, z_1)$ is any point on a sensed line L, the direction of which we wish to describe. The *direction angles* of L are the smallest angles, considered positive, through which L must be conceived rotated in turn about P_1, so as to have the same respective direction and sense as each of the coordinate axes. We shall designate the radian measure of these angles between L and the x-axis, y-axis, and z-axis by α, β, and γ, respectively, as indicated in Figure 15–3. It happens that $\cos \alpha$, $\cos \beta$, and $\cos \gamma$ are more useful than α, β, and γ, themselves, and we designate these so-called *direction cosines* by $l = \cos \alpha$, $m = \cos \beta$, and $n = \cos \gamma$. If the line L is not sensed, the set of direction cosines adapted to either sense of the line may be used to describe its direction.

Let $P_2(x_2, y_2, z_2)$ be any other point of L, in the positive direction from P_1. If D is the associated measure of distance between P_1 and P_2, the figure shows that $l = (x_2 - x_1)/D$, $m = (y_2 - y_1)/D$, and $n = (z_2 - z_1)/D$.

But then

$$l^2 + m^2 + n^2 = \frac{(x_2 - x_1)^2 + (y_2 - y_1)^2 + (z_2 - z_1)^2}{D^2} = \frac{D^2}{D^2} = 1,$$

and we have the following result:

> The sum of the squares of the direction cosines of any straight line is equal to 1.

The direction cosines of a line are then not independent, and the third one can be determined—except for sign—from the other two.

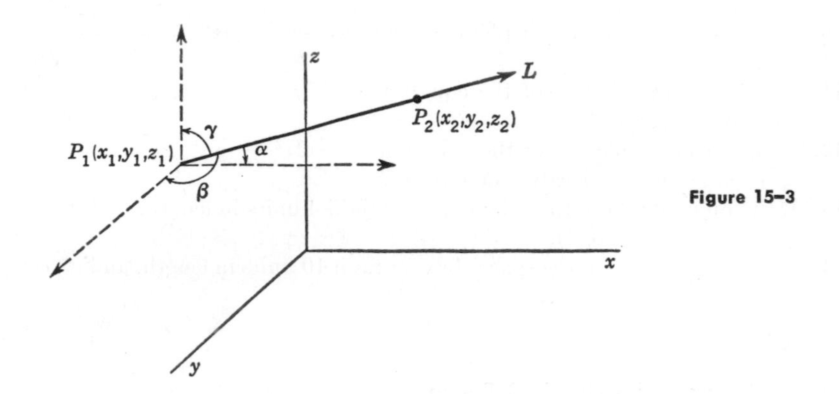

Figure 15–3

Any three numbers that are proportional to the direction cosines of a line are called *direction numbers* of the line. Thus, if a, b, and c are direction numbers of the line L above, we have $a = kl$, $b = km$, and $c = kn$, where k is some real number. From this it follows that $a^2 + b^2 + c^2 = k^2(l^2 + m^2 + n^2) = k^2$ and so $k = \pm 1/\sqrt{a^2 + b^2 + c^2}$. If direction numbers, a, b, c are given for a line, its corresponding direction cosines l, m, n can be found as follows: $l = a/(\pm\sqrt{a^2 + b^2 + c^2})$, $m = b/(\pm\sqrt{a^2 + b^2 + c^2})$, $n = c/(\pm\sqrt{a^2 + b^2 + c^2})$; the sign of the radical is chosen either positive throughout or negative throughout, according to the positive sense of the line. We note in passing that if $P_1(x_1, y_1, z_1)$ and $P_2(x_2, y_2, z_2)$ are any two points of a line, the numbers $x_2 - x_1, y_2 - y_1, z_2 - z_1$ are direction numbers of the line. In listing direction numbers or direction cosines of a line, we shall always assume the order of listing established above.

ILLUSTRATION 1. Find the direction cosines of the line containing the points $P_1(1, 3, 5)$ and $P_2(2, -1, 4)$, if the positive sense is from P_1 to P_2.

Solution. From the above observation, we see that $1, -4, -1$ are direction numbers of the line. If we visualize the positions of P_1 and P_2, we find that the positive sense of segment P_1P_2 is from the first to the second octant; thus $\pi/2 \leq \beta \leq \pi$, and $\cos \beta$, i.e., m, is negative. Since k is then positive, and $\sqrt{1^2 + (-4)^2 + (-1)^2} = 3\sqrt{2}$, we must have $l = \sqrt{2}/6$, $m = -2\sqrt{2}$, and $n = -\sqrt{2}/6$.

ILLUSTRATION 2. Direction numbers of a line are 2, -1, -3. Determine the direction cosines of the line, if its positive sense is chosen so that $0 \leq \gamma \leq \pi/2$.

Solution. In this case $a = 2$, $b = -1$, and $c = -3$, so that $a^2 + b^2 + c^2 = 14$. Since $\cos \gamma$ is positive, k must be chosen negative, i.e., $k = -1/\sqrt{14}$, and $l = -2/\sqrt{14} = -\sqrt{14}/7$, $m = 1/\sqrt{14} = \sqrt{14}/14$, and $n = 3\sqrt{14}/14$.

It should also be observed—as we already have with respect to distance—that if an analysis with angles is to have geometric significance, the unit of distance must be the same on all coordinate axes. We shall assume that this is the case, whenever distances or angles are involved.

PROBLEM SET 15.2

1. Find the direction cosines of the line containing the given two points, and sensed from the first to the second: (*a*) $(2, -1, 4)$, $(-3, 5, 2)$; (*b*) $(-3, 0, 2)$, $(4, -2, -5)$; (*c*) $(0, 0, -4)$, $(-5, 7, 0)$; (*d*) $(-6, 6, 4)$, $(-2, 4, -3)$.
2. Find a set of direction numbers for the line containing the given two points: (*a*) $(-2, 5, 3)$, $(0, 4, -3)$; (*b*) $(3, -3, 2)$, $(3, 0, -6)$; (*c*) $(6, 1, -3)$, $(-1, 5, -4)$; (*d*) $(2, 3, 4)$, $(-3, 0, -2)$.
3. Assume that γ radians is an acute angle, and determine the direction cosines of the line having the given direction numbers: (*a*) 2, -1, 4; (*b*) -2, 3, -5; (*c*) 3, -4, -5; (*d*) -9, 2, -6.
4. Assume that γ radians is an obtuse angle, and determine the direction cosines of the line having the given direction numbers: (*a*) 3, -2, 1; (*b*) -2, -3, 1; (*c*) 3, 2, -1; (*d*) 0, -2, -6.
5. Determine a set of direction angles of a line, that has the following direction numbers: $a = -3$, $b = 3$, $c = 3\sqrt{2}$.
6. Determine the direction cosines of a line, with two of its direction angles specified below and the third assumed to be acute: (*a*) $\alpha = \pi/6$, $\beta = 2\pi/3$; (*b*) $\alpha = \pi/3$, $\gamma = 3\pi/4$; (*c*) $\beta = \pi/6$, $\gamma = \pi/2$; (*d*) $\beta = \pi/4$, $\gamma = \pi/4$.
7. Write down the direction cosines of the coordinate axes.
8. Find $\cos \gamma$, if $\alpha = \pi/3$ and $\beta = 3\pi/4$. What are two possible solutions for γ?
9. Show that the line containing the origin and the point (a, b, c) has direction numbers a, b, c.
10. The direction cosines of a line segment containing $P_1(-2, 6, -5)$ are $-3/7$, $2/7$, $-6/7$. Determine the coordinates of the point P_2, located on the segment 14 units on the positive side of P_1.

15.3 The Angle Between Two Directed Lines

It should have been observed that the direction cosines of a line determine the sense of the line as well as its direction; in a plane, however, the slope of a line determines its direction, but no indication of sense is included. In most problems of plane geometry, we are not concerned with the sense of a line, and so slope is a satisfactory measure of direction. While it is also true that we are seldom concerned with the sense of a line in solid geometry, its direction cosines automatically give the sense along with its direction. Hence it will frequently be just as convenient to refer to sensed as to unsensed lines in 3-space. We first remove the ambiguity that is generally present in the notion of "the" angle between two sensed lines.

DEFINITION. By *the angle between* two sensed lines that intersect, we shall mean the angle, of numerically smallest measure, considered positive, through which either line can be considered rotated about their point of intersection, so as to agree in direction and sense with the other. If the angle between two sensed lines is ϕ radians, it follows from our definition that $0 \leq \phi \leq \pi$.

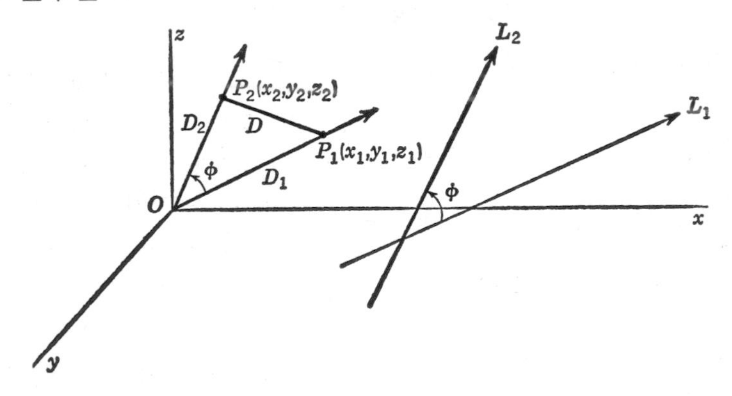

Figure 15–4

DEFINITION. By *the angle between* two sensed lines or line segments that do not intersect, we shall mean the angle between two intersecting lines having the same respective directions and senses as the given lines or segments.

In particular, the angle between two parallel lines or line segments is 0 or π radians, according as they have the same or opposite sense. We now wish to determine the angle between two sensed lines, having known direction cosines.

With reference to Figure 15–4, let L_1 and L_2 be two lines having direction cosines l_1, m_1, n_1 and l_2, m_2, n_2, respectively. The segments OP_1 and OP_2 are line segments having the same direction and sense as L_1 and L_2, respectively, and our above definition now implies that the angle between OP_1 and OP_2 is the same as the angle between L_1 and L_2. Let P_1 be the point (x_1, y_1, z_1) and P_2 be the point (x_2, y_2, z_2), with D_1 and D_2 the respective measures of length of the segments OP_1 and OP_2. If ϕ is the radian measure of the angle between L_1 and L_2, i.e., the angle between OP_1 and OP_2, an application of the Law of Cosines to triangle OP_1P_2 gives us $D^2 = D_1^2 + D_2^2 - 2D_1D_2 \cos \phi$, where D is the measure of length of segment P_1P_2. But $D_1^2 = x_1^2 + y_1^2 + z_1^2$ and $D_2^2 = x_2^2 + y_2^2 + z_2^2$, while $D^2 = (x_1 - x_2)^2 + (y_1 - y_2)^2 + (z_1 - z_2)^2$. If we substitute these expressions in the equation involving D, D_1, and D_2, and simplify, the result may be expressed in the form

$$\cos \phi = \frac{x_1x_2 + y_1y_2 + z_1z_2}{D_1D_2}.$$

Since $x_1/D_1 = l_1, y_1/D_1 = m_1, z_1/D_1 = n_1$, and $x_2/D_2 = l_2, y_2/D_2 = m_2, z_2/D_2 = n_2$, we can also write this result as

$$\cos \phi = l_1l_2 + m_1m_2 + n_1n_2.$$

Thus, the angle between two sensed lines can be determined from a knowledge of their direction cosines.

Our definition of the angle between two sensed lines requires that the angle between two mutually perpendicular lines is $\pi/2$ radians. Since $\cos \pi/2 = 0$, the lines L_1 and L_2 are mutually perpendicular if and only if $l_1l_2 + m_1m_2 + n_1n_2 = 0$. An equivalent condition can be given in terms of direction numbers of a line, since we saw in the preceding section how the direction cosines of a line are related to its direction numbers. If a_1, b_1, c_1 and a_2, b_2, c_2 are respective direction numbers of two lines, an application of this result to the expression for $\cos \phi$ gives

$$\cos \phi = \pm \frac{a_1a_2 + b_1b_2 + c_1c_2}{\sqrt{a_1^2 + b_1^2 + c_1^2}\,\sqrt{a_2^2 + b_2^2 + c_2^2}}.$$

It now appears that a necessary and sufficient condition for two lines to be perpendicular is that $a_1a_2 + b_1b_2 + c_1c_2 = 0$, a condition which uses only direction numbers of the lines.

ILLUSTRATION 1. Determine the angle between two lines having direction numbers $-3, 0, 4$ and $0, -\sqrt{3}, 1$, respectively, choosing the positive sense of each line so that γ radians is an acute angle.

Solution. The direction cosines of the two lines are $-3/5, 0, 4/5$ and $0, -\sqrt{3}/2, 1/2$, and so if the desired angle is ϕ radians, we must have $\cos \phi = 0 + 0 + 2/5 = 0.4$. It follows that $\phi = 0.4115$, approximately.

ILLUSTRATION 2. Show that the line containing the points $(7, -5, 4)$ and $(5, 3, 6)$ is perpendicular to the line containing the points $(3, -1, 2)$ and $(9, -1, 8)$.

Solution. Direction numbers for the first line are $2, -8, -2$ while direction numbers for the second line are $6, 0, 6$. Since $(2)(6) + (-8)(0) + (-2)(6) = 12 - 12 = 0$, an application of the above criterion shows that the lines are mutually perpendicular.

PROBLEM SET 15.3

1. Find the angle between two lines having the indicated direction cosines: (*a*) $-2/3, 2/3, -1/3$; $7/9, 4/9, -4/9$; (*b*) $2/3, -2/15, 11/15$; $-6/11, 2/11, 9/11$.
2. Find the acute angle between two lines having the indicated direction numbers: (*a*) $1, -2, 3$; $6, -6, 7$; (*b*) $3, 4, -2$; $-3, 2, 5$.
3. Show that the coplanar points $(2, 2, 4)$, $(-2, 4, -3)$, $(7, 5, 2)$, and $(3, 7, -5)$ are the vertices of a rectangle.
4. Direction numbers of two lines are $2, -3, 1$ and $1, 4, -1$, respectively. If $3, b, c$ are direction numbers of a line that is perpendicular to both these lines, determine b and c.
5. Direction numbers of two lines are $-3, 1, 2$ and $5, 1, -1$, respectively. If $a, -2, c$ are direction numbers of a line that is perpendicular to both these lines, determine a and c.
6. If the direction angles of a line are equal, determine this common angle.
7. Determine the equal angles of the isosceles triangle, having vertices at $(2, 2, -3)$, $(-3, 6, -2)$, and $(-3, 2, -7)$.
8. Find direction numbers of a line that is perpendicular to the plane of the triangle having its vertices at $(1, 1, 1)$, $(7, 4, 6)$, and $(5, 2, 4)$.
9. Determine the angles of a triangle having its vertices at (a, b, c), (b, c, a), and (c, a, b), where a, b, and c are real numbers that are not all equal, but otherwise arbitrary.
10. The vertices of a triangle are $(0, 0, 8)$, $(0, 6, 0)$, and $(2, 0, 0)$. Determine the angle at the vertex that lies on the y-axis.

15.4 Planes

In this section we consider planes, which in many ways may be considered the simplest of all geometric surfaces. They play a role in solid geometry which is comparable to that played by straight lines in plane geometry, and they have already been used in a description of our coordinate system of 3-space. We shall see presently that a rectangular graph of a function from $R^{\#} \times R^{\#}$ to $R^{\#}$ is a set of points that lie in a plane, provided the rule of mapping is an equation of the first degree; and conversely, the locus of such an equation is a plane.

A plane is of infinite extent, but it is customary to indicate one on a geometrical diagram by showing segments of its lines of intersection with the coordinate planes. These lines of intersection are known as the *traces* of the plane in the coordinate planes. In Figure 15–5, we have indicated a plane, by showing the segments AB, BC, and AC of its traces in the yz, xy, and xz planes, respectively. The line segment from the origin, which terminates in and is perpendicular to a plane, is the *normal* of the plane, the positive sense of the normal being in this direction. If a plane includes the origin as one of its points, and the direction cosines of its normal are l, m, and n, we shall agree to consider as the positive sense of the normal that which makes positive the first of l, m, n that is not zero.

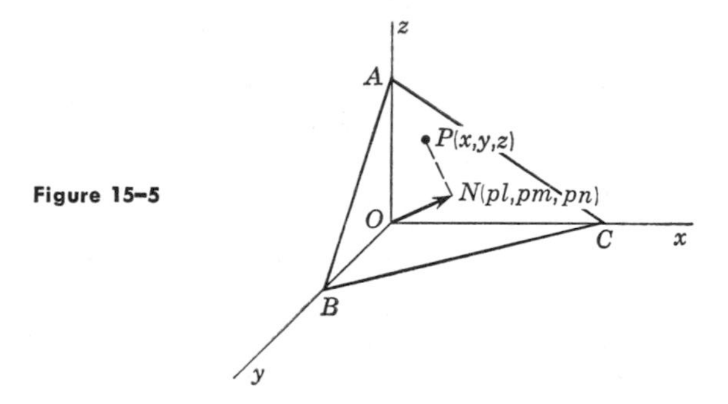

Figure 15–5

Let us now suppose that the length of the normal of the plane in Figure 15–5 is p units, $p \geq 0$, while the direction cosines of this normal are l, m, n. If N is the foot of the normal of the plane, we can characterize the plane as the locus of all points P such that NP is perpendicular to the normal. The definitions of the circular functions now imply that N is the point (pl, pm, pn), and if $P(x, y, z)$ is any point on the locus, a set of direction numbers for the segment NP is $x - pl$, $y - pm$, $z - pn$. The condition for perpendicularity then requires that $l(x - pl) + m(y - pm) + n(z - pn) = 0$. Since this equation must be satisfied by the coordinates of an arbitrary point in the plane, it constitutes an equation of the plane. If we now use the fact that $l^2 + m^2 + n^2 = 1$, this equation can be simplified to the form $lx + my + nz = p$, the so-called *normal* equation of the plane. We state this result in the following form:

> The *normal* equation of a plane is $lx + my + nz = p$, where l, m, n are the direction cosines, and p units is the length, of its normal.

The form of the normal equation shows that any plane has an equation which is of the first degree in x, y, and z, with respect to a Cartesian coordinate system. We now consider an arbitrary equation of the first degree in x, y, and z, such as $Ax + By + Cz = D$. Let us divide both members of this equation by $\pm\sqrt{A^2 + B^2 + C^2}$, choosing that sign which makes the resulting right member positive; or, if $D = 0$, we choose that sign of the radical which makes positive the first of the coefficients of x, y, and z that is not 0. This equation may now be seen to be the normal equation of a plane. For we note that the right member is positive or 0; and the sum of the squares of the coefficients of x, y, and z is equal to 1, so that these coefficients are the direction cosines of some line segment which we may identify with the normal to the plane. It is also important to note that the coefficients A, B, C of the original equation are direction numbers of this normal. We have then shown that the locus of any first-degree equation is a plane, and it then follows immediately that the graph of a function defined on $R^{\#} \times R^{\#}$ to $R^{\#}$ by a first-degree equation, as a subset of the locus of this equation, consists of points which lie on a plane.

ILLUSTRATION 1. If $2x - y + 2z + 9 = 0$ is the given equation of a plane, determine its normal equation. Also find the length and direction cosines of its normal, as well as equations of its traces in the coordinate planes.

Solution. In order to reduce the equation to normal form, we add -9 to both members, divide both members by -3, and obtain $(-2/3)x + (1/3)y + (-2/3)z = 3$. The direction cosines of the normal are now seen to be $-2/3, 1/3, -2/3$, while the length of the normal is 3 units. Equations of the traces in the coordinate planes may be obtained from the original equation, by separately replacing x, y, and z by 0: $y - 2z - 9 = 0$ (yz-plane); $2x + 2z + 9 = 0$ (xz-plane); $2x - y + 9 = 0$ (xy-plane). A sketch of the plane is shown in Figure 15–6.

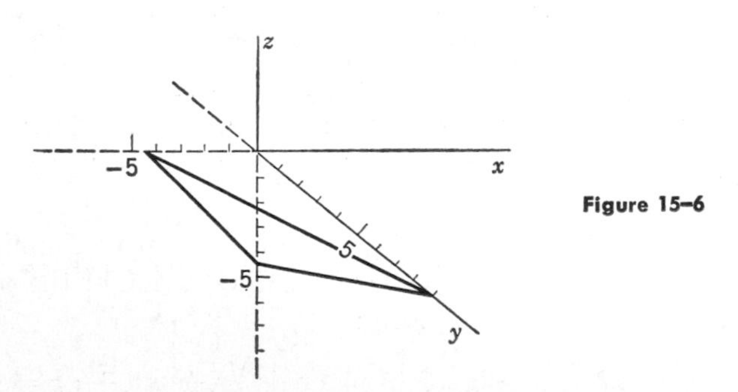

Figure 15–6

If two planes intersect, two supplementary dihedral angles are formed, and it can be shown that one of these angles is equal in magnitude to the angle between the normals to the planes. We remove the ambiguity with the following definition.

DEFINITION. The *angle between two intersecting planes* is an acute (or possibly right) angle, equal to either the angle between their normals or to the supplement of this angle.

Inasmuch as we know how to determine the angle between two lines, if their direction cosines are known, and the direction cosines of the normal to a plane are known from its normal equation, the problem of determining the angle between two planes is solved. We noted earlier that if the given equation of a plane is $Ax + By + Cz + D = 0$, the coefficients A, B, C are direction numbers of the normal to the plane. Hence if $A_1x + B_1y + C_1z + D_1 = 0$ and $A_2x + B_2y + C_2z + D_2 = 0$ are the given equations of two planes, it is clear that a necessary and sufficient condition for them to be mutually perpendicular, is that $A_1A_2 + B_1B_2 + C_1C_2 = 0$.

ILLUSTRATION 2. If $8x - y + z = 2$ and $3x + y - z = 4$ are equations of two planes, determine the angle between the planes.

Solution. The normal equations of these planes are $(8/\sqrt{66})x + (-1/\sqrt{66})y + (1/\sqrt{66})z = 2/\sqrt{66}$ and $(3/\sqrt{11})x + (1/\sqrt{11})y + (-1/\sqrt{11})z = 4/\sqrt{11}$. If the angle between the planes is ϕ radians, we must have $\cos \phi = (8/\sqrt{66})(3/\sqrt{11}) + (-1/\sqrt{66})(1/\sqrt{11}) + (1/\sqrt{66})(-1/\sqrt{11}) = 4\sqrt{6}/11 - \sqrt{6}/33 = \sqrt{6}/3 = 0.8165$, approximately. It follows that an approximation for ϕ is 0.6152, and so the desired angle is approximately 0.6152 radians.

PROBLEM SET 15.4

1. Write an equation of a plane, if its normal satisfies the indicated conditions: (*a*) $l = -1/2$, $m = 1/2$, $n = -1/\sqrt{2}$; $p = 2$; (*b*) $l = 1/3$, $m = 2/3$, $n = -2/3$; $p = 5$.
2. The normal of a plane has $-2, 3, -2$ as a set of direction numbers. If the normal is sensed so that γ radians is an acute angle, and its length is 3 units, write an equation of the plane.
3. Put each of the following equations in the normal form of an equation of a plane: (*a*) $3x - 2y + z - 5 = 0$; (*b*) $x + 3y - 5z + 4 = 0$; (*c*) $2x + 4z + 5 = 0$; (*d*) $4y - 5z - 6 = 0$.
4. Put each of the following equations in the normal form of an equation of a plane: (*a*) $2x + 4y - z = 0$; (*b*) $4y - 5z = 0$.
5. Determine the angle between the planes having the given equations: (*a*) $3x - 4y + z = 5$, $x + y - 2z = 2$; (*b*) $x - 2y + 3z + 6 = 0$, $2x + y - z + 9 = 0$; (*c*) $3x + 4y - 9 = 0$, $5x - 12y + 8 = 0$.
6. Write an equation of a plane, if the foot of the normal of the plane is the point (*a*) $(2, -3, 6)$; (*b*) $(3, 4, -1)$; (*c*) $(1, -1, -2)$; (*d*) $(-2, -3, 1)$.
7. Find an equation of the plane, satisfying the following conditions: (*a*) $\alpha = 3\pi/4$, $\beta = 2\pi/3$, $\gamma = \pi/3$, $p = 3$; (*b*) $\alpha = 2\pi/3$, $\beta = \pi/6$, $\gamma = \pi/2$, $p = 10$.
8. The given equation of a plane is $3x - 2y + 5z + 2 = 0$. (*a*) Put the equation in normal form. (*b*) What are the direction cosines of its normal?

(*c*) What is the distance of the plane from the origin? (*d*) What are equations of the traces of the plane in the coordinate planes? (*e*) Make a sketch of the plane, from the traces discussed in (*d*).

9. Show that the locus, consisting of all points that are equidistant from $(-2, 3, 5)$ and $(3, -8, 1)$ is a plane, and that the plane is perpendicular to the line segment joining the given points.

10. Determine an equation of the plane containing the point $(-2, 3, 5)$, and perpendicular to the line segment joining the points $(2, -5, 3)$ and $(0, -3, 2)$.

11. Let $D = \{(x, y) \mid (x, y) \in R^\# \times R^\#, |x| \leq 2, |y| \leq 2\}$. If f is the function defined on D by $f(x, y) = 3x - 2y + 1$, for each (x, y) in D, what numbers are represented by $f(1, -1)$ and $f(0, -2)$? Describe the graph of f.

12. If (x, y) is an element in the domain of a function F, defined on $R^\# \times R^\#$ by the equation $2x - 5y + 2z - 6 = 0$, what number is represented by (*a*) $F(0, 0)$; (*b*) $F(1, 1)$; (*c*) $F(-2, 3)$?

15.5 Further Remarks on Planes

The problem of determining the distance from a point to a plane is very similar to the problem of plane geometry, discussed in Section 14.4, of determining the distance from a point to a line. The methods of solution are similar and, as in the earlier problem, there are essentially two cases to be considered: (*a*) the point and plane are on the same side of the origin; (*b*) the point and plane are on opposite sides of the origin. We shall consider case (*a*) first.

Let us then suppose that the point $P(x_1, y_1, z_1)$ is on the same side of the origin as the plane that has $lx + my + nz = p$ as its normal equation. We now consider another plane containing the point P, and parallel to the given plane. Since the normals of these two planes have the same direction and sense, in this case, the normal equation of the second plane can be written in the form $lx + my + nz = p'$. If the distance between the planes is D units, it is clear that this is also the distance from P to the given plane, and $D = |p' - p|$. Since $P(x_1, y_1, z_1)$ is a point in the second plane, we must have $lx_1 + my_1 + nz_1 = p'$, and so $D = |lx_1 + my_1 + nz_1 - p|$.

In case (*b*), the point P lies on the opposite side of the origin from the given plane, and so if we consider a parallel plane containing P, as in case (*a*), the normals to the two planes will be parallel but will have opposite senses. The direction cosines of the normal of the second plane are then the negatives of the corresponding direction cosines for the given plane, and so the normal equation of the plane containing P has the form $-lx - my - nz = p'$. Since $P(x_1, y_1, z_1)$ is a point in this plane, we must have $p' = -lx_1 - my_1 - nz_1$. If the distance between the planes is D units, we see in this case that $D = p' + p = -lx_1 - my_1 - nz_1 + p = |lx_1 + my_1 + nz_1 - p|$, and so the result is the same for both cases. We now have the following procedure for determining the distance from a point to a plane, provided an equation of the plane is known:

> Determine the normal equation of the plane, and add $-p$ to both members, so that the resulting equation has the form $lx + my + nz - p = 0$. The absolute value of the left member of this equation, if x, y, and z are replaced by the corresponding coordinates of a given point, is the associated measure of distance from the point to the plane.

ILLUSTRATION 1. Find the distance from the point $(-2, 3, 1)$ to the plane having $x + 3y - 2z + 5 = 0$ for an equation.

Solution. The appropriately altered normal equation of the plane is $(-1/\sqrt{14})x + (-3/\sqrt{14})y + (2/\sqrt{14})z - 5/\sqrt{14} = 0$. If we now replace x by -2, y by 3, and z by 1 in the left member of this equation, the result is $2/\sqrt{14} - 9/\sqrt{14} + 2/\sqrt{14} - 5/\sqrt{14} = -10/\sqrt{14}$, and so the desired distance is $10/\sqrt{14}$ or $5\sqrt{14}/7$ units.

The general equation of the first degree, $Ax + By + Cz + D = 0$, has only three arbitrary coefficients, since we may divide both members by any non-zero coefficient, thereby replacing it by 1. It then appears that a plane can be made to satisfy, in general, three independent conditions.

ILLUSTRATION 2. Find an equation of the plane that contains the three points $(2, -4, -1)$, $(3, -8, -2)$, and $(4, 4, 2)$.

Solution. Let us assume that $Ax + By + Cz + D = 0$ is the desired equation, with its coefficients to be determined by the conditions. Since the points are in the plane, the following equations are satisfied:

$$\begin{aligned} 2A - 4B - C &= -D \\ 3A - 8B - 2C &= -D \\ 4A + 4B + 2C &= -D. \end{aligned}$$

If we solve these equations for A, B, and C, by putting the augmented coefficient matrix in reduced echelon form, the final matrix obtained is

$$\begin{pmatrix} 1 & 0 & 0 & -D \\ 0 & -4 & 0 & 5D \\ 0 & 0 & 1 & 4D \end{pmatrix}.$$

The general solution is then $A = -D$, $B = -5D/4$, and $C = 4D$; and if we let D be any non-zero number, we obtain a particular solution. For example, if $D = -4$, we obtain $A = 4$, $B = 5$, and $C = -16$, and the resulting equation of the plane is $4x + 5y - 16z = 4$.

ILLUSTRATION 3. The given equation of a plane is $3x + y - 5z = 12$. Find an equation of the plane that contains the points $(2, 1, 0)$ and $(5, 0, -7)$, and is perpendicular to the given plane.

Solution. Let us assume that the desired equation is $Ax + By + Cz + D = 0$, with the coefficients to be determined. Since the two points lie in the plane, the following equations are satisfied:

$$\begin{aligned} 2A + B \qquad &= -D \\ 5A \qquad - 7C &= -D. \end{aligned}$$

The condition of perpendicularity, applied to direction numbers of the normals of the planes, gives us the third equation, $3A + B - 5C = 0$.

The reduced echelon form of the augmented coefficient matrix of these equations is easily found to be

$$\begin{pmatrix} 3 & 0 & 0 & -2D \\ 0 & 3 & 0 & D \\ 0 & 0 & 3 & -D \end{pmatrix},$$

and so $A = -2D/3$, $B = D/3$, and $C = -D/3$. If we let $D = -3$, we obtain a particular solution, $A = 2, B = -1, C = 1, D = -3$, and the resulting equation is seen to be $2x - y + z - 3 = 0$.

If $(a, 0, 0)$, $(0, b, 0)$, and $(0, 0, c)$ are the three points in which a plane intercepts the coordinate axes, an application of Illustration 2 gives the so-called *intercept* equation of the plane: $x/a + y/b + z/c = 1$.

PROBLEM SET 15.5

1. Find an equation of the plane that contains the points $(2, 2, -2)$, $(4, 6, 4)$, and $(8, -1, 2)$,
2. Find an equation of the plane that contains the points $(0, 0, 0)$, $(1, 4, 2)$, and $(-3, 2, 4)$.
3. Find an equation of the plane that contains the points $(1, -2, 3)$ and $(2, 1, -4)$, and is perpendicular to the plane having $x - 3y + 2z - 5 = 0$ as an equation.
4. An equation of a given plane is $2x + y + 3z + 7 = 0$. Find an equation of the plane that contains the points $(-1, 2, 4)$ and $(5, -1, 3)$, and is perpendicular to the given plane.
5. If an equation of a given plane is $3x - 2y + z - 5 = 0$, determine an equation of a parallel plane containing the point $(1, -3, 4)$.
6. Establish the *intercept* equation of a plane, mentioned above.
7. Write down an equation of a plane, if its x, y, and z intercepts are 3, -5, and 1, respectively.
8. Prove that the following four points are coplanar: $(0, 0, -6)$, $(1, 1, -5)$, $(2, -2, 0)$, $(-1, -3, -5)$.
9. Find an equation of the plane containing the point $(2, -6, 1)$, and having x-intercept 2 and y-intercept -3.

10. Equations of two given parallel planes are $3x - y + 2z = 1$ and $3x - y + 2z = 6$. Determine an equation of a third parallel plane that lies midway between the two given planes.

11. An equation of a given plane is $x - y + 2z = 5$. Find equations of the planes that contain the points $(1, 1, 1)$ and $(-1, 3, -1)$, and make an angle of $\pi/3$ radians with the given plane.

12. The given equations of two planes are $2x + y - z = 4$ and $x - y + 2z = 0$. Determine an equation of the plane that contains the point $(0, -1, 1)$, and the line of intersection of the given planes.

15.6 Straight Lines

In spite of its geometric simplicity, a straight line in 3-space is somewhat difficult to describe analytically, since it is not the locus of a single equation. For if we consider a straight line to be the graph of a relation from $R^\# \times R^\#$ to $R^\#$, it is clear that the domain of this relation is very restricted; in the usual symbolism, this domain is the complete solution set of a linear equation in x and y, the graph of this solution set being itself a straight line or a single point in the xy-plane.

Let L be a straight line in 3-space, containing the point $Q(x_1, y_1, z_1)$ and having a, b, c as direction numbers. We can regard L as the locus comprising all points $P(x, y, z)$, such that the line segment QP has a, b, c as direction numbers. Since QP has direction numbers $x - x_1, y - y_1, z - z_1$, and since corresponding members of two sets of direction numbers bear the same ratio to each other, it follows that $x - x_1 = ka$, $y - y_1 = kb$, and $z - z_1 = kc$, where k is a real number dependent on the position of P. If we write these equations in the form $x = x_1 + ka$, $y = y_1 + kb$, $z = z_1 + kc$, we can consider them to be *parametric equations* of L, with k the parameter. For it is clear that each number k determines a point (x, y, z) on L, and we have seen that there is a real number k determined by each point (x, y, z) on L. If we use the symbolism $R^\# \times R^\# \times R^\#$ for the set of all triples of real numbers, it is clear that these parametric equations define a relation F on $R^\#$ to $R^\# \times R^\# \times R^\#$; the given straight line is then the graph of the range of this relation.

If each of the direction numbers a, b, c of L is non-zero, we can solve each of the parametric equations for k and equate the results, obtaining what are known as *symmetric equations* of the line:

$$\frac{x - x_1}{a} = \frac{y - y_1}{b} = \frac{z - z_1}{c}.$$

The line L is the graph of the complete solution set of these equations, i.e., L is the locus of these equations, with reference to the established coordinate system. If we regard these equations as the rule of mapping of a function f from $R^{\#} \times R^{\#}$ to $R^{\#}$, with $f(x, y) = z$, the domain of f is the solution set of $(x - x_1)/a = (y - y_1)/b$. If $a = 0$, the symmetric form of the equations of L is not valid, and the following equations are required: $x - x_1 = 0$, $(y - y_1)/b = (z - z_1)/c$; it is easy to take care of other special cases, in a similar manner.

If a straight line contains two given points (x_1, y_1, z_1) and (x_2, y_2, z_2), direction numbers of the line are $x_2 - x_1$, $y_2 - y_1$, $z_2 - z_1$. In case each of these numbers is non-zero, the preceding result gives us the following equations of the line:

$$\frac{x - x_1}{x_2 - x_1} = \frac{y - y_1}{y_2 - y_1} = \frac{z - z_1}{z_2 - z_1}.$$

If one or more of the direction numbers is zero, equations of the line can be found as in the general procedure mentioned previously. We may refer to these equations as *two-point* equations of the line.

It is also possible to consider a straight line as the unique intersection of any two planes that contain it, and thus any *simultaneous* equations of the planes constitute a pair of equations of the line. If equations of the planes are $E = 0$ and $F = 0$, the locus of any equation of the form $k_1E + k_2F = 0$, with k_1 and k_2 real numbers not both 0, is also a plane containing the same straight line. Hence, if we use this method of describing a line, either or both the original equations can be replaced by equations of this type.

The *projecting planes* of a line, that is not parallel to one of the coordinate axes, are three planes that contain the line and are respectively perpendicular to the coordinate planes. One of the direction numbers of the normal of such a plane is 0, and so the coefficient of either x, y, or z is 0 in an equation of a projecting plane. Equations of the three projecting planes of a line can be found by a proper choice of k_1 and k_2 in the equation $k_1E + k_2F = 0$, so that any particular coefficient is 0. Equations of these planes are useful for sketching purposes, and in determining symmetric equations of a line.

ILLUSTRATION 1. Determine symmetric equations of the straight line containing the points $(2, -1, 3)$ and $(-3, 5, -6)$. What are the direction cosines of the line, if the positive sense is from the first of the points to the second?

Solution. Direction numbers of the line are $5, -6, 9$ and so its equations may be given in symmetric form as $\dfrac{x - 2}{5} = \dfrac{y + 1}{-6} = \dfrac{z - 3}{9}$. The first point is in the second octant, while the second is in the eighth, so the specified sense of the line implies that $\cos \gamma < 0$. The desired direction cosines of the line are then $-5/\sqrt{142}$, $6/\sqrt{142}$, $-9/\sqrt{142}$.

ILLUSTRATION 2. The given equations of two intersecting planes are

$x - y - 2z - 1 = 0$, and $x + 3y - z - 5 = 0$. Write, in symmetric form, equations of the line of intersection, find equations of the projecting planes, and use two of these equations to sketch the line.

Solution. In the notation used above, $E = x - y - 2z - 1$ and $F = x + 3y - z - 5$. We now use multipliers k_1 and k_2 in the equation $k_1E + k_2F = 0$, so that the coefficients of x, y, and z are each 0 in turn, and obtain the following equations of the projecting planes: $4y + z - 4 = 0$; $4x - 7z - 8 = 0$; $x + 7y - 9 = 0$.

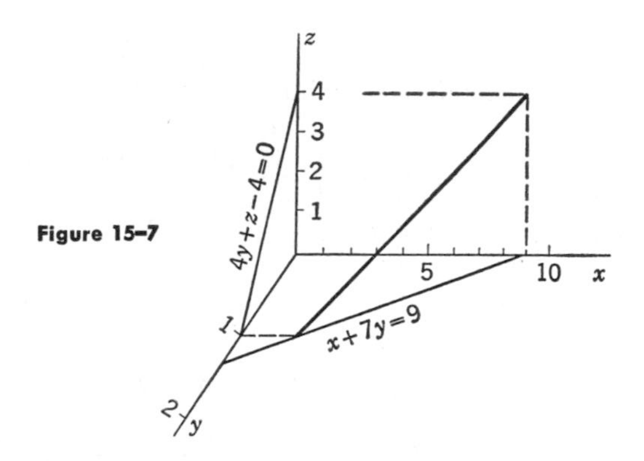

Figure 15–7

It is now easy to find two points on the line, considered as points of the intersection of the projecting planes; for example, we obtain the points (2, 1, 0) and (9, 0, 4) by respectively replacing z and y by 0 in the equations of these planes. Direction numbers of the line are now seen to be 7, -1, 4, and so the following symmetric equations of the line may be given: $\dfrac{x-2}{7} = \dfrac{y-1}{-1} = \dfrac{z}{4}$. For the sketch, shown in Figure 15–7, we have used the projecting planes that are perpendicular to the yz and xy planes.

PROBLEM SET 15.6

1. Write, in symmetric form, equations of the line that (*a*) has direction numbers 2, -4, 3 and contains the point $(1, 2, -3)$; (*b*) is perpendicular to the plane having the equation $3x + 4y + 12z - 3 = 0$, and contains the point $(2, 5, -8)$; (*c*) contains the point $(3, -2, 0)$, and is parallel to the line containing the points $(2, -4, 6)$ and $(1, 4, -3)$.
2. Find, in symmetric form, equations of the line, defined as the intersection of the planes having the equations $x - 2y + z - 1 = 0$ and $2x + 3y - z - 5 = 0$.
3. Make a sketch of a line, if equations of two of its projecting planes are $2x + z = 6$ and $3x + 6y = 10$.

4. Write parametric equations of a line that has direction numbers 2, 4, −5 and contains the point (2, −4, 3).
5. If $x - 2y - z + 10 = 0$ and $7x - 6y + 3z + 6 = 0$ are given as equations of two planes, write in symmetric form, equations of their line of intersection.
6. Use two of the projecting planes of the line in Problem 5 to make a sketch of the line.
7. Find, in symmetric form, equations of the line containing the points (1, 3, 5), (−5, 6, −1), and (5, 1, 9).
8. The set of all real simultaneous solutions of the equations $3x + 3y - 2z + 4 = 0$ and $5x + 6y - 3z - 3 = 0$ is a function, the graph of which is a straight line. Determine an equation of the plane that is perpendicular to this line, and that contains the point (−1, 2, 6).
9. Write symmetric equations of the line that contains the point (1, 3, −3), if two of its direction angles are specified by $\alpha = \pi/3$ and $\beta = \pi/6$.
10. A function f is defined as the set of all real simultaneous solutions of the equations $2x - y = 1$ and $y + 4z = 35$, while F is defined in a similar manner by the equations $x - y = 0$ and $6x - z + 3 = 0$. Show that the graph of f is a line that is perpendicular to the graph of F.

15.7 Cylinders, Spheres, and Surfaces of Revolution

We now discuss some surfaces of solid geometry, that have easily recognizable equations.

DEFINITION. A *cylinder* is a surface such that all planes parallel to some given plane intersect the surface in congruent plane figures. The bounding curve of one of these plane figures is a *directrix curve* of the cylinder. Each point of a directrix curve is on a line, which lies entirely on the cylinder, and is known as an *element* of the cylinder.

The type of a cylinder depends on the directrix curve, and whether or not the elements of the cylinder are perpendicular to a directrix. Thus, we may speak of a *right circular*, *skew elliptical*, or *right parabolic* cylinder, for example, where these names are self-explanatory. We shall consider only right cylinders in this section.

In Figure 15–8, we have shown a portion of a right parabolic cylinder, its directrix curve in the xy-plane being the locus of the equation $y^2 = x$. If $P(x, y, z)$ is an arbitrary point of the cylinder, there is a corresponding point $P_1(x, y, 0)$ on the directrix curve in the xy-plane, having coordinates satisfying the equation $y^2 = x$. However, since this equation does not involve z, and the x and y coordinates of P and P_1 are identical, it follows that the coordinates of P also satisfy the same equation. Inasmuch as P is an arbitrary point of the cylinder, it appears that $y^2 = x$ is an equation of the cylinder. This reasoning can be extended to obtain the following result:

> If the elements of a cylinder are perpendicular to one of the coordinate planes, an equation of the directrix curve in that plane may be taken for an equation of the cylinder.

ILLUSTRATION 1. Discuss the locus of the equation $x^2 + 4z^2 = 8$.

Solution. Since the equation does not involve y, the locus is a right cylinder with elements parallel to the y-axis. An equation of the directrix curve in the xz-plane is $x^2 + 4z^2 = 8$, and so this curve is an ellipse. The surface, a portion of which is shown in Figure 15–9, may then properly be called a right elliptic cylinder.

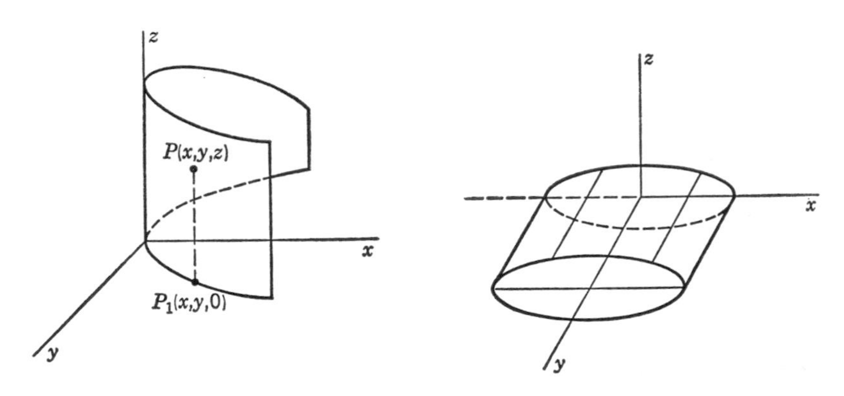

Figure 15–8 Figure 15–9

We have previously made some reference to a *sphere* in Problems 11 through 14 of Section 15.1. A *sphere* may be defined as the locus comprising all points of 3-space that are equidistant from some given point. If an equation in x, y, and z has equal coefficients for x^2, y^2, and z^2, and no terms in xy, yz, or xz, the locus of this equation is a sphere, unless the real solution set of the equation is empty. This follows from the fact that such an equation can be put in a form which shows that an arbitrary point (x, y, z) of the locus is an invariant distance from some particular point.

ILLUSTRATION 2. Determine the center and length of the radii of the sphere, defined as the locus of the equation $x^2 + y^2 + z^2 + 4x - 8y + 2z - 4 = 0$.

Solution. If we "complete the squares" in x, y, and z, the equation can be written in the form $(x + 2)^2 + (y - 4)^2 + (z + 1)^2 = 25$. We can see from this equation that the center is at $(-2, 4, -1)$, and the radii are 5 units in length.

DEFINITION. A surface, that may be conceived to have been generated by revolving a plane curve about a line in its plane, is known as a *surface of revolution.* The line, about which the revolution is conceived to have taken place, is the *axis of revolution.*

In our discussion of surfaces of revolution, we shall confine our remarks to surfaces for which the axis of revolution is one of the coordinate axes. In Figure 15–10, we have shown a portion of a *paraboloid of revolution,* which can be considered the result of revolving the locus of $z = x^2$

about the z-axis. An arbitrary point $P(x, y, z)$ on the surface is on the circle "generated" by some point $Q(x_1, 0, z)$ of the locus of $z = x^2$ in the xz-plane. The length of a radius of this circle is x_1 units, and so $x^2 + y^2 = x_1^2 = z$, the last equality following from the fact that Q is on the parabolic

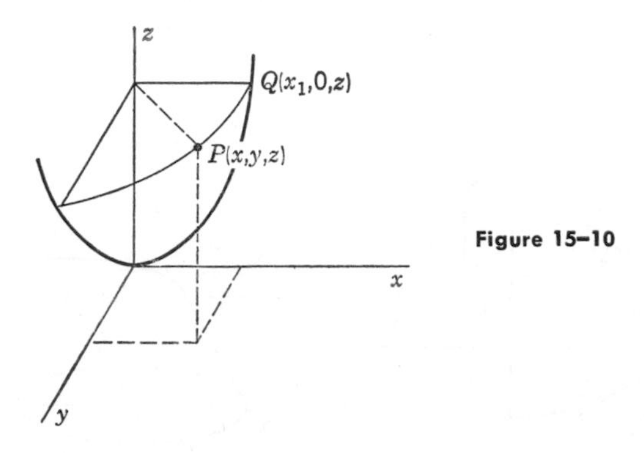

Figure 15–10

locus. The equation $x^2 + y^2 = z$ is then an equation of the surface of revolution, and we note that this equation of the surface of revolution may be obtained from the given equation of the "revolved" locus by a replacement of x by $\sqrt{x^2 + y^2}$. We can generalize this to obtain the following result:

> If a curve in the xz-plane is considered revolved about the z-axis, an equation of the resulting surface of revolution can be obtained by replacing x by $\sqrt{x^2 + y^2}$ in the given equation of the curve. A similar remark applies to the other surfaces of revolution of the type under discussion.

An equation of a surface of revolution can always be recognized from the observation that at least one of x, y, or z occurs only as a component of an expression $x^2 + y^2$, $y^2 + z^2$, or $x^2 + z^2$.

ILLUSTRATION 3. If the locus of $y^2 = x^3$ in the xy-plane is considered revolved about the x-axis, find an equation of the resulting surface of revolution.

Solution. In accordance with the above procedure, we replace y by $\sqrt{y^2 + z^2}$ and obtain $y^2 + z^2 = x^3$ as a desired equation. Since the directrix curve is a semi-cubical parabola, this surface may be referred to as a *semi-cubical paraboloid of revolution.*

PROBLEM SET 15.7

1. Sketch a portion of the locus of each of the following equations in 3-space: (*a*) $y^2 = 3x$; (*b*) $xy = 5$; (*c*) $y^2 + z^2 = 10$; (*d*) $z = \sin x$.
2. Sketch a portion of the locus of each of the following equations in 3-space: (*a*) $2x + 3y - 6 = 0$; (*b*) $z = x^3$; (*c*) $y = e^x$; (*d*) $z = \ln x$.
3. Determine the center and length of the radii of the sphere, having the following equation: (*a*) $x^2 + y^2 + z^2 - 6x + 2y - z + 4 = 0$; (*b*) $x^2 + y^2 + z^2 + x + 3y - 2z - 2 = 0$.
4. Find an equation of the surface of revolution considered generated by revolving the plane curve, having the given equation, about the indicated axis: (*a*) $x^2 = 2z$, z-axis; (*b*) $y = x^3$, x-axis; (*c*) $x^2 + y^2 = 5$, y-axis.
5. Find an equation of the surface of revolution considered generated by revolving the plane curve, having the given equation, about the indicated axis: (*a*) $y = \cos z$, z-axis; (*b*) $z = e^y$, z-axis; (*c*) $xy = 1$, y-axis.
6. The locus of $y = 3x$ in the xy-plane is considered revolved about the x-axis. Find an equation of the resulting *right circular cone*.
7. Identify the locus of each of the following equations in 3-space, and sketch a portion of each: (*a*) $x^2 = 2z$; (*b*) $2x^2 + 2z^2 = y$; (*c*) $x^2 + y^2 + z^2 + 4x - 2z = 0$; (*d*) $x^2 = 4(y^2 + z^2)$; (*e*) $x = \ln z$; (*f*) $x^2 + y^2 + z^2 = 0$.
8. Identify the locus of each of the following equations in 3-space, and sketch a portion of each: (*a*) $x = \cos z$; (*b*) $z = e^{\sqrt{x^2+y^2}}$; (*c*) $x^2 + y^2 = 2z$; (*d*) $y = 2x$.
9. What can be said about the graph of a relation, defined on a set of ordered pairs (x, y) of $R^\# \times R^\#$ by an equation (*a*) $x^2 + y^2 + z^2 = 4$; (*b*) $2x^2 + 2z^2 - 3y = 5$; (*c*) $x = 5z$; (*d*) $y = x$?
10. Describe the graph of the function defined as the following set of ordered triples: $\{(x, y, z) \mid (x, y, z) \in R^\# \times R^\# \times R^\#, z = \sqrt{4 - y^2}\}$.

15.8 The Loci of More General Equations

The problem of sketching the graph of a relation on a subset of $R^\# \times R^\#$ is similar to that of sketching the graph of a relation on a subset of $R^\#$; in the former case, we graph the ordered triples (x, y, z) of the relation, while in the latter case we graph the ordered pairs of the relation. However, the 3-dimensional graphing problem for the triples is more difficult to accomplish with accuracy. The rule of mapping of any relation to be considered will be given by an equation in x, y, and z where, as usual, (x, y) is an arbitrary element of the domain with z a corresponding element of the range. The loci of these equations will be surfaces, and it is with these surfaces that we are to be most concerned. Unless the student is a skilled draftsman, he is advised not to attempt a detailed sketch of a surface, but merely to include enough line segments and arcs of curves to give a clear impression. In addition, if the surface has symmetrical portions in several octants, it is feasible to limit the sketch to one octant. The following guides may be helpful in making a sketch of a 3-dimensional surface.

INTERCEPTS. The intercepts of the surface on the x-axis (y-axis, z-axis) can be found by replacing both y and z (x and z, x and y) by 0 in the equation, and solving for x (y, z).

TRACES. These are the curves in which the surface intersects the coordinate planes, and equations for these traces can be found by replacing the appropriate representative coordinate in the given equation of the surface by 0. For example, if we replace z by 0, we obtain an equation of the trace in the xy-plane.

SYMMETRY. The following tests for symmetry are stated without proof, but their validity will be apparent from previous discussions of plane symmetry.

1. A surface is symmetric with respect to the yz-plane, if a replacement of x by $-x$ in an equation of the surface, results in an equivalent equation. A similar test applies for the other coordinate planes.

2. A surface is symmetric with respect to the z-axis, if a replacement of x by $-x$ and y by $-y$ in an equation of the surface, results in an equivalent equation. A similar test applies for the other coordinate axes.

3. A surface is symmetric with respect to the origin, if a replacement of x by $-x$, y by $-y$, and z by $-z$ in an equation of the surface results in an equivalent equation.

SECTIONS PARALLEL TO THE COORDINATE PLANES. If the traces do not give sufficient information, equations of cross sections parallel to the coordinate planes may be obtained by replacing a representative coordinate in an equation of the surface by some given number k.

ILLUSTRATION. Analyze the equation and sketch a portion of the locus of

$$y^2 + 6z^2 - 9x - 9 = 0.$$

Solution. We shall analyze the equation according to the above items.

1. Intercepts. $y = \pm 3$; $x = -1$; $z = \pm\sqrt{6}/2$.
2. Traces. yz-plane: $y^2 + 6z^2 = 9$, an ellipse.
   xz-plane: $z^2 = 3(x+1)/2$, a parabola.
   xy-plane: $y^2 = 9(x+1)$, a parabola.
3. Symmetry. The surface is symmetric with respect to the xz- and xy-planes, and so an adequate sketch may include portions in only the first and fourth octants.
4. Cross Sections. If $x = k$, $y^2 + 6z^2 = 9(k+1)$; an ellipse, center on x-axis.
   If $y = k$, $6z^2 = 9x + 9 - k^2$; a parabola, axis on xy-plane, parallel to x-axis.

If $z = k$, $y^2 = 9x + 9 - 6k^2$; a parabola, axis on xz-plane, parallel to x-axis.

A sketch of the surface in the first and fourth octants is shown in Figure 15–11.

The locus of a second-degree equation in x, y, and z is known as a *quadric surface*, the general form of an equation of such a surface being $Ax^2 + By^2 + Cz^2 + Dxy + Exz + Fyz + Gx + Hy + Iz + J = 0$. These surfaces in 3-space correspond to the conic sections of plane geometry,

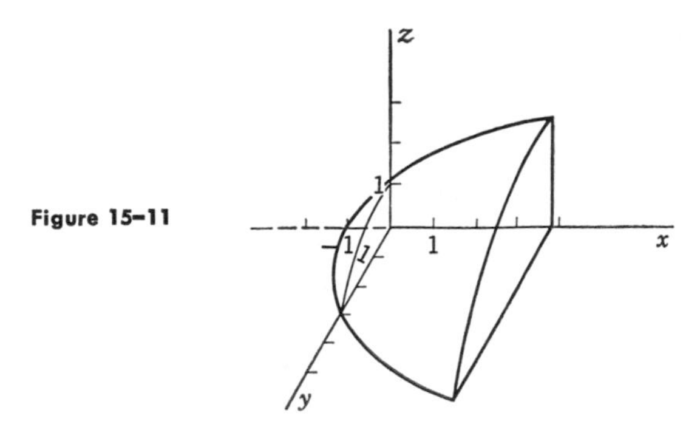

Figure 15–11

and it can be shown that their intersections with arbitrary planes are, in fact, conics. As is the case with conics, equations of quadric surfaces assume simple "standard" forms, if the coordinate planes are suitably chosen. We shall now list some of the more common quadric surfaces, along with their standard equations with respect to suitable coordinate systems, and have included some partial sketches. It is to be understood, of course, that the loci discussed in the preceding section are also quadric surfaces, with a few simple exceptions.

Ellipsoid:

$$x^2/a^2 + y^2/b^2 + z^2/c^2 = 1.$$

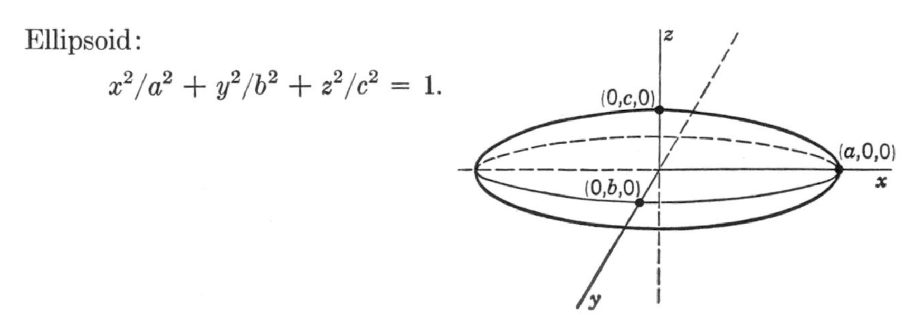

Figure 15–12

Hyperboloid of One Sheet:

$$x^2/a^2 + y^2/b^2 - z^2/c^2 = 1.$$

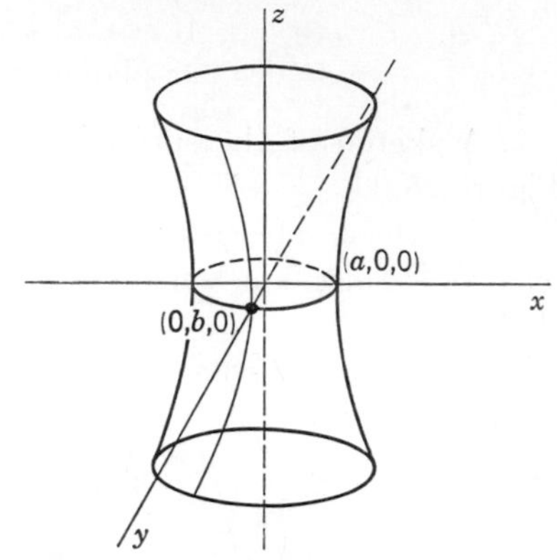

Figure 15–13

Hyperboloid of Two Sheets:

$$x^2/a^2 - y^2/b^2 - z^2/c^2 = 1.$$

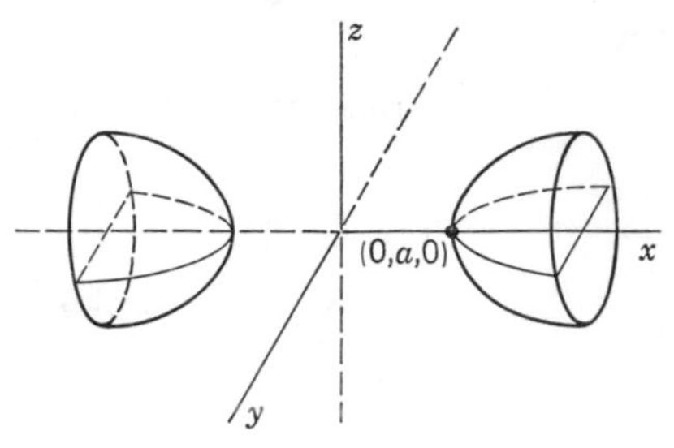

Figure 15–14

Elliptic Paraboloid:

$$x^2/a^2 + y^2/b^2 = z.$$

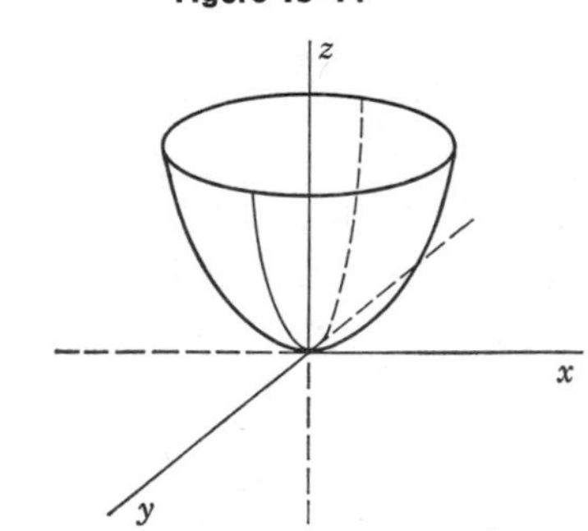

Figure 15–15

Hyperbolic Paraboloid:

$$x^2/a^2 - y^2/b^2 = z.$$

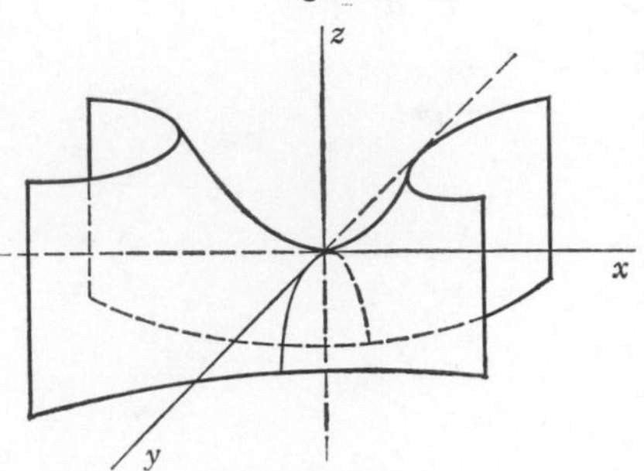

Figure 15–16

Quadric Cone:

$$x^2/a^2 + y^2/b^2 = z^2/c^2.$$

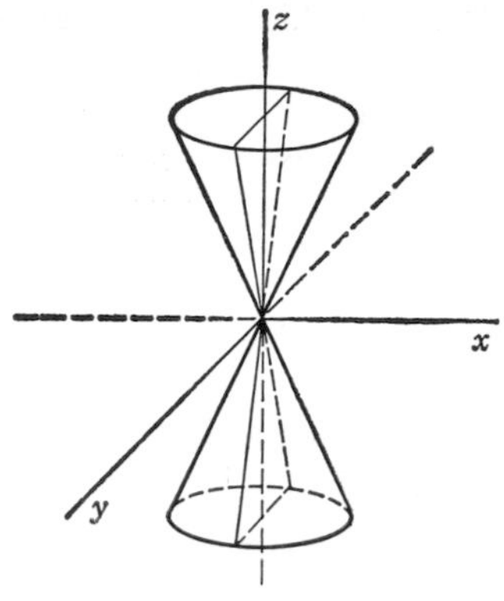

Figure 15–17

PROBLEM SET 15.8

Make a partial sketch of the locus of each of the following equations, and identify each surface.

1. $x^2/25 + y^2/9 + z^2/4 = 1.$
2. $x^2/36 - y^2/16 - z^2/9 = 1.$
3. $9x^2 + 16y^2 = 144z^2.$
4. $x^2 - 4z^2 = 6x^2.$
5. $x^2 - y^2/9 - z^2/16 = 1.$
6. $x^2 + y^2 + z^2 = 25.$
7. $y^2 = 5x^2 + 10x.$
8. $xy = 5.$
9. $3y^2 + 5z^2 = 15x.$
10. $y^2/4 - z^2/9 = x.$
11. $xy = z^2 + z.$
12. $x + y = z^2.$
13. $8x = 16 - y^2 - 4z^2.$
14. $y^2 + 6z^2 - 9x = 18.$

REVIEW TEST A

1. The vertices of a triangle in 3-space are: $A(2, 3, -2)$, $B(-5, -7, 2)$, $C(3, -4, 5)$. Find the direction cosines of the sensed line segment from (*a*) A to B; (*b*) C to B.
2. Determine the interior angle at the vertex B of the triangle in Problem 1.
3. If the line containing $(2, 1, 3)$ and $(-3, 2, -4)$ is perpendicular to the line containing $(3, -4, 2)$ and $(1, 2, a)$, determine the number a.
4. Determine an equation of the plane containing the points $(1, 1, 8)$, $(2, 1, 5)$, and $(-2, -2, 2)$.
5. Find the approximate distance from the point $(1, -2, 4)$ to the plane in Problem 4.
6. Determine the approximate distance between the two planes having the given equations $x + y - 2z + 6 = 0$ and $2x + 2y - 4z - 7 = 0$.
7. Find equations of the straight line containing the points $(1, 1, -2)$ and $(-2, -3, 4)$.

8. If the locus of $x^2 + 2y^3 - 4 = 0$ is considered revolved about the y-axis, what is an equation of the resulting surface of revolution?

9. Determine an equation of the plane that has 2, -2, and 3 for x, y, and z intercepts, respectively.

10. Identify the locus of each of the following equations, and describe its traces in the coordinate planes: (*a*) $x^2 + 2y^2 + 5x + y = 4$; (*b*) $x^2 + 2y^2 - 3z^2 = 0$; (*c*) $z^2 + 2x^2 + 2y^2 = 16$; (*d*) $y + 4x^2 - 3z^2 + 2z - x = 10$.

11. Determine an equation of the sphere that contains the point $(5, -1, -1)$ and has its center at $(-2, 3, -4)$.

12. Show that the three lines joining the points $(8, 12, 9)$, $(9, -12, 8)$, and $(-12, -1, 12)$ with the origin are mutually perpendicular.

REVIEW TEST B

1. The vertices of a triangle in 3-space are: $A(-2, -3, 5)$, $B(1, 5, 4)$, $C(2, -4, -3)$. Find the direction cosines of the sensed line segment from (*a*) A to B; (*b*) A to C.

2. Determine the interior angle at the vertex A of the triangle in Problem 1.

3. Line L_1 contains the points $(3, -2, 1)$ and $(1, 2, -4)$, while line L_2 contains $(0, 1, 2)$ and $(-2, 1, -3)$. If the points $(0, 1, 2)$ and $(1, a, b)$ are on a line perpendicular to both L_1 and L_2, determine the numbers a and b.

4. If $(1, -2, 9)$, $(4, 2, 4)$ and $(-3, -3, 7)$ are elements of a relation having a rule of mapping given by an equation of the form $Ax + By + Cz + D = 0$, determine the simplest solutions for A, B, C, and D, and the resulting equation.

5. Determine the approximate distance from the point $(-2, 3, 5)$ to the locus in Problem 4.

6. If the given equations of two planes are $2x - y + 3z + 5 = 0$ and $6x - 3y + 9z - 2 = 0$, determine the approximate distance between the planes.

7. Find an equation of the straight line having direction numbers 1, -2, 3, if $(2, 1, -4)$ is one of its points.

8. If the given equations of two planes are $x + y - 2z + 2 = 0$ and $x + 3y + z - 2 = 0$, determine the acute angle between the planes.

9. Identify the locus of each of the following equations, and describe its traces in the coordinate planes: (*a*) $2x^2 - 3y^2 + 4z^2 = 5$; (*b*) $4x^2 + 2y^2 + z^2 = 20$; (*c*) $2x^2 + 2y^2 + 2z^2 + 4x = 15$; (*d*) $x^2 - 2y^2 - 4z^2 = 6$.

10. The direction cosines of the line segment joining the point P with the point P_1 are $2/3$, $-1/3$, $2/3$. If the coordinates of P_1 are $(2, 1, -3)$ and the distance from P to P_1 is 6 units, find the coordinates of P.

11. Two lines L_1 and L_2 have direction cosines l_1, m_1, n_1 and l_2, m_2, n_2, respectively. If the angle between L_1 and L_2 is θ radians, show that

$$\sin^2 \theta = \begin{vmatrix} m_1 & n_1 \\ m_2 & n_2 \end{vmatrix}^2 + \begin{vmatrix} n_1 & l_1 \\ n_2 & l_2 \end{vmatrix}^2 + \begin{vmatrix} l_1 & m_1 \\ l_2 & m_2 \end{vmatrix}^2 .$$

12. A straight line L is defined as the intersection of the planes having the equations $x + y + z = 3$ and $x - 3y + 2z = 2$. Find an equation of the line that is parallel to L and contains the point $(2, -4, 6)$. Also find an equation of the plane that is perpendicular to L and contains the given point.

REFERENCES

Books

MARCH, H. W. AND H. C. WOLFF, *Calculus*, New York, McGraw-Hill, 1917. (Chap. 14.)

MILNE, WILLIAM E. AND D. R. DAVIS, *Introductory College Mathematics*, New York, Ginn, 1941. (Pp. 389–414.)

16

PERMUTATIONS, COMBINATIONS, AND THE BINOMIAL THEOREM

And I believe that the Binomial Theorem and a Bach fugue are, in the long run, more important than all the battles of history.

JAMES HILTON†

16.1 The Fundamental Counting Principle

The topics to be discussed in this chapter arise in many different places in mathematics. However, our principal interest in them lies in their usefulness in the development of the brief survey of probability and statistics in Chapter 17. The student is urged to review Section 1.1, at this point.

If a college student has 5 sport shirts and 6 pairs of slacks, all different, in how many different outfits can he appear on the campus? Since he can select any one of the 5 shirts, and can match *each* choice of shirt with any one of 6 pairs of slacks, it is clear that he can be outfitted in $5 \cdot 6$ or 30 different ways. If there are 3 candidates for president, and 2 for vice president of an organization, in how many ways can these two offices be filled? Since any one of 3 persons can be president, and *each* of these can be associated with either of 2 persons as vice president, there are $3 \cdot 2$ or 6 different ways of filling the offices. These two results are illustrative of the following important principle.

THE FUNDAMENTAL COUNTING PRINCIPLE. If one event can take place in any one of m ways, and *after it has happened* a second event can take place in any one of n ways, the *sequence* of the two events can take place in mn ways.

This principle, which involves nothing more than common sense, can be readily extended to include sequences of more than two events, each of which can happen in a given number of ways.

It is important to realize in a counting problem, that the counting procedure *depends on what we are counting.* If we are merely counting the

† Reprinted from *This Week* magazine, December 19, 1937. Copyright, 1937, by the United Newspaper Magazine Corporation.

total number of ways in which unrelated events can happen, we add the numbers of ways in which the separate events can happen. If, on the other hand, we are counting *sequences* of events, we must *multiply* these numbers together, since the way in which any one event happens affects the sequence of events. It was this latter type of counting that we used in the two problems above, the sequences of events being ordered pairs in each case. If A is the set of ways in which one event can happen, while B is the set of ways in which a second event can happen, after the first event has occurred, it may be seen that the number of ways in which the sequence of the two events can happen is the cardinal number of the set $A \times B$.

ILLUSTRATION 1. Three men, traveling together, plan to spend a night in either Washington or Baltimore, there being 5 hotels in Washington and 4 hotels in Baltimore that can accommodate them. In how many ways can they take up quarters for the night, if no two of them stay in the same hotel?

Solution. If they stay in Washington, the Fundamental Counting Principle implies that they can be housed in $5 \cdot 4 \cdot 3$ or 60 different ways. If they stay in Baltimore, the same reasoning shows that the number of different ways is $4 \cdot 3 \cdot 2$ or 24. Since the choices in Washington are in no way dependent on the choices in Baltimore, the total number of ways in which the men can be accommodated is $60 + 24$ or 84.

ILLUSTRATION 2. If $A = \{1, 3, 5, 7, 9\}$ and $B = \{2, 4, 6, 8\}$, how many elements are there in the set $A \cup B$ and in the set $A \times B$?

Solution. The sets A and B have no elements in common, and so the number of elements in $A \cup B$ is the sum of the cardinal numbers of A and B; this number, the cardinal number of $A \cup B$ is then $5 + 4$ or 9. The elements of $A \times B$ are sequences, in this case ordered pairs. Since the first member of an ordered pair of $A \times B$ can be any one of 5 numbers, while there are 4 choices for an associated second member, the Fundamental Counting Principle implies that there are $5 \cdot 4$ or 20 different ordered pairs of $A \times B$. The cardinal number of $A \times B$ is then 20.

PROBLEM SET 16.1

1. Find the 8th term of each of the following infinite sequences, assuming that the terms follow the established pattern: (*a*) $1, 2, 1, 2, \cdots$; (*b*) $2, 4, 6, 8, \cdots$; (*c*) $1, 4, 7, 10 \cdots$; (*d*) $1, 1, 1, 1, \cdots$; (*e*) $3, 6, 12, 24, \cdots$; (*f*) $1, 3, 9, 27, \cdots$.

2. Find the 10th term of the sequence that has the following nth term: (*a*) $n(n + 1)$; (*b*) $(n + 1)(n + 2)$; (*c*) $n^2 + 2n$; (*d*) $n(n + 1)(n + 2)$; (*e*) $n(n + 1) + 1$; (*f*) $n^2 + 2n + 2$.

3. How many ordered triples (a_1, a_2, a_3) can be formed from the elements of the set $\{1, 2, 3\}$, if (*a*) no element is repeated in a triple; (*b*) $a_1 = a_2$, and a_3 is a different number?

4. How many 3-letter code words can be made, if the first two letters can be any consonants and the last letter can be any vowel?
5. A lady has recently purchased 3 pairs of shoes, 4 dresses, and 2 hats. In how many ways can she appear with (*a*) a new outfit of shoes, dress and hat; (*b*) exactly one new article of clothing?
6. A student is taking 4 courses in each of which he can receive a grade of A, B, C, D, or E. How many different sets of grades can he receive?
7. A man living in Jacksonville has a choice of 3 routes to Atlanta, a choice of 2 routes from Atlanta to Chicago, and a choice of 2 routes from Chicago to Minneapolis. In how many ways can he make the trip from Jacksonville to Minneapolis?
8. If four colors are available, in how many ways can a map of four countries be colored, no two countries having the same color?
9. A signal device consists of 4 rows of lights, each with a red, an amber, and a green light. If at most one light can be lit in each row, how many different signals can be sent with the device?
10. A finite sequence is defined as follows: $a_1 = 2$, $a_2 = 7$, $a_3 = 10$, $a_4 = 12$, $a_5 = 15$, $a_6 = 16$. If a new sequence is defined by $b_n = a_n + pa_{n+1}$, for $n < 6$, and $b_6 = a_6$, write down the terms of this sequence where (*a*) $p = 2$; (*b*) $p = 4$; (*c*) $p = 5$.
11. How many different 4-digit numbers can be symbolized, using the digits of the set $\{1, 2, 3, 4\}$, if (*a*) any digit may be repeated; (*b*) the first digit is even, and none are repeated; (*c*) the last digit is even, and repetitions are allowed; (*d*) the first and last digits are even, and none are repeated?
12. How many 5-letter code words can be made, if the first and last letters may be selected from the set $\{b, d, s, t\}$, the second and fourth may be any vowel, and the middle letter may be any member of the set $\{j, k, m\}$, using any one letter only once in one code word?
13. A signalman can hold a flag in each hand, and can put each flag in any one of 4 positions. How many different signals can he send, if he uses only one pattern for each signal? If he uses two successive patterns, how many different signals can he send?
14. Information can be recorded on "punched" cards, by punching holes at the proper spots. If each card has 80 columns, and 12 spots in each column, how many different messages can be recorded on a card, if not more than one hole can be punched in any one column?
15. If $A = \{1, 2, 5, 7, 8, 9\}$ and $B = \{6, 10, 11\}$, compare the number of elements in $A \cup B$ with the number in $A \times B$. Compare the number, if $B = \{2, 6, 10\}$.

16.2 Permutations and Combinations

A study of combinations and permutations is concerned with the number of ways in which a subset of a finite set of objects can be selected, or selected and then arranged in different orders. If order is of importance, we refer to the different arrangements as *permutations*, while if order is to be disregarded the different selections are known as *combinations*. The problems of permutations and combinations involve very little in their solutions but counting and applications of the Fundamental Counting Principle. It is possible to develop some useful formulas, but the student is urged to think the problem through carefully, before applying any of them. Moreover, it may happen that a problem is not solvable with an application of a single formula, but some combination of formulas may be needed.

Permutations may be classified as *linear* or *circular* according as the elements of the set are considered arranged along a straight line or on a circle. It is clear that the notion of a linear permutation is similar to that of a finite sequence, which explains why the Fundamental Counting Principle is applicable to problems involving permutations. It may be that some of the elements of the basic set are indistinguishable, though distinct, and so if we identify permutations which differ only in rearrangements of these elements, we are left with *distinguishable* permutations. In the present section, however, we shall be concerned only with *linear* permutations of elements that are distinguishable, along with associated problems involving combinations.

The first question before us is this: in how many ways can we select r objects from a total of n distinguishable objects, $r \leq n$, and arrange them to form different permutations? Let us represent this number by $P_{n,r}$, the *number of permutations of* n *things taken* r *at a time*. The problem is to count the number of sequences of r elements that can be formed, all elements being selected from the same set containing originally n elements. There are then n choices for the first element, $n - 1$ choices for the second, $n - 2$ choices for the third, and so on with $n - r + 1$ choices for the rth element. An application of the general Fundamental Counting Principle then yields $P_{n,r} = n(n - 1)(n - 2) \cdots (n - r + 1)$. It is convenient to define the symbol $\underline{|n}$† (read "factorial n") for the product of all the positive integers from 1 to n, inclusive; for some purposes, it is also useful to identify $\underline{|0}$ with 1. The above formula can then be written in compact form as, $P_{n,r} = \underline{|n}/\underline{|n - r}$. In case $r = n$, i.e., all the elements of the basic set are selected and permuted in all possible ways, we obtain the *number of permutations of* n *things taken all at a time*. If we represent this number by P_n, the previous result with $r = n$ yields $P_n = \underline{|n}$.

Since a set of r objects can be permuted in $\underline{|r}$ ways, the number of *permutations* of n things taken r at a time is $\underline{|r}$ times as great as the number

† Many authors use $n!$ instead of $\underline{|n}$.

of *combinations* of n things taken r at a time. If we use the symbol $C_{n,r}$† to represent this latter number, we can express this observation in the form $C_{n,r} = \underline{|n}/(\underline{|n-r}\,\underline{|r})$. It is clear that $C_{n,n} = 1$, since there can be only one selection of n elements from a set containing only n elements. In view of our definition of $\underline{|0}$, this formula, as well as the formula for $P_{n,r}$, remains valid if $r = n$.

ILLUSTRATION 1. How many different 5-digit integer symbols can be formed by using distinct digits of the set $\{1, 2, 3, 4, 5, 6, 7, 8, 9\}$?

Solution. Since each arrangement of digits produces a different symbol, the problem is to count the number of ways in which 5 digits can be selected from the set and then permuted. But this number is $P_{9,5}$, which is $9 \cdot 8 \cdot 7 \cdot 6 \cdot 5$ or 15,120.

ILLUSTRATION 2. In how many ways can a selection of 5 books be made from a collection of 8 different books, if (*a*) one specified book is to be included; (*b*) one specified book is to be excluded?

Solution.

(*a*) Since a specified book is to be included, the choice involves only 4 books. We have then to count the number of ways in which 4 books can be *selected* (not arranged) from a total of 7 books, and this number is $C_{7,4}$, i.e., $\dfrac{7 \cdot 6 \cdot 5 \cdot 4}{4 \cdot 3 \cdot 2 \cdot 1}$ or 35.

(*b*) Since a specified book is excluded, we have merely to count the number of ways in which 5 books can be selected from a collection of 7 different books. This number is $C_{7,5}$, i.e., $\dfrac{7 \cdot 6 \cdot 5 \cdot 4 \cdot 3}{5 \cdot 4 \cdot 3 \cdot 2 \cdot 1}$ or 21.

The following illustration shows that problems arise for which no single formula is adequate.

ILLUSTRATION 3. In how many ways can a party of at least 4 be selected from a group of 7 people?

Solution. We must consider parties consisting of 4, 5, 6, and 7 people, respectively.

(*a*) A party of 4 can be selected in $C_{7,4}$ ways, where

$$C_{7,4} = (7 \cdot 6 \cdot 5 \cdot 4)/(4 \cdot 3 \cdot 2 \cdot 1) = 35.$$

(*b*) A party of 5 can be selected in $C_{7,5}$ ways, where

$$C_{7,5} = (7 \cdot 6 \cdot 5 \cdot 4 \cdot 3)/(5 \cdot 4 \cdot 3 \cdot 2 \cdot 1) = 21.$$

(*c*) A party of 6 can be selected in $C_{7,6}$ ways, where

$$C_{7,6} = (7 \cdot 6 \cdot 5 \cdot 4 \cdot 3 \cdot 2)/(6 \cdot 5 \cdot 4 \cdot 3 \cdot 2 \cdot 1) = 7.$$

(*d*) A party of 7 can be selected in only 1 way.

---

† The symbol $\binom{n}{r}$ is also frequently used in this connection.

The total number of ways in which a party of the desired type can be selected is then $35 + 21 + 7 + 1$ or 64.

PROBLEM SET 16.2

1. Find the numbers represented by (*a*) $\underline{|5}$; (*b*) $\underline{|6}$; (*c*) $\underline{|7}$; (*d*) $3 \cdot \underline{|6}$; (*e*) $2 \cdot \underline{|3}$; (*f*) $(\underline{|3})(\underline{|5})$.
2. Find the numbers represented by (*a*) $P_{5,3}$; (*b*) $P_{6,4}$; (*c*) $P_{10,3}$; (*d*) $C_{7,3}$; (*e*) $C_{6,3}$; (*f*) $C_{10,3}$.
3. Write each of the following as a multiple of $\underline{|n}$, with n as large as possible: (*a*) $9\underline{|8}$; (*b*) $12\underline{|8} - 7\underline{|6}$; (*c*) $4\underline{|7} - 6\underline{|5}$; (*d*) $\underline{|3}\,\underline{|6} + \underline{|7}$.
4. In how many ways can a group of 5 soldiers be chosen from a platoon of 15?
5. How many different 3-digit integer symbols can be formed, by using distinct digits from the set $\{3, 4, 5, 6, 7\}$? How many 2-digit or 3-digit integer symbols can be so formed?
6. In how many ways can the letters of each of the following words be arranged: (*a*) SET; (*b*) NUMBER; (*c*) WORDS; (*d*) LOGARITHM?
7. In how many ways can a class of 30 students choose a committee of (*a*) 4 students; (*b*) 6 students; (*c*) not more than 4 students?
8. A plane is determined by 3 points. How many planes are determined by 4 points, if no 4 of them are coplanar?
9. How many different "singles" tennis matches could be arranged with a group of (*a*) 10 players; (*b*) 8 players?
10. Show that $C_{n,r} = C_{n,n-r}$.
11. A deck of playing cards has 4 suits, each suit having 3 "face cards" (king, queen, jack), an ace, and 9 other cards numbered from 2 to 10, inclusive. Two cards with the same picture or number are said to have the same rank. (*a*) A poker hand consists of 5 cards. How many different poker hands are there in a deck of playing cards? (*b*) A poker hand contains a "pair" if it contains 2 cards of the same rank. How many different poker hands are there with at least one "pair"? (*c*) A "full house" is a poker hand with 3 cards of the same rank and a "pair" of another rank. How many different "full houses" are there in a deck of playing cards? (*d*) A bridge deal consists of 4 hands of 13 cards each, the order of the hands relative to the dealer being important. How many different bridge deals are possible from a deck of playing cards? (*e*) How many bridge deals are there in which the dealer gets all the aces, kings, and queens?
12. In how many ways can a committee of 5 be appointed from 6 Italians, 4 Frenchmen, and 7 Americans, if each nationality is to be represented?
13. In how many points do 12 coplanar straight lines intersect, if no 2 of them are parallel?
14. How many different team arrangements can be made with 9 ball players, if only two of them can catch and only one can pitch?
15. In how many different ways can 7 books be arranged on a shelf, if a certain 2-volume work is not to be separated?

16. In how many ways can 2 black and 3 white balls be drawn from a box containing 5 black and 8 white balls, all distinguishable?

17. How many different football "elevens" can be formed from a squad of 25 men, if only 4 can play as "ends" and only 6 can play as "backs," and these 10 can play in no other position?

18. In how many ways can 1 English and 4 Latin books be placed on a shelf, so that the English book is in the middle, the selection being made from 7 Latin and 3 English books?

19. A boat is to be manned by 8 men, of whom 2 can row only on the bow side and 1 can row only on the stroke side. In how many ways can the crew be arranged?

16.3 Further Discussion of Permutations and Combinations

In the preceding section we considered only *linear* permutations, i.e., permutations equivalent to a linear or sequential arrangement of the elements. Let us now turn our attention to *circular* permutations, where the elements may be considered arranged on a circle. In this type of permutation, if each element is displaced the same number of positions in the same direction (i.e., all clockwise or all counter-clockwise), the new arrangement is said to be a *cyclic* permutation of the original and is not distinguishable from it. For example, the keys on a ring can be moved as a unit around the ring, without disturbing the arrangement of the keys. If there are n objects, all distinguishable, in a circular arrangement, there will be n such cyclic permutations corresponding to the n different possible displacements. Since the corresponding linear permutations would be distinguishable, there are n times as many distinguishable linear permutations as there are distinguishable circular permutations of a set of n objects. It then follows that the number of distinguishable circular permutations of n objects is P_n/n or $|\underline{n-1}$. A similar argument will show that the number of distinguishable circular permutations of n objects taken r at a time is $P_{n,r}/r$ or $|\underline{n}/(r|\underline{n-r})$.

ILLUSTRATION 1. How many seating arrangements are possible for 10 people at a round table?

Solution. The above formula for circular permutations can be applied here, directly, and the result is $|\underline{9}$ or 362,880 different arrangements.

We now return to the subject of linear permutations, but let us assume that the elements are not all distinguishable from each other. If we are permuting n elements, of which s are indistinguishable, the permutations which differ only in rearrangements of these s elements will not be distinguishable permutations. Since there are $|\underline{s}$ such permutations, the number of permutations of n objects, all of which are distinguishable, will be $|\underline{s}$ times as great as the number if s are indistinguishable. It follows that the number of permutations of n objects, of which s are indistinguishable, is $\underline{|n}/\underline{|s}$. If there are an additional t objects, indistinguishable from each other, a similar argument will give the number of distinguishable permutations as $\underline{|n}/(\underline{|s}\,\underline{|t})$, and the argument can be extended, easily. We note that there is *no* formula for the number of distinguishable permutations of n objects taken r at a time, $r < n$, if some of the objects are indistinguishable.

ILLUSTRATION 2. How many distinguishable permutations can be made of the letters of the word ASSASSINATION?

Solution. The word contains 13 letters of which 4 are S, 3 are A, 2 are N, and 2 are I, while the remaining letters T and O appear only once. A direct application of the above result gives the desired number of permutations as $\underline{|13}/(\underline{|4}\,\underline{|3}\,\underline{|2}\,\underline{|2})$ or 10,810,800.

In the following illustration, some techniques are used in the solution of a problem which can not be solved by a direct application of any of the above formulas.

ILLUSTRATION 3. From 3 peaches, 4 apples, and 2 oranges, how many selections of fruit can be made, if (*a*) any number may be taken; (*b*) at least one of each kind must be taken? Assume that no two pieces of fruit are identical.

Solution.

(*a*) In this case, there are two possibilities as far as each piece of fruit is concerned: either it is selected or it is not selected. Since there are 9 pieces of fruit, the total number of possible selections is 2^9 or 512. As this number includes the case when none are taken, the number of actual selections of fruit will be 511.

(*b*) In this case, there may be selected 1, 2, or 3 peaches, 1, 2, 3, or 4 apples, and 1 or 2 oranges. The number of selections of peaches is then $C_{3,1} + C_{3,2} + C_{3,3}$, i.e., $3 + 3 + 1$ or 7; the number of selections of apples is $C_{4,1} + C_{4,2} + C_{4,3} + C_{4,4}$, i.e., $4 + 6 + 4 + 1$ or 15; and the number of selections of oranges is $C_{2,1} + C_{2,2}$, i.e., $2 + 1$ or 3. The Fundamental Counting Principle then implies that, under the circumstances of the problem, the number of distinguishable selections of fruit is $7 \cdot 15 \cdot 3$ or 315.

PROBLEM SET 16.3

1. In how many ways can 5 keys be arranged on a ring?
2. In how many ways can 5 keys be selected from a group of 10 keys, and arranged on a ring?
3. A group of 5 women and a group of 6 men are to be seated at separate round tables. How many seating arrangements are possible?
4. How many distinguishable permutations can be made of the letters of the word: (*a*) MISSISSIPPI; (*b*) SYZYGY; (*c*) INDIANA; (*d*) DIVISIBLE?

5. From 2 apples, 2 oranges, and 3 grapefruit (all pieces distinguishable), a selection of fruit is to be made. How many selections are possible if (*a*) any number of pieces may be selected; (*b*) at least one piece of each kind must be selected?
6. How many symbols of distinct whole numbers can be formed by placing in juxtaposition all members of the set $\{1, 2, 3, 4, 3, 2, 1\}$ of distinct, but partially indistinguishable, digits?
7. Find n and r if $P_{n,r} = 24$ and $C_{n,r} = 4$.
8. In how many ways can at least 3 and not more than 5 people be chosen from a group of 7 people?
9. A committee of 5 is to be chosen from a group of 10 people. In how many ways can the committee be formed, if two particular people agree to serve only if they are both chosen?
10. In how many ways can 5 prizes be given away to 6 boys, if each boy is eligible for all the prizes?
11. A committee of 7 men is to be chosen from a group of 12 and seated at a round table. In how many ways can the committee be chosen and seated?
12. A bracelet is to be made by linking together 5 different sections. If the jeweler has 10 different linkage sections available, in how many ways can the bracelet be made?
13. A man wishes to invite one or more of 7 friends to dinner. In how many ways can he do this?

14*. Find the number of ways in which (*a*) a selection and (*b*) an arrangement can be made of 4 letters taken from the letters of the word REHEARSE.

15*. Apply the directions of Problem 14 to the letters of the word ARRANGE.

16.4 The Binomial Theorem

If a and b are arbitrary numbers, it is possible to obtain an expression equal to $(a + b)^n$, for any positive integer n, by multiplying together n factors each equal to $a + b$. In particular, the following "expansions" are well known to the student: $(a + b)^1 = a + b$; $(a + b)^2 = a^2 + 2ab + b^2$; $(a + b)^3 = a^3 + 3a^2b + 3ab^2 + b^3$. The corresponding expression equal to $(a + b)^n$, for any real number n, is known as the *binomial expansion*, the theorem that establishes the existence of such an expansion being known as the *Binomial Theorem*.

The terms of $(a + b)^2$, i.e., $(a + b)(a + b)$, arise from the multiplication of each term of the first factor by each term of the second factor. There are four such products, which we may list as a^2, ab, ba, b^2, and when similar terms are combined the resulting sum is $a^2 + 2ab + b^2$. Similarly, the various terms of $(a + b)^3$, i.e., $(a + b)(a + b)(a + b)$, arise when all possible products are formed by multiplying together one term from each factor. There are eight such products, in this case, which we may list as a^3, aab, baa, abb, bab, bba, aba, b^3; on combining like terms, the resulting sum is $a^3 + 3a^2b + 3ab^2 + b^3$.

The terms of the expansion of $(a + b)^n$, for any positive integer n, arise in the same way as they did for the cases $n = 2$ and $n = 3$. Thus, the expansion of $(a + b)^n$ is the sum of all possible products obtainable, by multiplying together n terms, one from each of the n factors. If we select r of the terms to be b, and the remainder $n - r$ terms to be a, each such product will equal $a^{n-r}b^r$. Since it is possible to make this selection in $C_{n,r}$ ways, the number of such terms in the expansion will be $C_{n,r}$, which is then the coefficient of $a^{n-r}b^r$. In view of the fact that r can be any integer from 0 to n, inclusive, the expansion of $(a + b)^n$ can now be written down as follows:

$$(a + b)^n = a^n + C_{n,1}a^{n-1}b + C_{n,2}a^{n-2}b^2 + \cdots + C_{n,r}a^{n-r}b^r + \cdots + C_{n,n-1}ab^{n-1} + b^n.$$

The coefficients 1, $C_{n,1}$, $C_{n,2}$, $\cdots$, $C_{n,r}$, $\cdots$, $C_{n,n-1}$, 1 are referred to as the *binomial coefficients.* Though it has not much practical value, it is possible to obtain these coefficients, for any integer n, by a device known as *Pascal's Triangle*, displayed in Figure 16–1. The rows of the "triangle," which have been formed in an obvious manner, are the binomial coefficients for successive integers n beginning with $n = 0$.

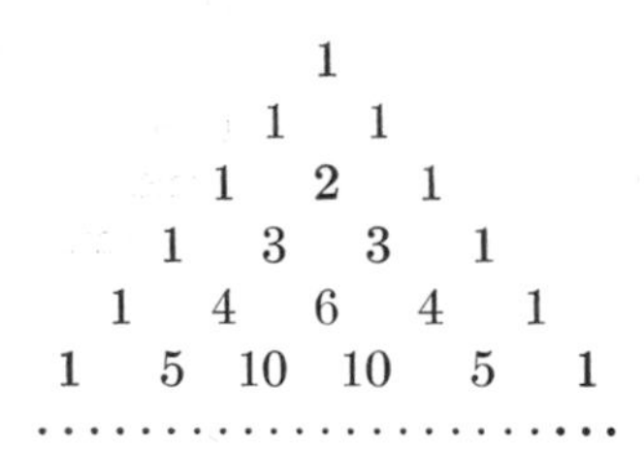

Figure 16–1

ILLUSTRATION 1. Write down the binomial expansion of $(1/2 + x^2)^5$.

Solution. This is the case of the general expansion with $a = 1/2$, $b = x^2$, and $n = 5$. The desired expansion is then

$$(1/2)^5 + 5(1/2)^4(x^2)^1 + \frac{5\cdot4}{2}(1/2)^3(x^2)^2 + \frac{5\cdot4\cdot3}{3\cdot2}(1/2)^2(x^2)^3 + \frac{5\cdot4\cdot3\cdot2}{4\cdot3\cdot2}(1/2)^1(x^2)^4 + (x^2)^5,$$

which on simplification becomes $(1/32) + (5/16)x^2 + (5/4)x^4 + (5/2)x^6 + (5/2)x^8 + x^{10}$.

An examination of the $(r + 1)$th term of the binomial expansion of $(a + b)^n$ reveals that this term involves the number r in a conspicuous manner:

1. The numerator of the coefficient formally contains the product of r consecutively descending integers beginning with n.

2. The denominator of the coefficient formally contains the factor $\underline{|r}$.

3. The exponent of b is r and the exponent of a is $n - r$.

It is then easy, with the above observation as a memory device, to write down any particular term without the complete expansion.

ILLUSTRATION 2. Write down the 5th term of the binomial expansion of $(\sqrt{a} - 2x)^8$.

Solution. The conspicuous number, associated with the 5th term, is 4. Hence, using the above memory device, the 5th term is seen to be $\frac{8 \cdot 7 \cdot 6 \cdot 5}{4 \cdot 3 \cdot 2} (\sqrt{a})^{8-4}(-2x)^4$, i.e., $1120\, a^2x^4$.

PROBLEM SET 16.4

Give the complete binomial expansion in Problems 1 through 6.

1. $(2x - 3)^5$.
2. $(1 - xy)^6$.
3. $(2x - 2/3)^7$.
4. $(1/2 + 2a)^8$.
5. $(1 + 1/x)^8$.
6. $(1 - 1/x)^{10}$.
7. Determine the 6th term of the binomial expansion of $(2x - 1/x)^{12}$.
8. Determine the 5th term of the binomial expansion of $(x^2 + 3a/x)^{15}$.
9. Find the two middle terms of the binomial expansion of $(3a - a^3/6)^9$.
10. Find the term of the binomial expansion of $(3x^2/2 - 1/3x)^9$ that is independent of x.
11. Find the term independent of x in the binomial expansion of $(x - 1/x^2)^{3n}$.
12. Write out the general binomial expansion of $(x + h)^n$.
13. Let x be a limit point in the domain of a function f, defined on its domain by $f(t) = t^n$, for some positive integer n. Use the result of Problem 12 to show that f is differentiable at x and $f'(x) = nx^{n-1}$.
14. Prove that $C_{n,1} + C_{n,2} + \cdots + C_{n,n-1} + C_{n,n} = 2^n - 1$, without actually adding the individual terms of the left member.

16.5 Further Remarks on the Binomial Expansion

While the binomial expansion has been developed to apply to a binomial, i.e., a polynomial with two terms, it is possible to group the terms of any polynomial as a binomial, and so the binomial expansion becomes applicable. For example, the binomial expansion can be used for $(1 + 2x + x^2)^6$, if we write it in the form $(\overline{1 + 2x} + x^2)^6$.

It may be shown that the binomial expansion, which we have proven for any positive integral exponent n, is valid under certain circumstances, for an arbitrary real number n. If n is not a positive integer, this binomial expansion does not terminate, and the usefulness of such an infinite series is dependent on its *convergence*. In more detailed studies of infinite series, it is shown that the binomial expansion of $(1 + x)^n$ is valid and converges for any real number n, provided $|x| < 1$. Since $(a + b)^n = a^n(1 + b/a)^n$, we see that a convergent expansion of $(a + b)^n$ can be obtained, if $|b/a| < 1$. Inasmuch as a convergent series can be approximated by the first few terms, we can often use a binomial expansion for approximate computations.

ILLUSTRATION 1. Find the first four terms of the binomial expansion of $(4 + 3/x)^{1/2}$.

Solution. Assuming the validity of the binomial expansion for $n = 1/2$, we write $4 + 3/x$ as $4\left(1 + \dfrac{3}{4x}\right)$ and apply the general result with $a = 1$, and $b = \dfrac{3}{4x}\cdot$ We then obtain

$$(4 + 3/x)^{1/2} = 2\left(1 + \frac{3}{4x}\right)^{1/2}$$

$$= 2\left[1 + (1/2)\frac{3}{4x} + \frac{(1/2)(-1/2)\left(\frac{3}{4x}\right)^2}{2} + \frac{(1/2)(-1/2)(-3/2)\left(\frac{3}{4x}\right)^3}{3\cdot 2} + \cdots\right]$$

$$= 2\left(1 + \frac{3}{8x} - \frac{9}{128x^2} + \frac{27}{1024x^3} + \cdots\right).$$

The first four terms will be an approximation of the complete expansion if $\left|\dfrac{3}{4x}\right| < 1$, i.e., if $|x| > 3/4$.

ILLUSTRATION 2. Compute a 3-significant digit approximation for $(8.4)^{1/3}$.

Solution.

$$(8.4)^{1/3} = [8(1 + 0.4/8)]^{1/3} = 2(1 + 0.05)^{1/3}$$

$$= 2\left[1 + (1/3)(0.05) + \frac{(1/3)(-2/3)(0.05)^2}{1\cdot 2} + \cdots\right]$$

$$= 2(1 + 0.0167 - 0.0003 + \cdots) = 2.03,$$

approximately.

ILLUSTRATION 3. Develop an approximate formula for the maximum range of unobstructed vision, at an elevation of h feet above the surface of the earth, assuming the earth is a sphere of radius 3960 miles.

Solution. If we use r miles as the length of a radius of the earth, and d miles as the maximum range, the right triangle in Figure 16–2 shows that

$(r + h/5280)^2 = d^2 + r^2$, i.e., $r^2(1 + h/5280r)^2 = d^2 + r^2$. Using only the first two terms of the binomial expansion of $(1 + h/5280r)^2$, we obtain $r^2(1 + 2h/5280r) = d^2 + r^2$, i.e., $d^2 = 2rh/5280 = 2(3960)h/5280 = 3h/2$.

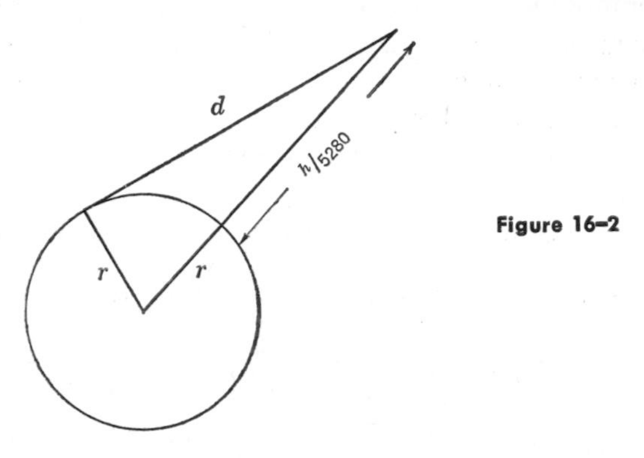

Figure 16–2

Thus, the maximum range of unobstructed vision at a height of h feet is $\sqrt{3h/2}$ miles.

PROBLEM SET 16.5

In Problems 1 through 6, find the first four terms of the binomial expansions, and state the conditions for convergence.

1. $(1 + 2/x)^{1/2}$.
2. $(2 - 3/4x)^{1/4}$.
3. $(2x - 1/a)^{2/3}$.
4. $(1 - x)^{-2}$.
5. $(2 + 3x)^{-1}$.
6. $(8 + 5/a)^{1/3}$.
7. Use the binomial expansion to expand $(1 + 2x + 3x^2)^4$.
8. Use the binomial expansion to expand $(2x - 1/2 + a)^6$.
9. Use the binomial expansion to compute an approximation for $(4.12)^{1/2}$.
10. Use the binomial expansion to compute an approximation for $(8.34)^{1/3}$.
11. The period of a simple pendulum of length L inches is T seconds, where $T = \sqrt{L}/6.253$. Moreover, this pendulum beats seconds if $L = (6.253)^2 = 39.10$. Find the approximate period of the pendulum if its length is increased to 39.15 inches. (Hint: Replace L by $L + h$, and apply the binomial expansion to $\sqrt{L + h}$.)
12. Show that the approximate formulas given below are valid if $|x| < 1$: (*a*) $\sqrt{1 + x} = 1 + x/2$; (*b*) $\sqrt[3]{1 + x} = 1 + x/3$; (*c*) $(1 + x)^{-2/3} = 1 - 2x/3$; (*d*) $(1 - x)^{-1} = 1 + x$.
13. Find the approximate percent increase in the area of a circle, if its radii are increased in length from 100 to 101 inches.
14. Find the approximate percent increase in the volume of a sphere, if its radii are increased in length from 100 to 101 inches.

15. Find an approximation for H from the following formula, and state the limitations that must be placed on p and q for the new result to be valid: $H = (2/p)\sqrt{1-q} + p\sqrt{1+2q/p^2}$.
16. If the length of the pendulum in Problem 11 is decreased to 38.8 inches, find the approximate change in the period.
17. Use the formula of Illustration 3 to compute an approximation for the maximum range of unobstructed vision at an altitude above the earth of 50 yards.

REVIEW TEST A

1. Find the number represented by $\dfrac{\underline{|12}\,\underline{|8}}{10\,\underline{|7}\,\underline{|9}}$.
2. How many different permutations can be made by taking 5 letters from the letters of the word DRAUGHT?
3. A town council has 20 councillors and 10 aldermen. How many committees can be formed, each consisting of 4 councillors and 2 aldermen?
4. Determine the number n so that the ratios $C_{2n,3}:C_{n,2}$ and 44:3 shall be equal.
5. Using each of the 6 distinct, but not entirely distinguishable, digits of the set $\{1, 1, 3, 3, 4, 5\}$, how many distinct integer symbols can be formed?
6. There are 24 letters in the Greek alphabet. How many different Greek-letter fraternity names with 3 letters can be formed, if the second and third letters are to be unlike?
7. How many different bridge hands of 13 cards, containing A K Q J 10 9 8 7 6 of any one suit, are possible?
8. Four letters are chosen from the letters of the word COMMITTEE and arranged in a sequence. Determine the number of possible selections and distinguishable arrangements.
9. Give the complete binomial expansion of $(2x - 3/y)^5$.
10. Find the term independent of x in the binomial expansion of $\left(x/2 - \dfrac{5}{3x^2}\right)^{12}$.
11. Find the first four terms of the binomial expansion of $(8 + 4x)^{1/3}$, and give the limitations on x if the expansion is to be convergent.
12. Use the binomial expansion to approximate $1/\sqrt{47}$ to 4 decimal places.

REVIEW TEST B

1. Find the number represented by $\dfrac{4\,\underline{|10} + 8\underline{|9}}{\underline{|8} + \underline{|9}}$.
2. How many different changes can be rung with a peal of 7 bells, if the tenor bell is always to be last?

3. A class consists of 15 boys and 10 girls. In how many ways can a president, secretary, and treasurer be chosen for the class, if the president is to be a boy?
4. How many permutations can be made of the letters of the word ARTICLE, if vowels are to occupy the first and last positions?
5. A student is eligible for any number of 6 different prizes. In how many different ways might he be a winner?
6. How many basketball teams can be formed from a squad of 21 men, if 3 of them can play at center, 8 can play forward, and the remaining 10 can play guard?
7. How many different bridge hands of 13 cards, that contain all the aces and kings, are possible from a deck of playing cards?
8. Three letters are chosen from the letters of the word DIFFERENT. Find the number of possible selections and distinguishable arrangements.
9. Give the complete binomial expansion of $(x/2 - 2y)^4$.
10. Determine the 12th term of the binomial expansion of $(x/2 - 2/y)^{20}$.
11. Find the first three terms of the binomial expansion of $1/\sqrt[3]{1 - 3x}$, and give the limitations on x if the expansion is to be convergent.
12. Use the binomial expansion to approximate $1/\sqrt[3]{128}$ to 4 decimal places.

REFERENCES

Books

ALBERT, A. A., *College Algebra,* New York, McGraw-Hill, 1946. (Chap. 1.)

HALL, HENRY S. AND SAMUEL R. KNIGHT, *Higher Algebra,* London, MacMillan, 1950. (Chaps. 11, 13, and 14.)

American Mathematical Monthly

BALLANTINE, J. P., "$C_{n,r}$ Where the n Things Include Identities," Vol. 57, p. 626 (1950).

COOLIDGE, J. P., "The Story of the Binomial Theorem," Vol. 56, p. 147 (1949).

FULTON, C. M., "A Simple Proof of the Binomial Theorem," Vol. 59, p. 243 (1953).

17
PROBABILITY AND STATISTICS

Well, hardly ever!
GILBERT AND SULLIVAN

17.1 Introduction

In recent years, the science of statistics has become of great practical importance, with every business and industrial enterprise of at least moderate size having its own staff of statisticians. It is the purpose of this chapter to give the student some small indication of the nature of this relatively new branch of mathematics.

The subject of statistics may be said to be concerned with the collection, presentation, analysis, and interpretation of sets of data. There are four major aspects of the subject, and we comment briefly on each of them.

1. After a set of data has been collected, it is convenient to have certain *descriptive measures* to apply to the set. To anyone familiar with them, these measures will present a condensed picture of the whole set. For example, the average grade on an examination usually gives the instructor and students an indication of the class performance.

2. A *universe* or *population* of data is the complete set, from which a sample may be drawn. One of the important roles of statistical analysis is to predict the nature of an unknown universe, from a knowledge of the nature of a properly drawn sample. The familiar Gallup poll is an analysis of this type.

3. Sometimes, it is desirable to make predictions about the nature of a sample, when the universe of the sample is completely known. The analyses of games of chance involve this aspect of statistics.

4. The branch of statistics known as *quality control* is concerned with the comparison of samples drawn from an unknown universe. Samples of a manufactured product are tested for certain defects, and as long as the results stay within certain predetermined limits, the production of the article is said to be "under control." If the samples show too great discrepancies, a fault in production is indicated, and an investigation should be undertaken to determine the source of the trouble.

In the present chapter we can, of course, touch on only a few of these topics. Because of the nature of statistics, it is only natural that probability should be a basic tool, and it is with a brief discussion of this subject that we open the chapter.

17.2 Simple Probability

When an experiment is performed, it frequently happens that the result may assume any one of several recognizably different forms. For example, if a ball is drawn at random from a bag, known to contain both black and white balls, there are two possible results: (1) the ball is black; (2) the ball is white. If the bag is known to contain at least two balls of each color and two random draws are made, there are three possible results: (1) both balls are white; (2) both balls are black; (3) one ball is white and the other ball is black. If the bag contains more white balls than black balls, it is clear that a random draw is more "likely" to produce a white than a black ball. It is one of the principal purposes of the theory of probability to put a *numerical measure* on the "likelihood" that the result of an experiment will have a certain designated form—for example, that a random draw from the above bag will produce a white ball. The connection between probability and games of chance is, of course, quite obvious, but in recent years the theory of probability has assumed a position of importance in other fields of science including physics. In fact, in the opinion of many modern scholars, the ultimate building blocks of the universe may depend more on the laws of probability than on the laws of Newtonian physics.

In the language of probability, an experiment is known as a *trial*, while the set of all possible outcomes of the trial is the *universe* U. For example, if the trial is a toss of two coins, there are four possible outcomes comprising the set U, which we may list as: TT, HH, TH, HT. If the trial is a throw of a pair of 6-faced dice, it is clear that there are 36 possible outcomes, and in this case U will contain 36 members. After the outcome of a trial is known, it is always possible to say whether or not a certain *event* has occurred. For example, we may be interested in the *event of 2 heads* in a toss of a pair of coins, or in the *event of a sum of 7* in a throw of a pair of dice. More generally, an *event* is a result of a trial, the occurrence of which is known with the outcome of the trial. *It is meaningful to discuss an event* E *only if it is clear for every outcome of the trial whether or not* E *has occurred.* In Chapter 4, we considered the notion of whether or not an ordered pair of a certain kind satisfied a relation, and then found it convenient to identify the relation with all such ordered pairs that do satisfy it. In the same vein, *we now propose to identify the event* E *with the set of all outcomes of a trial in which* E *has occurred.* Furthermore, we shall say that an outcome is *favorable* to an event E, and the trial is a *success*, if the event occurs as a result of the outcome, which is the same thing as saying that the outcome is a member of the set now identified with E. For example, if the trial is a toss of a coin, the event of throwing a head may now be identified symbolically with the outcome H; in this case, the event has a single member. If the trial is a throw of a pair of dice, the event of throwing 7 has the following six outcomes as members: 1, 6; 6, 1; 2, 5; 5, 2; 3, 4; 4, 3. It is clear, of course, that the same outcome may be a member of more than one event. For example, the outcome 2, 2 in a throw of a pair of dice, is a member of the event of throwing 4 and also of the event of throwing doublets. If the probability of an event is determined from theoretical consideration, we are dealing with an example of *theoretical* or *a priori* probability; on the other hand, if the computation is based on sets of observed data, the resulting probability is known as *empirical*. We shall consider both types, briefly.

It is difficult to give a good definition of probability, but for our purposes the following one will prove satisfactory. We shall use the symbolism of the algebra of sets of Chapter 1, including $N(A)$ for the cardinal number of a finite set A.

DEFINITION. Let U be the universe or set of all possible outcomes of a trial, all outcomes considered equally likely. Then, if an event E is a subset of U, the (a priori) probability $p(E)$ of E is $N(E)/N(U)$, and the probability $p(E')$that E will not occur is $N(E')/N(U)$.

It follows from this definition that $p(U) = 1$ and $p(U') = 0$. Thus, if an event contains all possible outcomes, it is sure to succeed and the numerical probability of this event is 1; on the other hand, if the event contains no possible outcomes, it is sure to fail and the numerical measure of the probability of this event is 0. If E is a non-empty subset of U, $p(E)$ is a rational number between 0 and 1. Since $N(E) + N(E') = N(U)$, the definition also implies that $p(E) + p(E') = 1$ or $p(E') = 1 - p(E)$, a result that is often useful. If $N(E) = a$ and $N(E') = b$, in the above definition, we can also say that the odds are *a to b in favor of* or *b to a against* the event E.

Our notation quite correctly implies that we are thinking of p as a *function* on the set of subsets of the universe U of possible outcomes of a trial. The value $p(E)$, at the event E, of this *probability distribution* function or simply *probability* function, is then the probability of the event. Before attempting a problem in probability, it is desirable to have clearly in mind the nature of the *trial*, the *universe* U of possible outcomes, and the subset E of outcomes constituting the *event*. The central idea of probability is this: if the probability $p(E)$ of an event E in a random trial is known, the "expected" or "probable" number of successes, i.e., outcomes that belong to E, in n trials is $p(E) \cdot n$. There is, of course, no guarantee that there will be exactly this number, *but* if the probability has been computed correctly, as the number of trials increases, the number of successes should approach the number $p(E) \cdot n$ as a limit.

ILLUSTRATION 1. Determine the probability of throwing a number greater than 3 in a single throw of an ordinary die, having faces numbered from 1 to 6.

Solution. The *trial* is a throw of the die, the *universe* U is the set of all possible outcomes of this throw, while the *event* E is the subset of outcomes in which a number greater than 3 appears. There are three possible outcomes belonging to E, a throw of 4, 5, or 6, and so $N(E) = 3$. Since $N(U) = 6$, we find that $p(E) = N(E)/N(U) = 3/6 = 1/2$, which is the desired probability.

ILLUSTRATION 2. What is the probability of throwing 5 in a single throw of a pair of dice?

Solution. The *trial* is a throw of a pair of dice, the *universe* U is the set of all possible outcomes of the throws, while the *event* E is the set of outcomes in which the sum of the numbers that turn up on the dice is 5. If we assume that the dice are distinguishable in some way, they can land in any one of $6 \cdot 6$ or 36 different ways, i.e., $N(U) = 36$. The outcome will be favorable to the event if the faces read any one of the following pairs of numbers: 1, 4; 4, 1; 2, 3; 3, 2. Thus, $N(E) = 4$ and the desired probability $p(E)$ is $N(E)/N(U)$, which is 4/36 or 1/9.

ILLUSTRATION 3. Find the probability of throwing at least one ace in a single throw of a pair of dice.

Solution. The *trial* is a throw of a pair of dice, the *universe* U is the set of all possible outcomes of the throw, while the *event* E is the set of outcomes in which at least one ace appears. We shall find $p(E')$ and use $p(E) = 1 - p(E')$. The dice can fall in any one of $6 \cdot 6$ or 36 different ways, if we consider them distinguishable, and so $N(U) = 36$. Of these outcomes, there are $5 \cdot 5$ or 25 that contain no aces, and so $N(E') = 25$. Hence $p(E') = 25/36$, and so $p(E) = 1 - 25/36 = 11/36$, the desired probability.

ILLUSTRATION 4. From a bag containing 4 white and 6 black balls, 3 balls are drawn at random. What are the odds against them being all white?

Solution. The *trial* is a draw of 3 balls, the *universe* U is the set of all possible draws of 3 balls, all the balls assumed to be distinguishable, while the *event* E is the set of draws in which 3 white balls appear. The total number of ways in which 3 balls may be drawn from the bag is $C_{10,3}$ or 120, which is $N(U)$ for this problem. The number of ways in which 3 white balls can be drawn is $C_{4,3}$ or 4, which is $N(E)$. It follows that the probability that E will occur is $N(E)/N(U)$ or 1/30, and so the odds against the balls being all black are 29 to 1.

Note. In the solutions of the problems in Illustrations 2, 3, and 4, we have assumed that the objects involved were distinguishable, which was a matter of convenience rather than necessity. If we should not make this assumption, the numbers $N(E)$ and $N(U)$ would be proportionally reduced.

We have remarked that if the probability of an event E is $p(E)$ in a single trial, the "probable" number of successes or favorable outcomes in n trials is $p(E) \cdot n$. This notion is used in our definition of the *empirical* probability of an event. When this concept of probability is used, it is impossible to list all the members of the universe U or of the event E, but it is still possible to obtain an approximation to $N(E)/N(U)$, i.e., $p(E)$. This number will be an approximation to the probability that in a future trial, the outcome will be favorable to E.

DEFINITION. If there have been a outcomes of n trials that have been favorable to an event E, the *empirical probability* $p(E)$ that E will occur in a future trial is a/n. The empirical probability $p(E')$ that E will not occur is $(n - a)/n$, and so $p(E) + p(E') = 1$, as before.

The probability of a head in a single throw of a coin is 1/2 *only if* the coin is true. Thus, if 756 heads turned up in 1000 throws of a well-worn coin, a better estimate of the probability of throwing a head with this coin is 756/1000, i.e., 0.756. In a similar manner, the probability that a person of age x will live to age $x + 1$ can be computed from a mortality table. The Commissioners' 1941 Standard Ordinary Mortality Table, based on 1,000,000 lives at age 1, lists 454,548 survivors at age 70, with 26,955 of these dying before age 71. The probability that a person in the category of the table will survive to age 70 is then 0.454548, while the probability that such a person who has already reached age 70 will survive to age 71 is 427,593/454,548, i.e., 0.940699.

PROBLEM SET 17.2

The following table is a portion of the Commissioners' Standard Ordinary Mortality Table, which is needed in some of the problems of this set.

At Age	*Number Surviving*	*Deaths*
1	1,000,000	5,770
..	....	.....
70	454,548	26,955
71	427,593	27,481
72	400,112	27,872
73	372,240	28,104
74	344,136	28,154
75	315,982	28,009

1. Find the probability that a person in the category of the above table will survive to age 73.
2. Find the probability that a person in the category of the above table, who has reached age 73, will die before reaching age 74.
3. Let A and B be two persons in the category of the above table, who are both alive at age 72. Find the probability that (a) B will be alive at age 73; (b) A will be alive at age 75.
4. Of 7384 men on a certain college campus, 1230 were found to be over 6 feet in height. Determine the probability that a man drawn from this group at random will be over 6 feet in height.
5. A bag contains 4 red and 5 white balls. If 2 balls are drawn, what are the odds in favor of them being both red?
6. In a single throw of a pair of dice, find the probability of a throw of (a) 3; (b) 4.
7. In a single throw of a pair of dice, find the probability that at least one ace is thrown.
8. Find the probability of throwing more than 8 in a single throw of a pair of dice.
9. Two cards are drawn at random from a pack of playing cards. Find the probability that one is a queen and the other is a king.
10. Four playing cards are accidentally dropped while a deck is being shuffled. Find the probability that the dropped cards are one from each suit.
11. If an integer between 1 and 50 is chosen at random, what is the probability that it is divisible by 4?
12. How many different bridge hands are possible from a deck of 52 playing cards? What is the probability of drawing a hand containing all hearts?
13. A "full house" is a poker hand of 5 cards consisting of 3 cards of the same rank and a pair of another rank; a "royal flush" is a hand consisting of A K Q J 10 of the same suit. Compare the probabilities of a royal flush and a full house in a random poker hand.
14. The letters of the word FATHER are placed at random in a row. What is the probability that the two vowels come together?
15. If 13 persons take random places at a round table, show that the odds are 5 to 1 against two particular persons sitting together.
16. A bag contains a penny, a nickel, a dime, a quarter, and a half-dollar. If two coins are drawn at random from the bag, find the probability that the coins are worth less than a half-dollar.
17. On a certain multiple-choice examination, 7 answers are listed for each problem, four incorrect and three correct. If 2 answers are to be checked for each problem, what is the probability that a student who guesses will get a satisfactory answer for any one problem?
18. A dresser drawer contains 10 black and 10 white socks. What is the probability that a random grab of 2 socks will produce 2 socks of the same color?

17.3 Compound Events

In the preceding section we outlined the essential notion of *a priori* probability: if a trial has n possible outcomes, all equally likely and of which a are favorable to an event, the probability that the outcome of a random trial will be favorable to the event is a/n. Most problems in elementary probability require nothing but this elementary notion for their solution. However, it sometimes happens, especially when empirical probability is involved, that a problem can be solved more easily after it has been broken down into several simpler problems. We wish to emphasize that this is a matter of choice rather than of necessity.

In this section we are going to consider *compound* events, that are the result of two or more ordinary events occurring in succession. For example, if 2 balls are drawn in succession from a bag containing 5 white and 5 black balls, we may wish to know the probability that both balls will be black. It should be observed, in this case, that while the two trials of drawing a ball involve the same physical act, the probabilities of drawing a black ball are not the same in both instances: the probability of drawing a black ball the second time depends on whether or not a black ball was drawn the first time. If we let E be the event of drawing a black ball the first time, and F be the event of drawing a black ball the second time, we are concerned here with the probability of *both events in succession*, and we can conveniently indicate this probability by $p(E \times F)$. If U_1 and U_2 are the universes associated with E and F, respectively, our notation implies that we are considering $E \times F$ as a set of ordered pairs of $U_1 \times U_2$.

As an aid in the determination of $p(E \times F)$, for two events E and F, it is convenient to consider first the *probability* $p(F \mid E)$ *of event* F *after event* E *has occurred.* The universe, associated with event F after event E has occurred, is the set $E \times U_2$, and so $p(F \mid E) = N(E \times F)/N(E \times U_2)$. But this latter fraction can be written as $[N(E \times F)/N(U_1 \times U_2)]/N(E \times U_2)/N(U_1 \times U_2)$, and since $N(E \times U_2)/N(U_1 \times U_2) = N(E)/N(U_1)$, it follows that $p(F \mid E) = p(E \times F)/p(E)$. The more useful form of this result is $p(E \times F) = p(E) \cdot p(F \mid E)$, which we state in the following theorem.

THEOREM. Let $p(E)$ be the probability of an event E, and $p(F \mid E)$ be the probability of an event F after event E has occurred. Then, if $p(E \times F)$ is the probability that the *sequence* of events E and F will occur, $p(E \times F) = p(E) \cdot p(F \mid E)$.

Two events E and F are said to be *independent* if the probability of the occurrence of one does not depend on the occurrence of the other. For example, the event of drawing a black ball from a bag, from which one drawing has already been made, is independent of the first drawing *if the first ball has been replaced.* It is evident that $p(F \mid E) = p(F)$, if events E and F are independent, and so we have an immediate corollary to the preceding theorem.

Corollary. If E and F are independent events, $p(E \times F) = p(E) \cdot p(F)$.

Let us now apply the theorem to the problem, mentioned above, of drawing 2 black balls from a bag containing 5 black and 5 white balls. In this case, event E is the first drawing of a black ball, while event F is the drawing of a second black ball after one black ball has been drawn. Since there are initially 5 black balls, out of a total of 10, we have $p(E) = 5/10 = 1/2$. After a black ball has been drawn, there are 4 black balls remaining, and so $p(F \mid E) = 4/9$. An application of the theorem then yields the desired probability $p(E \times F)$ as $(1/2)(4/9)$ or $2/9$.

ILLUSTRATION 1. Two cards are drawn in succession from a deck of playing cards. Find the probability that the first is an ace, and the second is a queen if (*a*) the first card is replaced before the second draw; (*b*) the first card is not replaced.

Solution.

(*a*) The compound event here is a sequence of two events, the first event E being a draw of an ace, while the second event F is a draw of a queen after the first card has been replaced. These two events are clearly independent, and so $p(E) = p(F) = 4/52 = 1/13$. By the corollary of the theorem, the desired probability $p(E \times F)$ is $(1/13)(1/13)$ or $1/169$.

(*b*) In this case the events, which we shall still label E and F, are not independent. For the first draw, $p(E) = 1/13$, as before, but at the time of the second draw we must assume that one ace is missing. Hence $p(F \mid E) = 4/51$, and so $p(E \times F) = (1/13)(4/51) = 4/663$.

The results, pertaining to a sequence of two events, can be readily extended to any finite sequence of events. For example, if E, F, and G are three events, $p(E \times F \times G) = p(E) \cdot p(F \mid E) \cdot p(G \mid F \mid E)$, where $p(G \mid F \mid E)$ is the probability of event G after both events E and F have occurred in sequence.

ILLUSTRATION 2. Find the probability of throwing heads and tails alternately, in three successive throws of a coin.

Solution. Let E, F, and G be the successive alternate throws of the coin, these events being clearly independent. Either outcome of the first throw is favorable to E and so $p(E) = 1$. The outcome of the second throw must be opposite to that of the first throw, and so $p(F) = 1/2$. Similarly, $p(G) = 1/2$, and an application of an extension to the corollary above gives $p(E \times F \times G) = 1 \cdot (1/2) \cdot (1/2) = 1/4$, where we have used the fact that $p(F \mid E) = p(F)$ and $p(G \mid F \mid E) = p(G)$.

PROBLEM SET 17.3

1. A bag contains 4 red and 5 white balls. If two successive draws of 1 ball each are made, determine the probability that both balls will be red.

2. Three cards are drawn at random from an ordinary deck of 52 playing cards. Find the probability that they will consist of an ace, a king, and a queen.
3. The odds against A solving a certain problem are 3 to 5, and the odds in favor of B solving the same problem are 5 to 4. What is the probability that both A and B will solve the problem?
4. A pair of dice is thrown twice. What is the probability of 7 on the first throw and 11 on the second?
5. A bag contains 10 counters, marked from 1 to 10. If 2 counters are drawn successively, the first replaced before the second drawing, find the probability that (*a*) both draws will produce the same counter; (*b*) both counters will be even.
6. What is the probability of throwing 10 in two successive throws of a pair of dice?
7. If a certain man reaches age 72, he is to have a 1/3 chance of obtaining a sum of money. What is the probability that he will get this money, if he is now 70 years of age? (Use the table given in Problem Set 17.2.)
8. A fraternity of a small college has 60 members, of whom 15 belong to the fraternity football team. If the college has 800 male students, what is the probability that a man selected at random from the campus population will belong to the fraternity football team?
9. Two tennis players are so matched that the odds are 2 to 1 in favor of the winner of the previous game. What is the probability that the winner of the first game will win the set of 6 straight games?
10. Let A and B be two persons in the category of the mortality table given in Problem Set 17.2. If they are both alive at age 70, determine the probability that (*a*) both A and B will be alive at age 72; (*b*) A will be alive at age 72, but B will die at age 71; (*c*) both will die at age 71.

17.4 Compositions of Events

In the preceding section we constructed Cartesian products of events, that were sets with possibly different universes. These Cartesian products are sequences of events, and we were able to discover their probabilities of occurrence. We now return to a consideration of events, that are subsets of the *same* universe U, and study the probabilities associated with various compositions of such events.

Two events are said to be *mutually exclusive*, if they have no elements in common, which is equivalent to the condition that their intersection is the empty set. For example, both a head and a tail cannot occur in a single toss of a coin, and so these events are mutually exclusive. In general, for any events E and F of a universe U, the event $E \cap F$ is the subset of U that consists of all elements common to E and F, and so $p(E \cap F)$, i.e., $N(E \cap F)/N(U)$, is the probability that the outcome of a trial will be favorable to *both* E and F. For example, in a random draw of a card from a deck of playing cards, we may be interested in the probability that the card will be both a face card and a black card. If E is the event of drawing a face card, and F is the event of drawing a black card, it is evident that $N(E \cap F) = 6$, and so $p(E \cap F) = 6/52 = 3/26$.

It may be intuitively evident that if E and F are subsets of the same universe U, the probabilities $p(E \times F)$ and $p(E \cap F)$ are the same. However, let us repeat the type of proof that was given in the preceding section. If we assume that E has taken place, E may be considered to be the universe of $E \cap F$. Thus, again writing $p(F \mid E)$ for the probability of F, after E has occurred, $p(F \mid E) = N(E \cap F)/N(E) = [N(E \cap F)/N(U)] \cdot [N(U)/N(E)] = p(E \cap F)/p(E)$, and so $p(E \cap F) = p(E) \cdot p(F \mid E)$.

It sometimes happens that we are interested in the probability of *either* event E or event F, without preference as to which one occurs. For example, the respective events under consideration may be a throw of 5 and a throw of 7, with either one being considered a success. It is evident here that the probability of a success is 2/6 or 1/3, but the general situation is described by the following theorem. In harmony with set notation, we are using $p(E \cup F)$ for the probability that either E or F or both will occur.

THEOREM. If E and F are events associated with a given trial, then $p(E \cup F) = p(E) + p(F) - p(E \cap F)$.

Proof. The proof follows directly as an application of the result of Problem 17 of Problem Set 1.4. Thus, $N(E \cup F) = N(E) + N(F) - N(E \cap F)$, and so $p(E \cup F) = N(E \cup F)/N(U) = N(E)/N(U) + N(F)/N(U) - N(E \cap F)/N(U) = p(E) + p(F) - p(E \cap F)$, as asserted.

Corollary. If E and F are mutually exclusive, $p(E \cup F) = p(E) + p(F)$.

ILLUSTRATION 1. Find the probability of either 4 or 5 in a single throw of a pair of dice.

Solution. Let E be a throw of 4 and F be a throw of 5, with U the universe of throws of the dice. The dice can land in any one of 36 ways, and so $N(U) = 36$, considering them all distinguishable. Of these, 3 are favorable to E (1, 3; 3, 1; 2, 2) and 4 are favorable to F (1, 4; 4, 1; 2, 3; 3, 2). Hence $p(E) = 3/36 = 1/12$ and $p(F) = 4/36 = 1/9$. The corollary of the theorem then shows that $p(E \cup F) = 1/12 + 1/9 = 7/36$, since the two events are mutually exclusive.

ILLUSTRATION 2. What is the probability of a doublet or 6 in a single throw of a pair of dice?

Solution. Let E be a throw of a doublet and F be a throw of 6, with U the universe of throws of the dice. The dice can land in any one of 36 ways, considered distinguishable, and so $N(U) = 36$. Of these, 6 are favorable to E and 5 are favorable to F, so that $p(E) = 6/36 = 1/6$ and $p(F) = 5/36$. A doublet and 6 can occur simultaneously in only one way (with a pair of 3's), and so $p(E \cap F) = 1/36$. [The same result can be obtained with the formula $p(E \cap F) = p(E) \cdot p(F \mid E)$. Thus, since $p(E) = 1/6$ and $p(F \mid E) = 1/6$, it follows that $p(E \cap F) = (1/6)(1/6) = 1/36$.] An application of the theorem then shows that $p(E \cup F) = 1/6 + 5/36 - 1/36 = 10/36 = 5/18$.

ILLUSTRATION 3. A purse has two compartments, one containing 1 gold and 3 silver coins, and the other containing 2 gold and 2 silver coins, all coins of the same size. What is the probability that a random draw of a coin will be a gold one?

Solution. There are two mutually exclusive compound events to be considered here. Let the first one be $E_1 \times F_1$, with E_1 the selection of the first compartment and F_1 the drawing of a gold coin from it; and let $E_2 \times F_2$ be the second compound event, with E_2 the selection of the second compartment and F_2 the drawing of a gold coin from it. An application of the corollary to the theorem shows that $p(E_1 \times F_1) = (1/2)(1/3) = 1/6$, since the probability of selecting the first compartment is 1/2, and after it has been selected, the probability that a gold coin will be drawn from it is 1/3. A similar analysis yields $p(E_2 \times F_2) = (1/2)(2/4) = 1/4$ as the probability of the second compound event. Inasmuch as these are mutually exclusive, the corollary to the theorem shows that the desired probability is $1/3 + 1/4$ or $7/12$.

PROBLEM SET 17.4

1. In a single throw of two dice, find the probability of throwing (*a*) 8; (*b*) less than 8.
2. Two cards are drawn at random from a deck of 52 playing cards. Find the probability that they are both face cards or have numbers larger than 8.
3. The odds against a certain event are 5 to 2, and the odds in favor of an event independent of the first are 6 to 5. Find the probability that at least one of the events will happen.
4. A counter is drawn from a bag, containing 20 counters marked from 1 to 20. Find the probability that the counter selected has a number that is a multiple of 3 or 5.
5. What is the probability of throwing doublets at least twice in three throws of a pair of dice?
6. It has been estimated that the probability that a certain candidate will be nominated for one office is 1/3 and for another office 1/6. If the probability that he will be elected, after having been nominated, is considered to be 1/2, determine the probability that he will be elected to at least one of the offices.
7. In a game of bridge, South is the dummy and North notices that the ace of spades is in neither his hand nor the dummy's. What is the probability that East holds the ace of spades?

8. The odds in favor of a good review of a certain book, by three independent critics, are 5 to 2, 4 to 3, and 2 to 3, respectively. Find the probability that a majority of the reviews will be favorable.
9. What is the probability of obtaining at least one head in a single toss of 5 coins?
10. A certain race horse is to be ridden in a race by one of two jockeys B and C. The odds are 2 to 1 that B will be selected, in which case the probability of a win is 1/2; if C rides the horse, the probability of a win is 2/3. What are the odds that the horse will win?

17.5 Repeated Trials

A special case of the theorem in Section 17.3 and its generalization, which is of great interest, occurs when the several events are identical along with their associated universes. Thus, if the probability of the occurrence of an event in a single trial is known, this result will enable us to compute the probability that it will occur exactly r times in n trials. In order to simplify the notation, let p be the probability $p(E)$ of an event E in a single trial, with q the probability $p(E')$ that the event will not occur; it is clear, of course, that $p + q = 1$. It then turns out that the probability of the occurrence of the event r times in n trials is the $(r + 1)$th term of the binomial expansion of $(q + p)^n$. For if we select any *particular* set of r trials out of the total number n of trials, the probability that E will occur in each of these and fail to occur in every other one is $p^r q^{n-r}$. But r particular trials can be selected in $C_{n,r}$ different ways; and since the events, associated with the various trials are independent, the probability that E will occur in *any* r trials and fail in the others is $C_{n,r}p^r q^{n-r}$. If we expand $(q + p)^n$ by the binomial theorem, the result is $q^n + C_{n,1}q^{n-1}p + C_{n,2}q^{n-2}p^2 + \cdots + C_{n,r}q^{n-r}p^r + \cdots + p^n$. It then appears that the respective terms of this expansion will be the probabilities that the event E will occur exactly $0, 1, 2, \cdots, r, \cdots, n$ times in n trials. Let us now associate with an event E the function B, defined on the set $\{1, 2, 3, \cdots, n\}$ of integers by $B(x) = C_{n,x}p^x q^{n-x}$, for each x in the domain of B. This function is known as the *Bernoulli* or *binomial* distribution function of E; the value $B(x)$, of B at x, is the probability that E will occur exactly x times out of n trials.

ILLUSTRATION 1. In 5 throws of a pair of dice, determine the probability of throwing at least 3 doublets.

Solution. The probability of throwing at least 3 doublets is the sum of the probabilities of throwing 3, 4, and 5 doublets. Since the probability of throwing a doublet in a single throw of 2 dice is 6/36 or 1/6, the probability of throwing doublets at least 3 times is the sum of the last 3 terms of the binomial expansion of $(5/6 + 1/6)^5$. The desired probability is then $C_{5,3}(5/6)^2(1/6)^3 + C_{5,4}(5/6)(1/6)^4 + C_{5,5}(1/6)^5$, which reduces to 23/3888.

We now introduce a new idea. Suppose there are 100 tickets in a lottery for a prize of \$100. Since a holder of *all* the tickets would be sure to win, the money value to him of each ticket could be considered to be \$1. More generally, if p is the probability of success in a certain venture, and $\$M$ is the monetary reward for being a winner, we say that a participant in the venture has an *expectation* of $\$pM$. We might also say that the *probable value* of his winnings is $\$pM$, the notions of "expectation" and "probable value" being essentially the same. The word "expectation" as used above has the technical meaning given to it, and we do not imply that a person playing a game of chance will necessarily win his "expectation"; in fact, it may not be possible for him to do so! However, if the player continues the game indefinitely, his *average* win will approach his expectation.

ILLUSTRATION 2. A person is to win \$10 in a dice game, if he throws exactly 2 aces in 5 throws. Determine his expectation.

Solution. The probability p of throwing an ace in a single throw of a die is 1/6. It follows that the probability of 2 aces in 5 throws is then $C_{5,2}(5/6)^3(1/6)^2$, which reduces to 625/3888. His expectation is accordingly \$10(625)/3888 or approximately \$1.61.

In many games of chance, it is possible for a player to win various amounts on different outcomes of the game. A player's expectation in such a game is the *sum* of his expectations according to the different outcomes. For example, in a dice game a player may win \$1 if he rolls a 5, and \$5 if he rolls a 6, in a single roll of a die. His expectation is the sum of his expectations on the two possible wins, and since $(1/6)1 + (1/6)5 = 6/6 = 1$, his expectation is \$1.

ILLUSTRATION 3. One purse contains 5 dimes and 2 nickels, while a second purse contains only 5 dimes. A coin is transferred from the first purse to the second, and after the transfer, a coin is taken from the second and placed in the first purse. What is the probable value of the contents of the first purse?

Solution. There are three possibilities: (*a*) a nickel was removed and returned; (*b*) a nickel was removed and replaced by a dime; (*c*) a dime was removed and replaced by a (possibly different) dime. The probability of (*a*) is $(2/7)(1/6)$ or $2/42$; the probability of (*b*) is $(2/7)(5/6)$ or $10/42$; and the probability of (*c*) is $(5/7)(5/6)$ or $25/42$. The probable value of the contents of the first purse in cents is then $60(2/42) + 55(10/42) + 60(25/42)$, which equals $2170/42$, i.e., approximately 52 cents.

PROBLEM SET 17.5

1. The probability that A will win a game with B is 3/5. Find the probability that A will win at least 3 games out of 5.

2. A coin is tossed 5 times. What is the probability of obtaining (*a*) exactly 2 heads; (*b*) exactly 4 heads; (*c*) at least 3 heads?
3. Two coins are drawn from a bag containing three gold coins of value $5 each, and 4 silver coins of value $2 each. Find the expectation of the draw.
4. In a lottery, 300 tickets are sold for 10 cents each, the holder of the lucky number in a draw to receive $10. What is the expectation of a holder of a single ticket? Was the lottery a fair one from a mathematical point of view?
5. A boy aged 10 years is to receive $10,000 when he reaches the age of 21. Determine his present expectation. (According to the Commissioners' 1941 Mortality Table, out of 971,804 lives at age 10, there are 949,171 still living at age 21.)
6. If the probability of a marksman hitting a target is 1/4, find the probability of at least 7 hits in 10 attempts.
7. In 5 throws of a single die, determine the probability of throwing (*a*) 3 aces exactly; (*b*) 3 aces at least.
8. An urn contains 3 white and 4 black balls. If 2 balls are withdrawn, without their colors being noticed, what is the probability that another draw will produce a white ball?
9. Two purses contain gold and silver coins of the same size, the first one containing 3 gold coins and 2 silver coins, the second one containing only 3 silver coins. A coin is transferred from the first purse to the second, and after the transfer 2 coins are moved from the second purse to the first. If the gold coins are worth $5 each and silver coins are worth $2 each, what is the probable value of the contents of the first purse?

10*. A and B throw for a stake of $22, to be won by the first one to throw 5 with a single die. If A has the first throw, what are the odds in favor of his winning? What is his expectation? (Hint: the probabilities are sums of infinite series.)

17.6 Frequency Distributions

Up to this point, we have been concerned with the probabilities of events that have finite universes. For example, the universe of ways in which a pair of dice can fall is 36, which is a finite number. As we progress to a consideration of some of the elements of statistics, our universe—or *population* as it is frequently known in this setting—will often be quite large; in fact, for theoretical considerations, it will sometimes be considered infinite. Since statistical considerations always involve *numerical measures* of quantities, we shall often regard these measures as imbedded in the universe or population $R^{\#}$ of all real numbers. In any study of statistics, we are concerned either in fact or in theory, with sets of numerical data, and one of the first steps in an analysis of such a set is to arrange the items in an array, which exhibits their *frequency distribution.* These sets will always be subsets of $R^{\#}$.

Suppose that we are interested in an analysis of the number of heads that appear, when 6 coins are tossed 40 times simultaneously. The following table exhibits the results of one such experiment.

Number of heads	0	1	2	3	4	5	6
Frequency	2	3	10	12	8	4	1

The various subsets, into which the items are grouped in such an array, are known as *classes*, the *class mark* being the identifying measure of the items in any given class. The number of items in a class is known as its *class frequency*. In the above array we have 7 natural classes, with integral class marks from 0 to 6; the frequencies lie between 1 and 12, 6 heads appearing once and 3 heads appearing 12 times. This is an example of a frequency distribution involving only a finite number of items.

If the number of distinct elements in such a set of data is large, or even drawn from a continuum of numbers, the method of grouping is not so natural as in the preceding example. In such a case, each class will contain all those numbers of the data that lie within a certain *class interval*, the middle number of this interval being known as the *class mark*. In effect, we are then considering all the elements of a class to be equal to the class mark. This method of grouping not only simplifies the work connected with a set of data, but also frequently reveals trends in the data that might not otherwise be noticed. There are no fixed rules for the number of classes in a frequency distribution, but the usual number is between 10 and 20. The class boundaries should be chosen in such a way, that each item lies unambiguously in only one class. In the following array, we present the results of a survey of the heights in centimeters of 1000 college men, with x_i and f_i representing, respectively, the class mark and class frequency of the ith class.

i	1	2	3	4	5	6	7
Class	155–157	158–160	161–163	164–166	167–169	170–172	173–175
x_i	156	159	162	165	168	171	174
f_i	3	7	30	52	90	150	180

i	8	9	10	11	12	13	15
Class	176–178	179–181	182–184	185–187	188–190	191–193	194–196
x_i	177	180	183	186	189	192	195
f_i	176	135	110	55	8	2	2

There are many different ways of exhibiting a frequency distribution, graphically, but one of the best is by means of a frequency *histogram*. The class intervals of the distribution are marked on a uniform horizontal scale, while a uniform vertical scale is chosen that includes all the frequencies of the various classes. A rectangle is then constructed on each indicated class interval as a base, having its measure of height equal to the corresponding class frequency. This set of rectangles constitutes the frequency histogram of the data.

If the class interval is taken as the unit of horizontal measurement, and the unit frequency as the unit of vertical measurement, with the two units of equal length on the graph, the associated measure of area of any rectangle is equal to the corresponding class frequency. Furthermore, the

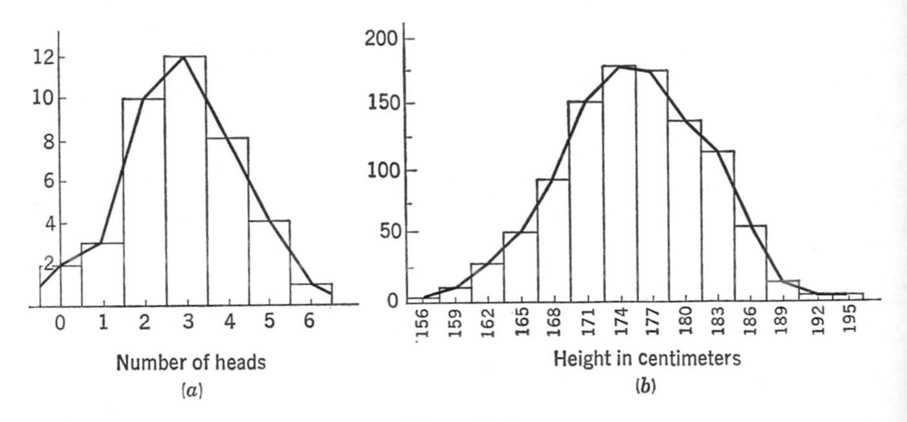

Figure 17–1

measure of area of the histogram, up to and including the upper boundary of a class, is equal to the cumulative frequency up to and including this class; the total frequency including all classes, i.e., the number of individual items in the data, is equal to the measure of area of the whole histogram. At a later point in our analysis, this area point of view will become of great importance.

A slight variation from the frequency histogram is the frequency *polygon* of a distribution. This is formed from the frequency histogram by joining the midpoints of the tops of successive rectangles with line segments. The polygon may be terminated by joining the first and last of these midpoints, respectively, with the midpoints of the lower vertical boundary of the first, and the upper vertical boundary of the last, of the rectangles. In Figure 17–1, we have shown frequency histograms and polygons for the two distributions previously discussed. Notice that the units of length on the vertical and horizontal scales are different, in both instances, and so considerations of area are not geometrically valid.

PROBLEM SET 17.6

1. Five coins were tossed simultaneously 50 times, with the results tabulated below; x is the number of heads, and f is the corresponding frequency. Construct a frequency histogram and frequency polygon of this data.

x	0	1	2	3	4	5
f	1	16	21	10	1	1

2. Toss 5 coins 50 times, tabulate the results, and construct a frequency histogram and frequency polygon of the distribution. Compare these with the ones constructed in Problem 1.
3. The following table lists the weights in pounds of 625 college freshmen. Construct the corresponding frequency histogram and frequency polygon.

Weight	105	116	127	138	149	160	171	182	193
Frequency	15	40	141	162	125	86	40	12	4

4. The following table records the results of a short quiz, with x the grade and f the corresponding frequency. Construct the frequency histogram and frequency polygon of this data.

x	0	1	2	3	4	5	6	7	8	9	10
f	2	2	5	6	7	12	12	15	10	5	4

5. The following is a set of actual measurements of length of a steel rod. Classify the data into 10 classes and construct the corresponding frequency histogram and frequency polygon.

10.31, 10.32, 10.31, 10.34, 10.25, 10.27, 10.31, 10.32, 10.33, 10.26,

10.29, 10.30, 10.30, 10.31, 10.27, 10.28, 10.31, 10.33, 10.30, 10.29

6. A survey of the monthly food costs of 50 college students was made, with the following results:

$32	$46	$29	$59	$75	$57	$36	$76	$65	$64	$38	$80	$72	$58
30	54	66	72	58	49	35	80	25	35	69	67	58	62
63	74	82	57	72	66	54	60	50	51	63	54	54	55
60	73	59	68	70	62	57	60						

Use approximately a dozen classes to tabulate the above data, and construct a frequency histogram and frequency polygon to represent it graphically.

7. Open a non-mathematical book at random and record the number of e's per line on the two facing pages. Construct a frequency distribution chart and histogram of the results.
8. The following table records the numbers of cases of measles in a certain town for one year, according to the age in years of the victim:

Age	0–2	3–5	6–8	9–11	12–14	15–17	18–20	21–23	24–26	27–29
Frequency	6	10	20	30	28	15	4	2	1	1

Construct the corresponding frequency histogram and polygon.

17.7 The Mean and Standard Deviation

While a frequency histogram or polygon does a good job of summarizing certain aspects of a set of numbers in a concise and readily understandable form, it nevertheless gives very little quantitative information. Therefore some arithmetic description of the data is desired, and we shall discuss here two numerical characteristics of a frequency distribution, the *central tendency* and the *variation*.

A measure of *central tendency* of a frequency distribution is a number, about which the elements of the data tend to concentrate. There are several such measures in common use, but the most familiar—and only one that we shall mention—is the *arithmetic mean* or *mean* of the distribution. This is what is usually meant by the word "average"; for instance, the student has this in mind when he wants to know the "class average" on an examination. If a frequency distribution of N items has h classes, the ith class having frequency f_i and class mark x_i, the *mean* $\bar{x}$ is defined by:

$$\bar{x} = \left(\sum_{i=1}^{h} x_i f_i\right) \Big/ N.$$

Referring to the data on the number of heads occurring in 40 simultaneous throws of 6 coins, as given in Section 17.6, the mean of this distribution is found to be $(0 + 4 + 20 + 36 + 32 + 20 + 6)/40$, i.e., $\bar{x} = 118/40 = 2.95$. In a similar manner, the mean height of the 1000 college men, whose heights were listed in the other set of data of that section, is $\left(\sum_{i=1}^{14} x_i f_i\right) \Big/ 1000 = 175{,}209/1000$, i.e., 175 centimeters, approximately.

The mean can be shown to have the following geometric interpretation: if a vertical line is drawn through the mean reading on the horizontal scale of a frequency histogram, it will pass through the centroid of the histogram. Hence, the mean determines a point on the horizontal axis, about which a sheet of homogeneous metal in the shape of the histogram could be balanced on a knife edge.

It is a familiar fact that two distinct pairs of numbers may have the same mean; for example, the numbers 2 and 10 have the same mean 6 as the numbers 4 and 8. For a similar reason, two entirely different frequency distributions may have the same mean, and so this number by itself does not always give a satisfactory description of the data in question. In order to put a proper valuation on this measure of central tendency, we must know to what extent the items of the data tend to concentrate about it. The scattering of the items of a set from the mean is called *variation* (or *dispersion*), the variation being small if the items are well clustered about the mean. We now introduce the most common measure of variation, called the *standard deviation.*

The difference between an item of a set of data and the mean is known as the *deviation from the mean* of the item. If all these deviations are squared and the mean of this set of squares determined, this number is known as the *variance* of the distribution. If we use the usual notation, and indicate variance by s^2, we have

$$s^2 = \frac{\sum_{i=1}^{h} (x_i - \bar{x})^2 f_i}{N}.$$

The positive square root of the variance is the *standard deviation*, and so if we indicate this measure by s, we have

$$s = \sqrt{\frac{\sum_{i=1}^{h} (x_i - \bar{x})^2 f_i}{N}}.$$

If this formula is used to determine the standard deviation of a set of data, any small error in $\bar{x}$ will be magnified many times, and so it is desirable to replace this formula by an equivalent but more practical one. Thus

$$\begin{aligned}
\sum_{i=1}^{h} (x_i - \bar{x})^2 f_i &= \sum_{i=1}^{h} x_i^2 f_i - \sum_{i=1}^{h} 2\bar{x} x_i f_i + \sum_{i=1}^{h} \bar{x}^2 f_i \\
&= \sum_{i=1}^{h} x_i^2 f_i - 2\bar{x} \sum_{i=1}^{h} x_i f_i + \bar{x}^2 \sum_{i=1}^{h} f_i \\
&= \sum_{i=1}^{h} x_i^2 f_i - 2\bar{x}(N\bar{x}) + \bar{x}^2 N = \sum_{i=1}^{h} x_i^2 f_i - N\bar{x}^2.
\end{aligned}$$

It follows that

$$s^2 = \frac{\sum_{i=1}^{h} x_i^2 f_i}{N} - \bar{x}^2$$

and

$$s = \sqrt{\frac{\sum_{i=1}^{h} x_i^2 f_i}{N} - \bar{x}^2}.$$

ILLUSTRATION. Use the data, presented at the beginning of Section 17.6, on the number of heads appearing when 6 coins were tossed 40 times, and determine the mean and standard deviation of the distribution.

Solution. The following table gives the pertinent computation.

i	1	2	3	4	5	6	7
x_i	0	1	2	3	4	5	6
f_i	2	3	10	12	8	4	1
$x_i f_i$	0	3	20	36	32	20	6
x_i^2	0	1	4	9	16	25	36
$x_i^2 f_i$	0	3	40	108	128	100	36

We now obtain $\bar{x} = \left(\sum_{i=1}^{7} x_i f_i\right) \Big/ 40 = 117/40 = 2.9$ and

$$s = \sqrt{\sum_{i=1}^{7} (x_i^2 f_i) \Big/ N - \bar{x}^2} = \sqrt{10.4 - 8.4} = \sqrt{2} = 1.4,$$

approximately.

PROBLEM SET 17.7

1. Find the mean and standard deviation of the data given in Problem 1 of Problem Set 17.6.
2. Find the mean and standard deviation of the data given in Problem 3 of Problem Set 17.6.
3. Find the mean and standard deviation of the data given in Problem 4 of Problem Set 17.6.

4. Find the mean and standard deviation of the data given in Problem 8 of Problem Set 17.6.
5. Decide whether or not the mean would be a good measure of central tendency for each of the following sets of ungrouped data: (*a*) $\{3, 5, 8, 4, 3, 7, 5\}$; (*b*) $\{5, 5, 6, 75, 80\}$; (*c*) $\{20, 50, 30, 25, 35, 3000\}$.
6. Two frequency distributions have the same means, but their standard deviations are quite different. Discuss the significance of this.
7. One additional item is included in a frequency distribution. What effect does this have on the mean if the item is (*a*) larger than the mean; (*b*) smaller than the mean; (*c*) the same as the mean?
8. Two frequency distributions have the same variance but quite different means. Discuss the significance of this.
9. Prove that the (algebraic) sum of the deviations of the items x_i from the mean $\bar{x}$ of a distribution is 0. (Hint: show that $\sum_{i=1}^{N} (x_i - \bar{x})f_i = 0$.)
10. Toss 5 coins simultaneously 50 times, and make a frequency distribution table of the number of heads occurring. Determine the mean, variance, and standard deviation of the distribution.

17.8 Relative Frequency Histograms; Binomial Distributions

We now return to a consideration of frequency histograms. It will be recalled that if the class interval is taken as the unit of horizontal measurement, and the unit frequency is taken as the unit of vertical measurement, with both units of equal geometric length, the associated measure of area of any one of the rectangles is the frequency of that class. Furthermore, the total area under the histogram is measured by the total frequency of the data. If we divide the frequency of any one class by the total frequency, we obtain what is known as the *relative frequency* of the class, this being a number less than 1. If we now construct another histogram, using relative frequency instead of frequency on the vertical axis, the result is a *relative frequency histogram* with total area 1 square unit. The associated polygon may be called a *relative frequency polygon.* Using the data on 40 tosses of 6 coins, given early in Section 17.6, we can easily compute the relative frequencies as shown in the table below.

Number of Heads	0	1	2	3	4	5	6
Frequency	2	3	10	12	8	4	1
Relative Frequency	0.05	0.075	0.25	0.3	0.2	0.1	0.025

Notice that the sum of the relative frequencies is 1. The associated relative frequency histogram and polygon are shown in Figure 17–2, where we have enlarged the vertical scale for ease in reading.

For statistical purposes, an experimental set of data is usually known as a *sample*, drawn from some underlying *population* of elements. As usual, let N be the total frequency of a sample, and let f_i be the frequency of the ith class in a frequency distribution of the sample. It is then apparent that the relative frequency f_i/N is a measure of the empirical probability that an item drawn at random from the population will fall in the ith class; and as the size N of the sample increases, this measure of

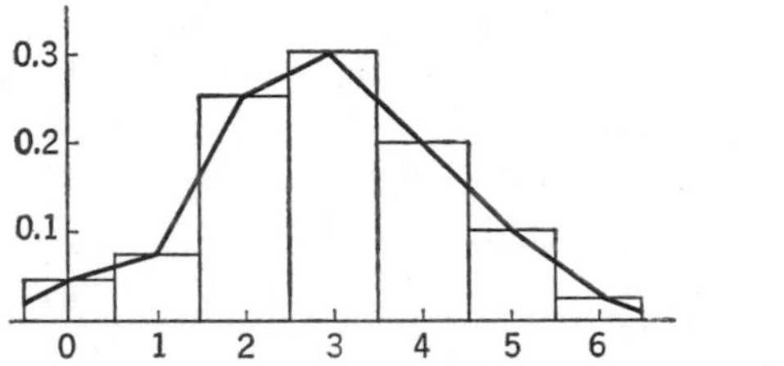

Figure 17–2

the empirical probability becomes more reliable. This implies that the associated measure of area of the ith rectangle, in the relative frequency histogram, is a measure of the empirical probability that an item drawn at random from the population will lie in the ith class.

The histogram of Figure 17–2 was constructed from experimental data on 40 actual tosses of 6 coins, using relative frequencies or, as we may now say, empirical probabilities. In this particular case, a more accurate histogram for ideal coins could have been constructed from theoretical considerations, since it is easy to compute the theoretical probability of obtaining any number of heads in a toss of 8 coins. As a matter of fact, if p and q are the respective probabilities of success and failure of an event in a single trial, the probability of exactly x successes in n trials is $C_{n,x}q^{n-x}p^x$, as we saw in Section 17.5. In harmony with the language of that section, we say that the successes in n trials have a *binomial* or *Bernoulli* distribution, if they are distributed according to this rule. It is worthy of note that a binomial distribution is completely determined by p, the probability of success in a single trial, and n, the number of trials. The distribution in Figure 17–2 is an experimental approximation to the theoretical binomial distribution in which $p = q = 1/2$ and $n = 6$. We now state the following important theorem, without proof.

THEOREM. Let p and q be the respective probabilities of success and failure of an event in a single trial. Then the mean μ and standard deviation σ of the binomial distribution of successes in n trials is given by $\mu = np$ and $\sigma = \sqrt{npq}$.

ILLUSTRATION. A single die is thrown 6 times. If we consider a success the appearance of 1 or 6, determine the binomial probability distribution of the number of successes. Also find the mean and standard deviation of the frequency distribution.

Solution. Since a success is the appearance of 1 or 6, the probability p of success in a single trial is 2/6 or 1/3. Thus, $q = 2/3$, and the following table gives us the relative frequency or, in this case, the binomial probability distribution.

Successes	Relative Frequency	Successes	Relative Frequency
0	$(2/3)^6 = 64/729$	4	$15(2/3)^2(1/3)^4 = 60/729$
1	$6(2/3)^5(1/3) = 192/729$	5	$6(2/3)(1/3)^5 = 12/729$
2	$15(2/3)^4(1/3)^2 = 240/729$	6	$(1/3)^6 = 1/729$
3	$20(2/3)^3(1/3)^3 = 160/729$		

An application of the above theorem to this distribution gives $\mu = 6(2/3) = 4$ and $\sigma = \sqrt{6(2/3)(1/3)} = 1.15$, approximately.

PROBLEM SET 17.8

1. Construct a relative frequency histogram and polygon from the data in Problem 1 of Problem Set 17.6.
2. Construct a relative frequency histogram and polygon from the data in Problem 3 of Problem Set 17.6.
3. Construct a relative frequency histogram and polygon from the data in Problem 8 of Problem Set 17.6.
4. In a throw of a single die, the appearance of 5 is to be considered a success. Construct a table of the binomial distribution of successes in 10 throws. Find the mean and standard deviation of the distribution.
5. The probability that a certain baseball player will make a hit in a single time at bat is 1/3. Assuming that the frequency of hits in 30 times at bat has a binomial distribution, find the mean and standard deviation of the distribution.
6. Toss 5 coins simultaneously 40 times, and make a relative frequency distribution chart of the number of heads appearing. Compare the results with the corresponding binomial distribution, with $p = 1/2$ and $n = 5$.

17.9 Testing Hypotheses

It is sometimes desirable to obtain information from a sample, concerning the nature of the underlying population from which the sample was drawn. For example, suppose we have tossed a coin 7 times and have obtained 7 heads. Is the coin biased, or is it likely a true coin? The procedure that we use, in an attempt to answer this question, is to *make a hypothesis* about the coin, and then either accept or reject the hypothesis on the basis of some level of probability. In the above instance, let us make the hypothesis that the coin is true, i.e., we are assuming that the probability of obtaining a head in a single throw is 1/2. The distribution of heads is binomial, and the probability of obtaining 7 heads in 7 throws is $(1/2)^7 = 1/128 = 0.0078$, approximately. Since this is a very small number, the event is quite unlikely, and so we reject the hypothesis that the coin is true. On the other hand, if we make the hypothesis that the coin is warped, so that the probability of a head in a single throw is 0.8, the probability of 7 heads in 7 throws would be $(0.8)^7$, i.e., approximately 0.206. Since this probability is relatively large, we would accept this hypothesis on the coin.

In order to have a definite rule for accepting or rejecting a hypothesis, we must decide in advance on some *critical* level of probability. There is no universal agreement on this, but for the purposes of this book, we shall consider 0.01 as the critical level, i.e., if the probability of an event is less than 0.01 under a certain hypothesis, we shall reject the hypothesis, and otherwise accept it. It should be understood, of course, that the acceptance of a hypothesis does not imply that we consider the hypothesis necessarily true; it simply means that our information is such that we are not in a position to reject it. It must be remembered in all considerations of statistics, that it is possible for a very improbable event to actually happen.

ILLUSTRATION 1. A pair of dice is rolled 5 times, and on each roll the total count is 7. Test the hypothesis, at the 0.01 level, that the dice are true.

Solution. A pair of dice can land in any one of 36 ways, of which 6 give a total count of 7, and so the probability of 7 in a single roll is 6/36 or 1/6. The probability of 5 successive rolls of 7 is then $(1/6)^5$ or 0.00013, approximately. Since this is much less than 0.01, we reject the hypothesis that the dice are true.

ILLUSTRATION 2. The probability that a certain ball player will make a hit has been estimated to be 1/2, for any one time at bat, but on one occasion he makes only 1 hit out of 6 times at bat. Test the hypothesis that he was hitting normally.

Solution. The probability of his obtaining only 1 hit out of 6 times at bat, using $p = 1/2$, is $6(1/2)(1/2)^5 = 6/64$, i.e., 0.094, approximately. Since this exceeds our critical level of 0.01, we accept the hypothesis that the batting was normal.

PROBLEM SET 17.9

1. A coin is tossed 8 times and 8 heads result. If p is the probability of obtaining a head on a single toss, test each of the following hypotheses at the 0.01 level: (*a*) $p = 1/2$; (*b*) $p = 1/10$; (*c*) $p = 4/7$; (*d*) $p = 3/4$.
2. A die is rolled 6 times, with the 6 turning up 3 times. At the 0.01 level, test the hypothesis that the die is true.
3. Toss a coin 12 times and record the number of heads. At the 0.01 level, test the hypothesis that the coin is true.
4. The probability that A will beat B at a game of tennis is 4/5, but in one set A lost with a score of 2–6. Test the hypothesis that A was playing a normal game, using the 0.01 level.
5. A pair of dice is rolled 6 times, with the total count 7 on 5 of the rolls. At the 0.01 level, test the hypothesis that the dice are true.
6. A manufacturer has found from experience that 2% of this product is rejected because of flaws. A new lot of 10 units comes up for inspection and 5 are rejected. Test the hypothesis, at the 0.01 level, that the manufacturing process is operating normally.
7. It has been found that approximately 20% of seed of a certain type germinates. Would an explanation be needed, if only 1 seed germinates out of 10 seeds planted?

17.10 Normal Distributions

It is evident that if n is a large number, the computation of probabilities with a binomial distribution function can become very tedious. We shall see in this section, however, that it is possible to avoid much of this unpleasant arithmetic and obtain satisfactory results by another method. This will be accomplished with the aid of *normal* distribution functions. These functions are "normal" in the sense that they serve as mathematical models for many frequency distributions occurring in nature and industry. But, on the other hand, there are perfectly respectable distribution functions that are not of this type, and these should not be regarded as "abnormal."

We have seen that the domain of a binomial distribution function is a discrete set of integers $\{0, 1, 2, \cdots, n\}$, and an associated distribution may properly be said to be *discrete*. It is a characteristic of the relative frequency histogram of a discrete distribution, that the values of the distribution function, i.e., the various probabilities, are the measures of area of the corresponding rectangles comprising this histogram. In particular, the total area of the histogram is 1 square unit, and the measure of area of the rectangles having class marks in a given subset of integers is the probability that the outcome of a random trial will be a number of this set. We now wish to use this area characteristic of a relative frequency histogram to generalize the notion of a distribution function to include those having the set $R^{\#}$ of all real numbers for domains. A distribution with this type of distribution function may be said to be *continuous*. While it is clear that a continuous distribution can never occur in practice, we shall see that such theoretical distributions can be used to advantage in the solution of many practical problems.

DEFINITION. Let $R^{\#}$ be the universe of outcomes of a trial, with $p[\alpha < x < \beta]$ the probability that the outcome x of the trial will satisfy the inequality $\alpha < x < \beta$. Then the distribution function, associated with the outcomes, is a function f on $R^{\#}$ such that $\int_{\alpha}^{\beta} f(x)\, dx = p[\alpha < x < \beta]$.

Inasmuch as the outcome of a trial of this type must be a real number, the probability is 1 that $x \in R^{\#}$, which in turn implies that the total area under the graph of f is 1 square unit. It is then a consequence of our definition that f is a generalization of the notion of a discrete distribution function, the graph of f corresponding to a relative frequency histogram or polygon. The only type of continuous distribution that we consider here is the *normal* type, which we have already mentioned and which we now define.

DEFINITION. A distribution is said to be *normal* if it has a distribution function f, defined on $R^{\#}$ by

$$f(x) = \frac{1}{\sigma\sqrt{2\pi}} e^{-\frac{1}{2}\left(\frac{x-\mu}{\sigma}\right)^2},$$

for each real x, and real numbers μ and σ.

If we define the mean and standard deviation of a normal distribution in a manner analogous to the discrete case, it turns out that μ is the mean and σ is the standard deviation. Hence a normal distribution, as we have defined it, is completely determined by its mean and standard deviation.

Our present interest in normal distributions lies in their relationship to binomial distributions. Let us then consider a binomial distribution with mean μ and standard deviation σ, where $\mu = np$ and $\sigma = \sqrt{npq}$ in the usual notation. If we define $t = (x - \mu)/\sigma$, it is possible to conceive of the binomial distribution of theoretical outcomes t, along with the distribution of actual outcomes x. In Figure 17–3*a*, we have shown a portion of the relative frequency histogram of t, with $p = q = 1/2$ and $n = 16$; in Figure 17–3*b*, a comparison histogram is shown for t with $n = 100$. It is certainly plausible, from an inspection of the two histograms, that if n is sufficiently large, the relative frequency histogram and polygon for the distribution of t will tend to assume the shape of a smooth curve. It can be shown by more advanced mathematics that *this curve is the graph of the* *normal distribution function with mean* 0 *and standard deviation* 1. If we represent this *standard normal* function by ϕ, we are then implying that

$$\phi(t) = \frac{1}{\sqrt{2\pi}} e^{-\frac{1}{2}t^2},$$

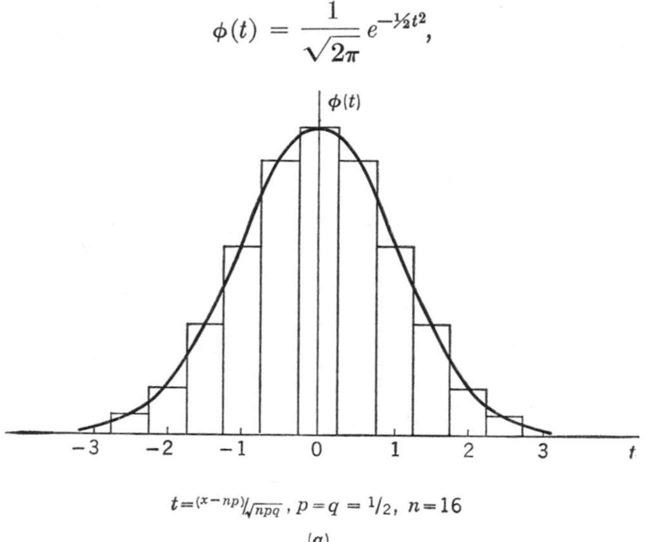

$t = (x - np)/\sqrt{npq}$, $p = q = 1/2$, $n = 16$

(a)

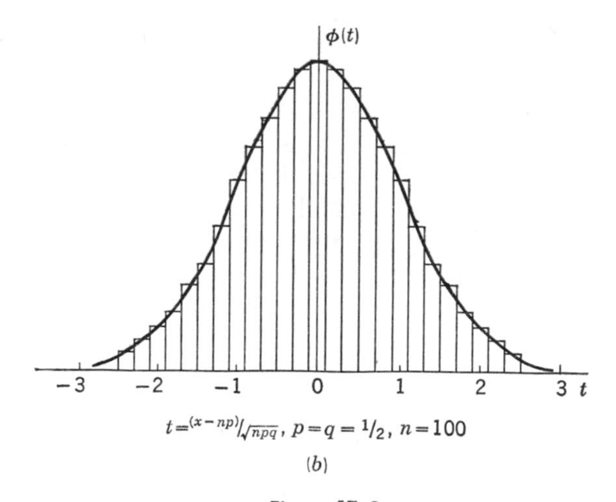

$t = (x - np)/\sqrt{npq}$, $p = q = 1/2$, $n = 100$

(b)

Figure 17–3

for each real number t. It is clear that the common vertical scale for the two graphs of Figure 17–3 is many times that used for the horizontal axes.

The standard normal distribution function ϕ has been tabulated in considerable detail. In Table 5 we have given a portion of this tabulation, and have included the corresponding tabulation for $\int_0^t \phi(t)\,dt$, which is especially useful in probability considerations. For example, if ϕ is the distribution function associated with the outcomes of a certain trial, the probability that the trial will produce an outcome t such that $\alpha < t < \beta$, i.e., $p[\alpha < t < \beta]$, is $\int_\alpha^\beta \phi(t)\,dt$; and it is clear that this integral can be evaluated from a tabulation of $\int_0^t \phi(t)\,dt$. We have seen that, associated with an arbitrary binomial distribution, there is a theoretical binomial distribution, the relative frequency histogram of which is approximated, for large n, by the graph of ϕ. Hence the data on ϕ can be adapted for the solution of problems involving any binomial distribution. This was our reason for introducing normal distributions, and in particular the standard normal distribution function ϕ.

In Section 17.9, we considered a level of probability of 0.01 as critical in the acceptance or rejection of a hypothesis. We shall continue to use this level, but if our populations are assumed to have a normal distribution, we shall use the function ϕ for the determination of probabilities. It can be shown that the area under the graph of ϕ between $t = -2.58$ and $t = 2.58$ comprises all but 0.01 units of the total area. Hence, with 0.01 as the critical level of probability—sometimes known as the 0.01 *significance* level—we shall consider as very improbable the occurrence of t outside the interval $[-2.58, 2.58]$. We shall reject any hypothesis that allows such an occurrence.

ILLUSTRATION 1. A coin is tossed 400 times. Would it be reasonable to have 250 heads appear?

Solution. We test the hypothesis that the coin is true with $p = 1/2$. The distribution of heads is binomial, with $\mu = np = 400(1/2) = 200$, and $\sigma = \sqrt{npq} = \sqrt{400(1/2)(1/2)} = \sqrt{100} = 10$. Since n is quite large we may approximate it by the standard normal distribution with $t = (x - 200)/10$. But if $x = 250$, $t = 5$, which is far outside the allowable interval $[-2.58, 2.58]$, and so we reject the hypothesis that the coin is true. We conclude that the appearance of 250 heads with a true coin would be unreasonable.

ILLUSTRATION 2. If we assume that approximately 9% of the total population of the country are between 20 and 24 years of age, would it be reasonable for a city of 12,000 to have 1300 in this age group?

Solution. Let us take as our hypothesis that the distribution of people in the given age group is binomial, with $p = 0.09$ and $n = 12{,}000$. For this distribution, $\mu = (0.09)(12{,}000) = 1080$, and $\sigma = \sqrt{12{,}000(0.09)(0.91)} = \sqrt{982.8} = 31.3$, approximately. Since n is large, the distribution may be approximated by the standard normal distribution with $t = (x - 1080)/31.3$. But if $x = 1300$, $t = 7$, approximately, and since 7 is outside our allowable limits on t, we must reject the hypothesis that the city has an average population. It would be reasonable to assume the existence of special circumstances that are responsible for the large number of people in the given age group in this city.

ILLUSTRATION 3. A die is thrown 90 times. Use the normal curve approximation to find the probability of obtaining more than 20 aces.

Solution. The distribution of aces is binomial, with $p = 1/6$ and $n = 90$.

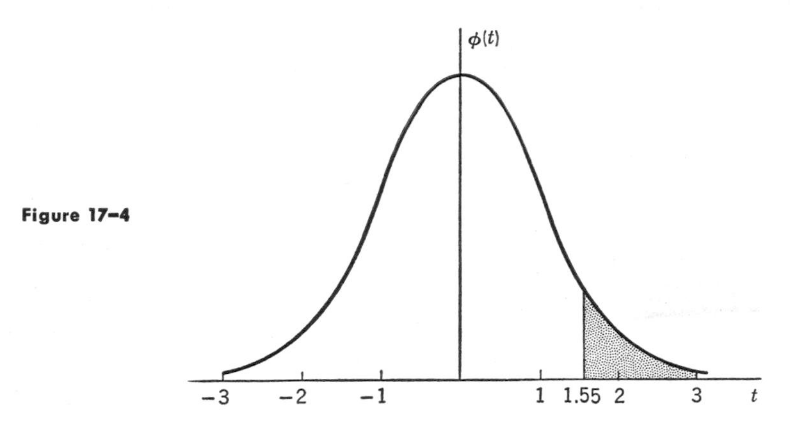

Figure 17–4

For this distribution, $\mu = np = 90(1/6) = 15$, and $\sigma = \sqrt{90(1/6)(1/6)} = 5\sqrt{2}/2 = 3.54$, approximately. For the standard normal distribution, $t = (x - 15)/3.54$, and if $x = 20.5$, $t = 1.55$. (Note that we use $x = 20.5$, the *upper boundary* of the histogram rectangle with class number 20.) We find from Table 5 that $\int_0^{1.55} \phi(t)\,dt = 0.43943$ and, since the area under the left half of the graph of ϕ is 0.5 units, the total area to the left of $t = 1.55$ is approximately 0.939 units. It follows that the area to the right of $t = 1.55$ is 0.061 units, and so the desired probability is 0.061. The role of the graph of ϕ in this problem is illustrated in Figure 17–4.

PROBLEM SET 17.10

1. A die is thrown 90 times. Find the approximate probability of obtaining more than (*a*) 17 aces; (*b*) 18 aces.
2. A coin is tossed 200 times and 115 heads appear. Is an explanation needed?
3. It has been found that about 20% of seed of a certain type germinates. Would it be unreasonable to expect less than 40, from a sample of 400 of the seeds, to germinate?
4. A manufacturer finds that approximately 2% of his product has to be

rejected because of flaws. A new lot of 1000 units comes up for inspection. (*a*) How many units might reasonably be expected to be rejected? (*b*) What is the approximate probability that less than 25 units will be rejected?

5. A pair of dice is thrown 90 times. Use the standard normal distribution to determine the approximate probability that more than 20 throws of 7 will occur. What is the approximate probability that less than 12 throws of 7 will occur?
6. A true die is rolled 450 times, with a success defined to be the appearance of either 1 or 6. Use the standard normal distribution to determine the approximate probability of throwing between 140 and 160 successes.
7. On a true-false test consisting of 100 questions, a student obtained 55 correct and 45 incorrect answers. What is the probability that he would have obtained a higher score by guessing?
8. A manufacturer finds from past experience that approximately 5% of his product is defective. A new operator turns out 400 pieces during his first day at work, of which 40 pieces are defective. Is the new operator to be considered satisfactory?
9. If 75% of the voters in a city are known to be in favor of a certain bill, what is the probability that, in a random sample of 100 voters, more than 65 will be in favor of the bill?
10. A coin is tossed 12 times. Find the probability, both by the binomial distribution and by the standard normal distribution, of obtaining (*a*) 4 heads; (*b*) at most 4 heads; (*c*) at least 4 heads.

11*. Verify that the points of inflection of the graph of the standard normal distribution function are $(1, 1/\sqrt{2\pi e})$ and $(-1, 1/\sqrt{2\pi e})$.

17.11 Distribution of Sample Means

A great many of the problems of statistics are attacked by the methods of sampling. We would like to be able to analyze a sample of elements, and from these results to deduce some conclusions about the population from which the sample was drawn. While we do not consider all aspects of this problem here, we do try to indicate some of the simpler relationships between a sample and its parent population. The procedure that we use is to test a hypothesis, such as was done for binomial distributions. Thus, we assume that the parent population has a certain mean and standard deviation and, from the mean and standard deviation of the sample, deduce whether or not our assumption is plausible.

The methods of statistics apply only to large samples, and it is convenient to think of our population as extremely large or even infinite in size. There are then a great many samples of any size N that can be drawn from the population, and each of these samples has its own mean and standard deviation. This set of means can now be considered to constitute a new population, a *population of sample means*, which is certainly related to the original population but different from it. Let $\mu_{\bar{x}}$ and $\sigma_{\bar{x}}$ be the mean and standard deviation, respectively, of this population of sample means. Then, *it can be shown* that if μ and σ are the respective mean and standard deviation of the parent population, $\mu_{\bar{x}} = \mu$ and $\sigma_{\bar{x}} = \sigma/\sqrt{N}$. The formula for $\sigma_{\bar{x}}$ shows that $\sigma_{\bar{x}}$ decreases as the size N of the sample is increased, which implies that the sample means cluster more closely about the population mean. This, in turn, implies—as we would expect—that the larger the sample the more closely its mean fits the population mean.

It is a most important fact, which we do not attempt to prove here, that the population of sample means has a distribution that is approximately normal, for many different types of sampled populations. This is often true, moreover, even when the parent population is not normal. For the purposes of the following illustrations and problems, we shall assume without justification that all the populations of sample means that are mentioned are normal.

ILLUSTRATION 1. The light bulbs manufactured by a certain company have been found to have an average burning time of 600 hours, with a standard deviation of 15 hours. What is the probability that a sample of 100 of these bulbs will have a mean burning time of 605 hours?

Solution. The parent population of bulb-hours has a mean μ of 600 and a standard deviation of 15. For the population of sample means, $\mu_{\bar{x}} = 600$ and $\sigma_{\bar{x}} = 15/\sqrt{100} = 1.5$. If we use the standard normal distribution to approximate this distribution, $t = (x - 600)/1.5$, and if $x = 605$, $t = 5/1.5 = 3.33$, approximately. From Table 5, $\int_0^{3.33} \phi(t)\,dt =$ 0.49957, and so $p[t > 3.33] = 0.00043$, the desired probability.

ILLUSTRATION 2. The population of marks on a college entrance examination has a normal distribution, with a mean of 72 and a standard deviation of 16. If a sample of 100 of the tested students obtained a mean score of 75, should we conclude that the sample was random?

Solution. For the parent population, $\mu = 72$ and $\sigma = 16$, while for samples of size 100, $\mu_{\bar{x}} = 72$ and $\sigma_{\bar{x}} = 16/\sqrt{100} = 16/10 = 1.6$. If we approximate the distribution of means by the standard normal distribution, $t = (x - 72)/1.6$, and if $x = 75$, $t = 3/1.6 = 1.875$. Since $t < 2.58$, we accept the hypothesis that the sample is random.

PROBLEM SET 17.11

1. An ordinary die is rolled 100 times, the appearance of an ace or 6 being considered a success. Determine the set of "likely" numbers of successes.

2. A manufacturer of a certain type of light bulb has found that the mean life of his bulbs is 700 hours, with a standard deviation of 20 hours. What is the probability that a sample of 100 of these bulbs will have a mean life in excess of 705 hours?

3. On a College Entrance examination, given to a large group of students, the average grade was 74 with a standard deviation of 9. If a group of 64 of these students has a mean grade of 69, is it probable that the group was selected in some special manner?
4. On a certain large cattle ranch, it has been found that the average percentage of cattle developing some disease is 8, with a standard deviation of 0.8. After the administering of a vaccine to 64 of the cattle, it was found that only 1 of these developed any disease. Should it be concluded that the vaccine was of any benefit?
5. The average number of sunny days in July, in a certain location over a period of years, has been found to be 27, with a standard deviation of 2.4. Would a July with only 23 sunny days be considered unlikely for this location?
6. The average weight of 2-year-old beef cattle of a certain type has been found to be 450 pounds, with a standard deviation of 15 pounds. After an experiment in breeding, the average weight of a sample of 25 cattle of the same age has been found to be 460 pounds. Is the increase in weight due likely to errors in sampling or was the experiment in breeding a success?
7. The probability of throwing a head with a certain imperfect coin has been found to be 0.7. What is the probability of more than 20 heads out of 36 throws with this coin?
8. If 8 is thrown 5 times in 20 throws of a pair of dice, would you suspect that the dice are imperfect?
9. The mean breaking strength of a certain type of fiber is 4.5 pounds, with a standard deviation of 0.3 pounds. If a bundle of 100 of these fibers broke under a weight of 440 pounds, should these fibers be considered susbtandard?

REVIEW TEST A

1. A basket of chocolate bars contains 5 *Milky Ways*, 4 *Baby Ruths*, and 6 *Jersey Milks*. What is the probability that a random grab of a bar will produce a *Baby Ruth?*
2. A peanut-vending machine is not operating properly, and after a series of tests, the following probabilities have been assigned to it: the probability that nothing comes out is 1/2; the probability of getting both peanuts and your money back is 2/7. Find the probability of getting either (but not both) your money back or peanuts in a single try.
3. A man bets "dollars to doughnuts" that horse A will outrun horse B in a race. If the bet is fair, what is the probability that A will win, assuming that doughnuts are 2 for 5¢?
4. In a bridge game, what is the probability that you will hold both the king and queen of at least one suit?
5. A punch board contains 20 punches, 2 of which pay $5 and 5 of which pay $1.

If you are the first to play the board, determine your expectation on the first punch.

6. On inspecting 1000 resistors at an electronics factory, 20 were found to be defective. What is the probability that, in a random sample, not more than 1 will be found to be defective?

7. Four coins were tossed simultaneously 60 times. The following table lists the results, with x the number of heads in a toss and f the number of tosses in which x heads occurred. Fill in the table, and compute the mean and standard deviation of the distribution of heads.

x	0	1	2	3	4	5
f	1	15	25	12	4	3
xf						
x^2f						

8. A pair of dice is thrown 180 times. Use the standard normal distribution to determine the probability that 7 will appear at least 25 times.

9. A newspaper polled a random sample of 1000 voters, living in the southern section of a city, and found that 550 favored a certain candidate for office; a similar poll of 600 people in the northern section revealed that 350 of these favored the candidate. Should it be inferred that the two sections of the city are equally in favor of the candidate?

10. If has been found from a check of the output of skilled workers at a certain factory that, on the average, 4 articles out of 1000 are defective. If an apprentice turns out 7 defective articles in a batch of 700, should he be considered ready for a skilled classification?

11. An auditorium will accommodate 2100 people. It has been found that, on the average, 1 out of every 10 persons who buy a ticket for a concert, fails to use it. Approximately how many tickets may the management sell, if it is willing to run a risk of 1:6 of being overcrowded?

12. The average grade on an entrance examination for all 3600 students entering Green Ivy College was 76.4, with a standard deviation of 8.8. If the average grade of the 64 students who majored in mathematics was 78, should any significance be attached to this result?

REVIEW TEST B

1. A shelf in a man's library contains 7 mathematics books, 5 history books, 4 natural science books, and 2 books on the history of mathematics. What is the probability that a random selection of a book will produce one of a mathematical nature?

2. What odds should a man give on a bet that 7 or 11 will turn up on a single throw of a pair of dice?

3. A student estimates that his odds for passing mathematics, physics, and chemistry are respectively 3 to 2, 1 to 4, and 1 to 1. What are the odds in favor of his passing all three courses?

4. In 4 throws of a pair of dice, what is the probability of throwing doublets at least twice?

5. Counters marked 1, 2, 3 are placed in a box, and one is withdrawn at random and then replaced. If this operation is repeated 3 times, what is the probability of obtaining a total of 6 on the three draws?

6. It has been found that when a certain bombsight on a military plane is used, the target is hit 75 times out of 100 tries. In an enemy action involving a bomber using this sight, it has been estimated that the probability of interception before reaching enemy territory is 1/2. If 3 bombers take part in a raid, each carrying 2 bombs, what is the probability that at least 2 hits will be made on a target?

7. The following table shows the distribution of aces, when 4 dice were thrown 50 times, with x representing the number of aces and f the number of throws in which x aces appeared. Fill in the table and compute the mean and standard deviation of the distribution of aces.

x	0	1	2	3	4
f	8	21	15	4	2
xf					
x^2f					

8. A pair of dice is tossed 144 times. Use the standard normal curve approximation to determine the probability that a sum of 4 will appear not more than 10 times.

9. Out of 60 tosses of 2 coins, 2 heads appeared 20 times. Are the coins to be considered normal?

10. The probability that a certain disease will be fatal is 1/10. In a certain city, where the air is constantly polluted with smoke, 10 victims of the disease died, out of a total of 30. Does this indicate that the air pollution had any effect on the patients?

11. A school field house holds 2000 people. The student body totals 1500 people, and they all hold season tickets to events in the auditorium. If approximately 1/3 of the students fail to use their tickets for any given event, how many cash tickets can be sold with safety for each event?

12. It has been found that the mean life of a certain type of battery is 3 years with a standard deviation of 0.48 years. Find the probability that a sample of 25 of these batteries will have a mean life of 3.2 years.

REFERENCES

Books

ALLENDOERFER, C. B. and C. O. OAKLEY, *Principles of Mathematics*, New York, McGraw-Hill, 1955. (Chap. 13.)

HALL, HENRY S. and SAMUEL R. KNIGHT, *Higher Algebra*, London, MacMillan, 1950. (Chap. 32.)

HUFF, D., *How To Lie With Statistics*, New York, Norton, 1954.

MOOD, A. M., *Introduction to the Theory of Statistics*, New York, McGraw-Hill, 1950. (Chap. 2.)

NEWSOM, CARROLL V. and HOWARD EVES, *Introduction to College Mathematics*, New York, Prentice-Hall, 1954. (Chaps. 6 and 7.)

WILKS, S. S., *Elementary Statistical Analysis*, Princeton, Princeton University Press, 1948.

American Mathematical Monthly

HALMOS, P. R., "The Foundations of Probability," Vol. 51, p. 493 (1944).

KENNEY, J. F., "Some Topics in Mathematical Statistics," Vol. 46, p. 59 (1939).

APPENDIX

REVIEW OF HIGH-SCHOOL ALGEBRA

The following review of high-school algebra is given without explanations, and should be regarded principally as a problem source. We have included, however, a few of the basic underlying principles and rules.

Arithmetic of Fractions

BASIC PRINCIPLE. If both numerator and denominator of a fraction are multiplied (or divided) by the same non-zero number, the fraction is replaced by an equivalent fraction.

Example.

$$\begin{aligned} 1/2 &= (1\cdot 2)/(2\cdot 2) = 2/4; \\ &= (1\cdot 5)/(2\cdot 5) = 5/10; \text{ etc.} \end{aligned}$$

$$15/9 = \frac{15/3}{9/3} = 5/3.$$

RULE FOR ADDITION AND SUBTRACTION. Use the above basic principle to express all the fractions with the same common denominator. Then perform the indicated operations with the numerators, place the result over the common denominator, and reduce to lowest terms.

Example. $2/3 + 1/2 - 1/4 - 1/6 = 8/12 + 6/12 - 3/12 - 2/12$ $= (8 + 6 - 3 - 2)/12 = 9/12 = 3/4.$

RULE FOR MULTIPLICATION. Write the indicated product of all the numerators over the indicated product of all the denominators, and use the basic principle to simplify, if possible. Multiply together all the resulting numerators and also all the resulting denominators, to obtain the final result.

Example.

$$\frac{2}{3}\cdot\frac{1}{4}\cdot\frac{1}{5}\cdot\frac{3}{8} = \frac{\overset{1}{\cancel{2}}\cdot 1\cdot 1\cdot \overset{1}{\cancel{3}}}{\underset{1}{\cancel{3}}\cdot\underset{2}{\cancel{4}}\cdot 5\cdot 8} = \frac{1}{80}.$$

RULE FOR DIVISION. Invert the divisor and proceed as for multiplication.

Example.

$$(2/3) \div (4/5) = (2/3)(5/4) = \frac{\overset{1}{\cancel{2}}\cdot 5}{3\cdot\underset{2}{\cancel{4}}} = 5/6.$$

PROBLEMS

1. Explain the process of "cancellation" in terms of the Basic Principle enunciated above.
2. Express each of the following numbers as a prime power product: (*a*) 64; (*b*) 36; (*c*) 72; (*d*) 160; (*e*) 42; (*f*) 18; (*g*) 125; (*h*) 60; (*i*) 80; (*j*) 90; (*k*) 102.
3. Determine the greatest common divisor of the integers in each of the following collections: (*a*) 8, 12, 15; (*b*) 21, 15, 42; (*c*) 2, 4, 8, 18; (*d*) 30, 45, 105, 120; (*e*) 3, 7, 13.
4. Reduce each of the following fractions by dividing numerator and denominator by the same number: (*a*) 4/12; (*b*) 32/48; (*c*) 7/21; (*d*) 70/21; (*e*) 90/24; (*f*) 120/260.
5. Replace each of the following fractions by an equivalent fraction, after multiplying numerator and denominator by 5: (*a*) 2/3; (*b*) 3/4; (*c*) 5/3; (*d*) 4/6; (*e*) 4/9.
6. Replace each of the following fractions by an equivalent fraction, after multiplying numerator and denominator by 10: (*a*) 4/3; (*b*) 2/7; (*c*) 5/8; (*d*) 5/6; (*e*) 3/4.
7. Find the sum of the numbers in each of the following collections: (*a*) 2/3, 3/4, 5/8, 1/2; (*b*) 1/2, 2/3, 3/4, 4/5; (*c*) 1/3, 3/7, 1/15, 3/10.
8. In each of the following pairs of fractions, subtract the second member from the first: (*a*) 5, 2/3; (*b*) 3/4, 2/3; (*c*) 5/7, 3/8; (*d*) 4, 3/7; (*e*) 12/5, 2.
9. Simplify each of the following expressions: (*a*) $3/2 + 2/3 - 1/8 - 1/4$; (*b*) $3/5 - 2/3 + 5/8 - 1/3 + 5/6$; (*c*) $3/7 + 8/3 - 3/5 + 2/9$.
10. Simplify each of the following expressions: (*a*) $(2/3)(1/4)(3/8)(4/3)$; (*b*) $(4/5)(10/3)(2/5)(3/10)$; (*c*) $(5/8)(4/3)(2/3)(5)(1/2)$.
11. Divide the first member of each of the following pairs of numbers by the second: (*a*) 3/4, 2/3; (*b*) 1/2, 4/5; (*c*) 3/8, 4/5; (*d*) 3/7, 6; (*e*) 8, 1/4; (*f*) 4/3, 6.
12. Simplify each of the following expressions: (*a*) $3/4 + (2/3)(1/4)$; (*b*) $(5/6)(2/3) + (1/4)(2/3) - (1/3)(1/8)$; (*c*) $(2/3)(4/5) - (3/8)(1/2)$; (*d*) $(5/6)(2/3) \div (3/7)(2/9)$; (*e*) $3/4 \div [(2/3)(1/2) - 1/8]$
13. From the sum of $7 + 7/8$ and $3 + 3/4$ subtract the sum of $2 + 1/5$ and $4 + 1/2$.
14. Subtract $5 + 7/8$ from $16 + 3/4$; subtract $27 + 3/4$ from $15 + 5/12$.
15. In building a fence, a man used steel posts 6 1/2 feet long. If he drove each post 2 1/4 feet into the ground, how much of each post was above ground?
16. What is the cost of 55 1/2 feet of sash cord at 3/4¢ per foot?
17. A filling station advertised 6 1/4 gallons of gasoline for $1.00. What was the exact price per gallon?
18. Find the sum of 5/2 and its reciprocal; find the sum of $3 + 2/3$ and its reciprocal.

Arithmetic of Signed Numbers

RULES FOR ADDITION.

(*a*) To add two signed numbers having the same sign, add their absolute values (i.e., the numbers without the signs) and attach the common sign.

Example. $(-2/3) + (-3/4) = -(8/12 + 9/12) = -17/12$; $(+1/2) + (+1/4) = +(2/4 + 1/4) = +3/4$.

(*b*) To add two signed numbers having unlike signs, subtract the smaller absolute value from the larger, and attach the sign of the larger.

Example. $3/4 - 5/8 = +(6/8 - 5/8) = 1/8$;
$2/3 - 5/6 = -(5/6 - 4/6) = -1/6$.

RULE FOR SUBTRACTION. Change the sign of the number to be subtracted (the subtrahend) and proceed as in addition.

Example. Subtracting $-1/3$ from $3/4$ is the same as adding $1/3$ to $3/4$, and the result is $13/12$.

RULES FOR MULTIPLICATION.

(*a*) The product of two signed numbers having like sign is positive;

(*b*) the product of two signed numbers having unlike signs is negative.

The above rules imply, of course, that the product of an even number of negative factors is positive, and the product of an odd number of negative factors is negative.

Example. $(2/3)(-1/4)(-3/2) = 1/4$;
$(-2/3)(-1/4)(-3/2) = -1/4$.

RULE FOR DIVISION. The rule of signs for division is the same as the rule for multiplication, with the word "product" replaced by the word "quotient."

Example. $(-4/5) \div (-2/3) = 6/5$; $(4/5) \div (-2/3) = -6/5$

PROBLEMS

1. Give the absolute value of each of the following: (*a*) 6; (*b*) -7; (*c*) -4; (*d*) $3/5$; (*e*) $-5/7$.
2. Find the sum of the numbers in each of the following collections: (*a*) 7, 4, 5, 1; (*b*) $-3, -5, -2, -8, -3$; (*c*) $-2/3, -3/4, -1/6, -5/12, -3/8$; (*d*) $3/5, 2/3, 3/8$.
3. Find the sum of the numbers in each of the following collections: (*a*) $6, 3, -8, -4$; (*b*) $12, -7, 6, -33, 5$; (*c*) $-4, 12, -9, -3, 5$; (*d*) $-5, 8, 14, -3, -16$.
4. Find the sum of the numbers in each of the following collections: (*a*) $2/3, -3/4, 5/8, -1/8$; (*b*) $3/2, -5/7, 7/8, -1/2, 6/7$; (*c*) $3/4, -2/5, 4/7, 7/8, -1/2, 3/4$.
5. Subtract the second number from the first in each of the following pairs: (*a*) $3/4, -2/7$; (*b*) $-5/3, 2/5$; (*c*) $5, -3/4$; (*d*) $-2/7, 3$; (*e*) $-4/3, -2/5$; (*f*) $3/5, -4$; (*g*) $-1, -5/4$.

6. Multiply together the numbers in each of the following collections, and reduce the result to lowest terms: (*a*) $2/3, -4/5, -3/4$; (*b*) $-2, -4/5, -5$; (*c*) $3/5, -6/7, -3, -5/2$.
7. Divide the first number by the second in each of the following pairs: (*a*) $3/4, -5/4$; (*b*) $-2/3, -6/5$; (*c*) $5, -4/5$; (*d*) $6/5, -4$.
8. Simplify each of the following expressions: (*a*) $(2/3)(-5/2)(-3/4)(-6)$; (*b*) $[(-4)(-2/3)(-6/7)] \div [(-5/2)(7/4)]$; (*c*) $(61/12)(-15/4) + (-3/2)(-2/5)$.

Note. If a sign of aggregation is preceded by a negative sign, change all the signs within the sign of aggregation when it is removed; if the preceding sign is positive, the signs within remain the same.

9. Simplify each of the following: (*a*) $1/2 - 2[3 + 5(1 - 1/2)]$; (*b*) $3 - 3[1/2 - (2 + 1/4)] - 1$; (*c*) $2\{3[1 - 2/3] + 1\} - 2$; (*d*) $3 - 2\{(1 - 1/2) \times (2 + 2/3) - 1\}$.
10. Simplify each of the following:

(*a*) $\dfrac{2\{3 + [5 - 2(1 - 1/2)]\}}{2 + 4[1 - (1/2)(2 - 1/3)]}$; (*b*) $1 - \dfrac{1}{2 - \dfrac{1}{3 - 1/2}}$;

(*c*) $\dfrac{1}{2 + 3[2 - (1/2)(3 - 2/3)]}$.

Algebraic Expressions

BASIC PRINCIPLE. The laws of combination for algebraic expressions are the same as those of arithmetic; the symbols are treated merely as unknown numbers.

Example.

$$2x^2 - [3y^2 + \{x^2 - (y^2 + 2x^2) + 4y^2\} - 2x^2]$$
$$= 2x^2 - [3y^2 + x^2 - y^2 - 2x^2 + 4y^2 - 2x^2]$$
$$= 2x^2 - 3y^2 - x^2 + y^2 + 2x^2 - 4y^2 + 2x^2 = 5x^2 - 6y^2.$$

SPECIAL PRODUCTS.

(*a*) The product of the sum and difference of any two numbers.

$$(x + y)(x - y) = x^2 - y^2.$$

Example. $(3x + 5y)(3x - 5y) = 9x^2 - 25y^2$.

(*b*) Powers of binomials.

$$(x + y)^2 = x^2 + 2xy + y^2$$
$$(x - y)^2 = x^2 - 2xy + y^2$$
$$(x + y)^3 = x^3 + 3x^2y + 3xy^2 + y^3$$
$$(x - y)^3 = x^3 - 3x^2y + 3xy^2 - y^3$$

Example.

$$(2x + 3y)^2 = 4x^2 + 12xy + 9y^2.$$

$$\begin{aligned}(3x - 2y)^3 &= 27x^3 - 3(9x^2)(2y) + 3(3x)(4y^2) - 8y^3\\ &= 27x^3 - 54x^2y + 36xy^2 - 8y^3.\end{aligned}$$

(*c*) The product of two binomials with a common term.

$$(x + a)(x + b) = x^2 + (a + b)x + ab.$$

Example. $(x + 2)(x - 5) = x^2 - 3x - 10.$

(*d*) The product of two general binomials.

$$(ax + b)(cx + d) = acx^2 + (bc + ad)x + bd.$$

Example.

$$\begin{aligned}(2a - 4b)(3a + 2b) &= (2a)(3a) + (4 - 12)ab - (4b)(2b)\\ &= 6a^2 - 8ab - 8b^2.\end{aligned}$$

PROBLEMS

1. Simplify each of the following: (*a*) $(-4x)(2x^2)$; (*b*) $3ab - 2ab + ab$; (*c*) $(2x)(-3x)(-4x)$; (*d*) $(-ay)(by)(-3)$; (*e*) $(-6xy)(2x) + 5x^2y$.

2. Find the sum of the quantities in each of the following collections: (*a*) $8a$, $-3a$, $9a$, $2a$; (*b*) $12ab$, $-5ab$, $-2ab$; (*c*) $2ab$, $-6ab$, $4ac$; (*d*) $2a^2$, $-3a$, $5b$, $5a$.

3. Subtract $12a - 7c$ from $6a - 7b - 10c$.

4. Subtract $12x^2 - 3x + 1$ from $-2x^2 + 9x - 7$.

5. (*a*) Subtract $18abc$ from $3abc$; (*b*) subtract $-5m$ from $-8m^2$; (*c*) subtract $-6x^2 + 4y$ from $2x^2 - 4y$.

6. (*a*) Subtract $2a + 3b + 5c$ from $5a - 8b + 11c$; (*b*) subtract $7x + 5y$ from $-6x + 4y$; (*c*) subtract $-6x^2 - 8$ from $3x^2 - 2y + 7$.

7. Simplify each of the following: (*a*) $3xy - 2xy + 9y - 2xy$; (*b*) $3x^2 - 2x^2 + (9y - 2x^2)$; (*c*) $7a - 4[(2a + 6b) - b^2 + c] - 4(2 - c)$.

8. Simplify each of the following: (*a*) $ab - 4b^2 - (2a^2 + b^2) - (-5a^2 - 3b^2)$; (*b*) $x - \{y - z - [x - (-x + y) - z]\} + (2x - y)$; (*c*) $-1\{-1 - [-1 - (-1)]\}$.

9. Expand each of the following products: (*a*) $(2x + 5y)(2x - 5y)$; (*b*) $(3x^2 + 2y^2)(3x^2 - 2y^2)$; (*c*) $(2x + y)^2$; (*d*) $(x - 2y)^3$.

10. Expand each of the following products: (*a*) $(5x - 2y)(5x + 2y)$; (*b*) $(x^2y - 3a)(x^2y + 3a)$; (*c*) $(2x - 6y)(2x + 6y)$; (*d*) $(3x - y)^3$.

11. Expand each of the following products: (*a*) $(2a - x)^2$; (*b*) $(1 + x)^3$; (*c*) $(2x - 1)^3$; (*d*) $(x + 2)(x + 3)$; (*e*) $(3xy - z)(3xy + 7z)$.

12. Expand each of the following products: (*a*) $(x - 2y)(2x - 2y)$; (*b*) $(a + 7b)(2a - 3b)$; (*c*) $(x^2 - 3)(x^2 + 4)$; (*d*) $[x/2 + 5y][x/2 - 5y]$; (*e*) $[x/2 - y/4]^2$.

13. Expand each of the following products: (a) $(6x - 1/2)^2$; (b) $(2 + 3x)^3$; (c) $(5m^3 - 6s^2)(5m^3 + s^2)$; (d) $(3xy - 7)^2$.
14. Simplify each of the following:

(a) $\dfrac{3m^2 + 2m - 5m^3}{m}$; (b) $\dfrac{4x^3 - 2x^2}{2x}$;

(c) $\dfrac{x^4 - 12x^3 + 6x^2}{x^2}$; (d) $\dfrac{a^2b^2 - a^3b^3 + ab^5}{ab^2}$;

(e) $\dfrac{15xy^2z}{3xz}$.

15. Find the product of each of the following pairs of algebraic quantities: (a) $5mn^2$, $-4mn^2$; (b) $3b^2c$, $4bc^2$; (c) $5ty^3$, $-8y^2z$; (d) $2x^2y$, $-4x + 7y$, $-xy$; (e) a, $-a$, $-a$, $-a$.
16. Expand each of the following: (a) $(2x - y + 3z)^2$; (b) $(x - 2y)(1 - x)^2$; (c) $(x^2 - 6)^2(2x + 1)$; (d) $(x - 3y)(2x + y)(x + y)$; (e) $(2x + y - z)^3$.

Factoring

The following are some of the more important factoring types.

(a) Perfect squares. $x^2 \pm 2xy + y^2 = (x \pm y)^2$.

Example. $x^2 - 8xy + 16y^2 = (x - 4y)^2$.

(b) Difference of two squares. $x^2 - y^2 = (x + y)(x - y)$.

Example. $9a^2 - 4b^2 = (3a + 2b)(3a - 2b)$.

(c) Trinomial with leading coefficient of 1.

$$x^2 + (a + b)x + ab = (x + a)(x + b).$$

Example. $x^2 - 6x - 16 = (x - 8)(x + 2)$.

(d) Sum of two cubes. $x^3 + y^3 = (x + y)(x^2 - xy + y^2)$.

Example. $8x^3 + y^3 = (2x + y)(4x^2 - 2xy + y^2)$.

(e) Difference of two cubes. $x^3 - y^3 = (x - y)(x^2 + xy + y^2)$.

Example. $27x^3 - 8y^3 = (3x - 2y)(9x^2 + 6xy + 4y^2)$.

(f) General trinomial, by inspection.

$$ax^2 + bx + c = (px + r)(qx + s).$$

Example. $6x^2 - 7x + 2 = (3x - 2)(2x - 1)$.

(g) Grouping.

Example.
$$\begin{aligned} 2x - 2y + ax - ay &= 2(x - y) + a(x - y) \\ &= (x - y)(2 + a). \end{aligned}$$

PROBLEMS

Factor each of the following expressions completely, by first factoring out any common monomial, and then using one of the above type forms.

1. $9x^8 - 4y^6$.
2. $225 - a^6$.
3. $r^4 - 11r^2 + 30$.
4. $16x^2 + 30x + 9$.
5. $3y^3 + 24$.
6. $6x^2 + 7x - 3$.
7. $c^3 + 27d^3$.
8. $x^2 - 16x + 48$.
9. $y^3 - 27z^3$.
10. $4x^2 - 3x - 7$.
11. $6 - t - 15t^2$.
12. $25t^4 - 1$.
13. $36a^2 - 132a + 121$.
14. $u^6 + u^3 - 110$.
15. $3x^4 - 12$.
16. $x^8 - y^8$.
17. $x^5 - xy^4 - x^4y + y^5$.
18. $x^4 - x^3y - xy^3 + y^4$.
19. $x^3 - 3x^2 + 3x - 1$.
20. $(x + y)^2 - a^2$.
21. $c^2 - (a + b)^2$.
22. $x^3y^3 + 1$.
23. $8 - 27x^3$.
24. $24m^2 + 22mn - 21n^2$.
25. $16x^2 - 6x - 27$.
26. $9 + 35x - 4x^2$.
27. $2x^4 + 11x^2y^2 - 21y^4$.
28. $(x - y)^2 - 4z^2$.
29. $(5x - 7)^2 - 1$.
30. $x^2 - (y - x)^2$.
31. $(3y + 5)^2 - (2y - 9)^2$.
32. $x^4y^4 - 9y^4$.
33. $x^2(2x + 1)^2 - (2y - 9)^2$.
34. $(x^2 - 4y^2) + x(x + 2y)$.
35. $a^2x + a^2y + abx + aby$.
36. $a^2x^3 - 64x^3y^2$.
37. $a^2x^2 - a^2y^2 + abx^2 - aby^2$.
38. $x^3 + x^2 + x + 1$.
39. $2 + 3x - 8x^2 - 12x^3$.
40. $56 - 32a + 21a^2 - 12a^3$.
41. $x^3 + (y - z)^3$.
42. $(m + n)^3 + 8t^3$.
43. $27a^3 - (a - b)^3$.
44. $(x + y)^2 - x^2y^2$.

Algebraic Fractions

An algebraic fraction should be treated exactly as an arithmetic fraction, as far as all simplifications and operations are concerned. The rules given previously still hold, and we illustrate their applications with a few examples. We shall assume that each fraction is defined.

Example.

$$\frac{n^2 - 36}{n^2} \cdot \frac{5n^2}{n^2 + n - 42} = \frac{(n - 6)(n + 6)}{n^2} \cdot \frac{5n^2}{(n + 7)(n - 6)}$$
$$= \frac{5n^2(n - 6)(n + 6)}{n^2(n + 7)(n - 6)} = \frac{5(n + 6)}{n + 7}.$$

Example.

$$\frac{2}{3x - 6} - \frac{1}{2x + 1} - \frac{1}{6x - 12} = \frac{2}{3(x - 2)} - \frac{1}{2x + 1} - \frac{1}{6(x - 2)}$$

$$= \frac{2\cdot 2(2x+1)}{6(x-2)(2x+1)} - \frac{6(x-2)}{6(x-2)(2x+1)} - \frac{2x+1}{6(x-2)(2x+1)}$$

$$= \frac{8x+4-6x+12-2x-1}{6(x-2)(2x+1)}$$

$$= \frac{15}{6(x-2)(2x+1)} = \frac{5}{2(x-2)(2x+1)}.$$

Example.

$$\frac{4}{4m^2-1} - \frac{5}{6m^2+m-1} = \frac{4}{(2m-1)(2m+1)} - \frac{5}{(2m+1)(3m-1)}$$

$$= \frac{4(3m-1)}{(2m-1)(2m+1)(3m-1)} - \frac{5(2m-1)}{(2m-1)(2m+1)(3m-1)}$$

$$= \frac{12m-4-10m+5}{(2m-1)(2m+1)(3m-1)} = \frac{2m+1}{(2m-1)(2m+1)(3m-1)}.$$

Example.

$$\frac{a/b-b/a}{1/a+1/b} = \frac{(a^2-b^2)/ab}{(b+a)/ab} = \frac{(a+b)(a-b)}{ab}\cdot\frac{ab}{a+b} = a-b.$$

PROBLEMS

Simplify each of the following expressions as much as possible.

1. $\frac{x}{2}+\frac{y}{6}+\frac{x}{3}$.
2. $\frac{x}{2}-\frac{(x-4)}{4}$.
3. $\frac{a-1}{a}-\frac{b+4}{b}$.
4. $\frac{5}{4x}+\frac{3}{5x^2}-\frac{7}{10x^3}$.
5. $\frac{x-y}{xy}+\frac{y-z}{yz}+\frac{z-x}{xz}$.
6. $\frac{2x+1}{5}-\frac{2x-1}{7}-\frac{x-3}{10}$.
7. $\frac{x-2}{x-1}+\frac{x+2}{x+1}$.
8. $\frac{x}{x+1}-\frac{2x}{x+2}+\frac{x}{x+3}$.
9. $\frac{2y-3}{y-2}+\frac{y+3}{3y-2}$.
10. $\frac{a}{x+a}-\frac{b}{x+b}$.
11. $\frac{3}{2+a-6a^2}-\frac{1}{1+a-2a^2}$.
12. $\frac{x+2}{x-2}-\frac{x^2+4}{x^2-4}$.

13. $\dfrac{4a^2 + 8a + 3}{2a^2 - 5a + 3} \cdot \dfrac{6a^2 - 9a}{4a^2 - 1}$.

14. $x + \dfrac{1}{x - 1/x}$.

15. $\dfrac{x + 2}{x} + \dfrac{x}{x - 3} - \dfrac{3}{x + 3}$.

16. $\dfrac{x - 1}{x^2 - 1} - \dfrac{x - 2}{x^2 - 4}$.

17. $\dfrac{1}{3 + x} + \dfrac{1}{3 - x} + \dfrac{6}{x^2 - 9}$.

18. $\dfrac{2x - 5}{x - 2} + x - 3$.

19. $\left(\dfrac{x}{y} - \dfrac{y}{x}\right) \div \left(x - \dfrac{x^2}{x + y}\right)$.

20. $\left(x - \dfrac{1}{x}\right) \div \left(x + \dfrac{1}{x} - 2\right)$.

21. $\dfrac{1 - 4/x + 3/x^2}{x - 9/x}$.

22. $\dfrac{x}{1 - \dfrac{1 - x}{1 + x}}$.

23. $[x^4 - 1/x^4] \div [(x - 1)/x]$.

24. $(x - 1/x) \div [(x + 1/x - 2)]$.

Equations: Linear and Quadratic

BASIC PRINCIPLE. An equality remains true if both members are transformed in the same way. For example, the same number may be added to both members, or both members may by multiplied or divided by the same number, except that division by 0 must be avoided.

(*a*) Linear. $ax = b$.

Applications of the above basic principle allow us to isolate the terms involving x, for any linear equation, on one side of the equality sign. The simplified equation may then be written in the form $ax = b$, and the solution can be obtained by dividing both members by a $(\neq 0)$.

Example.

$$3x - 4 + x = 6x + 2$$
$$3x + x - 6x = 2 + 4$$
$$-2x = 6, \; x = 6/(-2) = \mathbf{-3}.$$

(*b*) Quadratic. $ax^2 + bx + c = 0$.

Any quadratic equation can be put into the form $ax^2 + bx + c = 0$, by combining terms and applying the basic principle. There are then three methods of solution.

1. Factoring. This method is based on the important fact that if the product of two real or complex numbers is zero, at least one of the numbers is zero.

Example.

$$3x^2 + 5x - 2 = 0$$
$$(3x - 1)(x + 2) = 0$$
$$3x - 1 = 0 \text{ or } x + 2 = 0$$
$$x = 1/3 \quad \text{or} \quad x = \mathbf{-2}.$$

2. Completing the Square. An expression of the form $x^2 + ax$ can be made into a perfect square by adding to it the square of half the coefficient of x, i.e., $(a/2)^2$.

Example.

$$\begin{aligned} 3x^2 + 5x - 2 &= 0 \\ x^2 + (5/3)x &= 2/3 \\ x^2 + (5/3)x + 25/36 &= 2/3 + 25/36 \\ (x + 5/6)^2 &= 49/36 \\ x + 5/6 &= \pm 7/6 \end{aligned}$$

$$x = 1/3 \quad \text{or} \quad x = -2.$$

3. Formula. The formula is merely a condensation of the method of completing the square. The solutions of the equation $ax^2 + bx + c = 0$ are then $x = \dfrac{-b \pm \sqrt{b^2 - 4ac}}{2a}$.

Example. $3x^2 + 5x - 2 = 0.$

In this case, $a = 3$, $b = 5$ and $c = -2$. An application of the formula then gives

$$x = \frac{-5 \pm \sqrt{25 + 24}}{6} = \frac{-5 \pm 7}{6} = -2 \text{ or } 1/3.$$

Of the three methods, the method of factoring should be tried first. If this method fails, it is usually desirable to apply the formula.

PROBLEMS

Solve each of the following equations and check your result.

1. $2x + 2 = 7x - 18.$

2. $1 - x = 2 - 3x.$

3. $2 - 3x + 5 = -6x - 2.$

4. $5x + 6 = -7x.$

5. $(2x - 7) - (x - 5) = 0.$

6. $2(3x - 1) = 9(x - 2) - 7.$

7. $(x + 3)^2 - (x + 2)^2 = 1.$

8. $3 - (x - 1) = -1 - 2(5 - x).$

9. $2x^2 + 5x - 3 = 0.$

10. $6x^2 = x + 35.$

11. $x^2 + 5x - 3 = 0.$

12. $x^2 - 5x = -4.$

13. $3x^2 + 4x = 7.$

14. $x^2 + 5x = 36.$

15. $8x^2 - 22x - 90 = 0.$

16. $x^2 - 105x + 2700 = 0.$

17. $(1/4)x^2 - (3/2)x + 2 = 0.$

18. $s^2 = 5s + 6.$

19. $3r^2 - 2r = 40.$

20. $u^4 - 29u^2 + 100 = 0.$

21. $2y + 5/2 = 5/(4y).$

22. $t^2 - 6t = 6.$

23. $9y^2 - 12y - 8 = 0.$

24. $4x^2 + 4x - 5 = 0.$

25. $8y^2 - 8y - 3 = 0.$

26. $x^2 = 5 + (4/3)x.$

27. $\dfrac{x}{x-1} - \dfrac{x-1}{x} = \dfrac{x^2+2x-1}{x^2-1}$.

28. $x^2 + 100/(x^2) = 29$.

29. $\dfrac{1}{x-1} - \dfrac{1}{x+1} = \dfrac{1}{24}$.

30. $\dfrac{1}{x} + \dfrac{1}{x-3} - \dfrac{7}{3x-5} = 0$.

31. $(x + 1/x)^2 - (16/3)(x + 1/x) + 7 = 1/3$.

32. $x^6 - 12x^3 + 35 = 0$.

33. $(1/5)x^2 - (1/30)x - 1/2 = 0$.

34. $\dfrac{2x-7}{x^2-4} = \dfrac{10x-3}{5x(x+2)}$.

35. $6a^2 - 10a + 4 = 0$.

36. $1 + 2x - 15x^2 = 0$.

37. $18x^2 - 3x - 66 = 0$.

38. $1 - 20p - 10p^2 = 0$.

39. $t + 1/t = a + 1/a$.

40. $\dfrac{x-3}{x-2} - \dfrac{x+4}{x} = \dfrac{3}{2}$.

Simultaneous Linear Equations

1. TWO EQUATIONS IN TWO UNKNOWNS. Two methods are in common use, *elimination by addition and subtraction*, and *elimination by substitution*.

(*a*) Elimination by addition and subtraction. Both members of each equation are multiplied by some number, so that when corresponding members are now added (or subtracted) one of the unknowns has a coefficient 0. The other unknown is then found by the methods of the preceding section.

Example. $7x - 2y = 4$ (1)

$9x - 3y = 3$ (2)

Multiply both members of (1) by 3: $21x - 6y = 12$ (3)

Multiply both members of (2) by 2: $18x - 6y = 6$ (4)

Subtract the members of (4) from the corresponding members of (3): $3x = 6$, and so $x = 2$.

Substitute $x = 2$ in (1): $14 - 2y = 4$, $2y = 10$, and $y = 5$.

Check: (1) $7\cdot2 - 2\cdot5 = 14 - 10 = 4$

(2) $9\cdot2 - 3\cdot5 = 18 - 15 = 3$

(*b*) Elimination by substitution. One of the equations is solved for one of the unknowns in terms of the other; this solution is then substituted in the other equation, which is solved by the methods of the preceding section. The other unknown is found by substitution in either equation.

Example. $4x - y = 6$ (1)

$3x - 4y = 11$ (2)

Solve (1) for y in terms of x: $y = 4x - 6$.

Substitute $4x - 6$ for y in (2): $3x - 4(4x - 6) = 11$

$$3x - 16x + 24 = 11$$

$$13x = 13$$

$$x = 1, \qquad y = 4x - 6 = -2.$$

Check: (1) $4 \cdot 1 - (-2) = 4 + 2 = 6$

(2) $3 \cdot 1 - 4(-2) = 3 + 8 = 11.$

2. THREE EQUATIONS IN THREE UNKNOWNS. By successive elimination of the same unknown from two pairs of the equations, we obtain two equations in two unknowns, that may be solved by methods 1*a* and 1*b*.

Example.

$$2x + y - 3z = 1 \qquad (1)$$

$$x - y + 2z = 1 \qquad (2)$$

$$x + 3y - z = 6 \qquad (3)$$

Eliminate y from (1) and (2) by addition of the corresponding members:

$$3x - z = 2 \qquad (4)$$

Eliminate y from (2) and (3), by multiplying the members of (2) by 3 and adding the members of this new equation to the corresponding members of (3):

$$4x + 5z = 9 \qquad (5)$$

We now solve (4) and (5) by the method of elimination by substitution.

$$z = 3x - 2$$

$$4x + 5(3x - 2) = 9$$

$$4x + 15x - 10 = 9$$

$$19x = 19, \qquad x = 1, \qquad z = 3x - 2 = 1.$$

If we substitute $x = 1$ and $z = 1$ in (1), we obtain the solution for y.

$$2 \cdot 1 + y - 3 \cdot 1 = 1$$

$$2 + y - 3 = 1$$

$$y = 2.$$

The complete solution is then $x = 1$, $y = 2$, $z = 1$.

Check: (1) $2 \cdot 1 + 2 - 3 \cdot 1 = 2 + 2 - 3 = 1$

(2) $1 - 2 + 2 \cdot 1 = 1 - 2 + 2 = 1$

(3) $1 + 3 \cdot 2 - 1 = 1 + 6 - 1 = 6$

PROBLEMS

Solve and check each of the following systems of linear equations.

1. $2x + 5y = 4$
$4x - 10y = 48.$

2. $x - y = 1$
$x + y = 9.$

3. $y = 2x + 3$
$x = 2y - 3.$

4. $2x - 7y = 5$
$5x + 2y = 5.$

5. $2(x + y) = 16$
$3(x - y) = 6.$

6. $x + y/5 = 17$
$x - y = 5.$

7. $3x + 4y = 24$
$5x - 3y = 11.$

8. $3x - 4y = -6$
$x + 5y = 17.$

9. $7x + 9y = 41$
$x + 4y = 14.$

10. $5x + 3y = 5$
$9x + 5y = 8.$

11. $x - y - z = -6$
$2x + y + z = 0$
$3x - 5y + 8z = 13.$

12. $x + 2y + z = 7$
$x + y - z = 2$
$3x - y + 2z = 12.$

13. $2x - y + 3z = 4$
$x + 3y + 3z = -2$
$3x + 2y - 6z = 6.$

14. $x + 2y + z = 0$
$2x + y + 2z = 3$
$4x - 6y + 3z = 14.$

15. $x/2 + y/3 = 9$
$x/3 + z/2 = 8$
$y/2 + z/3 = 13.$

16. $1/x + 1/y + 2/z = 1$
$2/x + 1/y - 2/z = 1$
$3/x + 4/y - 4/z = 2.$

17. A man can row downstream 3 miles in 20 minutes, but the return trip takes him 1 hour. What is his speed in still water, and what is the speed of the current?

18. Find two integers, the respective sum and difference of which are 95 and 15.

Exponents

Note. In the following definitions and laws, the base number a will be a positive integer.

DEFINITION. $\sqrt[n]{a}$ is the positive nth root of a, i.e., the positive number such that $(\sqrt[n]{a})^n = a$.

DEFINITION. $a^n = a \cdot a \cdot a \cdot \cdots \cdot a$ to n factors, if n is a positive integer. $a^{1/r} = \sqrt[r]{a}$ and $a^{n/r} = (\sqrt[r]{a})^n = \sqrt[r]{a^n}$, if n and r are positive integers.

$$a^0 = 1.$$

$$a^{-n} = 1/a^n, \text{ for any number } n.$$

LAWS OF EXPONENTS.
1. $a^x \cdot a^y = a^{x+y}.$
2. $a^x/a^y = a^{x-y}.$
3. $(a^x)^y = a^{xy}.$
4. $a^x \cdot b^x = (ab)^x.$

Example.

$$3^{2/3} \cdot 3^{5/3} = 3^{2/3+5/3} = 3^{7/3} = 3^{2+1/3} = 9 \cdot 3^{1/3} = 9\sqrt[3]{3}.$$

Example.

$$\left[\frac{8x^{1/2}}{x^{2/3}}\right]^{2/3} = \frac{8^{2/3} \cdot x^{1/3}}{x^{4/9}} = 4 \cdot x^{(1/3-4/9)} = 4 \cdot x^{-1/9} = \frac{4}{\sqrt[9]{x}} \cdot$$

PROBLEMS

1. Write each of the following quantities in exponential form: (*a*) $\sqrt{a}$; (*b*) $\sqrt[4]{x^3}$; (*c*) $\sqrt[5]{a^7}$; (*d*) $\sqrt{a^3}$; (*e*) $\sqrt[3]{a+2}$.

2. Write each of the following quantities in exponential form: (*a*) $\sqrt{3}$; (*b*) $\sqrt[3]{2^5}$; (*c*) $\sqrt[5]{4^4}$; (*d*) $\sqrt{5}$; (*e*) $\sqrt[3]{2+x}$.

3. Find an integer equal to (*a*) $9^{1/2}$; (*b*) $81^{3/2}$; (*c*) $125^{5/3}$; (*d*) $64^{5/6}$; (*e*) $16^{1/4}$.

4. Write each of the following quantities in radical form: (*a*) $a^{1/3}$; (*b*) $x^{5/6}$; (*c*) $b^{n/3}$; (*d*) $n^{3/4}$; (*e*) $s^{7/6}$.

5. Write each of the following as a single exponential quantity: (*a*) $x^2 \cdot x^{n+1}$; (*b*) $a^{n-2} \cdot a^{3+n}$; (*c*) $u^{n+r} \cdot u^{n-r}$; (*d*) $(p^7)^3$; (*e*) $(a^4)^3$.

6. Write each of the following as a single exponential quantity: (*a*) $x^{3n} \div x^n$; (*b*) $10^{2r+1} \div 10^r$; (*c*) $u^{n+r} \div u^{n-r}$; (*d*) $(x^5/x^4)^4$; (*e*) $(p^3q^3)^s$; (*f*) $(r^2s^2)^5$; (*g*) $e^{n+5} \div e^3$.

7. Simplify each of the following expressions: (*a*) $x^{1/3}x^{7/3}$; (*b*) $a^{1/4}a^{1/5}$; (*c*) $a^{3/4}a^{2/3}$; (*d*) $x^{1/5}x^{3/10}$.

8. Simplify each of the following expressions: (*a*) $(a^{2/3})^{1/4}$; (*b*) $(x^{3/5})^{5/6}$; (*c*) $(a^{5/12})^4$; (*d*) $(a^2b^{1/2})^{1/2}$.

9. Simplify each of the following expressions: (*a*) $x^{1/2}/x^{1/2}$; (*b*) $[x^5/x^{2/3}]^{3/5}$; (*c*) $[9x^{3/4}/4x^{2/5}]^{3/2}$; (*d*) $(8a^{3/8}b^{9/4})^{4/9}$.

10. Find a rational fraction equal to (*a*) 2^{-1}; (*b*) $16^{-3/4}$; (*c*) 3^{-2}; (*d*) $7^{-1}/49^{-1/2}$; (*e*) 1^{-1}.

11. Find a rational fraction equal to (*a*) $2/3^{-2}$; (*b*) $1^{-8}/8^{-1}$; (*c*) $32^{-1/5}/2^{-1}$; (*d*) $512^{-1/3}$.

12. Write each of the following quantities in an equivalent form without negative exponents: (*a*) a^2b^{-2}; (*b*) $(a+b)^{-3}$; (*c*) $3x^{-2}y^{-1/2}$; (*d*) x^4/y^{-5}; (*e*) $1/x^{-2}$.

13. Write each of the following quantities as an equivalent expression with denominator 1: (*a*) $1/x^2$; (*b*) $(xy^2)/(c^3d^4)$; (*c*) $(2a^3b^{-3})/(4r^{-2}t^5)$; (*d*) $ab^{1/2}/(x^{-1/3}y^{s/t})$.

14. Simplify each of the following: (*a*) $(a^{-5}/a^{-4})^{-7}$; (*b*) $(x^{-4}/x^{-6})^{-2}$; (*c*) $\left[\frac{a^{-3}b}{x^3y^{-2}}\right]^{-3}$; (*d*) $(r^{-3/4})^{-2/3}$.

Equations Involving Radicals

(*a*) If only one radical is involved, isolate this term on one side of the equation, and raise both members to an appropriate power to eliminate the radical. Each answer should be checked, since this process frequently introduces extraneous roots. It should be recalled here that $\sqrt{a}$ is the *positive* square root of a, if a is a positive real number.

Example. $\sqrt{x-3} = x - 5$. Squaring both members, we obtain

$$x - 3 = (x-5)^2 = x^2 - 10x + 25$$
$$x^2 - 11x + 28 = 0$$
$$(x-7)(x-4) = 0$$
$$x = 7 \quad \text{or} \quad x = 4.$$

Check: $x = 7$. $\sqrt{4} = 7 - 5$ which checks;
$x = 4$. $\sqrt{1} \neq 4 - 1$, so 4 is extraneous and $x = 7$ is the only root.

(*b*) If more than one radical expression occurs in the equation, it may be necessary to repeat the procedure in (*a*). First isolate one radical—preferably the most complicated—and rationalize it by raising both members to an appropriate power; then isolate the remaining radical, and repeat the procedure.

Example.

$$\sqrt{2x+3} - \sqrt{5x+1} + 1 = 0$$
$$\sqrt{5x+1} = \sqrt{2x+3} + 1$$
$$5x + 1 = 2x + 3 + 2\sqrt{2x+3} + 1$$
$$2\sqrt{2x+3} = 3x - 3$$
$$4(2x+3) = 9x^2 - 18x + 9$$
$$9x^2 - 26x - 3 = 0$$
$$(x-3)(9x+1) = 0$$
$$x = 3 \quad \text{or} \quad x = -1/9.$$

Check: $x = 3$. $\sqrt{9} - \sqrt{16} + 1 = 0$, which checks this solution. The number $-1/9$ does not check, and so must be discarded as extraneous.

PROBLEMS

Solve and check each of the following equations.

1. $\sqrt{x+4} = 3.$
2. $\sqrt{3x-5} - 5 = 0.$
3. $\sqrt[3]{x-1} = 4.$
4. $\sqrt{11x-8} = 6.$
5. $\sqrt{x+11} = 1 - x.$
6. $\sqrt{3x-2} + 3 = 0.$
7. $\sqrt{x-5} + 2 = 0.$
8. $\sqrt{4x+1} - \sqrt{2x-3} = 2.$
9. $\sqrt{x-7} - \sqrt{5x-4} = \sqrt{3x+1}.$
10. $\sqrt{3x-11} = \sqrt{5-x}.$
11. $x - \sqrt{x} - 6 = 0.$
12. $\sqrt{10-x} - \sqrt{10+x} + 2 = 0.$
13. $\sqrt{6x+4} + \sqrt{2x} - 6 = 0.$
14. $\sqrt{2x+1} - \sqrt{5x-4} + 1 = 0.$
15. $1/\sqrt{x} + 1/\sqrt{4x} = 3.$
16. $1/(\sqrt{x} + \sqrt{4x}) = 3.$
17. $\sqrt{3x+4} + \sqrt{5-x} = 5.$
18. $(\sqrt{x} + \sqrt{3})/\sqrt{x+3} = 1.$

Ratio and Proportion

DEFINITION. The *ratio* of a number a to a number b, written $a:b$, is a measure of *comparison* of the numbers; we define $a:b = c:d$, if and only if $a/b = c/d$.

Note. If a ratio is used to express the relative size of two quantities, these quantities must be measured in the same units.

Example. If the respective lengths of diameters of two trees are $2'3''$ and $8''$, the ratio of the lengths of their diameters is $27:8$.

DEFINITION. A proportion is a statement of equality of two ratios. Thus, if $a:b$ and $c:d$ are equal ratios, this fact may be indicated by writing $a:b = c:d$ or $a:b :: c:d$. In view of our definition of equality for ratios, it follows that $a:b = c:d$ if and only if $a/b = c/d$. The numbers b and c are known as the *means* and a and d the *extremes* of the above proportion.

THEOREM. In any proportion, the product of the means is equal to the product of the extremes.

Example. If $2:9 = 4:x$, this theorem implies that $2x = 36$, and so $x = 18$.

DEFINITIONS. If $a:x = x:b$, then x is a *mean proportional* to a and b. If $a:b = b:x$, then x is a *third proportional* to a and b. If $a:b = c:x$, then x is a *fourth proportional* to a, b, and c.

PROBLEMS

1. Simplify each of the following ratios: (*a*) 4:8; (*b*) 5/2:13/4; (*c*) 13/4:9/2; (*d*) 2:17/8; (*e*) $(x^2 - y^2):(x + y)$.
2. Find the ratio of the first to the second of each of the following pairs of measurements of length: (*a*) 2 inches, 3 feet; (*b*) 8 inches, 2 1/4 feet; (*c*) 4 feet, 2 yards; (*d*) 5 centimeters, 45 millimeters.
3. Find the ratio of the first to the second of each of the following pairs of measurements of time: (*a*) 15 minutes, 1 1/2 hours; (*b*) 8 hours, 2 days; (*c*) 24 seconds, 10 minutes.
4. Express each of the following ratios in simplified form: (*a*) $(1 + 1/a):(1 - 1/a^2)$; (*b*) $[1/(x - 1)]:[2/(x^2 - 4x + 3)]$; (*c*) $(1/x):(3/x^2)$.
5. Separate 125 into two parts in the ratio 3:2.
6. Two numbers are in the ratio 2:5, while if 1 is added to each they are in the ratio 3:7. Find the numbers.
7. Solve each of the following proportions for the unknown member: (*a*) $2:5 = x:8$; (*b*) $3:x = 4:18$; (*c*) $4:7 = x:21$; (*d*) $x:12 = 3:4$.
8. Find the mean proportional to each of the following pairs of numbers: (*a*) 3, 12; (*b*) 8, 2; (*c*) 2, 32; (*d*) 3, 8; (*e*) 5, 12.
9. Find the third proportional to a and b if (*a*) $a = 4, b = 9$; (*b*) $a = 3, b = 10$; (*c*) $a = 8, b = 24$.
10. Find the fourth proportional to $a, b,$ and c given that (*a*) $a = 2, b = 3, c = 4$; (*b*) $a = 7, b = 11, c = 21$; (*c*) $a = -3, b = 8, c = 10$.
11. Solve the following proportion for x: $(2 - x):(2 + x) = (1 - x):(1 + x)$.
12. Solve the following proportion for x: $x:(x - 2) = 3:4$.

TEST ON REVIEW MATERIAL

1. Add the numbers in each of the following collections: (*a*) 1/2, −2/3, 3/4, −2; (*b*) −5/6, 3/5, 2/15, −5/12.
2. Divide the first number by the second in each of the following pairs: (*a*) −5/4, 2/3; (*b*) 5/6, −3/7; (*c*) 3/5, 5; (*d*) 4, −2/5.
3. Simplify each of the following expressions:

$$(a)\ \frac{\dfrac{x}{x-1} - 1}{\dfrac{x}{1-x} + 1}; \qquad (b)\ \frac{\dfrac{1}{x+3} + 1}{x - \dfrac{12}{x+1}}.$$

4. (*a*) From the sum of $x^2/2$, $-5x^2/4$, and $2 - 3x + x^2$, subtract the sum of $2x^2/3$ and $-5x$. (*b*) Divide $a/b - b/a$ by $1/b - 1/a$, and simplify the result.
5. Factor completely each of the following expressions: (*a*) $m^2 - 4n^2$; (*b*) $t^2 + 6t - 55$; (*c*) $1 - y^6$.

6. Factor completely each of the following expressions: (*a*) $am + bm + b + a$; (*b*) $(1 - x)^2 - (x - y)^2$; (*c*) $12x^2 + 25x - 7$.

7. Factor completely each of the following expressions: (*a*) $1 - x^2 - 2xy - y^2$; (*b*) $(x + 1)^3 - 9(x + 1)^2 + 8(x + 1)$.

8. Use the quadratic formula to solve each of the following equations: (*a*) $2s^2 - 5s + 1 = 0$; (*b*) $2x^2 + 3x + 1 = 0$.

9. Solve each of the following quadratic equations, by first factoring the left member: (*a*) $2x^2 - x - 1 = 0$; (*b*) $6x^2 + 5x - 6 = 0$.

10. Solve each of the following quadratic equations by completing squares in the left members: (*a*) $4x^2 - x - 5 = 0$; (*b*) $2y^2 - 4y - 1 = 0$.

11. Solve each of the following systems of linear equations, and check:

(*a*) $x + y = 11$
$2x - 3y = 22.$

(*b*) $2y + 5z = 2$
$4y + z = 13.$

12. Solve each of the following systems of equations, and check:

(*a*) $x + y = 18$
$y + z = 13$
$x + z = 5.$

(*b*) $1/x + 1/y = 7$
$1/y + 1/z = 11/2$
$1/z + 1/x = 5/2.$

13. (*a*) Write each of the following in radical form: $2^{1/2}, 3^{2/3}, 4^{3/2}, 6^{-1/2}, 2^{-2/3}$. (*b*) Write each of the following in exponential form: $\sqrt[5]{5}, \sqrt[3]{3^2}, 1/\sqrt{3}, 3/\sqrt[3]{5^2}$.

14. Simplify each of the following expressions: (*a*) $(x^{-2}y^3y^{-2})/(3x^2y^{-5}z)$; (*b*) $[(12x^3)(4x^{-2})^3(xy)^2]/[(3xy)^3(2x^{-3})^2]$.

15. (*a*) The heights of two posts are 18 inches and 3 1/2 feet, respectively. What is the ratio of their heights? (*b*) Solve the following proportion for x: $3:11/2 = (x - 1):(x + 1)$.

16. Solve for x: $\sqrt{3x + 7} + \sqrt{x + 1} - 2 = 0$.

17. Solve for y: $\sqrt{3y - 2} - 2 = 8/\sqrt{3y - 2}$.

LIST OF SYMBOLS

N	set of all natural numbers.
I	set of all integers.
$\bar{R}$	set of all rational numbers.
$R^{\#}$	set of all real numbers.
$=$	is equal to.
$\neq$	is not equal to.
$<$	is less than.
$\nless$	is not less than.
$>$	is greater than
$\ngtr$	is not greater than.
$\in$	is a member of.
$\notin$	is not a member of.
$\subseteq$	is included in.
$\subset$	is properly included in.
$\cup$	union or join.
$\cap$	intersection or meet.
$\rightarrow$	implies.
$\leftrightarrow$	is equivalent to.
$A \times B$	Cartesian product of set A with set B.
$\lvert a \rvert$	absolute value of a.
A'	complement of set A.
$f(x)$	value of function f at x.
$f'(x)$	value of the derivative of f at x.
$\sum$	summation.
$x \rightarrow \infty$	x becomes infinite, i.e., x exceeds any finite number.
$[a, b]$	interval of real numbers between a and b, inclusive.
$\lim_{x \rightarrow a} f(x)$	limit of $f(x)$ as x tends to a.
$\int f(x)\, dx$	antiderivative of f.
$\int_a^b f(x)\, dx$	definite integral of f from a to b.
$\int_a^x f(t)\, dt$	indefinite integral of f.
$[x]$	greatest integer not greater than x.
$C_{n,r}$	number of combinations of n things taken r at a time.

$P_{n,r}$	number of permutations of n things taken r at a time.
P_n	number of permutations of n things.
$\lfloor n$	factorial n, i.e., $n(n-1)(n-2)\cdots(3)(2)(1)$.
$N(A)$	the cardinal number of the set A.
$\doteq$	equals, approximately.
$p(E)$	probability of event E.
$p(F \mid E)$	probability of event F after event E has occurred.
$p(E \cap F)$	probability of events E and F occurring simultaneously.
$p(E \cup F)$	probability of either event E or event F or both occurring.
μ	mean of a population.
σ	standard deviation of a population.
$\bar{x}$	mean of a sample.
s	standard deviation of a sample.
$\mu_{\bar{x}}$	mean of a population of sample means.
$\sigma_{\bar{x}}$	standard deviation of a population of sample means.

TABLE 1

Four-Place Common Logarithms of Numbers

N	0	1	2	3	4	5	6	7	8	9
10	0000	0043	0086	0128	0170	0212	0253	0294	0334	0374
11	0414	0453	0492	0531	0569	0607	0645	0682	0719	0755
12	0792	0828	0864	0899	0934	0969	1004	1038	1072	1106
13	1139	1173	1206	1239	1271	1303	1335	1367	1399	1430
14	1461	1492	1523	1553	1584	1614	1644	1673	1703	1732
15	1761	1790	1818	1847	1875	1903	1931	1959	1987	2014
16	2041	2068	2095	2122	2148	2175	2201	2227	2253	2279
17	2304	2330	2355	2380	2405	2430	2455	2480	2504	2529
18	2553	2577	2601	2625	2648	2672	2695	2718	2742	2765
19	2788	2810	2833	2856	2878	2900	2923	2945	2967	2989
20	3010	3032	3054	3075	3096	3118	3139	3160	3181	3201
21	3222	3243	3263	3284	3304	3324	3345	3365	3385	3404
22	3424	3444	3464	3483	3502	3522	3541	3560	3579	3598
23	3617	3636	3655	3674	3692	3711	3729	3747	3766	3784
24	3802	3820	3838	3856	3874	3892	3909	3927	3945	3962
25	3979	3997	4014	4031	4048	4065	4082	4099	4116	4133
26	4150	4166	4183	4200	4216	4232	4249	4265	4281	4298
27	4314	4330	4346	4362	4378	4393	4409	4425	4440	4456
28	4472	4487	4502	4518	4533	4548	4564	4579	4594	4609
29	4624	4639	4654	4669	4683	4698	4713	4728	4742	4757
30	4771	4786	4800	4814	4829	4843	4857	4871	4886	4900
31	4914	4928	4942	4955	4969	4983	4997	5011	5024	5038
32	5051	5065	5079	5092	5105	5119	5132	5145	5159	5172
33	5185	5198	5211	5224	5237	5250	5263	5276	5289	5302
34	5315	5328	5340	5353	5366	5378	5391	5403	5416	5428
35	5441	5453	5465	5478	5490	5502	5514	5527	5539	5551
36	5563	5575	5587	5599	5611	5623	5635	5647	5658	5670
37	5682	5694	5705	5717	5729	5740	5752	5763	5775	5786
38	5798	5809	5821	5832	5843	5855	5866	5877	5888	5899
39	5911	5922	5933	5944	5955	5966	5977	5988	5999	6010
40	6021	6031	6042	6053	6064	6075	6085	6096	6107	6117
41	6128	6138	6149	6160	6170	6180	6191	6201	6212	6222
42	6232	6243	6253	6263	6274	6284	6294	6304	6314	6325
43	6335	6345	6355	6365	6375	6385	6395	6405	6415	6425
44	6435	6444	6454	6464	6474	6484	6493	6503	6513	6522
45	6532	6542	6551	6561	6571	6580	6590	6599	6609	6618
46	6628	6637	6646	6656	6665	6675	6684	6693	6702	6712
47	6721	6730	6739	6749	6758	6767	6776	6785	6794	6803
48	6812	6821	6830	6839	6848	6857	6866	6875	6884	6893
49	6902	6911	6920	6928	6937	6946	6955	6964	6972	6981
50	6990	6998	7007	7016	7024	7033	7042	7050	7059	7067
51	7076	7084	7093	7101	7110	7118	7126	7135	7143	7152
52	7160	7168	7177	7185	7193	7202	7210	7218	7226	7235
53	7243	7251	7259	7267	7275	7284	7292	7300	7308	7316
54	7324	7332	7340	7348	7356	7364	7372	7380	7388	7396
N	0	1	2	3	4	5	6	7	8	9

Four-Place Common Logarithms of Numbers

N	0	1	2	3	4	5	6	7	8	9
55	7404	7412	7419	7427	7435	7443	7451	7459	7466	7474
56	7482	7490	7497	7505	7513	7520	7528	7536	7543	7551
57	7559	7566	7574	7582	7589	7597	7604	7612	7619	7627
58	7634	7642	7649	7657	7664	7672	7679	7686	7694	7701
59	7709	7716	7723	7731	7738	7745	7752	7760	7767	7774
60	7782	7789	7796	7803	7810	7818	7825	7832	7839	7846
61	7853	7860	7868	7875	7882	7889	7896	7903	7910	7917
62	7924	7931	7938	7945	7952	7959	7966	7973	7980	7987
63	7993	8000	8007	8014	8021	8028	8035	8041	8048	8055
64	8062	8069	8075	8082	8089	8096	8102	8109	8116	8122
65	8129	8136	8142	8149	8156	8162	8169	8176	8182	8189
66	8195	8202	8209	8215	8222	8228	8235	8241	8248	8254
67	8261	8267	8274	8280	8287	8293	8299	8306	8312	8319
68	8325	8331	8338	8344	8351	8357	8363	8370	8376	8382
69	8388	8395	8401	8407	8414	8420	8426	8432	8439	8445
70	8451	8457	8463	8470	8476	8482	8488	8494	8500	8506
71	8513	8519	8525	8531	8537	8543	8549	8555	8561	8567
72	8573	8579	8585	8591	8597	8603	8609	8615	8621	8627
73	8633	8639	8645	8651	8657	8663	8669	8675	8681	8686
74	8692	8698	8704	8710	8716	8722	8727	8733	8739	8745
75	8751	8756	8762	8768	8774	8779	8785	8791	8797	8802
76	8808	8814	8820	8825	8831	8837	8842	8848	8854	8859
77	8865	8871	8876	8882	8887	8893	8899	8904	8910	8915
78	8921	8927	8932	8938	8943	8949	8954	8960	8965	8971
79	8976	8982	8987	8993	8998	9004	9009	9015	9020	9025
80	9031	9036	9042	9047	9053	9058	9063	9069	9074	9079
81	9085	9090	9096	9101	9106	9112	9117	9122	9128	9133
82	9138	9143	9149	9154	9159	9165	9170	9175	9180	9186
83	9191	9196	9201	9206	9212	9217	9222	9227	9232	9238
84	9243	9248	9253	9258	9263	9269	9274	9279	9284	9289
85	9294	9299	9304	9309	9315	9320	9325	9330	9335	9340
86	9345	9350	9355	9360	9365	9370	9375	9380	9385	9390
87	9395	9400	9405	9410	9415	9420	9425	9430	9435	9440
88	9445	9450	9455	9460	9465	9469	9474	9479	9484	9489
89	9494	9499	9504	9509	9513	9518	9523	9528	9533	9538
90	9542	9547	9552	9557	9562	9566	9571	9576	9581	9586
91	9590	9595	9600	9605	9609	9614	9619	9624	9628	9633
92	9638	9643	9647	9652	9657	9661	9666	9671	9675	9680
93	9685	9689	9694	9699	9703	9708	9713	9717	9722	9727
94	9731	9736	9741	9745	9750	9754	9759	9763	9768	9773
95	9777	9782	9786	9791	9795	9800	9805	9809	9814	9818
96	9823	9827	9832	9836	9841	9845	9850	9854	9859	9863
97	9868	9872	9877	9881	9886	9890	9894	9899	9903	9908
98	9912	9917	9921	9926	9930	9934	9939	9943	9948	9952
99	9956	9961	9965	9969	9974	9978	9983	9987	9991	9996
N	0	1	2	3	4	5	6	7	8	9

TABLE 2

Four-Place Values of the Circular Functions

x (degrees)	θ (radians)	$\sin\theta(x^\circ)$	$\csc\theta(x^\circ)$	$\cos\theta(x^\circ)$	$\sec\theta(x^\circ)$	$\tan\theta(x^\circ)$	$\cot\theta(x^\circ)$		
0.0	0.0000	0.00000	—	1.0000	1.0000	0.00000	—	1.5708	**90.0**
0.1	0.0017	0.00175	572.96	1.0000	1.0000	0.00175	573.0	1.5691	89.9
0.2	0.0035	0.00349	286.48	1.0000	1.0000	0.00349	286.5	1.5673	89.8
0.3	0.0052	0.00524	190.99	1.0000	1.0000	0.00524	191.0	1.5656	89.7
0.4	0.0070	0.00698	143.24	1.0000	1.0000	0.00698	143.24	1.5638	89.6
0.5	0.0087	0.00873	114.59	1.0000	1.0000	0.00873	114.59	1.5621	**89.5**
0.6	0.0105	0.01047	95.495	0.9999	1.0001	0.01047	95.49	1.5603	89.4
0.7	0.0122	0.01222	81.853	0.9999	1.0001	0.01222	81.85	1.5586	89.3
0.8	0.0140	0.01396	71.622	0.9999	1.0001	0.01396	71.62	1.5568	89.2
0.9	0.0157	0.01571	63.665	0.9999	1.0001	0.01571	63.66	1.5551	89.1
1.0	0.0175	0.01745	57.299	0.9998	1.0002	0.01746	57.29	1.5533	**89.0**
1.1	0.0192	0.01920	52.090	0.9998	1.0002	0.01920	52.08	1.5516	88.9
1.2	0.0209	0.02094	47.750	0.9998	1.0002	0.02095	47.74	1.5499	88.8
1.3	0.0227	0.02269	44.077	0.9997	1.0003	0.02269	44.07	1.5481	88.7
1.4	0.0244	0.02443	40.930	0.9997	1.0003	0.02444	40.92	1.5464	88.6
1.5	0.0262	0.02618	38.202	0.9997	1.0003	0.02619	38.19	1.5446	**88.5**
1.6	0.0279	0.02792	35.815	0.9996	1.0004	0.02793	35.80	1.5429	88.4
1.7	0.0297	0.02967	33.708	0.9996	1.0004	0.02968	33.69	1.5411	88.3
1.8	0.0314	0.03141	31.836	0.9995	1.0005	0.03143	31.82	1.5394	88.2
1.9	0.0332	0.03316	30.161	0.9995	1.0006	0.03317	30.14	1.5376	88.1
2.0	0.0349	0.03490	28.654	0.9994	1.0006	0.03492	28.64	1.5359	**88.0**
2.1	0.0367	0.03664	27.290	0.9993	1.0007	0.03667	27.27	1.5341	87.9
2.2	0.0384	0.03839	26.050	0.9993	1.0007	0.03842	26.03	1.5324	87.8
2.3	0.0401	0.04013	24.918	0.9992	1.0008	0.04016	24.90	1.5307	87.7
2.4	0.0419	0.04188	23.880	0.9991	1.0009	0.04191	23.86	1.5289	87.6
2.5	0.0436	0.04362	22.926	0.9990	1.0010	0.04366	22.90	1.5272	**87.5**
2.6	0.0454	0.04536	22.044	0.9990	1.0010	0.04541	22.02	1.5254	87.4
2.7	0.0471	0.04711	21.229	0.9989	1.0011	0.04716	21.20	1.5237	87.3
2.8	0.0489	0.04885	20.471	0.9988	1.0012	0.04891	20.45	1.5219	87.2
2.9	0.0506	0.05059	19.766	0.9987	1.0013	0.05066	19.74	1.5202	87.1
3.0	0.0524	0.05234	19.107	0.9986	1.0014	0.05241	19.081	1.5184	**87.0**
3.1	0.0541	0.05408	18.492	0.9985	1.0015	0.05416	18.464	1.5167	86.9
3.2	0.0559	0.05582	17.914	0.9984	1.0016	0.05591	17.886	1.5149	86.8
3.3	0.0576	0.05756	17.372	0.9983	1.0017	0.05766	17.343	1.5132	86.7
3.4	0.0593	0.05931	16.862	0.9982	1.0018	0.05941	16.832	1.5115	86.6
3.5	0.0611	0.06105	16.380	0.9981	1.0019	0.06116	16.350	1.5097	**86.5**
3.6	0.0628	0.06279	15.926	0.9980	1.0020	0.06291	15.895	1.5080	86.4
3.7	0.0646	0.06453	15.496	0.9979	1.0021	0.06467	15.464	1.5062	86.3
3.8	0.0663	0.06627	15.089	0.9978	1.0022	0.06642	15.056	1.5045	86.2
3.9	0.0681	0.06802	14.703	0.9977	1.0023	0.06817	14.669	1.5027	86.1
4.0	0.0698	0.06976	14.336	0.9976	1.0024	0.06993	14.301	1.5010	**86.0**
4.1	0.0716	0.07150	13.987	0.9974	1.0026	0.07168	13.951	1.4992	85.9
4.2	0.0733	0.07324	13.654	0.9973	1.0027	0.07344	13.617	1.4975	85.8
4.3	0.0750	0.07498	13.337	0.9972	1.0028	0.07519	13.300	1.4957	85.7
4.4	0.0768	0.07672	13.035	0.9971	1.0030	0.07695	12.996	1.4940	85.6
		$\cos\theta(x^\circ)$	$\sec\theta(x^\circ)$	$\sin\theta(x^\circ)$	$\csc\theta(x^\circ)$	$\cot\theta(x^\circ)$	$\tan\theta(x^\circ)$	θ (radians)	x (degrees)

Four-Place Values of the Circular Functions

x (degrees)	θ (radians)	sin θ(x°)	csc θ(x°)	cos θ(x°)	sec θ(x°)	tan θ(x°)	cot θ(x°)		
4.5	0.0785	0.07846	12.745	0.9969	1.0031	0.07870	12.706	1.4923	**85.5**
4.6	0.0803	0.08020	12.469	0.9968	1.0032	0.08046	12.429	1.4905	85.4
4.7	0.0820	0.08194	12.204	0.9966	1.0034	0.08221	12.163	1.4888	85.3
4.8	0.0838	0.08368	11.951	0.9965	1.0035	0.08397	11.909	1.4870	85.2
4.9	0.0855	0.08542	11.707	0.9963	1.0037	0.08573	11.664	1.4853	85.1
5.0	0.0873	0.08716	11.474	0.9962	1.0038	0.08749	11.430	1.4835	**85.0**
5.1	0.0890	0.08889	11.249	0.9960	1.0040	0.08925	11.205	1.4818	84.9
5.2	0.0908	0.09063	11.034	0.9959	1.0041	0.09101	10.988	1.4800	84.8
5.3	0.0925	0.09237	10.826	0.9957	1.0043	0.09277	10.780	1.4783	84.7
5.4	0.0942	0.09411	10.626	0.9956	1.0045	0.09453	10.579	1.4765	84.6
5.5	0.0960	0.09585	10.433	0.9954	1.0046	0.09629	10.385	1.4748	**84.5**
5.6	0.0977	0.09758	10.248	0.9952	1.0048	0.09805	10.199	1.4731	84.4
5.7	0.0995	0.09932	10.068	0.9951	1.0050	0.09981	10.019	1.4713	84.3
5.8	0.1012	0.10106	9.8955	0.9949	1.0051	0.10158	9.845	1.4696	84.2
5.9	0.1030	0.10279	9.7283	0.9947	1.0053	0.10334	9.677	1.4678	84.1
6.0	0.1047	0.10453	9.5668	0.9945	1.0055	0.10510	9.514	1.4661	**84.0**
6.1	0.1065	0.10626	9.4105	0.9943	1.0057	0.10687	9.357	1.4643	83.9
6.2	0.1082	0.10800	9.2593	0.9942	1.0059	0.10863	9.205	1.4626	83.8
6.3	0.1100	0.10973	9.1129	0.9940	1.0061	0.11040	9.058	1.4608	83.7
6.4	0.1117	0.11147	8.9711	0.9938	1.0063	0.11217	8.915	1.4591	83.6
6.5	0.1134	0.11320	8.8337	0.9936	1.0065	0.11394	8.777	1.4573	**83.5**
6.6	0.1152	0.11494	8.7004	0.9934	1.0067	0.11570	8.643	1.4556	83.4
6.7	0.1169	0.11667	8.5711	0.9932	1.0069	0.11747	8.513	1.4539	83.3
6.8	0.1187	0.11840	8.4457	0.9930	1.0071	0.11924	8.386	1.4521	83.2
6.9	0.1204	0.12014	8.3238	0.9928	1.0073	0.12101	8.264	1.4504	83.1
7.0	0.1222	0.12187	8.2055	0.9925	1.0075	0.12278	8.144	1.4486	**83.0**
7.1	0.1239	0.12360	8.0905	0.9923	1.0077	0.12456	8.028	1.4469	82.9
7.2	0.1257	0.12533	7.9787	0.9921	1.0079	0.12633	7.916	1.4451	82.8
7.3	0.1274	0.12706	7.8700	0.9919	1.0082	0.12810	7.806	1.4434	82.7
7.4	0.1292	0.12880	7.7642	0.9917	1.0084	0.12988	7.700	1.4416	82.6
7.5	0.1309	0.13053	7.6613	0.9914	1.0086	0.13165	7.596	1.4399	**82.5**
7.6	0.1326	0.13226	7.5611	0.9912	1.0089	0.13343	7.495	1.4382	82.4
7.7	0.1344	0.13399	7.4635	0.9910	1.0091	0.13521	7.396	1.4364	82.3
7.8	0.1361	0.13572	7.3684	0.9907	1.0093	0.13698	7.300	1.4347	82.2
7.9	0.1379	0.13744	7.2757	0.9905	1.0096	0.13876	7.207	1.4329	82.1
8.0	0.1396	0.13917	7.1853	0.9903	1.0098	0.14054	7.115	1.4312	**82.0**
8.1	0.1414	0.14090	7.0972	0.9900	1.0101	0.14232	7.026	1.4294	81.9
8.2	0.1431	0.14263	7.0112	0.9898	1.0103	0.14410	6.940	1.4277	81.8
8.3	0.1449	0.14436	6.9273	0.9895	1.0106	0.14588	6.855	1.4259	81.7
8.4	0.1466	0.14608	6.8454	0.9893	1.0108	0.14767	6.772	1.4242	81.6
8.5	0.1484	0.14781	6.7655	0.9890	1.0111	0.14945	6.691	1.4224	**81.5**
8.6	0.1501	0.14954	6.6874	0.9888	1.0114	0.15124	6.612	1.4207	81.4
8.7	0.1518	0.15126	6.6111	0.9885	1.0116	0.15302	6.535	1.4190	81.3
8.8	0.1536	0.15299	6.5366	0.9882	1.0119	0.15481	6.460	1.4172	81.2
8.9	0.1553	0.15471	6.4637	0.9880	1.0122	0.15660	6.386	1.4155	81.1
		cos θ(x°)	sec θ(x°)	sin θ(x°)	csc θ(x°)	cot θ(x°)	tan θ(x°)	θ (radians)	x (degrees)

Four-Place Values of the Circular Functions

x (degrees)	θ (radians)	sin θ(x°)	csc θ(x°)	cos θ(x°)	sec θ(x°)	tan θ(x°)	cot θ(x°)		
9.0	0.1571	0.15643	6.3925	0.9887	1.0125	0.15838	6.314	1.4137	**81.0**
9.1	0.1588	0.15816	6.3228	0.9874	1.0127	0.16017	6.243	1.4120	80.9
9.2	0.1606	0.15988	6.2546	0.9871	1.0130	0.16196	6.174	1.4102	80.8
9.3	0.1623	0.16160	6.1880	0.9869	1.0133	0.16376	6.107	1.4085	80.7
9.4	0.1641	0.16333	6.1227	0.9866	1.0136	0.16555	6.041	1.4067	80.6
9.5	0.1658	0.16505	6.0589	0.9863	1.0139	0.16734	5.976	1.4050	**80.5**
9.6	0.1676	0.16677	5.9963	0.9860	1.0142	0.16914	5.912	1.4032	80.4
9.7	0.1693	0.16849	5.9351	0.9857	1.0145	0.17093	5.850	1.4015	80.3
9.8	0.1710	0.17021	5.8751	0.9854	1.0148	0.17273	5.789	1.3998	80.2
9.9	0.1728	0.17193	5.8164	0.9851	1.0151	0.17453	5.730	1.3980	80.1
10.0	0.1745	0.1736	5.7588	0.9848	1.0154	0.1763	5.671	1.3963	**80.0**
10.1	0.1763	0.1754	5.7023	0.9845	1.0157	0.1781	5.614	1.3945	79.9
10.2	0.1780	0.1771	5.6470	0.9842	1.0161	0.1799	5.558	1.3928	79.8
10.3	0.1798	0.1788	5.5928	0.9839	1.0164	0.1817	5.503	1.3910	79.7
10.4	0.1815	0.1805	5.5396	0.9836	1.0167	0.1835	5.449	1.3893	79.6
10.5	0.1833	0.1822	5.4874	0.9833	1.0170	0.1853	5.396	1.3875	**79.5**
10.6	0.1850	0.1840	5.4362	0.9829	1.0174	0.1871	5.343	1.3858	79.4
10.7	0.1868	0.1857	5.3860	0.9826	1.0177	0.1890	5.292	1.3840	79.3
10.8	0.1885	0.1874	5.3367	0.9823	1.0180	0.1908	5.242	1.3823	79.2
10.9	0.1902	0.1891	5.2883	0.9820	1.0184	0.1926	5.193	1.3806	79.1
11.0	0.1920	0.1908	5.2408	0.9816	1.0187	0.1944	5.145	1.3788	**79.0**
11.1	0.1937	0.1925	5.1942	0.9813	1.0191	0.1962	5.097	1.3771	78.9
11.2	0.1955	0.1942	5.1484	0.9810	1.0194	0.1980	5.050	1.3753	78.8
11.3	0.1972	0.1959	5.1034	0.9806	1.0198	0.1998	5.005	1.3736	78.7
11.4	0.1990	0.1977	5.0593	0.9803	1.0201	0.2016	4.959	1.3718	78.6
11.5	0.2007	0.1994	5.0159	0.9799	1.0205	0.2035	4.915	1.3701	**78.5**
11.6	0.2025	0.2011	4.9732	0.9796	1.0209	0.2053	4.872	1.3683	78.4
11.7	0.2042	0.2028	4.9313	0.9792	1.0212	0.2071	4.829	1.3666	78.3
11.8	0.2059	0.2045	4.8901	0.9789	1.0216	0.2089	4.787	1.3648	78.2
11.9	0.2077	0.2062	4.8496	0.9785	1.0220	0.2107	4.745	1.3631	78.1
12.0	0.2094	0.2079	4.8097	0.9781	1.0223	0.2126	4.705	1.3614	**78.0**
12.1	0.2112	0.2096	4.7706	0.9778	1.0227	0.2144	4.665	1.3596	77.9
12.2	0.2129	0.2113	4.7321	0.9774	1.0231	0.2162	4.625	1.3579	77.8
12.3	0.2147	0.2130	4.6942	0.9770	1.0235	0.2180	4.586	1.3561	77.7
12.4	0.2164	0.2147	4.6569	0.9767	1.0239	0.2199	4.548	1.3544	77.6
12.5	0.2182	0.2164	4.6202	0.9763	1.0243	0.2217	4.511	1.3526	**77.5**
12.6	0.2199	0.2181	4.5841	0.9759	1.0247	0.2235	4.474	1.3509	77.4
12.7	0.2217	0.2198	4.5486	0.9755	1.0251	0.2254	4.437	1.3491	77.3
12.8	0.2234	0.2215	4.5137	0.9751	1.0255	0.2272	4.402	1.3474	77.2
12.9	0.2251	0.2233	4.4793	0.9748	1.0259	0.2290	4.366	1.3456	77.1
13.0	0.2269	0.2250	4.4454	0.9744	1.0263	0.2309	4.331	1.3439	**77.0**
13.1	0.2286	0.2267	4.4121	0.9740	1.0267	0.2327	4.297	1.3422	76.9
13.2	0.2304	0.2284	4.3792	0.9736	1.0271	0.2345	4.264	1.3404	76.8
13.3	0.2321	0.2300	4.3469	0.9732	1.0276	0.2364	4.230	1.3387	76.7
13.4	0.2339	0.2317	4.3150	0.9728	1.0280	0.2382	4.198	1.3369	76.6
		cos θ(x°)	sec θ(x°)	sin θ(x°)	csc θ(x°)	cot θ(x°)	tan θ(x°)	θ (radians)	x (degrees)

Four-Place Values of the Circular Functions

x (degrees)	θ (radians)	sin θ(x°)	csc θ(x°)	cos θ(x°)	sec θ(x°)	tan θ(x°)	cot θ(x°)		
13.5	0.2356	0.2334	4.2837	0.9724	1.0284	0.2401	4.165	1.3352	**76.5**
13.6	0.2374	0.2351	4.2527	0.9720	1.0288	0.2419	4.134	1.3334	76.4
13.7	0.2391	0.2368	4.2223	0.9715	1.0293	0.2438	4.102	1.3317	76.3
13.8	0.2409	0.2385	4.1923	0.9711	1.0297	0.2456	4.071	1.3299	76.2
13.9	0.2426	0.2402	4.1627	0.9707	1.0302	0.2475	4.041	1.3282	76.1
14.0	0.2443	0.2419	4.1336	0.9703	1.0306	0.2493	4.011	1.3265	**76.0**
14.1	0.2461	0.2436	4.1048	0.9699	1.0311	0.2512	3.981	1.3247	75.9
14.2	0.2478	0.2453	4.0765	0.9694	1.0315	0.2530	3.952	1.3230	75.8
14.3	0.2496	0.2470	4.0486	0.9690	1.0320	0.2549	3.923	1.3212	75.7
14.4	0.2513	0.2487	4.0211	0.9686	1.0324	0.2568	3.895	1.3195	75.6
14.5	0.2531	0.2504	3.9939	0.9681	1.0329	0.2586	3.867	1.3177	**75.5**
14.6	0.2548	0.2521	3.9672	0.9677	1.0334	0.2605	3.839	1.3160	75.4
14.7	0.2566	0.2538	3.9408	0.9673	1.0338	0.2623	3.812	1.3142	75.3
14.8	0.2583	0.2554	3.9147	0.9668	1.0343	0.2642	3.785	1.3125	75.2
14.9	0.2601	0.2571	3.8890	0.9664	1.0348	0.2661	3.758	1.3107	75.1
15.0	0.2618	0.2588	3.8637	0.9659	1.0353	0.2679	3.732	1.3090	**75.0**
15.1	0.2635	0.2605	3.8387	0.9655	1.0358	0.2698	3.706	1.3073	74.9
15.2	0.2653	0.2622	3.8140	0.9650	1.0363	0.2717	3.681	1.3055	74.8
15.3	0.2670	0.2639	3.7897	0.9646	1.0367	0.2736	3.655	1.3038	74.7
15.4	0.2688	0.2656	3.7657	0.9641	1.0372	0.2754	3.630	1.3020	74.6
15.5	0.2705	0.2672	3.7420	0.9636	1.0377	0.2773	3.606	1.3003	**74.5**
15.6	0.2723	0.2689	3.7186	0.9632	1.0382	0.2792	3.582	1.2985	74.4
15.7	0.2740	0.2706	3.6955	0.9627	1.0388	0.2811	3.558	1.2968	74.3
15.8	0.2758	0.2723	3.6727	0.9622	1.0393	0.2830	3.534	1.2950	74.2
15.9	0.2775	0.2740	3.6502	0.9617	1.0398	0.2849	3.511	1.2933	74.1
16.0	0.2793	0.2756	3.6280	0.9613	1.0403	0.2867	3.487	1.2915	**74.0**
16.1	0.2810	0.2773	3.6060	0.9608	1.0408	0.2886	3.465	1.2898	73.9
16.2	0.2827	0.2790	3.5843	0.9603	1.0413	0.2905	3.442	1.2881	73.8
16.3	0.2845	0.2807	3.5629	0.9598	1.0419	0.2924	3.420	1.2863	73.7
16.4	0.2862	0.2823	3.5418	0.9593	1.0424	0.2943	3.398	1.2846	73.6
16.5	0.2880	0.2840	3.5209	0.9588	1.0429	0.2962	3.376	1.2828	**73.5**
16.6	0.2897	0.2857	3.5003	0.9583	1.0435	0.2981	3.354	1.2811	73.4
16.7	0.2915	0.2874	3.4799	0.9578	1.0440	0.3000	3.333	1.2793	73.3
16.8	0.2932	0.2890	3.4598	0.9573	1.0446	0.3019	3.312	1.2776	73.2
16.9	0.2950	0.2907	3.4399	0.9568	1.0451	0.3038	3.291	1.2758	73.1
17.0	0.2967	0.2924	3.4203	0.9563	1.0457	0.3057	3.271	1.2741	**73.0**
17.1	0.2985	0.2940	3.4009	0.9558	1.0463	0.3076	3.251	1.2723	72.9
17.2	0.3002	0.2957	3.3817	0.9553	1.0468	0.3096	3.230	1.2706	72.8
17.3	0.3019	0.2974	3.3628	0.9548	1.0474	0.3115	3.211	1.2689	72.7
17.4	0.3037	0.2990	3.3440	0.9542	1.0480	0.3134	3.191	1.2671	72.6
17.5	0.3054	0.3007	3.3255	0.9537	1.0485	0.3153	3.172	1.2654	**72.5**
17.6	0.3072	0.3024	3.3072	0.9532	1.0491	0.3172	3.152	1.2636	72.4
17.7	0.3089	0.3040	3.2891	0.9527	1.0497	0.3191	3.133	1.2619	72.3
17.8	0.3107	0.3057	3.2712	0.9521	1.0503	0.3211	3.115	1.2601	72.2
17.9	0.3124	0.3074	3.2535	0.9516	1.0509	0.3230	3.096	1.2584	72.1
		cos θ(x°)	sec θ(x°)	sin θ(x°)	csc θ(x°)	cot θ(x°)	tan θ(x°)	θ (radians)	x (degrees)

Four-Place Values of the Circular Functions

x (degrees)	θ (radians)	$\sin \theta(x°)$	$\csc \theta(x°)$	$\cos \theta(x°)$	$\sec \theta(x°)$	$\tan \theta(x°)$	$\cot \theta(x°)$		
18.0	0.3142	0.3090	3.2361	0.9511	1.0515	0.3249	3.078	1.2566	**72.0**
18.1	0.3159	0.3107	3.2188	0.9505	1.0521	0.3269	3.060	1.2549	71.9
18.2	0.3176	0.3123	3.2017	0.9500	1.0527	0.3288	3.042	1.2531	71.8
18.3	0.3194	0.3140	3.1848	0.9494	1.0533	0.3307	3.024	1.2514	71.7
18.4	0.3211	0.3156	3.1681	0.9489	1.0539	0.3327	3.006	1.2497	71.6
18.5	0.3229	0.3173	3.1515	0.9483	1.0545	0.3346	2.989	1.2479	**71.5**
18.6	0.3246	0.3190	3.1352	0.9478	1.0551	0.3365	2.971	1.2462	71.4
18.7	0.3264	0.3206	3.1190	0.9472	1.0557	0.3385	2.954	1.2444	71.3
18.8	0.3281	0.3223	3.1030	0.9466	1.0564	0.3404	2.937	1.2427	71.2
18.9	0.3299	0.3239	3.0872	0.9461	1.0570	0.3424	2.921	1.2409	71.1
19.0	0.3316	0.3256	3.0716	0.9455	1.0576	0.3443	2.904	1.2392	**71.0**
19.1	0.3334	0.3272	3.0561	0.9449	1.0583	0.3463	2.888	1.2374	70.9
19.2	0.3351	0.3289	3.0407	0.9444	1.0589	0.3482	2.872	1.2357	70.8
19.3	0.3368	0.3305	3.0256	0.9438	1.0595	0.3502	2.856	1.2339	70.7
19.4	0.3386	0.3322	3.0106	0.9432	1.0602	0.3522	2.840	1.2322	70.6
19.5	0.3403	0.3338	2.9957	0.9426	1.0608	0.3541	2.824	1.2305	**70.5**
19.6	0.3421	0.3355	2.9811	0.9421	1.0615	0.3561	2.808	1.2287	70.4
19.7	0.3438	0.3371	2.9665	0.9415	1.0622	0.3581	2.793	1.2270	70.3
19.8	0.3456	0.3387	2.9521	0.9409	1.0628	0.3600	2.778	1.2252	70.2
19.9	0.3473	0.3404	2.9379	0.9403	1.0635	0.3620	2.762	1.2235	70.1
20.0	0.3491	0.3420	2.9238	0.9397	1.0642	0.3640	2.747	1.2217	**70.0**
20.1	0.3508	0.3437	2.9099	0.9391	1.0649	0.3659	2.733	1.2200	69.9
20.2	0.3526	0.3453	2.8960	0.9385	1.0655	0.3679	2.718	1.2182	69.8
20.3	0.3543	0.3469	2.8824	0.9379	1.0662	0.3699	2.703	1.2165	69.7
20.4	0.3560	0.3486	2.8688	0.9373	1.0669	0.3719	2.689	1.2147	69.6
20.5	0.3578	0.3502	2.8555	0.9367	1.0676	0.3739	2.675	1.2130	**69.5**
20.6	0.3595	0.3518	2.8422	0.9361	1.0683	0.3759	2.660	1.2113	69.4
20.7	0.3613	0.3535	2.8291	0.9354	1.0690	0.3779	2.646	1.2095	69.3
20.8	0.3630	0.3551	2.8161	0.9348	1.0697	0.3799	2.633	1.2078	69.2
20.9	0.3648	0.3567	2.8032	0.9342	1.0704	0.3819	2.619	1.2060	69.1
21.0	0.3665	0.3584	2.7904	0.9336	1.0711	0.3839	2.605	1.2043	**69.0**
21.1	0.3683	0.3600	2.7778	0.9330	1.0719	0.3859	2.592	1.2025	68.9
21.2	0.3700	0.3616	2.7653	0.9323	1.0726	0.3879	2.578	1.2008	68.8
21.3	0.3718	0.3633	2.7529	0.9317	1.0733	0.3899	2.565	1.1990	68.7
21.4	0.3735	0.3649	2.7407	0.9311	1.0740	0.3919	2.552	1.1973	68.6
21.5	0.3752	0.3665	2.7285	0.9304	1.0748	0.3939	2.539	1.1956	**68.5**
21.6	0.3770	0.3681	2.7165	0.9298	1.0755	0.3959	2.526	1.1938	68.4
21.7	0.3787	0.3697	2.7046	0.9291	1.0763	0.3979	2.513	1.1921	68.3
21.8	0.3805	0.3714	2.6927	0.9285	1.0770	0.4000	2.500	1.1903	68.2
21.9	0.3822	0.3730	2.6811	0.9278	1.0778	0.4020	2.488	1.1886	68.1
22.0	0.3840	0.3746	2.6695	0.9272	1.0785	0.4040	2.475	1.1868	**68.0**
22.1	0.3857	0.3762	2.6580	0.9265	1.0793	0.4061	2.463	1.1851	67.9
22.2	0.3875	0.3778	2.6466	0.9259	1.0801	0.4081	2.450	1.1833	67.8
22.3	0.3892	0.3795	2.6354	0.9252	1.0808	0.4101	2.438	1.1816	67.7
22.4	0.3910	0.3811	2.6242	0.9245	1.0816	0.4122	2.426	1.1798	67.6
		$\cos \theta(x°)$	$\sec \theta(x°)$	$\sin \theta(x°)$	$\csc \theta(x°)$	$\cot \theta(x°)$	$\tan \theta(x°)$	θ (radians)	x (degrees)

Four-Place Values of the Circular Functions

x (degrees)	θ (radians)	$\sin \theta(x^\circ)$	$\csc \theta(x^\circ)$	$\cos \theta(x^\circ)$	$\sec \theta(x^\circ)$	$\tan \theta(x^\circ)$	$\cot \theta(x^\circ)$		
22.5	0.3927	0.3827	2.6131	0.9239	1.0824	0.4142	2.414	1.1781	**67.5**
22.6	0.3944	0.3843	2.6022	0.9232	1.0832	0.4163	2.402	1.1764	67.4
22.7	0.3962	0.3859	2.5913	0.9225	1.0840	0.4183	2.391	1.1746	67.3
22.8	0.3979	0.3875	2.5805	0.9219	1.0848	0.4204	2.379	1.1729	67.2
22.9	0.3997	0.3891	2.5699	0.9212	1.0856	0.4224	2.367	1.1711	67.1
23.0	0.4014	0.3907	2.5593	0.9205	1.0864	0.4245	2.356	1.1694	**67.0**
23.1	0.4032	0.3923	2.5488	0.9198	1.0872	0.4265	2.344	1.1676	66.9
23.2	0.4049	0.3939	2.5384	0.9191	1.0880	0.4286	2.333	1.1659	66.8
23.3	0.4067	0.3955	2.5282	0.9184	1.0888	0.4307	2.322	1.1641	66.7
23.4	0.4084	0.3971	2.5180	0.9178	1.0896	0.4327	2.311	1.1624	66.6
23.5	0.4102	0.3987	2.5078	0.9171	1.0904	0.4348	2.300	1.1606	**66.5**
23.6	0.4119	0.4003	2.4978	0.9164	1.0913	0.4369	2.289	1.1589	66.4
23.7	0.4136	0.4019	2.4879	0.9157	1.0921	0.4390	2.278	1.1572	66.3
23.8	0.4154	0.4035	2.4780	0.9150	1.0929	0.4411	2.267	1.1554	66.2
23.9	0.4171	0.4051	2.4683	0.9143	1.0938	0.4431	2.257	1.1537	66.1
24.0	0.4189	0.4067	2.4586	0.9135	1.0946	0.4452	2.246	1.1519	**66.0**
24.1	0.4206	0.4083	2.4490	0.9128	1.0955	0.4473	2.236	1.1502	65.9
24.2	0.4224	0.4099	2.4395	0.9121	1.0963	0.4494	2.225	1.1484	65.8
24.3	0.4241	0.4115	2.4300	0.9114	1.0972	0.4515	2.215	1.1467	65.7
24.4	0.4259	0.4131	2.4207	0.9107	1.0981	0.4536	2.204	1.1449	65.6
24.5	0.4276	0.4147	2.4114	0.9100	1.0989	0.4557	2.194	1.1432	**65.5**
24.6	0.4294	0.4163	2.4022	0.9092	1.0998	0.4578	2.184	1.1414	65.4
24.7	0.4311	0.4179	2.3931	0.9085	1.1007	0.4599	2.174	1.1397	65.3
24.8	0.4328	0.4195	2.3841	0.9078	1.1016	0.4621	2.164	1.1380	65.2
24.9	0.4346	0.4210	2.3751	0.9070	1.1025	0.4642	2.154	1.1362	65.1
25.0	0.4363	0.4226	2.3662	0.9063	1.1034	0.4663	2.145	1.1345	**65.0**
25.1	0.4381	0.4242	2.3574	0.9056	1.1043	0.4684	2.135	1.1327	64.9
25.2	0.4398	0.4258	2.3486	0.9048	1.1052	0.4706	2.125	1.1310	64.8
25.3	0.4416	0.4274	2.3400	0.9041	1.1061	0.4727	2.116	1.1292	64.7
25.4	0.4433	0.4289	2.3314	0.9033	1.1070	0.4748	2.106	1.1275	64.6
25.5	0.4451	0.4305	2.3228	0.9026	1.1079	0.4770	2.097	1.1257	**64.5**
25.6	0.4468	0.4321	2.3144	0.9018	1.1089	0.4791	2.087	1.1240	64.4
25.7	0.4485	0.4337	2.3060	0.9011	1.1098	0.4813	2.078	1.1222	64.3
25.8	0.4503	0.4352	2.2976	0.9003	1.1107	0.4834	2.069	1.1205	64.2
25.9	0.4520	0.4368	2.2894	0.8996	1.1117	0.4856	2.059	1.1188	64.1
26.0	0.4538	0.4384	2.2812	0.8988	1.1126	0.4877	2.050	1.1170	64.0
26.1	0.4555	0.4399	2.2730	0.8980	1.1136	0.4899	2.041	1.1153	63.9
26.2	0.4573	0.4415	2.2650	0.8973	1.1145	0.4921	2.032	1.1135	63.8
26.3	0.4590	0.4431	2.2570	0.8965	1.1155	0.4942	2.023	1.1118	63.7
26.4	0.4608	0.4446	2.2490	0.8957	1.1164	0.4964	2.014	1.1100	63.6
26.5	0.4625	0.4462	2.2412	0.8949	1.1174	0.4986	2.006	1.1083	**63.5**
26.6	0.4643	0.4478	2.2333	0.8942	1.1184	0.5008	1.997	1.1065	63.4
26.7	0.4660	0.4493	2.2256	0.8934	1.1194	0.5029	1.988	1.1048	63.3
26.8	0.4677	0.4509	2.2179	0.8926	1.1203	0.5051	1.980	1.1030	63.2
26.9	0.4695	0.4524	2.2103	0.8918	1.1213	0.5073	1.971	1.1013	63.1
		$\cos \theta(x^\circ)$	$\sec \theta(x^\circ)$	$\sin \theta(x^\circ)$	$\csc \theta(x^\circ)$	$\cot \theta(x^\circ)$	$\tan \theta(x^\circ)$	θ (radians)	x (degrees)

Four-Place Values of the Circular Functions

x (degrees)	θ (radians)	$\sin \theta(x^\circ)$	$\csc \theta(x^\circ)$	$\cos \theta(x^\circ)$	$\sec \theta(x^\circ)$	$\tan \theta(x^\circ)$	$\cot \theta(x^\circ)$		
27.0	0.4712	0.4540	2.2027	0.8910	1.1223	0.5095	1.963	1.0996	**63.0**
27.1	0.4730	0.4555	2.1952	0.8902	1.1233	0.5117	1.954	1.0978	62.9
27.2	0.4747	0.4571	2.1877	0.8894	1.1243	0.5139	1.946	1.0961	62.8
27.3	0.4765	0.4586	2.1803	0.8886	1.1253	0.5161	1.937	1.0943	62.7
27.4	0.4782	0.4602	2.1730	0.8878	1.1264	0.5184	1.929	1.0926	62.6
27.5	0.4800	0.4617	2.1657	0.8870	1.1274	0.5206	1.921	1.0908	**62.5**
27.6	0.4817	0.4633	2.1584	0.8862	1.1284	0.5228	1.913	1.0891	62.4
27.7	0.4835	0.4648	2.1513	0.8854	1.1294	0.5250	1.905	1.0873	62.3
27.8	0.4852	0.4664	2.1441	0.8846	1.1305	0.5272	1.897	1.0856	62.2
27.9	0.4869	0.4679	2.1371	0.8838	1.1315	0.5295	1.889	1.0838	62.1
28.0	0.4887	0.4695	2.1301	0.8829	1.1326	0.5317	1.881	1.0821	**62.0**
28.1	0.4904	0.4710	2.1231	0.8821	1.1336	0.5340	1.873	1.0804	61.9
28.2	0.4922	0.4726	2.1162	0.8813	1.1347	0.5362	1.865	1.0786	61.8
28.3	0.4939	0.4741	2.1093	0.8805	1.1357	0.5384	1.857	1.0769	61.7
28.4	0.4957	0.4756	2.1025	0.8796	1.1368	0.5407	1.849	1.0751	61.6
28.5	0.4974	0.4772	2.0957	0.8788	1.1379	0.5430	1.842	1.0734	**61.5**
28.6	0.4992	0.4787	2.0890	0.8780	1.1390	0.5452	1.834	1.0716	61.4
28.7	0.5009	0.4802	2.0824	0.8771	1.1401	0.5475	1.827	1.0699	61.3
28.8	0.5027	0.4818	2.0757	0.8763	1.1412	0.5498	1.819	1.0681	61.2
28.9	0.5044	0.4833	2.0692	0.8755	1.1423	0.5520	1.811	1.0664	61.1
29.0	0.5061	0.4848	2.0627	0.8746	1.1434	0.5543	1.804	1.0647	**61.0**
29.1	0.5079	0.4863	2.0562	0.8738	1.1445	0.5566	1.797	1.0629	60.9
29.2	0.5096	0.4879	2.0498	0.8729	1.1456	0.5589	1.789	1.0612	60.8
29.3	0.5114	0.4894	2.0434	0.8721	1.1467	0.5612	1.782	1.0594	60.7
29.4	0.5131	0.4909	2.0371	0.8712	1.1478	0.5635	1.775	1.0577	60.6
29.5	0.5149	0.4924	2.0308	0.8704	1.1490	0.5658	1.767	1.0559	**60.5**
29.6	0.5166	0.4939	2.0245	0.8695	1.1501	0.5681	1.760	1.0542	60.4
29.7	0.5184	0.4955	2.0183	0.8686	1.1512	0.5704	1.753	1.0524	60.3
29.8	0.5201	0.4970	2.0122	0.8678	1.1524	0.5727	1.746	1.0507	60.2
29.9	0.5219	0.4985	2.0061	0.8669	1.1535	0.5750	1.739	1.0489	60.1
30.0	0.5236	0.5000	2.0000	0.8660	1.1547	0.5774	1.7321	1.0472	**60.0**
30.1	0.5253	0.5015	1.9940	0.8652	1.1559	0.5797	1.7251	1.0455	59.9
30.2	0.5271	0.5030	1.9880	0.8643	1.1570	0.5820	1.7182	1.0437	59.8
30.3	0.5288	0.5045	1.9821	0.8634	1.1582	0.5844	1.7113	1.0420	59.7
30.4	0.5306	0.5060	1.9762	0.8625	1.1594	0.5867	1.7045	1.0402	59.6
30.5	0.5323	0.5075	1.9703	0.8616	1.1606	0.5890	1.6977	1.0385	**59.5**
30.6	0.5341	0.5090	1.9645	0.8607	1.1618	0.5914	1.6909	1.0367	59.4
30.7	0.5358	0.5105	1.9587	0.8599	1.1630	0.5938	1.6842	1.0350	59.3
30.8	0.5376	0.5120	1.9530	0.8590	1.1642	0.5961	1.6775	1.0332	59.2
30.9	0.5393	0.5135	1.9473	0.8581	1.1654	0.5985	1.6709	1.0315	59.1
31.0	0.5411	0.5150	1.9416	0.8572	1.1666	0.6009	1.6643	1.0297	**59.0**
31.1	0.5428	0.5165	1.9360	0.8563	1.1679	0.6032	1.6577	1.0280	58.9
31.2	0.5445	0.5180	1.9304	0.8554	1.1691	0.6056	1.6512	1.0263	58.8
31.3	0.5463	0.5195	1.9249	0.8545	1.1703	0.6080	1.6447	1.0245	58.7
31.4	0.5480	0.5210	1.9194	0.8536	1.1716	0.6104	1.6383	1.0228	58.6
		$\cos \theta(x^\circ)$	$\sec \theta(x^\circ)$	$\sin \theta(x^\circ)$	$\csc \theta(x^\circ)$	$\cot \theta(x^\circ)$	$\tan \theta(x^\circ)$	θ (radians)	x (degrees)

Four-Place Values of the Circular Functions

x (degrees)	θ (radians)	sin θ(x°)	csc θ(x°)	cos θ(x°)	sec θ(x°)	tan θ(x°)	cot θ(x°)		
31.5	0.5498	0.5225	1.9139	0.8526	1.1728	0.6128	1.6319	1.0210	**58.5**
31.6	0.5515	0.5240	1.9084	0.8517	1.1741	0.6152	1.6255	1.0193	58.4
31.7	0.5533	0.5255	1.9031	0.8508	1.1753	0.6176	1.6191	1.0175	58.3
31.8	0.5550	0.5270	1.8977	0.8499	1.1766	0.6200	1.6128	1.0158	58.2
31.9	0.5568	0.5284	1.8924	0.8490	1.1779	0.6224	1.6066	1.0140	58.1
32.0	0.5585	0.5299	1.8871	0.8480	1.1792	0.6249	1.6003	1.0123	**58.0**
32.1	0.5603	0.5314	1.8818	0.8471	1.1805	0.6273	1.5941	1.0105	57.9
32.2	0.5620	0.5329	1.8766	0.8462	1.1818	0.6297	1.5880	1.0088	57.8
32.3	0.5637	0.5344	1.8714	0.8453	1.1831	0.6322	1.5818	1.0071	57.7
32.4	0.5655	0.5358	1.8663	0.8443	1.1844	0.6346	1.5757	1.0053	57.6
32.5	0.5672	0.5373	1.8612	0.8434	1.1857	0.6371	1.5697	1.0036	**57.5**
32.6	0.5690	0.5388	1.8561	0.8425	1.1870	0.6395	1.5637	1.0018	57.4
32.7	0.5707	0.5402	1.8510	0.8415	1.1883	0.6420	1.5577	1.0001	57.3
32.8	0.5725	0.5417	1.8460	0.8406	1.1897	0.6445	1.5517	0.9983	57.2
32.9	0.5742	0.5432	1.8410	0.8396	1.1910	0.6469	1.5458	0.9966	57.1
33.0	0.5760	0.5446	1.8361	0.8387	1.1924	0.6494	1.5399	0.9948	**57.0**
33.1	0.5777	0.5461	1.8312	0.8377	1.1937	0.6519	1.5340	0.9931	56.9
33.2	0.5794	0.5476	1.8263	0.8368	1.1951	0.6544	1.5282	0.9913	56.8
33.3	0.5812	0.5490	1.8214	0.8358	1.1964	0.6569	1.5224	0.9896	56.7
33.4	0.5829	0.5505	1.8166	0.8348	1.1978	0.6594	1.5166	0.9879	56.6
33.5	0.5847	0.5519	1.8118	0.8339	1.1992	0.6619	1.5108	0.9861	**56.5**
33.6	0.5864	0.5534	1.8070	0.8329	1.2006	0.6644	1.5051	0.9844	56.4
33.7	0.5882	0.5548	1.8023	0.8320	1.2020	0.6669	1.4994	0.9826	56.3
33.8	0.5899	0.5563	1.7976	0.8310	1.2034	0.6694	1.4938	0.9809	56.2
33.9	0.5917	0.5577	1.7929	0.8300	1.2048	0.6720	1.4882	0.9791	56.1
34.0	0.5934	0.5592	1.7883	0.8290	1.2062	0.6745	1.4826	0.9774	**56.0**
34.1	0.5952	0.5606	1.7837	0.8281	1.2076	0.6771	1.4770	0.9756	55.9
34.2	0.5969	0.5621	1.7791	0.8271	1.2091	0.6796	1.4715	0.9739	55.8
34.3	0.5986	0.5635	1.7745	0.8261	1.2105	0.6822	1.4659	0.9721	55.7
34.4	0.6004	0.5650	1.7700	0.8251	1.2120	0.6847	1.4605	0.9704	55.6
34.5	0.6021	0.5664	1.7655	0.8241	1.2134	0.6873	1.4550	0.9687	**55.5**
34.6	0.6039	0.5678	1.7610	0.8231	1.2149	0.6899	1.4496	0.9669	55.4
34.7	0.6056	0.5693	1.7566	0.8221	1.2163	0.6924	1.4442	0.9652	55.3
34.8	0.6074	0.5707	1.7522	0.8211	1.2178	0.6950	1.4388	0.9634	55.2
34.9	0.6091	0.5721	1.7478	0.8202	1.2193	0.6976	1.4335	0.9617	55.1
35.0	0.6109	0.5736	1.7434	0.8192	1.2208	0.7002	1.4281	0.9599	**55.0**
35.1	0.6126	0.5750	1.7391	0.8181	1.2223	0.7028	1.4229	0.9582	54.9
35.2	0.6144	0.5764	1.7348	0.8171	1.2238	0.7054	1.4176	0.9564	54.8
35.3	0.6161	0.5779	1.7305	0.8161	1.2253	0.7080	1.4124	0.9547	54.7
35.4	0.6178	0.5793	1.7263	0.8151	1.2268	0.7107	1.4071	0.9529	54.6
35.5	0.6196	0.5807	1.7221	0.8141	1.2283	0.7133	1.4019	0.9512	**54.5**
35.6	0.6213	0.5821	1.7179	0.8131	1.2299	0.7159	1.3968	0.9495	54.4
35.7	0.6231	0.5835	1.7137	0.8121	1.2314	0.7186	1.3916	0.9477	54.3
35.8	0.6248	0.5850	1.7095	0.8111	1.2329	0.7212	1.3865	0.9460	54.2
35.9	0.6266	0.5864	1.7054	0.8100	1.2345	0.7239	1.3814	0.9442	54.1
		cos θ(x°)	sec θ(x°)	sin θ(x°)	csc θ(x°)	cot θ(x°)	tan θ(x°)	θ (radians)	x (degrees)

Four-Place Values of the Circular Functions

x (degrees)	θ (radians)	sin θ(x°)	csc θ(x°)	cos θ(x°)	sec θ(x°)	tan θ(x°)	cot θ(x°)		
36.0	0.6283	0.5878	1.7013	0.8090	1.2361	0.7265	1.3764	0.9425	**54.0**
36.1	0.6301	0.5892	1.6972	0.8080	1.2376	0.7292	1.3713	0.9407	53.9
36.2	0.6318	0.5906	1.6932	0.8070	1.2392	0.7319	1.3663	0.9390	53.8
36.3	0.6336	0.5920	1.6892	0.8059	1.2408	0.7346	1.3613	0.9372	53.7
36.4	0.6353	0.5934	1.6852	0.8049	1.2424	0.7373	1.3564	0.9355	53.6
36.5	0.6370	0.5948	1.6812	0.8039	1.2440	0.7400	1.3514	0.9338	**53.5**
36.6	0.6388	0.5962	1.6772	0.8028	1.2456	0.7427	1.3465	0.9320	53.4
36.7	0.6405	0.5976	1.6733	0.8018	1.2472	0.7454	1.3416	0.9303	53.3
36.8	0.6423	0.5990	1.6694	0.8007	1.2489	0.7481	1.3367	0.9285	53.2
36.9	0.6440	0.6004	1.6655	0.7997	1.2505	0.7508	1.3319	0.9268	53.1
37.0	0.6458	0.6018	1.6616	0.7986	1.2521	0.7536	1.3270	0.9250	**53.0**
37.1	0.6475	0.6032	1.6578	0.7976	1.2538	0.7563	1.3222	0.9233	52.9
37.2	0.6493	0.6046	1.6540	0.7965	1.2554	0.7590	1.3175	0.9215	52.8
37.3	0.6510	0.6060	1.6502	0.7955	1.2571	0.7618	1.3127	0.9198	52.7
37.4	0.6528	0.6074	1.6464	0.7944	1.2588	0.7646	1.3079	0.9180	52.6
37.5	0.6545	0.6088	1.6427	0.7934	1.2605	0.7673	1.3032	0.9163	**52.5**
37.6	0.6562	0.6101	1.6390	0.7923	1.2622	0.7701	1.2985	0.9146	52.4
37.7	0.6580	0.6115	1.6353	0.7912	1.2639	0.7729	1.2938	0.9128	52.3
37.8	0.6597	0.6129	1.6316	0.7902	1.2656	0.7757	1.2892	0.9111	52.2
37.9	0.6615	0.6143	1.6279	0.7891	1.2673	0.7785	1.2846	0.9093	52.1
38.0	0.6632	0.6157	1.6243	0.7880	1.2690	0.7813	1.2799	0.9076	**52.0**
38.1	0.6650	0.6170	1.6207	0.7869	1.2708	0.7841	1.2753	0.9058	51.9
38.2	0.6667	0.6184	1.6171	0.7859	1.2725	0.7869	1.2708	0.9041	51.8
38.3	0.6685	0.6198	1.6135	0.7848	1.2742	0.7898	1.2662	0.9023	51.7
38.4	0.6702	0.6211	1.6099	0.7837	1.2760	0.7926	1.2617	0.9006	51.6
38.5	0.6720	0.6225	1.6064	0.7826	1.2778	0.7954	1.2572	0.8988	**51.5**
38.6	0.6737	0.6239	1.6029	0.7815	1.2796	0.7983	1.2527	0.8971	51.4
38.7	0.6754	0.6252	1.5994	0.7804	1.2813	0.8012	1.2482	0.8954	51.3
38.8	0.6772	0.6266	1.5959	0.7793	1.2831	0.8040	1.2437	0.8936	51.2
38.9	0.6789	0.6280	1.5925	0.7782	1.2849	0.8069	1.2393	0.8919	51.1
39.0	0.6807	0.6293	1.5890	0.7771	1.2868	0.8098	1.2349	0.8901	**51.0**
39.1	0.6824	0.6307	1.5856	0.7760	1.2886	0.8127	1.2305	0.8884	50.9
39.2	0.6842	0.6320	1.5822	0.7749	1.2904	0.8156	1.2261	0.8866	50.8
39.3	0.6859	0.6334	1.5788	0.7738	1.2923	0.8185	1.2218	0.8849	50.7
39.4	0.6877	0.6347	1.5755	0.7727	1.2941	0.8214	1.2174	0.8831	50.6
39.5	0.6894	0.6361	1.5721	0.7716	1.2960	0.8243	1.2131	0.8814	**50.5**
39.6	0.6912	0.6374	1.5688	0.7705	1.2978	0.8273	1.2088	0.8796	50.4
39.7	0.6929	0.6388	1.5655	0.7694	1.2997	0.8302	1.2045	0.8779	50.3
39.8	0.6946	0.6401	1.5622	0.7683	1.3016	0.8332	1.2002	0.8762	50.2
39.9	0.6964	0.6414	1.5590	0.7672	1.3035	0.8361	1.1960	0.8744	50.1
40.0	0.6981	0.6428	1.5557	0.7660	1.3054	0.8391	1.1918	0.8727	**50.0**
40.1	0.6999	0.6441	1.5525	0.7649	1.3073	0.8421	1.1875	0.8709	49.9
40.2	0.7016	0.6455	1.5493	0.7638	1.3093	0.8451	1.1833	0.8692	49.8
40.3	0.7034	0.6468	1.5461	0.7627	1.3112	0.8481	1.1792	0.8674	49.7
40.4	0.7051	0.6481	1.5429	0.7615	1.3131	0.8511	1.1750	0.8657	49.6
		cos θ(x°)	sec θ(x°)	sin θ(x°)	csc θ(x°)	cot θ(x°)	tan θ(x°)	θ (radians)	x (degrees)

Four-Place Values of the Circular Functions

x (degrees)	θ (radians)	$\sin\theta(x^\circ)$	$\csc\theta(x^\circ)$	$\cos\theta(x^\circ)$	$\sec\theta(x^\circ)$	$\tan\theta(x^\circ)$	$\cot\theta(x^\circ)$		
40.5	0.7069	0.6494	1.5398	0.7604	1.3151	0.8541	1.1708	0.8639	**49.5**
40.6	0.7086	0.6508	1.5366	0.7593	1.3171	0.8571	1.1667	0.8622	49.4
40.7	0.7103	0.6521	1.5335	0.7581	1.3190	0.8601	1.1626	0.8604	49.3
40.8	0.7121	0.6534	1.5304	0.7570	1.3210	0.8632	1.1585	0.8587	49.2
40.9	0.7138	0.6547	1.5273	0.7559	1.3230	0.8662	1.1544	0.8570	49.1
41.0	0.7156	0.6561	1.5243	0.7547	1.3250	0.8693	1.1504	0.8552	**49.0**
41.1	0.7173	0.6574	1.5212	0.7536	1.3270	0.8724	1.1463	0.8535	48.9
41.2	0.7191	0.6587	1.5182	0.7524	1.3291	0.8754	1.1423	0.8517	48.8
41.3	0.7208	0.6600	1.5151	0.7513	1.3311	0.8785	1.1383	0.8500	48.7
41.4	0.7226	0.6613	1.5121	0.7501	1.3331	0.8816	1.1343	0.8482	48.6
41.5	0.7243	0.6626	1.5092	0.7490	1.3352	0.8847	1.1303	0.8465	**48.5**
41.6	0.7261	0.6639	1.5062	0.7478	1.3373	0.8878	1.1263	0.8447	48.4
41.7	0.7278	0.6652	1.5032	0.7466	1.3393	0.8910	1.1224	0.8430	48.3
41.8	0.7295	0.6665	1.5003	0.7455	1.3414	0.8941	1.1184	0.8412	48.2
41.9	0.7313	0.6678	1.4974	0.7443	1.3435	0.8972	1.1145	0.8395	48.1
42.0	0.7330	0.6691	1.4945	0.7431	1.3456	0.9004	1.1106	0.8378	**48.0**
42.1	0.7348	0.6704	1.4916	0.7420	1.3478	0.9036	1.1067	0.8360	47.9
42.2	0.7365	0.6717	1.4887	0.7408	1.3499	0.9067	1.1028	0.8343	47.8
42.3	0.7383	0.6730	1.4859	0.7396	1.3520	0.9099	1.0990	0.8325	47.7
42.4	0.7400	0.6743	1.4830	0.7385	1.3542	0.9131	1.0951	0.8308	47.6
42.5	0.7418	0.6756	1.4802	0.7373	1.3563	0.9163	1.0913	0.8290	**47.5**
42.6	0.7435	0.6769	1.4774	0.7361	1.3585	0.9195	1.0875	0.8273	47.4
42.7	0.7453	0.6782	1.4746	0.7349	1.3607	0.9228	1.0837	0.8255	47.3
42.8	0.7470	0.6794	1.4718	0.7337	1.3629	0.9260	1.0799	0.8238	47.2
42.9	0.7487	0.6807	1.4690	0.7325	1.3651	0.9293	1.0761	0.8221	47.1
43.0	0.7505	0.6820	1.4663	0.7314	1.3673	0.9325	1.0724	0.8203	**47.0**
43.1	0.7522	0.6833	1.4635	0.7302	1.3696	0.9358	1.0686	0.8186	46.9
43.2	0.7540	0.6845	1.4608	0.7290	1.3718	0.9391	1.0649	0.8168	46.8
43.3	0.7557	0.6858	1.4581	0.7278	1.3741	0.9424	1.0612	0.8151	46.7
43.4	0.7575	0.6871	1.4554	0.7266	1.3763	0.9457	1.0575	0.8133	46.6
43.5	0.7592	0.6884	1.4527	0.7254	1.3786	0.9490	1.0538	0.8116	**46.5**
43.6	0.7610	0.6896	1.4501	0.7242	1.3809	0.9523	1.0501	0.8098	46.4
43.7	0.7627	0.6909	1.4474	0.7230	1.3832	0.9556	1.0464	0.8081	46.3
43.8	0.7645	0.6921	1.4448	0.7218	1.3855	0.9590	1.0428	0.8063	46.2
43.9	0.7662	0.6934	1.4422	0.7206	1.3878	0.9623	1.0392	0.8046	46.1
44.0	0.7679	0.6947	1.4396	0.7193	1.3902	0.9657	1.0355	0.8029	**46.0**
44.1	0.7697	0.6959	1.4370	0.7181	1.3925	0.9691	1.0319	0.8011	45.9
44.2	0.7714	0.6972	1.4344	0.7169	1.3949	0.9725	1.0283	0.7994	45.8
44.3	0.7732	0.6984	1.4318	0.7157	1.3972	0.9759	1.0247	0.7976	45.7
44.4	0.7749	0.6997	1.4293	0.7145	1.3996	0.9793	1.0212	0.7959	45.6
44.5	0.7767	0.7009	1.4267	0.7133	1.4020	0.9827	1.0176	0.7941	**45.5**
44.6	0.7784	0.7022	1.4242	0.7120	1.4044	0.9861	1.0141	0.7924	45.4
44.7	0.7802	0.7034	1.4217	0.7108	1.4069	0.9896	1.0105	0.7906	45.3
44.8	0.7819	0.7046	1.4192	0.7096	1.4093	0.9930	1.0070	0.7889	45.2
44.9	0.7837	0.7059	1.4167	0.7083	1.4118	0.9965	1.0035	0.7871	45.1
45.0	0.7854	0.7071	1.4142	0.7071	1.4142	1.0000	1.0000	0.7854	**45.0**
		$\cos\theta(x^\circ)$	$\sec\theta(x^\circ)$	$\sin\theta(x^\circ)$	$\csc\theta(x^\circ)$	$\cot\theta(x^\circ)$	$\tan\theta(x^\circ)$	θ (radians)	x (degrees)

TABLE 3

Five-Place Natural Logarithms

This table contains logarithms of numbers from 1 to 10 to the base e. To obtain **the natural logarithms of other numbers use the formulas:**

$$\log_e (10^r N) = \log_e N + \log_e 10^r$$

$$\log_e \left(\frac{N}{10^r}\right) = \log_e N - \log_e 10^r$$

$\log_e 10 = 2.302585$ | $\log_e 10^4 = 9.210340$
$\log_e 10^2 = 4.605170$ | $\log_e 10^5 = 11.512925$
$\log_e 10^3 = 6.907755$ | $\log_e 10^6 = 13.815511$

N	0	1	2	3	4	5	6	7	8	9
1.0	0.0 0000	0995	1980	2956	3922	4879	5827	6766	7696	8618
1.1	0.0 9531	*0436	*1333	*2222	*3103	*3976	*4842	*5700	*6551	*7395
1.2	0.1 8232	9062	9885	*0701	*1511	*2314	*3111	*3902	*4686	*5464
1.3	0.2 6236	7003	7763	8518	9267	*0010	*0748	*1481	*2208	*2930
1.4	0.3 3647	4359	5066	5767	6464	7156	7844	8526	9204	9878
1.5	0.4 0547	1211	1871	2527	3178	3825	4469	5108	5742	6373
1.6	0.4 7000	7623	8243	8858	9470	*0078	*0682	*1282	*1879	*2473
1.7	0.5 3063	3649	4232	4812	5389	5962	6531	7098	7661	8222
1.8	0.5 8779	9333	9884	*0432	*0977	*1519	*2078	*2594	*3127	*3658
1.9	0.6 4185	4710	5233	5752	6269	6783	7294	7803	8310	8813
2.0	0.6 9315	9813	*0310	*0804	*1295	*1784	*2271	*2755	*3237	*3716
2.1	0.7 4194	4669	5142	5612	6081	6547	7011	7473	7932	8390
2.2	0.7 8846	9299	9751	*0200	*0648	*1093	*1536	*1978	*2418	*2855
2.3	0.8 3291	3725	4157	4587	5015	5442	5866	6289	6710	7129
2.4	0.8 7547	7963	8377	8789	9200	9609	*0016	*0422	*0826	*1228
2.5	0.9 1629	2028	2426	2822	3216	3609	4001	4391	4779	5166
2.6	0.9 5551	5935	6317	6698	7078	7456	7833	8208	8582	8954
2.7	0.9 9325	9695	*0063	*0430	*0796	*1160	*1523	*1885	*2245	*2604
2.8	1.0 2962	3318	3674	4028	4380	4732	5082	5431	5779	6126
2.9	1.0 6471	6815	7158	7500	7841	8181	8519	8856	9192	9527
3.0	1.0 9861	*0194	*0526	*0856	*1186	*1514	*1841	*2168	*2493	*2817
3.1	1.1 3140	3462	3783	4103	4422	4740	5057	5373	5688	6002
3.2	1.1 6315	6627	6938	7248	7557	7865	8173	8479	8784	9089
3.3	1.1 9392	9695	9996	*0297	*0597	*0896	*1194	*1491	*1788	*2083
3.4	1.2 2378	2671	2964	3256	3547	3837	4127	4415	4703	4990
3.5	1.2 5276	5562	5846	6130	6413	6695	6976	7257	7536	7815
3.6	1.2 8093	8371	8647	8923	9198	9473	9746	*0019	*0291	*0563
3.7	1.3 0833	1103	1372	1641	1909	2176	2442	2708	2972	3237
3.8	1.3 3500	3763	4025	4286	4547	4807	5067	5325	5584	5841
3.9	1.3 6098	6354	6609	6864	7118	7372	7624	7877	8128	8379
4.0	1.3 8629	8879	9128	9377	9624	9872	*0118	*0364	*0610	*0854
4.1	1.4 1099	1342	1585	1828	2070	2311	2552	2792	3031	3270
4.2	1.4 3508	3746	3984	4220	4456	4692	4927	5161	5395	5629
4.3	1.4 5862	6094	6326	6557	6787	7018	7247	7476	7705	7933
4.4	1.4 8160	8387	8614	8840	9065	9290	9515	9739	9962	*0185
4.5	1.5 0408	0630	0851	1072	1293	1513	1732	1951	2170	2388
4.6	1.5 2606	2823	3039	3256	3471	3687	3902	4116	4330	4543
4.7	1.5 4756	4969	5181	5393	5604	5814	6025	6235	6444	6653
4.8	1.5 6862	7070	7277	7485	7691	7898	8104	8309	8515	8719
4.9	1.5 8924	9127	9331	9534	9737	9939	*0141	*0342	*0543	*0744
5.0	1.6 0944	1144	1343	1542	1741	1939	2137	2334	2531	2728
N	0	1	2	3	4	5	6	7	8	9

Five-Place Natural Logarithms

N	0	1	2	3	4	5	6	7	8	9
5.0	1.6 0944	1144	1343	1542	1741	1939	2137	2334	2531	2728
5.1	1.6 2924	3120	3315	3511	3705	3900	4094	4287	4481	4673
5.2	1.6 4866	5058	5250	5441	5632	5823	6013	6203	6393	6582
5.3	1.6 6771	6959	7147	7335	7523	7710	7896	8083	8269	8455
5.4	1.6 8640	8825	9010	9194	9378	9562	9745	9928	*0111	*0293
5.5	1.7 0475	0656	0838	1019	1199	1380	1560	1740	1919	2098
5.6	1.7 2277	2455	2633	2811	2988	3166	3342	3519	3695	3871
5.7	1.7 4047	4222	4397	4572	4746	4920	5094	5267	5440	5613
5.8	1.7 5786	5958	6130	6302	6473	6644	6815	6985	7156	7326
5.9	1.7 7495	7665	7843	8002	8171	8339	8507	8675	8842	9009
6.0	1.7 9176	9342	9509	9675	9840	*0006	*0171	*0336	*0500	*0665
6.1	1.8 0829	0993	1156	1319	1482	1645	1808	1970	2132	2294
6.2	1.8 2455	2616	2777	2938	3098	3258	3418	3578	3737	3896
6.3	1.8 4055	4214	4372	4530	4688	4845	5003	5160	5317	5473
6.4	1.8 5630	5786	5942	6097	6253	6408	6563	6718	6872	7026
6.5	1.8 7180	7334	7487	7641	7794	7947	8099	8251	8403	8555
6.6	1.8 8707	8858	9010	9160	9311	9462	9612	9762	9912	*0061
6.7	1.9 0211	0360	0509	0658	0806	0954	1102	1250	1398	1545
6.8	1.9 1692	1839	1986	2132	2279	2425	2571	2716	2862	3007
6.9	1.9 3152	3297	3442	3586	3730	3874	4018	4162	4305	4448
7.0	1.9 4591	4734	4876	5019	5161	5303	5445	5586	5727	5869
7.1	1.9 6009	6150	6291	6431	6571	6711	6851	6991	7130	7269
7.2	1.9 7408	7547	7685	7824	7962	8100	8238	8376	8513	8650
7.3	1.9 8787	8924	9061	9198	9334	9470	9606	9742	9877	*0013
7.4	2.0 0148	0283	0418	0553	0687	0821	0956	1089	1223	1357
7.5	2.0 1490	1624	1757	1890	2022	2155	2287	2419	2551	2683
7.6	2.0 2815	2946	3078	3209	3340	3471	3601	3732	3862	3992
7.7	2.0 4122	4252	4381	4511	4640	4769	4898	5027	5156	5284
7.8	2.0 5412	5540	5668	5796	5924	6051	6179	6306	6433	6560
7.9	2.0 6686	6813	6939	7065	7191	7317	7443	7568	7694	7819
8.0	2.0 7944	8069	8194	8318	8443	8567	8691	8815	8939	9063
8.1	2.0 9186	9310	9433	9556	9679	9802	9924	*0047	*0169	*0291
8.2	2.1 0413	0535	0657	0779	0900	1021	1142	1263	1384	1505
8.3	2.1 1626	1746	1866	1986	2106	2226	2346	2465	2585	2704
8.4	2.1 2823	2942	3061	3180	3298	3417	3535	3653	3771	3889
8.5	2.1 4007	4124	4242	4359	4476	4593	4710	4827	4943	5060
8.6	2.1 5176	5292	5409	5524	5640	5756	5871	5987	6102	6217
8.7	2.1 6332	6447	6562	6677	6791	6905	7020	7134	7248	7361
8.8	2.1 7475	7589	7702	7816	7929	8042	8155	8267	8380	8493
8.9	2.1 8605	8717	8830	8942	9054	9165	9277	9389	9500	9611
9.0	2.1 9722	9834	9944	*0055	*0166	*0276	*0387	*0497	*0607	*0717
9.1	2.2 0827	0937	1047	1157	1266	1375	1485	1594	1703	1812
9.2	2.2 1920	2029	2138	2246	2354	2462	2570	2678	2786	2894
9.3	2.2 3001	3109	3216	3324	3431	3538	3645	3751	3858	3965
9.4	2.2 4071	4177	4284	4390	4496	4601	4707	4813	4918	5024
9.5	2.2 5129	5234	5339	5444	5549	5654	5759	5863	5968	6072
9.6	2.2 6176	6280	6384	6488	6592	6696	6799	6903	7006	7109
9.7	2.2 7213	7316	7419	7521	7624	7727	7829	7932	8034	8136
9.8	2.2 8238	8340	8442	8544	8646	8747	8849	8950	9051	9152
9.9	2.2 9253	9354	9455	9556	9657	9757	9858	9958	*0058	*0158
10.0	2.3 0259	0358	0458	0558	0658	0757	0857	0956	1055	1154
N	**0**	**1**	**2**	**3**	**4**	**5**	**6**	**7**	**8**	**9**

TABLE 4

Values and Logarithms of Exponential Functions

x	e^x	$\text{Log}_{10}\, e^x$	e^{-x}	x	e^x	$\text{Log}_{10}\, e^x$	e^{-x}
0.00	1.0000	.00 000	1.00 000	**0.50**	1.6487	.21 715	.60 653
0.01	1.0101	.00 434	0.99 005	0.51	1.6653	.22 149	.60 050
0.02	1.0202	.00 869	.98 020	0.52	1.6820	.22 583	.59 452
0.03	1.0305	.01 303	.97 045	0.53	1.6989	.23 018	.58 860
0.04	1.0408	.01 737	.96 079	0.54	1.7160	.23 452	.58 275
0.05	1.0513	.02 171	.95 123	**0.55**	1.7333	.23 886	.57 695
0.06	1.0618	.02 606	.94 176	0.56	1.7507	.24 320	.57 121
0.07	1.0725	.03 040	.93 239	0.57	1.7683	.24 755	.56 553
0.08	1.0833	.03 474	.92 312	0.58	1.7860	.25 189	.55 990
0.09	1.0942	.03 909	.91 393	0.59	1.8040	.25 623	.55 433
0.10	1.1052	.04 343	.90 484	**0.60**	1.8221	.26 058	.54 881
0.11	1.1163	.04 777	.89 583	0.61	1.8404	.26 492	.54 335
0.12	1.1275	.05 212	.88 692	0.62	1.8589	.26 926	.53 794
0.13	1.1388	.05 646	.87 810	0.63	1.8776	.27 361	.53 259
0.14	1.1503	.06 080	.86 936	0.64	1.8965	.27 795	.52 729
0.15	1.1618	.06 514	.86 071	**0.65**	1.9155	.28 229	.52 205
0.16	1.1735	.06 949	.85 214	0.66	1.9348	.28 663	.51 685
0.17	1.1853	.07 383	.84 366	0.67	1.9542	.29 098	.51 171
0.18	1.1972	.07 817	.83 527	0.68	1.9739	.29 532	.50 662
0.19	1.2092	.08 252	.82 696	0.69	1.9937	.29 966	.50 158
0.20	1.2214	.08 686	.81 873	**0.70**	2.0138	.30 401	.49 659
0.21	1.2337	.09 120	.81 058	0.71	2.0340	.30 835	.49 164
0.22	1.2461	.09 554	.80 252	0.72	2.0544	.31 269	.48 675
0.23	1.2586	.09 989	.79 453	0.73	2.0751	.31 703	.48 191
0.24	1.2712	.10 423	.78 663	0.74	2.0959	.32 138	.47 711
0.25	1.2840	.10 857	.77 880	**0.75**	2.1170	.32 572	.47 237
0.26	1.2969	.11 292	.77 105	0.76	2.1383	.33 006	.46 767
0.27	1.3100	.11 726	.76 338	0.77	2.1598	.33 441	.46 301
0.28	1.3231	.12 160	.75 578	0.78	2.1815	.33 875	.45 841
0.29	1.3364	.12 595	.74 826	0.79	2.2034	.34 309	.45 384
0.30	1.3499	.13 029	.74 082	**0.80**	2.2255	.34 744	.44 933
0.31	1.3634	.13 463	.73 345	0.81	2.2479	.35 178	.44 486
0.32	1.3771	.13 897	.72 615	0.82	2.2705	.35 612	.44 043
0.33	1.3910	.14 332	.71 892	0.83	2.2933	.36 046	.43 605
0.34	1.4049	.14 766	.71 177	0.84	2.3164	.36 481	.43 171
0.35	1.4191	.15 200	.70 469	**0.85**	2.3396	.36 915	.42 741
0.36	1.4333	.15 635	.69 768	0.86	2.3632	.37 349	.42 316
0.37	1.4477	.16 069	.69 073	0.87	2.3869	.37 784	.41 895
0.38	1.4623	.16 503	.68 386	0.88	2.4109	.38 218	.41 478
0.39	1.4770	.16 937	.67 706	0.89	2.4351	.38 652	.41 066
0.40	1.4918	.17 372	.67 032	**0.90**	2.4596	.39 087	.40 657
0.41	1.5068	.17 806	.66 365	0.91	2.4843	.39 521	.40 252
0.42	1.5220	.18 240	.65 705	0.92	2.5093	.39 955	.39 852
0.43	1.5373	.18 675	.65 051	0.93	2.5345	.40 389	.39 455
0.44	1.5527	.19 109	.64 404	0.94	2.5600	.40 824	.39 063
0.45	1.5683	.19 543	.63 763	**0.95**	2.5857	.41 258	.38 674
0.46	1.5841	.19 978	.63 128	0.96	2.6117	.41 692	.38 289
0.47	1.6000	.20 412	.62 500	0.97	2.6379	.42 127	.37 908
0.48	1.6161	.20 846	.61 878	0.98	2.6645	.42 561	.37 531
0.49	1.6323	.21 280	.61 263	0.99	2.6912	.42 995	.37 158
0.50	1.6487	.21 715	.60 653	**1.00**	2.7183	.43 429	.36 788
x	e^x	$\text{Log}_{10}\, e^x$	e^{-x}	x	e^x	$\text{Log}_{10}\, e^x$	e^{-x}

From *Rinehart Mathematical Tables, Formulas, and Curves.*

Values and Logarithms of Exponential Functions

x	e^x	$\text{Log}_{10}\, e^x$	e^{-x}	x	e^x	$\text{Log}_{10}\, e^x$	e^{-x}
1.00	2.7183	.43 429	.36 788	**1.50**	4.4817	.65 144	.22 313
1.01	2.7456	.43 864	.36 422	1.51	4.5267	.65 578	.22 091
1.02	2.7732	.44 298	.36 059	1.52	4.5722	.66 013	.21 871
1.03	2.8011	.44 732	.35 701	1.53	4.6182	.66 447	.21 654
1.04	2.8292	.45 167	.35 345	1.54	4.6646	.66 881	.21 438
1.05	2.8577	.45 601	.34 994	**1.55**	4.7115	.67 316	.21 225
1.06	2.8864	.46 035	.34 646	1.56	4.7588	.67 750	.21 014
1.07	2.9154	.46 470	.34 301	1.57	4.8066	.68 184	.20 805
1.08	2.9447	.46 904	.33 960	1.58	4.8550	.68 619	.20 598
1.09	2.9743	.47 338	.33 622	1.59	4.9037	.69 053	.20 393
1.10	3.0042	.47 772	.33 287	**1.60**	4.9530	.69 487	.20 190
1.11	3.0344	.48 207	.32 956	1.61	5.0028	.69 921	.19 989
1.12	3.0649	.48 641	.32 628	1.62	5.0531	.70 356	.19 790
1.13	3.0957	.49 075	.32 303	1.63	5.1039	.70 790	.19 593
1.14	3.1268	.49 510	.31 982	1.64	5.1552	.71 224	.19 398
1.15	3.1582	.49 944	.31 664	**1.65**	5.2070	.71 659	.19 205
1.16	3.1899	.50 378	.31 349	1.66	5.2593	.72 093	.19 014
1.17	3.2220	.50 812	.31 037	1.67	5.3122	.72 527	.18 825
1.18	3.2544	.51 247	.30 728	1.68	5.3656	.72 961	.18 637
1.19	3.2871	.51 681	.30 422	1.69	5.4195	.73 396	.18 452
1.20	3.3201	.52 115	.30 119	**1.70**	5.4739	.73 830	.18 268
1.21	3.3535	.52 550	.29 820	1.71	5.5290	.74 264	.18 087
1.22	3.3872	.52 984	.29 523	1.72	5.5845	.74 699	.17 907
1.23	3.4212	.53 418	.29 229	1.73	5.6407	.75 133	.17 728
1.24	3.4556	.53 853	.28 938	1.74	5.6973	.75 567	.17 552
1.25	3.4903	.54 287	.28 650	**1.75**	5.7546	.76 002	.17 377
1.26	3.5254	.54 721	.28 365	1.76	5.8124	.76 436	.17 204
1.27	3.5609	.55 155	.28 083	1.77	5.8709	.76 870	.17 033
1.28	3.5966	.55 590	.27 804	1.78	5.9299	.77 304	.16 864
1.29	3.6328	.56 024	.27 527	1.79	5.9895	.77 739	.16 696
1.30	3.6693	.56 458	.27 253	**1.80**	6.0496	.78 173	.16 530
1.31	3.7062	.56 893	.26 982	1.81	6.1104	.78 607	.16 365
1.32	3.7434	.57 327	.26 714	1.82	6.1719	.79 042	.16 203
1.33	3.7810	.57 761	.26 448	1.83	6.2339	.79 476	.16 041
1.34	3.8190	.58 195	.26 185	1.84	6.2965	.79 910	.15 882
1.35	3.8574	.58 630	.25 924	**1.85**	6.3598	.80 344	.15 724
1.36	3.8962	.59 064	.25 666	1.86	6.4237	.80 779	.15 567
1.37	3.9354	.59 498	.25 411	1.87	6.4883	.81 213	.15 412
1.38	3.9749	.59 933	.25 158	1.88	6.5535	.81 647	.15 259
1.39	4.0149	.60 367	.24 908	1.89	6.6194	.82 082	.15 107
1.40	4.0552	.60 801	.24 660	**1.90**	6.6859	.82 516	.14 957
1.41	4.0960	.61 236	.24 414	1.91	6.7531	.82 950	.14 808
1.42	4.1371	.61 670	.24 171	1.92	6.8210	.83 385	.14 661
1.43	4.1787	.62 104	.23 931	1.93	6.8895	.83 819	.14 515
1.44	4.2207	.62 538	.23 693	1.94	6.9588	.84 253	.14 370
1.45	4.2631	.62 973	.23 457	**1.95**	7.0287	.84 687	.14 227
1.46	4.3060	.63 407	.23 224	1.96	7.0993	.85 122	.14 086
1.47	4.3492	.63 841	.22 993	1.97	7.1707	.85 556	.13 946
1.48	4.3929	.64 276	.22 764	1.98	7.2427	.85 990	.13 807
1.49	4.4371	.64 710	.22 537	1.99	7.3155	.86 425	.13 670
1.50	4.4817	.65 144	.22 313	**2.00**	7.3891	.86 859	.13 534
x	e^x	$\text{Log}_{10}\, e^x$	e^{-x}	x	e^x	$\text{Log}_{10}\, e^x$	e^{-x}

Values and Logarithms of Exponential Functions

x	e^x	$\text{Log}_{10}\, e^x$	e^{-x}	x	e^x	$\text{Log}_{10}\, e^x$	e^{-x}
2.00	7.3891	.86 859	.13 534	**2.50**	12.182	1.08 574	.082 085
2.01	7.4633	.87 293	.13 399	2.51	12.305	1.09 008	.081 268
2.02	7.5383	.87 727	.13 266	2.52	12.429	1.09 442	.080 460
2.03	7.6141	.88 162	.13 134	2.53	12.554	1.09 877	.079 659
2.04	7.6906	.88 596	.13 003	2.54	12.680	1.10 311	.078 866
2.05	7.7679	.89 030	.12 873	**2.55**	12.807	1.10 745	.078 082
2.06	7.8460	.89 465	.12 745	2.56	12.936	1.11 179	.077 305
2.07	7.9248	.89 899	.12 619	2.57	13.066	1.11 614	.076 536
2.08	8.0045	.90 333	.12 493	2.58	13.197	1.12 048	.075 774
2.09	8.0849	.90 768	.12 369	2.59	13.330	1.12 482	.075 020
2.10	8.1662	.91 202	.12 246	**2.60**	13.464	1.12 917	.074 274
2.11	8.2482	.91 636	.12 124	2.61	13.599	1.13 351	.073 535
2.12	8.3311	.92 070	.12 003	2.62	13.736	1.13 785	.072 803
2.13	8.4149	.92 505	.11 884	2.63	13.874	1.14 219	.072 078
2.14	8.4994	.92 939	.11 765	2.64	14.013	1.14 654	.071 361
2.15	8.5849	.93 373	.11 648	**2.65**	14.154	1.15 088	.070 651
2.16	8.6711	.93 808	.11 533	2.66	14.296	1.15 522	.069 948
2.17	8.7583	.94 242	.11 418	2.67	14.440	1.15 957	.069 252
2.18	8.8463	.94 676	.11 304	2.68	14.585	1.16 391	.068 563
2.19	8.9352	.95 110	.11 192	2.69	14.732	1.16 825	.067 881
2.20	9.0250	.95 545	.11 080	**2.70**	14.880	1.17 260	.067 206
2.21	9.1157	.95 979	.10 970	2.71	15.029	1.17 694	.066 537
2.22	9.2073	.96 413	.10 861	2.72	15.180	1.18 128	.065 875
2.23	9.2999	.96 848	.10 753	2.73	15.333	1.18 562	.065 219
2.24	9.3933	.97 282	.10 646	2.74	15.487	1.18 997	.064 570
2.25	9.4877	.97 716	.10 540	**2.75**	15.643	1.19 431	.063 928
2.26	9.5831	.98 151	.10 435	2.76	15.800	1.19 865	.063 292
2.27	9.6794	.98 585	.10 331	2.77	15.959	1.20 300	.062 662
2.28	9.7767	.99 019	.10 228	2.78	16.119	1.20 734	.062 039
2.29	9.8749	.99 453	.10 127	2.79	16.281	1.21 168	.061 421
2.30	9.9742	.99 888	.10 026	**2.80**	16.445	1.21 602	.060 810
2.31	10.074	1.00 322	.09 9261	2.81	16.610	1.22 037	.060 205
2.32	10.176	1.00 756	.09 8274	2.82	16.777	1.22 471	.059 606
2.33	10.278	1.01 191	.09 7296	2.83	16.945	1.22 905	.059 013
2.34	10.381	1.01 625	.09 6328	2.84	17.116	1.23 340	.058 426
2.35	10.486	1.02 059	.09 5369	**2.85**	17.288	1.23 774	.057 844
2.36	10.591	1.02 493	.09 4420	2.86	17.462	1.24 208	.057 269
2.37	10.697	1.02 928	.09 3481	2.87	17.637	1.24 643	.056 699
2.38	10.805	1.03 362	.09 2551	2.88	17.814	1.25 077	.056 135
2.39	10.913	1.03 796	.09 1630	2.89	17.993	1.25 511	.055 576
2.40	11.023	1.04 231	.09 0718	**2.90**	18.174	1.25 945	.055 023
2.41	11.134	1.04 665	.08 9815	2.91	18.357	1.26 380	.054 476
2.42	11.246	1.05 099	.08 8922	2.92	18.541	1.26 814	.053 934
2.43	11.359	1.05 534	.08 8037	2.93	18.728	1.27 248	.053 397
2.44	11.473	1.05 968	.08 7161	2.94	18.916	1.27 683	.052 866
2.45	11.588	1.06 402	.08 6294	**2.95**	19.106	1.28 117	.052 340
2.46	11.705	1.06 836	.08 5435	2.96	19.298	1.28 551	.051 819
2.47	11.822	1.07 271	.08 4585	2.97	19.492	1.28 985	.051 303
2.48	11.941	1.07 705	.08 3743	2.98	19.688	1.29 420	.050 793
2.49	12.061	1.08 139	.08 2910	2.99	19.886	1.29 854	.050 287
2.50	12.182	1.08 574	.08 2085	**3.00**	20.086	1.30 288	.049 787
x	e^x	$\text{Log}_{10}\, e^x$	e^{-x}	x	e^x	$\text{Log}_{10}\, e^x$	e^{-x}

Values and Logarithms of Exponential Functions

x	e^x	$\text{Log}_{10}\, e^x$	e^{-x}	x	e^x	$\text{Log}_{10}\, e^x$	e^{-x}
3.00	20.086	1.30 288	.04 9787	**3.50**	33.115	1.52 003	.030 197
3.01	20.287	1.30 723	.04 9292	3.51	33.448	1.52 437	.029 897
3.02	20.491	1.31 157	.04 8801	3.52	33.784	1.52 872	.029 599
3.03	20.697	1.31 591	.04 8316	3.53	34.124	1.53 306	.029 305
3.04	20.905	1.32 026	.04 7835	3.54	34.467	1.53 740	.029 013
3.05	21.115	1.32 460	.04 7359	**3.55**	34.813	1.54 175	.028 725
3.06	21.328	1.32 894	.04 6888	3.56	35.163	1.54 609	.028 439
3.07	21.542	1.33 328	.04 6421	3.57	35.517	1.55 043	.028 156
3.08	21.758	1.33 763	.04 5959	3.58	35.874	1.55 477	.027 876
3.09	21.977	1.34 197	.04 5502	3.59	36.234	1.55 912	.027 598
3.10	22.198	1.34 631	.04 5049	**3.60**	36.598	1.56 346	.027 324
3.11	22.421	1.35 066	.04 4601	3.61	36.966	1.56 780	.027 052
3.12	22.646	1.35 500	.04 4157	3.62	37.338	1.57 215	.026 783
3.13	22.874	1.35 934	.04 3718	3.63	37.713	1.57 649	.026 516
3.14	23.104	1.36 368	.04 3283	3.64	38.092	1.58 083	.026 252
3.15	23.336	1.36 803	.04 2852	**3.65**	38.475	1.58 517	.025 991
3.16	23.571	1.37 237	.04 2426	3.66	38.861	1.58 952	.025 733
3.17	23.807	1.37 671	.04 2004	3.67	39.252	1.59 386	.025 476
3.18	24.047	1.38 106	.04 1586	3.68	39.646	1.59 820	.025 223
3.19	24.288	1.38 540	.04 1172	3.69	40.045	1.60 255	.024 972
3.20	24.533	1.38 974	.04 0762	**3.70**	40.447	1.60 689	.024 724
3.21	24.779	1.39 409	.04 0357	3.71	40.854	1.61 123	.024 478
3.22	25.028	1.39 843	.03 9955	3.72	41.264	1.61 558	.024 234
3.23	25.280	1.40 277	.03 9557	3.73	41.679	1.61 992	.023 993
3.24	25.534	1.40 711	.03 9164	3.74	42.098	1.62 426	.023 754
3.25	25.790	1.41 146	.03 8774	**3.75**	42.521	1.62 860	.023 518
3.26	26.050	1.41 580	.03 8388	3.76	42.948	1.63 295	.023 284
3.27	26.311	1.42 014	.03 8006	3.77	43.380	1.63 729	.023 052
3.28	26.576	1.42 449	.03 7628	3.78	43.816	1.64 163	.022 823
3.29	26.843	1.42 883	.03 7254	3.79	44.256	1.64 598	.022 596
3.30	27.113	1.43 317	.03 6883	**3.80**	44.701	1.65 032	.022 371
3.31	27.385	1.43 751	.03 6516	3.81	45.150	1.65 466	.022 148
3.32	27.660	1.44 186	.03 6153	3.82	45.604	1.65 900	.021 928
3.33	27.938	1.44 620	.03 5793	3.83	46.063	1.66 335	.021 710
3.34	28.219	1.45 054	.03 5437	3.84	46.525	1.66 769	.021 494
3.35	28.503	1.45 489	.03 5084	**3.85**	46.993	1.67 203	.021 280
3.36	28.789	1.45 923	.03 4735	3.86	47.465	1.67 638	.021 068
3.37	29.079	1.46 357	.03 4390	3.87	47.942	1.68 072	.020 858
3.38	29.371	1.46 792	.03 4047	3.88	48.424	1.68 506	.020 651
3.39	29.666	1.47 226	.03 3709	3.89	48.911	1.68 941	.020 445
3.40	29.964	1.47 660	.03 3373	**3.90**	49.402	1.69 375	.020 242
3.41	30.265	1.48 094	.03 3041	3.91	49.899	1.69 809	.020 041
3.42	30.569	1.48 529	.03 2712	3.92	50.400	1.70 243	.019 841
3.43	30.877	1.48 963	.03 2387	3.93	50.907	1.70 678	.019 644
3.44	31.187	1.49 397	.03 2065	3.94	51.419	1.71 112	.019 448
3.45	31.500	1.49 832	.03 1746	**3.95**	51.935	1.71 546	.019 255
3.46	31.817	1.50 266	.03 1430	3.96	52.457	1.71 981	.019 063
3.47	32.137	1.50 700	.03 1117	3.97	52.985	1.72 415	.018 873
3.48	32.460	1.51 134	.03 0807	3.98	53.517	1.72 849	.018 686
3.49	32.786	1.51 569	.03 0501	3.99	54.055	1.73 283	.018 500
3.50	33.115	1.52 003	.03 0197	**4.00**	54.598	1.73 718	.018 316
x	e^x	$\text{Log}_{10}\, e^x$	e^{-x}	x	e^x	$\text{Log}_{10}\, e^x$	e^{-x}

TABLE 4

Values and Logarithms of Exponential Functions

x	e^x	$\text{Log}_{10} e^x$	e^{-x}	x	e^x	$\text{Log}_{10} e^x$	e^{-x}
4.00	54.598	1.73 718	.01 8316	**4.50**	90.017	1.95 433	.011 109
4.01	55.147	1.74 152	.01 8133	4.51	90.922	1.95 867	.010 998
4.02	55.701	1.74 586	.01 7953	4.52	91.836	1.96 301	.010 889
4.03	56.261	1.75 021	.01 7774	4.53	92.759	1.96 735	.010 781
4.04	56.826	1.75 455	.01 7597	4.54	93.691	1.97 170	.010 673
4.05	57.397	1.75 889	.01 7422	**4.55**	94.632	1 97 604	.010 567
4.06	57.974	1.76 324	.01 7249	4.56	95.583	1.98 038	.010 462
4.07	58.557	1.76 758	.01 7077	4.57	96.544	1.98 473	.010 358
4.08	59.145	1.77 192	.01 6907	4.58	97.514	1.98 907	.010 255
4.09	59.740	1.77 626	.01 6739	4.59	98.494	1.99 341	.010 153
4.10	60.340	1.78 061	.01 6573	**4.60**	99.484	1.99 775	.010 052
4.11	60.947	1.78 495	.01 6408	4.61	100.48	2.00 210	.009 9518
4.12	61.559	1.78 929	.01 6245	4.62	101.49	2.00 644	.009 8528
4.13	62.178	1.79 364	.01 6083	4.63	102.51	2.01 078	.009 7548
4.14	62.803	1.79 798	.01 5923	4.64	103.54	2.01 513	.009 6577
4.15	63.434	1.80 232	.01 5764	**4.65**	104.58	2.01 947	.009 5616
4.16	64.072	1.80 667	.01 5608	4.66	105.64	2.02 381	.009 4665
4.17	64.715	1.81 101	.01 5452	4.67	106.70	2.02 816	.009 3723
4.18	65.366	1.81 535	.01 5299	4.68	107.77	2.03 250	.009 2790
4.19	66.023	1.81 969	.01 5146	4.69	108.85	2.03 684	.009 1867
4.20	66.686	1.82 404	.01 4996	**4.70**	109.95	2.04 118	.009 0953
4.21	67.357	1.82 838	.01 4846	4.71	111.05	2.04 553	.009 0048
4.22	68.033	1.83 272	.01 4699	4.72	112.17	2.04 987	.008 9152
4.23	68.717	1.83 707	.01 4552	4.73	113.30	2.05 421	.008 8265
4.24	69.408	1.84 141	.01 4408	4.74	114.43	2.05 856	.008 7386
4.25	70.105	1.84 575	.01 4264	**4.75**	115.58	2.06 290	.008 6517
4.26	70.810	1.85 009	.01 4122	4.76	116.75	2.06 724	.008 5656
4.27	71.522	1.85 444	.01 3982	4.77	117.92	2.07 158	.008 4804
4.28	72.240	1.85 878	.01 3843	4.78	119.10	2.07 593	.008 3960
4.29	72.966	1.86 312	.01 3705	4.79	120.30	2.08 027	.008 3125
4.30	73.700	1.86 747	.01 3569	**4.80**	121.51	2.08 461	.008 2297
4.31	74.440	1.87 181	.01 3434	4.81	122.73	2.08 896	.008 1479
4.32	75.189	1.87 615	.01 3300	4.82	123.97	2.09 330	.008 0668
4.33	75.944	1.88 050	.01 3168	4.83	125.21	2.09 764	.007 9865
4.34	76.708	1.88 484	.01 3037	4.84	126.47	2.10 199	.007 9071
4.35	77.478	1.88 918	.01 2907	**4.85**	127.74	2.10 633	.007 8284
4.36	78.257	1.89 352	.01 2778	4.86	129.02	2.11 067	.007 7505
4.37	79.044	1.89 787	.01 2651	4.87	130.32	2.11 501	.007 6734
4.38	79.838	1.90 221	.01 2525	4.88	131.63	2.11 936	.007 5970
4.39	80.640	1.90 655	.01 2401	4.89	132.95	2.12 370	.007 5214
4.40	81.451	1.91 090	.01 2277	**4.90**	134.29	2.12 804	.007 4466
4.41	82.269	1.91 524	.01 2155	4.91	135.64	2.13 239	.007 3725
4.42	83.096	1.91 958	.01 2034	4.92	137.00	2.13 673	.007 2991
4.43	83.931	1.92 392	.01 1914	4.93	138.38	2.14 107	.007 2265
4.44	84.775	1.92 827	.01 1796	4.94	139.77	2.14 541	.007 1546
4.45	85.627	1.93 261	.01 1679	**4.95**	141.17	2.14 976	.007 0834
4.46	86.488	1.93 695	.01 1562	4.96	142.59	2.15 410	.007 0129
4.47	87.357	1.94 130	.01 1447	4.97	144.03	2.15 844	.006 9431
4.48	88.235	1.94 564	.01 1333	4.98	145.47	2.16 279	.006 8741
4.49	89.121	1.94 998	.01 1221	4.99	146.94	2.16 713	.006 8057
4.50	90.017	1.95 433	.01 1109	**5.00**	148.41	2.17 147	.006 7379
x	e^x	$\text{Log}_{10} e^x$	e^{-x}	x	e^x	$\text{Log}_{10} e^x$	e^{-x}

Values and Logarithms of Exponential Functions

x	e^x	$\text{Log}_{10}\, e^x$	e^{-x}	x	e^x	$\text{Log}_{10}\, e^x$	e^{-x}
5.00	148.41	2.17 147	.00 67379	**7.50**	1 808.0	3.25 721	.000 5531
5.05	156.02	2.19 319	.00 64093	7.55	1 900.7	3.27 892	.000 5261
5.10	164.02	2.21 490	.00 60967	7.60	1 998.2	3.30 064	.000 5005
5.15	172.43	2.23 662	.00 57994	7.65	2 100.6	3.32 235	.000 4760
5.20	181.27	2.25 833	.00 55166	7.70	2 208.3	3.34 407	.000 4528
5.25	190.57	2.28 005	.00 52475	**7.75**	2 321.6	3.36 578	.000 4307
5.30	200.34	2.30 176	.00 49916	7.80	2 440.6	3.38 750	.000 4097
5.35	210.61	2.32 348	.00 47482	7.85	2 565.7	3.40 921	.000 3898
5.40	221.41	2.34 519	.00 45166	7.90	2 697.3	3.43 093	.000 3707
5.45	232.76	2.36 690	.00 42963	7.95	2 835.6	3.45 264	.000 3527
5.50	244.69	2.38 862	.00 40868	**8.00**	2 981.0	3.47 436	.000 3355
5.55	257.24	2.41 033	.00 38875	8.05	3 133.8	3.49 607	.000 3191
5.60	270.43	2.43 205	.00 36979	8.10	3 294.5	3.51 779	.000 3035
5.65	284.29	2.45 376	.00 35175	8.15	3 463.4	3.53 950	.000 2887
5.70	298.87	2.47 548	.00 33460	8.20	3 641.0	3.56 121	.000 2747
5.75	314.19	2.49 719	.00 31828	**8.25**	3 827.6	3.58 293	.000 2613
5.80	330.30	2.51 891	.00 30276	8.30	4 023.9	3.60 464	.000 2485
5.85	347.23	2.54 062	.00 28799	8.35	4 230.2	3.62 636	.000 2364
5.90	365.04	2.56 234	.00 27394	8.40	4 447.1	3.64 807	.000 2249
5.95	383.75	2.58 405	.00 26058	8.45	4 675.1	3.66 979	.000 2139
6.00	403.43	2.60 577	.00 24788	**8.50**	4 914.8	3.69 150	.000 2035
6.05	424.11	2.62 748	.00 23579	8.55	5 166.8	3.71 322	.000 1935
6.10	445.86	2.64 920	.00 22429	8.60	5 431.7	3.73 493	.000 1841
6.15	468.72	2.67 091	.00 21335	8.65	5 710.1	3.75 665	.000 1751
6.20	492.75	2.69 263	.00 20294	8.70	6 002.9	3.77 836	.000 1666
6.25	518.01	2.71 434	.00 19305	**8.75**	6 310.7	3.80 008	.000 1585
6.30	544.57	2.73 606	.00 18363	8.80	6 634.2	3.82 179	.000 1507
6.35	572.49	2.75 777	.00 17467	8.85	6 974.4	3.84 351	.000 1434
6.40	601.85	2.77 948	.00 16616	8.90	7 332.0	3.86 522	.000 1364
6.45	632.70	2.80 120	.00 15805	8.95	7 707.9	3.88 694	.000 1297
6.50	665.14	2.82 291	.00 15034	**9.00**	8 103.1	3.90 865	.000 1234
6.55	699.24	2.84 463	.00 14301	9.05	8 518.5	3.93 037	.000 1174
6.60	735.10	2.86 634	.00 13604	9.10	8 955.3	3.95 208	.000 1117
6.65	772.78	2.88 806	.00 12940	9.15	9 414.4	3.97 379	.000 1062
6.70	812.41	2.90 977	.00 12309	9.20	9 897.1	3.99 551	.000 1010
6.75	854.06	2.93 149	.00 11709	**9.25**	10 405	4.01 722	.000 0961
6.80	897.85	2.95 320	.00 11138	9.30	10 938	4.03 894	.000 0914
6.85	943.88	2.97 492	.00 10595	9.35	11 499	4.06 065	.000 0870
6.90	992.27	2.99 663	.00 10078	9.40	12 088	4.08 237	.000 0827
6.95	1 043.1	3.01 835	.00 09586	9.45	12 708	4.10 408	.000 0787
7.00	1 096.6	3.04 006	.00 09119	**9.50**	13 360	4.12 580	.000 0749
7.05	1 152.9	3.06 178	.00 08674	9.55	14 045	4.14 751	.000 0712
7.10	1 212.0	3.08 349	.00 08251	9.60	14 765	4.16 923	.000 0677
7.15	1 274.1	3.10 521	.00 07849	9.65	15 522	4.19 094	.000 0644
7.20	1 339.4	3.12 692	.00 07466	9.70	16 318	4.21 266	.000 0613
7.25	1 408.1	3.14 863	.00 07102	**9.75**	17 154	4.23 437	.000 0583
7.30	1 480.3	3.17 035	.00 06755	9.80	18 034	4.25 609	.000 0555
7.35	1 556.2	3.19 206	.00 06426	9.85	18 958	4.27 780	.000 0527
7.40	1 636.0	3.21 378	.00 06113	9.90	19 930	4.29 952	.000 0502
7.45	1 719.9	3.23 549	.00 05814	9.95	20 952	4.32 123	.000 0477
7.50	1 808.0	3.25 721	.00 05531	**10.00**	22 026	4.34 294	.000 0454
x	e^x	$\text{Log}_{10}\, e^x$	e^{-x}	x	e^x	$\text{Log}_{10}\, e^x$	e^{-x}

TABLE 5
Normal Areas and Ordinates

t	$\phi(t)$	$\int_0^t \phi(t)dt$	t	$\phi(t)$	$\int_0^t \phi(t)dt$	t	$\phi(t)$	$\int_0^t \phi(t)dt$
.00	.39894	.00000	.45	.36053	.17364	.90	.26609	.31594
.01	.39892	.00399	.46	.35889	.17724	.91	.26369	.31859
.02	.39886	.00798	.47	.35723	.18082	.92	.26129	.32121
.03	.39876	.01197	.48	.35553	.18439	.93	.25888	.32381
.04	.39862	.01595	.49	.35381	.18793	.94	.25647	.32639
.05	.39844	.01994	.50	.35207	.19146	.95	.25406	.32894
.06	.39822	.02392	.51	.35029	.19497	.96	.25164	.33147
.07	.39797	.02790	.52	.34849	.19847	.97	.24923	.33398
.08	.39767	.03188	.53	.34667	.20194	.98	.24681	.33646
.09	.39733	.03586	.54	.34482	.20540	.99	.24439	.33891
.10	.39695	.03983	.55	.34294	.20884	1.00	.24197	.34134
.11	.39654	.04380	.56	.34105	.21226	1.01	.23955	.34375
.12	.39608	.04776	.57	.33912	.21566	1.02	.23713	.34614
.13	.39559	.05172	.58	.33718	.21904	1.03	.23471	.34850
.14	.39505	.05567	.59	.33521	.22240	1.04	.23230	.35083
.15	.39448	.05962	.60	.33322	.22575	1.05	.22988	.35314
.16	.39387	.06356	.61	.33121	.22907	1.06	.22747	.35543
.17	.39322	.06749	.62	.32918	.23237	1.07	.22506	.35769
.18	.39253	.07142	.63	.32713	.23565	1.08	.22265	.35993
.19	.39181	.07535	.64	.32506	.23891	1.09	.22025	.36214
.20	.39104	.07926	.65	.32297	.24215	1.10	.21785	.36433
.21	.39024	.08317	.66	.32086	.24537	1.11	.21546	.36650
.22	.38940	.08706	.67	.31874	.24857	1.12	.21307	.36864
.23	.38853	.09095	.68	.31659	.25175	1.13	.21069	.37076
.24	.38762	.09483	.69	.31443	.25490	1.14	.20831	.37286
.25	.38667	.09871	.70	.31225	.25804	1.15	.20594	.37493
.26	.38568	.10257	.71	.31006	.26115	1.16	.20357	.37698
.27	.38466	.10642	.72	.30785	.26424	1.17	.20121	.37900
.28	.38361	.11026	.73	.30563	.26730	1.18	.19886	.38100
.29	.38251	.11409	.74	.30339	.27035	1.19	.19652	.38298
.30	.38139	.11791	.75	.30114	.27337	1.20	.19419	.38493
.31	.38023	.12172	.76	.29887	.27637	1.21	.19186	.38686
.32	.37903	.12552	.77	.29659	.27935	1.22	.18954	.38877
.33	.37780	.12930	.78	.29431	.28230	1.23	.18724	.39065
.34	.37654	.13307	.79	.29200	.28524	1.24	.18494	.39251
.35	.37524	.13683	.80	.28969	.28814	1.25	.18265	.39435
.36	.37391	.14058	.81	.28737	.29103	1.26	.18037	.39617
.37	.37255	.14431	.82	.28504	.29389	1.27	.17810	.39796
.38	.37115	.14803	.83	.28269	.29673	1.28	.17585	.39973
.39	.36973	.15173	.84	.28034	.29955	1.29	.17360	.40147
.40	.36827	.15542	.85	.27798	.30234	1.30	.17137	.40320
.41	.36678	.15910	.86	.27562	.30511	1.31	.16915	.40490
.42	.36526	.16276	.87	.27324	.30785	1.32	.16694	.40658
.43	.36371	.16640	.88	.27086	.31057	1.33	.16474	.40824
.44	.36213	.17003	.89	.26848	.31327	1.34	.16256	.40988

Normal Areas and Ordinates

t	$\phi(t)$	$\int_0^t \phi(t)dt$	t	$\phi(t)$	$\int_0^t \phi(t)dt$	t	$\phi(t)$	$\int_0^t \phi(t)dt$
1.35	.16038	.41149	1.80	.07895	.46407	2.25	.03174	.48778
1.36	.15822	.41309	1.81	.07754	.46485	2.26	.03103	.48809
1.37	.15608	.41466	1.82	.07614	.46562	2.27	.03034	.48840
1.38	.15395	.41621	1.83	.07477	.46638	2.28	.02965	.48870
1.39	.15183	.41774	1.84	.07341	.46712	2.29	.02898	.48899
1.40	.14973	.41924	1.85	.07206	.46784	2.30	.02833	.48928
1.41	.14764	.42073	1.86	.07074	.46856	2.31	.02768	.48956
1.42	.14556	.42220	1.87	.06943	.46926	2.32	.02705	.48983
1.43	.14350	.42364	1.88	.06814	.46995	2.33	.02643	.49010
1.44	.14146	.42507	1.89	.06687	.47062	2.34	.02582	.49036
1.45	.13943	.42647	1.90	.06562	.47128	2.35	.02522	.49061
1.46	.13742	.42786	1.91	.06439	.47193	2.36	.02463	.49086
1.47	.13542	.42922	1.92	.06316	.47257	2.37	.02406	.49111
1.48	.13344	.43056	1.93	.06195	.47320	2.38	.02349	.49134
1.49	.13147	.43189	1.94	.06077	.47381	2.39	.02294	.49158
1.50	.12952	.43319	1.95	.05959	.47441	2.40	.02239	.49180
1.51	.12758	.43448	1.96	.05844	.47500	2.41	.02186	.49202
1.52	.12566	.43574	1.97	.05730	.47558	2.42	.02134	.49224
1.53	.12376	.43699	1.98	.05618	.47615	2.43	.02083	.49245
1.54	.12188	.43822	1.99	.05508	.47670	2.44	.02033	.49266
1.55	.12001	.43943	2.00	.05399	.47725	2.45	.01984	.49286
1.56	.11816	.44062	2.01	.05292	.47778	2.46	.01936	.49305
1.57	.11632	.44179	2.02	.05186	.47831	2.47	.01889	.49324
1.58	.11450	.44295	2.03	.05082	.47882	2.48	.01842	.49343
1.59	.11270	.44408	2.04	.04980	.47932	2.49	.01797	.49361
1.60	.11092	.44520	2.05	.04879	.47982	2.50	.01753	.49379
1.61	.10915	.44630	2.06	.04780	.48030	2.51	.01709	.49396
1.62	.10741	.44738	2.07	.04682	.48077	2.52	.01667	.49413
1.63	.10567	.44845	2.08	.04586	.48124	2.53	.01625	.49430
1.64	.10396	.44950	2.09	.04491	.48169	2.54	.01585	.49446
1.65	.10226	.45053	2.10	.04398	.48214	2.55	.01545	.49461
1.66	.10059	.45154	2.11	.04307	.48257	2.56	.01506	.49477
1.67	.09893	.45254	2.12	.04217	.48300	2.57	.01468	.49492
1.68	.09728	.45352	2.13	.04128	.48341	2.58	.01431	.49506
1.69	.09566	.45449	2.14	.04041	.48382	2.59	.01394	.49520
1.70	.09405	.45543	2.15	.03955	.48422	2.60	.01358	.49534
1.71	.09246	.45637	2.16	.03871	.48461	2.61	.01323	.49547
1.72	.09089	.45728	2.17	.03788	.48500	2.62	.01289	.49560
1.73	.08933	.45818	2.18	.03706	.48537	2.63	.01256	.49573
1.74	.08780	.45907	2.19	.03626	.48574	2.64	.01223	.49585
1.75	.08628	.45994	2.20	.03547	.48610	2.65	.01191	.49598
1.76	.08478	.46080	2.21	.03470	.48645	2.66	.01160	.49609
1.77	.08329	.46164	2.22	.03394	.48679	2.67	.01130	.49621
1.78	.08183	.46246	2.23	.03319	.48713	2.68	.01100	.49632
1.79	.08038	.46327	2.24	.03246	.48745	2.69	.01071	.49643

Normal Areas and Ordinates

t	$\phi(t)$	$\int_0^t \phi(t)dt$	t	$\phi(t)$	$\int_0^t \phi(t)dt$	t	$\phi(t)$	$\int_0^t \phi(t)dt$
2.70	.01042	.49653	3.15	.00279	.49918	3.60	.00061	.49984
2.71	.01014	.49664	3.16	.00271	.49921	3.61	.00059	.49985
2.72	.00987	.49674	3.17	.00262	.49924	3.62	.00057	.49985
2.73	.00961	.49683	3.18	.00254	.49926	3.63	.00055	.49986
2.74	.00935	.49693	3.19	.00246	.49929	3.64	.00053	.49986
2.75	.00909	.49702	3.20	.00238	.49931	3.65	.00051	.49987
2.76	.00885	.49711	3.21	.00231	.49934	3.66	.00049	.49987
2.77	.00861	.49720	3.22	.00224	.49936	3.67	.00047	.49988
2.78	.00837	.49728	3.23	.00216	.49938	3.68	.00046	.49988
2.79	.00814	.49736	3.24	.00210	.49940	3.69	.00044	.49989
2.80	.00792	.49744	3.25	.00203	.49942	3.70	.00042	.49989
2.81	.00770	.49752	3.26	.00196	.49944	3.71	.00041	.49990
2.82	.00748	.49760	3.27	.00190	.49946	3.72	.00039	.49990
2.83	.00727	.49767	3.28	.00184	.49948	3.73	.00038	.49990
2.84	.00707	.49774	3.29	.00178	.49950	3.74	.00037	.49991
2.85	.00687	.49781	3.30	.00172	.49952	3.75	.00035	.49991
2.86	.00668	.49788	3.31	.00167	.49953	3.76	.00034	.49992
2.87	.00649	.49795	3.32	.00161	.49955	3.77	.00033	.49992
2.88	.00631	.49801	3.33	.00156	.49957	3.78	.00031	.49992
2.89	.00613	.49807	3.34	.00151	.49958	3.79	.00030	.49992
2.90	.00595	.49813	3.35	.00146	.49960	3.80	.00029	.49993
2.91	.00578	.49819	3.36	.00141	.49961	3.81	.00028	.49993
2.92	.00562	.49825	3.37	.00136	.49962	3.82	.00027	.49993
2.93	.00545	.49831	3.38	.00132	.49964	3.83	.00026	.49994
2.94	.00530	.49836	3.39	.00127	.49965	3.84	.00025	.49994
2.95	.00514	.49841	3.40	.00123	.49966	3.85	.00024	.49994
2.96	.00499	.49846	3.41	.00119	.49968	3.86	.00023	.49994
2.97	.00485	.49851	3.42	.00115	.49969	3.87	.00022	.49995
2.98	.00471	.49856	3.43	.00111	.49970	3.88	.00021	.49995
2.99	.00457	.49861	3.44	.00107	.49971	3.89	.00021	.49995
3.00	.00443	.49865	3.45	.00104	.49972	3.90	.00020	.49995
3.01	.00430	.49869	3.46	.00100	.49973	3.91	.00019	.49995
3.02	.00417	.49874	3.47	.00097	.49974	3.92	.00018	.49996
3.03	.00405	.49878	3.48	.00094	.49975	3.93	.00018	.49996
3.04	.00393	.49882	3.49	.00090	.49976	3.94	.00017	.49996
3.05	.00381	.49886	3.50	.00087	.49977	3.95	.00016	.49996
3.06	.00370	.49889	3.51	.00084	.49978	3.96	.00016	.49996
3.07	.00358	.49893	3.52	.00081	.49978	3.97	.00015	.49996
3.08	.00348	.49897	3.53	.00079	.49979	3.98	.00014	.49997
3.09	.00337	.49900	3.54	.00076	.49980	3.99	.00014	.49997
3.10	.00327	.49903	3.55	.00073	.49981			
3.11	.00317	.49906	3.56	.00071	.49981			
3.12	.00307	.49910	3.57	.00068	.49982			
3.13	.00298	.49913	3.58	.00066	.49983			
3.14	.00288	.49916	3.59	.00063	.49983			

ANSWERS TO SELECTED PROBLEMS

CHAPTER 1

Problem Set 1.1.

1. *a*, *d*, *e*, *f*. **3.** (*b*) Concord, Hartford, Providence, Boston, Montpelier, Augusta. (*d*) Mercury, Venus, Earth, Mars, Jupiter, Saturn, Uranus, Neptune, Pluto. **4.** *b*, *d*. **5.** Sets: *a*, *c*, *d*. **7.** *a*, *e*. **8.** *b* and *d* are true. **11.** *c*, *e*. **12.** (*a*) Orange, peach, strawberry, and others. (*b*) Hydrogen, methane, acetylene, and others. **13.** *a*, *b*, *d*.

Problem Set 1.2.

3. Congruence, similarity, of equal area, etc. **4.** (*a*) $\{1, 2, 5\}$, $\{1, 2\}$, $\{1, 5\}$, $\{2, 5\}$; (*b*) $\{a, b, c, d\}$, $\{a, b, c\}$, $\{a, b, d\}$, $\{b, c, d\}$, $\{a, c, d\}$, $\{a, b\}$, $\{a, c\}$, $\{a, d\}$, $\{b, c\}$, $\{b, d\}$, $\{c, d\}$. **5.** $\{3, a, 5\}$, $\{3, a, *\}$, $\{3, 5, *\}$, $\{a, 5, *\}$, $\{3, a\}$, $\{a, 5\}$, $\{3, 5\}$, $\{5, *\}$, $\{a, *\}$, $\{3, *\}$, $\{3\}$, $\{a\}$, $\{5\}$, $\{*\}$, Z. **9.** (*a*) $B \subseteq A$; (*b*) $E \subseteq B$; (*c*) $E \subseteq A$; (*d*) $F \subseteq E$; (*e*) $E \subseteq C$; (*f*) $F \subseteq D$. **10.** $\{1, 2\}$, $\{1, 2, 3\}$, $\{1, 2, 4\}$, $\{1, 2, 5\}$, $\{1, 2, 3, 4\}$, $\{1, 2, 3, 5\}$, $\{1, 2, 4, 5\}$, $\{1, 2, 3, 4, 5\}$. **12.** (*a*) Z; (*b*) Finite; (*c*) Z; (*d*) Infinite; (*e*) Infinite; (*f*) Infinite. **13.** (*a*) No; it has the empty set Z as a member; (*b*) $\{1, 3\}$, $\{1\}$, $\{3\}$, Z; (*c*) Yes. **15.** (*a*) $b = a$; (*b*) $b \neq a$; (*c*) $b = a$.

Problem Set 1.3.

1. (*a*) (2, 1), (2, 2), (4, 1), (4, 2), $(a, 1)$, $(a, 2)$; (*b*) $(a, 3)$, (a, y), $(a, 1)$, $(x, 3)$, (x, y), $(x, 1)$, $(y, 3)$, (y, y), $(y, 1)$; (*c*) (3, 3), $(3, y)$, (3, 1), $(x, 3)$, (x, y), $(x, 1)$, $(a, 3)$, (a, y), $(a, 1)$. **2.** (1, 1), (1, 2), (1, 3), (2, 1), (2, 2), (2, 3), (3, 1), (3, 2), (3, 3). **4.** (*a*) 16; (*b*) 4; (*c*) 12; (*d*) 4. **5.** (*a*) On diagonal bisecting lattice region; (*b*) Reflection of (a, b) in diagonal; (*c*) On horizontal line through the vertical item 2; (*d*) On vertical line through the horizontal item 3. **6.** (*a*) $x = y$; (*b*) $x \neq y$; (*c*) $x = 3, y = 1$; (*d*) $x = y$. **7.** 16, including the set Z and the whole set; there are also 16 possible ordered pairs. **8.** (*a*) A square integer; (*b*) The single element $\{1, 1\}$. **9.** (1, 1, 1), (2, 2, 2), (1, 1, 2), (1, 2, 1), (2, 1, 1), (1, 2, 2),

(2, 1, 2), (2, 2, 1). **10.** (*a*) {2, *a*}, {2, *}, {*a*, *}; (*b*) {2, *a*, *}, {2, *a*}, {2, *}, {*a*, *}, {2}, {*a*}, {*}, *Z*; (*c*) (2, 2), (*a*, *a*), (*, *), (2, *a*), (2, *), (*a*, 2), (*a*, *), (*, 2), (*, *a*).

Problem Set 1.4.

1. (*a*) 4 and 2, 3; (*b*) 3, 2, *c* and *a*, *b*; (*c*) No members and all members of *A*. **2.** (*a*) 1, 2, 4, 6, and 4, 6; (*b*) *a*, *x*, *y*, 2, 1, 6 and *a*, *x*, *y*; (*c*) 1, 3, *x*, *y*, *a* and *x*, *a*. **3.** (2, 2), (2, 1), (2, 5), (1, 2), (1, 1), (1, 5), (5, 2), (5, 1), (5, 5); 2, 1, 5; 2, 1, 5. **4.** (*a*) *Z*; (*b*) *B*; (*c*) *A* (or *B*); (*d*) *A*. **7.** (*a*) 2, 3; (*b*) 3; (*c*) 2, 3, 4, 5; (*d*) (3, 3); (*e*) (3, 3), (3, 4), (3, 5), (4, 5), (4, 3), (4, 4), (5, 3), (5, 4), (5, 5), (4, 6), (5, 6), (6, 4), (6, 5), (6, 6). **10.** (*a*) 2, 3, 4, 5; (*b*) 1, 3, 5; (*c*) 3; (*d*) 1, 4; (*e*) 2, 4. **11.** (*a*) None; (*b*) 1, 3, 5, 7, 9, 11, 13, 15; (*c*) 1, 3, 5, 6, 7, 9, 11, 12, 13, 15; (*d*) 2, 4, 8, 10, 14; (*e*) All members of *U*; (*f*) All members of *C*; (*g*) 2, 4, 8, 10, 14. **14.** (*a*) Empty; (*b*) Neither; (*c*) Universal; (*d*) Empty; (*e*) Neither; (*f*) Empty. **15.** The sets are disjoint in both cases. **18.** 30. **19.** 35; 5. **21.** (*a*) {1, 2, 3, 5}, {1, 2}; (*b*) {1, 1, 2, 2, 3, 5}, *Z*.

Problem Set 1.6.

3. Least common multiple; $U = 110$. **5.** No. **6.** (*a*) X_1, X_2, and X_3 are all energized; (*b*) Either X_1 or X_2 is energized; (*c*) Either X_2 is energized or X_1 is not; (*d*) At least one of X_1, X_2, X_3 is energized. **9.** *c*. **11.** 100.

Review Test A, Chapter 1.

1. (*a*) 3, 7, 9, 11, 13, 17, 19; (*b*) 11, 13, 17, 19, 23. **2.** (*a*) 11, 13, 17, 19; (*b*) 3, 7, 9, 11, 13, 17, 19, 23. **3.** (1, 1), (1, 0), (2, 1), (2, 0); $A \times B$. **4.** Lincoln. **5.** $E = \{3, a\}, F = \{5, b\}$. **6.** (*a*) $D \subset C$; (*b*) $E \subset C$. $D \cap E$ is the empty set. **7.** (*b*, *a*), (*b*, *b*), (*b*, 2), (*a*, *a*), (*a*, 2), (2, 2), (2, *a*). **8.** 2, 8. **9.** {{1, 3}, {1}, {3}, *Z*} and all 16 subsets of this set, including the empty set *Z*. Note that we do not identify *Z* with the set whose single member is *Z*. **10.** No. The set of chocolate sundaes without chocolate is the same empty set as the set of pineapple sundaes without pineapple. **11.** The set of points common to both the triangle and rectangle, but not in or on the circle. **12.** $A = B$ if and only if *A* is a subset of *B* and *B* is a subset of *A*.

Review Test B, Chapter 1.

1. (*a*) Arkansas, Illinois, Iowa, Kentucky, Louisiana, Tennessee, Minnesota, Mississippi, Missouri, Wisconsin; (*b*) Maine, Maryland, Massachusetts, Michigan, Minnesota, Mississippi, Missouri, Montana. **2.** (*a*) Minnesota, Mississippi, Missouri; (*b*) Arkansas, Illinois, Iowa, Kentucky, Louisiana, Tennessee, Maine, Maryland, Massachusetts, Michigan, Minnesota, Mississippi, Missouri, Montana, Wisconsin. **3.** (1, 1), (3, 1), (4, 1), (1, 5), (3, 5), (4, 5); $A \times B$. **4.** The 16 subsets of *A* (including *Z*). **5.** (1, 1), (1, 3), (1, 5), (3, 1),

(3, 3), (3, 5), (5, 1), (5, 3), (5, 5). **6.** 1, 3, 5, 7, 9, 10. **7.** The 15 proper subsets of A (including Z). **8.** 2, 3, 4, 6, 7, 8, 9, 10. **9.** The set of subsets of $\{\{0, 1\}, \{0\}, \{1\}, Z\}$; there are 16 such sets, including Z. Notice that we do not identify the set having the single member Z with Z. **10.** Any two properties *and* their denials; for example "red" and "not red." **11.** The *vertices* of the triangle comprising C. **12.** Put their members in a one-to-one correspondence; or count them, and check that they have the same cardinal numbers.

CHAPTER 2

Problem Set 2.2.

1. $3 + 6$, $7 - 2$, $8 - 4$, $2 + 1$, $12/3$. **2.** $5 - 2 = x$ where $x + 2 = 5$, i.e., $x = 3$; $6/2 = x$ where $2x = 6$, i.e., $x = 3$; $7 - 3 = x$ where $x + 3 = 7$, i.e., $x = 4$; $20/5 = x$ where $5x = 20$, i.e., $x = 4$. **3.** $5 > 2$, $5 < 7$, $5 > 5 - 3$, $5 = 10 - 5$, $5 > 1$, $5 > 10/5$, $5 = 20/4$, $5 < 12 - 2$. **4.** $m - n$ and m/n are not natural numbers for all natural numbers m and n. **11.** No; $m + nr \neq (m + n)(m + r)$. **12.** Let $m - (n + r) = x$ and $(m - n) - r = y$. Then $x + (n + r) = m$ and $y + r = m - n$ or $(y + r) + n = m$. From this $x + (n + r) = (y + r) + n$, etc. **13.** 4, 5, 6, 7. **14.** 1, 2. **15.** (*a*) 4, 5; (*b*) 2, 3, 4; (*c*) 6, 7.

Problem Set 2.3.

1. (*a*) 43; (*b*) 6; (*c*) 3; (*d*) 26. **2.** (*a*) 17/12; (*b*) 65/63; (*c*) 5/3; (*d*) 116/63. **3.** (*a*) 4/15; (*b*) 2/25; (*c*) 35/18; (*d*) 11/12. **4.** (*a*) $5 \cdot 10 = 50$ and $5 \cdot 4 + 5 \cdot 6 = 20 + 30 = 50$; (*b*) $3 \cdot 6 = 18$ and $3 \cdot 2 + 3 \cdot 4 = 6 + 12 = 18$; distributive law. **5.** $2(7 - 2) + 5 = 2 \cdot 5 + 5 = 10 + 5 = 15$; one way only. **7.** (*a*) 4; (*b*) 147/5; (*c*) 6/5; (*d*) 21. **14.** (*a*) associative law of multiplication; (*b*) associative and commutative laws of multiplication.

Problem Set 2.4.

1. (*a*) 203/450; (*b*) $-5/108$; (*c*) 5/96; (*d*) $-66/13$; (*e*) $-10/21$. **2.** (*a*) $-153/60$; (*b*) $-5/3$. **3.** (*a*) $-1/128$; (*b*) 38/15. **11.** -1, 0, 1, 2, 3. **12.** -1, 0, 1. **13.** -2, -1, 0, 1, 2, 3, 4, 5, 6. **14.** 6, 7, -1, -2. **15.** 3.

Problem Set 2.5.

1. 2.6457. **2.** (*a*) $0.\overline{6}$; (*b*) $-0.\overline{571428}$; (*c*) $-0.\overline{5}$; (*d*) $0.8\overline{0}$. **3.** (*a*) 1436/999; (*b*) $-20621/9999$; (*c*) $517452/99999 = 172484/33333$. **4.** (*a*) greater than; (*b*) equal to; (*c*) less than. **6.** 1.7320. **7.** (*a*) 4.3778; (*b*) 4.5825. **9.** Rational integer, irrational, irrational, rational integer, rational integer, irrational, rational integer, irrational. **10.** $3 = 3/1 = 3.\bar{0} = 2.\bar{9}$.

14.

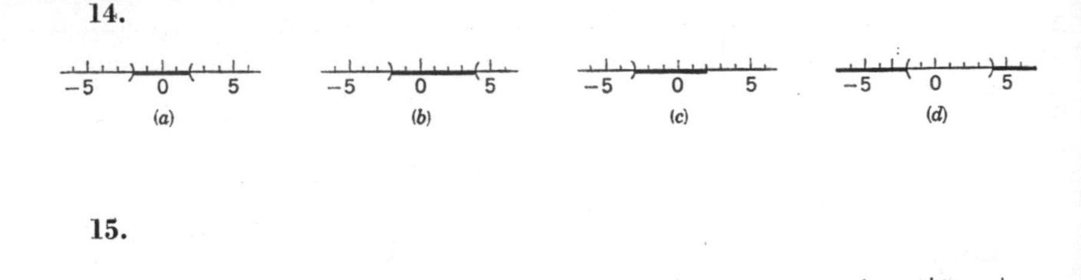

15.

(a) (b) (c) (d)

Note. An arc at the end of a segment indicates that the end point is not to be included in the shaded portion.

Review Test A.

1. $N \subset I \subset \bar{R} \subset R^{\#}$. **2.** (*a*) 4, $-3/2$, $\sqrt{25}$, $4.\overline{216}$, $1/3$; (*b*) $\sqrt[3]{5}$, π. **3.** $\sqrt{25} > 4.\overline{216} > 4 > \pi > \sqrt[3]{5} > 1/3 > -3/2$. **4.** 0, -1, 1. **5.** Put the two sets in a one-to-one correspondence. Put each set in a one-to-one correspondence with the first six natural numbers, i.e., count them. **6.** (*a*), (*e*), (*g*), (*h*). **7.** (*a*) 1; (*b*) 0, 1, -1; (*c*) any rational number between (but not including) -2 and 2; (*d*) All real numbers on the interval $[-2, 2]$.

8. (*a*)
$$\begin{aligned}(a+b)(c+d) &= (a+b)c + (a+b)d \quad \text{[distributive law]}\\ &= c(a+b) + d(a+b)\\ &\qquad \text{[commutative law of multiplication]}\\ &= ca + cb + da + db \quad \text{[distributive law]}\\ &= ac + bc + ad + bd\\ &\qquad \text{[commutative law of multiplication]}\end{aligned}$$

(*b*)
$$\begin{aligned}(ab)(cd) &= [(ab)c]d \quad \text{[associative law of multiplication]}\\ &= [a(bc)]d \quad \text{[associative law of multiplication]}\\ &= [(bc)a]d \quad \text{[commutative law of multiplication]}\\ &= [(bc)(ad)] \quad \text{[associative law of multiplication]}\\ &= (cb)(ad) \quad \text{[commutative law of multiplication]}\end{aligned}$$

9. $-(a+b)$ is a unique number with the property that $(a+b) + [-(a+b)] = 0$. Since $(a+b) + (-a-b) = a + b + (-a) + (-b) = a + (-a) + b + (-b) = 0$, it follows that $-(a+b) = -a - b$. **10.** (*a*) 6; (*b*) 14; (*c*) 7/4. **11.** (*a*) false, e.g., $4 + 9 = 13$, not the square of an integer; (*b*) true, $a^2b^2 = (ab)^2$; (*c*) false, e.g., $3/4 \div 5/7 = 21/20$, and $5/7 \div 3/4 = 20/21$; (*d*) true, $a/b + c/d = (ad+bc)/bd = c/d + a/b$; (*e*) true, an odd positive integer multiplied by an odd positive integer is an odd positive integer. **12.** 3.1622.

Review Test B.

1. (*c*). **2.** (*a*) $2 = \sqrt{4}$, -5, $3/2$, $5/3$, 0, $-1/2$, $1.\overline{234}$, 1; (*b*) $\sqrt{3}$, $\sqrt[3]{9}$. **3.** $-5 < -1/2 < 0 < 1 < 1.\overline{234} < 3/2 < 5/3 < \sqrt{3} < 2$ (or $\sqrt{4}$) $< \sqrt[3]{9}$. **4.** -2, -1, 0, 1, 2, 3, 4, 5, 6. **5.** Assume $\sqrt{5} = r/s$, with r and s integers having no common factors ($\neq 1$); then $r = \sqrt{5}s$, and we obtain a contradiction as in the illustration of the first paragraph of Section 2.5. **6.** Assume $x + \sqrt{2} = r$, with r rational; then $\sqrt{2} = r - x$ is rational, a contradiction.

7. (*a*)
$$\begin{aligned}(a + b) - a &= -a + (a + b) && \text{[commutative law of addition]}\\ &= (-a + a) + b && \text{[associative law of addition]}\\ &= 0 + b && \text{[definition of } -a\text{]}\\ &= b && \text{[definition of 0]}\end{aligned}$$

(*b*)
$$\begin{aligned}x(y + 2t) &= xy + x(2t) && \text{[distributive law]}\\ &= x(2t) + xy && \text{[commutative law of addition]}\\ &= (x2)t + xy && \text{[associative law of multiplication]}\\ &= (2x)t + xy && \text{[commutative law of multiplication]}\\ &= 2xt + xy && \text{[associative law of multiplication]}\end{aligned}$$

8. (*a*) $x = 0$; (*b*) $x = 0$, or $y = 0$, or both $x = 0$ and $y = 0$; (*c*) $x \neq 0$, $y \neq 0$. **9.** Because the circumference of a circle cannot be measured exactly by any measuring unit which is a straight line segment, such as the diameter of a circle. No, $22/7$ is an approximation for π. **10.** $715/333$. **11.** $2 - 4$, $6 - 6$, $8/3$. **12.** They are conceptually distinct; however, their operating rules are identical and so in practice we may consider them the same number.

CHAPTER 3

Problem Set 3.1.

1. (*a*) 16; (*b*) 16; (*c*) undefined; (*d*) 8; (*e*) 1/36; (*f*) 16; (*g*) undefined; (*h*) 5; (*i*) -8. **2.** (*a*) $\sqrt[3]{25}$; (*b*) $\sqrt[3]{1296}$; (*c*) $\sqrt[5]{16}$; (*d*) $\sqrt[3]{1/36}$; (*e*) $1/16$; (*f*) $\sqrt[5]{-1/125}$. **3.** (*a*) $(5x^3)^{1/4}$; (*b*) $5^{1/2}$; (*c*) $4^{-1/3}$; (*d*) $(3/2)^{1/5}$; (*e*) $(5x)^{2/3}$; (*f*) $(-3/4)^{2/5}$. **4.** $(-2)^{5/3}$, $(-3)^{7/5}$. **5.** (*a*) ab; (*b*) a^5b^4; (*c*) b^7; (*d*) 2^53^7; (*e*) xy^2. **6.** (*a*) $ab^2c^{-3}d^{-4}$; (*b*) $3\cdot 4^{-1}x^3y^{-3}r^2t^{-5}$; (*c*) $x^{-3}\,(a + bx + cx^2 + dx^4)$. **7.** (*a*) $3/a^2$; (*b*) x^2; (*c*) $2a^3/x^2y^{1/2}$; (*d*) x^4y^5; (*e*) $3a^{4/3}/5b^2$; (*f*) $-1/a^6$. **10.** (*a*) xy^4b^3/a^2; (*b*) $a^5x/(3b^3y^2)$; (*c*) $b/(a^2x^3y^{1/4})$. **12.** (*a*) $[xy(x^2 + y^2)]/(x^3 + y^3)$; (*b*) $(x - y)/(x + y)$; (*c*) $1/(x^3 + y^3)$.

Problem Set 3.2.

1. $1.23412(10)^2$, $1.68(10)^{-3}$, $2.46(10)^{-4}$, $3.64589(10)^5$, $1.289605(10)^3$, $6.7(10)^{-7}$, $7.854358(10)^3$. **3.** $2.4(10)^3$, $2.40(10)^3$, $2.400(10)^3$, $2.4000(10)^3$, $2.40000(10)^3$. **5.** $1(10)^{100}$; $1(10)^{1000\cdots0\text{(100 zeros)}}$. **7.** (*a*) 312.74; (*b*) -260.00. **9.** 9335 square feet. **11.** 200 cubic feet. **13.** 410 cubic inches. **15.** (*a*) 600,000; (*b*) 140,000,000.

Problem Set 3.3.

1. (*a*) 0.1023 + 2; (*b*) 0.5391 + 5; (*c*) 0.2711; (*d*) 0.3852 + 1; (*e*) 0.9333 + 5. **2.** (*a*) 0.3911 − 1; (*b*) 0.1461 − 3; (*c*) 0.3802 − 1. **3.** (*a*) 0.0913 − 1 = −0.9087; (*b*) 0.2695 − 4 = −3.7305; (*c*) 0.4537 − 2 = −1.5463. **4.** (*a*) $x = \log_5 6$; (*b*) $3 = \log_2 8$; (*c*) $2 = \log 100$; (*d*) $a = \log_{\sqrt{2}} b$. **5.** (*a*) $3^x = 5$; (*b*) $10^3 = 1000$; (*c*) $b^5 = 12$; (*d*) $b^x = \sqrt{2}$. **6.** (*a*) 4; (*b*) 2; (*c*) 4; (*d*) 2; (*e*) −3; (*f*) −3. **7.** (*a*) 0; (*b*) 0.001; (*c*) 0.2; (*d*) 4; (*e*) 1/4; (*f*) −2.

Problem Set 3.4.

1. (*a*) 0.9024 + 0; (*b*) 0.7077 + 5; (*c*) 0.3862 − 6; (*d*) 0.9296 + 2. **2.** (*a*) 0.5744 + 2; (*b*) 0.2334 + 2; (*c*) 0.7376 − 5. **3.** (*a*) 0.58 − 4; (*b*) 0.957 + 0; (*c*) 0.6 + 21. **4.** (*a*) 0.15 − 2; (*b*) 0.0427 + 0; (*c*) 0.640 − 2. **5.** (*a*) 0.229 − 1; (*b*) 0.711 − 1; (*c*) 0.075 − 1. **6.** (*a*) 0.573 − 2; (*b*) 0.369 − 2; (*c*) 0.858 − 2. **7.** (*a*) 26.55; (*b*) 2.13; (*c*) 0.04692. **8.** (*a*) 7.792; (*b*) 10,000; (*c*) 0.3514. **9.** (*a*) 2.784; (*b*) 0.3244; (*c*) 538.5.

Problem Set 3.5.

1. (*a*) $4.38(10)^{17}$; (*b*) 0.355. **2.** (*a*) 1.01; (*b*) $2.46(10)^{-8}$. **3.** (*a*) 0.912; (*b*) −2.05. **4.** (*a*) 0.007746; (*b*) 55,600. **5.** (*a*) $6.4(10)^8$; (*b*) 2.831. **6.** −0.0974. **7.** (*a*) −0.7103; (*b*) 0.1803. **8.** (*a*) 0.213. **9.** (*a*) 3.081. **10.** (*a*) −2.475.

Review Test A.

1. (*a*) $x \cdot x \cdot x$; (*b*) $\sqrt[3]{x^2}$; (*c*) $1/x^2$; (*d*) 1. **2.** $ab(a + b)$. **3.** $2/u$. **4.** $10^{0.3010}$, $10^{-0.3010}$, $10^{-0.4771}$, $10^{0.6990}$, 10^0. **5.** $5(10)^7$. **6.** $10^{0.2486}$. **7.** 0.336. **8.** 2.5. **9.** 4.87. **10.** 1/2. **11.** 328. **12.** 2.50.

Review Test B.

1. (*a*) $y \cdot y \cdot y \cdot y$; (*b*) $\sqrt[3]{y^4}$; (*c*) $1/\sqrt{y}$; (*d*) y. **2.** $x^{-1/3}$. **3.** $-xy$. **4.** 0.0838. **5.** $7(10)^8$. **6.** $10 \leq |x| \leq 100$. **7.** 15.4. **8.** 1. **9.** 15.8. **10.** (*a*) (1/6) log 3 − (1/6) log 2; (*b*) log 2 − (2/3) log 5; (*c*) 3 log 2 + log 3. **11.** 1.3. **12.** 245.

CHAPTER 4

Problem Set 4.1.

1. (*a*) (1, 3), (1, 4), (1, 8), (3, 4), (3, 8), (4, 8); (*b*) (1, 1), (1, 3), (1, 4), (1, 8), (3, 3), (3, 4), (3, 8), (4, 4), (4, 8), (8, 8); (*c*) (2, 3), (3, 4), (3, 8); (*d*) (2, 3), (2, 4), (2, 8), (3, 2), (3, 4), (3, 8), (4, 2), (4, 3), (4, 8), (8, 2), (8, 3), (8, 4). **3.** (*a*) "is less than"; (*b*) "is greater than"; (*c*) "is not equal to." (There are many other equally correct answers.) **4.** (*a*) "is a subset of" in the power set of I; (*b*) "is the Chief Executive of" from the set of 49 States to the set of State Governors; (*c*) "divides" in I; (*d*) "is prime to" in I; (*e*) "is the author of" from the set of all books to the set of all authors of books; (*f*) "is opposite in sign to" in I. (There may be other equally correct answers.) **6.** (*a*) $(R^{\#}, \bar{R})$, $(R^{\#}, I)$, $(R^{\#}, N)$, (I, N), $(\bar{R}, I)$, $(\bar{R}, N)$; (*b*) $(\bar{R}, R^{\#})$, $(I, R^{\#})$, $(N, R^{\#})$, (N, I), $(I, \bar{R})$, $(N, \bar{R})$. **7.** (*a*) (1, 1), (2, 2), (3, 3), (4, 4); (*c*) (4, 2), (2, 2), (3, 3), (4, 4). **8.** (*a*) First: 1, 2, 3, 4; Second: 1, 2, 3, 4. (*c*) First: 2, 3, 4; Second: 2, 3, 4. **9.** (Florida, Tallahassee), (California, Sacramento), (Michigan, Lansing), (Georgia, Atlanta), (Ohio, Columbus), (West Virginia, Charleston). **11.** (1, 2), (1, 4), (1, 6), (2, 2), (2, 4), (2, 6), (3, 6), (4, 4), (6, 6).

Problem Set 4.2.

1. (*a*) $-11/3$; (*b*) $5/7$; (*c*) $11/4$; (*d*) $-6/11$. **2.** (*a*) $(y^2 + 5)/(y + 1)$; (*b*) $(4 - y^2 - y^3)/(2y - 1)$; (*c*) $(3y + 5)/(2y^2 - y^3)$; (*d*) $(y^2 + 3y - 5)/2$. **3.** (*a*) $(2 + x - 3x^2)/2x$; (*b*) $2x/(2x^2 - x)$; (*c*) $(3 - x^2)/(2x + 1)$; (*d*) $-(x + 5)/2$. **4.** (*a*) $6R2$, $(2, 6) \in R$; (*b*) 7R12, $(12, 7) \in R$; (*c*) Joe R Mary, (Mary, Joe) $\in R$. **5.** (*a*) (4, 1), (6, 2), (5, 2); (*b*) (4, 1), (6, 2). **6.** (*a*) $\{1, 2, 5\}$; (*b*) $\{1, 3, 4, 6\}$. **7.** (*a*) (3, 1), (4, 2); (*b*) domain is the set $\{x \mid x \in N, x > 2\}$, while the range is N.

9.

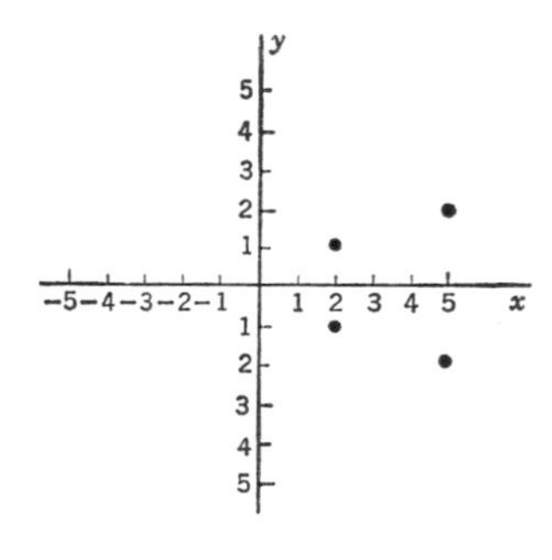

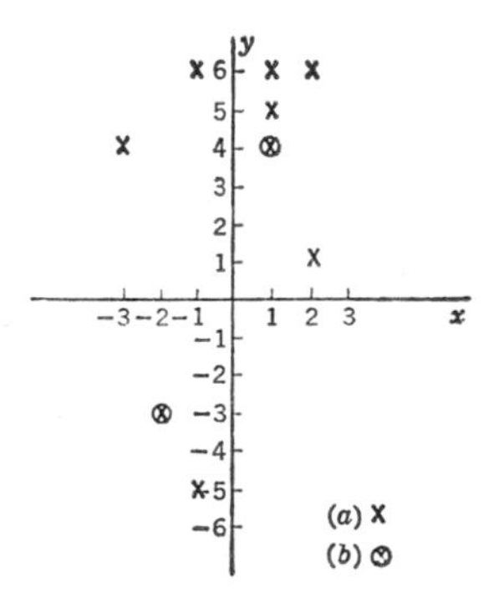

13. Domain of R_1: $\{-2, -1, 1, 2\}$.
Range of R_1: $\{-5, -3, 1, 4, 6\}$.
Domain of R_2: $\{-3, -2, -1, 1\}$.
Range of R_2: $\{-3, 4, 5, 6\}$.

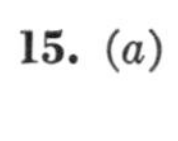

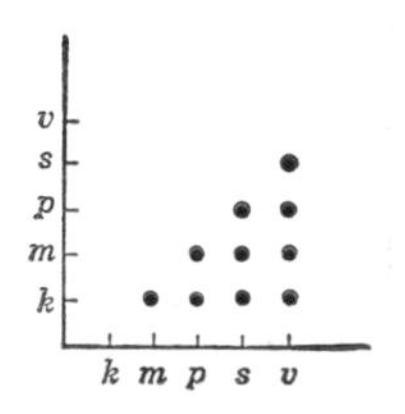

(b) Domain: $\{m, p, s, v\}$.
Range: $\{m, p, s, k\}$.

Problem Set 4.3.

1. 0, -9, 1, -44. **2.** (a) 1, 3; (b) $3 + 3h + h^2$, $3 - 3h + h^2$; (c) 25/6. **3.** (a) 1, -2; (b) 2, 4, 6, 8, 10; (c) -3, -2, 0, 1. **4.** (a) 9, 126, 1001; (b) No; (c) 20. **5.** 27. **6.** a, b. **8.** $(-5, 24)$, $(-3, 8)$, $(0, -1)$, $(1, 0)$, $(2, 3)$.

10.

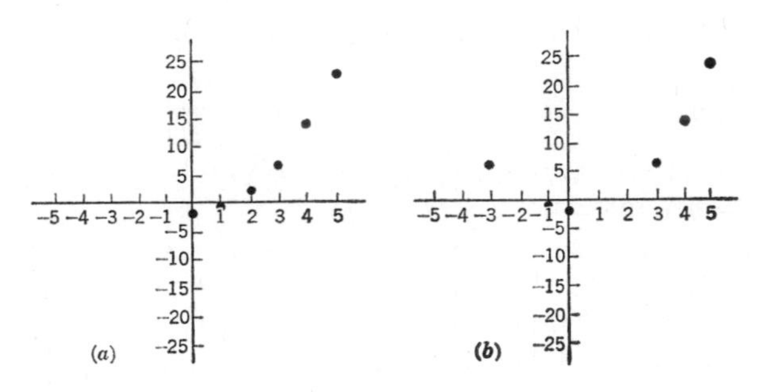

13. (a) 4, 5; (b)

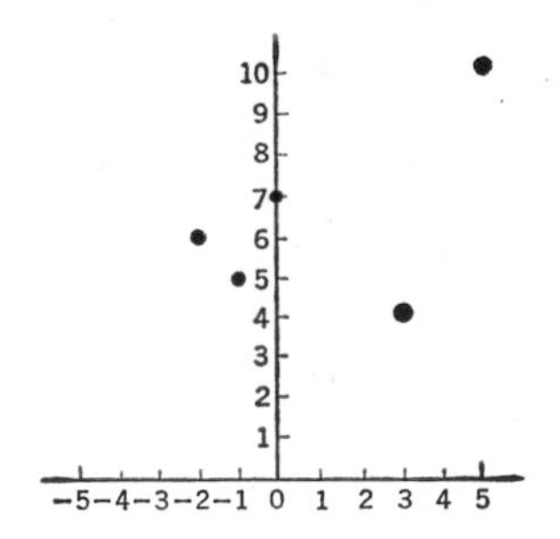

(c) 13/5. **14.** (a) Domain: $\{-4, -3, -2, -1, 0, 1, 2, 3, 4\}$; Range: $\{-2, -1, 1, 2\}$; (b) -1, 2; (c) -1, 2; (d) No.

15. (a)

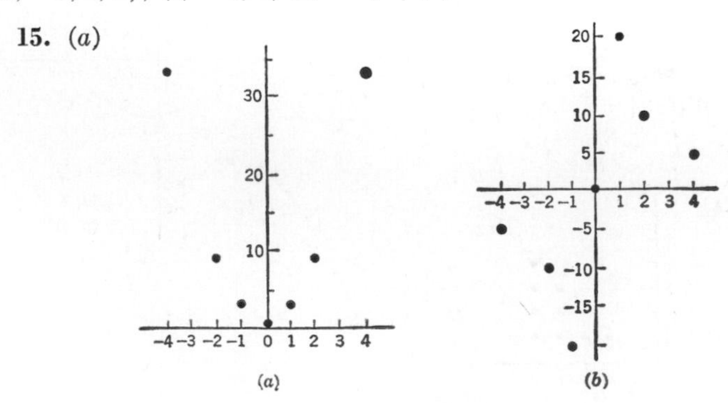

16. (0, 1), (1, 0), (−1, 1), (0, −1), (1, 0), (−1, −1). **17.** (*a*) Domain is I, and range is the set of all integers expressible as the cube of an integer; (*d*) Domain is I, and the range is the set of all integers expressible as 16 less than the square of an integer. **19.** 1, 0, 0. **21.** 3, 5.

Problem Set 4.4.

1. $\{x \mid x \in R^{\#}, |x| \geq \sqrt{5}\}$. **2.** $R^{\#}$. **3.** $R^{\#}$. **4.** $\{x \mid x \in R^{\#}, |x| \geq 2\sqrt{3}\}$. **5.** $\{x \mid x \in R^{\#}, |x| > 1\}$. **6.** $\{x \mid x \in R^{\#}, |x| \leq 5\}$. **7.** $\{x \mid x \in R^{\#}, x \neq 0\}$. **8.** $\{x \mid x \in R^{\#}, x \neq 1\}$. **9.** $\{x \mid x \in R^{\#}, x < 0$ or $x > 2$. **10.** $R^{\#}$.

11.

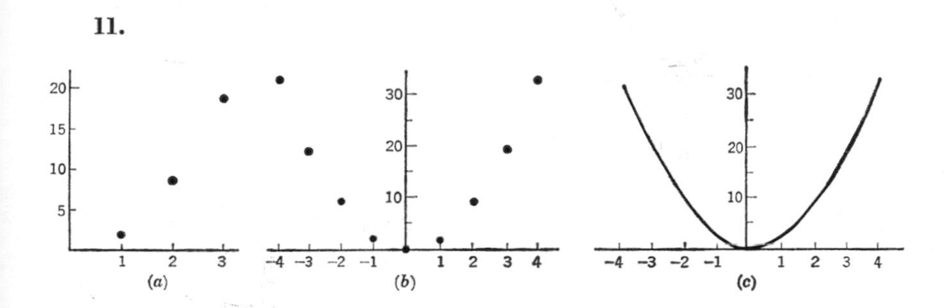

(*a*) (*b*) (*c*)

13.

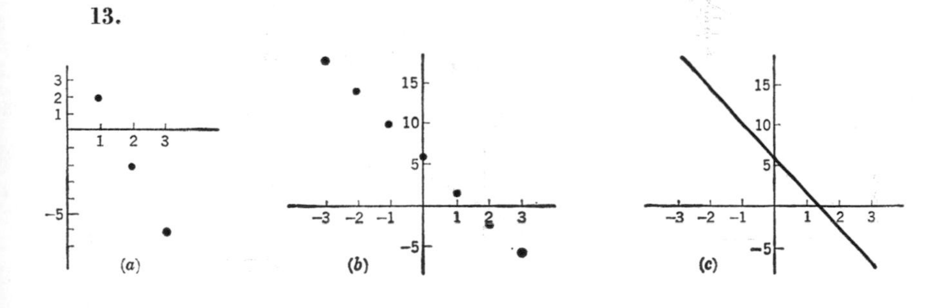

(*a*) (*b*) (*c*)

15.

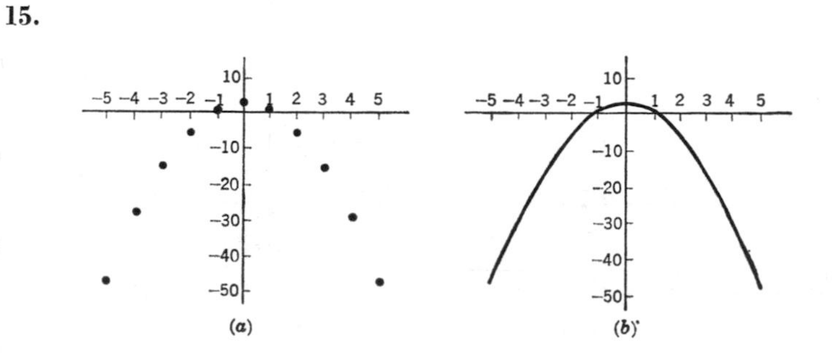

(*a*) (*b*)

17.

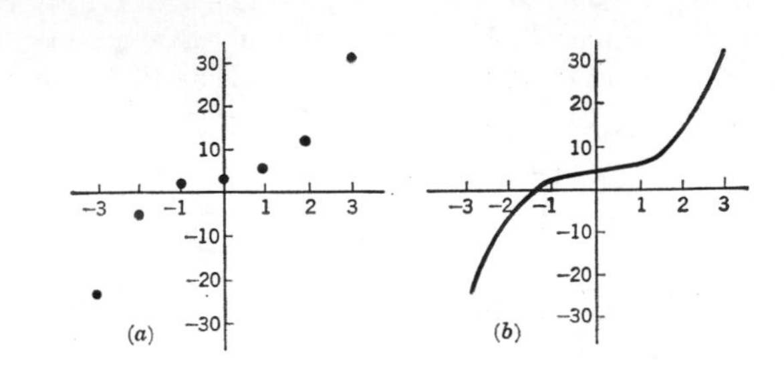

19.

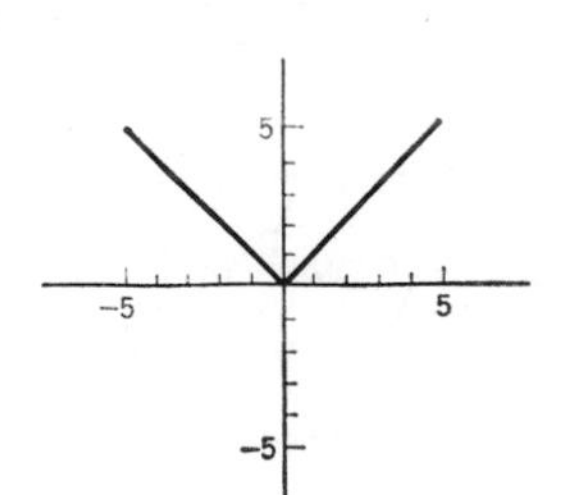

20.

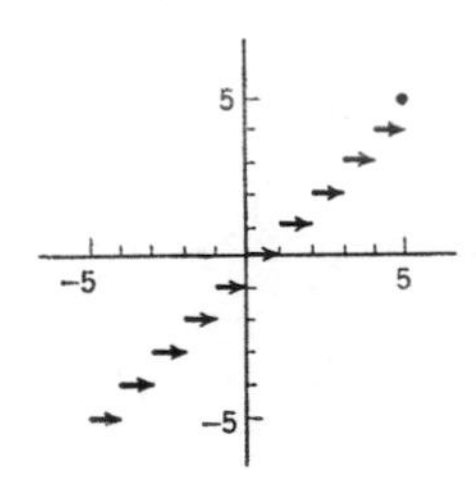

21.

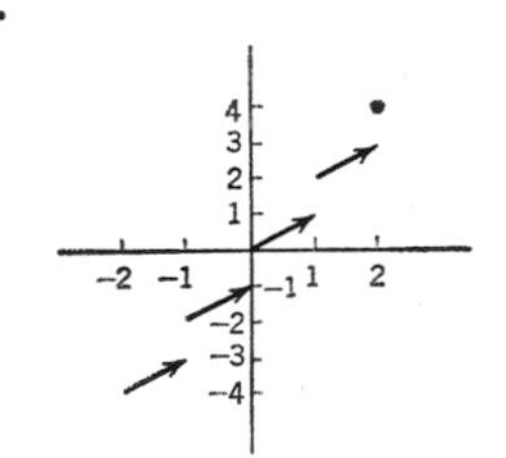

23.

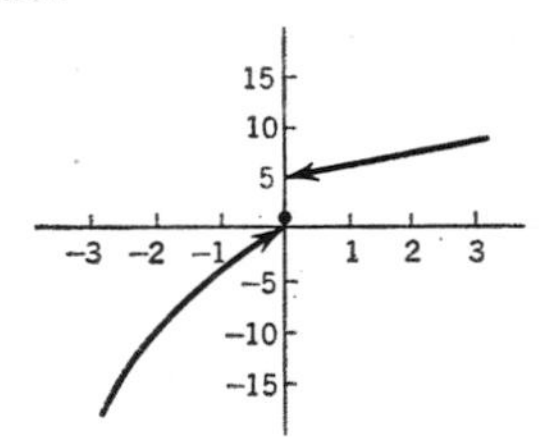

25.

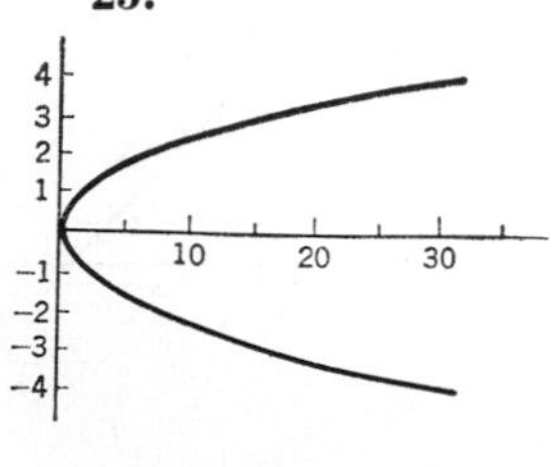

27.

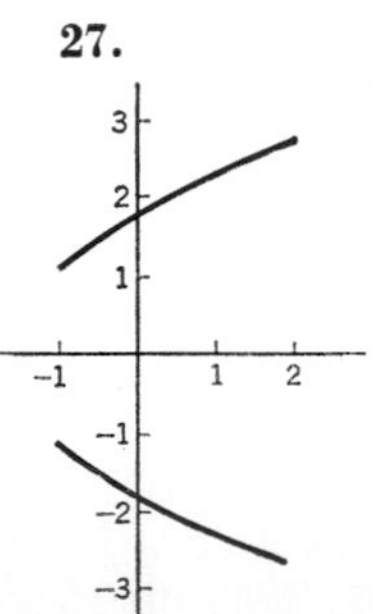

29.

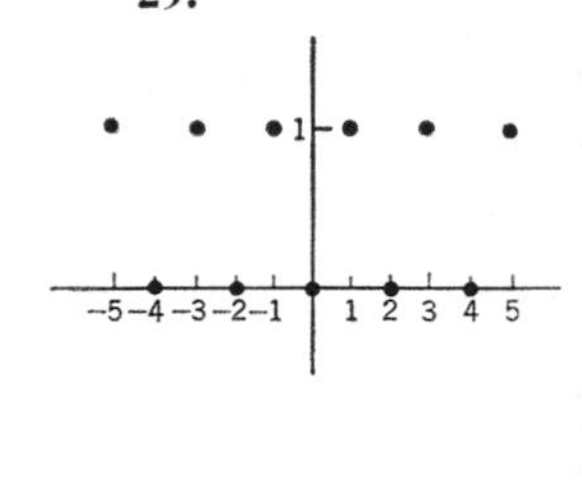

30.

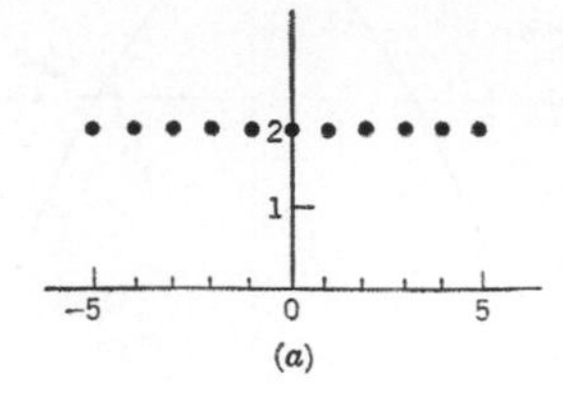

(a)

1

−5 0 5

(b)

Problem Set 4.5.

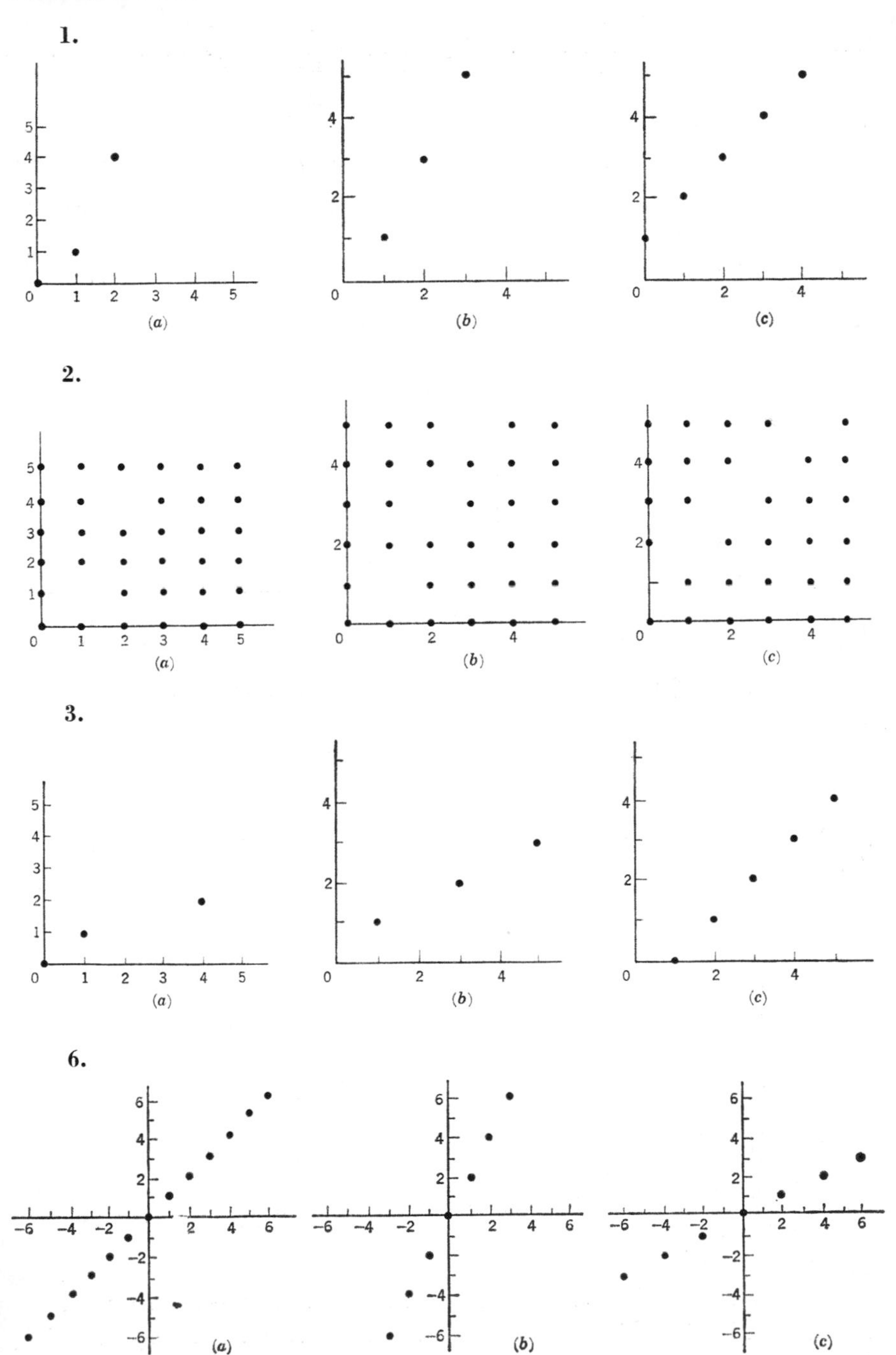

7. (*a*) Neither; (*b*) symmetric; (*c*) symmetric; (*d*) both; (*e*) both. **9.** *b*, *f*. **11.** *a*, *d*, *e*. **14.** (*a*) Both; (*b*) symmetric; (*c*) neither; (*d*) transitive; (*e*) transitive; (*f*) transitive; (*g*) both. **15.** *a*, *d*, *g*. **19.** 5, -1, 4, -1. **20.** 6, 15, 0, -16, 1.

Review Test A.

1. (*c*), (*d*). **2.** (*a*) $-2, 3, 5$; (*b*) 0, 1, 2, 4. **3.** (1, 0), (2, 3), (3, 8), (4, 15), (5, 24). **4.** $(-1, 1)$, $(-1, -1)$, $(-2, 0)$, $(2, 2)$, $(2, -2)$, $(7, 3)$, $(7, -3)$, $(14, 4)$, $(14, -4)$.

5.

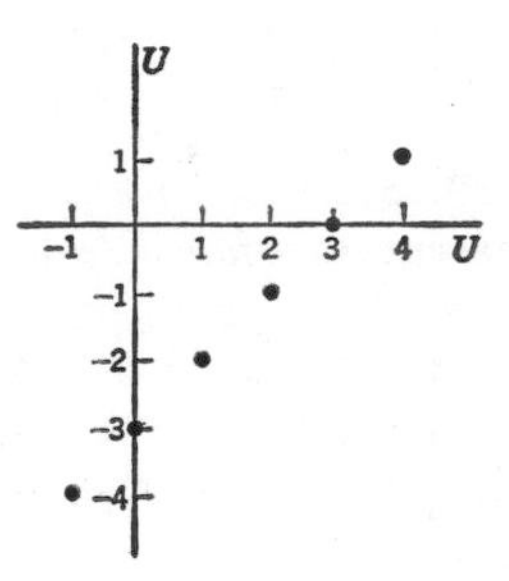

6. (*a*) 2. (*b*) 1/2. **7.** 54. **8.** $-2/7$. **9.** (*a*) domain and range both I; (*b*) the set $\{\pm 1, \pm 2, \pm 3, \pm 4, \pm 6, \pm 12\}$ is the domain and range; (*c*) domain $\{1, 6\}$, range $\{3, 2\}$. **10.** $V = \dfrac{\pi h^2(20 - h)}{3}$. **11.** (*a*) Symmetric; (*b*) neither; (*c*) symmetric; (*d*) reflexive. **12.** Each is the inverse function of the other.

Review Test B.

1. (*a*) 1; (*b*) 5; (*c*) 1; (*d*) 4. **2.** $f_1 : f_1(1) = 0$, $f_1(2) = 1$; $f_2 : f_2(1) = 1$, $f_2(2) = 0$. **3.** $(-3, -5)$, $(-2, -4)$, $(-1, -3)$, $(0, -2)$, $(1, -1)$, $(2, 0)$, $(3, 1)$.

4. **5.**

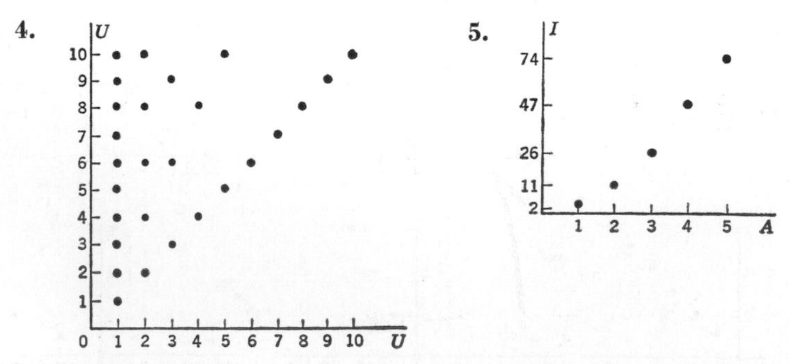

6. (*a*) 7/9; (*b*) 14. **7.** 8. **8.** $4x + 2h$. **9.** (*a*) The complete set $\bar{R}$ constitutes the domain and range; (*b*) both the domain and the range are the set of all non-zero rational numbers; (*c*) domain: $\{x \mid x \in \bar{R}, x \geq -1\}$, range: all non-negative rational numbers. **10.** $L = 2\sqrt{400 - d^2}$. **11.** Relation defined by $2y^3 = x - 1$ on $[-3, 3]$.

12.

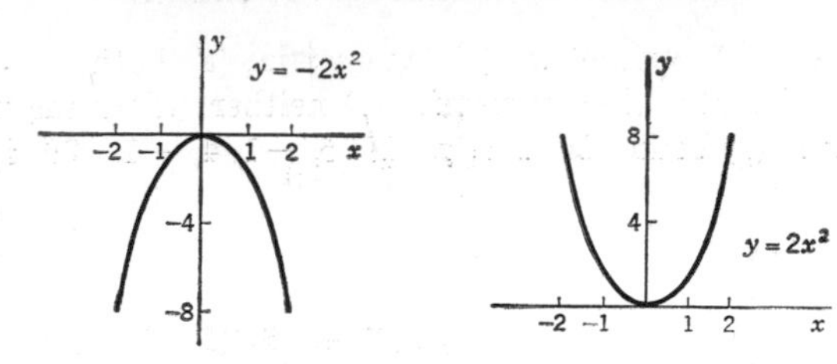

CHAPTER 5

Problem Set 5.2.

1. x^4, x^2, $x^{5/3}$, $x^{3/2}$, $x^{2/3}$, $x^{1/3}$, $x^{1/4}$. **3.** The points of the curve defined by $y = x^3$ lie below those of the curve defined by $y = x^2$. **5.** Parabolic: $y = x^3$, $y = x^{1/2}$, $y = x$, $y = x^{1/3}$, $y = x^{2/3}$; hyperbolic: $yx^2 = 1$, $y = x^{-1/2}$, $xy = 1$, $yx^4 = 1$, $y = x^{-2}$, $y = x^{-6}$. **6.** All *except* $x^{1/2}$, $x^{-3/2}$, and $x^{-1/4}$. **7.** 1, 3; 1; 1, 2; 1; 1; 1; 1, 3; 1, 2. **9.** 1, 2; 1, 3; 1, 3; 1, 3; 1; 1. **15.** (*a*) No, the graph defined by $y^2 = x$ contains the graph of $y = x^{1/2}$ as well as a symmetric portion in the 4th quadrant; (*b*) yes.

17.

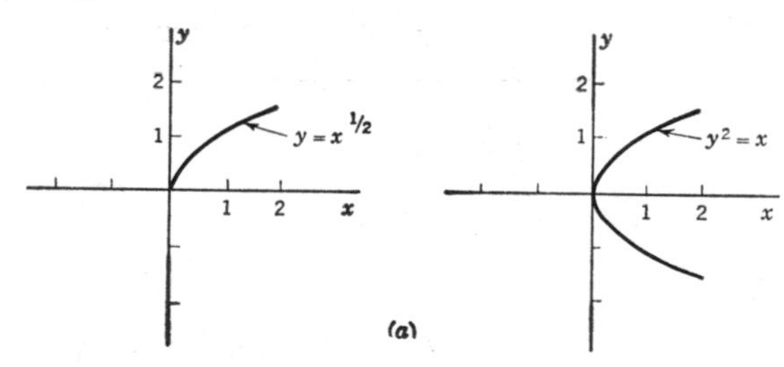

19.

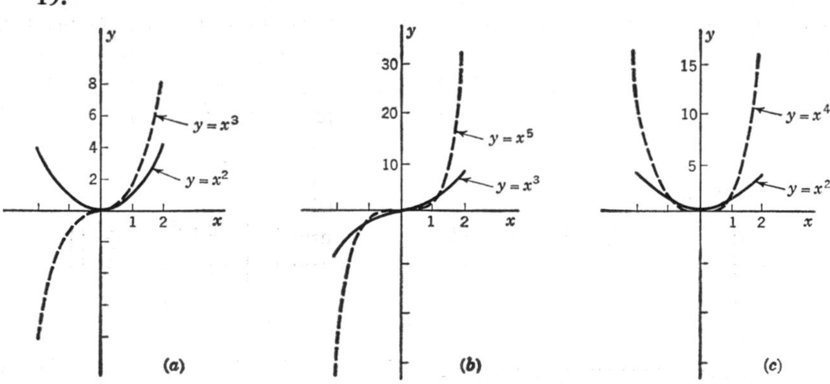

Problem Set 5.4.

1. (*a*) 1, 1; (*b*) −1, 0; (*c*) −8, 1; (*d*) −2, 6; (*e*) 0, 10; (*f*) 3, 0. **2.** (*a*) −2/3; (*b*) 2/3; (*c*) 4; (*d*) undefined. **3.** (*a*) and (*c*); (*b*) and (*f*). **5.** Because $\log_a 1 = 0$ for every $a > 0$.

7.

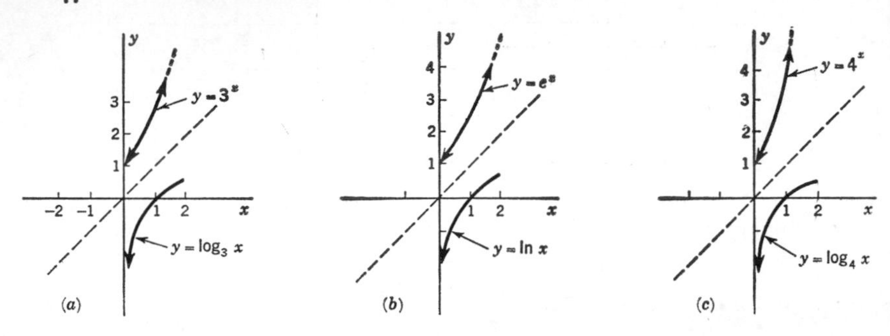

9. $\ln 2.567 = 0.94275$, $\ln 1.543 = 0.43374$, $\ln 24.86 = 3.21328$. **10.** 1.002 1.001. **12.** (*c*) 66 meters.

15.

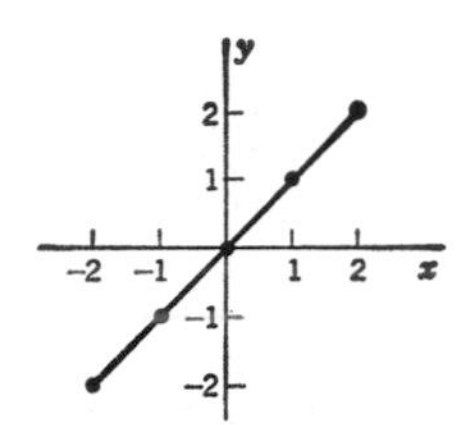

Problem Set 5.5.

4. (*a*) −0.4; (*b*) −0.6; (*c*) 0.7; (*d*) −0.7; (*e*) 0; (*f*) 1. **6.** (*a*) −1.2; (*b*) 2; (*c*) 2; (*d*) −2; (*e*) 1.2; (*f*) 7.1. **8.** (*a*) 1/2; (*b*) 0.5; (*c*) −0.2; (*d*) 2; (*e*) 3; (*f*) −0.9. **11.** 1, 1, 2, 4, 2, 1, 1, 4, 2. **12.** (*a*) 3, 4; (*b*) 1, 4; (*c*) 2, 3; (*d*) 1, 3; (*e*) 1, 3; (*f*) 2, 3; (*g*) 1, 4; (*h*) 3, 4; (*i*) 2, 3; (*j*) 2, 3. **13.** (*a*) $\pi/2$; (*b*) π; (*c*) $3\pi/2$; (*d*) π; (*e*) π; (*f*) $\pi/2$. **14.** (*a*) $\{\theta \mid \theta \in R^{\#}, \theta \neq (2n+1)\pi/2\}$; (*b*) $\{\theta \mid \theta \in R^{\#}, \theta \neq n\pi\}$; (*c*) $\{\theta \mid \theta \in R^{\#}, \theta \neq (2n+1)\pi/2\}$; (*d*) $\{\theta \mid \theta \in R^{\#}, \theta \neq n\pi\}$.

Problem Set 5.7.

5. sin: $\{y \mid y \in R^{\#}, -1 \leq y \leq 1\}$ csc: $\{y \mid y \in R^{\#}, |y| \geq 1\}$
cos: $\{y \mid y \in R^{\#}, -1 \leq y \leq 1\}$ sec: $\{y \mid y \in R^{\#}, |y| \geq 1\}$
tan: $\{y \mid y \in R^{\#}\}$ cot: $\{y \mid y \in R^{\#}\}$

6. $\sin\theta = 2$, $\sec\theta = 2/3$, $\cos\theta = -5$.

8. (*a*) $-\sqrt{2}/2$, $\sqrt{2}/2$, -1; (*b*) $-\sqrt{2}/2$, $-\sqrt{2}/2$, 1; (*c*) $\sqrt{2}/2$, $\sqrt{2}/2$, 1; (*d*) $-\sqrt{2}/2$, $-\sqrt{2}/2$, 1; (*e*) $-1/2$, $\sqrt{3}/2$, $1/\sqrt{3}$; (*f*) $-\sqrt{3}/2$, $1/2$, $-\sqrt{3}$. **9.** (*a*) $-1/2$, $-\sqrt{3}/2$, $1/\sqrt{3}$; (*b*) $\sqrt{3}/2$, $-1/2$, $\sqrt{3}$; (*c*) $\sqrt{3}/2$, $1/2$, $\sqrt{3}$; (*d*) $\sqrt{3}/2$, $-1/2$, $-\sqrt{3}$; (*e*) $-\sqrt{3}/2$, $1/2$, $\sqrt{3}$; (*f*) 0, −1, 0. **15.** 4/5. **16.** $-\sqrt{5}/3$. **17.** $2\sqrt{2}$. **18.** 0.31. **19.** $-\sqrt{5}/3$. **20.** 0.64.

21.

x	$\sin x$	$\cos x$	$\tan x$
$\pi/2 - \theta$	$\cos\theta$	$\sin\theta$	$\cot\theta$
$\pi/2 + \theta$	$\cos\theta$	$-\sin\theta$	$-\cot\theta$
$3\pi/2 - \theta$	$-\cos\theta$	$-\sin\theta$	$\cot\theta$
$3\pi/2 + \theta$	$-\cos\theta$	$\sin\theta$	$-\cot\theta$

22.

x	$\sin x$	$\cos x$	$\tan x$
$\pi - \theta$	$\sin\theta$	$-\cos\theta$	$-\tan\theta$
$\pi + \theta$	$-\sin\theta$	$-\cos\theta$	$\tan\theta$
$-\theta$	$-\sin\theta$	$\cos\theta$	$-\tan\theta$

Problem Set 5.8.

1. The domain of the basic Cosine function is $\{x \mid x \in R^{\#},\ 0 \le x \le \pi\}$. **3.** The arc Tan relation is a *function*. **4.** No, the domain of the Sin function is $\{x \mid x \in R^{\#},\ -\pi/2 \le x \le \pi/2\}$. **5.** Yes, since the domain of the Cos function is $\{x \mid x \in R^{\#},\ 0 \le x \le \pi\}$. **6.** (*a*) $\sqrt{2}/2$; (*b*) $-\pi/6$; (*c*) $-\pi/3$; (*d*) -1; (*e*) $2\pi/3$; (*f*) $2\pi/3$. **9.** (*a*) $\pi/3$; (*b*) 0; (*c*) $-\pi/4$; (*d*) π. **10.** (*a*) $\sqrt{3}/2$; (*b*) $\sqrt{5}/3$; (*c*) $-\sqrt{5}/2$; (*d*) $-2\sqrt{2}$. **11.** (*a*) $-\pi/4$; (*b*) $\pi/3$; (*c*) $2\pi/3$; (*d*) $-\pi/3$.

Review Test A.

1. (*a*) 1, 2; concave down. (*b*) 1; concave up. (*c*) 1, 2; concave up.

2.

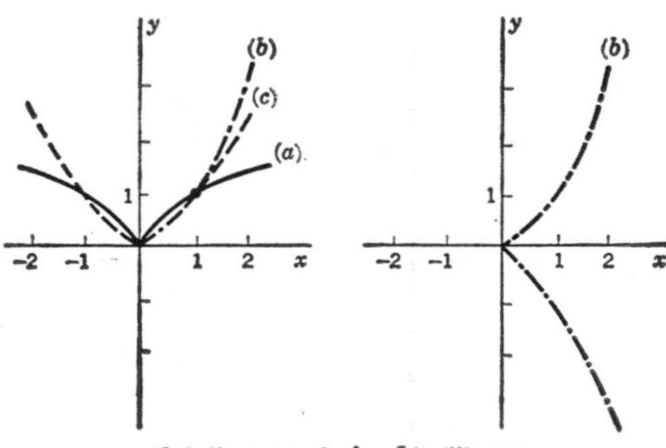

(Only the curve of $y^4 = x^7$ is different)

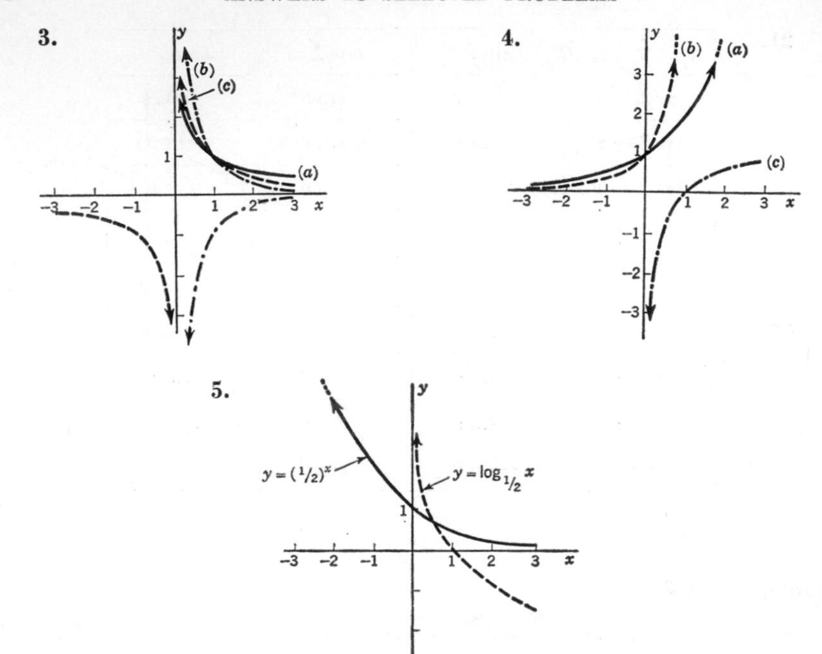

6. 5/4. **7.** 10.2. **8.** 18 centuries. **9.** (*a*) $-\sqrt{3}/2$; (*b*) $-\sqrt{2}$; (*c*) $-2\sqrt{3}/3$. **10.** (*a*) negative; (*b*) negative; (*c*) negative. **11.** (*a*) π, $-\pi$; (*b*) $3\pi/4$, $-\pi/4$; (*c*) $3\pi/4$, $-3\pi/4$. **12.** (*a*) $(4 - \pi)/4$; (*b*) $-\pi/4$.

Review Test B.

1. (*a*) 1, 2; concave up. (*b*) 1, 3; concave down. (*c*) 1; concave up.

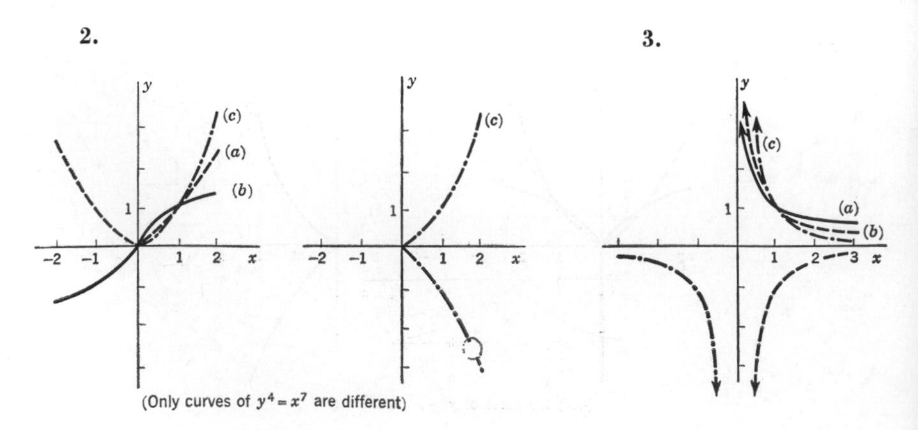

4.

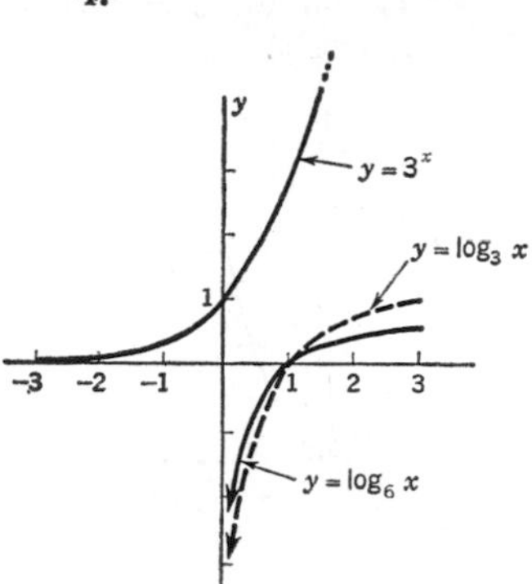

5.

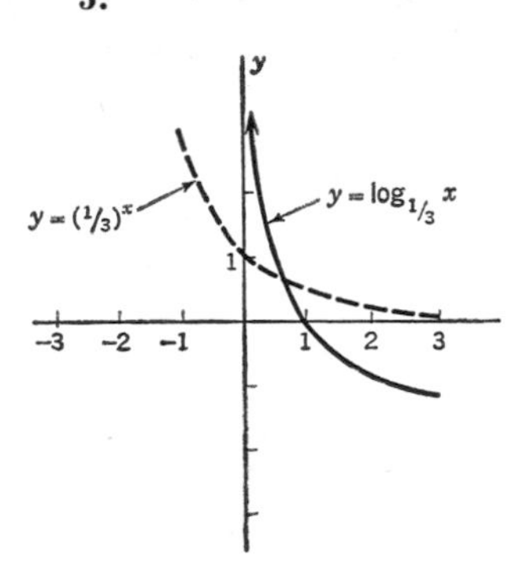

6. 1/2. **7.** 6.5. **8.** 0.25 centuries. **9.** (*a*) negative; (*b*) positive; (*c*) positive. **10.** (*a*) $-\sqrt{2}/2$; (*b*) $-1/\sqrt{3}$; (*c*) $1/\sqrt{3}$. **11.** (*a*) $7\pi/6$, $-\pi/6$; (*b*) $4\pi/3$, $-\pi/3$; (*c*) $\pi/4$, $-3\pi/4$. **12.** (*a*) $(\sqrt{3} + 2\pi)/3$; (*b*) 1/2.

CHAPTER 6

Problem Set 6.1.

1. (*a*) x-axis; (*b*) x-axis, y-axis, and origin; (*c*) origin; (*d*) x-axis, y-axis, and origin; (*e*) origin; (*f*) y-axis; (*g*) x-axis, y-axis, and origin; (*h*) y-axis. **2.** (*a*) $y = -2x^{2/3}$; (*b*) $y^3 = -x^2$; (*c*) $y = -x^4$; (*d*) $y^4 = x^3$; (*e*) $y = -x$ **3.** (*a*) $y^2 = -x$; (*b*) $y^3 = x^2$; (*c*) $y = x^4$; (*d*) $y = -1/x^3$; (*e*) $y = -1/x^5$. **4.** (*a*) $x = y^2$; (*b*) $x^2 = y^5$; (*c*) $x = y^{2/3}$; (*d*) $x = 1/y^3$; (*e*) $x^4 = 1/y^2$. **5.** (*a*) $y = -x^2$; (*b*) $y^3 = x^5$; (*c*) $y^3 = 1/x^5$; (*d*) $y = -1/x^4$; (*e*) $y = 1/x^3$.

6.

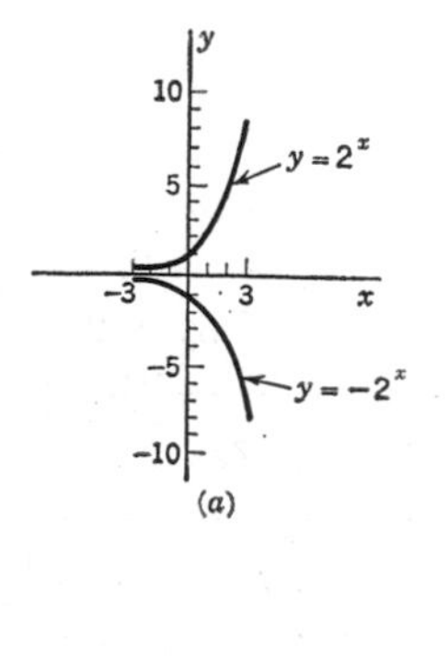

(*a*)

7.

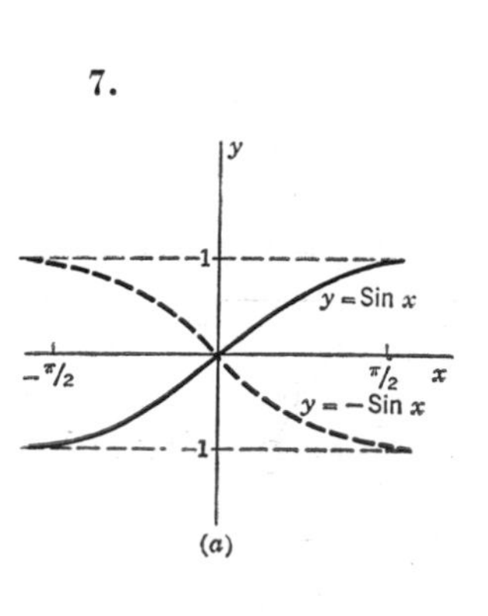

(*a*)

8.

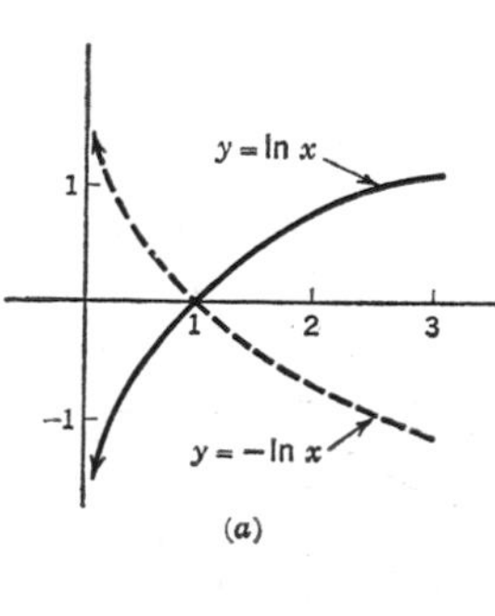

(*a*)

9. (*a*) $y = -\operatorname{Sin} x$; (*b*) $y = -e^x$; (*c*) $y = -\operatorname{arc\,Cos} x$; (*d*) $y = -\ln x$. **10.** (*a*) $x = e^y$; (*b*) $x = \log_6 y$; (*c*) $x = \operatorname{Sec} y$; (*d*) $x = \operatorname{arc\,Cos} y$.

11.

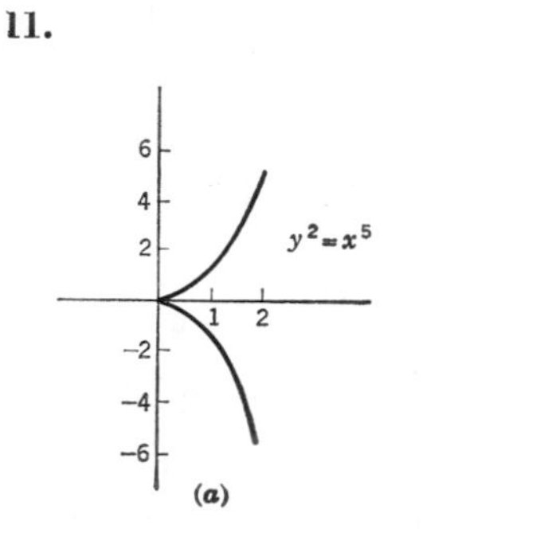

12.

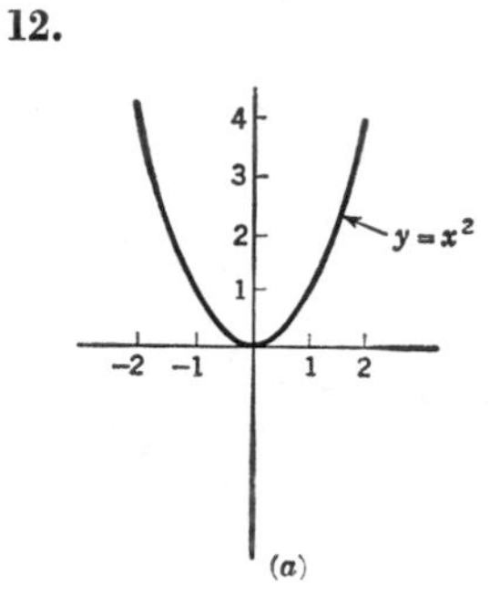

13. (*a*) y-axis; (*b*) none; (*c*) x-axis; (*d*) x-axis.

Problem Set 6.2.

1. (*a*) $2x$; (*b*) $\sqrt{3}x$; (*c*) $3x$; (*d*) $\sqrt{2}x$. **3.** (*a*) Ordinates multiplied by 4 or abscissas divided by 2, ordinates divided by 3 or abscissas multiplied by $\sqrt{3}$; (*b*) ordinates or abscissas multiplied by 2, ordinates or abscissas divided by 2; (*c*) graphs are identical; (*d*) reflection in the diagonal line. **5.** (*a*) Abscissas divided by 3, ordinates divided by 4 and new locus reflected in the x-axis; (*b*) abscissas multiplied by 2 and new locus reflected in the x-axis, ordinates divided by 6; (*c*) abscissas divided by 3 and the new locus reflected in the x-axis, both the ordinates and the abscissas divided by 3; (*d*) abscissas divided by 2, abscissas multiplied by 2. **7.** (*a*) Abscissas divided by 2 or ordinates multiplied by $2\sqrt{2}$, abscissas multiplied by $\sqrt{2}$ or ordinates divided by $\sqrt{2}$; (*b*) abscissas divided by 2 or ordinates multiplied by $\sqrt[3]{2}$ and new locus reflected in either axis, abscissas multiplied by 4/3 or ordinates divided by $\sqrt[3]{4/3}$; (*c*) abscissas divided by 6 or ordinates multiplied by $\sqrt{6}$, abscissas multiplied by 4 or ordinates divided by 2; (*d*) abscissas multiplied by 2/3 or ordinates divided by $\sqrt[3]{4/9}$, abscissas divided by $\sqrt{2}$ or ordinates multiplied by $\sqrt[3]{2}$ and new locus reflected in the x-axis. **9.** (*a*) Abscissas divided by 2 or ordinates multiplied by 4, ordinates multiplied by 3 or abscissas divided by $\sqrt[4]{9}$; (*b*) abscissas multiplied by $\sqrt[3]{2}$ or ordinates multiplied by 2, abscissas divided by $\sqrt[3]{3}$ or ordinates divided by 3; (*c*) abscissas multiplied by $\sqrt{3}$ or ordinates multiplied by 3, abscissas divided by 2 or ordinates divided by 4; (*d*) abscissas divided by 2 or ordinates multiplied by $\sqrt[3]{32}$, abscissas multiplied by $\sqrt[5]{8}$ or ordinates divided by 2. **11.** (*a*) $y = \operatorname{Sin} 2x$; (*b*) $y = 4 \operatorname{Sin} x$; (*c*) $y = -\operatorname{Sin} x$; (*d*) $3y = \operatorname{Sin} 2x$; (*e*) $x = \operatorname{Sin} y$. **13.** (*a*) $y = e^{2x}$; (*b*) $y = 4e^x$; (*c*) $y = -e^x$; (*d*) $3y = e^{2x}$; (*e*) $x = e^y$.

Problem Set 6.3.

1. (*a*) Abscissas divided by 2 or ordinates multiplied by 2, new locus translated 1 unit in the positive direction of x; (*b*) abscissas divided by $\sqrt{2}$ or ordinates multiplied by 2, new locus translated 2 units in the positive direction of x; (*c*) abscissas multiplied by $\sqrt[3]{2}$ or ordinates divided by 2, new locus translated 3 units in the positive direction of x. **3.** (*a*) Abscissas divided by 2, ordinates multiplied by 4, new locus translated 2 units in the negative direction of x and 4 units in the positive direction of y; (*b*) abscissas multiplied by 2, new locus translated 2 units in the negative direction of y; (*c*) abscissas divided by 3 or ordinates multiplied by 3, new locus translated 2 units in the positive direction of x and 4 units in the negative direction of y. **5.** (*a*) $y = 2(x - 2)^3$; (*b*) $y + 4 = 2x^3$; (*c*) $y = 6x^3$; (*d*) $y = 16x^3$. **7.** (*a*) $y = -e^x$; (*b*) $y = -e^{x/2}$; (*c*) $y = -e^{(x-2)/2}$. **9.** $y = \ln 2(x - 2)$: divide abscissas by 2 and translate new locus 1 unit in the positive direction of x; $y = \ln (2x - 2)$: translate locus 2 units in the positive direction of x and divide abscissas of new locus by 2.

Problem Set 6.4.

2.

4.

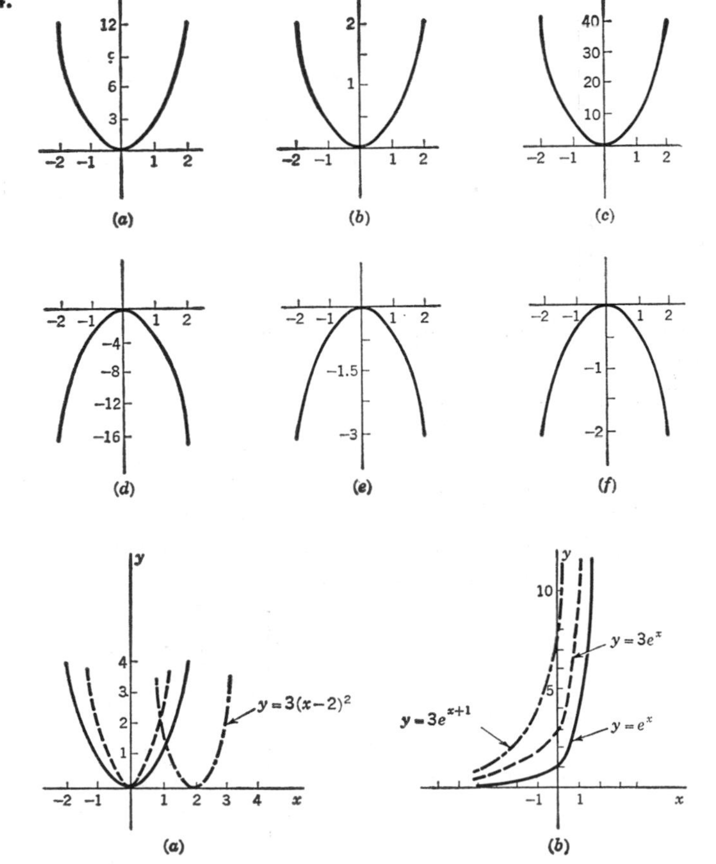

6. (*a*) (1/6, 11/12); (*b*) (1, 5); (*c*) (−1/3, 7/3); (*d*) (7/8, 1/4); (*e*) (19/3, 1/3); (*f*) (8, −1).

7. (*a*).

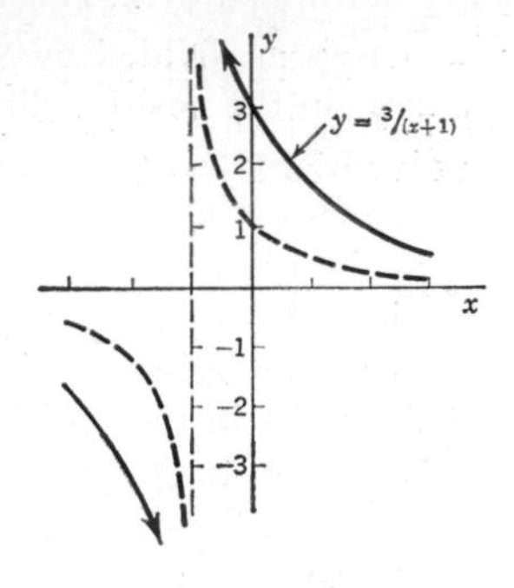

Problem Set 6.5.

1.

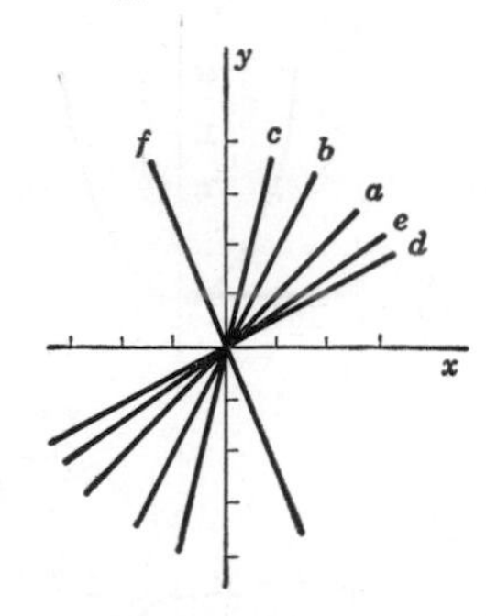

3.

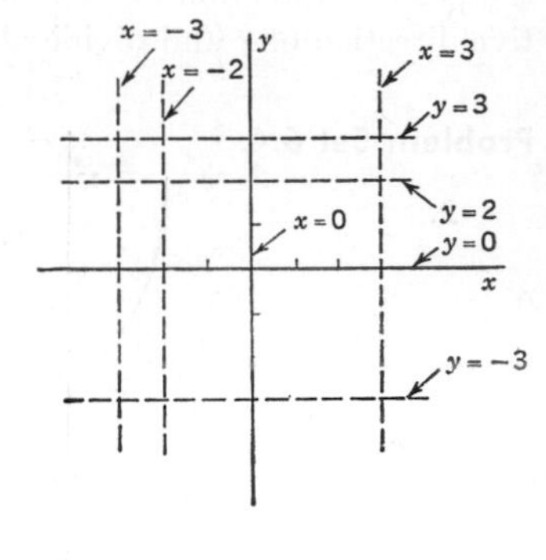

5. (*a*) 2, −3; (*b*) 5, 2; (*c*) 3/2, −4/3; (*d*) 5/3, 3/2. **6.** (*a*) $y = (2/3)x + 2/3$, 2/3, 2/3; (*b*) $y = -2x + 5/2$, −2, 5/2; (*c*) $y = -2x + 4/3$, −2, 4/3; (*d*) $y = (3/7)x + 2/7$, 3/7, 2/7. **7.** (*a*) $x/(-1) + y/(2/3) = 1$, −1, 2/3; (*b*) $x/(5/4) + y/(5/2) = 1$, 5/4, 5/2; (*c*) $x/(2/3) + y/(4/3) = 1$, 2/3, 5/2; (*d*) $x/(-2/3) + y/(2/7) = 1$, −2/3, 2/7. **8.** (*a*) $8x + 7y - 26 = 0$; (*b*) $2x + y + 1 = 0$; (*c*) $3x - 2y - 12 = 0$. **9.** (*a*) $x - 4y + 31 = 0$; (*b*) $5x + 3y - 6 = 0$; (*c*) $17x + y - 94 = 0$. **10.** −1. **11.** (*a*) $y = 3x$; (*b*) $2x + y + 3 = 0$; (*c*) $x = 2$; (*d*) $15x + 7y - 3 = 0$. **12.** (*a*) $2x - 3y + 12 = 0$; (*b*) $6x - 5y + 10 = 0$; (*c*) $2x + y + 3 = 0$. **13.** $x + y + 11 = 0$.

15.

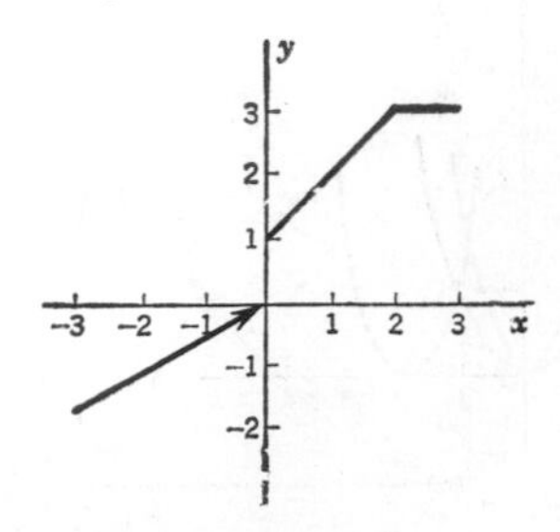

Problem Set 6.6.

1. (*a*) $4x + y - 13 = 0$; (*b*) $4x - y - 18 = 0$; (*c*) $3x - 4y - 12 = 0$; (*d*) $x - 2y + 14 = 0$. **3.** $9x + 20y - 45 = 0$. **5.** The family of parallel lines with slope 3. **7.** (*a*) $y = 3x + 12$; (*b*) $y = x/2 + 6$; (*c*) $2x + y + 5 = 0$. **9.** $E_1 + kE_2 = 0$ does not contain the line defined by $E_2 = 0$.

Problem Set 6.7.

2.

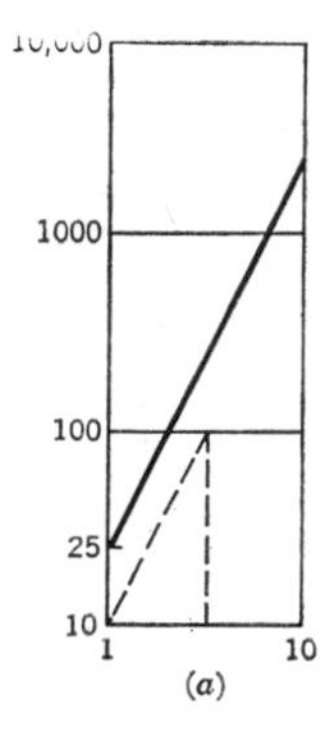

(*a*)

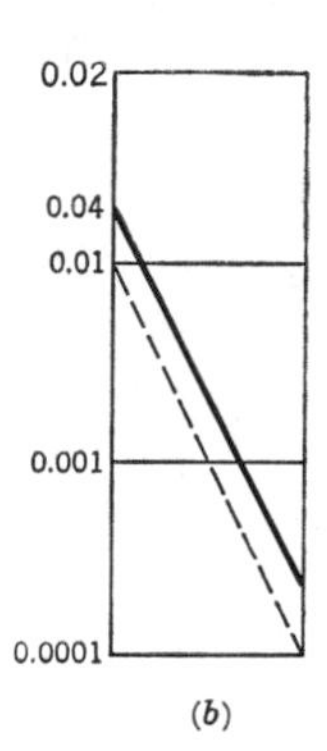

(*b*)

4. (*a*) $y = x^2$; (*b*) $y = 10x^{-2}$; (*c*) $y = 10x^{-1/2}$. **6.** (*a*) $y = 100x^{-1/2}$; (*b*) $y = 0.1x^4$; (*c*) $y = 400x^{-0.4}$; (*d*) $y = 320x^{1/2}$. **7.** $y = 3.5x^{1.58}$. **9.** $y = 1.3x^{1.2}$. **11.** $y = 0.016x^{-1.1}$. **13.** $y = 1.2x^{0.3}$.

Problem Set 6.8.

1.

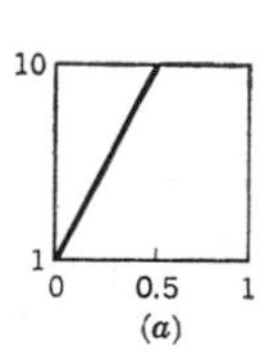

(*a*)

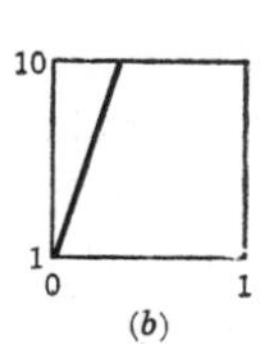

(*b*)

3. (*a*) $y = 10(10)^{-2x}$; (*b*) $y = 10^{2x}$; (*c*) $y = 10^{x/2}$. **5.** (*a*) $y = 5.62(10)^{x/20}$; (*b*) $y = 46.4(10)^{-2x/3}$; (*c*) $y = 0.00001(10)^{2x}$. **7.** (*a*) $y = 0.04(10)^{x/20}$; (*b*) $y = 4.55(10)^{-0.037x}$. **9.** $y = 80(10)^{-0.087x}$.

Problem Set 6.9.

4. [0, 60].

9.

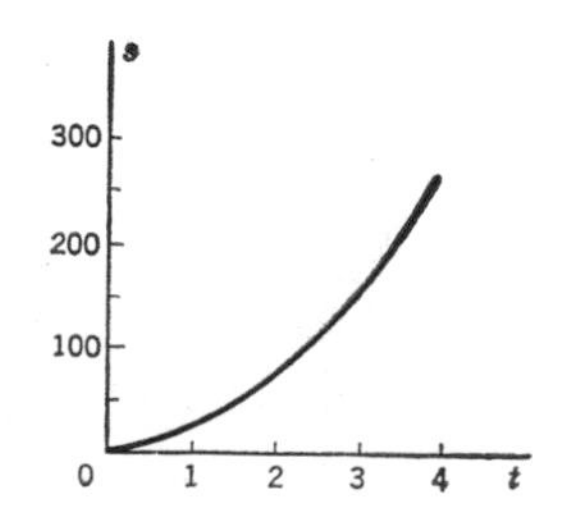

11.

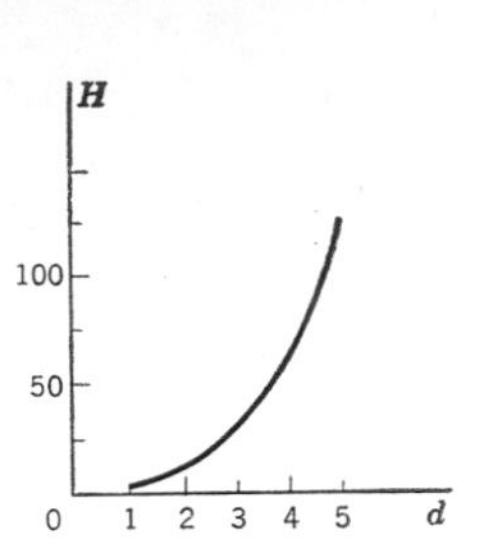

13.

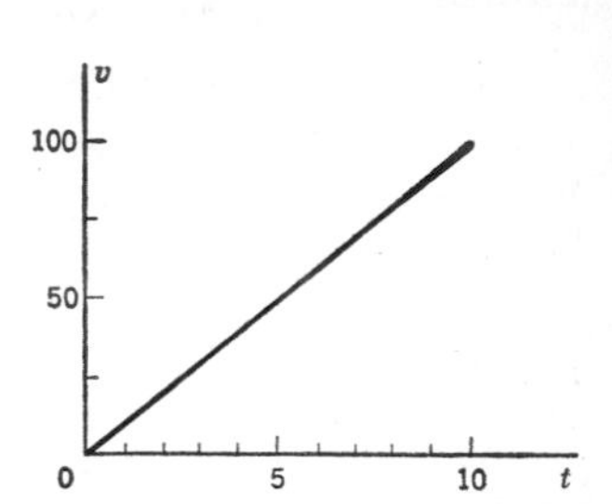

Review Test A.

1. (*a*) Ordinates multiplied by 3; (*b*) abscissas divided by 2; (*c*) translated 2 units in the positive direction of y; (*d*) translated 2 units in the positive direction of y and abscissas divided by 3. **2.** (*a*) Reflection in x-axis; (*b*) reflection in x-axis and ordinates multiplied by 2; (*c*) reflection in x-axis and ordinates divided by 2. **3.** (5/4, 7/8). **4.** y-axis 1 unit in the negative direction of x, and x-axis 7 units in the negative direction of y. **5.** $20\sqrt{3}/3$. **6.** $3x - 2y + 7 = 0$. **7.** $x + y + 1 = 0$. **8.** -3. **9.** The product of slope and y-intercept is 3. **10.** (*a*) $y = 10^{2x}$; (*b*) $y = 0.1(10)^x$ or $y = 10^{x-1}$. **11.** (*a*) $y = 0.001x^2$; (*b*) $y = 10^{4/3}x^{-2/3}$. **12.** 0.184.

Review Test B.

1. (*a*) Abscissas divided by 2 or ordinates multiplied by 4; (*b*) ordinates divided by 4 or abscissas multiplied by 2; (*c*) translated 2 units in the negative direction of x; (*d*) ordinates multiplied by 3 or abscissas divided by $\sqrt{3}$, followed by a translation 1 unit in the negative direction of y and 2 units in the positive direction of x. **2.** (*a*) Reflection in x-axis and ordinates multiplied by 2; (*b*) ordinates divided by 2 and reflection in x-axis; (*c*) ordinates multiplied by 2 or abscissas multiplied by 4. **3.** (1/4, 21/4). **4.** y-axis translated 1/4 unit in the positive direction of x, and x-axis translated 29/4 units in the positive direction of y. **5.** 161/15 or approximately 10.7 feet. **6.** $3x + 4y + 16 = 0$. **7.** $y = 2x$. **8.** $-8/3$. **9.** They contain the point (1, 0); the slope and y-intercept are numerically equal but opposite in sign. **10.** (*a*) $y = 0.1(10)^{2x/3}$; (*b*) $y = 10^{3/2}(10)^{-x/6}$ or $y = 10^{(9-x)/6}$. **11.** (*a*) $y = 10\sqrt{10}x^{1/2}$; (*b*) $y = 0.1x^{-2}$. **12.** 2.71.

CHAPTER 7

Problem Set 7.1.

1. (*a*) 5; (*b*) 12; (*c*) 10. **2.** (*a*) 5; (*b*) $2\sqrt{10}$; (*c*) $\sqrt{149}$; (*d*) 1. **3.** No. **6.** 5, $5\sqrt{5}$, $2\sqrt{10}$.

Problem Set 7.2.

10. (*a*) $\sin\theta$; (*b*) $(\sqrt{3}/2)\cos\theta + (1/2)\sin\theta$; (*c*) $(\sqrt{3}/2)\cos\theta + (1/2)\sin\theta$; (*d*) $(1 + \tan\theta)/(1 - \tan\theta)$; (*e*) $(\sqrt{3} + \tan\theta)/(\sqrt{3}\tan\theta - 1)$; (*f*) $(\sqrt{2}/2)\sin\theta - (\sqrt{2}/2)\cos\theta$. **12.** (*a*) 63/65, −16/65; (*b*) 220/221, −21/221. **13.** (*a*) −87/425, 366/425; (*b*) $(2 + \sqrt{5})/(4\sqrt{5})$, $(2\sqrt{15} - 1)/(4\sqrt{5})$. **14.** (*a*) $3\sin\theta - 4\sin^3\theta$; (*b*) $4\cos^3\theta - 3\cos\theta$; (*c*) $(3\tan\theta - \tan^3\theta)/(1 - 3\tan^2\theta)$. **15.** (*a*) $\sqrt{(2 - \sqrt{2})/2}$; (*b*) $\sqrt{(2 + \sqrt{3})/2}$; (*c*) $\sqrt{(2 + \sqrt{3})/2}$. **16.** (*a*) $-\sqrt{3}/2$; (*b*) 1/9; (*c*) $4\sqrt{2}/9$. **17.** (*a*) $\sqrt{(2 - \sqrt{3})/(2 + \sqrt{3})}$; (*b*) $\sqrt{(4 + \sqrt{7})/(4 - \sqrt{7})}$; (*c*) $-\sqrt{2}$. **18.** (*a*) $\sin\pi/4 + \sin 3\pi/4$; (*b*) $\cos\pi/6 + \cos\pi/2$; (*c*) $(\cos 3x - \cos 7x)/2$; (*d*) $(-\sin 5x + \sin 9x)/2$; (*e*) $(\cos x + \cos 9x)/2$; (*f*) $(\cos\pi/12 - \cos 17\pi/12)/2$. **19.** (*a*) $2\sin 13\pi/24\cos 5\pi/24$; (*b*) $-2\sin 7\pi/24\sin\pi/24$; (*c*) $2\cos 13\pi/24\sin 5\pi/24$; (*d*) $2\sin 4x\cos x$; (*e*) $-2\sin 7x\sin 3x$; (*f*) $2\cos 4x\cos 2x$. **20.** (*a*) $\sqrt{(2 + \sqrt{3})/2}$, $-\sqrt{(2 - \sqrt{3})/2}$, $-\sqrt{(2 + \sqrt{3})/(2 - \sqrt{3})}$; (*b*) $\sqrt{(2 - \sqrt{2})/2}$, $-\sqrt{(2 + \sqrt{2})/2}$, $\sqrt{(2 - \sqrt{2})/(2 + \sqrt{2})}$; (*c*) $-\sqrt{(2 - \sqrt{2})/2}$, $\sqrt{(2 + \sqrt{2})/2}$, $-\sqrt{(2 - \sqrt{2})/(2 + \sqrt{2})}$; (*d*) $-\sqrt{(2 + \sqrt{3})/2}$, $\sqrt{(2 - \sqrt{3})/2}$, $-\sqrt{(2 + \sqrt{3})/(2 - \sqrt{3})}$.

Problem Set 7.3.

25. $2\sin 6\theta\cos 2\theta$. **26.** $2\cos 6\theta\sin\theta$. **27.** $2\cos 11\theta/2\cos 5\theta/2$. **28.** $-2\sin 3\theta\sin 2\theta$. **29.** $\sin 2\theta + \sin 4\theta$. **30.** $-\sin\theta + \sin 9\theta$. **31.** $(\cos\theta/2 - \cos\theta)/2$. **32.** $(\cos\theta - \cos 7\theta/3)/2$. **33.** $-\sin\theta$. **34.** $-\sin\theta$. **35.** $-\tan\theta$. **36.** $-\cos\theta$. **37.** $-\sin\theta$. **38.** $\sin\theta$. **39.** $-\cot\theta$. **40.** $-\sin\theta$.

Problem Set 7.4.

1. (*a*) $2\pi/3$, 2; (*b*) $\pi/2$, 3; (*c*) $\pi/5$, 3; (*d*) 3π, 4; (*e*) 1, 7; (*f*) 2, 3. **2.** (*a*) $3/(2\pi)$ 0; (*b*) $2/\pi$, 0; (*c*) $5/\pi$, $-\pi/3$; (*d*) $1/(3\pi)$, $\pi/4$; (*e*) 1, 0; (*f*) 1/2, 0. **3.** They differ in phase by $\pi/4$. **4.** rk; the same. **5.** The first differs from the second in amplitude, and from the third in phase. **6.** $x = 10\cos 2t$, $y = 10\sin 2t$. **7.** $x = 3\cos\pi t$. **8.** $x = 3\cos\pi(t - 1/2)$. **9.** 2, π. **10.** They differ in amplitude and phase, but have the same period.

Problem Set 7.5.

1. (*a*) 2, 3/5; (*b*) 10, 3/2; (*c*) 50, 15; (*d*) 100, −3/5; (*e*) 0.25, −4; (*f*) 40, 400/3. **2.** (*a*) $2\pi/5$, $2\pi/3$; (*b*) 6π, 4π; (*c*) 30, 2; (*d*) $2\pi/5$, $2\pi/3$; (*e*) 15, 15/4; (*f*) $8\pi/3$, $\pi/50$. **3.** $y = 3\sin[(2\pi/75)(5x - 22t)]$, t in seconds. **4.** 8.83, 5.65, 3.77, 1.88. **5.** $y = \cos(300\pi t)\sin(\pi/10)x$. **6.** $y = \cos(300\pi t)\sin(3\pi x/20)$.

7. (*a*) A stationary wave of amplitude 10, wave length 2 and period 2/3; (*b*) a stationary wave of amplitude 2, wave length 12π, and period 10π. **8.** $y = 10 \cos (2\pi/15)t \sin (\pi/200)x$, with t in seconds, x in meters, and y in centimeters. **9.** $y = 8 \cos (\pi/5)t \sin (\pi/100)x$ with t in seconds, x in meters, and y in centimeters. **10.** $y = 5 \sin [(x + 12t - 10)/3]$; $y = 5 \sin [(x + 12t + 5)/3]$.

Problem Set 7.6.

1. (*a*) $5\pi/6$; (*b*) $9\pi/4$; (*c*) $3\pi/2$; (*d*) $85\pi/18$; (*e*) $4\pi/3$; (*f*) $\pi/6$; (*g*) $-5\pi/6$; (*h*) $-\pi/3$. **2.** (*a*) 45°; (*b*) 22.5°; (*c*) 30°; (*d*) 135°; (*e*) 157.5°; (*f*) 165°; (*g*) −150°. **3.** (*a*) 3.49 radians; (*b*) −6.04 radians; (*c*) 1.27 radians; (*d*) 4.30 radians. **4.** (*a*) 258°; (*b*) 286°; (*c*) −138°; (*d*) 212°. **5.** (*a*) 2π inches; (*b*) 7π inches; (*c*) 5π inches. **6.** (*a*) π inches; (*b*) 5π inches; (*c*) $49\pi/3$ inches; (*d*) $2\pi/3$ inches. **7.** (*a*) $36/\pi°$; (*b*) $270/\pi°$; (*c*) $360/\pi°$. **8.** 865,000 miles. **9.** (*a*) $\sqrt{2}/2$; (*b*) $\sqrt{3}/2$; (*c*) 1; (*d*) $\sqrt{2}/2$; (*e*) 1/2; (*f*) $-\sqrt{3}$; (*g*) $-\sqrt{2}/2$; (*h*) −1; (*i*) $-1/\sqrt{3}$; (*j*) $1/\sqrt{3}$. **10.** (*a*) 0.6046; (*b*) −0.8536; (*c*) 0.2364; (*d*) 1.0141; (*e*) 0.2622; (*f*) 0.5934; (*g*) −0.5045; (*h*) −0.8554. **11.** 11,000 miles. **12.** (*a*) 10π; (*b*) 100π. **15.** 88/3. **16.** $2000\pi/3$. **17.** 1.5 inches.

Problem Set 7.7.

1. $B = 28$, $b = 19$, $a = 35$. **3.** $B = 24$, $C = 66$, $a = 62$. **5.** $A = 25$, $C = 65$, $c = 32$. **9.** 385 feet. **11.** 930 feet. **13.** 21 feet. **15.** 667 feet. **17.** 3900 feet. **19.** 110 feet.

Problem Set 7.8.

1. (*a*) $A = 99$, $B = 43$, $c = 14$; (*b*) $B = 31.3$, $C = 120$, $a = 13.9$; (*c*) $A = 34.4$, $C = 15.1$, $b = 35.0$. **3.** 103 pounds. **5.** 427 yards. **7.** 240 miles per hour, N 53° E. **9.** 137 miles per hour, 8.4°. **11.** (*a*) 51 pounds, E 10° S; (*b*) 138 pounds, N 65° E.

Problem Set 7.9.

1. $A = 110$, $b = 5.3$, $c = 6.8$. **3.** $A = 59.2$, $C = 49.3$, $c = 119$. **5.** $B = 36.5$, $C = 25.7$, $c = 422$. **7.** CD has length of 360 feet, BD has length of 618 feet. **9.** 624 pounds at 20° and 302 pounds at 45°. **11.** 161 miles from B.

Review Test A.

1. 1.257. **2.** (*a*) −7; (*b*) 3/5. **3.** $4\sqrt{2}$. **4.** (*a*) $(2\sqrt{2} + 1)/(\sqrt{2} - 1)$; (*b*) $(-4/7)\sqrt{2}$; (*c*) $\sqrt{2+\sqrt{2}}/2$. **5.** (*a*) 0.6570; (*b*) 0.7055. **6.** $\sqrt{(2+\sqrt{3})/2}$. **7.** $1 - \cos 4x = 2 \sin^2 2x = 2(2 \sin x \cos x)^2 = 8 \sin^2 x \cos^2 x$. **8.** $\pi/6$. **9.** $a = 100$, $L = 6\pi$, $T = \pi/2$, $V = 12$. **10.** 5.5 miles. **11.** 110 feet. **12.** 640 feet, 660 feet.

Review Test B.

1. 0.6632. **2.** (*a*) $-3/4$; (*b*) $-25/24$. **3.** $\sqrt{\pi^2 + 4} = 3.7$, approximately. **4.** (*a*) $(\sqrt{3} - 1)/(2\sqrt{2})$; (*b*) $(\sqrt{3} - 1)/(2\sqrt{2})$; (*c*) $-\sqrt{2 - \sqrt{2}}/2$. **5.** -2.52; -2.60. **6.** $(6 - 4\sqrt{5})/15$. **7.** $1/(1 + \sin x) + 1/(1 - \sin x) = 2/[(1 + \sin x)(1 - \sin x)] = 2/\cos^2 x = 2 \sec^2 x$. **8.** $\pi/5$ inches per minute. **9.** (*a*) $a = 10$, $T = 3\pi$; (*b*) -5. **10.** 1850 feet. **11.** 48.2°, 73.4°, 58.4°. **12.** 6500 feet, 86°.

CHAPTER 8

Problem Set 8.1.

1. (*a*) 5; (*b*) 3; (*c*) -3; (*d*) -2, 1; (*e*) 0; (*f*) 2, -1.

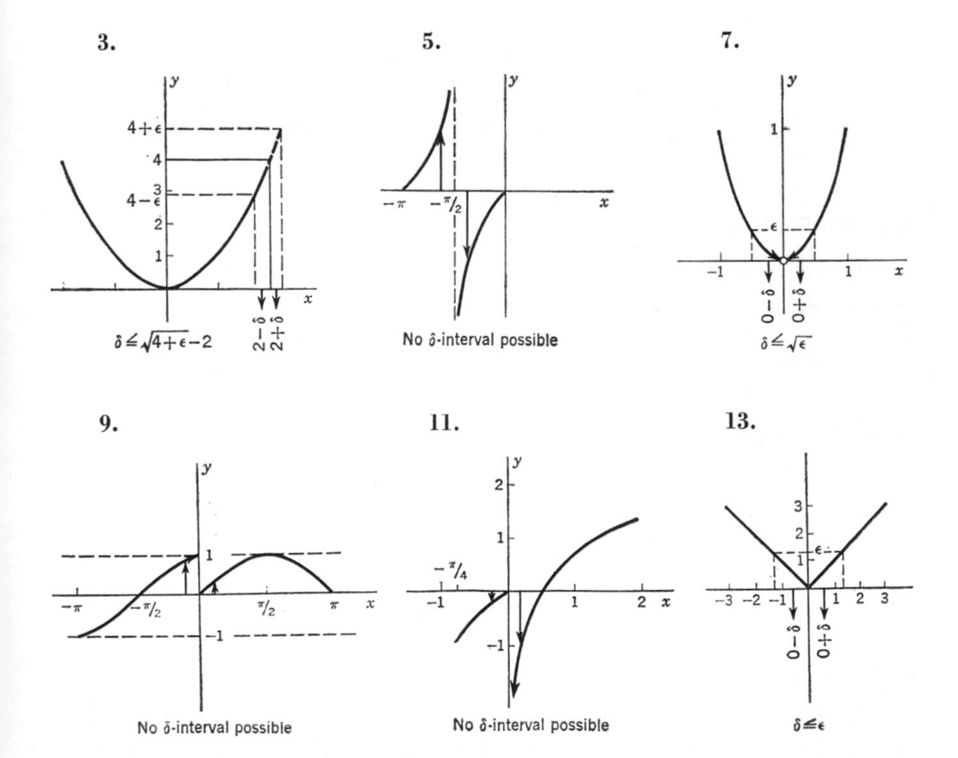

Problem Set 8.2.

1. (*a*) 2; (*b*) 2; (*c*) non-existent; (*d*) non-existent; (*e*) 2. **5.** 14. **7.** 0. **9.** 2. **11.** 0. **13.** 1. **15.** 0.

Problem Set 8.3.

1. (*a*) continuous; (*b*) undefined; (*c*) undefined; (*d*) continuous; (*e*) undefined. **3.** (*a*) 1; (*b*) 3; (*c*) 246/23; (*d*) 0; (*e*) $2/(2-\pi/2)$; (*f*) -2. **5.** (*a*) none; (*b*) $-5, -4, -3, -2, -1, 0, 1, 2, 3, 4, 5$; (*c*) none; (*d*) none; (*e*) every point of the interval.

Problem Set 8.4.

1. $E_{-1}(h) = 2x + h$. **3.** 0. **5.** $10x$. **7.** 3. **9.** $-1/(2x^2)$. **11.** $-1/(2x^{3/2})$. **13.** $3x^2 + 4x$. **15.** $12x^2$.

Problem Set 8.5.

1. 2. **3.** $8x + 6$. **5.** $12x^2 - 3$. **7.** $3x^2 - 4x$. **9.** $10x + 13$. **11.** 18. **13.** 12. **15.** 60. **17.** $6x + y - 5 = 0$.

Problem Set 8.6.

1. (*a*) $F(x) = u^3$, $u = x^2 + 1$; (*b*) $F(x) = e^u$, $u = x + 1$; (*c*) $F(x) = \cos u$, $u = x^2 - 2$. **3.** $12x^3 - 2$. **5.** $8x(x^2+1)^3$. **7.** $12x^3e^{3x^4}$. **9.** $48x/(6x^2+5)$. **11.** $6(9x^2+2)(3x^3+2x-5)^5$. **13.** $20x/(2x^2-3)$. **15.** $6xe^{3x^2}$. **17.** Yes, for (*a*) and (*b*).

Problem Set 8.7.

1. $6x$. **3.** $32x^7 - 14x$. **5.** $6x^5 - 1$. **7.** $x/(x+1) + \ln(x+1)$. **9.** $(x+2)/(x-1) + \ln(1-x)$. **11.** $6x - 3x^2 - 5x^4$. **13.** $-1/x^2 - 2/x^3$. **15.** $3x^2 \sec^2 3x + 2x \tan 3x$. **17.** $-2x \csc^2(x^2+1)$. **19.** $10x(x^2+1)^4$. **21.** $8x/(x^2-1)$. **23.** 1. **25.** $y = e^2(3x-2)$. **27.** $F'(x) = a^u f'(x) \ln a$.

Problem Set 8.8.

1. Maximum at (1, 4); minimum at (3, 0). **3.** Maximum at (5/2, 115/4). **5.** Maximum at (−1/2, 5/4). **7.** Minimum at (0, 0); maximum at (−2, −4). **9.** Maximum at $(e, 1/e)$. **11.** 4000 cubic feet. **13.** (*a*) $[-b/(2a), c - b^2/(4a)]$; (*b*) (−1/3, −10/3); (*c*) (1/4, 11/4); (*d*) (−1/3, 13/3). **15.** 40 by 40 and 30 by 60. **17.** 32, 32. **19.** $20\sqrt{5}$ or approximately 45 miles. **21.** 30. **23.** $A = \sqrt{3}$.

Problem Set 8.9.

1. The particle starts at a point 12 units on the negative side of the given point and moves with a velocity of constant measure 4 in the positive direction. **3.** The particle starts at a point 2 units on the positive side of the given point, moves in the negative direction until $t = 23$, and thereafter proceeds in the positive direction. **5.** The particle starts at the given point, moves in the positive direction until $t = 8/3$, and thereafter moves in the negative direction.

7. $A' = 2\pi rr'$. **9.** $8/(5\pi)$ or approximately 1/2 foot per second. **11.** 96 square inches per second. **13.** 20 feet per second. **15.** 480 feet per second. **17.** 25/3 feet per second. **19.** 50 feet per second.

Problem Set 8.10.

1. (3, 0), minimum; (1, 4), maximum; (2, 2) inflection. **3.** (2, 9), inflection. **5.** (0, 0), minumum; (−2, −4), maximum. **7.** 0, constantly. **9.** 2, constantly. **11.** 0 if $t = 4/3$, negative if $t > 4/3$, and positive if $0 < t < 4/3$. **15.** 165 feet per second. **17.** 2.

Review Test A.

1. Because, for any $\epsilon > 0$ we can choose $\delta = \epsilon$ and be assured that $|f(x) - c| < \epsilon$ whenever $0 < |x - c| < \delta$. In this case, $f(x) - c$ is precisely the same as $x - c$. **2.** (*a*) −4; (*b*) 3; (*c*) because the functions are continuous at those points. **3.** (*a*) 5/2; (*b*) 1; (*c*) because the canceled factors are not 0 in the limiting process. **4.** 0. **5.** (*a*) $12x^2 - 3$; (*b*) $24x^2 - 24x + 6$. **6.** (*a*) $2(2x + 1)(2x + 3)e^{2x}$; (*b*) $5x^2(1 + 3 \ln 3x)$. **7.** (−3, 12). **8.** (−1, 4). **9.** 100 rods. **10.** (0, 1), (2/3, 11/27); (*b*) $x < 0$ or $x > 2/3$; (*b*) $0 < x < 2/3$. **11.** $t = 2$. **12.** 1 foot per minute.

Review Test B.

1. Because, for any $\epsilon > 0$, we can choose $\delta = \epsilon/2$ and be assured that $|2x - 2c| < \epsilon$, provided $0 < |x - c| < \delta$. **2.** (*a*) −1; (*b*) 1/4; (*c*) because the functions are continuous at those points. **3.** (*a*) 3; (*b*) 2; (*c*) because the canceled factors are not 0 in the limiting process. **4.** $a = 0$. **5.** (*a*) $3x^2 - 4x + 1$; (*b*) $81x^2 - 54x + 9$. **6.** (*a*) $e^{3x}(3/x^2 - 2/x^3)$; (*b*) $\ln 3x + (x + 1)/x$. **7.** $y = 12x - 17$. **8.** −9.5; $x = -3/2$. **9.** 180 by 180 yards. **10.** (2, 13), maximum; (3, 11), inflection; (4, 9), minimum. **11.** 352 feet per second; 1942 feet in 11 seconds. **12.** $30\sqrt{3}$ square inches per second.

CHAPTER 9

Problem Set 9.1.

1. −59. **3.** 1/6561. **5.** 6561. **7.** 76. **9.** 140, 350. **11.** −3, 0, 3. **13.** 41/24, 17/12, 9/8, 5/6, 13/24. **15.** −7. **17.** −1/4, 1/8. **18.** $700. **19.** $584.93. **21.** 304. **22.** 80.

Problem Set 9.2.

1. (*a*) −88; (*b*) 54; (*c*) 390. **2.** (*a*) 15.75; (*b*) 7.875; (*c*) 2.65625. **3.** (*a*) 63; (*b*) 195; (*c*) −105/2. **4.** (*a*) 5; (*b*) 510; (*c*) 211/120. **5.** (*a*) 4/3; (*b*) 16/7;

(*c*) 125/9; (*d*) $10(2 - \sqrt{3})$. **6.** (*a*) 12/33; (*b*) 1211/3330; (*c*) 5/6. **7.** 90 inches. **8.** 37.5 feet. **9.** n^2. **10.** $n(n + 1)$. **11.** 6 feet. **12.** $3\sqrt{3}$ feet.

Problem Set 9.3.

1. $$\lim \sum_{i=1}^{n} x_i^3 h_n = \int_0^3 x^3\,dx.$$

3. $$\lim \sum_{i=1}^{n} (x_i^2 + 2)h_n = \int_1^4 (x^2 + 2)\,dx.$$

5. $$\lim \sum_{i=1}^{n} e^{2x_i}h_n = \int_0^3 e^{2x}\,dx.$$

7. $$\lim \sum_{i=1}^{n} e^{-2x_i}h_n = \int_{-1}^3 e^{-2x}\,dx.$$

9. $$\lim \sum_{i=1}^{n} \sin x_i h_n = \int_0^{\pi/2} \sin x\,dx.$$

11. $$\lim \sum_{i=1}^{n} (x_i^3 - 2)h_n = \int_2^5 (x^3 - 2)\,dx.$$

Problem Set 9.4.

1. (*a*) $x^4/4 + 2x^3/3 - 5x^2/2$; (*b*) $3x^5/5 - 4x^3/3 + x^2 - 3x$; (*c*) $x^4/2 + 3x^2/2$; (*d*) $x^6/6 - 5x^4/4$. **3.** (*a*) $-2/x^3 + 3$; (*b*) $4x - 3$. **5.** (*a*) 85/6; (*b*) 24; (*c*) 20; (*d*) −1/5. **7.** (*a*) 40; (*b*) 42; (*c*) 312; (*d*) −112. **9.** 39 units. **11.** $126.\overline{6}$ units.

Problem Set 9.5.

1. $x^3/3 - x^2 + 3x + C$. **3.** $(-1/3) \cos x^3 + C$. **5.** $(5/2) \ln (x^2 + 3) + C$ **7.** 16/3. **9.** $(\sin 2x - \sin 2)/2$. **11.** $\sqrt{3}/2$. **13.** $e^{\sin x} - 1$. **15.** −65/8. **17.** 1/3. **19.** 2 ln 4 or approximately 2.77 units.

Review Test A.

1. (*a*) Arithmetic, 11, 14; (*b*) arithmetic, 4, 0; (*c*) geometric, $-3\sqrt{3}$, 9; (*d*) arithmetic, 1, 7/6. **2.** $a_1 = 3$, $a_2 = 2$, $a_3 = 5/6$. **3.** $b_1 = 0$, $b_2 = -7/24$, $b_3 = -7/24$. **4.** (*a*) 45, 330; (*b*) $-13.\overline{3}$; (*c*) $366.\overline{6}$. **5.** $\dfrac{3^{10} - 1}{4(3^7)}$. **6.** 50/7. **7.** 0.5″, 55.5′ +. **8.** 20. **9.** (*a*) $x^3 - x^2 + x + C$; (*b*) $x^4/2 + (\cos 2x)/2 +$

$x^2/2 + C$; (c) $\frac{e^{2x}}{2} - \frac{\sin 3x}{3} + C$. **10.** (a) 26/15; (b) $\ln 2 + 1.5 - \frac{e^3(e^3 - 1)}{3}$ or -142.1, approximately. **11.** (a) $109.\bar{3}$ square units; (b) $e - 1$, or 1.82 square units, approximately. **12.** $\int_0^4 2x^2\,dx = \lim \left[\frac{4^3 n(n+1)(2n+1)}{3n^3}\right] = 128/3 = 42.\bar{6}$.

Review Test B.

1. (a) Arithmetic, -4, -8; (b) geometric, 1/24, 1/48; (c) geometric, $\sqrt{2}/4$, 1/4; (d) arithmetic, -6.5, -8. **2.** $a_1 = 0$, $a_2 = 2/3$, $a_3 = 3/2$. **3.** $b_1 = 9$, $b_2 = 3/4$, $b_3 = 36/25$. **4.** (a) 72, 555; (b) -16, -82.5. **5.** $(3^{12} - 2^{12})/3^{10}$. **6.** 6. **7.** 11, 17, 23, 29, 35, 41, 47, 53 feet. **8.** 729/16 or 45.5625 gallons. **9.** (a) $4x^3/3 + x^2 + 5x + C$; (b) $(\sin 2x)/2 - 3\ln x + C$; (c) $x^2/2 - e^{\sin x} + C$. **10.** (a) 2; (b) $[(e+1)^3 - 2]/3$ or approximately 17.89. **11.** (a) 42 square units; (b) 1/3 square units.

12. $\int_0^3 (x^2/2 + 1)\,dx = \lim\,[(1/2)(3/n)^3\{n(n+1)(2n+1)/6\}] = 15/2$ or 7.5.

CHAPTER 10

Problem Set 10.1.

1. (a) (21, 13); (b) (4, 2); (c) (12, -8). **2.** (a) (4, 12); (b) (7, -5); (c) (7, 1). **3.** (a) (-42, -9); (b) (-34, -2); (c) (8, 31). **4.** (a) ($-29/53$, $-31/53$); (b) ($-31/53$, $-29/53$); (c) ($-46/85$, $-48/85$).

Problem Set 10.2.

1. (a) $2 - 6i$; (b) $-3 + 4i$; (c) $-1 - i$; (d) $4i$; (e) -3. **2.** (a) $-2 - i$; (b) $-1 + 5i$; (c) $21 - 7i$ (d) $9 + 2i$. **3.** (a) $6 - 5i$; (b) $-7 - 9i$; (c) $-21 + 9i$; (d) $1 - 2i$. **4.** (a) $-2 + 16i$; (b) $2 - 34i$; (c) $8 + 21i$; (d) $20 + 10i$. **5.** (a) $9/5 - (7/5)i$; (b) $-1/5 + (8/5)i$. **6.** (a) $-2/5 + (14/5)i$; (b) $17 - 59i$. **7.** (a) $x = 2$, $y = 7$; (b) $x = 7$, $y = -6$. **9.** (a) $1/2 - (1/2)i$; (b) $-i$; (c) -1.

Problem Set 10.3.

1. $2 - 5i$, $-4 + 5i$, $-1 - i$, $4 - 6i$, $1 - i$. **2.** $\sqrt{2}$ cis $\pi/4$, $\sqrt{2}$ cis $3\pi/4$, 2 cis $\pi/3$, 2 cis $4\pi/3$, 2 cis $(-\pi/6)$, $2\sqrt{2}$ cis $5\pi/4$. **3.** $\sqrt{13}$ cis 0.9829, $\sqrt{10}$ cis 3.4633, $2\sqrt{5}$ cis (-0.4637), $3\sqrt{2}$ cis 3.9270. **4.** (a) 8 cis $13\pi/18$; (b) 2 cis $2\pi/3$; (c) (1/20) cis$(-17\pi/12)$; (d) 16 cis $\pi/3$. **5.** (a) 3125 cis 15;

(*b*) 32 cis 6.7; (*c*) 10,000 cis 3.12. **6.** (*a*) cis π; (*b*) $(4/\sqrt{2})$ cis $\pi/12$; (*c*) $128\sqrt{2}$ cis $3\pi/4$. **7.** $1,\ -1/2 + (\sqrt{3}/2)i,\ -1/2 - (\sqrt{3}/2)i$. **8.** $2i,\ -\sqrt{3} - i,\ \sqrt{3} - i$. **9.** $\pm 1,\ \pm i$. **10.** cis $\pi/8$, cis $5\pi/8$, cis $9\pi/8$, cis $13\pi/8$. **11.** $-128 - 128\sqrt{3}i$. **12.** $-3/4 - (7/32)i$. **13.** 70700 cis $\pi/4$. **14.** $14448 - 4033.5i$.

Problem Set 10.4.

1. (*a*) rational; (*b*) algebraic; (*c*) non-algebraic; (*d*) rational; (*e*) non-algebraic; (*f*) algebraic; (*g*) non-algebraic; (*h*) rational. **2.** (*a*) $x^3 - x^2 - 3x + 2$; (*b*) $-x^3 + ix^2 + (2i - 2)x + 4$; (*c*) $(1 + i)x^3 + (2 + i)x^2 + (4 - 2i)x + 8$; (*d*) $x^5 + x^3 - (2 + i)x^2 + 3$. **3.** (*a*) 5; (*b*) 2; (*c*) 3. **4.** (*a*) 5; (*b*) 2; (*c*) 3. **5.** (*a*) $x^3 - 19x + 30 = 0$; (*b*) $x^4 - 2x^3 - x^2 + 2x = 0$; (*c*) $x^3 - x^2 + x - 1 = 0$; (*d*) $x^3 - 2x^2 + 2x = 0$; (*e*) $x^3 - 2ix^2 - (2 + i)x + i - 1 = 0$; (*f*) $x - 2 - i = 0$. **6.** (*a*) $x^4 - 4x^2 = 0$; (*b*) $x^4 - 6x^2 + 8x - 3 = 0$; (*c*) $x^4 + (1 - 3i)x^3 - (3 + 3i)x^2 - (3 - i)x + 2 = 0$; (*d*) $x^3 - (2 + 3i)x^2 - (2 - 4i)x + 2 = 0$. **7.** (*a*) -1; (*b*) -7; (*c*) 17; (*d*) $2i + 1$; (*e*) $-6 - 3i$. **9.** (*a*) $\{2, -4, 3\}$; (*b*) $\{-2, 6, 4\}$; (*c*) $0, 3, (-1 \pm \sqrt{5})/2$; (*d*) $2, -1, (1 \pm \sqrt{7}i)/2$. **10.** (*a*) -56; (*b*) 9; (*c*) -48; (*d*) $-2i$; (*e*) $7 + 4i$; (*f*) 0. **11.** (*a*) not real; (*b*) real and rational; (*c*) not real; (*d*) not real; (*e*) not real; (*f*) real and rational. **12.** (*a*) $1/3 \pm (\sqrt{14}/3)i$; (*b*) $-5/4 \pm (\sqrt{33}/4)i$; (*c*) $2 \pm \sqrt{2}$. **13.** (*a*) $\sqrt{6}/2 + (\sqrt{2}/2)i$.

Problem Set 10.5.

4. (*a*) $A = 1/2,\ B = -1/4$. **5.** $A = 8,\ B = -3,\ C = 4,\ D = -5$. **7.** (*a*) $x^3 + 3x^2 + 2x + 1 = 0$; (*b*) $4x^4 - 3x^3 + 5x + 2 = 0$; (*c*) $2x^5 + 5x^2 + 4x + 1 = 0$; (*d*) $3x^3 + 2x^2 + 5x + 6 = 0$. **9.** (*a*) 3 or 1 positive, no negative; (*b*) 2 or 0 positive, 2 or 0 negative; (*c*) 3 or 1 positive, no negative; (*d*) 3 or 1 positive, no negative. **11.** (*a*) $x^2 - 2x + 2$; (*b*) $x^3 - 2x^2 + x - 2 = 0$; (*c*) $x^4 + 3x^2 + 6x + 10 = 0$; (*d*) $x^4 - 4x^3 + 6x^2 - 4x + 5 = 0$. **13.** (*a*) $(x^2 + 4x + 5)(2x - 3)$; (*b*) $(x^2 + 6x + 11)(x - 1)(x - 5)$.

Problem Set 10.6.

1. (*a*) $3x^3 + 6x^2 + 10x + 15,\ R = 31$; (*b*) $3x^3 - 6x^2 + 10x - 25,\ R = 51$; (*c*) $3x^3 + 15x^2 + 73x + 360,\ R = 1801$; (*d*) $3x^3 - 15x^2 + 73x - 370,\ R = 1851$; (*e*) $3x^3 + 9x^2 + 25x + 70,\ R = 211$; (*f*) $3x^3 - 9x^2 + 25x - 80,\ R = 241$; (*g*) $3x^3 + (3/2)x^2 - (5/4)x - 45/8,\ R = -29/16$; (*h*) $3x^3 - x^2 - (5/3)x - 40/9,\ R = 67/27$. **2.** (*a*) -4; (*b*) 8; (*c*) 58; (*d*) $-31/16$; (*e*) -1.6064. **5.** $\pm 6\sqrt{2}$. **10.** 0, 3. **13.** (*a*) -2; (*b*) 9.

Problem Set 10.7.

1. (*a*) $\{\pm 8, \pm 4, \pm 2, \pm 1, \pm 1/2\}$; (*b*) $\{\pm 5, \pm 1, \pm 5/3, \pm 1/3\}$; (*c*) $\{\pm 10, \pm 5, \pm 2, \pm 1, \pm 5/2, \pm 1/2\}$; (*d*) $\{\pm 10, \pm 5, \pm 2, \pm 1\}$. **2.** All real rational solutions are integers. **3.** (*a*) $\{\pm 1, \pm 1/2\}$; (*b*) $\{\pm 1, \pm 2, \pm 1/3, \pm 2/3\}$. (*c*)

$\{\pm 1, \pm 2, \pm 4, \pm 1/5, \pm 2/5, \pm 4/5\}$; (*d*) $\{0, \pm 1\}$. **7.** (*a*) $\{3/2, -1/3, -1 + \sqrt{3}i, -1 - \sqrt{3}i\}$; (*b*) $\{-3/2, -2, (-1 + \sqrt{3}i)/2, (-1 - \sqrt{3}i)/2\}$; (*c*) $\{5, 3/2, -2/3\}$; (*d*) $\{0, 1, 2, -5\}$.

Problem Set 10.8.

1. 0.347. **2.** 1.311. **3.** 1.213. **4.** 1.414. **5.** 0.654. **6.** 3.764. **7.** 0.791. **8.** 2.214.

Problem Set 10.9.

1. $3\pi/4, 7\pi/4, \pi/2$. **3.** $\pi/2, \pi, 3\pi/2$. **5.** $\pi/3, 2\pi/3, 4\pi/3, 5\pi/3$. **7.** $3\pi/4, 7\pi/4$. **9.** $\pi/4, 5\pi/4$. **11.** $0, 3\pi/4, \pi, 7\pi/4, 2\pi$. **13.** $\pi/4, 5\pi/4$, 1.325 (approx.), 4.467 (approx.). **15.** $0, 2\pi/3, 4\pi/3, 2\pi$. **17.** No solutions. **19.** $0, 2\pi/3, 2\pi$. **21.** $\pi/6, 5\pi/6, 7\pi/6, 11\pi/6$. **23.** $\pi/6, 5\pi/6, 3\pi/2$. **25.** 0.511; one solution. **26.** 0.357; two solutions. **27.** 4.493; infinitely many solutions. **28.** 0.480; infinitely many solutions. **29.** 2.123; one solution. **30.** 0.601; one solution.

Problem Set 10.10.

1. $x < 3$. **3.** $x \geq 1/3$. **5.** $-7/2 < x < 5/2$. **7.** $-5/3 \leq x \leq 1/3$. **9.** $x \geq 15/2$. **11.** No solution. **13.** $y > 10$ or $y < -2$. **15.** $-13/3 < x \leq 19/3$. **17.** $x \leq 2 - \sqrt{2}$, $x \geq 2 + \sqrt{2}$. **19.** $-5/4 \leq x \leq 1$. **21.** All real numbers.

Problem Set 10.11.

1. $1/3 < x < 3$. **3.** $x > -2/3$ or $x < -2$. **5.** $x \geq 2/3$ or $x \leq -7/2$. **7.** $x < -1$, $-2 < x < 3$. **9.** $1 < x < 2$. **11.** $x < 3$. **13.** $(2k - 1)\pi < x < 2k\pi$, for any integer k.

Review Test A.

1. Let $a = (a_1, a_2)$, $b = (b_1, b_2)$, and $c = (c_1, c_2)$. Then $a + (b + c) = \underline{(a_1, a_2)} + [\underline{(b_1, b_2)} + \underline{(c_1, c_2)}] = \underline{(a_1, a_2)} + [\underline{(b_1 + c_1, b_2 + c_2)}] = \underline{(a_1 + b_1 + c_1, a_2 + b_2 + c_2)} = \underline{(a_1 + b_1} + c_1, \underline{a_2 + b_2} + c_2)$. Similarly, $(a + b) + c$ equals this latter expression. **2.** $3/2 + (\sqrt{11}/2)i$, $3/2 - (\sqrt{11}/2)i$. **3.** $\sqrt{3} + i$. **4.** $\sqrt[6]{2}$ cis $(-\pi/12)$, $\sqrt[6]{2}$ cis $7\pi/12$, $\sqrt[6]{2}$ cis $5\pi/4$. **5.** $2, -3, (-1 \pm \sqrt{7}i)/2$. **6.** $-3/2, 1/3$. **7.** 0.3747, 2.7669. **8.** 1.36, 3.15. **9.** (*a*) $x < 3$ or $x > 4$; (*b*) $x \leq -2$ or $-1/2 \leq x \leq 1$. **10.** $A = 3, B = 9, C = 7, D = 2$. **11.** (*a*) $\{0, 1, 2, 3, 4, 5\}$; (*b*) $2 < x \leq 8$. **12.** (*a*) $k = 3, -5$; (*b*) $-1/4 + (\sqrt{3}/4)i$.

Review Test B.

1. Let $a = (a_1, a_2)$, $b = (b_1, b_2)$, and $c = (c_1, c_2)$. Then $a(b + c) = (a_1, a_2)[(b_1, b_2) + (c_1, c_2)] = (a_1, a_2)(b_1 + c_1, b_2 + c_2) = (a_1b_1 + a_1c_1 -$

$a_2b_2 - a_2c_2$, $a_2b_1 + a_2c_1 + a_1b_2 + a_2c_2$. Similarly, the expansion of $ab + ac$ yields the same result. **2.** $2\sqrt{2}$ cis $\pi/4$, $2\sqrt{2}$ cis $(-\pi/4)$. **3.** $-16 + 16i$. **4.** $\sqrt[8]{32}$ cis $\pi/16$, $\sqrt[8]{32}$ cis $9\pi/16$, $\sqrt[8]{32}$ cis $17\pi/16$, $\sqrt[8]{32}$ cis $25\pi/16$. **5.** 2, -4, $-2 \pm \sqrt{2}$. **6.** 3/4. **7.** $\pi/6$, $5\pi/6$, $7\pi/6$, $11\pi/6$. **8.** 3.093. **9.** (*a*) $\{0, 1, 2, 3, 4\}$; (*b*) $\{0, 1, 2\}$. **10.** (*a*) $-2 < x < 1/2$; (*b*) $-1/3 \leq x \leq 0$, $x > 3$. **11.** $A = 2$, $B = -9$, $C = 14$. **12.** (*a*) $t = -4 \pm \sqrt{16 + 2s}$; (*b*) $x = 5$, $y = 1/2$.

CHAPTER 11

Problem Set 11.1.

1. (2, 3). **3.** (2/3, 5/3). **5.** (5/3, 5/2). **7.** (2, 1). **9.** $(-1, -2)$. **11.** (2, 3).

Problem Set 11.2.

1. (*a*) $m = 3$, $n = 4$; (*b*) 2, 1, 4, -5. **2.** (*a*) 3, 4, 1, -2; (*b*) 4, 1, 0; (*c*) 2, 4, 0. **3.** (*a*) 19; (*b*) -7; (*c*) 5; (*d*) 10. **4.** (*a*) 19; (*b*) 7; (*c*) 5; (*d*) 10. **5.** 49. **7.** (*a*) 130; (*b*) 45; (*c*) 126. **13.** (*a*) $7x - x^2 - 25$; (*b*) $7x + 11$; (*c*) -5. **14.** (*a*) $xy^2 + yz^2 + zx^2 - x^2y - y^2z - z^2x$; (*b*) $xy - 3x^2$; (*c*) $2 + 5x - 5x^2$. **16.** $8x + 5y - 7 = 0$.

Problem Set 11.3.

1. (2, 3, 3). **3.** (35/11, 28/11, $-14/11$). **5.** (1, 2, 3). **7.** (2, -1, 3). **9.** (0, 0, 0).

Problem Set 11.4.

1. $\begin{pmatrix} 220 & 0 & 0 & -13 \\ 0 & 20 & 0 & 3 \\ 0 & 0 & 110 & -19 \end{pmatrix}$ **3.** $\begin{pmatrix} 24 & 0 & 0 & 52 & 29 \\ 0 & 12 & 0 & 56 & 25 \\ 0 & 0 & 3 & -10 & -2 \end{pmatrix}$

5. $\begin{pmatrix} 1 & 0 & 0 & 0 \\ 0 & 1 & 0 & 0 \\ 0 & 0 & 1 & 0 \\ 0 & 0 & 0 & 1 \end{pmatrix}$ **7.** $\begin{pmatrix} 2 & 0 & 0 & 0 & -1 \\ 0 & 1 & 0 & 0 & 3 \\ 0 & 0 & 2 & 0 & 1 \\ 0 & 0 & 0 & 1 & 2 \end{pmatrix}$

9. $\begin{pmatrix} 3 & 0 & 0 & 0 & 1 \\ 0 & 2 & 0 & 0 & -3 \\ 0 & 0 & 2 & 0 & -1 \\ 0 & 0 & 0 & 5 & -6 \end{pmatrix}$

Problem Set 11.5.

1. (*a*) $(-4/3,\ 2/3,\ 6/5)$; (*b*) $(-5/6,\ 9/2,\ 0)$; (*c*) $(0,\ 7/4,\ 5/8)$. **2.** (*a*) $x = 6/5$, $y = u$, $z = -2u + 1/2$; (*b*) $x = 9/4$, $y = \text{u}$, $z = 6/5$; (*c*) $x = 8/5$, $y = u$, $z = -2/3 - (4/3)u$. **3.** (*a*) $x = -5/2$, $y = u$, $z = 5u - 8$, $w = 7/4$; (*b*) $x = u$, $y = -2/5 - (6/5)u$, $z = v$, $w = -3/2 + 2v$. **5.** $x = 11u + 56$, $y = -6u - 30$, $z = u$. **7.** Inconsistent. **9.** $x = u$, $y = -2u$, $z = u$.

Problem Set 11.6.

1. $3/[2(x+1)] - 1/[2(x-1)]$. **3.** $-6/[5(x+2)] + 12/[5(2x-1)]$. **5.** $2/(x+2) + 3/(x+2)^2 - 2/(x+1)$. **7.** $x/(x^2+3)^2 + (1-3x)/(x^2+3)^3$. **9.** $-7/x + 2/x^2 + 1/x^3 + (7x+5)/(x^2+x+1) + (10x+1)/(x^2+x+1)^2$. **11.** $x + 1 - 1/(x-1) + (x+1)/(x^2+1)$. **13.** $1 + 1/[2(x-1)] - 1/[2(x+1)] - 1/(x^2+1)$. **15.** $2 + 11/(x-5) + 4/(x+2)$. **17.** $y = (-19/30)x^3 + (1/30)x^2 + (13/5)x + 3$.

Problem Set 11.7.

1. $\{(-4, 3),\ (3, 4)\}$. **3.** $(1, -2)$. **5.** $\{(4, 3),\ (-2, -6)\}$. **7.** $(2, 6)$. **9.** $\{(a^2, a),\ (a^2/2, a/2)\}$. **11.** $\left\{\left(\dfrac{-6+8i}{5}, \dfrac{12+4i}{5}\right), \left(\dfrac{-6-8i}{5}, \dfrac{-12-4i}{5}\right)\right\}$.

Problem Set 11.8.

1. $\{(3, 2), (3, -2), (-3, 2), (-3, -2)\}$. **3.** $\{(\sqrt{3}i, \sqrt{7}i), (\sqrt{3}i, -\sqrt{7}i), (-\sqrt{3}i, \sqrt{7}i), (-\sqrt{3}i, -\sqrt{7}i)\}$. **5.** $\{(2\sqrt{6}, \sqrt{6}), (-2\sqrt{6}, -\sqrt{6})\}$. **7.** $\{(1, -7), (-1, -7), (1, 3), (-1, 3)\}$. **9.** $\{(\sqrt{6}, -2\sqrt{6}), (-\sqrt{6}, 2\sqrt{6}), (-4, -2), (4, 2)\}$. **11.** $\{(3, 5), (1, -3), (-3, 5), (-1, -3)\}$.

Review Test A.

1. (*a*) $(1, -2)$; (*b*) $(1/2, -1, 2)$. **2.** $1(2) + 4(-6) - 3/2 = -28$. **3.** \$2500 at 4%, \$1500 at 6%. **4.** $(2, -1, 3)$. **5.** $x = 10u$, $y = -7u - 3/10$, $z = -16u + 18/5$, $w = 4u - 12/5$. **6.** $A = 1, B = 2$. **7.** $A = B = 1/2$, $C = 3/2$. **8.** $(5, 1)$, $(7, 5)$. **9.** $(3, 2)$, $(-3, -2)$, $(1, -1)$, $(-1, 1)$. **10.** $x = 7t$, $y = 19t$, $z = 11t$. **11.** 7.24 ohms, 2.76 ohms. **12.** 1, 3, -3.

Review Test B.

1. (*a*) $(-2, 3)$; (*b*) $(2, -1, -2)$. **2.** $3(4) + 4(6) = 36$. **3.** 189 miles per hour; 324 miles. **4.** $(-2, -3, 2)$. **5.** $x = 2u$, $y = -1/2 - 5u$, $z = -5/2 - 11u$, $w = -5/2 - 7u$. **6.** $A = -2$, $B = 3$. **7.** $A = -7/3$, $B = -5/3$, $C = 13/3$. **8.** $\{(1, -1), (2, -5/2)\}$. **9.** $\{(2, 3), (2, -3), (-2, 3), (-2, -3)\}$. **10.** $x = t$, $y = -2t$, $z = 4t$. **11.** 1, 25/3, 47/3. **12.** -10.

CHAPTER 12

Problem Set 12.2.

1.

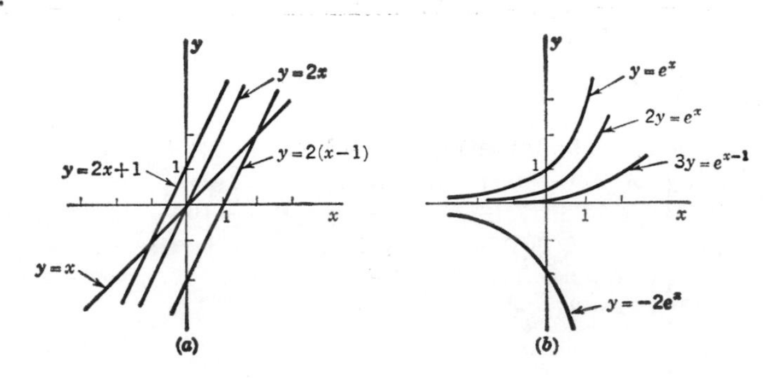

2.

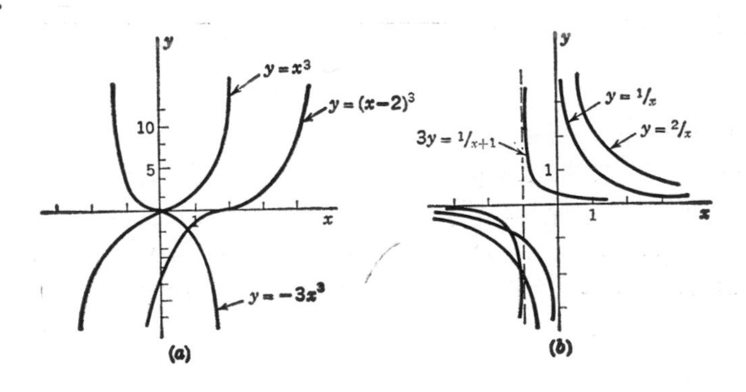

3.

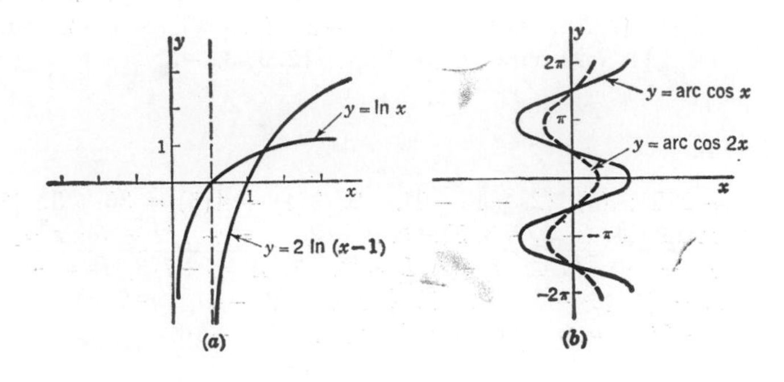

4.

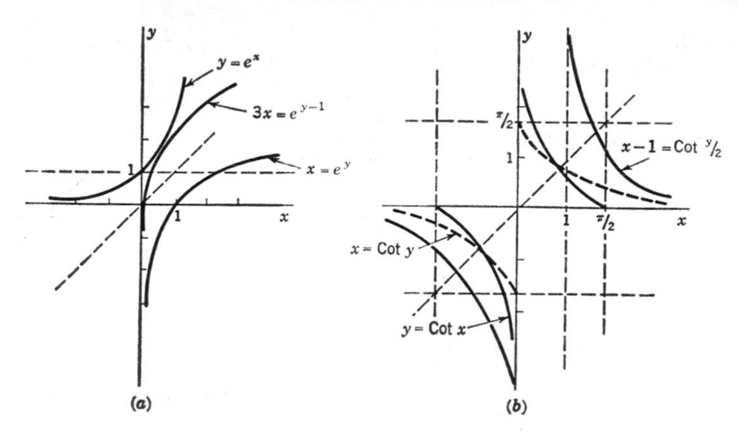
y
y = e^x
3x = e^{y-1}
x = e^y
1
1
x
(a)
y
π/2
1
x − 1 = Cot y/2
1
π/2
x
x = Cot y
y = Cot x
(b)

5.

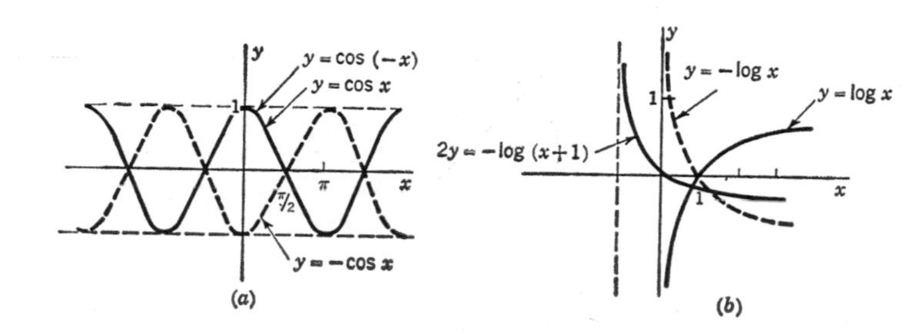
y
y = cos (−x)
y = cos x
1
π
x
π/2
y = −cos x
(a)
y
y = −log x
y = log x
1
2y = −log (x+1)
1
x
(b)

6.

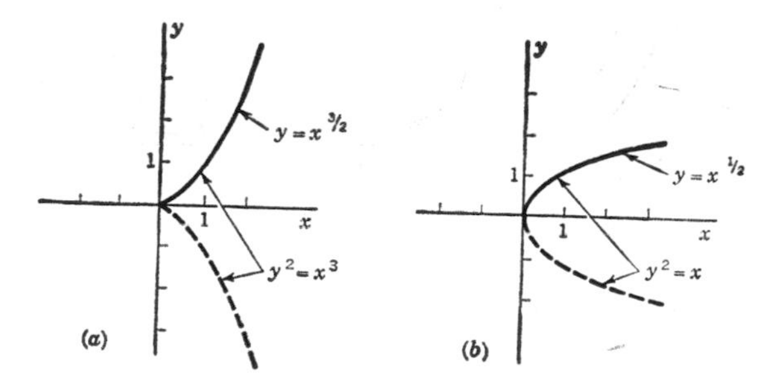
y
y = x^{3/2}
1
1
x
y² = x³
(a)
y
1
y = x^{1/2}
1
x
y² = x
(b)

7.

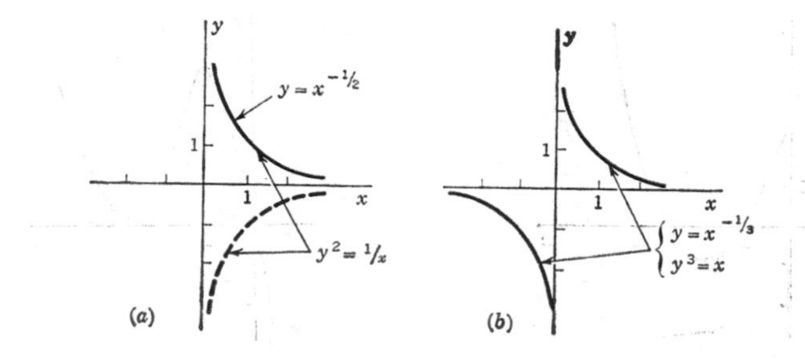
y
y = x^{−1/2}
1
1
x
y² = 1/x
(a)
y
1
1
x
y = x^{−1/3}
y³ = x
(b)

8.

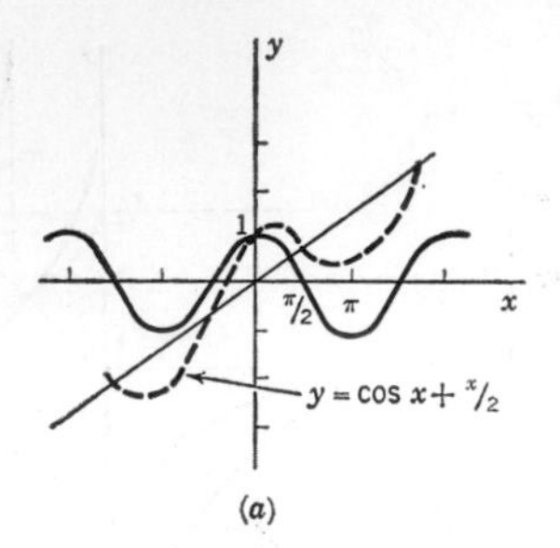

(a)

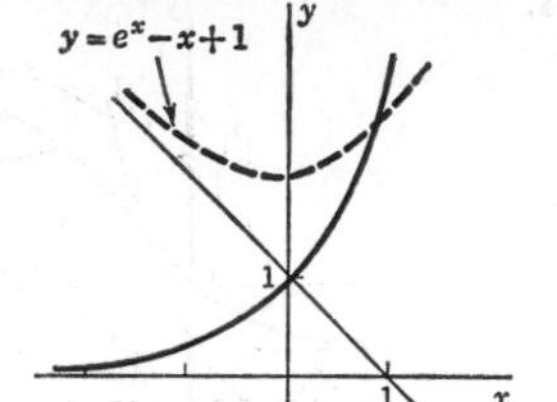

(b)

9.

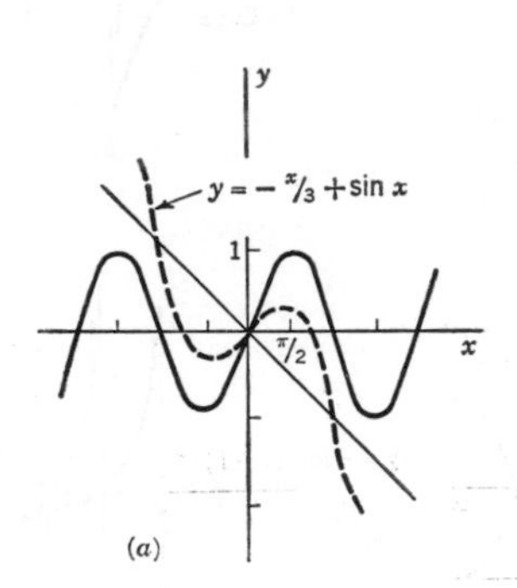

(a)

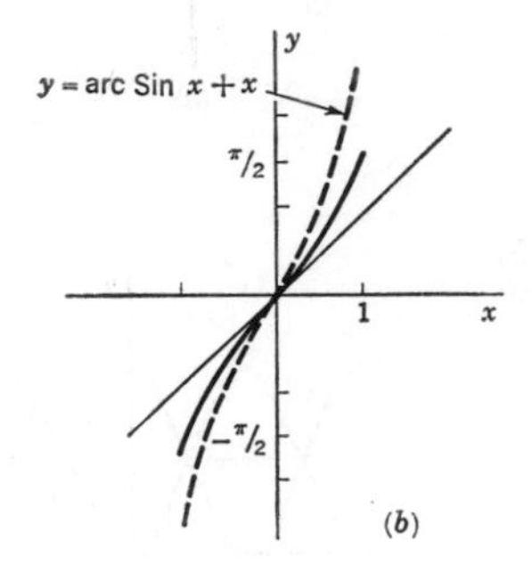

(b)

10.

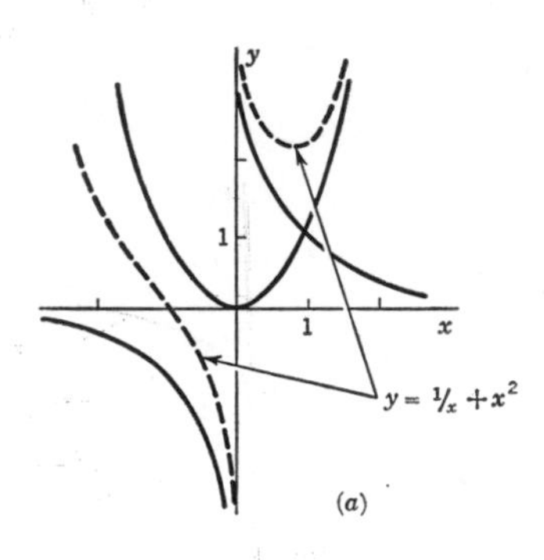

(a)

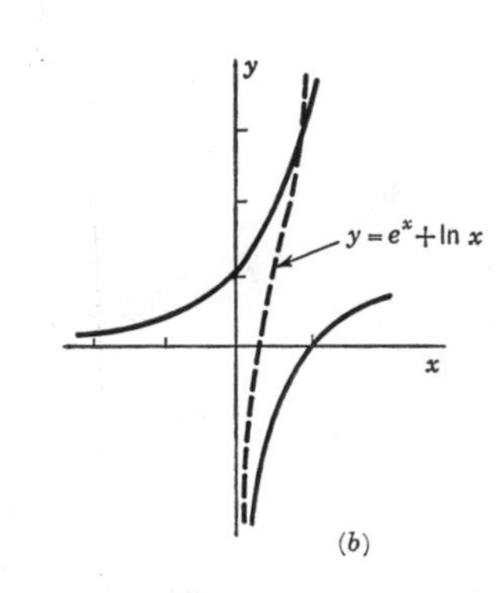

(b)

Problem Set 12.3.

1.

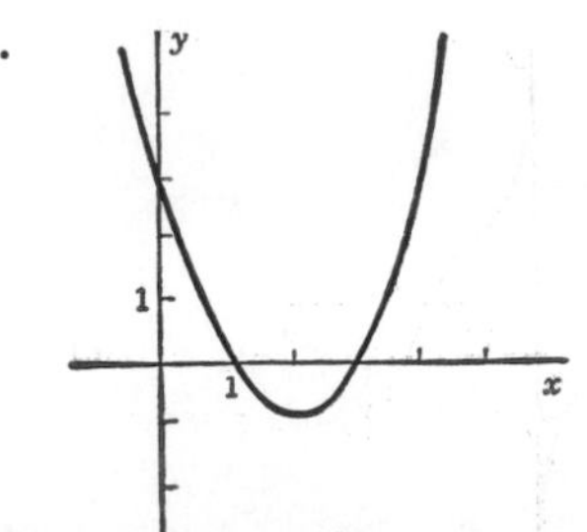

3.

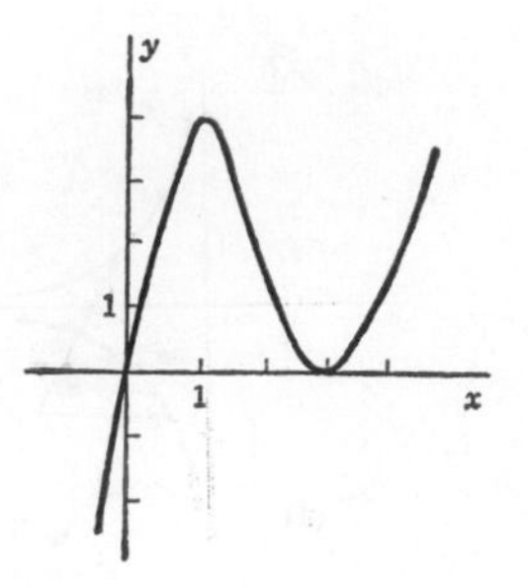

5.

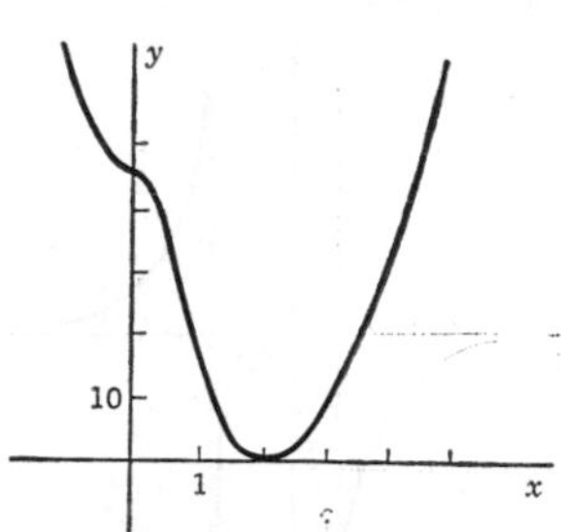

7.

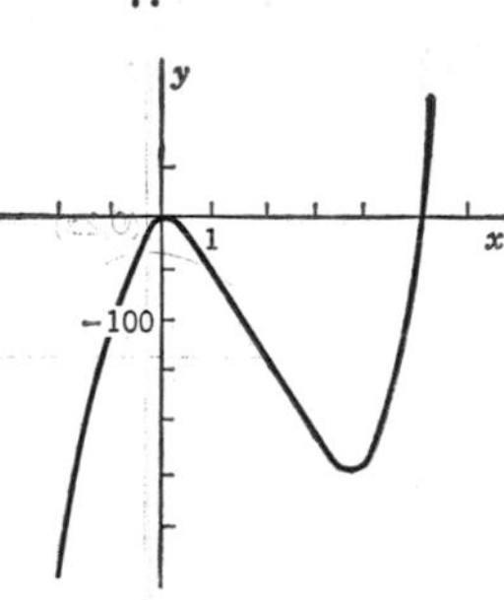

9.

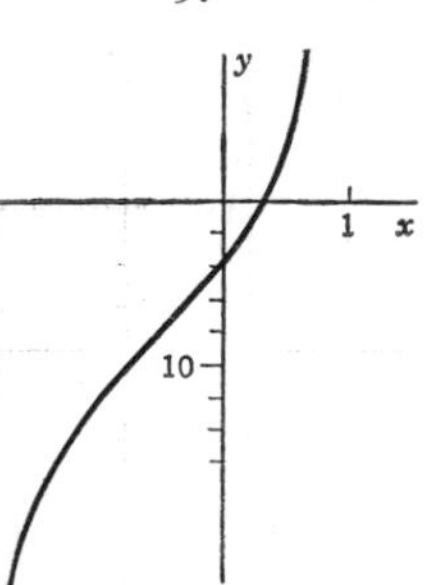

13. The set of all real numbers.

19.

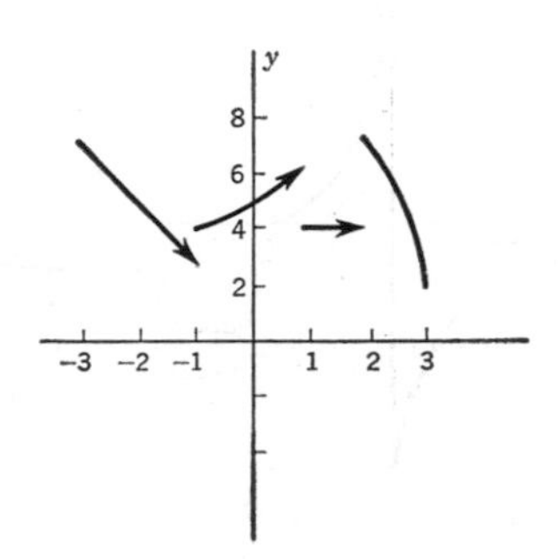

Problem Set 12.4.

1. $y = 1, x = \pm 2$. **3.** $y = 0, x = 0, x = \pm 2$. **5.** $x = 2$. **7.** $2x + 3y = 0$, $2x - 3y = 0$. **9.** $x = 0$, $y = 4$, $y = x - 4$. **11.** $x = 1$, $x - y + 1 = 0$, $x + y + 1 = 0$.

Problem Set 12.5.

1.

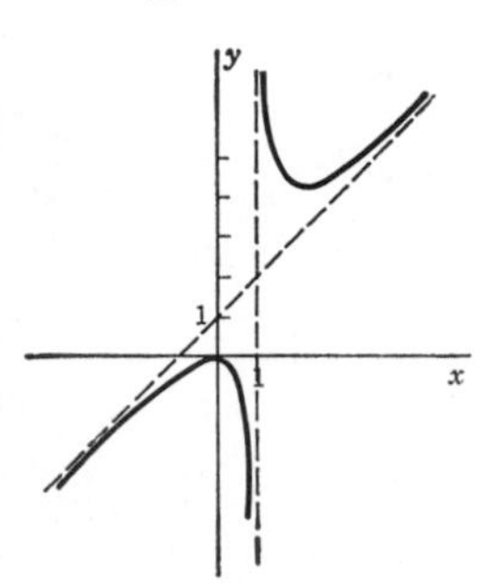

3.

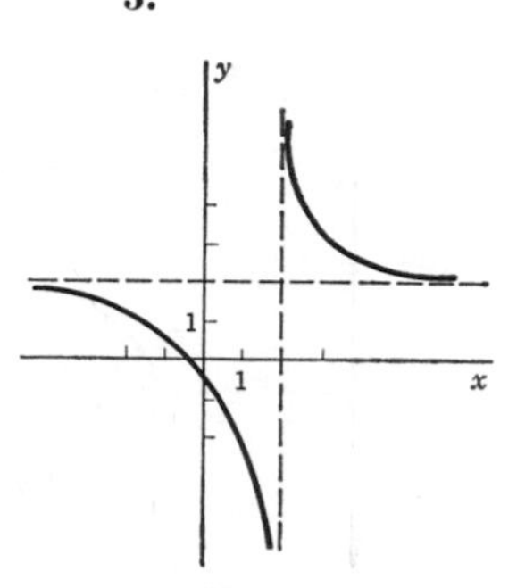

5.

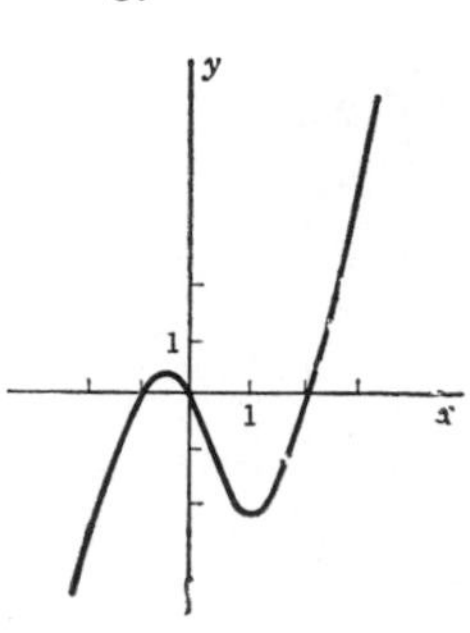

7.

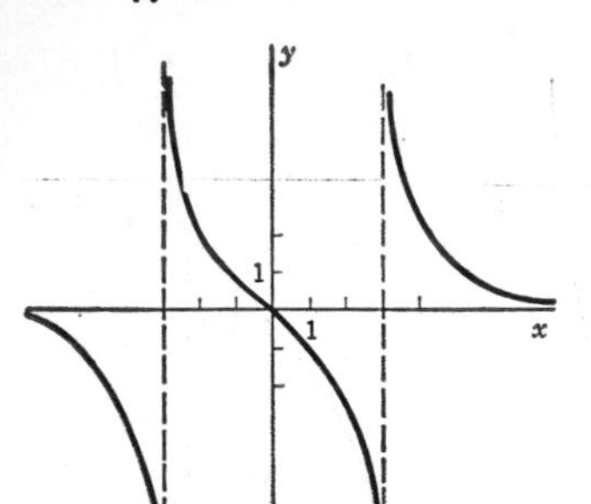

9.

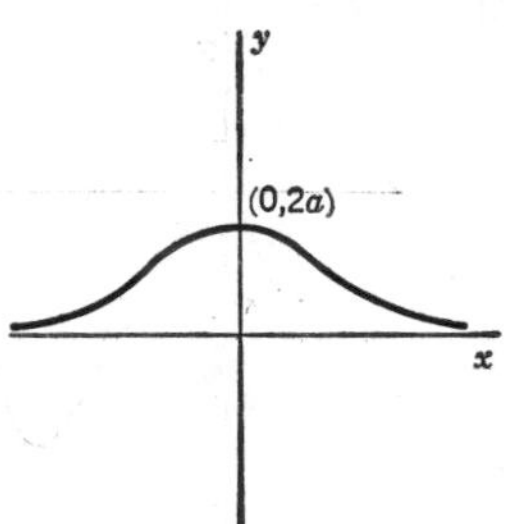

11.

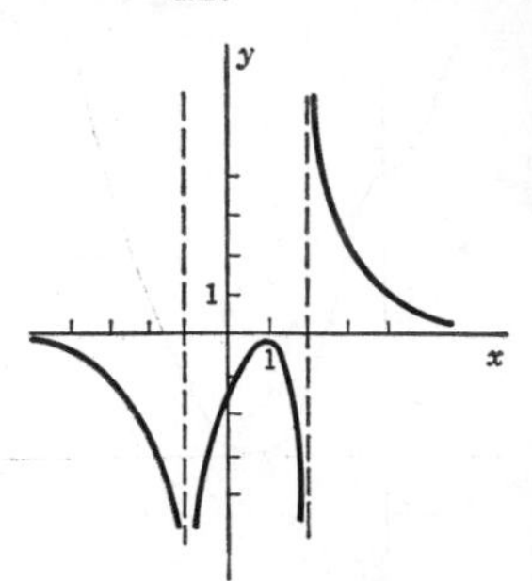

13.

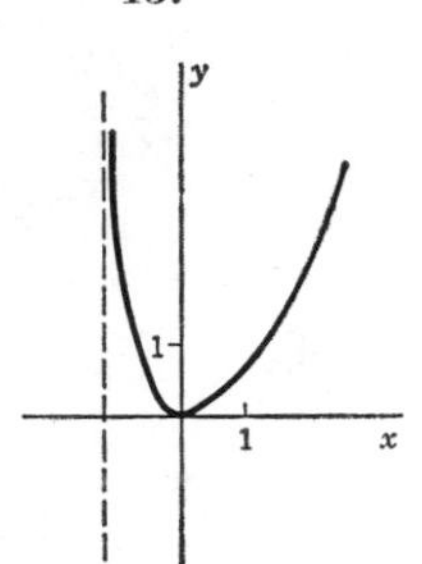

15.

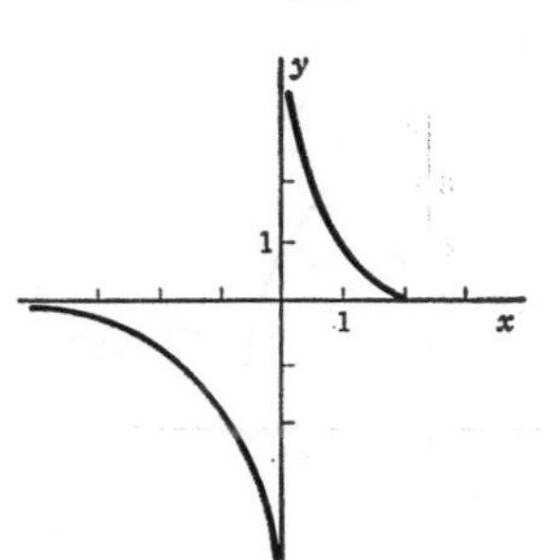

17.

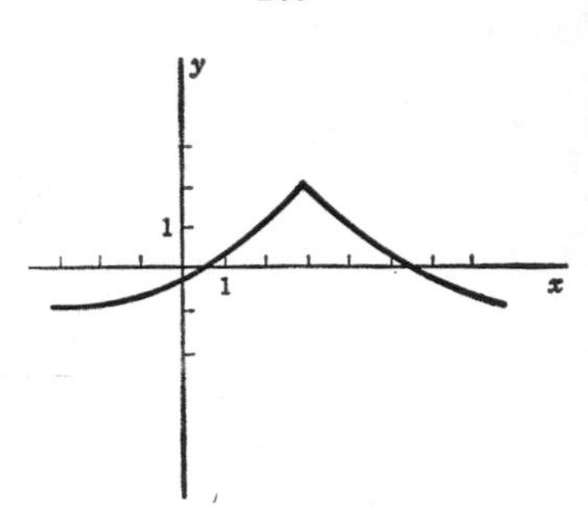

19.

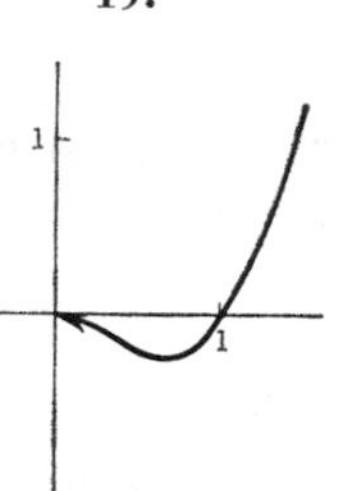

21.

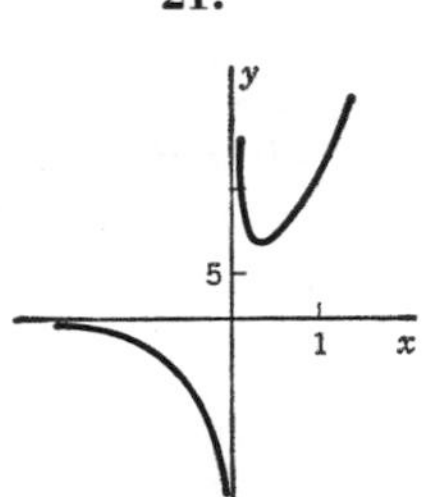

23.

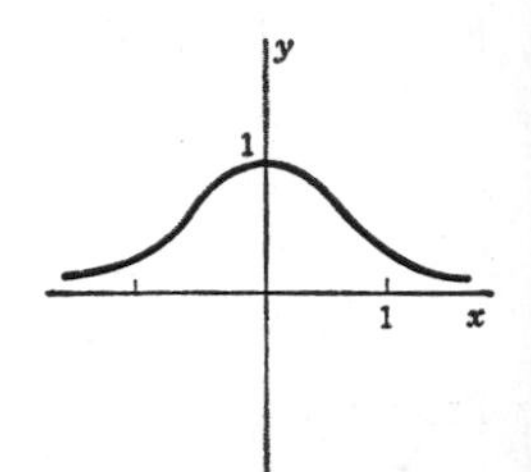

25.

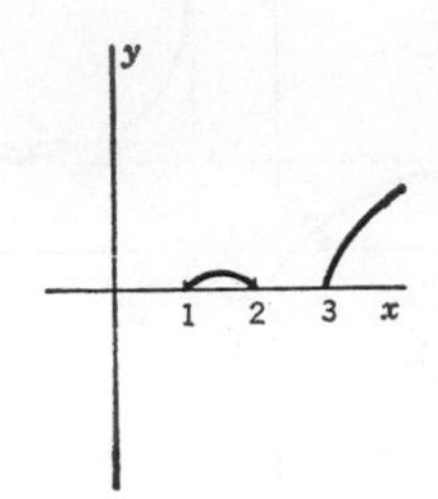

Problem Set 12.6.

1.

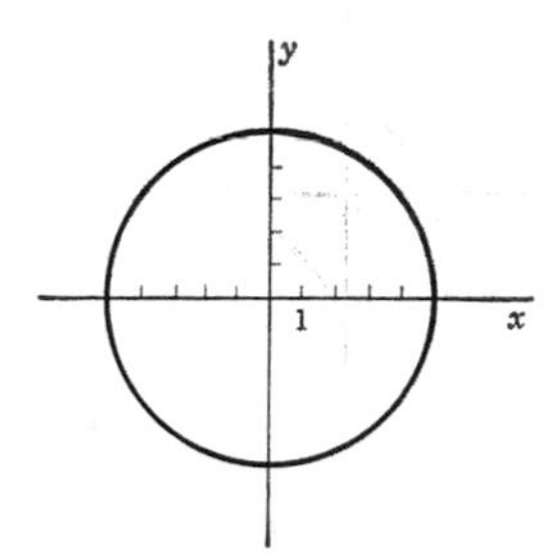

3.

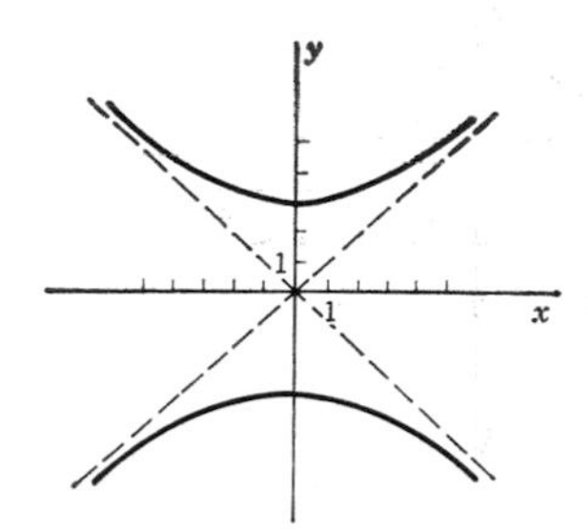

5.

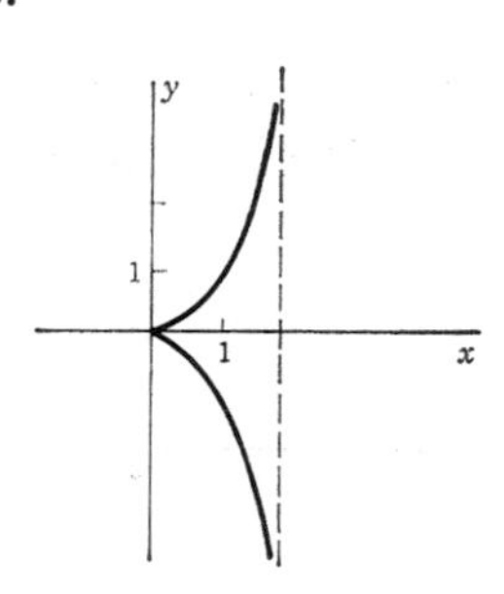

7.

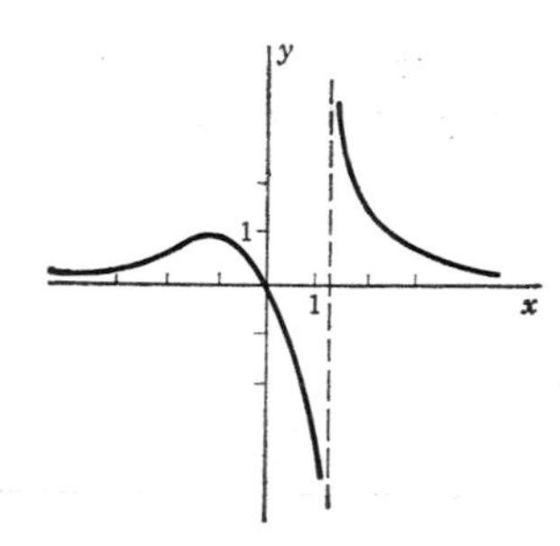

9.

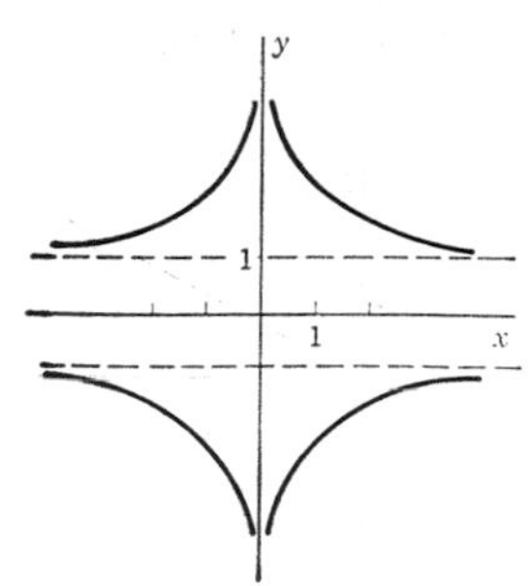

11.

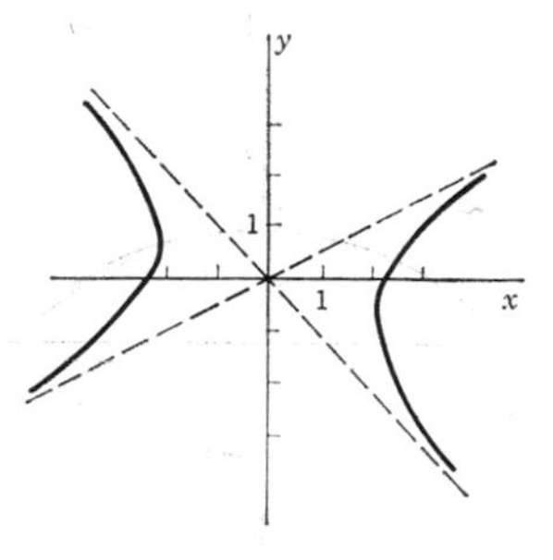

13.

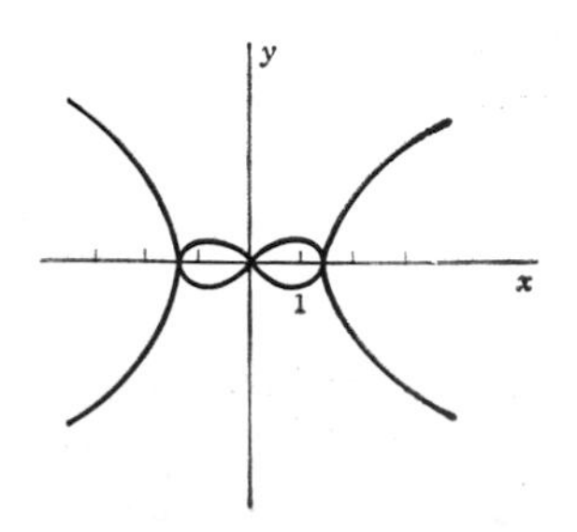

15.

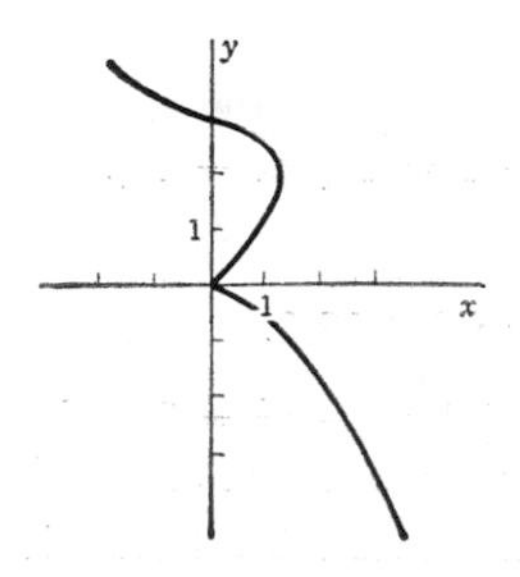

17.

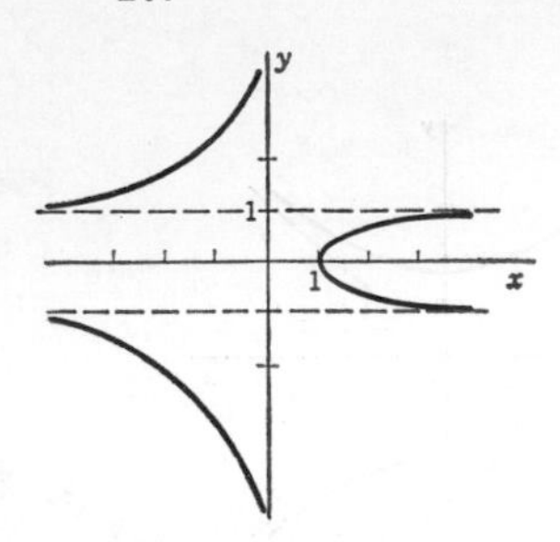

19.

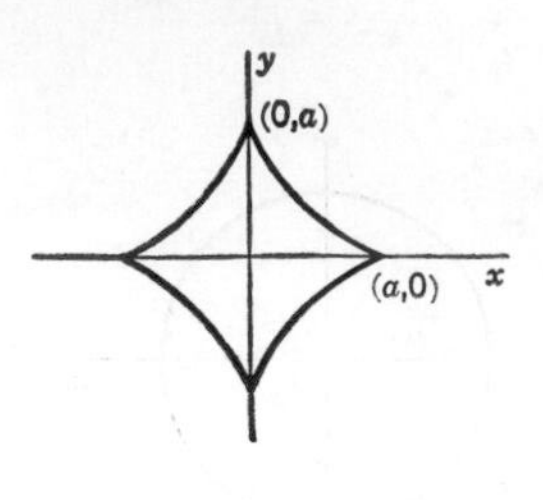

Problem Set 12.7.

1. (*a*) hyperbola; (*b*) ellipse; (*c*) ellipse; (*d*) parabola. **3.** (*a*) $y = -x$, $y = x/2$; (*b*) $y = -2x$, $y = x/2$; (*c*) $y = x$, $y = -3x$; (*d*) $y = 4x$, $y = -x$.

5.

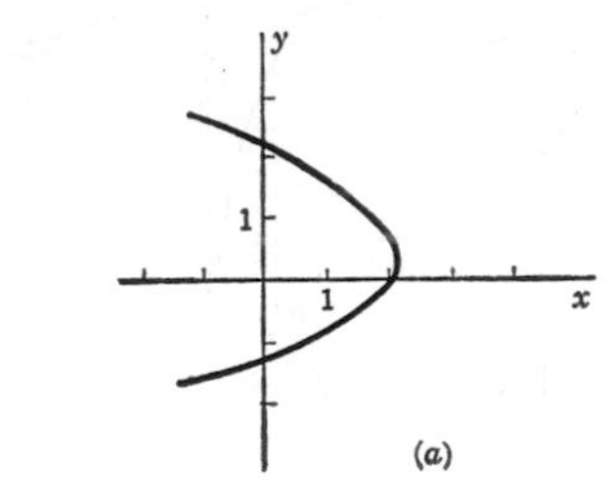

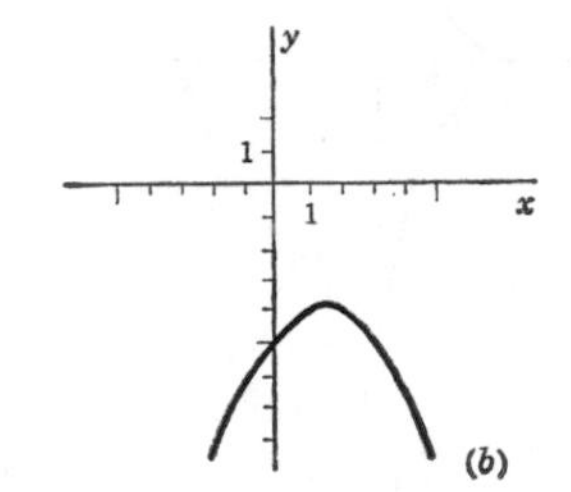

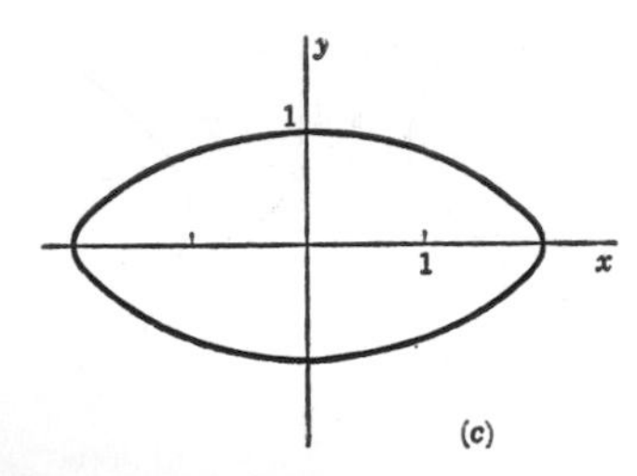

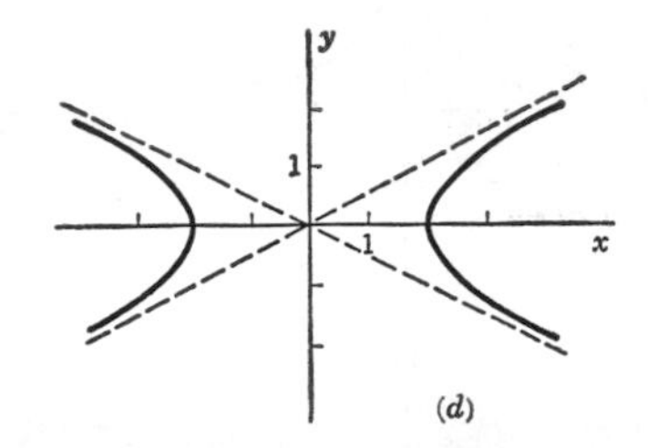

7. (*a*) The origin; (*b*) the two parallel lines with equations $y = \pm\sqrt{5/3}$; (*c*) two intersecting lines through the origin, with equations $3x + 2y = 0$ and $3x - 2y = 0$; (*d*) the line with equation $x = -1$. **9.** (*a*) $y + 1 = 4(x - 3)^2$; (*b*) $y + 1 = 1/[2(x - 3)]$.

Problem Set 12.8.

2. (*a*) $x^2 + y^2 = 24$; (*b*) $x^2 + y^2 = 4$; (*c*) $x^2 + y^2 = 100$. **3.** (*a*) A circle with center at the origin, and radius 2 units long; (*b*) a circle with center at the origin and radius $2\sqrt{3}$ units long; (*c*) a circle with center at the origin and radius

$\sqrt{10}$ units long; (*d*) a circle with center at the origin and radius $\sqrt{2/3}$ units long; (*e*) a "point circle" consisting of the origin; (*f*) a circle with center at the origin and radius $\sqrt{14/5}$ units long. **5.** (*a*) $x^2 + y^2 - 4x + 8y - 80 = 0$; (*b*) $x^2 + y^2 - 6x + 8y = 0$; (*c*) $x^2 + y^2 + 2x + 6y - 6 = 0$; (*d*) $x^2 + y^2 - 2x - 10y - 10 = 0$. **7.** (*a*) Center at (3/2, 0), radius $\sqrt{47/3}/2$ units long; (*b*) center at (0, −4), radius $2\sqrt{6}$ units long; (*c*) center at (−5/4, 0), radius 5/4 units long; (*d*) center at (0, 2), radius 2 units long. **8.** (*a*) Divide ordinates by 2; (*b*) divide abscissas by $\sqrt{2}$ and ordinates by 2; (*c*) divide abscissas by $\sqrt{2/5}$ and ordinates by $2/\sqrt{5}$.

Review Test A.

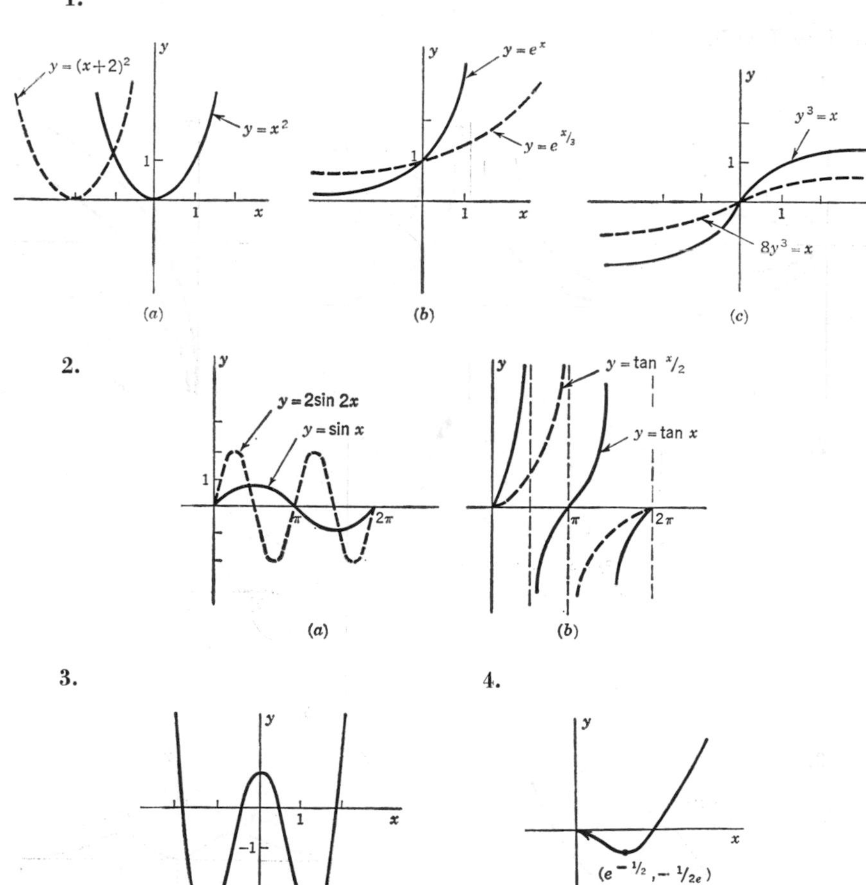

5. $x = 0$, $y = -2$, $y = 1$. **6.** $x + y + 1 = 0$.

7.

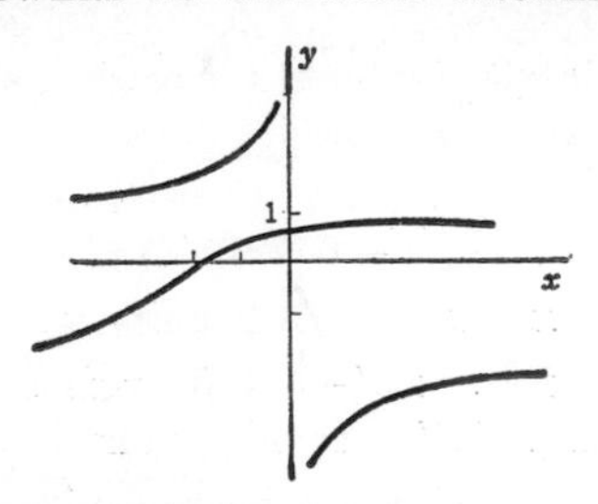

8. (*a*) ellipse; (*b*) hyperbola; (*c*) hyperbola. **9.** (1, −2), $5\sqrt{2}/2$. **10.** $x^2 + y^2 - 4x - 2y = 0$. **11.** (*a*), (*b*), (*c*): y positive and very large; (*d*) y negative and numerically large. **12.** $x^2 + y^2 = k(x + y)$.

Review Test B.

1.

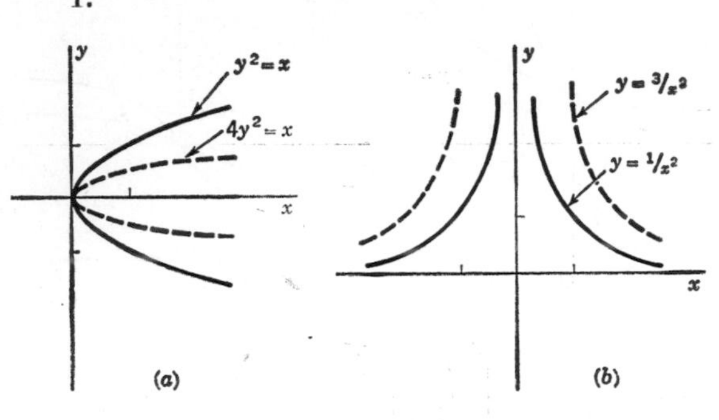

y = ln 2x
y = ln x
(c)

2.

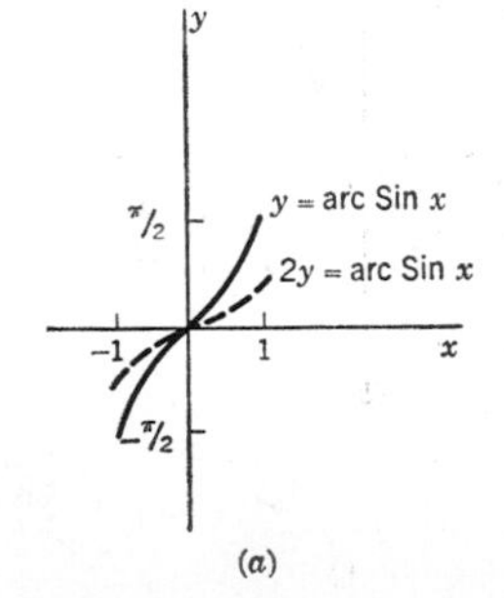

(a)

y = cos x
3y = cos x/2
(b)

3.

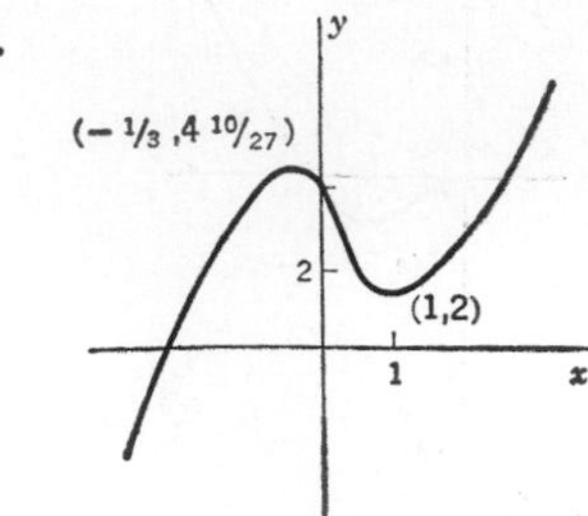

4.

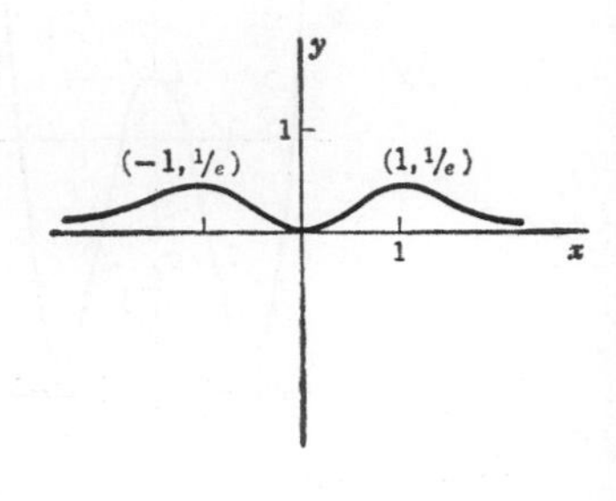

5. $x = 3, x = 2, y = 0$. **6.** $x - y + 1 = 0, x - 2y - 1 = 0$.

7.

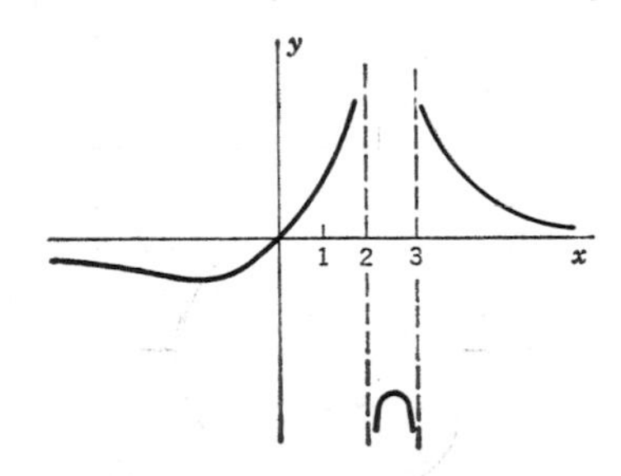

8. (*a*) parabola; (*b*) parabola; (*c*) ellipse. **9.** $(-1, 0)$, $4\sqrt{3}/3$. **10.** $x^2 + y^2 - 6x + 8y - 9 = 0$. **11.** (*a*), (*d*): y negative and numerically very large; (*b*), (*c*): y positive and very large. **12.** (*a*) x-axis; (*b*) origin; (*c*) origin.

CHAPTER 13

Problem Set 13.1.

1. $\pi/6, 7\pi/6, 13\pi/6, -5\pi/6, -11\pi/6, -17\pi/6$.

3.

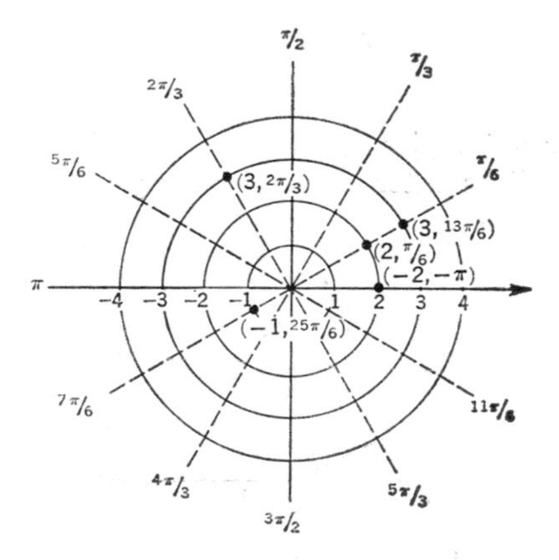

5. $(-3, 3\pi/2)$, $(3, 5\pi/2)$, $(-3, -\pi/2)$; $(3, 7\pi/6)$, $(-3, 13\pi/6)$, $(3, -5\pi/6)$; $(-4, 2\pi/3)$, $(4, 5\pi/3)$, $(-4, -4\pi/3)$. **7.** $(-1, 2 - \pi)$.

9. $d = 2\sqrt{7}$.

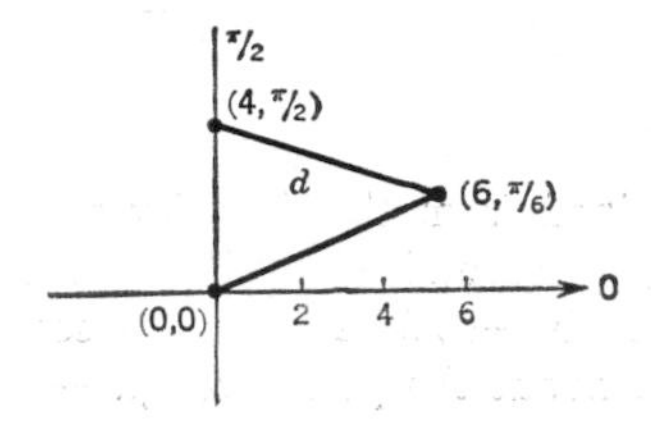

Problem Set 13.2.

1.

3.

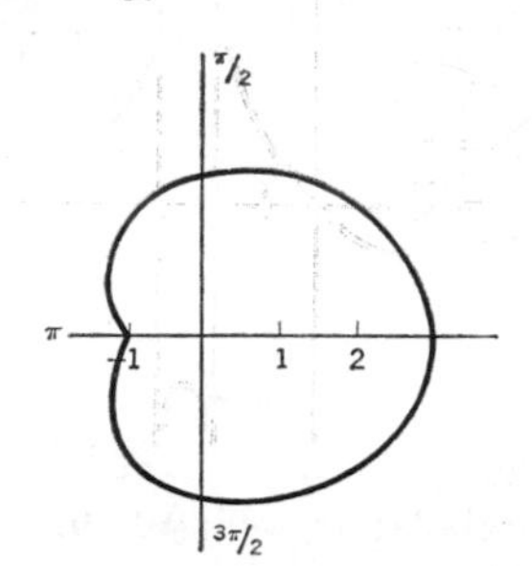

5.

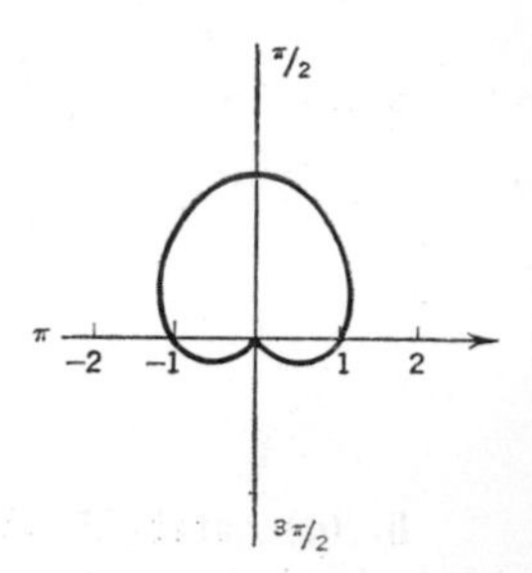

7.

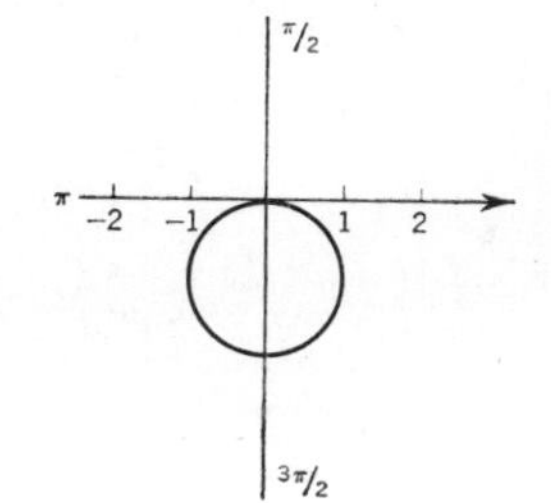

9.

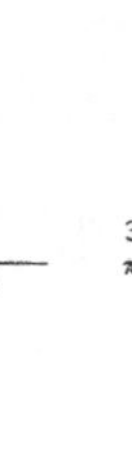

11.

13. The loci of $r = 5$ and $r = -5$ are identical; the loci of $\theta = \pi/4$ and $\theta = -\pi/4$ are straight lines, intersecting at an angle of $\pi/2$ radians.

15.

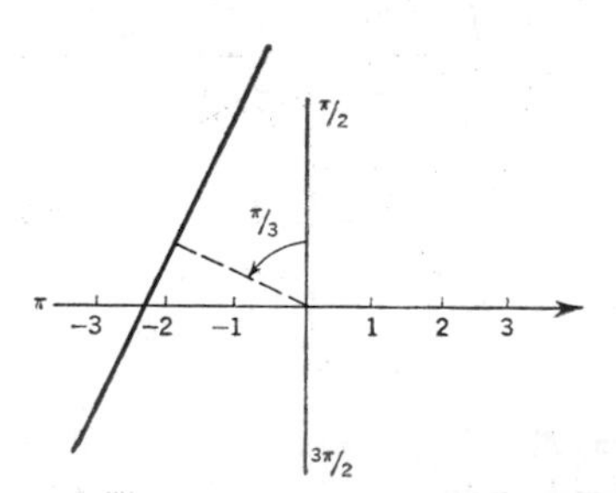

Problem Set 13.3.

2. (a) Second is obtained from the first, by rotating the latter about the pole through $\pi/3$ radians; (b) second is obtained from the first, by rotating the latter about the pole through $-\pi/6$ radians; (c) second is obtained from the first, by rotating the latter about the pole through $-2\pi/3$ radians.

3.

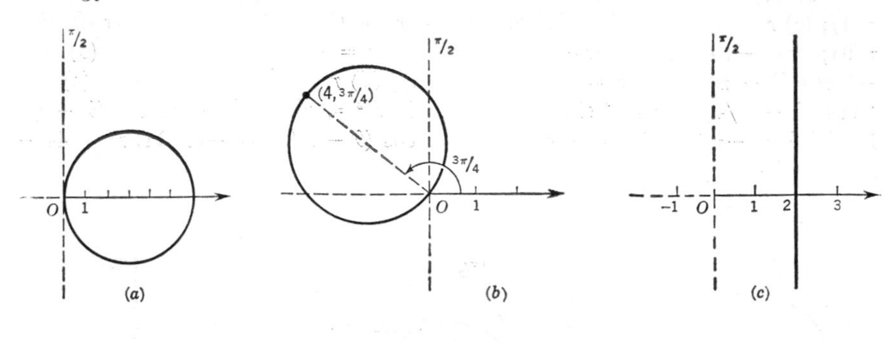

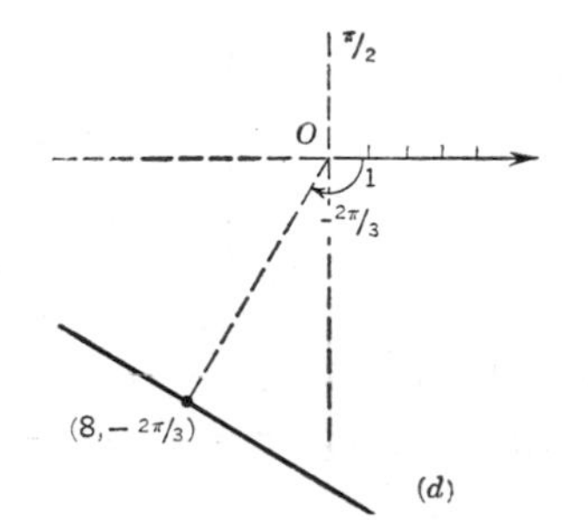

π/2

O 1 −π/6

(3, − π/6)

(e)

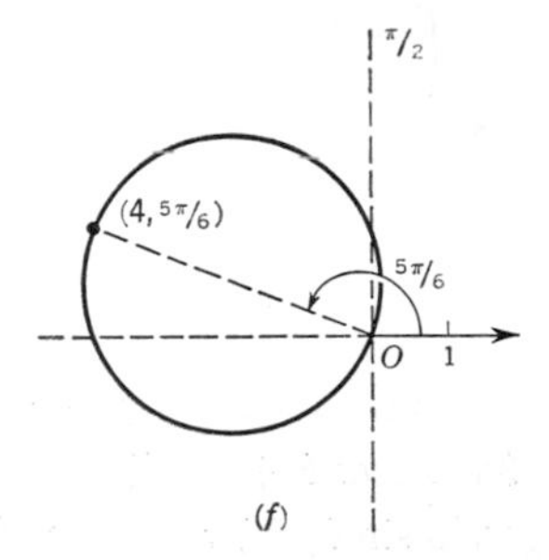

4.

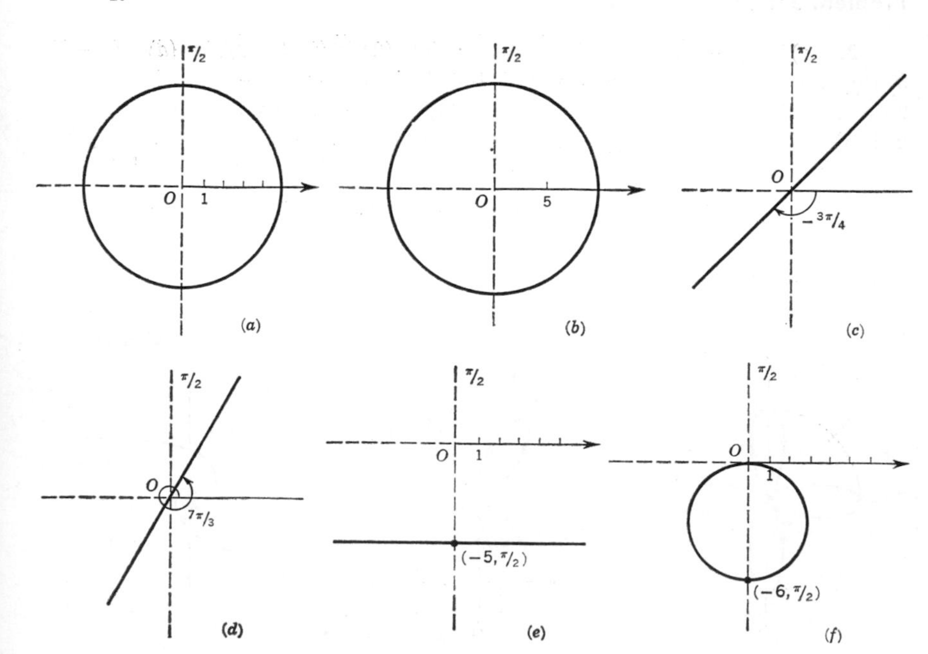

5. (*a*) $r = 10 \sin(\theta + \pi/6)$; (*b*) $r = -8 \sin(\theta - \pi/4)$ or $r = -8 \cos(\theta + \pi/4)$; (*c*) $r = 20 \sin(\theta + \pi/6)$. **6.** (*a*) $5 = r \cos(\theta - \pi/6)$; (*b*) $-2 = r \sin(\theta - \pi/6)$; (*c*) $-10 = r \sin(\theta - \pi/6)$. **8.** (*a*) $r = -6 \cos(\theta + \pi/3)$; (*b*) $r = -5 \cos(\theta - \pi/5)$; (*c*) $r = 8 \cos(\theta - \pi/6)$; (*d*) $r = 10 \sin(\theta - \pi/6)$; (*e*) $r = 4 \cos(\theta - \pi/4)$ or $r = 4 \sin(\theta + \pi/4)$. **9.** $R^2 = r^2 + c^2 - 2rc \cos(\theta - \gamma)$. **10.** (*a*) $\theta = -\pi/4$; (*b*) $4 = -r \cos\theta$; (*c*) $r \cos(\theta - \pi/6) = -5$. **11.** $r^2 + 44 - 24r \cos(\theta - 2\pi/3) = 0$.

13.

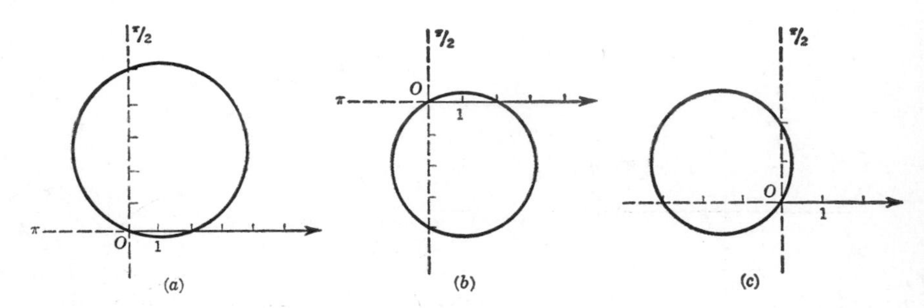

14. $5 = r \cos(\theta - \pi/6)$. **15.** (*a*) $r = 2 \cos\theta + 2\sqrt{3} \sin\theta$; (*b*) $r = 3\sqrt{2}(\cos\theta + \sin\theta)$; (*c*) $r = -4\sqrt{3} \cos\theta + 4 \sin\theta$; (*d*) $r = 4 \cos\theta - 4\sqrt{3} \sin\theta$; (*e*) $r = 6 \cos\theta + 6\sqrt{3} \sin\theta$.

Problem Set 13.4.

2. (*a*) $(1, -\sqrt{3})$; (*b*) $(\sqrt{2}, \sqrt{2})$; (*c*) $(3\sqrt{2}/2, 3\sqrt{2}/2)$; (*d*) $(0, -2)$. **3.** (*a*) $r = -8 \cos\theta$; (*b*) $r = 6 \cos\theta + 4 \sin\theta$. **4.** (*a*) $x - 3y = 6$; (*b*) $x + 2y = 10$. **5.** (*a*) $r^2(2 - 3 \sin 2\theta) = 0$; (*b*) $r^2(1 - 2r^2 \cos^4\theta) = 0$; (*c*) $r(r + 2 \sin\theta) = 8$. **7.** (*a*) $x^2 + y^2 - 2x + 4y = 0$; (*b*) $5(x^2 - y^2) = \pm 2(x^2 + y^2)^{3/2}$; (*c*) $2(x^2 + y^2) = 5x$. **9.** $x^2 + y^2 - ax \cos\omega - ay \sin\omega = 0$. **10.** $x^2 + y^2 - ax - by = 0$; $\sqrt{a^2 + b^2}/2$; $(a/2, b/2)$. **11.** $x^2 + y^2 = c^2$; $y = x \tan c$.

Problem Set 13.5.

1. **3.** **5.**

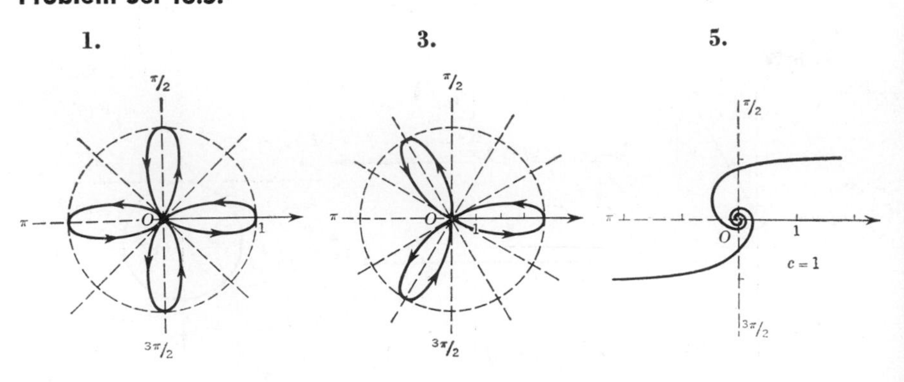

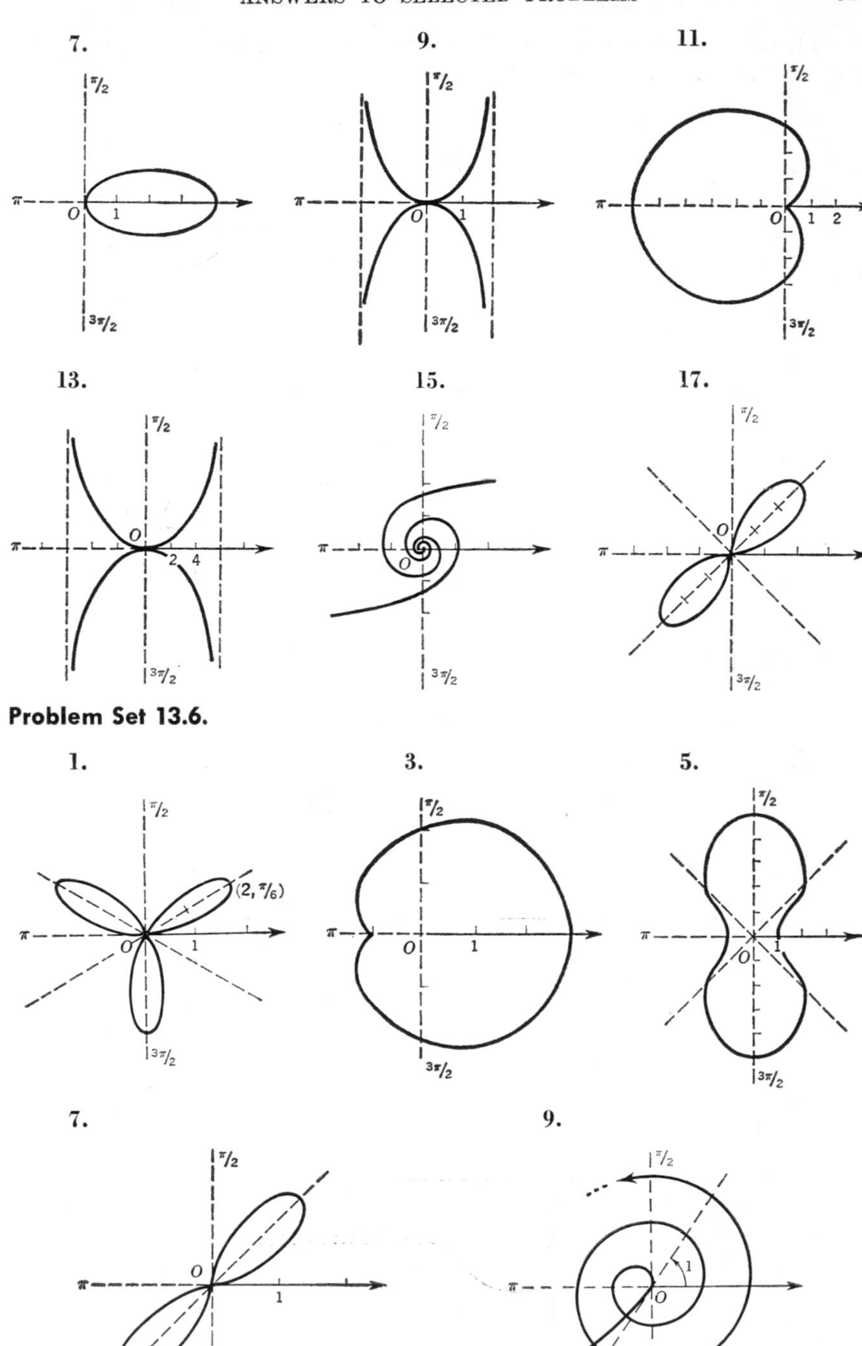

Problem Set 13.6.

11. $(2\sqrt{5}, \text{arc Cos } \sqrt{5}/5)$, $(2\sqrt{5}, -\text{arc Cos } \sqrt{5}/5)$. **13.** $(2 + 3\sqrt{2}/2, \pi/4)$; $\pi - \text{arc Cos } 2/3 \leq \theta \leq \pi - \text{arc Cos } 2/3$.

17. **18.**

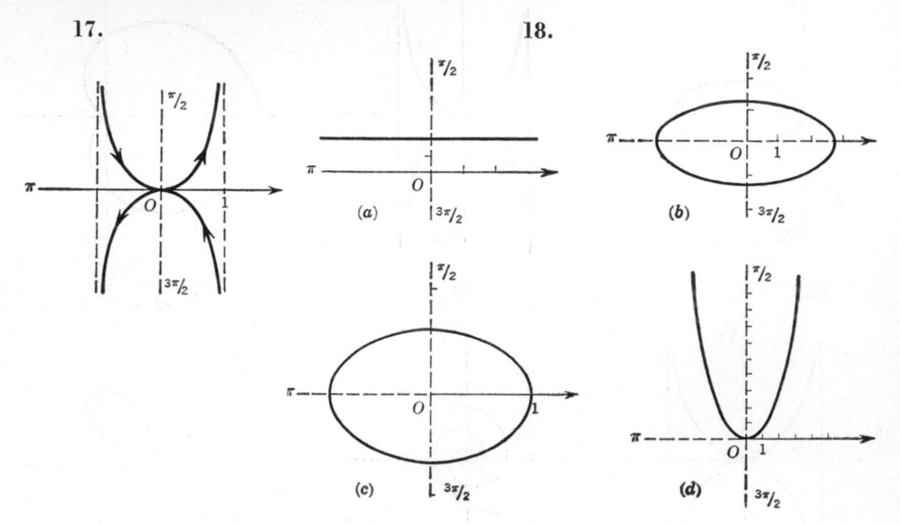

Review Test A.

1. $(\sqrt{2}, -\sqrt{2})$; $(1.98, -0.28)$; 1.1 units. **2.** $(2\sqrt{2}, 5\pi/4)$; $(\sqrt{5}, 5.176)$.

3.

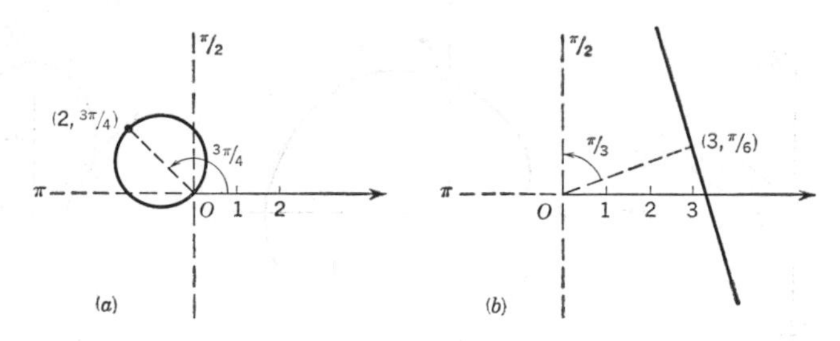

4. $1 = r \sin(\theta - \pi/3)$. **5.** $r = 4 \cos(\theta + \pi/3)$.

6.

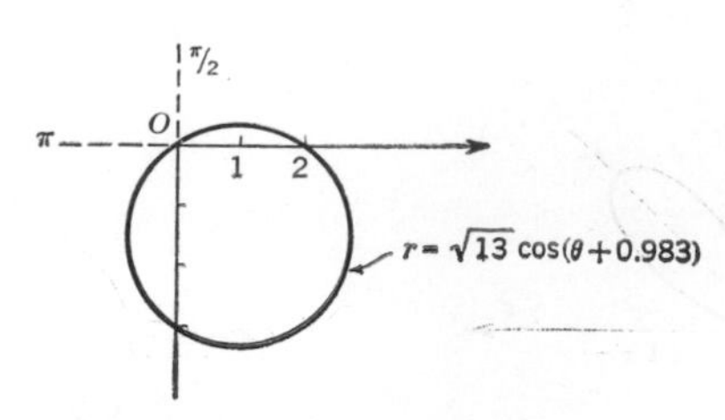

7. (*a*) $x^2 + y^2 - 2x - 3y = 0$; (*b*) $x^2 - 8y - 16 = 0$. **8.** (*a*) $r^2 = 36/(4 \cos^2 \theta - 9 \sin^2 \theta)$; (*b*) $\theta = \pi/4$. Symmetric with respect to polar axis.

9.

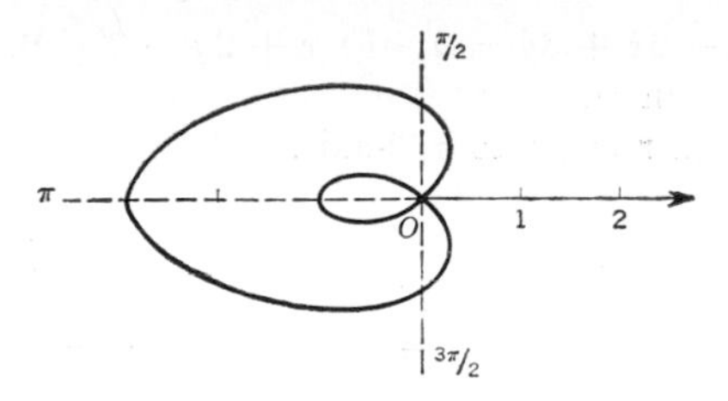

10.

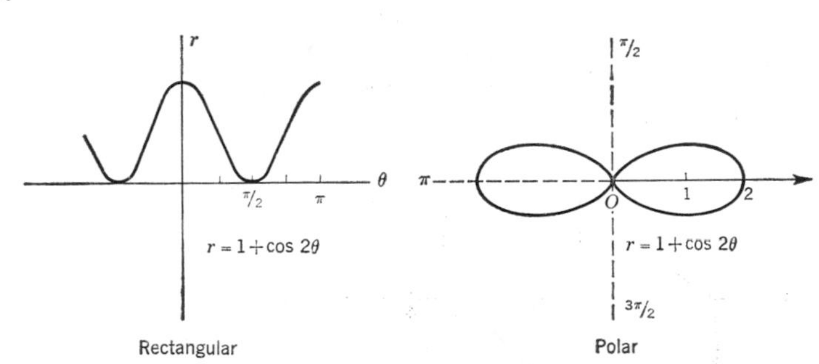

11. $[2\pi/3, 4\pi/3]$. **12.** $(4\sqrt{5}/5,\ 1.1072)$, $(0, 0)$; No, the latter pair is not in the intersection of the solution sets.

Review Test B.

1. $(3\sqrt{3}/2, -1.5)$; $(-0.416, -0.909)$; 3.1 units. **2.** $(2, 5\pi/6)$; $(\sqrt{10}, 0.322)$.

3.

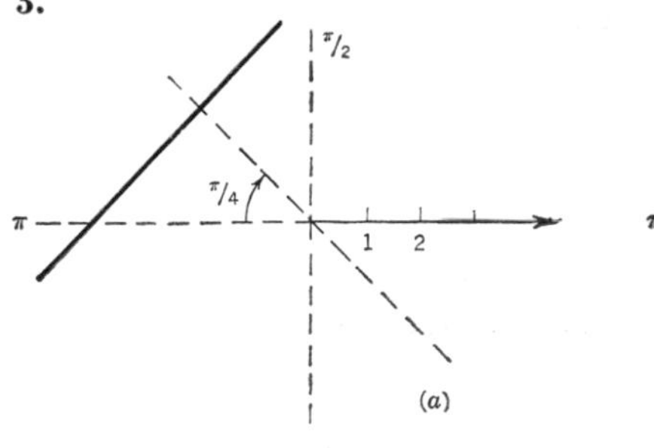

4. $\sqrt{3} = r \cos(\theta + 4\pi/3)$. **5.** $r = 3 \sin(\theta + 5\pi/4)$.

6. $r = \sqrt{10} \sin(\theta - 1.249)$.

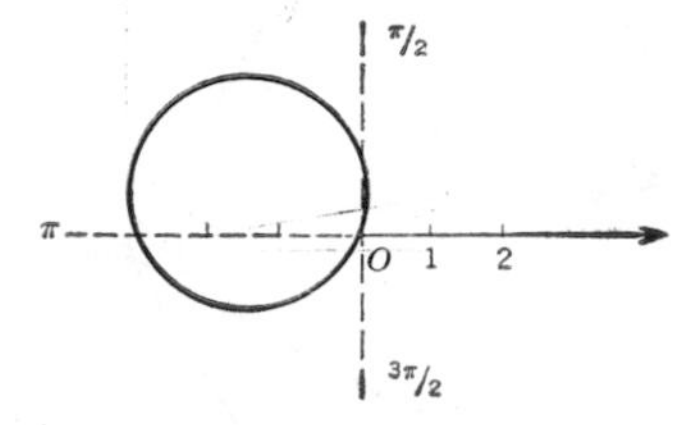

7. (*a*) $x^2 + y^2 - 2x + 3y = 0$; (*b*) $x + 2y - 3 = 0$. **8.** (*a*) $r = 4 \sin \theta$; (*b*) $r = 1/(2 \cos \theta - 3 \sin \theta)$.

9. Symmetric with respect to $\pi/2$-axis.

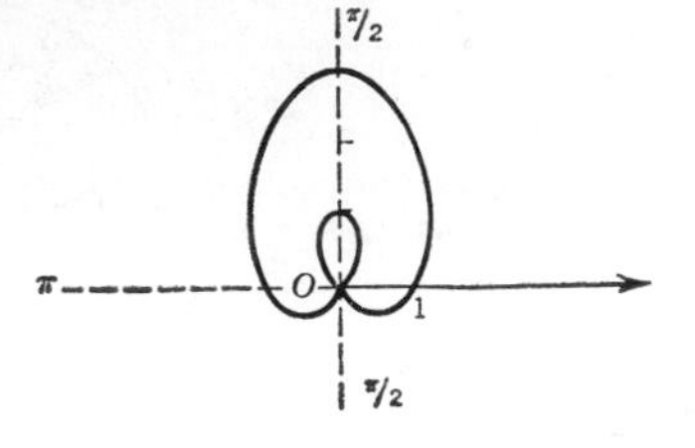

10.

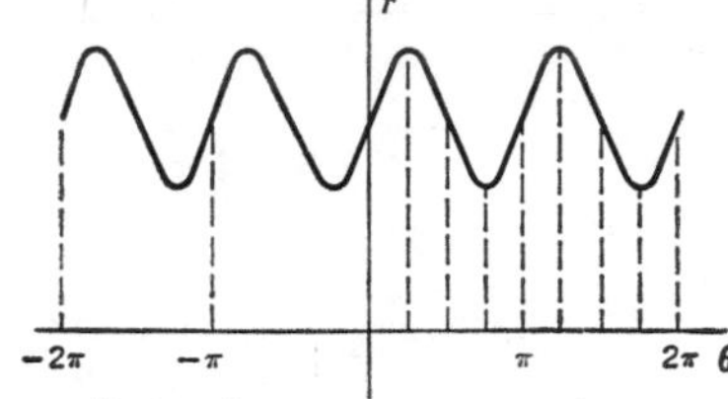

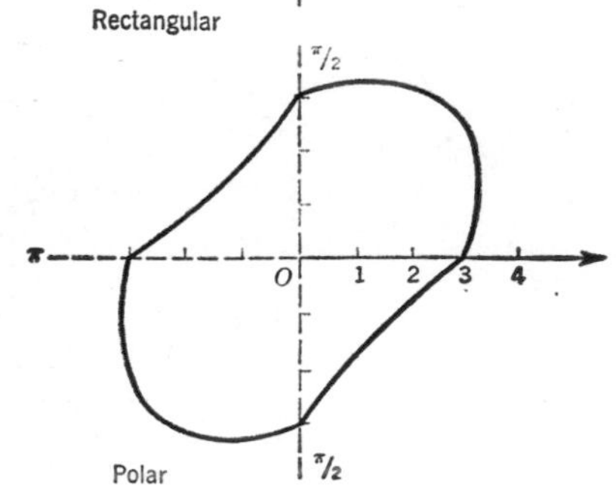

11. $[\pi/3, 2\pi/3]$. **12.** $(4 \cdot 41, 2.06)$, $(0, 0)$; no.

CHAPTER 14

Problem Set 14.1.

1. (*a*) $(-3, 2)$; (*b*) $(3, 7)$; (*c*) $(3/2, -6)$. **3.** $(2, -16)$. **5.** $(6/5, 18/5)$. **6.** $(15/2, 18)$. **7.** $5:9$. **9.** $\sqrt{349}/2$, $\sqrt{58}$, 7.5. **11.** $4x + 3y = 0$.

Problem Set 14.2.

1.

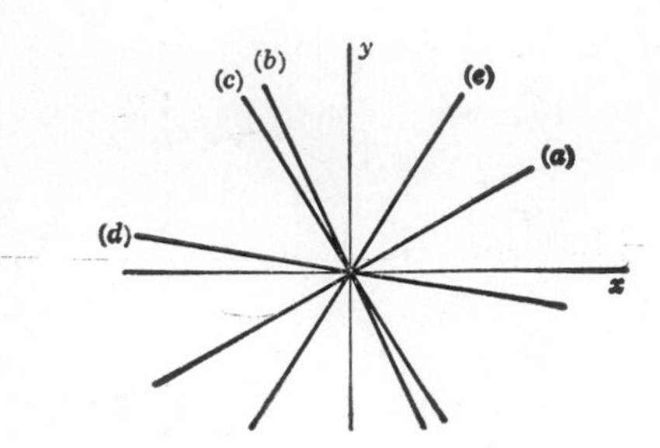

2.

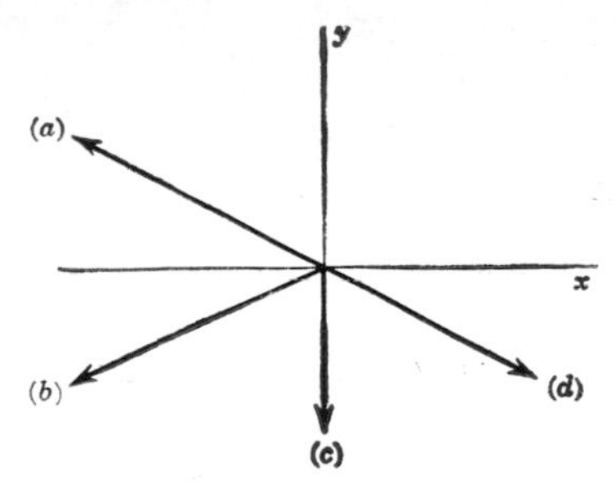

3. 0.5774, -2.185, -1.7321, -0.1425, 1.5574. **5.** (*a*) $-2/3$; (*b*) 3; (*c*) $-5/2$; (*d*) 1/2. **7.** (*a*) 2.5749; (*b*) 1.8926. **9.** $3x + y - 5 = 0$. **11.** $6x - y - 3 = 0$, $x + 6y - 19 = 0$. **13.** 0.1566. **15.** $x + 6y - 29 = 0$.

Problem Set 14.3.

1. $x^2 + 2xy + y^2 + (\sqrt{2}/2)x - (\sqrt{2}/2)y = 0$. **3.** $11x^2 + 2\sqrt{3}xy + 9y^2 = 4$. **5.** $9x^2 - 14\sqrt{3}xy - 5y^2 + 4 = 0$. **7.** (*a*) $x(-1/2) + y(\sqrt{3}/2) = 5$; (*b*) $x(-\sqrt{3}/2) + y(1/2) = 5$; (*c*) $x(\sqrt{2}/2) + y(-\sqrt{2}/2) = 5$. **8.** (*a*) $(3/5)x + (4/5)y = 6/5$; (*b*) $(-1/\sqrt{10})x + (3/\sqrt{10})y = 5/\sqrt{10}$. **9.** (*a*) $x(1) + y(0) = 5$; (*b*) $x(-1) + y(0) = 6$; (*c*) $x(0) + y(1) = 2$; (*d*) $x(0) + y(-1) = 2$. **10.** (*a*) $\sqrt{34}/17$; (*b*) $(6/5)\sqrt{5}$. **11.** $x(-\sqrt{3}/2) + y(1/2) = 5$, $x(\sqrt{3}/2) + y(-1/2) = 5$. **13.** $(5/13)x + (12/13)y = 48/13$. **17.** $\pi/8$. **18.** $2x^2 + y^2 = 4$. **19.** $3y^2 - 2x^2 = 5$.

Problem Set 14.4.

1. 3.2. **3.** $(8/5)\sqrt{5}$. **5.** $(2/17)\sqrt{34}$. **7.** 2.4. **9.** $(3/2)\sqrt{10}$. **11.** $(8/73)\sqrt{73}$. **12.** $4x + 3y + 35 = 0$, $4x + 3y - 25 = 0$. **13.** (8, 2), $(-6, 4)$.

Problem Set 14.5.

1. $x + y = 3$. **3.** (*a*) $x + 2 = 0$; (*b*) $3x - 7y + 32 = 0$; (*c*) $x^2 + y^2 + 2x + 6y - 26 = 0$. **8.** $8x^2 + 15y^2 - 24xy + 16x - 10y - 9 = 0$. **10.** $5x^2 - 4y^2 + 76x + 260 = 0$. **11.** $(x^2 + y^2)^2 - 2a^2(x^2 - y^2) + a^4 - c^4 = 0$. **12.** $xy = 2Amn/(m + n)^2$, $x > 0$, $y > 0$, with A the given measure of area.

Problem Set 14.7.

1. $r = 4/(2 - \cos\theta)$. **3.** $r = 24/(2 - 3\cos\theta)$. **7.** $p = 5$, $e = 1/2$. **8.** $p = 5/2$, $e = 2$. **9.** 10. **10.** $r\cos\theta = mk/(m + n)$, where $m:n$ is given ratio and k units is distance from 0 to given line.

Problem Set 14.8.

2. (*a*) $x - 3y + 6 = 0$; (*b*) $4x^2 - 4xy + y^2 - x = 0$; (*c*) $25x^2 - 4y^2 = 100$; (*d*) $x^2 - y^2 = 4$. **3.** $2x + 5y - 19 = 0$; $-2/5$. **5.** $x = 5(1 - m^2)/(1 + m^2)$, $y = 10m/(1 + m^2)$. **7.** $x = -18t$, $y = 5t$ (taking origin at initial position of ship). **9.** (*a*) 2; (*b*) -1; (*c*) $\pi/4$; (*d*) 1/2. **10.** $x = (880/3)t$, $y = 16t^2$ (with x positive in direction of flight and y positive downwards). **14.** $x = 10/m^2$, $y = 10/m$ (if we follow method of Illustration 3); the origin is omitted from the locus of these parametric equations.

Problem Set 14.9.

2. $2\pi a$; $(\pi a, 2a)$. **5.** (*a*) $6t$; (*b*) $-1/t^2$; (*c*) $-2\theta/3$; (*d*) $1/(5t^2)$. **7.** $8x - 3y - 32 = 0$. **9.** $(-8, 18)$. **11.** $x = \cos\phi + \phi\sin\phi$, $y = \sin\phi - \phi\cos\phi$. **12.** $(\sin\theta)/(1 - \cos\theta)$; $2x - 2y + 4a - a\pi$; $2x + 2y - a\pi$.

Problem Set 14.10.

1. $-1 \leq m \leq 1$. **3.** 5. **5.** $x^2 + y^2 = 10$; a circle with center at origin and radius $\sqrt{10}$ units in length. **7.** $\sqrt{3}x - y + 1 - 5\sqrt{3} = 0$. **9.** $2x - 9y - 73 = 0$. **11.** $4x + 3y - 10 = 0$. **13.** $x^2 + y^2 - 20x - 40y + 400 = 0$. **15.** $2x + y \pm 4\sqrt{5} = 0$. **17.** $3x - 4y - 25 = 0$. **19.** $3x - 2y - 20 = 0$. **21.** $18x - 30y + 125 = 0$. **23.** $2\sqrt{170}$. **25.** $x - 2y + 5 = 0$, $x + 2y + 5 = 0$. **27.** $12x + 5y \pm 2\sqrt{174} = 0$. **29.** $x^2 + y^2 - 16x - 4 = 0$. **31.** $\sqrt{26}$. **33.** $x^2 + y^2 + 14y = 0$.

Review Test A.

1. $(9/5, -1)$. **2.** 0.9273 radians. **3.** $12x - 16y + 9 = 0$.

4. Equation of OM: $y = x(1 - \cos\alpha)/\sin\alpha$. Determine coordinates of M to prove the assertion. **5.** $x^2 + y^2 = a^2$. Center at (0, 0), radius a units in length.

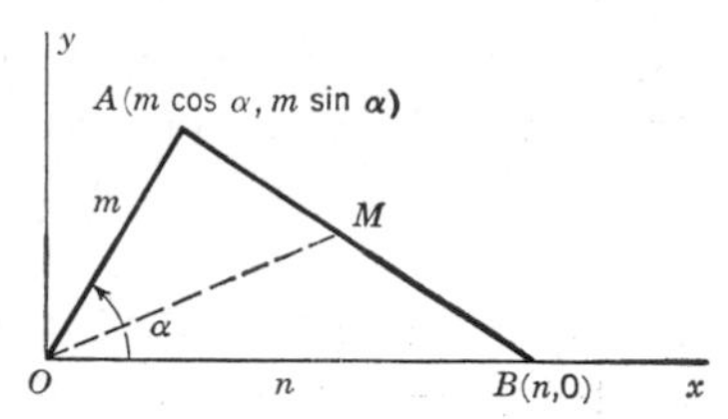

6. Show that the distances from P to the three lines are: y; $(\sqrt{3}x - y + a)/2$; $(\sqrt{3}x + y - a)/2$. Now square these expressions, add the results, and set equal to the prescribed number, noting that the equation defines a circle.

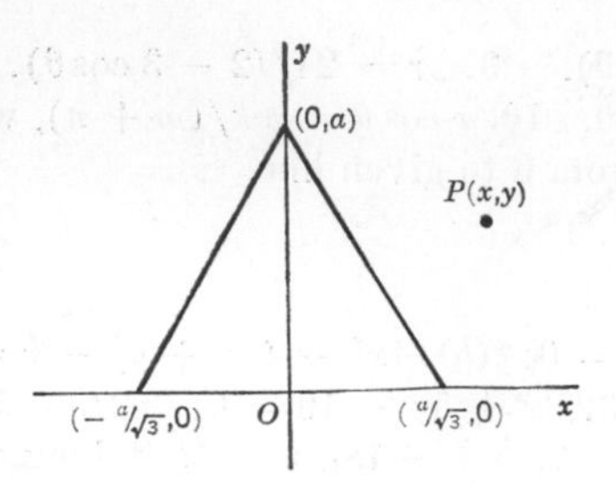

7. $x = a(\cos\theta + \theta\sin\theta)$, $y = a(\sin\theta - \theta\cos\theta)$. **8.** $11x - 22y + 37 = 0$. **9.** $x + 24y - 25 = 0$. **10.** $2x - y + 3 = 0$. **11.** $(x + 3)^2 + (y + 7)^2 = 117$. **12.** 67.5 square units.

Review Test B.

1. (12, 32). **2.** 0.3693 radians. **3.** $x + 2y - 3 = 0$, $3\sqrt{5}/5$.

4. Test the validity of the proposition to the sides OB and OA, and the

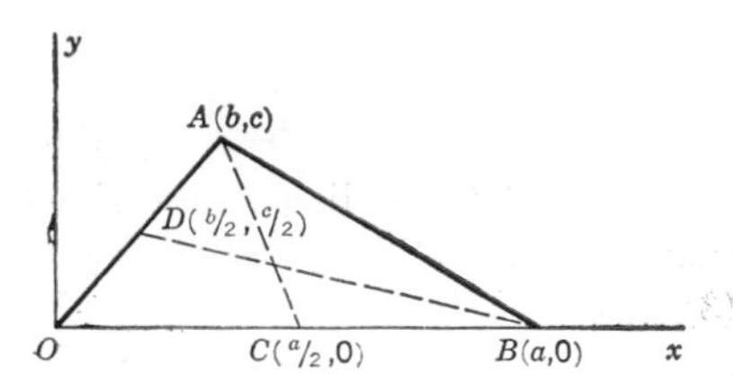

diagonals BD and AC. **5.** $y/x = t$. Thus $x = (3y/x)/(1 + y^3/x^3) = 3yx^2/(x^3 + y^3)$, and so $x^3 + y^3 - 3xy = 0$. **6.** $3x^2 + 4y^2 = 48$. **7.** $x = a\cos\theta(1 - \sin\theta)$, $y = a\sin\theta(1 - \sin\theta)$. **8.** $3x - 4y + 49 = 0$, $3x - 4y - 31 = 0$. **9.** 0.4999 radians. **10.** $\ln y + (\ln x)^2 = 0$. **11.** $3x - y - 8 = 0$.

12. Let $\angle QPT = \angle RPS = \beta$ radians, and $\angle RPF = \alpha$ radians. From slope of PR, i.e., $-2p/x_1$, and slope of PF, i.e., $(y_1 - p)/x_1$ show that $\tan\alpha = |-2x_1/2p| = \tan\beta$.

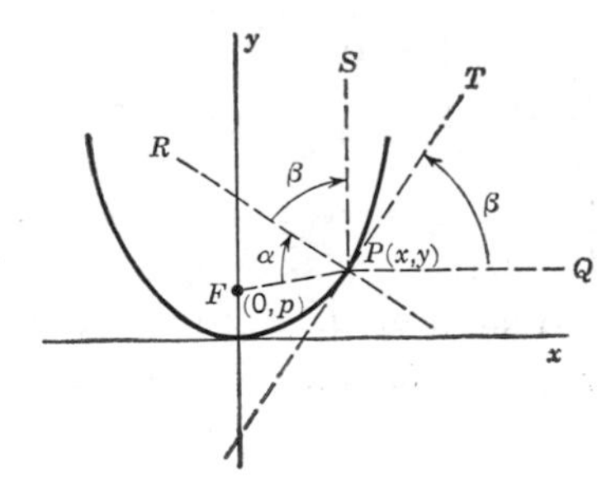

CHAPTER 15

Problem Set 15.1.

1. (a) 6; (b) 8; (c) 2; (d) 5. **3.** (a) $\sqrt{93}$; (b) $\sqrt{110}$; (c) $\sqrt{14}$; (d) $\sqrt{6}$. **5.** $2\sqrt{6}$. **7.** x-coordinate is 0. **10.** (a) On a plane parallel to and 5 units above the xy-plane; (b) on a plane parallel to and 2 units left of the yz-plane. **11.** On a sphere with center at the origin and radius 2 units in length. **13.** $x^2 + y^2 + z^2 + 4x - 10y - 6z + 22 = 0$.

Problem Set 15.2.

1. (*a*) $-5/\sqrt{65}$, $6/\sqrt{65}$, $-2/\sqrt{65}$; (*b*) $7/\sqrt{102}$, $-2/\sqrt{102}$, $-7/\sqrt{102}$; (*c*) $-\sqrt{10}/6$, $7\sqrt{10}/30$, $2\sqrt{10}/15$; (*d*) $-1/\sqrt{69}$, $-2/\sqrt{69}$, $-7/\sqrt{69}$. **3.** (*a*) $2/\sqrt{21}$, $-1/\sqrt{21}$, $4/\sqrt{21}$; (*b*) $2/\sqrt{38}$, $-3/\sqrt{38}$, $5/\sqrt{38}$; (*c*) $-3\sqrt{2}/10$, $2\sqrt{2}/5$, $\sqrt{2}/2$; (*d*) $9/11$, $-2/11$, $6/11$. **5.** $\alpha = 2\pi/3$, $\beta = \pi/3$, $\gamma = \pi/4$; or $\alpha = \pi/3$, $\beta = 2\pi/3$, $\gamma = 3\pi/4$. **7.** x-axis: 1, 0, 0; y-axis: 0, 1, 0; z-axis: 0, 0, 1. **8.** $\pm\sqrt{2}/2$; $\pi/4$, $3\pi/4$. **10.** $(-8, 10, -17)$.

Problem Set 15.3.

1. (*a*) arc Cos $(-2/27)$ or 1.497 radians, approximately; (*b*) arc Cos $(7/33)$ or 1.357 radians, approximately. **3.** Show that adjacent sides are perpendicular; for example, $(2)(3) + (2)(7) + (4)(-5) = 0$. **5.** $a = 6/7$, $c = 16/7$. **7.** arc Cos $(\sqrt{41}\sqrt{42}/82)$ or 1.0401 radians, approximately. **8.** -2, -1, 3. **9.** All angles are $\pi/3$ radians.

Problem Set 15.4.

1. (*a*) $x - y + \sqrt{2}z + 4 = 0$; (*b*) $x + 2y - 2z - 15 = 0$. **2.** $2x - 3y + 2z - 3\sqrt{17} = 0$. **3.** (*a*) $(3/\sqrt{14})x - (2/\sqrt{14})y + (1/\sqrt{14})z = 5/\sqrt{14}$; (*b*) $(-1/\sqrt{35})x - (3/\sqrt{35})y + (5/\sqrt{35})z = 4/\sqrt{35}$; (*c*) $(-1/\sqrt{5})x + (-2/\sqrt{5})z = \sqrt{5}/2$; (*d*) $(4/\sqrt{41})y + (-5/\sqrt{41})z = 6/\sqrt{41}$. **5.** (*a*) arc Cos $(\sqrt{156}/52)$ or 1.328 radians, approximately; (*b*) arc Cos $(\sqrt{21}/14$ or 1.237 radians, approximately; (*c*) arc Cos $(33/65)$ or 1.038 radians, approximately. **7.** (*a*) $\sqrt{2}x + y - z + 6 = 0$; (*b*) $x - \sqrt{3}y + 20 = 0$. **8.** (*a*) $(-3/\sqrt{38})x + (2/\sqrt{38})y + (-5/\sqrt{38})z = 2/\sqrt{38}$; (*b*) $-3/\sqrt{38}$, $2/\sqrt{38}$, $-5/\sqrt{38}$; (*c*) $\sqrt{38}/19$; (*d*) $3x - 2y + 2 = 0$, $3x + 5z + 2 = 0$, $2y - 5z - 2 = 0$. **10.** $2x - 2y + z + 2 = 0$. **11.** (*a*) 6, 5; (*b*) a section of a plane.

Problem Set 15.5.

1. $17x + 14y - 15z - 92 = 0$. **3.** $5x + 3y + 2z - 5 = 0$. **5.** $3x - 2y + z - 13 = 0$. **7.** $5x - 3y + 15z - 15 = 0$. **9.** $3x - 2y - 12z - 6 = 0$. **11.** $2x + y + z = 2$, $x + 2y - z = 4$.

Problem Set 15.6.

1. (*a*) $(x - 1)/(-2) = (y - 2)/(-4) = (z + 3)/3$; (*b*) $(x - 2)/3 = (y - 5)/4 = (z + 8)/12$; (*c*) $(x - 3)/1 = (y + 2)/(-8) = z/9$. **2.** $(x - 2)/2 = y/(-6) = (z + 1)/(-14)$. **4.** $x = 2 + 2k$, $y = -4 + 4k$, $z = 3 - 5k$. **5.** $(x - 6)/6 = (y - 8)/5 = z/(-4)$. **7.** $(x - 5)/6 = (y - 1)/(-3) = (z - 9)/6$. **8.** $3x - y + 3z - 13 = 0$. **9.** $z = -3$, $(x - 1)/1 = (y - 3)/\sqrt{3}$.

Problem Set 15.7.

3. (*a*) $(3, -1, 1/2), 5/2$; $(-1/2, -3/2, 1), \sqrt{22}/2$. **4.** (*a*) $x^2 + y^2 = 2z$; (*b*) $y^2 + z^2 = x^6$; (*c*) $x^2 + y^2 + z^2 = 5$. **5.** (*a*) $y^2 + z^2 = \cos^2 z$; (*b*) $x^2 + y^2 = \ln^2 z$; (*c*) $y^2(x^2 + z^2) = 1$. **6.** $9x^2 - y^2 - z^2 = 0$. **7.** (*a*) Parabolic cylinder; (*b*) paraboloid of revolution; (*c*) sphere; (*d*) right circular cone; (*e*) logarithmic cylinder; (*f*) point (the origin). **9.** (*a*) Points of a sphere; (*b*) points of a paraboloid of revolution; (*c*) points of a plane; (*d*) points of a plane.

Review Test A.

1. (*a*) $-7/\sqrt{165}, -10/\sqrt{165}, 4/\sqrt{165}$; (*b*) $-8/\sqrt{82}, -3/\sqrt{82}, -3/\sqrt{82}$. **2.** 0.8813 radians, approximately. **3.** 30/7. **4.** $3x - 5y + z = 6$. **5.** $11/\sqrt{35}$ or 1.86 units, approximately. **6.** $19\sqrt{6}/12$ or 3.88 units, approximately. **7.** $(x - 1)/3 = (y - 1)/4 = (z + 2)/(-6)$. **8.** $x^2 + 2y^2 + z^2 - 4 = 0$. **9.** $3x - 3y + 2z - 6 = 0$. **10.** (*a*) circular cylinder; xy: circle, xz: parallel lines, yz: parallel lines; (*b*) quadric cone; xy: origin, xz: intersecting lines, yz: intersecting lines; (*c*) ellipsoid; xy: circle, xz: ellipse, yz: ellipse; (*d*) hyperbolic paraboloid; xy: parabola, yz: parabola, xz: hyperbola. **11.** $(x + 2)^2 + (y - 3)^2 + (z + 4)^2 = 74$. **12.** $8(-12) + 12(-1) + 9(12) = 9(-12) + (-12)(-1) + 8(12) = 8(9) + 12(-12) + 9(8) = 0$.

Review Test B.

1. (*a*) $3/\sqrt{74}, 8/\sqrt{74}, -1/\sqrt{74}$; (*b*) $4/9, -1/9, -8/9$. **2.** 1.4152 radians, approximately. **3.** $a = 1$, $b = 8/5$. **4.** $x - 2y - z + 4 = 0$. **5.** $3\sqrt{6}/2$ or 3.67 units, approximately. **6.** $17\sqrt{126}/126$ or 1.51 units, approximately. **7.** $(x - 2)/1 = (y - 1)/(-2) = (z + 4)/3$. **8.** 1.3246 radians, approximately. **9.** (*a*) hyperboloid of one sheet; xy: hyperbola, yz: hyperbola, xz: ellipse; (*b*) ellipsoid; xy: ellipse, yz; ellipse, xz: ellipse; (*c*) sphere; xy: circle, yz: circle, xz: circle; (*d*) hyperboloid of two sheets; xy: hyperbola, yz: none, xz: hyperbola. **10.** $(6, -1, 1)$. **11.** Show that $\cos^2\theta = 1 - \sin^2\theta = (l_1l_2 + m_1m_2 + n_1n_2)^2$. **12.** $(x - 2)/1 = (y + 4)/3 = (z - 6)/(-4)$, $x + 3y - 4z + 34 = 0$.

CHAPTER 16

Problem Set 16.1.

1. (*a*) 2; (*b*) 16; (*c*) 22. **2.** (*a*) 110; (*b*) 132; (*c*) 120. **3.** (*a*) 6; (*b*) 6. **5.** (*a*) 24; (*b*) 9. **7.** 12. **9.** 81. **10.** (*a*) 16, 27, 34, 42, 47, 16. **11.** (*a*) 256; (*b*) 12; (*c*) 128; (*d*) 4. **13.** 16, 256. **15.** 9 in $A \cup B$, 18 in $A \times B$; 8 in $A \cup B$, 18 in $A \times B$.

Problem Set 16.2.

1. (*a*) 120; (*b*) 720; (*c*) 5,040; (*d*) 2,160; (*e*) 12; (*f*) 720. **2.** (*a*) 60; (*b*) 360; (*c*) 720; (*d*) 35; (*e*) 20; (*f*) 120. **3.** (*a*) $\underline{|9}$; (*b*) $95\underline{|7}$; (*c*) $27\underline{|6}$; (*d*) $13\underline{|6}$. **5.** 60; 80. **7.** (*a*) 27,405; (*b*) 593,775; (*c*) 31,930. **9.** (*a*) 45; (*b*) 28. **11.** (*a*) 2,598,960; (*b*) 1,281,072; (*c*) 3,744; (*d*) $(C_{52,13})(C_{39,13})(C_{26,13})$; (*e*) $40(C_{39,13})(C_{26,13})$. **13.** 66. **15.** 1,440. **17.** 120,120. **19.** 5,760.

Problem Set 16.3.

1. 24. **3.** 2880. **5.** (*a*) 127; (*b*) 63. **7.** 3. **9.** 112. **11.** 570,240. **13.** 127. **15.** (*a*) 18; (*b*) 276.

Problem Set 16.4.

1. $32x^5 - 240x^4 + 720x^3 - 1080x^2 + 810x - 243$. **3.** $128x^7 - (896/3)x^6 + (896/3)x^5 - (4480/27)x^4 + (4480/81)x^3 - (2688/243)x^2 + (896/729)x - 128/2187$. **5.** $1 + 8/x + 28/x^2 + 56/x^3 + 70/x^4 + 56/x^5 + 28/x^6 + 8/x^7 + 1/x^8$. **7.** $-101{,}376/x^5$. **9.** $189a^{17}/8$; $-21a^{19}/16$. **11.** $(-1/^n(\underline{|3n})/(\underline{|n}\,\underline{|2n})$.

Problem Set 16.5.

1. $1 + 1/x - 1/(2x^2) + 1/(4x^3)$; $|x| > 2$. **3.** $(2x)^{2/3}[1 - 1/(3ax) - 1/(36a^2x^2) - 1/(162a^3x^3)]$; $|x| > 1/(2a)$. **5.** $1/2 - 3x/4 + 9x^2/8 - 27x^3/16$; $|x| < 2/3$. **7.** $1 + 8x + 36x^2 + 104x^3 + 214x^4 + 150x^5 + 324x^6 + 216x^7 + 81x^8$. **9.** 2.02978. **11.** 1.00064. **13.** 2%. **15.** $p + 2/p$; $|q| < 1$, $p^2 > |2q|$. **17.** 15 miles.

Review Test A.

1. 1056. **2.** 2520. **3.** 218,025. **4.** 6. **5.** 180. **6.** 13,248. **7.** 493,640 **8.** 48, 738. **9.** $32x^5 - 240x^4/y + 720x^3/y^2 - 1080x^2/y^3 + 810x/y^4 - 243/y^5$ **10.** 34375/2304. **11.** $2 + x/3 - x^2/18$, $|x| < 2$. **12.** 0.1459.

Review Test B.

1. 216/5. **2.** 720. **3.** 4140. **4.** 720. **5.** 63. **6.** 3780. **7.** $C_{44,5}$ or 1,086,008. **8.** 33, 162. **9.** $x^4/16 - x^3y + 6x^2y^2 - 16xy^3 + 16y^4$. **10.** $-671{,}840x^9/y^{11}$. **11.** $1 + x + 2x^2$, $|x| < 1/3$. **12.** 0.1984.

CHAPTER 17

Problem Set 17.2.

1. 0.37224. **3.** (*a*) 0.93; (*b*) 0.79. **5.** 1:5. **7.** 11/36. **9.** 8/663. **11.** 6/25. **13.** 6/4165 for full house and 1/649740 for royal flush. **14.** 1/3. **16.** 3/5. **17.** 1/7.

Problem Set 17.3.

1. 1/6. **3.** 25/72. **5.** (*a*) 1/10; (*b*) 1/4. **7.** 0.29. **9.** 32/243.

Problem Set 17.4.

1. (*a*) 5/36; (*b*) 7/12. **3.** 52/77. **5.** 2/27. **6.** 1/4. **7.** 1/2. **8.** 146/245. **9.** 31/32.

Problem Set 17.5.

1. 2133/3125. **3.** $6.57, approximately. **5.** $9767.10. **7.** (*a*) 125/3888; (*b*) 23/648. **9.** $20.10. **10.** $12.

Problem Set 17.7.

1. 1.94, 0.92. **3.** 5.75, 2.38. **5.** (*a*) yes; (*b*) no; (*c*) no. **7.** (*a*) increases mean; (*b*) decreases mean; (*c*) leaves mean unchanged.

Problem Set 17.8.

4. $\mu = 1.67, \sigma = 1.18$. **5.** $\mu = 10, \sigma = 1.69$. **6.** $\mu = 2.5, \sigma = 1.12$.

Problem Set 17.9.

1. (*a*) reject; (*b*) reject; (*c*) accept; (*d*) accept. **2.** Accept. **5.** Reject. **7.** No explanation required.

Problem Set 17.10.

1. 0.240; 0.161. **3.** No. **5.** 0.060; 0.161. **7.** 0.136. **9.** 0.986. **10.** (*a*) 0.121, 0.119; (*b*) 0.194, 0.193; (*c*) 0.927. 0.925.

Problem Set 17.11.

1. 22 to 45. **3.** Yes($t = 4.4$). **5.** No($t = 1.667$). **7.** 0.956. **9.** Yes($t = -3.33$).

Review Test A.

1. 4/5. **2.** 3/14. **3.** 40/41. **4.** 4/17. **5.** 75¢. **6.** 0.98, approximately. **7.** $\bar{x} = 2.2, s = 1.09$. **8.** 0.86. **9.** Yes ($t = 2.1 < 2.58$). **10.** No ($t = 3.0 > 2.58$). **11.** 2310. **12.** No ($t = 1.46 < 2.58$).

Review Test B.

1. 1/2. **2.** 2 to 7. **3.** 3 to 47. **4.** 19/144. **5.** 7/27. **6.** 0.5, approximately. **7.** $\bar{x} = 1.42, s = 0.98$. **8.** 0.23. **9.** Yes ($t = 1.5 < 2.58$). **10.** Yes ($t = 4.3 > 2.58$). **11.** 1400. **12.** 0.019, approximately.

APPENDIX

Section 1.

1. Divide numerator and denominator by the number "canceled." **2.** (*a*) 2^6; (*b*) $2^2 \cdot 3^2$; (*c*) $2^3 \cdot 3^2$; (*d*) $2^5 \cdot 5$; (*e*) $2 \cdot 3 \cdot 7$; (*f*) $2 \cdot 3^2$; (*g*) 5^3; (*h*) $2^2 \cdot 3 \cdot 5$; (*i*) $2^4 \cdot 5$; (*j*) $2 \cdot 3^2 \cdot 5$; (*k*) $2 \cdot 3 \cdot 17$. **3.** (*a*) 1; (*b*) 3; (*c*) 2; (*d*) 15; (*e*) 1. **4.** (*a*) 1/3; (*b*) 2/3; (*c*) 1/3; (*d*) 10/3; (*e*) 15/4; (*f*) 6/13. **5.** (*a*) 10/15; (*b*) 15/20; (*c*) 25/15; (*d*) 20/30; (*e*) 20/45. **6.** (*a*) 40/30; (*b*) 20/70; (*c*) 50/80; (*d*) 50/60; (*e*) 30/40. **7.** (*a*) 2 13/24; (*b*) 2 43/60; (*c*) 1 9/70. **8.** (*a*) 4 1/3; (*b*) 1/12; (*c*) 19/56; (*d*) 3 4/7; (*e*) 2/5. **9.** (*a*) 1 19/24; (*b*) 1 7/120; (*c*) 2 226/315. **10.** (*a*) 1/12; (*b*) 8/25; (*c*) 1 7/18. **11.** (*a*) 9/8; (*b*) 5/8; (*c*) 15/32; (*d*) 1/14; (*e*) 32; (*f*) 2/9. **12.** (*a*) 11/12; (*b*) 49/72; (*c*) 83/240; (*d*) 5 5/6; (*e*) 3 3/5. **13.** 4 37/40. **14.** 10 7/8. **15.** 4 1/4 feet. **16.** 41 5/8¢. **17.** 16¢. **18.** 2 9/10; 3 31/53.

Section 2.

1. (*a*) 6; (*b*) 7; (*c*) 4; (*d*) 3/5; (*e*) 5/7. **2.** (*a*) +17; (*b*) −21; (*c*) −2 3/8; (*d*) 1 77/120. **3.** (*a*) −3; (*b*) −17; (*c*) 1; (*d*) −2. **4.** (*a*) 5/12; (*b*) 2 1/56; (*c*) 2 13/280. **5.** (*a*) 1/28; (*b*) −2 1/15; (*c*) 5 3/4; (*d*) −3 2/7; (*e*) −14/15; (*f*) 4 3/5; (*g*) 1/4. **6.** (*a*) 2/5; (*b*) −8; (*c*) −3 6/7. **7.** (*a*) −3/5; (*b*) 5/9; (*c*) −6 1/4; (*d*) −3/10. **8.** (*a*) −7 1/2; (*b*) 128/245; (*c*) −18 37/80. **9.** (*a*) −10 1/2; (*b*) 2 1/3; (*c*) 2; (*d*) 2 1/3. **10.** (*a*) 5 1/4; (*b*) 3/8; (*c*) 4 1/2.

Section 3.

1. (*a*) $-8x^3$; (*b*) $2ab$; (*c*) $24x^3$; (*d*) $3aby^2$; (*e*) $-7x^2y$. **2.** (*a*) $16a$; (*b*) $5ab$; (*c*) $4ac - 4ab$; (*d*) $2a^2 + 2a + 5b$. **3.** $-6a - 7b - 3c$. **4.** $-14x^2 + 12x - 8$. **5.** (*a*) $-15abc$; (*b*) $5m - 8m^2$; (*c*) $8x^2 - 8y$. **6.** (*a*) $3a - 11b + 6c$; (*b*) $-13x - y$; (*c*) $9x^2 - 2y + 15$. **7.** (*a*) $9y - xy$; (*b*) $9y - x^2$; (*c*) $4b^2 - 24b - a - 8$. **8.** (*a*) $3a^2 + ab - 2b^2$; (*b*) $3x - 2y$; (*c*) 1. **9.** (*a*) $4x^2 - 25y^2$; (*b*) $9x^4 - 4y^4$; (*c*) $4x^2 + 4xy + y^2$; (*d*) $x^3 - 6x^2y + 12xy^2 - 8y^3$. **10.** (*a*) $25x^2 - 4y^2$; (*b*) $x^4y^2 - 9a^2$; (*c*) $4x^2 - 36y^2$; (*d*) $27x^3 - 27x^2y + 9xy^2 - y^3$. **11.** (*a*) $4a^2 - 4ax + x^2$; (*b*) $1 + 3x + 3x^2 + x^3$; (*c*) $8x^3 - 12x^2 + 6x - 1$; (*d*) $x^2 + 5x + 6$; (*e*) $9x^2y^2 + 18xyz - 7z^2$. **12.** (*a*) $2x^2 - 6xy + 4y^2$; (*b*) $2a^2 + 11ab - 21b^2$; (*c*) $x^4 + x^2 = 12$; (*d*) $x^2/4 - 25y^2$; (*e*) $x^2/4 - xy/4 + y^2/16$. **13.** (*a*) $36x^2 - 6x + 1/4$; (*b*) $8 + 36x + 54x^2 + 27x^3$; (*c*) $25m^6 - 25m^3s^2 - 6s^4$; (*d*) $9x^2y^2 - 42xy + 49$. **14.** (*a*) $3m + 2 - 5m^2$; (*b*) $2x^2 - x$; (*c*) $x^2 - 12x + 6$; (*d*) $a - a^2b + b^3$; (*e*) $5y^2$. **15.** (*a*) $-20m^2n^4$; (*b*) $12b^3c^3$; (*c*) $-40ty^5z$; (*d*) $8x^4y^2 - 14x^3y^3$; (*e*) $-a^4$. **16.** (*a*) $4x^2 + y^2 + 9z^2 - 4xy + 12xz - 6yz$; (*b*) $x - 2x^2 + x^3 - 2y + 4xy - 2x^2y$; (*c*) $2x^5 + x^4 - 24x^3 - 12x^2 + 72x + 36$; (*d*) $2x^3 - 3x^2y - 8xy^2 - 3y^3$; (*e*) $8x^3 + y^3 - z^3 - 12xyz - 12x^2z + 12x^2y + 6xz^2 + 6xy^2 - 3y^2z + 3yz^2$.

Section 4.

1. $(3x^4 - 2y^3)(3x^4 + 2y^3)$. **2.** $(15 - a^3)(15 + a^3)$. **3.** $(r^2 - 5)(r^2 + 5)$. **4.** $(8x + 3)(2x + 3)$. **5.** $3(y + 2)(y^2 - 2y + 4)$. **6.** $(3x - 1)(2x + 3)$. **7.** $(c + 3d)(c^2 - 3cd + 9d^2)$. **8.** $(x - 12)(x - 4)$. **9.** $(y - 3z)(y^2 + 3yz + 9z^2)$. **10.** $(x + 1)(4x - 7)$. **11.** $(3 - 5t)(2 + 3t)$. **12.** $(5t^2 - 1)(5t^2 + 1)$. **13.** $(6a - 11)^2$. **14.** $(u^3 - 10)(u^3 + 11)$. **15.** $3(x - 2)(x + 2)$. **16.** $(x^4 + y^4)(x^2 + y^2)(x + y)(x - y)$. **17.** $(x^2 + y^2)(x - y)^2(x + y)$. **18.** $(x - y)^2(x^2 + xy + y^2)$. **19.** $(x - 1)^3$. **20.** $(x + y - a)(x + y + a)$. **21.** $(c + a + b)(c - a - b)$. **22.** $(xy + 1)(x^2y^2 - xy + 1)$. **23.** $(2 - 3x)(4 + 6x + 9x^2)$. **24.** $(2m + 3n)(12m - 7n)$. **25.** $(8x + 9)(2x - 3)$. **26.** $(1 + 4x)(9 - x)$. **27.** $(2x^2 - 3y^2)(x^2 + 7y^2)$. **28.** $(x - y - 2z)(x - y + 2z)$. **29.** $(5x - 6)(5x - 8)$. **30.** $y(2x - y)$. **31.** $(5y - 4)(y + 14)$. **32.** $y^4(x^2 - 3)(x^2 + 3)$. **33.** $(2x^2 + 2y + x - 9)(2x^2 + x - 2y + 9)$. **34.** $2(x + 2y)(x - y)$. **35.** (*a*) $(a + b)(x + y)$. **36.** $x^3(a - 8y)(a + 8y)$. **37.** $a(x - y)(x + y)(a + b)$. **38.** $(x^2 + 1)(x + 1)$. **39.** $(1 - 2x)(1 + 2x)(2 + 3x)$. **40.** $(7 - 4a)(8 + 3a^2)$. **41.** $(x + y - z)(x^2 + y^2 + z^2 - xy + xz - 2yz)$. **42.** $(m + n + 2l)(m^2 + n^2 + 4t^2 + 2mn - 2mt - 2nt)$. **43.** $(2a + b)(13a^2 - 5ab + b^2)$. **44.** $(x + y - xy)(x + y + xy)$.

Section 5.

1. $(5x + y)/6$. **2.** $(x + 4)/4$. **3.** $-(4a + b)/ab$. **4.** $(25x^2 + 12x - 14)/20x^3$ **5.** 0. **6.** $(x + 45)/70$. **7.** $2(x^2 - 2)/(x^2 - 1)$. **8.** $2x/[(x + 1)(x + 2)(x + 3)]$. **9.** $y(7y - 12)/[(y - 2)(3y - 2)]$. **10.** $x(a - b)/[(x + a)(x + b)]$. **11.** $1/[(1 - a)(1 + 2a)(2 - 3a)]$. **12.** $4x/(x^2 - 4)$. **13.** $3a(2a + 4)/[(2a - 1)(a - 1)]$. **14.** $x^3/(x^2 - 1)$. **15.** $2(x^3 + x^2 - 9)/[x(x - 3)(x + 3)]$. **16.** $1/[(x + 1)(x + 2)]$. **17.** 0. **18.** $(x^2 - 3x + 1)/(x - 2)$. **19.** $(x - y)(x + y)^2/[x^2y^2]$. **20.** $(x + 1)/(x - 1)$. **21.** $(x - 1)/[x(x + 3)]$. **22.** $(x + 1)/2$. **23.** $(x + 1)(x^2 + 1)(x^4 + 1)/x^3$. **24.** $(x + 1)/(x - 1)$.

Section 6.

1. 4. **2.** 1/2. **3.** −3. **4.** −1/2. **5.** 2. **6.** 7 2/3. **7.** −2. **8.** 5. **9.** 1/2, −3. **10.** −7/3, 5/2. **11.** $(-5 \pm \sqrt{37})/2$. **12.** 4, 1. **13.** −7/3, 1. **14.** −9, 4. **15.** −9/4, 5. **16.** 60, 45. **17.** 4, 2. **18.** 6, −1. **19.** 4, −10/3. **20.** ±2, ±5. **21.** $(-5 \pm \sqrt{65})/8$. **22.** $3 \pm \sqrt{15}$. **23.** $(6 \pm 2\sqrt{27})/9$. **24.** $(-1 \pm \sqrt{6})/2$. **25.** $(2 \pm \sqrt{10})4$. **26.** 3, −5/3. **27.** No solution. **28.** ±5, ±2. **29.** ±7. **30.** 5, −3. **31.** 1/3, 3, $(3 \pm \sqrt{5})/2$. **32.** $\sqrt[3]{7}$, $\sqrt[3]{5}$. **33.** 5/3, −3/2. **34.** −1/2. **35.** 2/3, 1. **36.** −1/5, 1/3. **37.** −11/6, 2. **38.** $(-10 \pm \sqrt{110})/10$. **39.** a, $1/a$. **40.** −1, 24/13.

Section 7.

1. $x = 7$, $y = -2$. **2.** $x = 5$, $y = 4$. **3.** $x = -1$, $y = 1$. **4.** $x = 15/13$, $y = -5/13$. **5.** $x = 5$, $y = 3$. **6.** $x = 15$, $y = 10$. **7.** $x = 4$, $y = 3$. **8.** $x = 2$,

$y = 3$. **9.** $x = 2, y = 3$. **10.** $x = -1/2, y = 5/2$. **11.** $x = -2, y = 1, z = 3$. **12.** $x = 3, y = 1, z = 2$. **13.** $x = 2, y = -1, z = -1/3$. **14.** $x = 2, y = -1, z = 0$. **15.** $x = 6, y = 18, z = 12$. **16.** $x = 2, y = 4, z = 8$. **17.** 6 m.p.h., 3 m.p.h. **18.** 55, 40.

Section 8.

1. (*a*) $a^{1/2}$; (*b*) $x^{3/4}$; (*c*) $a^{7/5}$; (*d*) $a^{3/2}$; (*e*) $(a + 2)^{1/5}$. **2.** (*a*) $3^{1/2}$; (*b*) $2^{5/3}$; (*c*) $4^{4/5}$; (*d*) $5^{1/2}$; (*e*) $(2 + x)^{1/3}$. **3.** (*a*) 3; (*b*) 729; (*c*) 3125; (*d*) 32; (*e*) 2. **4.** (*a*) $\sqrt[3]{a}$; (*b*) $\sqrt[6]{x^5}$; (*c*) $\sqrt[3]{b^n}$; (*d*) $\sqrt[4]{n^3}$; (*e*) $\sqrt[6]{s^7}$. **5.** (*a*) x^{n+3}; (*b*) a^{2n+1}; (*c*) u^{2n}; (*d*) p^{21}; (*e*) a^{12}. **6.** (*a*) x^{2n}; (*b*) 10^{r+1}; (*c*) u^{2r}; (*d*) x^4; (*e*) $(pq)^{3s}$; (*f*) $(rs)^{10}$; (*g*) e^{n+2}. **7.** (*a*) $x^{8/3}$; (*b*) $a^{9/20}$; (*c*) $a^{23/21}$; (*d*) $a^{1/2}$. **8.** (*a*) $a^{1/6}$; (*b*) $x^{1/2}$; (*c*) $a^{5/3}$; (*d*) $ab^{1/4}$. **9.** (*a*) 1; (*b*) $x^{13/5}$; (*c*) $(27/8)x^{21/40}$; (*d*) $2^{4/3}a^{1/6}b$. **10.** (*a*) 1/2; (*b*) 1/8; (*c*) 1/9; (*d*) 1; (*e*) 1. **11.** (*a*) 18;) (*b* 8; (*c*) 1; (*d*) 1/8. **12.** (*a*) a/b^2; (*b*) $1/(a + b)^3$; (*c*) $3/(x^2y^{1/2})$ (*d*) x^4y^5; (*e*) x^2. **13.** (*a*) x^{-2}; (*b*) $xy^2c^{-3}d^{-4}$; (*c*) $2^{-1}a^3b^{-3}r^2t^{-5}$; (*d*) $ab^{1/2}x^{1/3}y^{-s/t}$. **14.** (*a*) a^7; (*b*) $1/x^4$; (*c*) $(a^9x^9)/(b^3y^6)$; (*d*) $r^{1/2}$.

Section 9.

1. 5. **2.** 10. **3.** 65. **4.** 4. **5.** -2. **6.** No solution. **7.** No solution. **8.** 2, 6. **9.** No solution. **10.** 4. **11.** 9. **12.** 6. **13.** 2. **14.** 4. **15.** 1/4. **16.** 1/81. **17.** 4. **18.** 0.

Section 10.

1. (*a*) 1:2; (*b*) 10:13; (*c*) 13:18; (*d*) 16:17; (*e*) $(x - y):1$. **2.** (*a*) 1:18; (*b*) 8:27; (*c*) 2:3; (*d*) 10:9. **3.** (*a*) 1:2; (*b*) 1:6; (*c*) 1:25. **4.** (*a*) $a:(a - 1)$; (*b*) $(x - 3):2$; (*c*) $x:3$. **5.** 75, 50. **6.** 8, 20. **7.** (*a*) 16/5; (*b*) 27/2; (*c*) 12; (*d*) 9. **8.** (*a*) 6; (*b*) 4; (*c*) 8; (*d*) $2\sqrt{6}$; (*e*) $2\sqrt{15}$. **9.** (*a*) 81/4; (*b*) 100/3; (*c*) 72. **10.** (*a*) 6; (*b*) 33; (*c*) $-80/3$. **11.** $x = 0$. **12.** $x = -6$.

Test.

1. (*a*) $-1\,5/12$; (*b*) $-31/60$. **2.** (*a*) $-1\,7/8$; (*b*) $-1\,17/18$; (*c*) 3/25; (*d*) -10. **3.** (*a*) -1; (*b*) $(x + 1)/(x^2 - 9)$. **4.** (*a*) $2 + 2x - 5x^2/12$; (*b*) $a + b$. **5.** (*a*) $(m - 2n)(m + 2n)$; (*b*) $(t + 11)(t - 5)$; (*c*) $(1 + y^3)(1 - y)(1 + y + y^2)$. **6.** (*a*) $(a + b)(m + 1)$; (*b*) $(1 - y)(1 - 2x + y)$; (*c*) $(4x - 1)(3x + 7)$. **7.** (*a*) $(1 - x - y)(1 + x + y)$; (*b*) $x(x + 1)(x - 7)$. **8.** (*a*) $(5 \pm \sqrt{17})/4$; (*b*) $-1/2$, -1. **9.** (*a*) 1/2, -1; (*b*) 2/3, $-3/2$. **10.** (*a*) -1, 5/4; (*b*) $(2 \pm \sqrt{6})/2$. **11.** (*a*) $x = 11, y = 0$; (*b*) $y = 7/2, z = -1$. **12.** (*a*) $x = 5, y = 13, z = 0$; (*b*) $x = 1/2, y = 1/5, z = 2$. **13.** (*a*) $\sqrt{2}$, $\sqrt[3]{9}$, $\sqrt{64}$, $\sqrt{1/6}$, $\sqrt[3]{1/4}$; (*b*) $5^{1/5}$, $3^{2/3}$, $3^{-1/2}$, $3(5^{-2/3})$. **14.** (*a*) $y^6/(3x^4z)$; (*b*) $64x^2/(9y)$. **15.** (*a*) 3:7; (*b*) $x = 3\,2/5$. **16.** $x = -1$. **17.** $x = 6$.

INDEX

Boldface numbers refer to chapters; all other numbers refer to pages.